C000198744

# The UK Scanning Directory

## 6th Edition

**Interproducts**

*Publishers of Specialist Radio Books*

**Scotland**

The UK Scanning Directory

© Copyright Interproducts 1997

6th Edition published December 1997

All rights reserved. No part of this book may be reproduced or transmitted in any form or by any means electronic or mechanical, including photocopying, recording or by information storage and retrieval systems, without prior written permission of the publisher except in the case of brief quotations embodied in critical articles and reviews.

ISBN 1 900445 07 7

This book is sold *as is*, without warranty of any kind, either express of implied, respecting the contents of this book, including but not limited to implied warranties for the book's quality, performance, merchantibility, or fitness for any particular purpose. Neither Interproducts nor it's dealers or distributors shall be liable to the purchaser or any other person or entity with respect to any liability, loss or damage caused, alleged to be caused directly or indirectly by this book.

This book is designed and compiled purely for entertainment and educational purposes, and is not intended to be used in conjunction with any type or form of VHF/UHF scanning receiver, which may be in direct contravention of the Wireless Telegraphy Act, or as a professional guide. Neither the editorial team nor the publisher accept any responsibility for errors or omissions present in the text.

Published by
**Interproducts**
8 Abbot Street, Perth, PH2 0EB, Scotland
Telephone and Fax: (01738) 441199
email: interproducts@netmatters.co.uk

# *Introduction*

This 6th Edition of *The UK Scanning Directory* is the most comprehensive guide to the VHF and UHF bands on the market. It has been updated throughout, many new frequencies added and the larger format gives more frequencies on each page making it easier for reference. It is not only used by radio enthusiasts but by the military, government departments, police and industry.

There are many changes taking place with radio communication and the equipment is becoming more sophisticated. New radios have enabled users to switch to other bands, and this is especially true of the police who are changing their frequencies. The demand for radio communication continues to increase every year and this is reflected by the number of new users on the Personal Mobile Radio bands.

We have been ask to spiral bind *The UK Scanning Directory* as we did with the earlier editions, but because the book has become so large it is impractical.

Newcomers who would like to learn more about radio will find sections on scanning in magazines such as *Shortwave Magazine, Radio Active* and *Ham Radio Today* very helpful. All these magazines are available at good newsagents.

We have already begun collecting new frequencies, so why not send in your lists and receive on of the free publications detailed on page 485.

Editor
November 1997

# Using the UK Scanning Directory

Each page of *The UK Scanning Directory* is set out in five column; Base and Mobile frequencies, Mode, Location and User & Notes.

**Base Frequency:** This is the most acive frequency where most will be heard so the best one to monitor.

**Mobile Frequency:** In a Simplex arrangement, this frequency will be the same as the Base frequency. However, in a Duplex arrangement, this frequency will carry only signals from mobiles.

**Mode:** This is the mode that should be selected on your scanner for best reception.

**Location:** This is generally the area from where the signal originates. For example, if you are in Cambridge and you heard a signal on a particular frequency, then the location of the signal will be Cambridge.

**User & Notes:** This column contains details of who uses a particular frequency, their callsign, channel number and any other relevant notes.

Below is an example of a typical page.

Column 1:  Base & Repeater Transmit Frequency (Duplex)
Base & Mobile Transmit Frequency (Simplex)

Column 2:  Mobile Transmit Frequency (Duplex)
Mobile & Base Transmit Frequency (Simplex)

Column 3: Transmission Mode (i.e. AM, NFM, WFM, etc)

Column 4: Location (The approximate area where the signal will be heard, i.e. City, Town, District, Village, or County.

Column 5: User, Callsign & Remarks

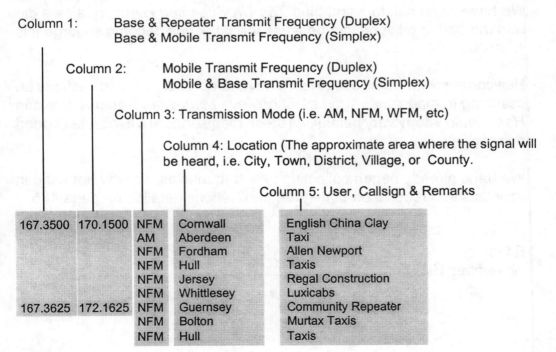

| 167.3500 | 170.1500 | NFM | Cornwall | English China Clay |
| | | AM | Aberdeen | Taxi |
| | | NFM | Fordham | Allen Newport |
| | | NFM | Hull | Taxis |
| | | NFM | Jersey | Regal Construction |
| | | NFM | Whittlesey | Luxicabs |
| 167.3625 | 172.1625 | NFM | Guernsey | Community Repeater |
| | | NFM | Bolton | Murtax Taxis |
| | | NFM | Hull | Taxis |

A great deal of confusion has arisen from the gaps left after certain frequencies, for example, the gaps that follow 167.3500/170.1500 in the above extract. These gaps have been introduced to make the page less cluttered and more user friendly. Any gaps that follow a frequency indicates that the same frequency applies of all entries below the first. Therefore, the 167.3500/170.1500 group means:

| | | | | |
|---|---|---|---|---|
| 167.3500 | 170.1500 | NFM | Cornwall | English China Clay |
| 167.3500 | 170.1500 | AM | Aberdeen | Taxi |
| 167.3500 | 170.1500 | NFM | Fordham | Allen Newport |
| 167.3500 | 170.1500 | NFM | Hull | Taxis |
| 167.3500 | 170.1500 | NFM | Jersey | Regal Construction |
| 167.3500 | 170.1500 | NFM | Whittlesey | Luxicabs |

If you are new to scanning the following list of the main users of the VHF/UHF bands will help you to quickly find their frequencies.

Due to overwhelming workload experienced by the editorial staff of *The UK Scanning Directory*, we are unable to answer queries by telephone, however, you can send them in writing.

## List of Abbreviations and Terms

| | |
|---|---|
| AA | Automobile Association |
| AFIS | Aerodrome Flight Information Service |
| AFSATCOM | US Air Force Satellite Communications |
| AM | Amplitude Modulation |
| ARA | Air Refuelling Area |
| ATC | Air Traffic Control or Air Training Corps |
| ATCC | Air Traffic Control Centre |
| ATIS | Aerodrome Terminal Information Service |
| AWACS | Airborne Warning & Control System |
| BAe | British Aerospace |
| BBC | British Broadcasting Corporation |
| BGS | British Geological Survey |
| BNFL | British Nuclear Fuels Ltd |
| BR | British Rail |
| BT | British Telecom |
| BTP | British Transport Police |
| CAC | Centralised Approach Control |
| CB | Citizen Band |
| CEGB | Central Electricity Generating Board |
| CMD | Command |
| Comms | Communications |
| CW | Continuous Wave (Morse) |
| DAB | Digital Audio Broadcasting |
| DATIS | Digital Aerodrome Terminal Information Service |
| DME | Distance Measuring Equipment |
| DTI | Department of Trade and Industry |
| DSRR | Digital Short Range Radios |
| FLTSATCOM | US Navy Satellite Communications |
| FM | Frequency Modulation |
| GCHQ | Government Communications Headquarters |
| GSM | New digital mobile phones |
| IBA | Independent Broadcasting Authority |
| IFR | Instrument Flight Rules |
| ILR | Independent Local Radio |
| ILS | Instrument Landing System |
| ITN | Independent Television News |
| ITV | Independent Television |
| LBS | Low Band Skip |
| LWT | London Weekend Television |
| MoD | Ministry of Defence |
| Mould | MoD National Home Defence Repeater Network |
| MRSA | Mandatory Radar Service Area |

| | |
|---|---|
| MWL | Mid-Wales Railway Line |
| NATO | North Atlantic Treaty Organisation |
| NASA | National Aeronautics and Space Administration |
| NB | Narrow Band |
| NCB | National Coal Board |
| NFM | Narrow Band FM |
| O/B | Outside Broadcast |
| Ops | Operations |
| PAR | Precision Approach Radar |
| PFA | Popular Flying Association |
| PMR | Private Mobile Radio |
| PR | Personal Radio |
| R | Runway (Left & Right) |
| RAF | Royal Air Force |
| RCA | Radiocommunications Agency |
| RN | Royal Navy |
| RTTY | Radio Teletype |
| SAR | Search and Rescue |
| SCS | Shopping Centre Security |
| Spec. | Specification |
| SRE | Surveillance Radar Element |
| SSB | Single-Side Band |
| SSTV | Slow Scan Television |
| Std | Standard |
| Surv. | Surveillance |
| TACAN | Tactical Air Navigation |
| TMA | Terminal Manoeuvring Area |
| TX | Transmission |
| UACC | Upper Air Control Centre |
| UHF | Ultra High Frequency (300 - 3000 MHz) |
| UKAEA | UK Atomic Energy Authority |
| USAF | US Air Force |
| USAFE | US Air Force Europe |
| USB | Upper Side Band |
| VFR | Visual Flight Rules |
| VHF | Very High Frequency (30 - 300 MHz) |
| VOLMET | Aviation Weather Broadcast |
| VOR | VHF Omni-Directional Radio Range |
| WFM | Wide Band FM |

# Longwave, Medium Wave and Shortwave Allocations

Many scanners now cover frequencies down to 100 kHz and allow access to the exciting world of Shortwave radio. Below is a list of frequency allocations, but if you want to learn more about receiving stations from around the world, turn to the back of this book for a list of publications what will introduce you fascinating subject.

| | |
|---|---|
| 148.5 - 283.5 kHz | Longwave Broadcasting AM |
| 283.5 - 320 kHz | Maritime NDB, Aeronautical Navigation |
| 320 - 405 kHz | Aeronautical Navigation NDB |
| 405 - 435 kHz | Aeronautical Navigation NDB, Maritime Mobiles |
| 435 - 495 kHz | Maritime Mobiles |
| 495 - 505 kHz | Mobile (Distress and Calling) |
| 505 - 526 kHz | Maritime Mobiles |
| 526 - 1626 kHz | Medium Wave Broadcasting |
| 1626 -2850 kHz | Maritime |
| 2850 -2000 kHz | 160 metres Amateur Radio |
| 2300 - 2495 kHz | 120 metres Tropical Braodcasting |
| 2851 - 3019 kHz | En-Route Aeronautical Mobiles |
| 3023 - 3152 kHz | Off-Route Aeronautical Mobiles |
| 3155 - 3200 kHz | Fixed and Land & Maritime Mobiles |
| 3200 - 3400 kHz | 90 metres Tropical Broadcasting and Fixed & Land Mobiles |
| 3401 - 3497 kHz | En-Route Aeronautical Mobiles |
| 3500 - 3800 kHz | 80 metres Amateur Radio |
| 3950 - 4000 kHz | 75 metres European Braodcasting |
| 4000 - 4435 kHz | Maritime Fixed & Mobiles |
| 4438 - 4650 kHz | Fixed and Land & Maritime Mobiles |
| 4651 - 4696 kHz | En-Route Aeronautical Mobiles |
| 4700 - 4995 kHz | Off-Route Aeronautical Mobiles |
| 4750 - 5060 kHz | 60 metres Tropical Broadcasting |
| 5060 - 5450 kHz | Fixed and Land & Maritime Mobiles |
| 5450 - 5477 kHz | Off-Route Aeronautical Mobiles |
| 5481 - 5676 kHz | En-Route Aeronautical Mobiles |
| 5680 - 5726 kHz | Off-Route Aeronautical Mobiles |
| 5730 - 5960 kHz | Fixed and Land & Maritime Mobiles |
| 5950 - 6200 kHz | 49 metres Broadcasting Band |
| 6200 - 6526 kHz | Maritime Mobiles |
| 6526 - 6682 kHz | En-Route Aeronautical Mobiles |
| 6685 - 6765 kHz | Off-Route Aeronautical Mobiles |
| 6765 - 7000 kHz | Fixed and Land Mobiles |
| 7000 - 7100 kHz | 40 metres Amateur Radio |
| 7100 - 7300 kHz | 41 metres Broadcasting Band |
| 7300 - 8100 kHz | Fixed and Land Mobiles |
| 8100 - 8195 kHz | Fixed and Maritime Mobiles |
| 8195 - 8812 kHz | Maritime Mobiles |
| 8816 - 8960 kHz | En-Route Aeronautical Mobiles |
| 8965 - 9037 kHz | Off-Route Aeronautical Mobiles |
| 9040 - 9500 kHz | Fixed |

| | |
|---|---|
| 9500 - 9900 kHz | 31 metres Broadcasting Band |
| 9900 - 9995 kHz | Fixed |
| 10006 - 10096 kHz | En-Route Aeronautical Mobiles |
| 10100 - 10150 kHz | 30 metres Amateur Radio |
| 10150 - 11175 kHz | Fixed and Land & Maritime Mobiles |
| 11175 - 11271 kHz | Off-Route Aeronautical Mobiles |
| 11276 - 11396 kHz | En-Route Aeronautical Mobiles |
| 11400 - 12230 kHz | Fixed |
| 11650 - 12050 kHz | 25 metres Broadcasting Band |
| 12230 - 13197 kHz | Maritime Mobiles |
| 13200 - 13257 kHz | Off-Route Aeronautical Mobiles |
| 13261 - 13357 kHz | En-Route Aeronautical Mobiles |
| 13360 - 13600 kHz | Fixed and Land & Maritime Mobiles |
| 13600 - 13800 kHz | 22 metres Broadcasting Band |
| 13800 - 14000 kHz | Fixed and Land Mobiles |
| 14000 - 14350 kHz | 20 metres Amateur Band |
| 14350 - 14990 kHz | Fixed and Land & Maritime Mobiles |
| 15010 - 15097 kHz | Off-Route Aeronautical Mobiles |
| 15100 - 15600 kHz | 19 metres Broadcasting Band |
| 15600 - 16360 kHz | Fixed |
| 16360 - 17407 kHz | Maritime Mobiles |
| 17410 - 17550 kHz | Fixed |
| 17550 - 17900 kHz | 16 metres Broadcasting Band |
| 17901 - 17967 kHz | En-Route Aeronautical Mobiles |
| 17970 - 18027 kHz | Off-Route Aeronautical Mobiles |
| 18030 - 18068 kHz | Fixed |
| 18068 - 18168 kHz | 16 metres Amateur Band |
| 18168 - 18780 kHz | Fixed |
| 18780 - 18900 kHz | Maritime Mobiles |
| 18900 - 19680 kHz | Fixed |
| 19680 - 19797 kHz | Maritime Mobiles |
| 19800 - 21000 kHz | Fixed & Land Mobiles |
| 21000 - 21450 kHz | 15 metres Amateur Band |
| 21450 - 21850 kHz | 13 metres Broadcasting Band |
| 21850 - 21870 kHz | Fixed |
| 21870 - 21924 kHz | Aeronautical Fixed |
| 21925 - 21998 kHz | En-Route Aeronautical Mobiles |
| 22000 - 22852 kHz | Maritime Mobiles |
| 22855 - 23000 kHz | Fixed |
| 23000 - 23200 kHz | Fixed and Land & Maritime Mobiles |
| 23200 - 23350 kHz | Off-Route Aeronautical Mobiles |
| 23350 - 24890 kHz | Fixed & Land Mobiles |
| 24890 - 24990 kHz | 12 metres Amateur Band |
| 24990 - 25070 kHz | Fixed & Land Mobiles |
| 25070 - 25210 kHz | Maritime Mobiles |
| 25210 - 25520 kHz | Fixed and Land & Maritime Mobiles |
| 25550 - 25600 kHz | Radio Astronomy |
| 25600 - 26100 kHz | 11 metres Broadcasting Band |
| 26100 - 26172 kHz | Maritime Mobiles |
| 26175 - 26235 kHz | Fixed and Land & Maritime Mobiles |

# Scanning and the Law

We are often asked about the legal position of scanning. In a nut shell 95% of what you listen to is illegal! According to the authorities all you can listen to are broadcasts and amateur radio. Tuning into the airband, ships or even the local dust cart is a no go area. If you hear a Mayday call from a fishing boat and inform the Coastguard you can be prosecuted and have your equipment confiscated.

Go to any airport or airshow and you will find many people tuned into the aircrafts and nobody minds. On the other hand during the past year we have learnt of several people who have been successfully prosecuted for listening to the police, even though they were not caught in the act. Because they had police frequencies in their scanner's memory this was enough to convict them, therefore store sensitive frequencies in your head. A helpful leaflet on this subject entitled *Receive only - Scanner etc. Information Sheet* (RA169) is obtainable free of charge from the Radiocommunications Agency, New King's Beam House, 22 Upper Ground, London, SE1 9SA (telephone 0171 211 0502). Therefore scanning should be done with common sense and discretion, and don't tell everybody in the pub how you hear PC Plod arrest your mother-in-law for shop lifting a bottle of gin.

A last thought. This is rather a hypercritical situation because governments listening into us more and more. For example your telephone calls are being monitored by GCHQ, Cheltenham, and the US listening post at Menwith Hill near Harrogate.

# Part 1

# Frequencies for the UK and Republic of Ireland

## 26.1000 - 27.5000 MHz   Fixed, Land and Mobile

## Except Aeronautical Mobile

26.1000 - 26.1750 MHz Maritime Mobile USB

26.100 0- 27.4500 MHz      One-way Paging systems and Alarms

| Base | Mobile | Mode | Location | User and Notes |
|------|--------|------|----------|----------------|
| 26.5880 | | NFM | Nationwide | Common Paging Channel |
| 26.8350 | | NFM | Nationwide | Short term hire pagers |
| 26.9200 | | NFM | Nationwide | Short term hire pagers |
| 26.9950 | | NFM | Nationwide | Vehicle alarms (radio keys) |
| 27.0450 | | NFM | Nationwide | Vehicle alarms (radio keys) |
| 27.0950 | | NFM | Nationwide | Vehicle alarms (radio keys) |
| 27.1200 | | NFM | Nationwide | Paging Test & Development |
| 27.1450 | | NFM | Nationwide | Vehicle alarms (radio keys) |
| 27.1950 | | NFM | Nationwide | Vehicle alarms (radio keys) |
| 27.4500 | | NFM | Nationwide | Short range alarm for the elderly and infirm |

General telementry and telecommand systems for industial,
scientific and medical apperatus

| Base | Mode | Location |
|------|------|----------|
| 26.9950 | NFM | Nationwide |
| 27.0450 | NFM | Nationwide |
| 27.0950 | NFM | Nationwide |
| 27.1450 | NFM | Nationwide |
| 27.1950 | NFM | Nationwide |

26.9650 - 27.4050 MHz   CEPT (UK & Europe) Citizen Band Radio

| Base | Mode | Location | User and Notes |
|------|------|----------|----------------|
| 26.96500 | NFM | Nationwide | Channel 01 |
| 26.97500 | NFM | Nationwide | Channel 02 |
| 26.98500 | NFM | Nationwide | Channel 03 |
| 27.00500 | NFM | Nationwide | Channel 04 |
| 27.01500 | NFM | Nationwide | Channel 05 |
| 27.02500 | NFM | Nationwide | Channel 06 |
| 27.03500 | NFM | Nationwide | Channel 07 |
| 27.05500 | NFM | Nationwide | Channel 08 |
| 27.06500 | NFM | Nationwide | Channel 09 |
| 27.07500 | NFM | Nationwide | Channel 10 |
| 27.08500 | NFM | Nationwide | Channel 11 |
| 27.10500 | NFM | Nationwide | Channel 12 |
| 27.11500 | NFM | Nationwide | Channel 13 |
| 27.12500 | NFM | Nationwide | Channel 14 |
| 27.13500 | NFM | Nationwide | Channel 15 |
| 27.15500 | NFM | Nationwide | Channel 16 |
| 27.16500 | NFM | Nationwide | Channel 17 |
| 27.17500 | NFM | Nationwide | Channel 18 |
| 27.18500 | NFM | Nationwide | Channel 19 |
| 27.20500 | NFM | Nationwide | Channel 20 |
| 27.21500 | NFM | Nationwide | Channel 21 |
| 27.22500 | NFM | Nationwide | Channel 22 |
| 27.23500 | NFM | Nationwide | Channel 24 |
| 27.24500 | NFM | Nationwide | Channel 25 |
| 27.25500 | NFM | Nationwide | Channel 23 |

| Base | Mobile | Mode | Location | User and Notes |
|------|--------|------|----------|----------------|
| 27.26500 | | NFM | Nationwide | Channel 26 |
| 27.27500 | | NFM | Nationwide | Channel 27 |
| 27.28500 | | NFM | Nationwide | Channel 28 |
| 27.29500 | | NFM | Nationwide | Channel 29 |
| 27.30500 | | NFM | Nationwide | Channel 30 |
| 27.31500 | | NFM | Nationwide | Channel 31 |
| 27.32500 | | NFM | Nationwide | Channel 32 |
| 27.33500 | | NFM | Nationwide | Channel 33 |
| 27.34500 | | NFM | Nationwide | Channel 34 |
| 27.35500 | | NFM | Nationwide | Channel 35 |
| 27.36500 | | NFM | Nationwide | Channel 36 |
| 27.37500 | | NFM | Nationwide | Channel 37 |
| 27.38500 | | NFM | Nationwide | Channel 38 |
| 27.39500 | | NFM | Nationwide | Channel 39 |
| 27.40500 | | NFM | Nationwide | Channel 40 |

### 26.960 - 27.280 MHz — GENERAL MODEL CONTROL

| Base | Mobile | Mode | Location | User and Notes |
|------|--------|------|----------|----------------|
| 26.99500 | | NFM | Nationwide | 'Brown' Model Channel |
| 27.04500 | | NFM | Nationwide | 'Red' Model Channel |
| 27.09500 | | NFM | Nationwide | 'Orange' Model Channel |
| 27.14500 | | NFM | Nationwide | 'Yellow' Model Channel |
| 27.19500 | | NFM | Nationwide | 'Green' Model Channel |
| 27.24500 | | NFM | Nationwide | 'Blue' Model Channel |

---

### 27.60125 - 27.99125 MHz UK CB

| Base | Mobile | Mode | Location | User and Notes |
|------|--------|------|----------|----------------|
| 27.60125 | 27.60125 | NFM | Nationwide | Channel 01 |
| 27.61125 | 27.61125 | NFM | Nationwide | Channel 02 |
| 27.62125 | 27.62125 | NFM | Nationwide | Channel 03 |
| 27.63125 | 27.63125 | NFM | Nationwide | Channel 04 |
| 27.64125 | 27.64125 | NFM | Nationwide | Channel 05 |
| 27.65125 | 27.65125 | NFM | Nationwide | Channel 06 |
| 27.66125 | 27.66125 | NFM | Nationwide | Channel 07 |
| 27.67125 | 27.67125 | NFM | Nationwide | Channel 08 |
| 27.68125 | 27.68125 | NFM | Nationwide | Channel 09 Emergency |
| 27.69125 | 27.69125 | NFM | Nationwide | Channel 10 |
| 27.70125 | 27.70125 | NFM | Nationwide | Channel 11 |
| 27.71125 | 27.71125 | NFM | Nationwide | Channel 12 |
| 27.72125 | 27.72125 | NFM | Nationwide | Channel 13 |
| 27.73125 | 27.73125 | NFM | Nationwide | Channel 14 Calling |
| 27.74125 | 27.74125 | NFM | Nationwide | Channel 15 |
| 27.75125 | 27.75125 | NFM | Nationwide | Channel 16 |
| 27.76125 | 27.76125 | NFM | Nationwide | Channel 17 |
| 27.77125 | 27.77125 | NFM | Nationwide | Channel 18 |
| 27.78125 | 27.78125 | NFM | Nationwide | Channel 19 Calling |
| 27.79125 | 27.79125 | NFM | Nationwide | Channel 20 |
| 27.80125 | 27.80125 | NFM | Nationwide | Channel 21 |
| 27.81125 | 27.81125 | NFM | Nationwide | Channel 22 |
| 27.82125 | 27.82125 | NFM | Nationwide | Channel 23 |
| 27.83125 | 27.83125 | NFM | Nationwide | Channel 24 |
| 27.84125 | 27.84125 | NFM | Nationwide | Channel 25 |
| 27.85125 | 27.85125 | NFM | Nationwide | Channel 26 |
| 27.86125 | 27.86125 | NFM | Nationwide | Channel 27 |

| Base | Mobile | Mode | Location | User and Notes |
|------|--------|------|----------|----------------|
| 27.87125 | 27.87125 | NFM | Nationwide | Channel 28 |
| 27.88125 | 27.88125 | NFM | Nationwide | Channel 29 |
| 27.89125 | 27.89125 | NFM | Nationwide | Channel 30 |
| 27.90125 | 27.90125 | NFM | Nationwide | Channel 31 |
| 27.91125 | 27.91125 | NFM | Nationwide | Channel 32 |
| 27.92125 | 27.92125 | NFM | Nationwide | Channel 33 |
| 27.93125 | 27.93125 | NFM | Nationwide | Channel 34 |
| 27.94125 | 27.94125 | NFM | Nationwide | Channel 35 |
| 27.95125 | 27.95125 | NFM | Nationwide | Channel 36 |
| 27.96125 | 27.96125 | NFM | Nationwide | Channel 37 |
| 27.97125 | 27.97125 | NFM | Nationwide | Channel 38 |
| 27.98125 | 27.98125 | NFM | Nationwide | Channel 39 |
| 27.99125 | 27.99125 | NFM | Nationwide | Channel 40 |

| Base | Mobile | Mode | Location | User and Notes |
|------|--------|------|----------|----------------|
| 28.0000 - 29.7000 MHz | | | 10M AMATEUR BAND | |
| 28.12000 | | SSB | Nationwide | Packet Radio |
| 28.21500 | | CW | Didcot | GB3RAL Beacon |
| 28.67500 | | SSB | Nationwide | Slow Scan TV and Fax |
| 29.20000 | | SSB | Nationwide | Packet Radio (FM 2.5 kHz) |
| 29.30000 | | SSB | Nationwide | Satellite downlinks |
| 29.60000 | | NFM | Nationwide | FM Calling Channel |

| Base | Mobile | Mode | Location | User and Notes |
|------|--------|------|----------|----------------|
| 29.7000 - 29.9700 MHz | | MoD TACTICAL CHANNELS 25 kHz SIMPLEX NFM | | |

| Base | Mobile | Mode | Location | User and Notes |
|------|--------|------|----------|----------------|
| 30.0050 - 31.0250 MHz | | NASA SPACE TO EARTH NFM SIMPLEX | | |
| 30.01000 | | NFM | Space | Downlink |

| Base | Mobile | Mode | Location | User and Notes |
|------|--------|------|----------|----------------|
| 30.0250 - 31.7000 MHz | | USAFE COMMUNICATIONS 25 kHz SIMPLEX | | |
| 30.0250 | | NFM | USAF Fairford | Base Security |
| 30.1250 | | NFM | Swansea | TA HQ Camp Communications |
| 30.1750 | | NFM | Salisbury Plain | Army |
| 30.2000 | | NFM | Salisbury Plain | Army |
| 30.3250 | | NFM | Salisbury Plain | Army |
| 30.3500 | | NFM | Nationwide | Army Forward Air Controllers |
| 30.4500 | | NFM | Nationwide | US Military MARS Network |
| 30.5000 | | NFM | London | US Embassy Security (Eagle) |
| | | NFM | USAF Fairford | Base Security |
| 30.9875 | | NFM | USAF Fairford | Base Security |
| 31.0000 | | NFM | USAF Fairford | Tanker Ground Ops |
| 31.1825 | | NFM | USAF Fairford | Fence Security |
| 31.2000 | | NFM | Salisbury Plain | Army |
| | | NFM | USAF Fairford | Ground Maintenance |
| 31.2125 | | NFM | Nationwide | Digital Signalling |
| 31.2500 | | NFM | USAF Fairford | Base Security |
| 31.3000 | | NFM | USAF Fairford | Base Medical Services |
| 31.4000 | | NFM | USAF Fairford | Tanker Ground Operations |
| 31.4375 | | NFM | Nationwide | Digital Signalling |
| 31.5000 | | NFM | Brighton | TA Barracks |
| | | NFM | Preston | TA Barracks |
| 31.6750 | | NFM | Salisbury Plain | Army |
| 31.7000 | | NFM | Salisbury Plain | Army |

**31.7250 - 31.7750 MHz   HOSPITAL PAGING OUTGOING SPEECH.**

**(RETURN SPEECH ONLY IN EMERGENCIES)**

| Base | Mobile | Mode | Location | User and Notes |
|------|--------|------|----------|----------------|
| 31.725 | 161.000 | NFM | Nationwide | Hospital Paging |
| 31.750 | 161.025 | NFM | Nationwide | Hospital Paging |
| | | NFM | Worcester | Ronkwood Hospital Paging |
| 31.775 | 161.050 | NFM | Nationwide | Hospital Paging |

**31.8000 - 34.9000 MHz   USAFE COMMUNICATIONS 25 kHz SIMPLEX**

| Base | Mobile | Mode | Location | User and Notes |
|------|--------|------|----------|----------------|
| 31.8000 | | AM | Nationwide | RAF Cadets Channel V12 |
| 31.9125 | | NFM | Nationwide | Digital Signalling |
| 31.9500 | | NFM | Salisbury Plain | Army |
| 32.2000 | | NFM | Nationwide | USAF Base Security |
| 32.2500 | | NFM | Salisbury Plain | Army |
| 32.3000 | | NFM | Brighton | TA Barracks |
| | | NFM | Preston | TA Barracks |
| | | NFM | USAF Fairford | Base Security |
| 32.3250 | | NFM | Salisbury Plain | Army |
| 32.3500 | | NFM | Salisbury Plain | Army |
| | | NFM | USAF Mildenhall | Security |
| 32.4250 | | NFM | Salisbury Plain | Army |
| 32.5250 | | NFM | Salisbury Plain | Army |
| 32.5750 | | NFM | Salisbury Plain | Army |
| 32.9000 | | NFM | Salisbury Plain | Army |
| 33.1250 | | NFM | Nationwide | Army Land Forces |
| 33.2000 | | NFM | Salisbury Plain | Army |
| 33.2500 | | NFM | USAF Lakenheath | Birdscare Operations |
| | | NFM | USAF Mildenhall | Birdscare Operations |
| 33.3000 | | NFM | Nationwide | USAF War Training |
| 33.5000 | | NFM | USAF Lakenheath | Birdscare Operations |
| | | NFM | USAF Mildenhall | Birdscare Operations |
| 33.6750 | | NFM | Brighton | TA Barracks |
| | | NFM | Preston | TA Barracks |
| 33.7000 | | NFM | USAF Mildenhall | Fire Control |
| 33.7750 | | NFM | Salisbury Plain | Army |
| 33.8625 | | NFM | USAF Mildenhall | Ambulance |
| 34.1000 | | NFM | Nationwide | USAF Medical |
| 34.1250 | | NFM | Salisbury Plain | Army |
| 34.1500 | | NFM | USAF Lakenheath | Crash Operations |
| | | NFM | USAF Mildenhall | Crash Operations |
| 34.3000 | | NFM | Salisbury Plain | Army |
| 34.4000 | | NFM | Nationwide | Army Forward Air Controllers |
| 34.7625 | | NFM | USAF Mildenhall | Security |
| 34.9000 | | NFM | USAF Lakenheath | Base Security |
| | | NFM | USAF Mildenhall | Security |

**34.9250 - 34.9750 MHz   LOW POWER ALARMS FOR ELDERLY AND**

**INFIRM ALARM FOR ELDERLY & INFIRM**

| Base | Mobile | Mode | Location | User and Notes |
|------|--------|------|----------|----------------|
| 34.9250 | | NFM | Nationwide | |
| 34.9500 | | NFM | Nationwide | |
| | | NFM | West Midlands | Emergency Alarms for the Elderly |
| 34.9750 | | NFM | Nationwide | |
| | | NFM | West Midlands | Emergency Alarms for the Elderly |

**35.0000 - 35.2500 MHz** RADIO CONTROLLED MODEL AIRCRAFT 10 kHz (100 mW MAX)

| Base | Mobile | Mode | Location | User and Notes |
| --- | --- | --- | --- | --- |
| 35.00000 | | NFM | Nationwide | Channel 60 |
| 35.01000 | | NFM | Nationwide | Channel 61 |
| 35.02000 | | NFM | Nationwide | Channel 62 |
| 35.03000 | | NFM | Nationwide | Channel 63 |
| 35.04000 | | NFM | Nationwide | Channel 64 |
| 35.05000 | | NFM | Nationwide | Channel 65 |
| 35.06000 | | NFM | Nationwide | Channel 66 |
| 35.07000 | | NFM | Nationwide | Channel 67 |
| 35.08000 | | NFM | Nationwide | Channel 68 |
| 35.09000 | | NFM | Nationwide | Channel 69 |
| 35.10000 | | NFM | Nationwide | Channel 70 |
| 35.11000 | | NFM | Nationwide | Channel 71 |
| 35.12000 | | NFM | Nationwide | Channel 72 |
| 35.13000 | | NFM | Nationwide | Channel 73 |
| 35.14000 | | NFM | Nationwide | Channel 74 |
| 35.15000 | | NFM | Nationwide | Channel 75 |
| 35.16000 | | NFM | Nationwide | Channel 76 |
| 35.17000 | | NFM | Nationwide | Channel 77 |
| 35.18000 | | NFM | Nationwide | Channel 78 |
| 35.19000 | | NFM | Nationwide | Channel 79 |
| 35.20000 | | NFM | Nationwide | Channel 80 |
| 35.21000 | | NFM | Nationwide | Channel 81 |
| 35.22000 | | NFM | Nationwide | Channel 82 |
| 35.23000 | | NFM | Nationwide | Channel 83 |
| 35.24000 | | NFM | Nationwide | Channel 84 |
| 35.25000 | | NFM | Nationwide | Channel 85 |

**35.2500 - 37.7500 MHz** MOD TACTICAL COMMUNICATIONS 25 kHz SIMPLEX

| Base | Mobile | Mode | Location | User and Notes |
| --- | --- | --- | --- | --- |
| 35.2500 | | NFM | Salisbury Plain | Army |
| 35.2750 | | NFM | Salisbury Plain | Army |
| 35.3500 | | NFM | Brecon Beacons | Army |
| 35.4000 | | NFM | Brecon Beacons | Army |
| 35.5750 | | NFM | Salisbury Plain | Army |
| 35.6000 | | NFM | USAF Mildenhall | Security |
| 35.6250 | | NFM | Salisbury Plain | Army |
| 35.7750 | | NFM | Salisbury Plain | Army |
| 35.9000 | | NFM | USAF Mildenhall | Security |
| 35.9750 | | NFM | Nationwide | Royal Signals |
| 36.0000 | | NFM | Brighton | TA Barracks |
| | | NFM | Preston | TA Barracks |
| 36.3500 | | NFM | Bovington | Army Training Camp |
| 36.7500 | | NFM | Nationwide | Army Forward Air Controllers |
| 36.8000 | | NFM | Nationwide | ATC Channel V12 |
| 36.8500 | | NFM | Salisbury Plain | Army |
| 37.2250 | | NFM | Stanford Battle Area | Army |
| 37.3000 | | AM | Nationwide | RAF Cadets Channel V11 |
| 37.3250 | | NFM | Salisbury Plain | Army |

**37.7500 - 38.2500 MHz** RADIO ASTRONOMY BAND

## 37.9000 - 40.1000 MHz MoD Tactical Communications 25 kHz Simplex

| Base | Mobile | Mode | Location | User and Notes |
|---|---|---|---|---|
| 38.0000 | | USB | Nationwide | Racal Comsec Spot |
| 38.1000 | | AM | Nationwide | RAF Cadets Channel V13 |
| 38.3200 | | NFM | Nationwide | Fish Tagging (salmon) |
| 38.5750 | | NFM | Senny Bridge | Army |
| 38.6250 | | NFM | Oakhampton | Army 657 Sqn Ops |
| 39.0000 | | NFM | Ludford Cove | Range Patrol Vessel |
| | | NFM | Salisbury Plain | Army |
| 39.5000 | | NFM | Nationwide | Army Tanks Channel |
| 39.6000 | | NFM | Ludford Cove | Army Patrol Vessel |
| 39.6500 | | NFM | Nationwide | Army Tanks Channel |
| 39.7500 | | NFM | Nationwide | Royal Signals Display |
| 39.9000 | | NFM | USAF Fairford | Base Security |
| 40.0000 | | NFM | Salisbury Plain | Army |
| 40.0500 | | NFM | Nationwide | Army Distress Frequency |
| 40.0800 | | NFM | London | Sky News Link |
| 40.2000 | | AM | Nationwide | RAF Cadets Channel V14 |
| 40.2750 | | NFM | London | Royal Military Police |

## 40.6650 - 40.9550 MHz    Radio Controlled Surface Models 10 kHz
### (e.g. cars and boats)

| Base | Mobile | Mode | Location | User and Notes |
|---|---|---|---|---|
| 40.66500 | | NFM | Nationwide | Channel 665 |
| 40.67500 | | NFM | Nationwide | Channel 675 |
| 40.68500 | | NFM | Nationwide | Channel 685 |
| 40.69500 | | NFM | Nationwide | Channel 695 |
| 40.70000 | | NFM | Bovington Camp | Army |
| | | NFM | Salisbury Plain | Army |
| 40.70500 | | NFM | Nationwide | Channel 705 |
| 40.71500 | | NFM | Nationwide | Channel 715 |
| 40.72500 | | NFM | Nationwide | Channel 725 |
| 40.73500 | | NFM | Nationwide | Channel 735 |
| 40.74500 | | NFM | Nationwide | Channel 745 |
| 40.75000 | | NFM | Bovington Camp | Army |
| | | NFM | Nationwide | Channel 755 |
| 40.76500 | | NFM | Nationwide | Channel 765 |
| 40.77500 | | NFM | Nationwide | Channel 775 |
| 40.78500 | | NFM | Nationwide | Channel 785 |
| 40.79500 | | NFM | Nationwide | Channel 795 |
| 40.80500 | | NFM | Nationwide | Channel 805 |
| 40.81500 | | NFM | Nationwide | Channel 815 |
| 40.82500 | | NFM | Nationwide | Channel 825 |
| 40.83500 | | NFM | Nationwide | Channel 835 |
| 40.84500 | | NFM | Nationwide | Channel 845 |
| 40.85500 | | NFM | Nationwide | Channel 855 |
| 40.86500 | | NFM | Nationwide | Channel 865 |
| 40.87500 | | NFM | Nationwide | Channel 875 |
| | | NFM | Salisbury Plain | Army |
| 40.88500 | | NFM | Nationwide | Channel 885 |
| 40.89500 | | NFM | Nationwide | Channel 895 |
| 40.90500 | | NFM | Nationwide | Channel 905 |
| 40.91500 | | NFM | Nationwide | Channel 915 |
| 40.92500 | | NFM | Nationwide | Channel 925 |
| 40.93500 | | NFM | Nationwide | Channel 935 |
| 40.94500 | | NFM | Nationwide | Channel 945 |
| 40.95500 | | NFM | Nationwide | Channel 955 |

## 41.0000 - 46.6000 MHz MoD Tactical Communications 25 kHz Simplex

| Base | Mobile | Mode | Location | User and Notes |
| --- | --- | --- | --- | --- |
| 41.1250 | | NFM | Salisbury Plain | Army |
| 42.0500 | | NFM | Jersey | Territorial Army |
| | | NFM | Salisbury Plain | Army |
| 42.1250 | | NFM | Nationwide | Army War Training |
| 42.3250 | | NFM | Salisbury Plain | Army |
| 42.5500 | | NFM | Salisbury Plain | Army |
| 43.1000 | | NFM | Salisbury Plain | Army |
| 43.2250 | | NFM | Salisbury Plain | Army |
| 43.5500 | | NFM | Salisbury Plain | Army |
| 43.7750 | | NFM | Salisbury Plain | Army |
| 44.0000 | | NFM | Bovington | Army Training Camp |
| | | NFM | Salisbury Plain | Army |
| 44.4250 | | NFM | Salisbury Plain | Army |
| 44.4500 | | NFM | Nationwide | Army War Training |
| 45.3000 | | NFM | Salisbury Plain | Army |
| | | NFM | Stanford Battle Area | Army |
| 45.4000 | | NFM | Senny Bridge | Army |
| 45.4250 | | NFM | Stanford Battle Area | Army |
| 45.7000 | | NFM | Wiltshire | Dunge Hill War Games |
| 45.7125 | | NFM | Nationwide | Army War Training |
| 46.0000 | | NFM | Nationwide | Royal Signals Display |
| 46.1250 | | NFM | Nationwide | Army War Training |
| 46.3250 | | NFM | Nationwide | Army War Training |

## 46.6100 - 46.9700 MHz   US Spec. Cordless Telephones Base
### (Split + 3.06 MHz)

| Base | Mobile | Mode | Location | User and Notes |
| --- | --- | --- | --- | --- |
| 46.61000 | 49.67000 | NFM | Nationwide | US Specification Channel 1 |
| 46.63000 | 49.84500 | NFM | Nationwide | US Specification Channel 2 |
| 46.67000 | 49.86000 | NFM | Nationwide | US Specification Channel 3 |
| 46.71000 | 49.77000 | NFM | Nationwide | US Specification Channel 4 |
| 46.73000 | 49.87500 | NFM | Nationwide | US Specification Channel 5 |
| 46.77000 | 49.83000 | NFM | Nationwide | US Specification Channel 6 |
| 46.80000 | 46.80000 | NFM | London | BBC Music Link |
| 46.83000 | 49.89000 | NFM | Nationwide | US Specification Channel 7 |
| 46.87000 | 49.93000 | NFM | Nationwide | US Specification Channel 8 |
| 46.93000 | 49.99000 | NFM | Nationwide | US Specification Channel 9 |
| 46.97000 | 49.97000 | NFM | Nationwide | US Specification Channel 10 |

## 47.0000 - 47.4000 MHz   Future PMR Allocation, currently MoD

## 47.309375 - 47.365625 MHz   Long Range and Vehicle Security Alarm Systems 12.5 kHz bandwidth

| Base | Mobile | Mode | Location | User and Notes |
| --- | --- | --- | --- | --- |
| 47.309375 | | NFM | Nationwide | Channel 1 (6.25 kHz bandwidth) |
| 47.318750 | | NFM | Nationwide | Channel 2 |
| 47.331250 | | NFM | Nationwide | Channel 3 |
| 47.343750 | | NFM | Nationwide | Channel 4 |
| 47.356250 | | NFM | Nationwide | Channel 5 |
| 47.365625 | | NFM | Nationwide | Channel 6 (6.25 kHz bandwith) |
| 47.400000 | | NFM | Nationwide | Vehicle theft paging alarms |
| | | NFM | London | BBC Music Link |

| Base | Mobile | Mode | Location | User and Notes |
|------|--------|------|----------|----------------|

**47.41875 - 47.43125 MHz   EXTENDED RANGE CORDLESS PHONES**

| Base | Mobile | Mode | Location | User and Notes |
|------|--------|------|----------|----------------|
| 47.41875 | 77.55000 | NFM | Nationwide | Extended Range Telephone |
| 47.43125 | 77.51250 | NFM | Nationwide | Extended Range Telephone |

**47.45625 - 47.54375 MHz   DTI APPROVED CORDLESS TELEPHONES**

| Base | Mobile | Mode | Location | User and Notes |
|------|--------|------|----------|----------------|
| 47.45625 | 1.64200 | NFM | Nationwide | Channel 1 |
| 47.46875 | 1.66200 | NFM | Nationwide | Channel 2 |
| 47.48125 | 1.68200 | NFM | Nationwide | Channel 3 |
| 47.49375 | 1.70200 | NFM | Nationwide | Channel 4 |
| 47.50625 | 1.72200 | NFM | Nationwide | Channel 5 |
| 47.51875 | 1.74200 | NFM | Nationwide | Channel 6 |
| 47.53125 | 1.76200 | NFM | Nationwide | Channel 7 |
| 47.54375 | 1.78200 | NFM | Nationwide | Channel 8 |

**47.5500 - 48.5500 MHz   BROADCASTING LINKS**

| Base | Mobile | Mode | Location | User and Notes |
|------|--------|------|----------|----------------|
| 47.57000 | | NFM | Cardiff | BBC Radio Wales studio sound Ch |
| 47.64500 | | NFM | Nationwide | BBC O/B |
| 47.94375 | | NFM | Nationwide | ITV Engineers Channel 1 |
| 47.94375 | | NFM | Stockport | TV Engineers |
| 47.95625 | | NFM | Nationwide | ITV Engineers Channel 2 |
| 47.96875 | | NFM | Nationwide | ITV Engineers Channel 3 |
| 48.05625 | | NFM | Isle of Wight | Isle of Wight Radio Feeder |
| 48.08125 | | NFM | London | Sky TV Talkback |

**48.4000 - 48.5000 MHz   CORDLESS RADIO MICROPHONES 12.5 kHz**

| Base | Mobile | Mode | Location | User and Notes |
|------|--------|------|----------|----------------|
| 48.40000 | | NFM | Nationwide | Channel 1 |
| 48.40625 | 52.85625 | NFM | Nationwide | ASP-Hi Talkback |
| 48.41250 | 52.86875 | NFM | Nationwide | ASP-Hi Talkback |
| 48.41250 | | NFM | Nationwide | Channel 2 |
| 48.42500 | 52.87125 | NFM | Nationwide | ASP-Hi Talkback |
| | | NFM | Nationwide | Channel 3 |
| 48.43750 | 52.90375 | NFM | Nationwide | ASP-Hi Talkback |
| 48.43750 | | NFM | Nationwide | Channel 4 |
| 48.45000 | 52.90625 | NFM | Nationwide | ASP-Hi Talkback |
| | | NFM | Nationwide | Channel 5 |
| 48.46250 | 52.91875 | NFM | Nationwide | ASP-Hi Talkback |
| | | NFM | Nationwide | Channel 6 |
| 48.47500 | 52.93125 | NFM | Nationwide | ASP-Hi Talkback |
| | | NFM | Nationwide | Channel 7 |
| 48.48750 | | NFM | Nationwide | Channel 8 |
| 48.50000 | 52.94375 | NFM | Nationwide | ASP-Hi Talkback |

**48.97500 - 48.98750 MHz   SHORT TERM HIRE PAGING**

| Base | Mobile | Mode | Location | User and Notes |
|------|--------|------|----------|----------------|
| 48.97500 | | NFM | Nationwide | |
| 48.98750 | | NFM | Nationwide | |

**49.0000 - 49.4875 MHz   ONE WAY NON SPEECH PAGING SYSTEMS 12.5 kHz**

| Base | Mobile | Mode | Location | User and Notes |
|------|--------|------|----------|----------------|
| 49.00000 | | NFM | Nationwide | Channel 1 |
| 49.01250 | | NFM | Nationwide | Channel 2 |
| 49.02500 | | NFM | Nationwide | Channel 3 |
| 49.03750 | | NFM | Nationwide | Channel 4 |
| 49.05000 | | NFM | Nationwide | Channel 5 |
| 49.06250 | | NFM | Nationwide | Channel 6 |

| Base | Mobile | Mode | Location | User and Notes |
|------|--------|------|----------|----------------|
| 49.07500 | | NFM | Nationwide | Channel 7 |
| 49.08750 | | NFM | Nationwide | Channel 8 |
| 49.10000 | | NFM | Nationwide | Channel 9 |
| 49.11250 | | NFM | Nationwide | Channel 10 |
| 49.12500 | | NFM | Nationwide | Channel 11 |
| 49.13750 | | NFM | Nationwide | Channel 12 |
| 49.15000 | | NFM | Nationwide | Channel 13 |
| 49.16250 | | NFM | Nationwide | Channel 14 |
| 49.17500 | | NFM | Nationwide | Channel 15 |
| 49.18750 | | NFM | Nationwide | Channel 16 |
| 49.20000 | | NFM | Nationwide | Channel 17 |
| 49.21250 | | NFM | Nationwide | Channel 18 |
| 49.22500 | | NFM | Nationwide | Channel 19 |
| 49.23750 | | NFM | Nationwide | Channel 20 |
| 49.25000 | | NFM | Nationwide | Channel 21 |
| 49.26250 | | NFM | Nationwide | Channel 22 |
| 49.27500 | | NFM | Nationwide | Channel 23 |
| 49.28750 | | NFM | Nationwide | Channel 24 |
| 49.30000 | | NFM | Nationwide | Channel 25 |
| 49.31250 | | NFM | Nationwide | Channel 26 |
| 49.32500 | | NFM | Nationwide | Channel 27 |
| 49.33750 | | NFM | Nationwide | Channel 28 |
| 49.35000 | | NFM | Nationwide | Channel 29 |
| 49.36250 | | NFM | Nationwide | Channel 30 |
| 49.37500 | | NFM | Nationwide | Channel 31 |
| 49.38750 | | NFM | Nationwide | Channel 32 |
| 49.40000 | | NFM | Nationwide | Channel 33 |
| 49.41250 | | NFM | Nationwide | Channel 34 |
| 49.48750 | | NFM | Nationwide | Channel 40 |

**49.4250 - 49.4750 MHz    HOSPITAL PAGING**

| Base | Mobile | Mode | Location | User and Notes |
|------|--------|------|----------|----------------|
| 49.42500 | 161.0000 | NFM | Bournemouth | Hospital Paging |
| | | NFM | Nationwide | Hospital Channel 35 |
| 49.43750 | 161.1000 | NFM | Nationwide | Hospital Channel 36 |
| 49.45000 | 164.2000 | NFM | Jersey | Hospital Cardiac Bleep & Voice |
| | | NFM | Nationwide | Hospital Channel 37 |
| 49.46250 | | NFM | Nationwide | Hospital Channel 38 |
| 49.47500 | | NFM | Nationwide | Hospital Channel 39 |

**49.5000 - 49.7875 MHz    BBC CORDLESS MICROPHONES NFM**

**49.6700 - 49.9700 MHz    US SPEC. CORDLESS TELEPHONES BASE
(SPLIT + 3.06 MHz)**

**49.8200 - 49.9875 MHz    LOW POWER DEVICES,WALKIE TALKIES, RADIO
CONTROLLED TOYS AND BABY MONITORS**

| Base | Mobile | Mode | Location | User and Notes |
|------|--------|------|----------|----------------|
| 49.82000 | | NFM | Nationwide | Channel 1 |
| 49.83000 | | NFM | Nationwide | Channel 2 |
| | | NFM | Nationwide | Channel A |
| | | NFM | Nationwide | Maxan Channel 1 |
| 49.84000 | | NFM | Milton Keynes | JD Sports |
| | | NFM | Nationwide | Channel 3 |
| | | NFM | Nationwide | Channel UK1 |
| 49.84500 | | NFM | Nationwide | Channel B |

| Base | Mobile | Mode | Location | User and Notes |
|------|--------|------|----------|----------------|
| 49.84500 | | NFM | Nationwide | Maxan Channel 2 |
| 49.85000 | | NFM | Nationwide | Channel 4 |
| 49.86000 | | NFM | Ayr | Sports division stock control |
| | | NFM | Nationwide | Channel 5 |
| | | NFM | Nationwide | Channel C |
| | | NFM | Nationwide | Maxan Channel 3 |
| 49.87000 | | NFM | Nationwide | Channel 6 |
| 49.87500 | | NFM | Nationwide | Channel D |
| | | NFM | Nationwide | Maxan Channel 4 |
| 49.88000 | | NFM | Nationwide | Channel UK2 |
| 49.89000 | | NFM | London | CSM motorcycle training |
| | | NFM | Nationwide | Channel 7 |
| 49.89000 | | NFM | Nationwide | Channel E |
| | | NFM | Nationwide | Maxan Channel 5 |
| 49.90000 | | NFM | Nationwide | Channel 8 |
| 49.90500 | | NFM | Nationwide | Tomy baby monitors |
| 49.91000 | | NFM | Nationwide | Channel 9 |
| 49.92000 | | NFM | Nationwide | Channel 10 |
| 49.93000 | | NFM | Nationwide | Channel 11 |
| 49.94000 | | NFM | Nationwide | Channel 12 |
| 49.95000 | | NFM | Nationwide | Channel 13 |
| 49.96000 | | NFM | Nationwide | Channel 14 |
| | | NFM | Nationwide | Channel UK3 |
| 49.97000 | | NFM | Nationwide | Channel 15 |
| 49.98000 | | NFM | Nationwide | Channel 16 |

**50.0000 - 52.0000 MHz   6M UK AMATEUR RADIO BAND ALL MODES**

| Base | Mobile | Mode | Location | User and Notes |
|------|--------|------|----------|----------------|
| 50.00000 | | CW | Buxton | Beacon (GB3BUX) |
| 50.04200 | | CW | St Austell | Beacon (GB3MCB) |
| 50.05000 | | CW | Potters Bar | Beacon (GB3NHQ) |
| 50.06000 | | CW | Inverness | Beacon (GB3RMK) |
| 50.06400 | | CW | Lerwick | Beacon (GB3LER) |
| 50.06500 | | CW | Jersey | Beacon (GB3IOJ) |
| 50.09000 | | CW | Nationwide | CW calling |
| 50.20000 | | USB | Nationwide | SSB calling |
| 50.27500 | | CW | Darlington | Beacon (GB3IFX) |
| 50.30000 | | CW | Nationwide | CW calling |
| 50.51000 | | SSB | Nationwide | Slow scan TV |
| 50.55000 | | SSB | Nationwide | Fax |
| 50.60000 | | SSB | Nationwide | RTTY (afsk) |
| 50.63000 | | SSB | Nationwide | Packet radio |
| 51.51000 | | SSB | Nationwide | FM calling (all modes) |

**52.0000 - 52.3875 MHz   BROADCASTING LINKS NFM**

**52.8500 - 52.9500 MHz   CORDLESS RADIO MICROPHONES 12.5 kHz**

| Base | Mobile | Mode | Location | User and Notes |
|------|--------|------|----------|----------------|
| 52.85000 | | NFM | Nationwide | Channel 1 |
| 52.86250 | | NFM | Nationwide | ASP Talkback Sound Links |
| | | NFM | Nationwide | Channel 2 |
| 52.87500 | | NFM | Nationwide | ASP Talkback Sound Links |
| | | NFM | Nationwide | Channel 3 |
| 52.88750 | | NFM | Nationwide | Channel 4 |
| 52.90000 | | NFM | Nationwide | ASP Talkback Sound Links |
| | | NFM | Nationwide | Channel 5 |

| Base | Mobile | Mode | Location | User and Notes |
|------|--------|------|----------|----------------|
| 52.91250 | | NFM | Nationwide | ASP Talkback Sound Links |
| | | NFM | Nationwide | Channel 6 |
| 52.92500 | | NFM | Nationwide | ASP Talkback Sound Links |
| 52.92500 | | NFM | Nationwide | Channel 7 |
| 52.93750 | | NFM | Nationwide | ASP Talkback Sound Links |
| | | NFM | Nationwide | Channel 8 |
| 52.95000 | | NFM | Nationwide | ASP Talkback Sound Links |
| 53.20000 | | NFM | Swansea | BBC Wales |
| 53.52500 | | NFM | Nationwide | BBC O/B Continuity |

**53.7500 - 55.7500 MHz    BBC 5W Cordless Microphones**

| Base | Mobile | Mode | Location | User and Notes |
|------|--------|------|----------|----------------|
| 53.57500 | | NFM | Taunton | BBC O/B Mics (Somerset Sound) |
| 53.75000 | | NFM | Nationwide | BBC O/B Microphone Ch. 1 |
| 53.85000 | | NFM | Nationwide | BBC O/B Microphone Ch. 2 |
| 53.95000 | | NFM | Nationwide | BBC O/B Microphone Ch. 3 |
| 54.05000 | | NFM | Nationwide | BBC O/B Microphone Ch. 4 |
| 54.15000 | | NFM | Nationwide | BBC O/B Microphone Ch. 5 |
| 54.25000 | | NFM | Nationwide | BBC O/B Microphone Ch. 6 |
| 54.35000 | | NFM | Nationwide | BBC O/B Microphone Ch. 7 |
| 54.45000 | | NFM | Nationwide | BBC O/B Microphone Ch. 8 |
| 54.55000 | | NFM | Nationwide | BBC O/B Microphone Ch. 9 |
| 54.65000 | | NFM | Nationwide | BBC O/B Microphone Ch. 10 |
| 54.76000 | | NFM | Nationwide | BBC O/B Microphone Ch. 11 |
| 54.85000 | | NFM | Nationwide | BBC O/B Microphone Ch. 12 |
| 54.95000 | | NFM | Nationwide | BBC O/B Microphone Ch. 13 |
| 55.05000 | | NFM | Nationwide | BBC O/B Microphone Ch. 14 |
| 55.15000 | | NFM | Nationwide | BBC O/B Microphone Ch. 15 |
| 55.25000 | | NFM | Nationwide | BBC O/B Microphone Ch. 16 |
| 55.35000 | | NFM | Nationwide | BBC O/B Microphone Ch. 17 |
| 55.45000 | | NFM | Nationwide | BBC O/B Microphone Ch. 18 |
| 55.55000 | | NFM | Nationwide | BBC O/B Microphone Ch. 19 |
| 55.65000 | | NFM | Nationwide | BBC O/B Microphone (spare) |

**55.7500 - 60.75000 MHz   Future PMR**

**54.000 - 60.000 MHz    MoD Tactical Communications 25 kHz Simplex**

| Base | Mobile | Mode | Location | User and Notes |
|------|--------|------|----------|----------------|
| 56.62500 | | NFM | Nationwide | Royal Signals Public Displays |

**60.7500 - 62.7500 MHz   BBC 5W Cordless and Outside Broadcast Mics**

| Base | Mobile | Mode | Location | User and Notes |
|------|--------|------|----------|----------------|
| 60.75000 | | NFM | Nationwide | BBC O/B Microphone Ch. 20 |
| 60.80000 | | NFM | Nationwide | BBC O/B Microphone |
| 60.85000 | | NFM | Nationwide | BBC O/B Microphone Ch. 21 |
| 60.90000 | | NFM | Nationwide | BBC O/B Microphone |
| 60.95000 | | NFM | Nationwide | BBC O/B Microphone Ch. 22 |
| 61.00000 | | NFM | Nationwide | BBC O/B Microphone |
| 61.05000 | | NFM | Nationwide | BBC O/B Microphone Ch. 23 |
| 61.10000 | | NFM | Nationwide | BBC O/B Microphone |
| 61.15000 | | NFM | Nationwide | BBC O/B Microphone Ch. 24 |
| 61.25000 | | NFM | Nationwide | BBC O/B Microphone Ch. 25 |
| 61.30000 | | NFM | Nationwide | BBC O/B Microphone |
| 61.35000 | | NFM | Nationwide | BBC O/B Microphone Ch. 26 |
| 61.40000 | | NFM | Nationwide | BBC O/B Microphone |
| 61.45000 | | NFM | Nationwide | BBC O/B Microphone Ch. 27 |

| Base | Mobile | Mode | Location | User and Notes |
|------|--------|------|----------|----------------|
| 61.50000 | | NFM | Nationwide | BBC O/B Microphone |
| 61.55000 | | NFM | Nationwide | BBC O/B Microphone Ch. 28 |
| 61.65000 | | NFM | Nationwide | BBC O/B Microphone Ch. 29 |
| 61.70000 | | NFM | Nationwide | BBC O/B Microphone |
| 61.75000 | | NFM | Nationwide | BBC O/B Microphone Ch. 30 |
| 61.80000 | | NFM | Nationwide | BBC O/B Microphone |
| 61.85000 | | NFM | Nationwide | BBC O/B Microphone Ch. 31 |
| 61.90000 | | NFM | Nationwide | BBC O/B Microphone |
| 61.95000 | | NFM | Nationwide | BBC O/B Microphone Ch. 32 |
| 62.05000 | | NFM | Nationwide | BBC O/B Microphone Ch. 33 |
| 62.15000 | | NFM | Nationwide | BBC O/B Microphone Ch. 34 |
| 62.20000 | | NFM | Nationwide | BBC O/B Microphone |
| 62.25000 | | NFM | Nationwide | BBC O/B Microphone Ch. 35 |
| 62.35000 | | NFM | Nationwide | BBC O/B Microphone Ch. 36 |
| 62.45000 | | NFM | Nationwide | BBC O/B Microphone Ch. 37 |
| 62.55000 | | NFM | Nationwide | BBC O/B Microphone Ch. 38 |
| 62.60000 | | NFM | Nationwide | BBC O/B Microphone |
| 62.65000 | | NFM | Nationwide | BBC O/B Microphones (Spare) |

62.75000 - 68.0000 MHz  FUTURE PMR

64.0000 - 68.0000 MHz  MoD TACTICAL COMMUNICATIONS

### 25 kHz SIMPLEX

#### BBC O/B MICROPHONES AND LINKS

| Base | Mobile | Mode | Location | User and Notes |
|------|--------|------|----------|----------------|
| 64.03750 | | NFM | Nationwide | BBC O/B Microphones |
| 67.01250 | | NFM | Nationwide | BBC O/B Control |
| 67.02500 | | NFM | Nationwide | BBC O/B Control |

68.08125 - 70.00625  PMR LOW BAND MOBILE SIMPLEX

| Base | Mobile | Mode | Location | User and Notes |
|------|--------|------|----------|----------------|
| 68.20000 | | NFM | Isle of Man | Highways & Transport |
| 68.48750 | | NFM | Doncaster | Carr Hill Parcels |
| 69.40000 | | NFM | RAC Network Q Rally | Rally Control |
| 69.45000 | | NFM | RAC Network Q Rally | Rally Control |
| 69.48750 | | NFM | RAC Network Q Rally | Rally Control |
| 69.98750 | | NFM | Nationwide | RAC Network Q Rally |

68.0000 - 69.5000 MHz  MoD, MOULD & TACTICAL COMMUNICATIONS

### 25 kHz

| Base | Mobile | Mode | Location | User and Notes |
|------|--------|------|----------|----------------|
| 68.0250 | 68.0250 | AM | Cheltenham | MoD Transport |
| 68.0250 | 68.0250 | AM | Nationwide | UKAEA Transport Movements |
| 68.1250 | 68.1250 | NFM | Brecon Beacons | Army Range Ops |
| 68.1500 | 79.3500 | NFM | Camberley | Army Stores |
| | | NFM | Maidenhead | Army Stores |
| | | NFM | Nationwide | Army Stores |
| 68.1500 | 68.1500 | NFM | Nationwide | Army Pye Channel 6 |
| 68.2000 | 78.4000 | NFM | Nationwide | Army Pye Channel 4 |
| 68.2500 | | FM | Northern Ireland | Ulster Defence Regiment |
| 68.2750 | | NFM | Dartmoor | Military Range |
| 68.3000 | 79.2250 | NFM | Nationwide | Army Pye Channel 1 |
| 68.3250 | | AM | Nationwide | Military Airfield Ground services |
| 68.3500 | | NFM | Dartmoor | Military Range |
| 68.3500 | 68.3500 | NFM | Nationwide | Army Pye Channel 5 |
| 68.3625 | | NFM | Nationwide | Army Cadet Force Ch 1 |
| 68.3875 | | NFM | Bristol | MoD Transport |

| Base | Mobile | Mode | Location | User and Notes |
|------|--------|------|----------|----------------|
| 68.4000 | 79.2500 | NFM | Nationwide | Army Pye Channel 2 |
| 68.4250 | | NFM | Dartmoor | Military Range |
| 68.4250 | 79.2750 | NFM | Nationwide | Army Pye Channel 3 |
| 68.4250 | | NFM | Northern Ireland | British Army |
| 68.5000 | 79.8000 | NFM | Nationwide | Army Pye Channel 7 |
| 68.5000 | | NFM | Rosyth | RN Dockyards Operations |
| 68.5250 | 79.7000 | NFM | Nationwide | Army Pye Channel 8 |
| 68.5625 | | AM | RAE Farnborough | Emergency Services |
| 68.6000 | 79.9500 | NFM | Nationwide | Army Pye Channel 9 |
| 68.6125 | | AM | RAE Farnborough | Tractor Control |
| 68.6250 | | NFM | Larkhill | Army Range |
| 68.6375 | | AM | Nationwide | Army Pye Channel 1 |
| | | NFM | Northern Ireland | British Army |
| | | AM | RAE Farnborough | ATC Ch 6 |
| 68.6875 | | AM | Cheltenham | MoD Transport |
| | | AM | Hampshire | MoD transport |
| | | AM | RAE Farnborough | Ground Services |
| 68.6938 | | AM | RAE Farnborough | Repair Workshop |
| 68.7625 | | NFM | Salisbury Plain | Army Transport (Tenor Base) |
| 68.7875 | | AM | Cheltenham | MoD Transport |
| 68.8688 | | AM | RAE Farnborough | Fire |
| 68.9063 | | AM | RAE Farnborough | Medical |
| 68.9875 | | NFM | Brecon Beacons | Mould |
| 69.0750 | 69.0750 | NFM | Okehampton | Military Range |
| 69.1250 | | NFM | Isle of Man | Highways & Transport |
| | | NFM | Northern Ireland | British Army |
| 69.1550 | | NFM | Northern Ireland | British Army |
| 69.1750 | 69.1750 | NFM | Okehampton | Military Range |
| 69.2000 | | NFM | Northern Ireland | British Army |
| 69.2500 | | NFM | Northern Ireland | British Army |
| 69.3000 | 69.3000 | AM | Smethwick | Sea Cadets |
| 69.3250 | | NFM | Brecon Beacons | Army |
| | | NFM | Northern Ireland | British Army |
| 69.3500 | | AM | Brecon Beacons | Army Cadets Hike Control |
| 69.3750 | | NFM | Northern Ireland | British Army |
| 69.4000 | | WFM | Nationwide | Eastern European Low Band Skip |
| | | NFM | Northern Ireland | British Army |
| 69.4750 | 84.5250 | NFM | Nationwide | 39 Inf Bgd/Sig Chan A9 |

## 69.5000 - 69.8000 MHz MoD Tactical Communications
### 25 kHz Simplex

| Base | Mobile | Mode | Location | User and Notes |
|------|--------|------|----------|----------------|
| 69.5000 | | NFM | Okehampton | Military Range |
| | | NFM | RN Rosyth | Security |
| 69.5500 | | NFM | Northern Ireland | British Army |
| 69.5750 | | NFM | Northern Ireland | Army Bomb Squad |
| 69.7000 | | WFM | Nationwide | Eastern European Low Band Skip |
| 69.7500 | | NFM | Northern Ireland | British Army |
| 69.7750 | | NFM | Isle of Man | Highways & Transport |
| 69.8000 | | NFM | Northern Ireland | British Army |

## 69.82225 - 69.9625 MHz Television O/B "System One" CMCR
### Studio Manager Talkback

| Base | Mobile | Mode | Location | User and Notes |
|------|--------|------|----------|----------------|
| 69.82250 | 74.70000 | NFM | Nationwide | BBC Studio Manager Ch. 3 |
| 69.82500 | | NFM | Manchester | ITN Studio Link |
| | | NFM | Nationwide | BBC CMCR Channel 7 |

| Base | Mobile | Mode | Location | User and Notes |
|---|---|---|---|---|
| 69.83500 | 75.26880 | NFM | Nationwide | BBC Studio Manager Ch. 4 |
| 69.83750 | | NFM | Nationwide | BBC CMCR Channel 8 |
| 69.83750 | | NFM | Scotland | BBC Scotland CMCR |
| 69.84750 | | NFM | Nationwide | BBC Studio Manager Ch. 5 |
| 69.85000 | | NFM | Nationwide | BBC CMCR Channel 9 |
| 69.86000 | | NFM | Nationwide | BBC Studio Manager Ch. 6 |
| 69.86250 | | NFM | Nationwide | BBC CMCR Channel 10 |
| 69.87250 | | NFM | Nationwide | BBC Studio Manager Ch. 7 |
| 69.87500 | | NFM | Nationwide | BBC CMCR Channel 11 |
| 69.88500 | | NFM | Nationwide | BBC Studio Manager Ch. 8 |
| 69.89750 | | NFM | Nationwide | BBC Studio Manager Ch. 9 |
| 69.90000 | | NFM | Birmingham | BBC Talkback |
| | | NFM | Goodwood | BBC Goodwood OB |
| | | NFM | Haydock Park | TV OB |
| | | NFM | Scotland | BBC Scotland Channel 12 |
| 69.90000 | 75.29375 | NFM | Swansea | BBC Wales O/B |
| 69.90750 | 75.28750 | NFM | Nationwide | BBC Studio Manager Ch. 2 |
| 69.92500 | | NFM | Nationwide | BBC Studio Continuity |
| 69.96250 | 75.26250 | NFM | Nationwide | BBC Studio Manager Ch. 1 |

## 69.82500 - 70.0000 MHz  MoD Tactical Communications 25 kHz

| Base | Mobile | Mode | Location | User and Notes |
|---|---|---|---|---|
| 69.82500 | | NFM | Northern Ireland | British Army |
| 69.84500 | | AM | Salisbury Plain | Army |
| 69.85000 | | NFM | Northern Ireland | British Army |
| 69.86250 | | NFM | RNAS Yeovilton | Radio Somerset link at air display |
| 69.95000 | | NFM | Northern Ireland | British Army |
| 69.98000 | | FM | Northern Ireland | Ulster Defence Regiment |

## 70.0000 - 70.5000 MHz  4m Amateur Radio Band

| Base | Mobile | Mode | Location | User and Notes |
|---|---|---|---|---|
| 70.00000 | | CW | Buxton | Beacon (GB3BUX) |
| 70.01000 | | CW | Camberley | Repeater (GB3REB) |
| 70.02000 | | CW | Dundee | Beacon (GB3ANG) |
| 70.02500 | | CW | St Austell | Beacon (GB3MCB) |
| 70.20000 | | CW | Nationwide | CW Calling Channel |
| | | SSB | Nationwide | SSB Calling Channel |
| 70.26000 | | AM | Nationwide | AM Calling Channel |
| 70.30000 | | NFM | Nationwide | FAX Calling Channel |
| | | NFM | Nationwide | RTTY Calling Channel |
| | | NFM | Salisbury Plain | Army |
| 70.31250 | | NFM | Nationwide | Packet Channel |
| 70.32500 | | NFM | Nationwide | Packet Channel |
| 70.35000 | | NFM | Nationwide | Raynet Channel |
| 70.37500 | | NFM | Nationwide | Raynet Channel |
| 70.40000 | | NFM | Nationwide | Raynet Channel |
| 70.45000 | | NFM | Nationwide | FM Calling Channel |
| 70.48750 | | NFM | Nationwide | Packet Channel |

## 70.5000 - 71.5000 MHz  Fire Brigades (England & Wales) 12.5 kHz
### [Mobile 80.5000 - 81.5000 MHz]

| Base | Mobile | Mode | Location | User and Notes |
|---|---|---|---|---|
| 70.5125 | 80.1875 | AM | Coventry | Fire Brigade (FB) |
| | | NFM | Northumberland | Fire Brigade (M2LJ) |
| 70.5125 | 80.4375 | AM | West Midlands | Fire Brigade (FBW) |
| 70.5250 | | AM | Ipswich | Fire Brigade |
| 70.5250 | 80.9625 | AM | London | Fire Brigade (FH) Ch 1 |
| 70.5250 | 80.7375 | AM | Manchester | Fire Brigade (FT) Ch 2 |

| Base | Mobile | Mode | Location | User and Notes |
|------|--------|------|----------|----------------|
| 70.5375 | 80.1125 | AM | North Yorkshire | Fire Brigade (M2LY) |
| 70.5375 | 80.1875 | AM | Nottinghamshire | Fire Brigade (M2NZ) |
| 70.5500 | 80.0000 | AM | Manchester | Fire Brigade HQ (FT) Ch 1 |
| 70.5625 | 80.9875 | AM | Lincolnshire | Fire Brigade (NV) |
| 70.5625 | 80.6000 | AM | Mid Glamorgan | Fire Brigade (WF) |
| 70.5750 | 80.4625 | AM | West Midlands | Fire Brigade (FBW) Ch 3 |
| 70.5875 | 80.1875 | AM | Hampshire | Fire Brigade (HX) Ch 2 |
| 70.5875 | 80.7625 | AM | Manchester | Fire Brigade (FT) Ch 3 |
| 70.6000 | 80.0000 | AM | Derbyshire | Fire Brigade (M2ND) |
| 70.6000 | 81.2625 | NFM | Warwickshire | Fire Brigade (M2YS) |
| 70.6125 | 80.1250 | AM | Dyfed | Fire Brigade (WD) |
|  |  | NFM | Surrey | Fire Brigade (HF) |
|  |  | NFM | West Yorkshire | Fire Brigade (M2XF) |
| 70.6250 | 80.6125 | AM | Essex | Fire Brigade (VD) Ch 1 |
|  |  | AM | Merseyside | Fire Brigade (M2FO) Ch 3 |
| 70.6375 | 80.0000 | AM | Doncaster | Fire Brigade (M2XV) |
| 70.6375 | 80.2125 | AM | East Sussex | Fire Brigade (KD) |
| 70.6375 | 80.1125 | AM | South Yorkshire | Fire Brigade (XV) |
| 70.6500 | 80.9875 | AM | Wiltshire | Fire Brigade (QM) |
| 70.6625 | 81.0000 | AM | Leicestershire | Fire Brigade (M2NK) |
| 70.6750 | 80.5500 | NFM | Lancashire | Fire Brigade (BE) Ch 1 |
| 70.6750 |  | AM | Liverpool | Fire Brigade |
| 70.6750 | 80.5250 | AM | South Glamorgan | Fire Brigade (WD) |
| 70.6875 | 81.1250 | AM | Hereford & Worcester | Fire Brigade (YB) |
| 70.7000 | 81.1250 | NFM | Gwent | Fire Brigade (WP) Ch 4 |
| 70.7000 | 80.0000 | NFM | Merseyside | Fire Brigade (M2FO) Ch 4 |
|  |  | AM | Norfolk | Fire Brigade (M2VF) |
| 70.7125 | 80.8000 | AM | Derbyshire | Fire Brigade (M2ND) |
| 70.7125 | 80.3500 | AM | East Sussex | Fire Brigade Ch 2 |
| 70.7125 |  | AM | Manchester | Fire Brigade |
| 70.7250 | 80.0375 | AM | Devon | Fire Brigade (M2QD) |
| 70.7250 | 80.6750 | AM | Essex | Fire Brigade (VD) Ch 2 |
| 70.7400 | 70.7400 | NFM | West Midlands | Data Link for Fire Brigade |
| 70.7500 | 80.7500 | AM | Northamptonshire | Fire Brigade (NO) |
| 70.7624 | 80.1500 | AM | East London | Fire Brigade (M2FE) Ch3 |
| 70.7625 | 80.9875 | NFM | West Yorkshire | Fire Brigade (M2XF) |
| 70.7750 | 80.5000 | AM | Cheshire | Fire Brigade (M2CF) |
|  |  | AM | Hampshire | Fire Brigade (HX) Ch 1 |
| 70.7875 | 80.8000 | AM | Cornwall | Fire Brigade (QA) |
| 70.8000 | 80.5125 | NFM | West Sussex | Fire Brigade (KW) |
| 70.8125 | 81.2125 | AM | Gwynedd | Fire Brigade (WC) |
| 70.8250 | 80.3250 | AM | Devon | Fire Brigade (M2QD) |
| 70.8250 | 80.7875 | AM | Manchester | Fire Brigade (FT) Ch 4 |
| 70.8375 | 80.0000 | AM | Cambridgeshire | Fire Brigade |
| 70.8375 | 80.0375 | NFM | Cumbria | Fire Brigade (BC) |
|  |  | AM | Galashiels | Fire Brigade (ZF) |
| 70.8375 | 80.1250 | AM | Kent | Fire Brigade (KF) |
| 70.8500 | 80.9625 | AM | Powys | Fire Brigade (WB) |
| 70.8625 | 80.5500 | AM | Dorset | Fire Brigade (QK) |
| 70.8750 | 80.6625 | NFM | West Yorkshire | Fire Brigade (M2XF) |
| 70.8875 | 80.2125 | AM | Durham | Fire Brigade (LF) |
|  |  | AM | Hertfordshire | Fire Brigade (M2KP) |
| 70.8875 | 80.9375 | AM | Staffordshire | Fire Brigade (YG) |
| 70.9000 | 80.0375 | AM | Hertfordshire | Fire Brigade (M2VI) |
| 70.9000 | 80.6000 | NFM | Lancashire | Fire Brigade (BE) Ch 2 |
| 70.9000 | 80.4000 | NFM | Suffolk | Fire Brigade (VN) |

| Base | Mobile | Mode | Location | User and Notes |
|---|---|---|---|---|
| 70.9125 | 80.0000 | NFM | Essex | Fire Brigade (M2VD) Ch3 |
| 70.9125 | | AM | London | Fire Brigade Data Channel |
| 70.9375 | | NFM | England & Wales | Fire Brigade Data Channel |
| 70.9500 | 80.0000 | AM | West Glamorgan | Fire Brigade (WZ) |
| 70.9625 | 80.1125 | AM | London | Fire Brigade (FS) |
| 70.9625 | 81.0875 | AM | Merseyside | Fire Brigade (M2FO) Ch 2 |
| 70.9750 | 80.6500 | AM | Shropshire | Fire Brigade (YU) |
| | | NFM | Stockport | Fire Brigade |
| 70.9875 | 80.0000 | NFM | Gwynedd | Fire Brigade (M2WC) |
| 71.0125 | 80.1750 | AM | Avon | Fire Brigade (M2QG) |
| | | AM | Bristol | Fire Brigade |
| 71.0375 | 81.0625 | AM | Merseyside | Fire Brigade (M2FO) |
| 71.0750 | | AM | Bristol | Fire Brigade |
| 71.0750 | 80.6250 | AM | Gloucester | Fire Brigade (QF) |
| 71.0750 | 80.1500 | AM | Humberside | Fire Brigade (XT) |
| 71.1000 | 80.3750 | AM | Humberside | Fire Brigade (XT) |
| 71.1000 | 80.6625 | AM | Oxfordshire | Fire Brigade (M2HI) |
| 71.1125 | 80.0000 | AM | Bedfordshire | Fire Brigade (M2VM) |
| | | AM | Cleveland | Fire Brigade (LT) |
| 71.1250 | 80.1125 | AM | Somerset | Fire Brigade (QI) |
| 71.1375 | 80.4500 | AM | Buckinghamshire | Fire Brigade (HK) |
| 71.1375 | 80.4375 | AM | North Yorkshire | Fire Brigade (LY) |
| 71.1500 | 80.5125 | AM | West Midlands | Fire Brigade (FBW) |
| 71.1625 | 80.8750 | AM | Clwyd | Fire Brigade (M2WK) |
| 71.1750 | 80.2125 | AM | London (North) | Fire Brigade (FN) Ch 4 |
| 71.1750 | 80.0000 | AM | North Yorkshire | Fire Brigade (LY) |
| 71.2000 | 80.2250 | NFM | Berkshire | Fire Brigade (M2HD) |
| 71.2000 | 80.0000 | NFM | Lancashire | Fire Brigade (M2BE) Ch2 |
| 71.2500 | 80.0000 | NFM | Gloucester | Fire Brigade (M2YP) |
| 71.2750 | 81.0625 | AM | Isle of Wight | Fire Brigade (HP) |
| 71.2750 | 81.0875 | NFM | Suffolk | Fire Brigade (VN) |
| 71.3000 | | AM | Tyne and Wear | Fire Brigade (LP) Ch 1 |
| 71.3125 | | NFM | England & Wales | Fire Brigade Data Channel |
| 71.3375 | | NFM | England & Wales | Fire Brigade Data Channel |
| 71.3375 | 80.0000 | NFM | London | Fire Brigade (M2FHO) Ch5 1200 Baud Data |
| 71.3375 | | NFM | Tyne and Wear | Fire Brigade (LP) Ch 2 |
| 71.3875 | | AM | Gloucestershire | Fire Brigade (QC) |
| 71.3875 | 80.0000 | NFM | Lancashire | Fire Brigade (BE) Ch 3 |
| 71.4000 | 81.2500 | NFM | Nationwide | RW Radio Engineers |
| 71.4250 | 80.5250 | AM | Cambridgeshire | Fire Brigade (VC) |
| 71.4500 | | AM | Nottinghamshire | Fire Brigade (NZ) |
| 71.4750 | | NFM | Nationwide | Police Radio Engineering |

### 71.50625 - 72.79375 MHz    PMR Low Band Mobiles 12.5 kHz
### (Base +10.5 MHz)

| Base | Mobile | Mode | Location | User and Notes |
|---|---|---|---|---|
| 71.51250 | 82.01250 | NFM | Birmingham | National Breakdown |
| 71.55000 | 82.05000 | NFM | Cambridge | Bidwells |
| | | NFM | Ipswich | Anglian Water |
| | | NFM | London | Baron Cars |
| 71.82500 | 82.32500 | NFM | Chelmsford | Southern Water |
| 71.86500 | 82.36500 | NFM | Nuneaton | Anglian Water |
| 71.90000 | 82.40000 | AM | Nationwide | Selective Call |
| 71.96250 | 82.46250 | NFM | Manchester | North West Water |

| Base | Mobile | Mode | Location | User and Notes |
|------|--------|------|----------|----------------|
| 71.98750 | 82.48750 | NFM | Nationwide | Automobile Association |
| 72.17500 | 85.67500 | NFM | Barrow | Barrow Five Taxis |
| 72.22500 | 82.72500 | NFM | Nationwide | BBC/IBA Microwave Links Setup |
| 72.27500 | 85.77500 | NFM | Blackpool | Red Cabs Taxis |
| 72.32500 | 82.82500 | NFM | Southampton | Taxis |
| 72.33750 | 72.33750 | AM | Jersey | Ideal Hire Cars Channel 2 |
| 72.38750 | 85.88750 | AM | Blackpool | Tower Taxis |
| 72.42500 | 85.92500 | AM | Blackpool | Radio Cabs |
| 72.43750 | 85.93750 | AM | Blackpool | Progress Taxis |
| 72.53750 | 83.03750 | AM | Methley Park | Private Hospital |
| 72.57500 | 83.07500 | AM | Lochaber | Ambulance Repeater |
| 72.65000 | 83.15000 | NFM | Kent | Tour de France French PMR |

## 72.8000 - 73.9250 MHz   MoD Tactical Communications
### 25 kHz Duplex

| Base | Mobile | Mode | Location | User and Notes |
|------|--------|------|----------|----------------|
| 72.80000 | | NFM | Brecon Beacons | Army Range Ops |
| 72.80000 | 74.80000 | NFM | Nationwide | Secure Government Mobiles |
| 72.81250 | | NFM | Southampton | Royal Navy Loading |
| 72.82500 | | NFM | USAF Fairford | Base Ops |
| 72.98750 | 72.98750 | NFM | HMS Drake | Naval Provost |
| 73.00000 | | NFM | Brecon Beacons | Army Range Ops |
| 73.00000 | 78.90000 | NFM | Nationwide | Army Pye Equipment Ch. 7 |
| 73.02500 | 78.65000 | NFM | Nationwide | Army Pye Equipment Ch. 8 |
| 73.10000 | | NFM | Aldershot | Military Police |
| 73.12500 | 78.40000 | NFM | Nationwide | Army Pye Equipment Ch. 1 |
| 73.15000 | 78.42500 | NFM | Nationwide | Army Pye Equipment Ch.2 |
| 73.20000 | | NFM | DRA Farnborough | Ground Movements |
| 73.20000 | 78.45000 | NFM | Nationwide | Army Pye Equipment Ch. 3 |
| 73.21250 | | NFM | Southampton | Royal Navy Transport |
| 73.22500 | 78.47500 | NFM | Nationwide | Army Pye Equipment Ch. 4 |
| 73.25000 | 78.50000 | NFM | Nationwide | Army Pye Equipment Ch. 5 |
| 73.25600 | | NFM | Midlands | Army Base Security |
| 73.27500 | | NFM | Kent | Tour de France French PMR |
| 73.32500 | 78.80000 | NFM | Nationwide | Army Pye Equipment Ch. 6 |
| 73.32500 | | NFM | Plymouth | Royal Marines |
| 73.33750 | | NFM | RN Portsdown | Base Ops |
| 73.35000 | | NFM | Nationwide | MoD Security Police |
| | | NFM | RAF High Wycombe | Security |
| 73.35000 | 73.35000 | NFM | West Midlands | USAF Police |
| 73.38750 | | NFM | Nationwide | Sea Cadets |
| 73.40000 | | NFM | Plymouth | MoD Operations |
| 73.42500 | | NFM | RN Faslane | Transport |
| 73.43750 | | AM | RAE Farnborough | Ground Control |
| 73.45000 | | NFM | RN Portsdown | Security |
| 73.46250 | | AM | RAE Farnborough | Ground Vehicles |
| 73.46875 | | AM | RAE Farnborough | Workshop Ch 5 |
| 73.47500 | 73.47500 | NFM | Nationwide | MoD Police |
| 73.48750 | | NFM | RAE Farnborough | Ground Service Ch 1 |
| 73.50000 | 78.65000 | NFM | Nationwide | Army Pye Equipment Ch. 1 |
| 73.51250 | | NFM | Nationwide | MoD Police |
| 73.52500 | 78.72500 | NFM | Nationwide | Army Pye Equipment Ch. 2 |
| 73.53750 | | NFM | Plymouth | MoD Operations |
| 73.55000 | 78.77500 | NFM | Nationwide | Army Pye Equipment Ch. 9 |
| 73.56250 | | NFM | RN Faslane | Security (Alpha Control) |
| 73.56750 | | NFM | RN Poole | Royal Marines |

| Base | Mobile | Mode | Location | User and Notes |
|------|--------|------|----------|----------------|
| 73.57500 | | NFM | Plymouth | Military Police |
| | | NFM | RN Dartmouth | Navy Ops |
| 73.61250 | | NFM | Plymouth | MoD Police |
| 73.63750 | | NFM | Plymouth | MoD Police |
| | | NFM | RAE Farnborough | Movements Control Ch 6 |
| 73.65000 | | NFM | London | MoD Police |
| 73.66875 | | NFM | RAE Farnborough | Fire Ch 4 |
| 73.70000 | 84.12500 | NFM | Nationwide | 61 Sig Sqn Channel 1 |
| 73.70000 | | NFM | Nationwide | Army Cadet Force |
| | | NFM | RN Faslane | MoD Police |
| 73.70625 | | NFM | RAE Farnborough | Medical Ch 2 |
| 73.72500 | 84.15000 | NFM | Nationwide | 61 Sig Sqn Channel 2 |
| 73.75000 | 84.17500 | NFM | Nationwide | 61 Sig Sqn Channel 3 |
| 73.77500 | 84.25000 | NFM | Nationwide | 61 Sig Sqn Channel 4 |
| 73.80000 | | NFM | Brecon Beacons | Army Range Control |
| 73.80000 | 84.27500 | NFM | Nationwide | 61 Sig Sqn Channel 5 |
| 73.82500 | 84.32500 | NFM | Nationwide | 61 Sig Sqn Channel 6 |
| 73.85000 | 84.35000 | NFM | Nationwide | 61 Sig Sqn Channel 7 |
| 73.85000 | | NFM | Nationwide | Army Cadet Force |
| | | NFM | Nationwide | MoD Police Ch 5 |
| 73.87500 | 84.37500 | NFM | Nationwide | 61 Sig Sqn Channel 8 |
| 73.90000 | 84.42500 | NFM | Nationwide | 61 Sig Sqn Channel 9 |
| 73.92500 | 84.47500 | NFM | Nationwide | 61 Sig Sqn Channel 10 |

**73.9250 - 74.1000 MHz    MoD Mould Repeaters 12.5 kHz Duplex**

| Base | Mobile | Mode | Location | User and Notes |
|------|--------|------|----------|----------------|
| 74.01250 | | NFM | Northamptonshire | Mould |
| 74.01250 | 74.01250 | NFM | Scarborough | Mould |
| 74.02500 | 79.01250 | NFM | Hampshire | Mould |
| | | NFM | Lincolnshire | Mould |
| | | NFM | West Midlands | Mould |
| 74.03750 | | NFM | Shropshire | Mould |
| | | NFM | Wiltshire | Mould |
| 74.05000 | | NFM | Brecon Beacons | Mould |
| | | NFM | Northamptonshire | Mould |
| | | NFM | Nottinghamshire | Mould |
| | | NFM | West Midlands | Mould |
| 74.06250 | | NFM | Manchester | Mould |
| | | NFM | Northamptonshire | Mould |
| | | NFM | West Midlands | Mould |
| | | NFM | West Yorkshire | Mould |
| 74.07500 | | NFM | Devon | Mould |
| | | NFM | Gwent | Mould |
| 74.08750 | | NFM | Gwent | Mould |
| | | NFM | Manchester | Mould |
| | | NFM | Tayside | Mould |
| | | NFM | West Midlands | Mould |

**74.1000 - 74.7875 MHz    MoD Mould & Tactical Channels 12.5 kHz**

| Base | Mobile | Mode | Location | User and Notes |
|------|--------|------|----------|----------------|
| 74.10000 | | NFM | RAF Honington | RAF police Ch 3 |
| 74.11250 | | NFM | Colchester | Barracks |
| | | NFM | Gwent | Mould Ch 1 |
| | | NFM | Manchester | Mould |
| | | NFM | West Midlands | Mould |
| 74.12500 | | NFM | Brecon Beacons | Mould |
| 74.12500 | | NFM | West Midlands | Mould |

| Base | Mobile | Mode | Location | User and Notes |
|------|--------|------|----------|----------------|
| 74.13750 | | NFM | Brecon Beacons | Mould |
| 74.15000 | | NFM | Shropshire | Mould |
| 74.15000 | | NFM | West Midlands | Mould |
| 74.16250 | | NFM | Manchester | Mould |
| | | NFM | Strathclyde | Mould |
| | | NFM | West Midlands | Mould |
| 74.18750 | | NFM | West Yorkshire | Mould |
| 74.20000 | | NFM | Nationwide | Military Transport Security |
| 74.20000 | 79.30000 | NFM | Nationwide | RAF Police Transport |
| | | NFM | Norfolk | Mould |
| 74.21250 | 79.21250 | NFM | Gwent | Mould |
| | | NFM | Strathclyde | Mould |
| 74.22500 | | NFM | Colchester | Mould |
| | | NFM | Lincolnshire | Mould |
| | | NFM | Nationwide | Royal Ordnance Corps |
| | | NFM | Nottinghamshire | Mould |
| | | NFM | Upper Heyford | Mould |
| | | NFM | West Midlands | Mould |
| 74.23750 | | NFM | Lincolnshire | Mould |
| | | NFM | Shropshire | Mould |
| | | NFM | Tayside | Mould |
| 74.25000 | 79.28750 | NFM | Colchester | Barracks |
| 74.25000 | 79.35000 | NFM | Norfolk | Mould |
| | | NFM | Suffolk | Mould |
| 74.26250 | | NFM | Gwent | Mould |
| 74.27500 | | NFM | Strathclyde | Mould |
| 74.31250 | | NFM | Gwent | Mould |
| | | NFM | Shropshire | Mould |
| 74.33750 | | NFM | Manchester | Mould |
| 74.35000 | 79.45000 | NFM | Brecon Beacons | Mould |
| 74.36250 | | NFM | Chester | Mould |
| | | NFM | Hampshire | Mould |
| 74.37500 | | NFM | Brecon Beacons | Mould |
| 74.38750 | 79.41250 | NFM | Devon | Mould |
| | | NFM | Gwent | Mould |
| 74.40000 | | NFM | Brecon Beacons | Mould |
| 74.41250 | | NFM | Brecon Beacons | Mould |
| | | NFM | Shropshire | Mould |
| 74.41250 | | NFM | West Yorkshire | Mould |
| 74.43750 | 79.66250 | NFM | Norfolk | Mould |
| | | NFM | Strathclyde | Mould |
| | | NFM | West Midlands | Mould |
| 74.45000 | 79.45000 | NFM | Brecon Beacons | Mould |
| 74.46250 | | NFM | Gwent | Mould |
| 74.46750 | 79.71250 | NFM | Gwent | Mould |
| 74.48750 | 79.92650 | NFM | Hampshire | Mould |
| | | NFM | Norfolk | Mould |
| | | NFM | Wiltshire | Mould |
| 74.51250 | | NFM | Brecon Beacons | Mould |
| | | NFM | West Midlands | Mould |
| 74.52500 | | NFM | Brecon Beacons | Mould |
| 74.53750 | | NFM | Brecon Beacons | Mould |
| | | NFM | Lincolnshire | Mould |
| | | NFM | West Midlands | Mould |
| 74.55000 | 79.55000 | NFM | Nationwide | RAF Police |
| 74.56250 | | NFM | Brecon Beacons | Mould |

| Base | Mobile | Mode | Location | User and Notes |
|------|--------|------|----------|----------------|
| 74.57500 | | NFM | Brecon Beacons | Mould |
| | | NFM | Manchester | Mould |
| 74.57500 | | NFM | Shropshire | Mould |
| | | NFM | West Yorkshire | Mould |
| 74.58750 | | NFM | Devon | Mould |
| | | NFM | Gwent | Mould |
| | | NFM | Hampshire | Mould |
| | | NFM | Wiltshire | Mould |
| 74.60000 | | NFM | Kent | Tour de France French PMR |
| | | NFM | West Midlands | Mould |
| 74.61250 | | NFM | Brecon Beacons | Mould |
| | | NFM | West Midlands | Mould |
| 74.62500 | | NFM | Brecon Beacons | Mould |
| | | NFM | Devon | Mould |
| 74.65000 | 79.61250 | NFM | Hants (Crabwood Farm) | Mould |
| 74.66250 | | NFM | Brecon Beacons | Mould |
| 74.67500 | 79.71250 | NFM | Gwent | Mould |
| | | NFM | Strathclyde | Mould |
| 74.68750 | 79.68750 | NFM | Cambridgeshire | Mould Ch 15 |
| 74.70000 | 79.71250 | NFM | Brecon Beacons | Mould |
| | | NFM | Gwent | Mould |
| | | NFM | Tayside | Mould |
| 74.71250 | | NFM | Oxfordshire | Mould |
| 74.72500 | | NFM | Brecon Beacons | Mould |
| | | NFM | Manchester | Mould |
| | | NFM | Shropshire | Mould |
| 74.73750 | | NFM | Hampshire | Mould |
| | | NFM | London | Mould |
| 74.75000 | | NFM | Devon | Mould |
| | | NFM | Manchester | Mould |
| | | NFM | Shropshire | Mould |
| 74.75000 | | NFM | Wiltshire | Mould |
| 74.76250 | | NFM | Gwent | Mould |
| 74.78750 | | NFM | Gwent | Mould |

## 74-8000 - 75.2500 MHz    CIVIL AVIATION OUTER, MIDDLE & INNER RUNWAY MARKERS

| Base | Mobile | Mode | Location | User and Notes |
|------|--------|------|----------|----------------|
| 75.00000 | | AM | Nationwide | Runway Marker Beacons |

## 75.2500 - 75.3000 MHz    BBC O/B TALKBACK & MoD TACTICAL COMMS

| Base | Mobile | Mode | Location | User and Notes |
|------|--------|------|----------|----------------|
| 75.02500 | | NFM | RAF Marham | Security |
| 75.25000 | | AM | Pendine (MoD) | Range Ops |
| | | AM | West Midlands | USAF Police |
| 75.26250 | 69.96250 | NFM | Nationwide | BBC O/B Talkback Ch 1 |
| 75.26860 | 69.83500 | NFM | Nationwide | BBC O/B Talkback Ch 4 |
| 75.28130 | 69.87250 | NFM | Nationwide | BBC O/B Talkback Ch 7 |
| 75.28750 | 69.90750 | NFM | Nationwide | BBC O/B Talkback Ch 2 |
| 75.29380 | 69.89750 | NFM | Nationwide | BBC O/B Talkback Ch 9 |

## 75.3000 - 76.7000 MHz    MoD POLICE, MOULD & USAFE SECURITY 12.5 kHz SIMPLEX

| Base | Mobile | Mode | Location | User and Notes |
|------|--------|------|----------|----------------|
| 75.30000 | | AM | Pendine (MoD) | Range Ops |
| | | AM | Porton Down | Security |
| | | AM | Suffolk | USAF Police |

| Base | Mobile | Mode | Location | User and Notes |
|------|--------|------|----------|----------------|
| 75.32500 | | NFM | Nationwide | USAF Ground Common |
| | | NFM | USAF Lakenheath | Ground Ops |
| | | NFM | USAF Mildenhall | Ground Ops |
| 75.40000 | | AM | Pendine (MoD) | Range Ops |
| | | AM | Suffolk | USAF Police |
| 75.45000 | | NFM | Nationwide | USAF Base Security |
| 75.47500 | | NFM | Brecon Beacons | Mould |
| 75.50000 | | AM | Christchurch | Military |
| | | AM | Glasgow | RAF Security |
| | | NFM | Gwent | Royal Air Force |
| | | NFM | Northamptonshire | Security |
| 75.57500 | | NFM | Nationwide | USAF Ground Common |
| | | NFM | USAF Lakenheath | Ground Ops |
| | | NFM | USAF Mildenhall | Ground Ops |
| 75.60000 | | NFM | Plymouth | MoD |
| 75.67500 | | NFM | Plymouth | MoD Dockyard Ops |
| | | NFM | USAF Lakenheath | Security |
| | | NFM | USAF Mildenhall | Security |
| 75.71250 | | NFM | Hampshire | Mould |
| | | NFM | Oxfordshire | Mould |
| 75.73750 | | NFM | London | Mould |
| | | NFM | Nationwide | Military Close Protection Ch 11 |
| 75.75000 | | NFM | Devon | Mould |
| | | NFM | Gwent | Mould |
| | | NFM | Wiltshire | Mould |
| 75.76250 | | NFM | Salisbury Plain | Close Support Group |
| 75.78750 | | NFM | Gwent | Mould |
| | | NFM | Lothian and Borders | Mould |
| 75.81250 | | NFM | Brecon Beacons | Army |
| 75.82500 | | NFM | London | Link for Remembrance Sunday |
| | | NFM | London | Used by military for state visits |
| | | NFM | London | Wellington Barracks and Buckingham Palace guards |
| | | NFM | Nationwide | Military Close Protection Ch 12 |
| | | NFM | Nationwide | T19 Tactical Support Team. |
| 75.82500 | | NFM | Nationwide | USAF Special Agents |
| 75.83750 | | NFM | East Anglia | MOD Police G Division |
| | | NFM | RN Faslane | Security (Charlie Control) |
| 75.83750 | | NFM | USAF Mildenhall | Security |
| 75.86250 | | NFM | Oxfordshire | Mould |
| 75.87500 | | NFM | Devon | Mould |
| | | NFM | Dorset | Territorial Army Mould |
| | | NFM | Gwent | Mould |
| | | NFM | London | Mould |
| | | NFM | Nationwide | Military Close Protection Ch 10 |
| 75.90000 | | NFM | Gwent | Mould |
| 75.91250 | | NFM | Gwent | Mould |
| 75.93750 | | NFM | Fife | Mould |
| 75.93750 | | NFM | Gwent | Mould |
| | | NFM | Hampshire | Mould |
| 75.93750 | | NFM | Tayside | Mould |
| 75.94000 | | NFM | Salisbury Plain | Army |
| 75.95000 | | NFM | Gwent | Mould |
| 75.96250 | | NFM | Hampshire | Mould |
| 75.97500 | | NFM | Nationwide | Royal Signals |
| 76.00000 | | NFM | Nationwide | USAF Police |

| Base | Mobile | Mode | Location | User and Notes |
|------|--------|------|----------|----------------|
| 76.01250 | | NFM | Gwent | Mould |
| | | NFM | Hampshire | Mould |
| | | NFM | Plymouth | MoD Dockyard Ops |
| 76.01250 | | NFM | West Midlands | Mould |
| 76.05000 | | NFM | USAF Lakenheath | Security |
| | | NFM | West Midlands | USAF Maintenance Ch 6 |
| 76.06250 | | NFM | Devon | Mould |
| | | NFM | Gwent | Mould |
| | | NFM | Nationwide | Military Close Protection Ch 15 |
| 76.07500 | | NFM | Hampshire | USAF |
| | | NFM | Wiltshire | USAF |
| 76.11250 | | NFM | Gwent | Mould |
| | | NFM | Hampshire | Mould |
| 76.12500 | | NFM | Gwent | Mould |
| | | NFM | West Midlands | Mould |
| 76.16250 | | NFM | Hampshire | Mould |
| 76.22500 | | NFM | Devon | Mould |
| | | NFM | Gwent | Mould |
| | | NFM | Nationwide | Military Close Protection Ch 16 |
| | | NFM | Nationwide | USAF Base to Mobile |
| | | NFM | USAF Mildenhall | Security |
| 76.25000 | | NFM | Brecon Beacons | Army |
| | | NFM | USAF Mildenhall | Security |
| 76.26250 | | NFM | Gwent | Army |
| 76.30000 | | NFM | RNAS Culdrose | Ground Services |
| | | NFM | RNAS Yeovilton | Navy Provosts |
| 76.32500 | | NFM | Devon | Mould |
| | | NFM | Hampshire | Mould |
| 76.32500 | | NFM | London | MoD Police Ruislip |
| | | NFM | Lothian and Borders | Mould |
| | | NFM | Nationwide | Military Close Protection Ch 14 |
| | | NFM | Tayside | Mould |
| | | NFM | USAF Lakenheath | Security |
| | | NFM | USAF Mildenhall | Security |
| 76.35000 | | NFM | USAF Lakenheath | Crystal Palace |
| 76.36250 | | NFM | Northamptonshire | Mould |
| | | NFM | West Midlands | Mould |
| 76.38750 | | NFM | Hampshire | Mould |
| 76.43750 | | NFM | Hampshire | Mould |
| | | NFM | London | Mould |
| | | NFM | Nationwide | Military Close Protection Ch 09 |
| | | NFM | Oxfordshire | Mould |
| | | NFM | Salisbury Plain | Army |
| | | NFM | West Midlands | Mould |
| 76.44000 | | NFM | Salisbury Plain | Army |
| 76.45000 | | NFM | USAF Fairford | Security |
| 76.47500 | | NFM | Hampshire | USAF |
| | | NFM | London | Mould |
| | | NFM | South Wales | Mould |
| 76.50000 | | NFM | London | MoD Police Ruislip |
| | | NFM | Nationwide | Military Close Protection Ch 13 |
| 76.52500 | | NFM | Camberley | WRAC Gate Security |
| 76.52500 | | FM | Neath, Glamorgan | Knight Hawk Security |
| | | NFM | USAF Lakenheath | Security |
| 76.56250 | | NFM | Kent | Tour de France (French) |
| 76.57500 | | NFM | USAF Lakenheath | Security Ch 2 |

| Base | Mobile | Mode | Location | User and Notes |
|---|---|---|---|---|
| 76.60000 | | NFM | Cumbria | Range Control |
| 76.61250 | | NFM | Hampshire | USAF |
| 76.67500 | | NFM | USAF Lakenheath | Security |
| 76.70000 | | NFM | Cumbria | Range Control |
| | | NFM | Nationwide | British Telecom Channel A |
| | | NFM | Nationwide | USAF Police |
| 76.72500 | | NFM | RAF Leeming | Ground |
| 76.73750 | | NFM | Nationwide | British Telecom Channel B |
| 76.75000 | | NFM | Nationwide | British Telecom Channel C |
| 76.76250 | | NFM | Nationwide | British Telecom Channel D |
| 76.82500 | | NFM | Nationwide | Thames TV Talkback |

**76.7000 - 78.0000 MHz — PMR LOW BAND MOBILES 12.5 kHz DUPLEX**

| Base | Mobile | Mode | Location | User and Notes |
|---|---|---|---|---|
| 77.13750 | | NFM | Hampshire | Motorway Surveyors |
| 77.21250 | | NFM | Hampshire | Netley Country Park Rangers |
| | | NFM | Leicester | Council Ch2 |
| 77.23750 | | NFM | Hampshire | New Forest Council |
| 77.25000 | | NFM | Hampshire | Motorway Surveyors |
| | | NFM | RNAS Culdrose | Ground Services |
| 77.25000 | 87.25000 | NFM | Stockton | Borough Council |
| 77.26250 | 87.26250 | NFM | Stockton | Borough Council |
| 77.28750 | | NFM | Galway | Tone Repeater |
| 77.70000 | | NFM | Swansea City | Royal Mail |
| 77.87500 | 77.87500 | NFM | Nationwide | ITN O/B Film Mobiles |
| 77.98750 | | NFM | Hampshire | Marchwood Miltary Port |

**78.800-79.000 MHz MoD & USAF, BBC O/B NETWORKS 12.5 kHz**

| Base | Mobile | Mode | Location | User and Notes |
|---|---|---|---|---|
| 78.00000 | 78.00000 | NFM | Hampshire | Army Ops |
| 78.05000 | | NFM | London | Military |
| 78.10000 | | AM | Nationwide | ATC Channel V3 |
| | | NFM | Nationwide | BBC O/B |
| | | AM | Nationwide | RAF Cadets Channel V1 |
| 78.11250 | | NFM | RN Faslane | Security (Papa Control) |
| 78.12500 | | NFM | Guilford | Army |
| 78.13750 | | NFM | Blandford | Royal Signals Security |
| 78.15000 | | NFM | Nationwide | BBC O/B Talkback Channel 1 |
| 78.15000 | 84.50000 | NFM | Okehampton | Military Range |
| 78.16250 | 84.66250 | NFM | Okehampton | Military Range |
| 78.16250 | 73.61250 | NFM | Plymouth | MoD Police |
| | | NFM | RN Faslane | Security (Bravo Control) |
| | | NFM | Salisbury Plain | MOD Police (Hippy Surveillance) |
| 78.17500 | 84.67500 | NFM | Okehampton | Military Range |
| 78.18750 | | NFM | Nationwide | BBC O/B Camera Channel 1 |
| 78.20000 | | NFM | Nationwide | BBC O/B Camera Channel 2 |
| 78.21250 | | NFM | Nationwide | BBC O/B Engineering Ch. 3 |
| 78.21550 | | NFM | Nationwide | BBC O/B |
| 78.22500 | 78.22500 | AM | Avon | Air Training Corps |
| | | NFM | Birmingham | BBC Microwave set up |
| | | NFM | Nationwide | BBC O/B Engineering Ch. 4 |
| 78.22750 | | NFM | Nationwide | BBC O/B |
| 78.23150 | | NFM | DRA Farnborough | DRA Security |
| | | NFM | Nationwide | BBC O/B Engineering Ch. 5 |
| 78.23750 | | NFM | Salisbury Plain | MOD Police (Hippy Surveillance) |
| 78.24000 | | NFM | Nationwide | BBC O/B Rigging |
| 78.25000 | | NFM | Nationwide | BBC O/B Lighting Channel 6 |

| Base | Mobile | Mode | Location | User and Notes |
|------|--------|------|----------|----------------|
| 78.25250 | | NFM | Nationwide | BBC O/B |
| 78.27500 | | NFM | Bovington | Army Camp Ch 3 |
| | | NFM | Colchester | Barracks |
| 78.27500 | | NFM | Hampshire | Army Ops |
| | | NFM | Waterbeach | Security |
| 78.28750 | | NFM | Colchester | Barracks Ch 4 |
| 78.30000 | | NFM | Aberystwyth | Royal Welsh Fusilliers TA Centre |
| | | NFM | Bovington | Army Camp Ch 4 |
| | | NFM | Colchester | Barracks Ch 2 |
| | | NFM | Middle Wallop | Military Police (army) |
| | | NFM | Nationwide | Combined Cadet Force |
| | | NFM | Stanford Battle Area | Stanford Ops |
| | | NFM | Waterbeach | Security |
| 78.31250 | | NFM | Aldershot | Military Police |
| | | NFM | Salisbury Plain | Military Police |
| 78.32500 | | NFM | Colchester | Barracks Ch 3 |
| | | NFM | Hampshire | Military Police |
| | | NFM | London | Bassington Barracks Military Police |
| | | NFM | Stanford Battle Area | Stanford Ops |
| | | NFM | Waterbeach | Security |
| | | NFM | West Moors | Army Ch 3 |
| 78.33750 | | NFM | London | MoD Police |
| 78.35000 | | NFM | USAF Fairford | Base Ops |
| 78.36250 | | NFM | Bovington | Army Camp Ch 6 |
| 78.36750 | | NFM | Portsmouth | RN Police |
| 78.37500 | | NFM | Aldershot | Army Camp Security |
| 78.38750 | | NFM | London | MoD Police |
| | | NFM | Portsmouth | RN Police |
| 78.40000 | 73.12500 | NFM | London | MoD Police |
| 78.40000 | | NFM | Nationwide | Army Equipment Channel 1 |
| 78.41250 | | NFM | Knightsbridge | Bomb Squad |
| 78.41250 | | NFM | London | MoD Police Chelsea Barracks |
| | | NFM | Middle Wallop | Ops (army) |
| | | NFM | RAF Northolt | Security |
| 78.42500 | 73.15000 | NFM | Nationwide | Army Equipment Channel 2 |
| 78.43750 | | NFM | Bovington | Army Camp Ch 6 |
| 78.45000 | | NFM | Middle Wallop | Crash (army) |
| 78.45000 | 73.20000 | NFM | Nationwide | Army Equipment Channel 3 |
| 78.47500 | 73.22500 | NFM | Nationwide | Army Equipment Channel 4 |
| 78.48750 | | NFM | Aldershot Camp | Army Security |
| | | NFM | Colchester | Military Police |
| | | NFM | Guildford | Military Police |
| 78.50000 | | NFM | Nationwide | Army Equipment Channel 5 |
| 78.52500 | | FM | Northern Ireland | Ulster Defence Regiment Police |
| | | NFM | Welford | USAF Bomb Disposal Units |
| 78.53750 | | NFM | Bovington | Army Camp Ch 1 |
| 78.55000 | | NFM | Shropshire | Army Fire Channel |
| 78.57500 | | NFM | RNAS Culdrose | Base Ops |
| | | NFM | RNAS Yeovilton | Crash Ops Ch 4 |
| | | NFM | USAF Fairford | IAT Tanker Ops |
| 78.60000 | | NFM | RAF Wittering | RAF Police Ch 52 |
| 78.61250 | | NFM | Bovington | Army Camp Ch 2 |
| 78.63750 | | NFM | Hampshire | MOD Police |
| 78.65000 | 73.50000 | NFM | Nationwide | Army Equipment Channel 1 |
| 78.67500 | 73.25000 | NFM | Nationwide | Army Equipment Channel 8 |
| 78.67500 | | NFM | RAF Wittering | RAF Police Ch 53 |

| Base | Mobile | Mode | Location | User and Notes |
|------|--------|------|----------|----------------|
| 78.68750 | | NFM | Portsmouth | RN Security |
| 78.69750 | 78.69750 | NFM | Nationwide | RAF Police |
| 78.70000 | | NFM | USAF Fairford | Base Ops |
| 78.77500 | 73.55000 | NFM | Hampshire | Army |
| | | NFM | London | MoD Police |
| | | NFM | Nationwide | Army Equipment Channel 9 |
| | | NFM | RAF Ternhill | Army Fire Channel |
| | | NFM | RNAS Portland | Tower |
| 78.80000 | | NFM | Great Malvern | RSRE Base Security |
| | | NFM | Hampshire | Army |
| 78.80000 | 149.50000 | NFM | London | MoD Police |
| 78.80000 | 73.35000 | NFM | Nationwide | Army Equipment Channel 6 |
| 78.80000 | | NFM | Poole | Royal Marines |
| 78.81250 | | NFM | Newbury | Army |
| 78.82000 | | NFM | Birmingham | ITV News Talkback |
| 78.82500 | | NFM | AAC Middle Wallop | Ops |
| | | NFM | Donington | Army Ordnance Depot Fire |
| | | NFM | London | MoD Police |
| 78.83750 | | NFM | Mildenhall | MoD police |
| 78.85000 | | NFM | AAC Middle Wallop | Ops |
| | | NFM | Brecon Beacons | Army |
| | | NFM | RAF Wittering | RAF Police Ch 54 |
| 78.87500 | | NFM | Nationwide | MoD Police |
| 78.90000 | 73.00000 | NFM | Nationwide | Army Equipment Channel 7 |
| 78.90000 | | NFM | RNAS Lee-On-Solent | Crash Ops |
| | | NFM | RNAS Yeovilton | Fuel & Maintenance |
| 78.95000 | | NFM | AAC Middle Wallop | Tower/Ground |
| | | NFM | RNAS Culdrose | Ops |
| | | NFM | RNAS Merryfield | Ops |
| 78.97500 | | NFM | Cheltenham | GCHQ Security and Transport |
| | | | | |
| **79.0000 - 80.0000 MHz** | | | **MoD and RAF Ground Services 12.5 kHz** | |
| 79.00000 | | NFM | RAF Coningsby | 56(R) Squadron Ops |
| | | NFM | RAF Leeming | Air Defence Channel |
| | | NFM | RAF Odiham | Ops |
| | | NFM | RAF Uxbridge | Ops |
| | | NFM | RNAS Yeovilton | Ground |
| 79.00000 | | NFM | RNAS Yeovilton | Tower/Ground Ch 3 |
| 79.02500 | | NFM | RAF Cottesmore | Tower |
| | | NFM | RAF Manston | Tower/Ground |
| | | NFM | RAF Valley | Q Control |
| 79.02500 | | NFM | Salisbury Plain | Army |
| 79.05000 | | NFM | RAF Coningsby | Tower |
| | | NFM | RAF Leuchars | Felix Control |
| | | NFM | RAF Lyneham | Crew Buses |
| | | AM | RAF Machrihanish | Tower |
| | | NFM | RAF Northolt | Paintbox Control |
| 79.07500 | | NFM | RAF Church Fenton | Tower/Ground |
| | | NFM | RAF Cosford | Tower/Ground |
| | | NFM | RAF Northolt | Tower Crash Tenders |
| 79.10000 | | NFM | Nationwide | RAF Police Channel 1 |
| | | NFM | RAF Valley | Tower/Ground |
| 79.12500 | | NFM | RAF Brize Norton | Ground Services |
| | | NFM | RAF Cottesmore | Ratchet Control/Line |
| | | NFM | RAF Manston | Maintenance |

| Base | Mobile | Mode | Location | User and Notes |
|---|---|---|---|---|
| 79.12500 | | NFM | RAF Manston | RAF Police (Seagull) |
| | | NFM | RAF Marham | Engineering |
| 79.12500 | | NFM | RAF St Athan | Loadmaster and Ground |
| 79.12500 | | NFM | RAF St Mawgan | Personnel Services |
| 79.13750 | | NFM | RAF Leuchars | Ground Services |
| 79.15000 | | NFM | Nationwide | RAF Police Channel 2 |
| | | NFM | RAF Linton-on-Ouse | Ground Services |
| 79.17500 | | NFM | RAF Lyneham | Tower/Ground |
| | | NFM | RAF Northolt | Forward Control |
| 79.18750 | | NFM | RAF Northolt | Link Repeater |
| 79.20000 | | NFM | Nationwide | RAF Police Channel 3 |
| | | NFM | RAF Coningsby | Ground Services |
| | | NFM | RAF Leeming | Saracen |
| | | NFM | RAF Newton | Police Training |
| 79.21250 | 74.11250 | NFM | Gwent | Mould |
| | | NFM | Manchester | Mould |
| | | NFM | Norfolk | Mould |
| | | NFM | RAE Aberporth | MoD Police |
| 79.22500 | 68.30000 | NFM | Nationwide | Army Channel 1 |
| 79.22500 | 79.22500 | NFM | RAF Cottesmore | Ops (Bravo) |
| 79.22500 | | NFM | RAF Kinloss | Ops (Moonshine Control) |
| | | NFM | RAF Leuchars | Ops (Zulu Control) |
| | | NFM | RAF Spadeadam | Ops |
| | | NFM | RAF Waddington | RAF Police (Whitecap Control) |
| | | NFM | RAF Wittering | RAF Police Ch 3/13 |
| 79.25000 | 68.40000 | NFM | Nationwide | Army Channel 2 |
| 79.25000 | | NFM | Nationwide | RAF Police Channel 4 |
| | | NFM | RAF Church Fenton | Marshallers |
| | | NFM | RAF Leuchars | Ground Ops |
| | | NFM | RAF Linton-on-Ouse | Ground Services |
| | | NFM | RAF Marham | Security |
| | | NFM | RAF Wittering | Ops |
| | | NFM | RAF Wittering | RAF Police |
| 79.26250 | | NFM | RAF Leeming | Ground |
| 79.27500 | 68.42500 | NFM | Nationwide | Army Channel 3 |
| 79.27500 | | NFM | RAF Lyneham | Ground Control |
| | | NFM | RAF Marham | Tower |
| | | NFM | RAF Northolt | Ground Control |
| | | NFM | RAF St Athan | Transport and Ground |
| | | NFM | RAF St Mawgan | RAF Police |
| | | NFM | RAF Valley | RAF Police (Livid Control) |
| | | NFM | RAF Wittering | Ops |
| 79.30000 | | NFM | Nationwide | RAF Police Channel 5 |
| | | NFM | RAF Coltishall | RAF Police (Whitecap Control) |
| | | NFM | RAF Coltishall | Tower |
| | | NFM | RAF Odiham | Tower |
| | | NFM | RAF Wittering | RAF Police |
| 79.32500 | | NFM | Galway | Galway Heating Oil Co. |
| | | NFM | Nationwide | RAF Police |
| | | NFM | RAE Farnborough | Ground Control |
| | | NFM | RAF Cosford | Ground Control |
| | | NFM | RAF Leeming | Ground |
| | | NFM | RAF Linton-on-Ouse | Ground Services |
| | | NFM | RAF Lossiemouth | Tower |
| | | NFM | RAF Waddington | Ground Services |

| Base | Mobile | Mode | Location | User and Notes |
|------|--------|------|----------|----------------|
| 79.35000 | | NFM | Nationwide | RAF Police Channel 6 |
| | | NFM | Nationwide | Royal Signals |
| | | NFM | RAF Coningsby | Ground Services |
| | | NFM | RAF Leuchars | Crash Ops |
| 79.35000 | | NFM | RAF Manston | RAF Police (Seagull) |
| | | NFM | RAF Waddington | Channel One |
| | | NFM | RAF Wittering | Ch I/11/51 |
| 79.37500 | | NFM | Gosport | RN Security (Tanzy Control) |
| | | NFM | RAF Church Fenton | RAF Police (Whitecap Control) |
| | | NFM | RAF Leuchars | Crash Ops |
| | | NFM | RAF Marham | Elfin |
| | | NFM | RAF Odiham | Ruler |
| 79.38750 | | NFM | RAF Leuchars | Ground Services |
| 79.40000 | | NFM | Nationwide | Army Channel 4 |
| | | NFM | Nationwide | RAF Police Channel 7 |
| | | NFM | RAF Coningsby | Ground Services |
| | | NFM | RAF Leeming | Air Defence Channel |
| | | NFM | RAF Leuchars | Ground Services |
| | | NFM | RAF Lyneham | Ops |
| | | NFM | RAF Northolt | RAF Police (Mayfly Control) |
| | | NFM | RAF Wittering | RAF Police Ch 7/17 |
| 79.41250 | 74.38750 | NFM | Gwent | Mould |
| 79.42500 | | NFM | RAF Brize Norton | Tower/Ground |
| | | NFM | RAF Kinloss | Tower |
| | | NFM | RAF Waddington | Tower/Ground |
| 79.45000 | | NFM | Nationwide | RAF Police Channel 8 |
| | | NFM | RAF Coltishall | Ops (Zero) |
| | | NFM | RAF Cosford | Charlie Control |
| | | NFM | RAF Leeming | Air Defence Channel |
| | | NFM | RAF Wittering | RAF Police |
| 79.47500 | | NFM | Lydd | Army Camp Security |
| | | NFM | Nationwide | RAF Police |
| | | NFM | RAF Coningsby | Line |
| | | NFM | RAF Cranwell | Ground Services |
| | | NFM | RAF Northolt | Ops (Papa Control) |
| 79.48750 | | NFM | Northern Ireland | RAF Repeater |
| 79.48750 | | NFM | Southend on Sea | MoD Repeater |
| 79.50000 | | NFM | Lydd | Army Camp Security |
| | | NFM | Nationwide | RAF Police Channel 9 |
| | | NFM | RAE Aberporth | MoD Police |
| | | NFM | RAF Neatishead | Security |
| | | NFM | RAF Waddington | Channel Four |
| | | NFM | RAF Wittering | Ops |
| | | NFM | RAF Wittering | RAF Police Ch 9/19 |
| | | NFM | USAF Mildenhall | Security |
| 79.52500 | | NFM | RAF Lossiemouth | Ops |
| | | NFM | RAF Newton | Ops (Tempo) |
| | | NFM | RAF Wittering | Ops/RAF Police |
| 79.53750 | | NFM | RAE Farnborough | Medical Ops |
| 79.55000 | | NFM | Nationwide | RAF Police Channel 10 |
| | | NFM | RAF Coningsby | Ground Services |
| 79.56250 | | NFM | RAF Ternhill | Army Staff Cars |
| 79.57500 | | NFM | RAF Leeming | Air Defence Channel |
| | | NFM | RAF Lossiemouth | Ops (Epoch Control) |

| Base | Mobile | Mode | Location | User and Notes |
|---|---|---|---|---|
| 79.60000 | | NFM | Nationwide | RAF Police Channel 11 |
| | | NFM | RAF Brize Norton | Ops (Brize Ops) |
| | | NFM | RAF Lossiemouth | Ops (Oxide Control) |
| | | NFM | RAF Manston | RAF Police (Seagull) |
| 79.61250 | | NFM | Cambridgeshire | Mould Ch 4 |
| 79.62500 | | NFM | RAF Wittering | Ground Services |
| 79.65000 | | NFM | Nationwide | RAF Police Channel 12 |
| | | NFM | RAF Benson | Tower |
| | | NFM | RAF Brize Norton | Loadmasters/Tower/Ground |
| | | NFM | RAF Coningsby | Ground Services |
| | | NFM | RAF Lyneham | Tower |
| 79.67500 | | NFM | RAF Brize Norton | Loadmaster |
| | | NFM | RAF Newton | Tower |
| | | NFM | RAF Northolt | Ops |
| | | NFM | RAF Valley | F Control |
| 79.68000 | | NFM | RAF Waddington | Channel 5 |
| 79.70000 | 68.15000 | NFM | Nationwide | Army Channel 6 |
| 79.70000 | 79.70000 | NFM | RAF Coningsby | Ground Services |
| | | NFM | RAF Leeming | Air Defence Channel |
| | | NFM | RAF Marham | Link |
| 79.71250 | 79.71250 | NFM | Colchester | Barracks |
| 79.71250 | 74.46750 | NFM | Gwent | Mould |
| 79.71250 | 79.71250 | NFM | Stanford Battle Area | Stanford Ops |
| 79.72500 | 74.72500 | NFM | RAF Cottesmore | Grady Control |
| 79.76250 | 74.26250 | NFM | Gwent | Mould |
| 79.77500 | | NFM | Colchester | Barracks |
| | | NFM | Nationwide | RAF Fire Channel |
| | | NFM | RAF Leeming | Air Defence Channel |
| | | NFM | RAF Northolt | Ops |
| 79.80000 | | NFM | Nationwide | Army Channel 7 |
| | | NFM | RAF Coningsby | Ground Services |
| 79.82500 | | NFM | Nationwide | RAF Police Convoys |
| | | NFM | RAF Wittering | RAF Police |
| 79.87500 | | NFM | RAF Odiham | 33 Squadron link |
| 79.90000 | 68.52500 | NFM | Nationwide | Army Channel 8 |
| 79.95000 | 68.60000 | NFM | Nationwide | Army Channel 9 |
| 79.95000 | 79.95000 | NFM | RAF Wittering | Ground Services |
| 79.98750 | 79.97500 | NFM | RAF Coningsby | 56(R) Squadron Ops |

## 80.0000 - 81.5000 MHz  FIRE BRIGADES (ENGLAND & WALES)
### [BASE 70.5000 - 71.5000 MHz]

| Base | Mobile | Mode | Location | User and Notes |
|---|---|---|---|---|
| 80.0125 | | NFM | Lancashire | Fire Brigade Ch 9 |
| | | AM | London | Fire Tender to Tender Ch 21 |
| | | AM | RAE Farnborough | Fire Brigade control Ch 21 |
| 80.0375 | | AM | Cumbria | Fire Mobiles |
| 80.0750 | | AM | London | Fire Tender to Tender Ch 22 |
| 80.2000 | | NFM | Norfolk | Fire Brigade |
| 80.2250 | | NFM | West Yorkshire | Fire Brigade Mobiles Ch3 |
| 80.4000 | | AM | Suffolk | Fire Brigade |
| 80.4125 | 71.1125 | AM | Bedfordshire | Fire Brigade |
| 80.5500 | | NFM | Lancashire | Fire Mobiles |
| 81.0375 | | NFM | Suffolk | Fire Brigade |
| 81.0875 | | NFM | Suffolk | Fire Brigade |
| 81.1250 | | NFM | Nationwide | Fire Brigade Channel |
| 81.2500 | | NFM | Galway | Tone Repeater |

| Base | Mobile | Mode | Location | User and Notes |
|------|--------|------|----------|----------------|
| 81.2625 | | NFM | Tayside | Link |
| 81.3125 | | NFM | Tayside | Link |
| 81.3500 | | NFM | Tayside | Link |

**80.5000 - 82.5000 MHz    RADIO ASTRONOMY**

**81.5000 - 83.5000 MHz    LOW BAND PMR (SIMPLEX & DUPLEX)**
**[SPLIT -13.5 MHz]**

| Base | Mobile | Mode | Location | User and Notes |
|------|--------|------|----------|----------------|
| 81.57500 | | NFM | England & Wales | Police Radio Engineering |
| 81.76250 | | NFM | London | HM Customs & Excise |
| 81.77500 | 68.27500 | NFM | Immingham | HM Customs & Excise |
| | | NFM | Nationwide | HM Customs & Excise |
| | | NFM | Nationwide | Network Q RAC Rally Marshall |
| 81.78750 | | NFM | Immingham | HM Customs & Excise |
| | | NFM | London | HM Customs & Excise |
| 81.78750 | 68.28750 | NFM | Nationwide | HM Customs & Excise |
| | | NFM | Oban | HM Customs & Excise |
| 81.80000 | 68.30000 | NFM | Poole | Repeater |
| 81.82500 | 81.82500 | AM | Nationwide | Police Motorway Units |
| 81.85000 | 68.35000 | NFM | Glasgow | Taxis |
| 81.88750 | 68.38750 | NFM | Sussex | PMR Repeater |
| 81.91250 | 68.41250 | NFM | Slough | Taxis |
| 81.92500 | 68.42500 | NFM | Birmingham | Taxis |
| | | NFM | Redcar | Taxis |
| 81.93750 | 68.43750 | NFM | Southall | Sky Cars |
| 81.95000 | 81.95000 | NFM | London | Fire Brigade HQ Ops Room |
| 81.96250 | 68.46250 | AM | Plymouth | Plymouth Taxis |
| 81.98750 | 68.48750 | NFM | Grimsby | Marine Gas and Oil |
| | | NFM | Kent | Courier Service |
| | | NFM | Kent | Doctors |
| | | NFM | Portsmouth | PMR |
| 82.00000 | 68.50000 | NFM | Sussex | PMR Repeater |
| 82.02500 | | NFM | Bexley Heath | Taxis |
| 82.03750 | | NFM | London | London Car Hire |
| 82.05000 | 68.55000 | NFM | Liverpool | HM Customs & Excise |
| | | NFM | Manchester | HM Customs & Excise |
| | | NFM | Nationwide | HM Customs & Excise |
| 82.06000 | | NFM | Worcester | Amber Taxis |
| 82.06250 | 68.56250 | NFM | Glasgow | Taxis |
| 82.10000 | 68.60000 | NFM | Glasgow | Taxis |
| 82.10000 | 71.60000 | AM | Swansea | Council Works Department |
| 82.10000 | 68.60000 | AM | Swansea | Ryan Mining Ch 1 |
| 82.11250 | 68.62150 | NFM | Edinburgh | Taxis |
| | | NFM | Glasgow | Taxis |
| 82.13750 | 68.63750 | NFM | Humberside | Snow ploughs |
| | | NFM | London | Building Supplier |
| | | NFM | Tonbridge | Medicall |
| 82.17500 | 85.17500 | NFM | Bristol Area | Maintenance Company |
| 82.18750 | 68.68750 | NFM | London | Contract Dustcart |
| 82.21250 | 68.71250 | AM | Swansea | Ryan Mining Ch 2 |
| 82.22500 | 68.72500 | NFM | Newcastle | PMR |
| 82.26500 | 68.76500 | NFM | Ayr | North of Scotland Water Authority |

| Base | Mobile | Mode | Location | User and Notes |
|------|--------|------|----------|----------------|
| 82.30000 | 68.80000 | NFM | Leicester | PMR |
| | | NFM | Sussex | PMR Repeater |
| | | NFM | Tunbridge Wells | Medicall |
| 82.43750 | 68.93750 | NFM | Glasgow | Taxis |
| | | NFM | Gravesend | Taxis |
| 82.52500 | 69.02500 | NFM | Nationwide | Road Construction Recovery |
| 82.53750 | | NFM | Walsall | Taxi |
| 82.55000 | | NFM | Lincoln | PMR |
| 82.78750 | | NFM | Nationwide | RAC Network Q Rally |
| 82.80000 | 86.43500 | NFM | Keilder Forest | RAC Rally |
| 82.80000 | 82.80000 | NFM | RAC Network 'Q' Rally | Rally Control |
| 82.81250 | 82.81250 | NFM | RAC Network 'Q' Rally | Rally Channel 3 |
| 82.90000 | 82.90000 | NFM | RAC Network 'Q' Rally | Ford Team |
| 82.92500 | 69.42500 | NFM | RAC Network 'Q' Rally | Subara Team |
| 82.95000 | | NFM | Nationwide | Network Q RAC Rally Recovery |
| 82.98750 | 69.48750 | NFM | RAC Network 'Q' Rally | Toyota Channel 2 |
| 83.06500 | | NFM | Birmingham | Building Suppliers |
| 83.07500 | | NFM | Birmingham | Severn Trent Water - Aqua Base |
| 83.24500 | | NFM | Dublin | Electricity |
| 83.35000 | 71.85000 | NFM | Swansea | Council works dept. |

## 83.4000 - 84.0000 MHz  LAND SEARCH AND RESCURE (SIMPLEX)

| Base | Mobile | Mode | Location | User and Notes |
|------|--------|------|----------|----------------|
| 84.30000 | | NFM | Nationwide | RAF Mountain Rescue Ch.1 |
| | | NFM | Brecon Beacons | RAF Mountain Rescue Ch1 |
| 84.32500 | | NFM | Nationwide | RAF Mountain Rescue Ch.2 |

## 83.996 - 84.004 MHz  INDUSTRIAL, SCIENTIFIC AND MEDICAL EQUIPMENT

## 84.0000 - 84.9750 MHz  MoD POLICE COMMUNICATIONS
### 25 kHz (SIMPLEX)

| Base | Mobile | Mode | Location | User and Notes |
|------|--------|------|----------|----------------|
| 84.05000 | | NFM | Tweed Valley | Mould |
| 84.08750 | | NFM | Nationwide | Military Close Protection Ch 3 |
| 84.12500 | | NFM | Nationwide | Army Cadet Force |
| 84.15000 | | NFM | Nationwide | Military Close Protection Ch 4 |
| 84.22500 | | NFM | Nationwide | RAF |
| 84.26250 | | NFM | Nationwide | Military Close Protection Ch 7 |
| 84.31250 | | NFM | Salisbury | MOD Police Larkhill Range |
| 84.33750 | | NFM | Blanford | MOD Police |
| 84.36250 | | NFM | Nationwide | Military Close Protection Ch 6 |
| 84.37500 | | NFM | Nationwide | Military Police |
| 84.38750 | | NFM | Nationwide | Military Police |
| 84.40000 | | NFM | Nationwide | Military Police |
| 84.41250 | | NFM | Nationwide | Military Police |
| 84.42500 | | NFM | Nationwide | Military Police |
| 84.43750 | | NFM | Nationwide | Military Police |
| 84.45000 | | NFM | Nationwide | Military Police |
| 84.46250 | | NFM | Nationwide | Military Police |
| 84.47500 | | NFM | Castlemartin | RAC Range |
| 84.47500 | | NFM | Nationwide | Military Police |
| 84.48750 | | NFM | Nationwide | Military Police Escorts |
| 84.50000 | | NFM | Nationwide | Military Police Escorts |
| 84.51250 | | NFM | Nationwide | Military Police |
| 84.52500 | | NFM | Aldershot | Military Police Data |
| 84.53750 | | NFM | Nationwide | Military Police |
| 84.55000 | | NFM | London | Military Police |

| Base | Mobile | Mode | Location | User and Notes |
|------|--------|------|----------|----------------|
| 84.56250 | | NFM | Nationwide | Military Police |
| 84.57500 | | NFM | Nationwide | Military Police |
| 84.58750 | | NFM | Nationwide | Military Police |
| 84.60000 | | NFM | Nationwide | Military Mountain Rescue |
| | | NFM | Southampton | Royal Navy |
| 84.61250 | | NFM | Southampton | Army Marchwood Camp shipping Office |
| 84.64000 | | NFM | Salisbury Plain | Defence Land Services |
| 84.65000 | | NFM | RN Faslane | Medics |
| 84.71250 | | NFM | Nationwide | Military Close Protection Ch 2 |
| 84.76250 | | NFM | Nationwide | Military Close Protection Ch 1 |
| 84.77500 | | NFM | Southampton | Royal Navy |
| 84.82500 | | NFM | Nationwide | RAF Helicopter Winchmen |
| 84.83750 | | NFM | Nationwide | Military Close Protection Ch 6 |
| | | NFM | Perth | Territorial Army |
| 84.85000 | | NFM | Nationwide | Military Close Protection Ch 5 |
| 84.92500 | | NFM | Southampton | Royal Navy |
| 84.97500 | | NFM | Ludford Cove | Army Range Control Ch 1 |

### 84.35000- 84.55000 MHz  REPUBIC OF IRELAND FIRE BRIGADE AND AMBULANCE SERVICE (DUPLEX)

| Base | Mobile | Mode | Location | User and Notes |
|------|--------|------|----------|----------------|
| 84.35000 | 74.12500 | NFM | Nationwide | Fire Brigade |
| 84.37500 | 74.15000 | NFM | Nationwide | Fire Brigade |
| 84.40000 | 74.17500 | NFM | Nationwide | Fire Brigade |
| 84.42500 | 74.20000 | NFM | Nationwide | Fire Brigade |
| 84.45000 | 74.22500 | NFM | Nationwide | Fire Brigade |
| 84.47500 | 74.25000 | NFM | Nationwide | Fire Brigade |
| 84.50000 | 74.27500 | NFM | Nationwide | Fire Brigade |
| 84.52500 | 74.30000 | NFM | Nationwide | Fire Brigade |
| 84.55000 | 74.32500 | NFM | Nationwide | Fire Brigade |
| 84.57500 | 74.35000 | NFM | Nationwide | Ambulance Service |
| 84.60000 | 74.37500 | NFM | Nationwide | Ambulance Service |
| 84.62500 | 74.40000 | NFM | Nationwide | Ambulance Service |
| 84.65000 | 74.42500 | NFM | Nationwide | Ambulance Service |
| 84.67500 | 74.45000 | NFM | Nationwide | Ambulance Service |
| 84.70000 | 74.47500 | NFM | Nationwide | Ambulance Service |
| 84.72500 | 74.50000 | NFM | Nationwide | Ambulance Service |
| 84.75000 | 74.52500 | NFM | Nationwide | Ambulance Service |
| 84.77500 | 74.55000 | NFM | Nationwide | Ambulance Service |
| 84.80000 | 74.57500 | NFM | Nationwide | Ambulance Service |
| 84.82500 | 74.60000 | NFM | Nationwide | Ambulance Service |

### 85.00625 - 87.5000 MHz  PMR LOW BAND BASE REPEATERS 12.5 kHz [SPLIT - 13.5 MHz]

| Base | Mobile | Mode | Location | User and Notes |
|------|--------|------|----------|----------------|
| 85.01250 | 71.51250 | NFM | Brighton | Focsa Street Cleaners |
| | | NFM | Bristol | Severn Trent Water |
| | | NFM | Ealing | PMR |
| | | NFM | Isle of Man | Isle of Man Water |
| | | AM | Jersey | Jersey Telecom |
| | | NFM | London | Breakdown services |
| | | NFM | Perth | North of Scotland Water Authority |
| | | NFM | Widnes | Skip Hire |
| 85.02500 | 71.52500 | NFM | Birmingham | Breakdown Company |
| | | NFM | Gedling | Gedling Borough Council |
| | | NFM | Ipswich | Council |
| | | NFM | Neath | Council |

| Base | Mobile | Mode | Location | User and Notes |
|---|---|---|---|---|
| 85.02500 | 71.52500 | NFM | Norfolk | County Highways |
| | | NFM | Peterborough | Peterborough Development Corp |
| | | NFM | Pickering | Council |
| | | NFM | Port Talbot | Council Services |
| 85.03750 | 71.53750 | NFM | Aberdeen | Roads Department |
| | | NFM | Ayr | East Ayrshire Road Dept. (Highways) |
| | | NFM | Cambridge | Regency Cars |
| | | NFM | Dumfries | Council Roads Department |
| | | NFM | Easington | Works Dept |
| 85.03750 | 71.53750 | NFM | Hastings | Council |
| | | NFM | Ipswich | Council Repeater |
| | | AM | Killwinning | Roads Department |
| | | AM | Leeds | Gritters/snow ploughs |
| | | AM | St Austell | Chris Perry Motors |
| | | NFM | Strathclyde | Strathclyde Council |
| 85.05000 | 71.55000 | NFM | Aylsham | East Coast Grain |
| | | NFM | Benington | Braceys |
| | | NFM | Cambridge | Trumpington Farms |
| | | NFM | Cleveland | Mastercare |
| | | NFM | Ipswich | Anglian Water |
| | | AM | Jersey | Abbey |
| | | NFM | London | Baron Transport |
| | | NFM | Norfolk | Farm Feed Co. |
| | | NFM | Perth | North of Scotland Water Authority |
| | | NFM | Peterborough | Royal Taxis |
| | | NFM | Reepham | Salle Farm Co. |
| | | NFM | Romford | Atlas Minicabs |
| | | NFM | Southampton | Taxis |
| | | NFM | Suffolk | Farm Feed Co. |
| 85.06200 | 71.56200 | NFM | Birmingham | Community ambulance |
| | | NFM | Caerphilly | Coddy Cabs |
| | | NFM | Cleveland | Mastercare |
| | | NFM | Hull | Moss Tyres |
| | | NFM | Kettering | A-Z Taxis |
| | | NFM | London | Diamond Cars |
| | | NFM | London | Lee Vans |
| | | NFM | Norfolk | James Abbotts Ltd |
| | | NFM | Suffolk | James Abbotts Ltd |
| | | NFM | Swansea | Bryan Twyn Taxis |
| | | NFM | West Midlands | Mastercare |
| | | NFM | Witham | Anglia Land Drainage |
| | | NFM | Birmingham | Ambuline Private Ambulance |
| 85.07500 | 71.57500 | AM | Derbyshire | Tilcon |
| | | NFM | Great Yarmouth | Wolsey Taxis |
| | | NFM | Ipswich | Anglian Water |
| | | NFM | Kendal | Vets |
| | | NFM | Lakenheath | H. Palmer |
| | | AM | Leeds | Gritter/Snow Ploughs |
| | | NFM | Little Downham | W.B. Chambers. |
| | | NFM | London | David Marshall |
| | | AM | Melksham | Dance Taxis |
| | | NFM | Perth | Taxi |
| | | NFM | Scunthorpe | Taxis |
| | | NFM | Woodchurch | Arrow Park Taxis |
| | | NFM | Wrexham | Trafford Estate |

| Base | Mobile | Mode | Location | User and Notes |
|---|---|---|---|---|
| 85.08750 | 71.58750 | NFM | Baldock | Winifred Express |
| | | NFM | Cambridge | Regency Cars |
| | | NFM | Colchester | Wooldridge |
| | | AM | Cornwall | County Council |
| | | NFM | Guernsey | Guernsey Gas Co. |
| | | NFM | Hillingdon | Sky Radio Cars |
| | | NFM | Newmarket | Six Mile Bottom Estate |
| 85.10000 | 71.60000 | NFM | Brecon | Welsh Water |
| | | NFM | Glasgow | Water Department |
| | | NFM | Grampian | North of Scotland Water Authority |
| 85.10000 | 71.60000 | NFM | Ipswich | Anglian Water |
| | | NFM | Neath | Welsh Water control room |
| | | NFM | Nottingham | Trent Water |
| 85.11250 | 71.61250 | NFM | Abergavenny | Welsh Water |
| | | NFM | Colchester | Roadworks Depot |
| | | NFM | Ipswich | Roadworks Depot |
| | | AM | Leeds | Yorkshire Water |
| | | NFM | Manchester | PMR |
| | | NFM | Norwich | Anglian Water |
| | | NFM | Stanway | Roadworks Depot |
| | | NFM | Thames Valley | Thames Valley Water |
| | | NFM | West Yorkshire | British Pipeline |
| 85.12500 | 71.62500 | NFM | Ayr | East Ayrshire Road Dept. (Highways) |
| | | NFM | Brighton | Skip Service |
| | | NFM | Essex | British Pipeline |
| | | NFM | Jersey | Jersey Electricity Company Ch 3 |
| | | NFM | Nationwide | British Pipeline |
| | | NFM | Strathclyde | Strathclyde Council |
| | | NFM | Edinburgh | British Telecom |
| | | NFM | Nationwide | British Telecom Channel 6 |
| 85.15000 | 71.65000 | NFM | Nationwide | British Telecom Channel 2 |
| 85.16250 | 71.66250 | NFM | Glasgow | Data Link |
| | | NFM | Lancaster | British Telecom |
| | | NFM | Morecambe | British Telecom |
| | | NFM | Nationwide | British Telecom Channel 4 |
| | | NFM | Perth | British Telecom |
| | | AM | Swansea | British Telecom Base |
| 85.17500 | 71.67500 | NFM | Dundee | BT Data Link |
| | | NFM | Jersey | Jersey Electricity Company Ch 2 |
| | | NFM | Nationwide | British Telecom Channel 1 |
| | | NFM | Perth | British Telecom |
| 85.18750 | 71.68750 | NFM | Edinburgh | British Telecom Voice Link |
| | | NFM | Nationwide | British Telecom Channel 5 |
| | | NFM | Perth | British Telecom Data Link |
| 85.20000 | 71.70000 | AM | Liverpool | Taxis |
| | | NFM | Nationwide | British Telecom Channel 3 |
| | | AM | York | British Telecom |
| 85.21000 | 71.71000 | NFM | Ayr | North of Scotland Water Authority |
| 85.21250 | 71.71250 | NFM | Bishop Stortford | Thames Water |
| | | NFM | Dundee | North of Scotland Water Authority |
| | | NFM | Folkestone | Southern Water |
| | | NFM | Glossop | Seven Trent Water |
| | | NFM | Gwent | South Wales Water |
| | | NFM | Hampshire | Water Board Ch 2 |
| | | NFM | Ipswich | Anglian Water |
| | | NFM | Lancaster | North West Water |

| Base | Mobile | Mode | Location | User and Notes |
|------|--------|------|----------|----------------|
| 85.21250 | 71.71250 | NFM | Lea Valley | Southern Water Channel 2 |
| 85.21250 | 71.71250 | NFM | Llanelli | Welsh Water |
| | | NFM | Montgomery | Severn Trent Water |
| | | NFM | Morecambe | North West Water |
| | | NFM | Saffron Walden | Southern Water |
| | | AM | Swansea City | South Wales Water Board |
| 85.22500 | 71.72500 | AM | Cardiff | South Glamorgan Council |
| | | NFM | Cardiff Area | Maintenance Company |
| | | AM | Cornwall | County Council |
| | | NFM | Dumbarton | Council |
| 85.22500 | 71.72500 | NFM | Dumfries | West of Scotland Water |
| | | NFM | Lea Valley | Southern Water Channel 4 |
| | | NFM | London | Chelsea Council |
| | | NFM | London | Westminster Council |
| | | NFM | North Wales | Welsh Water |
| | | NFM | Thames Valley | Thames Valley Water |
| 85.23750 | 71.73750 | NFM | Aberdeen | North of Scotland Water Authority |
| | | NFM | Borders | West of Scotland Water |
| | | NFM | Essex | Wessex Water |
| | | NFM | Gwynedd | Welsh Water |
| | | NFM | Nottingham | Trent Water |
| | | NFM | Perth | North of Scotland Water Authority |
| | | NFM | Suffolk | Suffolk Water |
| | | NFM | Thames Valley | Thames Valley Water |
| | | NFM | Walsall | Severn Trent Water |
| | | NFM | Whitehaven | North West Water |
| 85.25000 | 71.75000 | NFM | Ayr | North of Scotland Water Authority |
| | | NFM | Barrow | North West Water |
| | | NFM | Frimley | Surrey Water |
| | | NFM | Hampshire | Portsmouth Water |
| | | NFM | Jersey | Jersey Milk |
| | | NFM | Lancaster | North West Water |
| | | NFM | Leeds | Automobile Association |
| | | NFM | Letchwood | Thames Water |
| | | NFM | Morecambe | North West Water |
| | | NFM | Newcastle | Northumbrian Water |
| | | NFM | Norfolk | Anglian Water |
| | | NFM | Perth | North of Scotland Water Authority |
| | | NFM | Scarborough | Water Authority |
| | | NFM | Suffolk | Anglian Water |
| | | NFM | Surrey | Thames Water |
| | | NFM | West Yorkshire | Automobile Association |
| | | AM | York | Yorkshire Water |
| 85.26250 | 71.76250 | NFM | Avon | Severn Trent Water |
| | | NFM | Hampshire | Portsmouth Water |
| | | NFM | Huddersfield | Yorkshire Water |
| | | NFM | Kent | Kent Water |
| | | NFM | Nottinghamshire | Severn Trent Water |
| | | NFM | Taunton | Wessex Water |
| | | NFM | Thames Valley | Thames Valley Water |
| | | AM | York | Yorkshire Water |
| 85.27500 | 71.77500 | NFM | Cornwall | South West Water |
| | | AM | Driffield | Yorkshire Water |
| | | NFM | East Sussex | Southern Water |
| | | NFM | Ipswich | Anglian Water |
| | | NFM | Kent | Kent Water |

| Base | Mobile | Mode | Location | User and Notes |
|------|--------|------|----------|----------------|
| 85.27500 | 71.77500 | NFM | Manchester | North West Water |
| | | NFM | Norfolk | Anglian Water |
| | | NFM | Perth | North of Scotland Water Authority |
| | | NFM | Somerset | Council Housing |
| | | NFM | St. Helens | North West Water |
| | | NFM | Suffolk | Anglian Water |
| | | NFM | Tayside | North of Scotland Water Authority |
| | | NFM | West Yorkshire | Yorkshire Water |
| 85.28750 | 71.78750 | NFM | Anglia | Anglian Water Ch 13 |
| | | NFM | Brighton | Southern Water (Red Base) |
| 85.28750 | 71.78750 | NFM | Fort William | North of Scotland Water Authority |
| | | AM | Gwynedd | Welsh Water |
| | | NFM | Peterborough | Anglian Water |
| | | AM | Sussex | Southern Water |
| | | NFM | Tayside | North of Scotland Water Authority |
| | | NFM | Warrington | North West Water |
| | | NFM | Yorkshire | Yorkshire Water |
| 85.30000 | 71.80000 | NFM | Aberdeen | Council Dog Catcher |
| | | NFM | Breckland | Council HQ |
| | | NFM | Hampshire | Council Drainage |
| | | NFM | Ipswich | Community Repeater |
| | | NFM | London | Brent Council |
| | | NFM | Thames Valley | Thames Valley Water Ch 5 |
| 85.31250 | 71.81250 | NFM | Blackburn | North West Water |
| | | NFM | Brighton | Southern Water (Distribution) |
| | | NFM | Bristol | Water Authority |
| | | NFM | Humberside | Council |
| | | NFM | Huntingdon | Anglian Water |
| | | NFM | Newmarket | PMR |
| | | NFM | Sheffield | Yorkshire Water Board |
| | | NFM | Tayside | North of Scotland Water Authority |
| | | NFM | West Sussex | Wessex Water Ch 6 |
| | | NFM | Whitehaven | North West Water |
| 85.32500 | 71.82500 | NFM | Aberdeen | British Gas |
| | | AM | Ayr | West of Scotland Water |
| | | NFM | Bournemouth | Dorset Water |
| | | NFM | Brighton | Southern Water (Green Base) |
| | | NFM | Burnley | North West Water |
| | | NFM | Co. Durham | Electricians |
| | | NFM | Doncaster | Yorkshire Water |
| | | NFM | Edinburgh | East of Scotland Water |
| | | NFM | Folkestone | Community Repeater |
| | | NFM | Gloucester | Gloucester Water |
| | | NFM | Ipswich | Anglian Water |
| | | NFM | Merseyside | PMR |
| | | NFM | Northampton | Anglian Water |
| | | NFM | Pendle | Northwest Water |
| | | AM | Sheffield | Yorkshire Water |
| 85.33750 | 71.83750 | NFM | Aberdeen | North of Scotland Water Authority |
| | | NFM | Carlisle | North West Water |
| | | NFM | Gwent | Severn Trent Water |
| | | NFM | Humberside | Humberside Water |
| | | AM | Huntingdon | Anglian Water |
| | | NFM | Ipswich | Anglian Water |
| | | NFM | Kidderminster | Worcestershire Water |

| Base | Mobile | Mode | Location | User and Notes |
|------|--------|------|----------|----------------|
| 85.33750 | 71.83750 | NFM | Mold | Clwyd Water Board |
| | | NFM | Perth | North of Scotland Water Authority |
| | | NFM | Plymouth | South West Water |
| | | NFM | Sheffield | Yorkshire Water Board |
| | | NFM | Taunton | Wessex Water |
| | | NFM | Worcester | Severn Trent Water |
| 85.35000 | 71.85000 | NFM | Belfast | Water Board |
| | | NFM | Clwyd | Clwyd Council |
| | | NFM | East Sussex | Bottle Bank Clearance |
| | | NFM | Guernsey | Civil Defence |
| | | NFM | Hampshire | Bottle Bank Collection |
| 85.35000 | 71.85000 | NFM | Kent | Kent Water |
| | | NFM | Newcastle, Byker | North East Water |
| | | NFM | Portsmouth | City Council |
| | | NFM | Renfrew | Council |
| | | NFM | Saddleworth | Highways |
| | | NFM | Stowmarket | Council Highways |
| | | NFM | Swansea City | Council |
| | | NFM | Warrington | North West Water |
| 85.36250 | 71.86250 | NFM | Ayr | District Council |
| | | NFM | Chester | Car Transporters |
| | | NFM | Coventry | Severn Trent Water |
| | | NFM | Essex | Wessex Water |
| | | AM | Glamorgan | Welsh Water |
| | | NFM | Huntingdon | Anglian Water |
| | | NFM | Liverpool | North West Water |
| | | NFM | Tayside | North of Scotland Water Authority |
| | | NFM | Warwickshire | Severn Trent Water |
| | | NFM | Wirral | North West Water |
| | | NFM | Yorkshire | Yorkshire Water |
| 85.37500 | 71.87500 | NFM | Barnsley | Yorkshire Water |
| | | NFM | Belfast | NI Electricity |
| | | NFM | Bury St Edmunds | Council Highways |
| | | NFM | Leicester | Severn Trent Water |
| | | NFM | London | Thames Water Authority |
| | | NFM | West Sussex | Southern Water Engineer and Base |
| 85.38500 | 71.88500 | NFM | West Glasgow | Strathclyde Water |
| 85.38750 | 71.88750 | NFM | Belfast | Newtownabbey Council |
| | | NFM | Cambridge | Anglian Water |
| | | AM | Co. Durham | Yorkshire Water |
| | | NFM | Huntingdon | Anglian Water |
| | | NFM | Nottinghamshire | Severn Trent Water |
| | | NFM | Perth | North of Scotland Water Authority |
| | | AM | Wiltshire | Severn Trent Water Ch 2 |
| | | NFM | Wyre | Council |
| 85.40000 | 71.90000 | NFM | Hounslow | County Council |
| | | NFM | Kent | Kent Water |
| | | NFM | London | Hounslow CTCSS |
| | | NFM | Northampton | Social Services |
| | | NFM | Perth | North of Scotland Water Authority |
| | | NFM | Sheffield | County Council |
| | | NFM | Somerset | Tarmac Topmix |
| | | NFM | Yorkshire | Yorkshire Water |

| Base | Mobile | Mode | Location | User and Notes |
|------|--------|------|----------|----------------|
| 85.41250 | 71.91250 | NFM | Brighton | Southern Water (Drainage) |
| | | AM | Caernarfon | Welsh Water |
| | | NFM | Ipswich | Anglian Water |
| | | NFM | Manchester | PMR |
| | | NFM | Perth | North of Scotland Water Authority |
| | | NFM | Stoke-on-Trent | Severn Trent Water |
| | | NFM | West Midlands | Midland Water |
| | | NFM | West Sussex | Southern Water |
| | | NFM | Wye | Welsh Water Channel 33 |
| 85.42500 | 71.92500 | NFM | Guernsey | Fire Service |
| | | NFM | Ipswich | Community Repeater |
| | | NFM | Kent | Council |
| | | AM | Neath | Welsh Water |
| | | NFM | Northampton | Social Services |
| 85.42500 | 71.92500 | NFM | Tayside | North of Scotland Water Authority |
| | | NFM | Wales | Council Repeater |
| 85.43750 | 71.93750 | NFM | Alford | Roads Department |
| | | NFM | Cornwall | South West Water |
| | | NFM | Eastbourne | Eastbourne Water |
| | | NFM | Gloucestershire | Cotswolds Water |
| | | NFM | Gowerton | Welsh Water |
| | | NFM | Lea Valley | Southern Water |
| | | NFM | Leeds | Roadworks |
| | | NFM | Liverpool | North West Water |
| | | NFM | Merseyside | PMR |
| | | AM | Scunthorpe | Anglian Water |
| | | NFM | Surrey | Thames Water |
| | | NFM | Warrington | North West Water |
| 85.45000 | 71.95000 | NFM | Ayr | Skip Hire |
| | | AM | Bedford | Bedford Sewage |
| | | NFM | Cumnock | Council |
| | | NFM | Gwynedd | Welsh Water |
| | | NFM | Kent | Kent Water |
| | | NFM | Minehead | Somerset Water |
| | | NFM | Newport | Council Ch 3 |
| | | NFM | Norfolk | Anglian Water |
| | | NFM | Pitcaple | Roads Department |
| | | NFM | Suffolk | Anglian Water |
| | | NFM | Swansea | Dyfed Council |
| 85.46250 | 71.96250 | AM | Ayr | West of Scotland Water |
| | | NFM | Barrow | PMR |
| | | NFM | Bristol | Severn Trent Water |
| | | NFM | Haverfordwest | Welsh Water |
| | | NFM | Manchester | North West Water |
| | | NFM | Norfolk | Anglian Water |
| | | NFM | Suffolk | Anglian Water |
| | | NFM | Taunton | Wessex Water |
| | | NFM | West Sussex | Southern Water Ch 3 |
| 85.47500 | 71.97500 | NFM | Bristol | Automobile Association |
| | | NFM | Broadstairs | Chauffeur Service |
| | | NFM | Gatwick | Capital Coaches |
| | | NFM | Grampian | Transport |
| | | NFM | Hastings | Hastings Water |
| | | NFM | Kings Lynn | Dow Chemicals |

| Base | Mobile | Mode | Location | User and Notes |
|------|--------|------|----------|----------------|
| 85.48750 | 71.98750 | AM | Dumfries | Automobile Association |
| | | NFM | London | Automobile Association |
| | | NFM | Nationwide | Automobile Association Ch. 6 |
| 85.50000 | 72.00000 | NFM | Cardiff | Automobile Association |
| | | NFM | Dumfries | Automobile Association |
| | | NFM | London | Automobile Association |
| | | NFM | Midlands | Automobile Association |
| | | NFM | Nationwide | Automobile Association Ch. 2 |
| | | NFM | Nottingham | Automobile Association |
| 85.51250 | 72.01250 | NFM | Birmingham | Automobile Association |
| | | NFM | Coniston | Automobile Association |
| | | NFM | Ipswich | Automobile Association |
| | | NFM | London | Automobile Association |
| | | NFM | Nationwide | Automobile Association Ch. 4 |
| | | NFM | Perth | Automobile Association |
| 85.52500 | 72.02500 | NFM | Aberdeen | Automobile Association |
| | | NFM | Anglia | Automobile Association |
| | | NFM | Belfast | Automobile Association Ch 1 |
| | | NFM | Blackpool | Automobile Association |
| | | NFM | Glasgow | Automobile Association |
| | | NFM | Guernsey | Automobile Association |
| | | NFM | London | Automobile Association |
| | | NFM | Nationwide | Automobile Association Ch. 1 |
| | | NFM | Perth | Automobile Association |
| | | NFM | West Midlands | Automobile Association |
| 85.53750 | 72.03750 | NFM | Brighton | Automobile Association |
| | | NFM | Exeter | Automobile Association |
| | | NFM | London | Automobile Association |
| | | NFM | Milton Keynes | Automobile Association |
| | | NFM | Nationwide | Automobile Association Ch. 5 |
| | | NFM | Oakhampton | Automobile Association |
| | | NFM | Perth | Automobile Association |
| | | NFM | Warrington | Automobile Association |
| 85.55000 | 72.05000 | NFM | Aberdeen | Automobile Association |
| | | NFM | Bristol | Automobile Association |
| | | NFM | Ipswich | Automobile Association |
| | | NFM | London | Automobile Association |
| | | NFM | Nationwide | Automobile Association Ch. 3 |
| | | NFM | Norwich | Automobile Association |
| | | NFM | Whitehaven | Automobile Association |
| 85.56250 | 72.06250 | NFM | Edinburgh | Automobile Association |
| | | NFM | Guernsey | Water Board |
| | | NFM | Ipswich | Automobile Association |
| | | NFM | Lancaster | Automobile Association |
| | | NFM | Liverpool | Automobile Association |
| | | NFM | London | Automobile Association |
| | | NFM | Nationwide | Automobile Association Ch. 7 |
| | | NFM | Perth | Automobile Association |
| 85.57500 | 72.07500 | NFM | Belfast | NI Electricity |
| | | NFM | Berkshire | Thames Water Ch 3 |
| | | NFM | Jersey | Jersey Electricity Company Ch 1 |
| 85.58750 | 72.08750 | AM | Cumbria | Automobile Association |
| | | NFM | Ipswich | Automobile Association |
| | | AM | Lancashire | Automobile Association |
| | | NFM | London | Automobile Association |
| | | NFM | Nationwide | Automobile Association Ch. 8 |

| Base | Mobile | Mode | Location | User and Notes |
|---|---|---|---|---|
| 85.58750 | 72.08750 | NFM | Perth | Automobile Association Data |
| | | NFM | Whinfell | Automobile Association |
| 85.60000 | 72.10000 | NFM | Belfast | NI Electricity |
| | | NFM | Blackpool | Council Parks |
| | | NFM | Exeter | Council |
| | | NFM | Forest Heath | Council |
| | | NFM | Jersey | Civil Defence Link to France |
| | | NFM | Norfolk | Royal Automobile Club |
| | | NFM | Scarborough | Council |
| | | NFM | Suffolk | Royal Automobile Club |
| 85.61250 | 72.11250 | NFM | Humberside | Community Repeater |
| | | NFM | Lake District | Lake District National Park |
| | | NFM | London | Concord Ltd |
| | | NFM | Oldham | Courier |
| | | NFM | Poole | Poole Adventure Centre |
| 85.62500 | 72.12500 | NFM | Abbotts Ripton, Cambs | Fellows Estate |
| | | NFM | Bath | Silversails Taxis |
| | | NFM | Colchester | J. Collie Ltd |
| | | NFM | Liverpool | Taxi |
| | | NFM | London | Battersea Cars |
| | | NFM | London | Globe Bikes |
| | | NFM | London | Haden Carriers |
| | | NFM | Norfolk | Automobile Association |
| | | NFM | Suffolk | Automobile Association |
| | | NFM | Uxbridge | Cabline |
| 85.62750 | 72.12750 | NFM | Barrow in Furness | Furness Emergency Doctor Service |
| | | NFM | Salisbury | Defence Land Services |
| 85.63750 | 72.13750 | NFM | Aberdeen | Taxi |
| | | NFM | Exeter | TNT |
| | | NFM | Guernsey | Fruit Exporters |
| | | NFM | Solent | Solent Waters Rescue |
| 85.65000 | 72.15000 | AM | Altricham | Trafftax |
| | | NFM | Ealing | Trade Centre Ch 1 |
| | | NFM | Jersey | Civil Defence Link to France |
| | | NFM | London | Chequers Transport |
| | | NFM | London | Riva Communications Ltd |
| | | NFM | Norfolk | Royal Automobile Club |
| | | AM | Portsmouth | Taxis |
| | | NFM | Seaforth | Taxi |
| | | NFM | St Ives | Tyrell Contractors |
| | | NFM | Suffolk | Royal Automobile Club |
| 85.66250 | 72.16250 | NFM | Lochaber | Caledonian Canal |
| | | NFM | London | Anderson Young Ltd |
| | | NFM | London | Westland Market Tower |
| | | NFM | London | Wide Fulham |
| | | NFM | Maidenhead | Valley Taxis |
| | | NFM | Norfolk | M. Crouch Ltd |
| | | NFM | Suffolk | M. Crouch Ltd |
| 85.67500 | 72.17500 | NFM | Aberdeen | Taxi |
| | | NFM | Ayr | Taxi |
| | | NFM | Barrow in Furness | Barrow 5 Taxis |
| | | NFM | Brighton | Streamline Taxis |
| | | NFM | Chatteris | Allpress Farms |
| | | NFM | Colchester | Eastern Tractors |
| | | NFM | Jersey | LuxiCabs  Ch 1 |

| Base | Mobile | Mode | Location | User and Notes |
|---|---|---|---|---|
| 85.67500 | 72.17500 | NFM | London | Petchey & Velite Cars |
| | | NFM | Milton Keynes | Harper Cars |
| | | NFM | Norfolk | Hughes TV Servicing |
| | | NFM | Suffolk | Hughes TV Servicing |
| | | NFM | Thetford | Lloyd & Marriot Vets |
| | | NFM | Walsall Wood | Claridge TV & Radio |
| 85.68750 | 72.18750 | NFM | Exeter | TNT Carriers |
| | | NFM | London | Belsize Ltd |
| | | NFM | Milton Keynes | Skyline Taxis |
| | | NFM | Norfolk | Royal Automobile Club |
| | | NFM | Slough | Castle Radio Cars |
| | | NFM | Suffolk | Royal Automobile Club |
| | | NFM | Wishaw | Myles Taxis |
| 85.70000 | 72.20000 | NFM | Aberdeen | Shanks Transport |
| | | NFM | Grimsby | Stoneledge Haulage |
| | | AM | Hull | Redune Taxis |
| | | NFM | London | Echo Cars |
| | | NFM | Old Swan | Taxi |
| | | NFM | Scarborough | R&C Company |
| 85.71250 | 72.21250 | NFM | London | AA M25 Recovery |
| | | NFM | London | Summit Cars |
| | | NFM | Nationwide | Curry's Master Care |
| | | NFM | West Mersea | Grey |
| 85.72500 | 72.22500 | NFM | Bedford | Carlow Radio |
| | | NFM | Brighton | Rediffusion |
| | | NFM | Clackmannan | Council |
| | | NFM | Ipswich | RAC Motor Recovery |
| | | NFM | London | Ascot & Bracknell |
| | | NFM | Nationwide | Sitaclear Technology Ltd |
| | | NFM | Norfolk | Automobile Assocation A12 Recovery |
| | | NFM | Shrewsbury | Taxis |
| | | NFM | Suffolk | AA Recovery (A12) |
| | | NFM | Weasenham | Farms |
| 85.73750 | 72.23750 | NFM | Colchester | Fieldspray Ltd |
| | | NFM | Dundee | Deliveries |
| | | NFM | Eastbourne | Skip Hire |
| | | NFM | Edinburgh | Garage |
| | | NFM | Glasgow | Plant Hire |
| | | NFM | London | Swift & Safe |
| | | NFM | London, North | Network Cars & Courier Service |
| | | NFM | North Yorkshire | Taxis |
| | | AM | St Austell | Haul-U-Waste |
| 85.75000 | 72.25000 | NFM | A55 | Automobile Association |
| | | NFM | Guernsey | Warry's Bakery |
| | | NFM | Hitchin | Rorall Taxis |
| | | NFM | Lakenheath | Trevor Cobbold |
| | | NFM | London | American Cars |
| | | NFM | London | Putney Cars |
| | | NFM | Manchester | Taxis |
| | | NFM | Oldham | Taxis |
| | | NFM | Royton | Borough Taxis |
| 85.76250 | 72.26250 | NFM | Aberdeen | Port Maintenance |
| | | NFM | Cambridge | Plant Growing Institute |
| | | NFM | Culzean | National Trust for Scotland Rangers |
| | | NFM | London | Galaxy Cars |

| Base | Mobile | Mode | Location | User and Notes |
|------|--------|------|----------|----------------|
| 85.76250 | 72.26250 | NFM | Long Stratton | C.P.S Fuels |
| | | NFM | Norfolk | Automobile Association |
| | | NFM | Suffolk | Automobile Association |
| 85.77500 | 72.27500 | NFM | Alloa | Taxi |
| | | NFM | Blackpool | Red Cabs |
| | | NFM | Guernsey | Le Pelley Taxi |
| | | NFM | Leigh-on-Sea | Taxis |
| | | NFM | Levenshulme | Premier Cars |
| | | NFM | London | Allways Ltd |
| | | NFM | Manchester | Vehicle wheel clampers |
| | | NFM | Norfolk | Automobile Association |
| | | NFM | Norwich | R.C. Snelling |
| | | NFM | Oxford | LuxiCabs |
| 85.77500 | 72.27500 | NFM | Perth | Taxis |
| | | NFM | Sheffield | Hargreaves Clearwaste Co. |
| | | NFM | Slough | Scorpio Radio Cars |
| | | NFM | Stoke on Trent | Lucky Seven Taxis |
| | | NFM | Suffolk | Automobile Association |
| | | NFM | Warrington | Wheel Clampers |
| 85.78250 | 72.28250 | AM | Birmingham | Wimply Builders |
| 85.78750 | 72.28750 | NFM | Brighton | Automobile Association |
| | | NFM | Edinburgh | Taxis |
| | | NFM | Ipswich | Automobile Association |
| | | NFM | London | Automobile Association |
| | | NFM | Nationwide | Automobile Association Ch. 9 |
| 85.80000 | 72.30000 | NFM | Aberdeen | City Council |
| | | NFM | Anglia | Parcline Ltd |
| | | NFM | Brighton | Express Security Vans |
| | | NFM | Cardiff | Cardiff Garage Services |
| | | NFM | Hull | Security Express |
| | | NFM | Nationwide | Express Security Vans |
| | | NFM | Nationwide | Parceline Ltd |
| | | NFM | Plymouth | City Council Cleansing Dept |
| | | NFM | Warrington | Parcel Line |
| 85.81250 | 72.31250 | NFM | Aberdeen | Taxi |
| | | NFM | Haverfordwest | Vet Service |
| | | NFM | Nationwide | DTI Channel L0065 |
| 85.82500 | 72.32500 | NFM | Cornwall | Pye Transport |
| | | NFM | Guernsey | Huelin |
| | | NFM | Letchwood | Joe's Taxis |
| | | NFM | London | Kwik Cars |
| | | NFM | Norwich | Beeline Taxis |
| | | NFM | Shoreham | Taxi |
| | | NFM | Soham | P. Lyon |
| | | NFM | Southampton | Taxis |
| 85.83750 | 72.33750 | NFM | Blantyre | Ariel & Art Cabs |
| | | NFM | Cornwall | English China Clay |
| | | NFM | Guernsey | Falles Hire Cars |
| | | NFM | Jersey | Ideal Cars Channel 1 |
| | | NFM | Jersey | Rank Taxis Channel 3 |
| | | NFM | Littleport | J.C. Rains Ltd |
| | | NFM | London | Belsize Ltd |
| | | NFM | London | Courier 83 Ltd |
| | | NFM | Luton | James Early Ltd |
| | | AM | St Austell | Haul-U-Waste |

| Base | Mobile | Mode | Location | User and Notes |
|---|---|---|---|---|
| 85.85000 | 72.35000 | NFM | Cornwall | English China Clay |
| | | NFM | Kirkby | Taxis |
| | | NFM | Nationwide | Philips Transport Scheme |
| | | NFM | Nationwide | Philips Telecom Channel 2 |
| | | NFM | Newtown | Taxis |
| | | NFM | Skelmersdale | Taxis |
| | | NFM | Tyneside | Taxis |
| | | NFM | Widnes | Taxis |
| | | NFM | Wigan | Taxis |
| 85.86250 | 72.36250 | NFM | Guernsey | J.H. Mahy & Sons Ltd |
| | | NFM | Lanarkshire | Doctor deputy service |
| | | NFM | London | Fisher Sylvester Ltd |
| | | NFM | London | G & R Tyres |
| | | NFM | London | Pronto Cars |
| 85.87500 | 72.37500 | NFM | Nationwide | DTI 28 Day Hire |
| | | NFM | Nationwide | Philips Telecom Channel 1 |
| 85.88750 | 72.38750 | NFM | Aylsham | Aylsham Produce |
| | | NFM | Blackpool | Tower Taxis |
| | | NFM | Burnley | Delta Cabs |
| | | NFM | Coventry | Allens Taxis and Coaches |
| | | NFM | London | Teleportation Ltd |
| | | NFM | Neath | Car Rallying |
| | | NFM | Norfolk | East Coast Grain |
| | | AM | Perth | Tay Transport |
| | | NFM | Suffolk | Aylsham Produce |
| 85.90000 | 71.40000 | NFM | Burnley | Delta Cabs |
| | | NFM | Cambridge | John's of Cambridge |
| | | NFM | Diss, Norfolk | G.W. Padley |
| | | NFM | Edinburgh | TV Repairs |
| | | NFM | Jersey | Rank Taxis |
| | | AM | Kettering | Headlands Taxis |
| | | NFM | London | Sensechoice |
| | | NFM | Newcastle | Taxis |
| | | NFM | Spalding | Glen Heat and Irrigation |
| 85.91250 | 72.41250 | NFM | Aberdeen | Breakdown Services |
| | | NFM | Brigg | Gallowswood Recovery Service |
| | | NFM | Edinburgh | TV Repairs |
| | | NFM | Ipswich | Taxi |
| | | NFM | London | Anglo Spanish |
| | | NFM | London | Arrival Couriers |
| | | NFM | London | Central Motors |
| | | NFM | London | K Cars |
| | | NFM | Perth | Local deliveries |
| | | NFM | Perth | Tay Breakdown Service |
| 85.92500 | 72.42500 | NFM | Birmingham | Star Cars |
| | | NFM | Blackpool | Radio Cabs |
| | | NFM | Jersey | LuxiCabs Ch 2 |
| | | NFM | London | Laurie Buxton |
| | | NFM | London | Town & Country |
| | | NFM | Wigan | District Council |
| | | NFM | Wirral | Cleansing Dept |
| 85.93750 | 72.43750 | NFM | Bury | Moorside Taxis |
| | | NFM | Kent | Porlant Car Hire |
| | | NFM | London | Action Cars |

| Base | Mobile | Mode | Location | User and Notes |
|---|---|---|---|---|
| 85.95000 | 72.45000 | AM | Chichester | Taxis |
| | | NFM | Guernsey | Crossways Agricultural |
| | | NFM | Leigh-on-Sea | Taxis |
| | | NFM | London | Action Cars |
| | | NFM | London | Galaxy Bikes |
| | | NFM | London | Super Express |
| 85.96250 | 72.46250 | NFM | Great Massingham | Gilman Ltd |
| | | NFM | London | Globe Cars |
| | | NFM | Norfolk | Don Robin Farms |
| | | NFM | Guernsey | Stan Brouard Ltd |
| 85.97500 | 72.47500 | NFM | Hamilton | Bridge Cars |
| | | AM | Leeds | Amber Cars |
| | | NFM | Nationwide | Tarmac Roadstone |
| | | NFM | Norfolk | Stanway Taxis |
| | | NFM | Suffolk | Stanway Taxis |
| | | NFM | Woodbridge | Wm Kerr Farms |
| 85.98750 | 72.47500 | NFM | Jersey | Fetch & Carry |
| 85.98750 | 72.48750 | NFM | London | Avery Cars |
| | | NFM | London | City & Suburban |
| | | NFM | London | Commutercars |
| | | NFM | London | Parkward Ltd |
| | | NFM | London | Southampton Way Cars |
| | | NFM | St. Neots | Eyrsbury Plant Hire |
| 86.00000 | 72.50000 | NFM | Aberdeen | Oil rig maintenance |
| | | NFM | Irvine | Taxis |
| | | NFM | London | Kilburn Cars |
| | | NFM | London | Windmill Cars |
| | | NFM | Nationwide | Community Repeater |
| 86.01250 | 72.51250 | NFM | Birmingham | Murphy |
| | | NFM | Leeds | Hotpoint |
| | | NFM | Milton Keynes | Hotpoint |
| | | NFM | York | Hotpoint |
| 86.02500 | 72.52500 | AM | Ayr | Scottish Ambulance Service |
| | | NFM | Bedfordshire | Bedford Social Services |
| | | AM | Haddington | Scottish Ambulance Service |
| | | NFM | Humberside | Community Repeater |
| | | NFM | Merthyr | Mountain Rescue (S) |
| | | AM | Nationwide | Scottish Ambulance Service Ch L82 |
| | | NFM | Spay Valley | Scottish Ambulance Service |
| 86.03750 | 72.53750 | AM | Dundee | Scottish Ambulance Service |
| | | NFM | Eastbourne | Downland rangers |
| | | AM | Glasgow | Scottish Ambulance Service |
| | | AM | Guernsey | Public Works |
| | | AM | Lincolnshire | Community Repeater |
| | | AM | London | Medicall |
| | | AM | Nationwide | Scottish Ambulance Service Ch L83 |
| | | AM | Nationwide | St Johns Private Ambulance |
| 86.05000 | 72.55000 | AM | Elgin | Scottish Ambulance Service Ch L84 |
| | | AM | Fort Augustus | Scottish Ambulance Service Ch L84 |
| | | NFM | Lincolnshire | Comunity Repeater |
| | | NFM | London | Doctors callout |
| | | NFM | London | Medicall |
| | | AM | Nationwide | Scottish Ambulance Service Ch L84 |
| | | NFM | Peterborough | Repeater |
| | | NFM | Southampton | Taxis |

| Base | Mobile | Mode | Location | User and Notes |
|------|--------|------|----------|----------------|
| 86.06250 | 72.56250 | NFM | Anglesey | Council |
| | | NFM | Gt. Ashfield | G. Miles |
| | | AM | Nationwide | Scottish Ambulance Service Ch. L85 |
| | | NFM | Norfolk | Sandringham Estate |
| 86.07500 | 72.57500 | AM | Aberdeen | Scottish Ambulance Service |
| | | NFM | Annan | District Council |
| | | AM | Dumfries and Galloway | Scottish Ambulance Service |
| | | AM | Edinburgh | Scottish Ambulance Service |
| | | AM | Inverness | Scottish Ambulance Service |
| | | AM | Nationwide | Scottish Ambulance Service Ch.L86 |
| | | NFM | Wiltshire | Severn Trent Water Ch 1 |
| 86.08750 | 72.58750 | AM | Braemar | Scottish Ambulance Service |
| | | AM | Edinburgh | Scottish Ambulance Service |
| | | AM | Nationwide | Scottish Ambulance Ch. L87 |
| | | NFM | Norfolk | Cabban Breeze |
| | | NFM | Norfolk | Douglas Framlingham |
| 86.10000 | 72.60000 | NFM | Hadleigh | Lemon & Sutherland |
| | | AM | Motherwell | Scottish Ambulance Service |
| | | AM | Nationwide | Scottish Ambulance Service Ch. L88 |
| | | NFM | Newmarket | PMR |
| 86.11250 | 72.61250 | AM | Dumfermline | Scottish Ambulance Service |
| | | NFM | Humberside | Tyre Co. |
| | | AM | Lincolnshire | Community Repeater |
| | | AM | Nationwide | Scottish Ambulance Service Ch. L89 |
| 86.12500 | 72.62500 | AM | Airdrie | Scottish Ambulance Service |
| | | NFM | Cardiff | F.W. Morgan Builders |
| | | NFM | Cheshire | Courier Service |
| | | AM | Coatbridge | Scottish Ambulance Service |
| | | AM | Dumfries and Galloway | Scottish Ambulance Service |
| | | AM | Edinburgh | Scottish Ambulance Service |
| | | NFM | Guernsey | Guernsey Telecoms |
| | | AM | Kilmarnock | Scottish Ambulance Service |
| | | AM | Nationwide | Scottish Ambulance Service Ch. L90 |
| | | NFM | Norfolk | E.P.H. Radio Repeater |
| | | NFM | Sheffield | Community Repeater |
| 86.13750 | 72.63750 | AM | Jersey | De Gruchy Vets |
| | | NFM | Mid Wales | British Waterways |
| | | NFM | Norfolk | Storno Radio Telephone Co |
| | | AM | Perth | Scottish Ambulance Service |
| | | NFM | Suffolk | Storno Radio Telephone Co |
| 86.15000 | 72.65000 | AM | Nationwide | Scottish Ambulance Ch. L91 |
| 86.16250 | 72.66250 | AM | Glasgow | Scottish Ambulance |
| | | AM | Kent | County Council |
| | | AM | Lancashire | Regional Health Ambulance |
| | | NFM | Nationwide | Radiofone Channel |
| | | AM | Nationwide | Scottish Ambulance Ch. L92 |
| | | AM | Powys | Welsh Water |
| | | AM | Radnor | County Council |
| 86.17500 | 72.67500 | NFM | Belfast | NI Electricity |
| | | NFM | Newmarket | PMR |
| | | NFM | Norfolk | Ipswich Transport Ltd |
| | | NFM | Suffolk | Ipswich Transport Ltd |
| 86.18750 | 72.68750 | AM | Falkirk | Scottish Ambulance Service |
| | | NFM | Nationwide | Automobile Assoc. Channel 10 |
| | | AM | Nationwide | Scottish Ambulance Service Ch.L93 |

| Base | Mobile | Mode | Location | User and Notes |
|---|---|---|---|---|
| 86.20000 | 72.70000 | NFM | Bristol | Automobile Assoc. Channel 11 |
| | | NFM | Ipswich | Automobile Assoc. Channel 11 |
| | | NFM | Nationwide | Automobile Assoc. Channel 11 |
| | | NFM | Oban | Scottish Ambulance Service |
| 86.21250 | 72.71250 | NFM | East Sussex | County Council |
| | | NFM | London | Enterprise Ltd |
| | | NFN | Needham Market | Quinton Skip Hire |
| | | NFM | Norfolk | William Cory Heating |
| 86.22500 | 72.72500 | NFM | Belfast | NI Electricity |
| | | NFM | Burnley | Breakdown Recovery |
| | | FM | Cambridge | Vets |
| | | NFM | Carnforth | PMR |
| | | NFM | Humberside | Motorway maintenance |
| | | NFM | Ipswich | Doctors on Call |
| | | NFM | Norfolk | Ipswich Transport Ltd |
| | | NFM | Perth | Amtrac Delivery Service |
| | | NFM | Portsmouth | Taxis |
| 86.22500 | 72.72500 | NFM | Scunthorpe | Humberside Highways |
| | | NFM | Suffolk | Ipswich Transport Ltd |
| 86.23750 | 72.73750 | NFM | Armagh | Road Construction |
| | | NFM | Great Oakley | Oakley Skip Hire |
| | | NFM | Great Yarmouth | Container Depot |
| | | NFM | Ipswich | Deliveries |
| | | NFM | Kettering | Farmers |
| | | NFM | Perth | Deliveries |
| 86.25000 | 72.75000 | NFM | Aberdeen | Snowploughs |
| | | NFM | East Sussex | County Council |
| | | NFM | Hull | Hotpoint |
| | | NFM | Nationwide | Hotpoint Channel 1 |
| 86.26250 | 72.76250 | AM | Aberdeen | Council |
| | | NFM | Grampian | Taxis |
| | | AM | Humberside | Council |
| | | AM | Nationwide | Hotpoint Channel 2 |
| 86.27500 | 72.77500 | NFM | Belfast | NI Electricity |
| | | NFM | Bournemouth | Cryston Communications |
| | | NFM | Dumfries | Council |
| | | NFM | East Sussex | Wealdon (162.2Hz) |
| | | NFM | Hull | Cryston Communications |
| | | NFM | Leeds | Cryston Communications |
| | | NFM | Nationwide | Cryston Communications |
| 86.28750 | 75.78750 | NFM | Ashton under Lyme | Satellite Installation |
| | | NFM | Great Yarmouth | Container Depot |
| | | NFM | Ipswich | RSPCA |
| | | NFM | Irvine | North Ayrshire Council |
| | | NFM | Leeds | RSPCA |
| | | NFM | Perth | North of Scotland Water Authority |
| | | NFM | Wilmston | Vets |
| 86.30000 | 72.80000 | NFM | East Sussex | County Council |
| | | NFM | Nationwide | IBA Aerial Riggers |
| | | NFM | Nationwide | Vibroplant Plc |

| Base | Mobile | Mode | Location | User and Notes |
|---|---|---|---|---|
| **86.3125 - 86.7000 MHz** | | | **PMR Low Band 12.5 kHz (Simplex)** | |
| 86.31250 | 86.31250 | NFM | Nationwide | Mountain Rescue Channel 1 |
| | | AM | Nationwide | Park Ranger Service Ch 2 |
| | | AM | Nationwide | St Johns Ambulance Channel 1 |
| | | NFM | North Yorkshire Moors | Rangers |
| 86.32500 | 86.32500 | AM | Blackpool | Gino's Pizza Deliveries |
| | | NFM | Nationwide | Mountain Rescue Reserve |
| | | NFM | Nationwide | National Parks Ch 2 |
| 86.33750 | 86.33750 | NFM | Cumbria | Lakes Mountain Rescue Ch. 2 |
| | | NFM | Norwich | Sir Robin Lee |
| 86.35000 | 86.35000 | NFM | Cairngorm | Ski Lifts |
| | | NFM | Cumbria | Lakes Mountain Rescue Ch. 3 |
| | | NFM | Edinburgh | The Scottish Office |
| | | AM | Jersey | Shell Rally Ch 2 |
| | | NFM | Jersey | TV Aerial Erectors |
| | | NFM | Nationwide | Mountain Rescue Channel 3 |
| | | NFM | Nationwide | Red Cross |
| | | AM | Nationwide | St Johns Ambulance Channel 3 |
| 86.36250 | 86.36250 | NFM | Nationwide | Boy Scouts Channel 1 |
| 86.37500 | 86.37500 | NFM | Edinburgh | The Scottish Office |
| 86.37500 | 86.37500 | NFM | Jersey | A C Mauger, builder |
| | | NFM | Nationwide | REACT CB Emergency |
| | | NFM | Wakefield | Stanley Royal Hospital |
| 86.38750 | 86.38750 | NFM | Nationwide | National Parks Ch 1 |
| 86.40000 | 86.40000 | NFM | Felixstowe | Docks |
| | | NFM | Nationwide | National Park Rangers |
| | | NFM | North Yorkshire Moors | Rangers |
| | | NFM | Yorkshire | Yorkshire Dales Warden |
| 86.41250 | 86.41250 | NFM | Berkshire | Council Ch 3 |
| | | NFM | Nationwide | Mountain Rescue Channel 2 |
| | | AM | Nationwide | St Johns Ambulance Channel 2 |
| | | NFM | Peak National Parks | Mountain Rescue |
| 86.42500 | 86.42500 | NFM | Ettrick & Lauderdale | District Council |
| | | NFM | Nationwide | Forestry Commission Channel 3 |
| 86.43750 | 86.43750 | NFM | Isle of Man | Tudor Manx Rally |
| | | NFM | Jersey | Shell Rally Control Ch 1 |
| | | NFM | Nationwide | RAC Rally Medical/Safety |
| 86.45000 | 86.45000 | NFM | Avon | Severn Trent Water |
| | | AM | Blackpool | Private Ambulance |
| | | NFM | Nationwide | Forestry Commission Channel 2 |
| | | NFM | Nationwide | Wimpey Construction Ch. 1 |
| 86.46500 | 86.46500 | NFM | Glasgow, west | Skip Hire |
| 86.47500 | 86.47500 | NFM | Cheshire | Gallifords Civil Engineers |
| | | NFM | Linton | T.B. Fairy |
| | | NFM | Nationwide | Forestry Commission Channel 1 |
| | | NFM | Nationwide | Railtrack Incidents |
| 86.50000 | 86.50000 | NFM | Luton Airport | McAlpine Aviation |
| | | NFM | Nationwide | BNFL Nuclear Incident Ch 1 |
| | | NFM | Nationwide | ITC Aerial Riggers |
| | | NFM | Suffolk | Suffolk County Council |
| | | NFM | Swindon | Radio Taxis |
| 86.51250 | 86.51250 | NFM | Guernsey | St John Ambulance Link |
| 86.52500 | 86.52500 | NFM | Dunstable | Taleds Motors Co |
| | | NFM | Enfield | Weston Ltd |
| | | NFM | Nationwide | BBC O/B Riggers |
| | | NFM | Nationwide | BNFL Nuclear Incident Ch 2 |

| Base | Mobile | Mode | Location | User and Notes |
|------|--------|------|----------|----------------|
| 86.53750 | 86.53750 | NFM | Derbyshire | Middleton Top Rangers |
| | | NFM | North-West | PMR |
| 86.55000 | 86.55000 | NFM | Guernsey | Cobo Surgery |
| | | NFM | Nationwide | BNFL Nuclear Incident Ch. 3 |
| 86.56250 | 86.56250 | NFM | Aberdeen | Robert Gordon Univ. of Tech |
| | | NFM | Nationwide | DHL International |
| 86.62500 | 86.62500 | NFM | Nationwide | Boy Scouts Channel 2 |
| | | NFM | Nationwide | Wimpey Construction Ch. 2 |
| | | NFM | RAF Marham | Wimpey Construction Ch. 2 |
| | | AM | Sheffield | Council Repairs |
| 86.63750 | 86.63750 | NFM | Bedford | RSPB |
| | | NFM | Jersey | Telefitters |
| | | NFM | Nationwide | Wimpey Construction Ch. 3 |
| | | NFM | RAF Marham | Wimpey Construction Ch. 3 |
| | | NFM | Nationwide | Vickers Seismic Surveys |
| 86.67500 | 86.67500 | NFM | Nationwide | UKAEA Radiation Survey |
| 86.70000 | 86.70000 | NFM | Dungeness | Power Station |
| | | NFM | Nationwide | Automobile Assocation Emergency |

## 86.7125 - 87.5000 MHz PMR Low Band Base Duplex
### (Duplex Mobiles -10.5 MHz)

| Base | Mobile | Mode | Location | User and Notes |
|------|--------|------|----------|----------------|
| 86.70000 | 76.20000 | NFM | Nationwide | UK Emergency Channel 999 |
| | | NFM | Nationwide | UKAEA Health Physics Ch 2 |
| 86.71250 | 76.71250 | NFM | Nationwide | HM Customs & Excise Ch 1 |
| 86.72500 | 76.22500 | NFM | Nationwide | HM Customs & Excise Ch 2 |
| | | NFM | Tayside | North of Scotland Water Authority |
| 86.73750 | 76.23750 | NFM | Ipswich | Repeater |
| | | NFM | London | HM Custom Drugs Squad |
| | | NFM | Nationwide | HM Customs & Excise Ch 9 |
| 86.75000 | 76.25000 | NFM | Burnley | Plant Hire |
| | | NFM | Cwnbran | Gwent Council Ch 8 |
| | | NFM | Hornsea | East Coast Caravan Security |
| | | NFM | Lowestoft | Hughes TV Rentals |
| 86.76250 | 76.26250 | NFM | Llanelli | BT |
| | | NFM | Llanelli | Taxi |
| | | NFM | Tayside | Community Repeater |
| 86.77500 | 76.27500 | NFM | Merseyside | Plant Hire Company |
| | | NFM | Portsmouth | City Council |
| | | NFM | York | Yorkshire Parcels Group |
| 86.80000 | 76.30000 | NFM | Bradford | Community Transport |
| | | NFM | Brighton | Community Repeater |
| | | NFM | Dyfed | Vets |
| | | NFM | Hampshire | Council |
| | | NFM | London | Post Office Tower |
| | | NFM | Nationwide | Vibroplant |
| | | NFM | Oldham | Plant Hire |
| | | NFM | Sussex | Community Repeater |
| | | NFM | West Sussex | West Dock Air Call |
| 86.82500 | 76.32500 | NFM | Bristol | ITV Broadcast Link |
| | | NFM | Manchester | Granada TV Talkback |
| | | NFM | Thames Valley | ITN Ch 4 |
| | | NFM | Clwyd | Delivery Company |
| | | NFM | Co Durham | BT Aerial Riggers |
| | | NFM | Perth | North of Scotland Water Authority |

| Base | Mobile | Mode | Location | User and Notes |
|---|---|---|---|---|
| 86.86250 | 76.36250 | NFM | Manchester | Amtrak Express Parcels |
| | | NFM | Nationwide | RSPCA |
| | | NFM | Plymouth | Plymouth Vets |
| 86.87500 | 76.37500 | NFM | Lochaber | Council Roads Dept |
| | | NFM | Malvern | Abbey Taxi |
| 86.88750 | 76.38750 | NFM | Ballachulish | Highland Regional Council Roads/Snow Ploughs |
| | | NFM | Lothian & Borders | East of Scotland Water |
| 86.90000 | 76.40000 | NFM | Merseyside | Transport Company |
| | | NFM | Southwold | Suffolk Traffic |
| 86.91250 | 76.41250 | NFM | Lochaber | Highland Regional Council Roads |
| | | NFM | Wirral | A1 Breakdown |
| 86.93750 | 76.43750 | NFM | London | HM Customs & Excise Drugs Squad |
| | | NFM | Nationwide | HM Customs Ch 3 |
| | | NFM | Perth | North of Scotland Water Authority |
| 86.95000 | 76.45000 | NFM | Dover | HM Customs & Excise |
| | | NFM | Dundee | North of Scotland Water Authority |
| | | NFM | Fishguard Docks | HM Customs & Excise |
| | | NFM | Nationwide | HM Customs & Excise Ch 4 |
| 86.96250 | 76.46250 | NFM | Brighton | RSPCA |
| | | NFM | Grizedale Forest Park | Forestry Commission |
| | | NFM | Gwynedd | Forestry Commission |
| | | NFM | Lochaber | Forestry Commission |
| | | NFM | Nationwide | RSPCA Channel |
| | | NFM | Newtown | Wayside Forestry Commission |
| 86.97500 | 76.47500 | NFM | Bolton | BT |
| 86.97500 | 76.86250 | NFM | Manchester | North West Water |
| 86.98750 | 76.98750 | NFM | London | Guarda Security |
| 87.00000 | 77.00000 | NFM | Berkshire | Council |
| | | NFM | Cumbria | RAC Data Link |
| | | NFM | Edinburgh | Data Link |
| | | NFM | Guernsey | RAC |
| | | NFM | Lancashire | RAC Data Link |
| | | NFM | Nationwide | RAC Channel 2 |
| | | NFM | Wymondham | Ayton Asphalt |
| 87.01250 | 77.01250 | NFM | Glasgow | RAC Data Link |
| | | NFM | Ipswich | RAC Data Link |
| | | NFM | Nationwide | RAC Channel 4 |
| | | NFM | Newcastle | RAC Data Link |
| | | NFM | Stirling | RAC Data Link |
| | | NFM | York | RAC Data Link |
| 87.02500 | 77.02500 | NFM | Glasgow | Data Link |
| | | NFM | Ipswich | RAC |
| | | NFM | Nationwide | RAC Channel 1 |
| | | NFM | Newmarket | RAC Data Link |
| | | NFM | Perth | RAC Data Link |
| | | NFM | Stirling | RAC |
| 87.03750 | 77.03750 | NFM | East Durham | Private Message |
| | | NFM | Kent (Euro Tunnel) | Trans Manche Ltd |
| | | NFM | Nationwide | RAC Channel 5 |
| 87.04500 | 76.54500 | NFM | Neath | TA Barracks |
| 87.05000 | 77.05000 | NFM | Grimsby | Raylor Ltd |
| | | NFM | Leeds | Armor Guard |
| | | NFM | Leeds | Raylor Ltd |
| | | NFM | Lothian and Borders | RAC |

| Base | Mobile | Mode | Location | User and Notes |
|------|--------|------|----------|----------------|
| 87.05000 | 77.05000 | NFM | Nationwide | RAC Channel 3 |
| | | NFM | Perth | Data Link |
| | | NFM | Skelmersdale | Taxis |
| | | NFM | Teesside | Raylor Ltd |
| | | NFM | York | Raylor Ltd |
| 87.06250 | 77.06250 | NFM | Bishop Stortford | Rougewell Ltd |
| | | NFM | Gwent | Forestry Commission |
| | | NFM | Haywards Heath | Station Taxis |
| | | NFM | London | Statisted Containers Ltd |
| | | NFM | Neath | Forestry Commission |
| | | NFM | Perth | Taxi |
| | | NFM | Wrexham | Derek's Taxis |
| 87.07500 | 77.07500 | NFM | Bristol | Ace Taxis |
| | | NFM | Bury | Red Rose Taxis |
| | | NFM | Droitwich | NY Taxis |
| | | NFM | Glasgow | Taxis |
| | | NFM | Ipswich | Council |
| | | AM | Jersey | United Taxis |
| 87.07500 | 77.07500 | AM | London | Concorde Minicabs Wembley |
| | | NFM | St Ives | RAC |
| 87.08750 | 77.08750 | NFM | Chichester | Council Refuse |
| | | NFM | Halifax | Halifax Council |
| | | NFM | Jersey | Jersey Evening Post |
| | | NFM | Lancashire | Haulage Contractor |
| | | NFM | London | Savoy Rolls Royce |
| | | NFM | London | Stanstead Containers Ltd |
| | | NFM | Nationwide | RSPCA Channel Ch 2 |
| 87.10000 | 77.10000 | NFM | Barrow | PMR |
| | | NFM | Bolton | Road Maintenance |
| | | NFM | Brighton | Taxis |
| | | NFM | Guernsey | Gilroy's |
| | | NFM | Hove | Hove Streamline Taxis |
| | | NFM | Kendal | Builders |
| | | NFM | Leicester | ABC Taxis |
| | | NFM | London | B.J. Transport |
| | | NFM | London | J.R. Cars |
| | | NFM | Montrose | Council Housing |
| | | NFM | Preston | Taxis |
| | | NFM | Stockport | North West Water |
| 87.12500 | 77.12500 | NFM | Ayr | SRC Building & Works Depart. |
| | | NFM | Badergh | Council |
| | | NFM | Powys | Forestry Commission |
| | | NFM | Strathclyde | Strathclyde Council |
| 87.13750 | 71.13750 | NFM | Cardiff | Community Repeater |
| | | NFM | Fishguard | Highways Council |
| | | NFM | Hampshire | Council |
| | | NFM | Kent | Kent Council Highways Dept. |
| | | NFM | Leeds | Construction Co. |
| | | NFM | Liverpool | Street Lighting |
| 87.15000 | 72.65000 | NFM | Fishguard | District Council |
| | | NFM | Kent | Tour de France |
| | | NFM | Lancashire | County Highways Ch 1 |
| | | NFM | Nationwide | Radiofone Channel Ch 1 |
| | | NFM | Stirling | PMR |

| Base | Mobile | Mode | Location | User and Notes |
|------|--------|------|----------|----------------|
| 87.16250 | 77.16250 | NFM | Aberdeen | Council |
| | | NFM | Buckinghamshire | Council |
| | | NFM | Dumfermline | Fife Regional Council |
| | | AM | Kent | Kent Council Highways Dept. |
| | | NFM | Lincolnshire | Highways |
| | | NFM | N Yorkshire | Highways |
| | | NFM | Shropshire | County Council Emer. Planning |
| 87.17500 | 77.17500 | NFM | Bristol | Highways |
| | | NFM | Glasgow | Underground Control |
| | | NFM | Lake District | Lake District National Park |
| | | NFM | Lancashire | County Park Rangers |
| | | NFM | Nottinghamshire | Comunity Repeater |
| 87.18750 | 77.18750 | NFM | Cambridgeshire | Council |
| | | NFM | Chichester | West Sussex Council |
| | | NFM | Fife | Fife Regional Council Roads |
| | | NFM | Lancashire | Snowploughs & Gritters Ch 2 |
| | | NFM | Oxford | Council |
| | | NFM | Radnor | Powys Council Highways |
| | | NFM | Surrey | Council Ch 2 |
| 87.18750 | 77.18750 | AM | West Yorkshire | Highways |
| 87.20000 | 77.20000 | NFM | Bury | Bury Council |
| | | NFM | County Durham | County Council |
| | | NFM | Cumbria | Quarry |
| | | NFM | Foreham | Council |
| | | NFM | Surrey | Council |
| 87.21250 | 77.21250 | NFM | Aberfeldy | Council Gritters |
| | | NFM | Buckinghamshire | Council |
| | | NFM | Hertfordshire | Council |
| | | NFM | Humberside | Council |
| | | NFM | Nationwide | Council Common |
| | | NFM | Rushmoor | Council |
| | | NFM | Sheffield | Council Highways |
| | | NFM | Somerset | Council |
| | | NFM | Staffordshire | Council |
| 87.22500 | 77.22500 | NFM | Bristol Area | Skip Company |
| | | NFM | Kent | Tour de France |
| | | NFM | London | Vehicle Clamping |
| | | NFM | Oxford | City Council Ch 3 |
| 87.23750 | 77.23750 | NFM | Dundee | North of Scotland Water Authority |
| | | NFM | East Sussex | County Highways |
| | | NFM | Eastbourne | Council |
| | | NFM | Fife | Fife Regional Council |
| | | AM | Gwynedd | Gwynedd Council |
| | | NFM | Heysham | PMR |
| | | NFM | Lancashire | County Council Ch 3 |
| | | NFM | Manchester | Sheltered Housing Wardens |
| | | NFM | North West England | PMR |
| | | NFM | Oxfordshire | County Council Ch 1 |
| | | NFM | Perth | Perth & Kinross Council |
| 87.24000 | 77.24000 | NFM | Gwent Area | Highway Maintenance Company |
| 87.25000 | 77.25000 | NFM | Birmingham | City Council Engineers |
| | | NFM | Brecon | Powys County Highways |
| | | NFM | East Sussex | Emergency Centre |
| | | NFM | Hampshire | Council |
| | | NFM | Hertfordshire | Council |
| | | NFM | West Midlands | Snowploughs & Gritters |

| Base | Mobile | Mode | Location | User and Notes |
|------|--------|------|----------|----------------|
| 87.26250 | 77.26250 | NFM | Ayr | Local Council Services |
| | | NFM | England & Wales | Council Common |
| | | NFM | Gwent | Council |
| | | NFM | Leicester | Council |
| | | NFM | Oxfordshire | County Council |
| | | NFM | Perth | Perth & Kinross Council |
| | | NFM | Slough | Council |
| | | NFM | Stockton | CCC Engineers |
| | | AM | West Sussex | County Council |
| | | AM | Yorkshire | Trading Standards Office |
| 87.27500 | 77.47500 | NFM | Blackpool | Illuminations |
| | | NFM | Edinburgh | Council Roads Dept. |
| | | NFM | Hanley | Security |
| | | NFM | Lothian and Borders | Lothian Regional Council |
| | | NFM | West Yorkshire | Bus Inspectors |
| 87.28750 | 77.28750 | NFM | Fife | Fife Regional Council Drainage |
| 87.30000 | 77.30000 | NFM | Anglia | Breckland District Council |
| | | NFM | Derbyshire | Derbyshire Council Roads |
| 87.30000 | 77.30000 | AM | Dumfries | Snowploughs & Gritters |
| | | NFM | Hertfordshire | Council |
| | | NFM | Jersey | Waterworks |
| | | NFM | Mold | Clwyd County Council |
| | | NFM | Norfolk | Breckland District Council |
| | | NFM | Perth | North of Scotland Water Authority |
| 87.31250 | 77.31250 | NFM | Cardiff | Parcel Force Ch 2 |
| | | NFM | Perth | Perth & Kinross Council |
| | | NFM | Windsor | Royal Parks |
| 87.32500 | 77.32500 | NFM | Derbyshire | Council |
| | | NFM | Perth | Perth & Kinross Council |
| | | NFM | South Yorkshire | Council |
| 87.33750 | 77.33750 | NFM | Cardiff | Parcel Force Ch 1 |
| | | NFM | Edinburgh | Highways Control |
| | | NFM | Lancaster | Vet Service |
| | | NFM | Morecambe | Vet Service |
| 87.35000 | 77.35000 | NFM | Castle Douglas | Stewartry Council |
| | | NFM | Edinburgh | MacGas |
| | | NFM | Guernsey | Gaudion Skip Hire |
| | | NFM | Stoke | Civil Engineers |
| 87.36250 | 77.36250 | NFM | Castle Douglas | Forestry Commission |
| | | NFM | Glen Falloch | West Roads Department |
| | | NFM | Perth | Perth & Kinross Council |
| | | NFM | Saddleworth | Haulage Firm |
| | | NFM | Strathclyde | Forestry Commission |
| | | NFM | Tayside | Forestry Commission |
| | | AM | Jersey | Dr Scott Warren |
| 87.37500 | 77.37500 | NFM | Linconshire | Community Repeater |
| | | NFM | Oldham | Harris Deliveries |
| | | NFM | Yorkshire | RSPCA |
| 87.38750 | 77.38750 | NFM | Cardiff | Thorn Homeserve TV Repairs |
| | | NFM | Ipswich | Community Repeater |
| | | NFM | Perth | Community Repeater |
| | | NFM | Stoke | Garage |

| Base | Mobile | Mode | Location | User and Notes |
|------|--------|------|----------|----------------|
| 87.40000 | 77.40000 | NFM | Aberdeen | Aberdeen Skip Hire |
| | | NFM | Huntington | Doctors Scheme |
| | | NFM | Nationwide | Doctor Scheme |
| | | NFM | Perth | North of Scotland Water Authority |
| 87.41250 | 77.41250 | NFM | Bristol | Ace Skip Hire |
| | | NFM | Bristol | Magnum Scaffolding |
| | | NFM | Bristol | P.D.G Courier Service |
| | | NFM | Elvington | A1 Haulage |
| | | NFM | Elvington | Elvington Plant Hire |
| | | NFM | Elvington | Silverseal Auto Windscreens |
| | | NFM | Lochaber | Council Roads Dept |
| | | NFM | London | Onyx Cleansing Services |
| | | NFM | Perth | Perth & Kinross Council |
| | | NFM | Scotland | Council Highways Common |
| | | NFM | Staffordshire | JCB Drivers |
| 87.42500 | 77.42500 | NFM | Blackpool | County Highways |
| | | NFM | Guernsey | Remote Gas Detectors |
| | | NFM | Stirling | County Council (B) |
| 87.43750 | 77.43750 | NFM | Bedford | County Surveyors Ch 1 |
| | | NFM | Coris Mid Wales | Forestry Commission |
| | | NFM | Plymouth | City Engineers |
| 87.43750 | 77.43750 | NFM | Scotland | Council Highways Common |
| | | NFM | Southampton | M27 Motorway Maintenance |
| | | NFM | West Midlands | Council |
| | | NFM | Wigan | North West Water |
| 87.45000 | 77.45000 | NFM | Belfast | Dept. of Environment |
| | | NFM | Berkshire | Council Ch 1 |
| | | AM | Bristol | Sub Council Control |
| | | NFM | Cambridge | Highways Ch 3 |
| | | NFM | Haverfordwest | Preseli Pembroke Council |
| | | NFM | London | Infomation Service |
| | | NFM | Peterborough | Cotton TV Servicing |
| | | NFM | Wiltshire | Council Roads Dept |
| 87.46000 | 87.46000 | NFM | Pendle | Pendle Council |
| 87.46250 | 77.46250 | NFM | Berkshire | Council Surveyor Ch 2 |
| | | NFM | Essex | Highways Ch 2 |
| | | NFM | Fife | NE Fife Council Road Ch 5 |
| | | NFM | Hereford | Council |
| | | AM | Lincolnshire | Highways |
| | | NFM | Lothian & Borders | Roads Dept |
| | | NFM | West Midlands | Snowploughs & Gritters |
| | | NFM | West Sussex | West Sussex Council |
| | | NFM | Worcester | Council |
| 87.47500 | 77.47500 | NFM | Buckinghamshire | County Council |
| | | NFM | Morecambe | PMR |
| | | NFM | Nottingham | DGA Cars Ch 2 |
| | | NFM | Pembrokeshire | MoD Castlemartin |
| | | NFM | Peterborough | Cotton TV |
| | | NFM | Fife | Council Works Drainage |
| 87.48750 | 77.48750 | NFM | Gainsbrough | Grimsby Council |
| | | NFM | Liverpool | Taxi |
| | | NFM | Nottingham | DGA Cars Ch 1 |
| | | NFM | Peterborough | Royal Taxis |
| 87.50000 | 77.50000 | NFM | Cambridge | John Grieves |
| | | NFM | Leeds | Skip Hire |

| Base | Mobile | Mode | Location | User and Notes |
|---|---|---|---|---|
| 87.5000 - 88.000 | | | NATIONWIDE BROADCASTING | |
| 87.70000 | | WFM | Nationwide | RSL 28 Day Stations |
| 87.80000 | | WFM | Nationwide | RSL 28 Day Stations |
| 87.90000 | | WFM | Nottingham | Heatwave Radio |
| | | | | |
| 88.0000 - 90.2000 MHz | | | NATIONWIDE BBC RADIO 2, RTE AND LOCAL RADIO | |
| 88.100 | | WFM | Ballachulish | |
| | | WFM | Bowmore | |
| | | WFM | Cirencester | |
| | | WFM | Clettraval | |
| | | WFM | Clyro | |
| | | WFM | Deiniolen | |
| | | WFM | Ffestiniog | |
| | | WFM | Grantham | |
| | | WFM | Guildford | |
| | | WFM | Llanidloes | |
| | | WFM | Mallaig | |
| | | WFM | Manningtree | |
| | | WFM | North Hessary Tor | |
| | | WFM | Penifiler | |
| | | WFM | Sundale | |
| 88.200 | | WFM | Betws-Y-Coed | |
| | | WFM | Bexhill | |
| | | WFM | Calne | |
| | | WFM | Knock More | |
| | | WFM | Nailsworth | |
| | | WFM | Newbury | |
| | | WFM | Rheola | |
| | | WFM | Truskmore | RTE Radio 1 |
| 88.300 | | WFM | Bressay | |
| | | WFM | Castletownbere | RTE Radio 1 |
| | | WFM | Forfar | |
| | | WFM | Lethanhill | |
| | | WFM | Llwyn-Onn | |
| | | WFM | Lochgilphead | |
| | | WFM | Millburn Muir | |
| | | WFM | Moville | RTE Radio 1 |
| | | WFM | Ness of Lewis | |
| | | WFM | Rostrevor Forest | |
| | | WFM | Sutton Coldfield | |
| | | WFM | Ullapool | |
| | | WFM | Wensleydale | |
| | | WFM | Westwood | |
| | | WFM | Windermere | |
| 88.400 | | WFM | Campbeltown | |
| | | WFM | Carmel | |
| | | WFM | Douglas, Isle Of Man | |
| | | WFM | Ebbw Vale | |
| | | WFM | Folkestone | |
| | | WFM | Hebden Bridge | |
| | | WFM | Kenley | |
| 88.400 | | WFM | Peebles | |
| | | WFM | Penmaen Rhos | |
| | | WFM | Porth | |

| Base | Mobile | Mode | Location | User and Notes |
|------|--------|------|----------|----------------|
| 88.400 | | WFM | Walsden South | |
| | | WFM | Wharfdale | |
| 88.500 | | WFM | Barnstaple | |
| | | WFM | Blaenavon | |
| | | WFM | Cwmafan | |
| | | WFM | Dungarvan | RTE Radio 1 |
| | | WFM | Idle | |
| | | WFM | Plympton | |
| | | WFM | Pontop Pike | |
| | | WFM | Rothesay | |
| | | WFM | Rowbridge | |
| | | WFM | Skraig | |
| | | WFM | Three Rock | RTE Radio 1 |
| 88.600 | | WFM | Berwick On Tweed | |
| | | WFM | Bow Brickhall | |
| | | WFM | Llangeinor | |
| | | WFM | Ridge Hill | |
| | | WFM | Sheffield | BBC Radio Sheffield |
| | | WFM | Strachur | |
| | | WFM | Upperton | |
| | | WFM | Winter Hill | |
| 88.700 | | WFM | Abergavenny | |
| | | WFM | Ardgour | |
| | | WFM | Beacon Hill | |
| | | WFM | Ben Gullipen | |
| | | WFM | Cambret Hill | |
| | | WFM | Camlough | |
| | | WFM | Kirkconnel | |
| | | WFM | Londonderry | |
| | | WFM | Luddenden | |
| | | WFM | Meldrum | |
| | | WFM | Okehampton | |
| 88.800 | | WFM | Ballycastle | |
| | | WFM | Belmont | |
| | | WFM | Carnmoney Hill | |
| | | WFM | Chippenham | |
| | | WFM | County Mayo | RTE Radio 1 |
| | | WFM | Crystal Palace | |
| | | WFM | Isles of Scilly | |
| | | WFM | Jersey | BBC Radio Jersey |
| | | WFM | Maghera | RTE Radio 1 |
| | | WFM | Penaligon Downs | |
| | | WFM | Ton Pentre | |
| 88.900 | | WFM | Brecon | |
| | | WFM | Cambridge | |
| | | WFM | Carmarthen | |
| | | WFM | Chard | |
| | | WFM | Girvan | |
| | | WFM | Keighley | |
| | | WFM | Llangollen | |
| 88.900 | | WFM | Northampton | |
| | | WFM | Oban | |
| | | WFM | Todmorden | |
| | | WFM | Varteg Hill | |
| 89.000 | | WFM | Abertillery | |
| | | WFM | Bath City | |

| Base | Mobile | Mode | Location | User and Notes |
|------|--------|------|----------|----------------|
| 89.000 | | WFM | Blunsdon | |
| | | WFM | Chesterfield | |
| | | WFM | Churchdown Hill | |
| | | WFM | Croeserw | |
| | | WFM | Isle of Man | Manx Radio |
| | | WFM | Kendal | |
| | | WFM | Kirkton Mailer | |
| | | WFM | Minehead | |
| | | WFM | Port Ellen | |
| | | WFM | St Thomas | |
| 89.100 | | WFM | Ashkirk | |
| | | WFM | Brigport | |
| | | WFM | Combe Martin | |
| | | WFM | Conwy | |
| | | WFM | Egford Hill | |
| | | WFM | Kingussie | |
| | | WFM | Kippure | RTE Radio 1 |
| | | WFM | Larne | |
| | | WFM | Llandrindod Wells | |
| | | WFM | Llanfyllin | |
| | | WFM | Melvaig | |
| | | WFM | West Kilbride | |
| | | WFM | Wrotham | |
| 89.200 | | WFM | Aberdare | |
| | | WFM | Chalford | |
| | | WFM | Cork City | RTE Radio 1 |
| | | WFM | Holywell Hill | RTE Radio 1 |
| | | WFM | Ogmore Vale | |
| | | WFM | Pitlochry | |
| | | WFM | Pontypool | |
| | | WFM | Rosneath | |
| 89.300 | | WFM | Achill | RTE Radio 1 |
| | | WFM | County Galway | RTE Radio 1 |
| | | WFM | Crieff | |
| | | WFM | Daliburg | |
| | | WFM | Fort William | |
| | | WFM | Haverfordwest | |
| | | WFM | Holme Moss | |
| | | WFM | Ilchester Cresent | |
| | | WFM | Keelylang Hill | |
| | | WFM | Rhymney | |
| | | WFM | South Khapdale | |
| 89.400 | | WFM | Brougher Mountain | |
| | | WFM | Durris | |
| | | WFM | Hutton | |
| | | WFM | Kikeel | |
| | | WFM | Limerick City | RTE Radio 1 |
| 89.400 | | WFM | Llamdecwyn | |
| | | WFM | Machynlleth | |
| | | WFM | Newton | |
| | | WFM | Ventnor | |
| 89.500 | | WFM | Axe Valley | |
| | | WFM | Cahirciveen | RTE Radio 1 |
| | | WFM | Darvel | |
| | | WFM | Darwen | |
| | | WFM | Glengorm | |

| Base | Mobile | Mode | Location | User and Notes |
|---|---|---|---|---|
| 89.500 | | WFM | Innerleithen | |
| | | WFM | Kilvey Hill | |
| | | WFM | Oxford | |
| | | WFM | Pennar | |
| | | WFM | Salcombe | |
| 89.600 | | WFM | Channel Islands | |
| | | WFM | Fermdale | |
| | | WFM | Hastings | |
| | | WFM | Keswick Forest | |
| | | WFM | Limavady | |
| | | WFM | Llyswen | |
| | | WFM | Long Mountain | |
| | | WFM | Ludlow | |
| | | WFM | Mount Leinster | RTE Radio 1 |
| | | WFM | Rosemarkie | |
| | | WFM | Whalley | |
| | | WFM | Whitby | |
| 89.700 | | WFM | Barnoldswick | |
| | | WFM | Caterham | |
| | | WFM | Cornholme | |
| | | WFM | Eyemouth | |
| | | WFM | Kinlochleven | |
| | | WFM | Lyme Regis | |
| | | WFM | Mynydd Pencarreg | |
| | | WFM | Newhaven | |
| | | WFM | Redruth | |
| | | WFM | Stranraer | |
| | | WFM | Tacolneston | |
| | | WFM | Wearsdale | |
| | | WFM | Whitehaven | |
| 89.800 | | WFM | Beecroft Hill | |
| | | WFM | Croaghmoyle, Mayo | RTE Radio 1 |
| | | WFM | Eitshal | |
| | | WFM | Fanad | RTE Radio 1 |
| | | WFM | Fendale | |
| | | WFM | Grantown | |
| | | WFM | Hemdean | |
| | | WFM | Kingswear | |
| | | WFM | Llanddona | |
| | | WFM | Llanrhaeadr-ym-M | |
| | | WFM | Saddleworth | |
| | | WFM | Salisbury | |
| | | WFM | Stanton Moor | |
| 89.900 | | WFM | Athlone | RTE Radio 1 |
| | | WFM | Black Hill | |
| | | WFM | County Mayo | RTE Radio 1 |
| | | WFM | Haslingden | |
| | | WFM | Ivybridge | |
| | | WFM | Oliver's Mount | |
| | | WFM | Sheffield | |
| | | WFM | Wenvoe | |
| 90.000 | | WFM | Buxton | |
| | | WFM | High Wycombe | |
| | | WFM | Morecambe Bay | |
| | | WFM | Mullaghanish | RTE Radio 1 |
| | | WFM | Swingate | |

| Base | Mobile | Mode | Location | User and Notes |
|------|--------|------|----------|----------------|
| 90.000 | | WFM | Weymouth | |
| 90.100 | | WFM | Basingstoke | |
| | | WFM | Brighton | |
| | | WFM | Chatton | |
| | | WFM | Divis | |
| | | WFM | Dolgellau | |
| | | WFM | Llandinam | |
| | | WFM | Llandtfriog | |
| | | WFM | Marlborough | |
| | | WFM | Peterborough | |
| | | WFM | Rumster Forest | |
| | | WFM | Tullich | |
| 90.200 | | WFM | Clyro | BBC Radio 3 |
| | | WFM | Pendle Forest | |
| | | WFM | Woolmoor | |

**92.3000 -92.4000 MHz    NATIONWIDE BBC RADIO 3, RTE and LOCAL RADIO**

| Base | Mobile | Mode | Location | User and Notes |
|------|--------|------|----------|----------------|
| 90.300 | | WFM | Ballachulish | |
| | | WFM | Bowmore | |
| | | WFM | Cirencester | |
| | | WFM | Clettraval | |
| | | WFM | Deiniolen | |
| | | WFM | Ffestiniog | |
| | | WFM | Grantham | |
| | | WFM | Guildford | |
| | | WFM | Llandloes | |
| | | WFM | Mallaig | |
| | | WFM | Manningtree | |
| | | WFM | North Hessary Tor | |
| | | WFM | Penifiler | |
| | | WFM | Sandale | |
| 90.400 | | WFM | Betws-Y-Coed | |
| | | WFM | Calne | |
| | | WFM | County Mayo | RTE Radio 2 |
| | | WFM | Knock More | |
| | | WFM | Nailsworth | |
| | | WFM | Newbury | |
| | | WFM | Rheoloa | |
| 90.500 | | WFM | Bressay | |
| | | WFM | Forfar | |
| | | WFM | Lethanhill | |
| | | WFM | Llwyn-Onn | |
| | | WFM | Lochgilphead | |
| | | WFM | Millburn Muir | |
| | | WFM | Ness of Lewis | |
| | | WFM | Rostrevor Forest | |
| | | WFM | Sutton Coldfield | |
| | | WFM | Ullapool | |
| | | WFM | Wensleydale | |
| | | WFM | Westwood | |
| | | WFM | Windermere | |
| 90.600 | | WFM | Campbeltown | |
| | | WFM | Carmel | |
| | | WFM | Douglas, Isle Of Man | |

| Base | Mobile | Mode | Location | User and Notes |
|------|--------|------|----------|----------------|
| 90.600 | | WFM | Ebbw Vale | |
| | | WFM | Folkestone | |
| | | WFM | Hebden Bridge | |
| | | WFM | Kenley | |
| | | WFM | Peebles | |
| | | WFM | Penmaen Rhos | |
| | | WFM | Porth | |
| | | WFM | Walsden South | |
| | | WFM | Wharfdale | |
| 90.700 | | WFM | Barnstaple | |
| | | WFM | Blaenavon | |
| | | WFM | Cwmafan | |
| | | WFM | Dungarvan | RTE Radio 1 |
| | | WFM | Idle | |
| | | WFM | Plympton | |
| | | WFM | Pontop Pike | |
| | | WFM | Rothesay | |
| | | WFM | Rowbridge | |
| | | WFM | Skraig | |
| | | WFM | Three Rock | RTE Radio 1 |
| 90.800 | | WFM | Berwick | |
| | | WFM | Bow Brickhill | |
| | | WFM | Lllangeinor | |
| | | WFM | Ridge Hill | |
| | | WFM | Strachur | |
| | | WFM | Upperton | |
| | | WFM | Winter Hill | |
| 90.900 | | WFM | Abergavenny | |
| | | WFM | Ardgour | |
| | | WFM | Beacon Hill | |
| | | WFM | Belmont | |
| | | WFM | Ben Gullipen | |
| | | WFM | Blaenplwyf | |
| | | WFM | Cambret Hill | |
| | | WFM | Camlough | |
| | | WFM | Kirkconnel | |
| | | WFM | Londonderry | |
| 90.900 | | WFM | Luddenden | |
| | | WFM | Meldrum | |
| | | WFM | Okehampton | |
| 91.000 | | WFM | Ballycastle | |
| | | WFM | Belmont | |
| | | WFM | Carnmoney Hill | |
| | | WFM | Chippenham | |
| | | WFM | County Mayo | RTE Radio 2 |
| | | WFM | Crystal Palace | |
| | | WFM | Galway | RTE Radio 2 |
| | | WFM | Isles of Scilly | |
| | | WFM | Penaligon Downs | |
| | | WFM | Ton Pentre | |
| 91.100 | | WFM | Brecon | |
| | | WFM | Cambridge | |
| | | WFM | Carmarthen | |
| | | WFM | Chard | |
| | | WFM | Girvan | |
| | | WFM | Jersey | |

| Base | Mobile | Mode | Location | User and Notes |
|------|--------|------|----------|----------------|
| 91.100 | | WFM | Keighley | |
| | | WFM | Llangollen | |
| | | WFM | Northampton | |
| | | WFM | Oban | |
| | | WFM | Todmorden | |
| | | WFM | Varteg Hill | |
| 91.200 | | WFM | Abertillery | |
| | | WFM | Bath City | |
| | | WFM | Blunsdon | |
| | | WFM | Chesterfield | |
| | | WFM | Churchdown Hill | |
| | | WFM | Croeserw | |
| | | WFM | Isle of Man | Manx Radio |
| | | WFM | Kendal | |
| | | WFM | Kirkton Mailer | |
| | | WFM | Minehead | |
| | | WFM | Port Ellen | |
| | | WFM | St Thomas | |
| 91.300 | | WFM | Ashkirk | |
| | | WFM | Brigport | |
| | | WFM | Combe Martin | |
| | | WFM | Conwy | |
| | | WFM | Egford Hill | |
| | | WFM | Kingussie | |
| | | WFM | Kippure | RTE Radio 1 |
| | | WFM | Larne | |
| | | WFM | Llandrindod Wells | |
| | | WFM | Llanfyllin | |
| | | WFM | Melvaig | |
| | | WFM | West Kilbride | |
| | | WFM | Wrotham | |
| 91.400 | | WFM | Aberdare | |
| | | WFM | Chalford | |
| | | WFM | Cork City | RTE Radio 1 |
| | | WFM | Holywell Hill | RTE Radio 1 |
| 91.400 | | WFM | Ogmore Vale | |
| | | WFM | Pitlochry | |
| | | WFM | Pontypool | |
| | | WFM | Rosneath | |
| 91.500 | | WFM | County Galway | RTE Radio 1 |
| | | WFM | Crieff | |
| | | WFM | Daliburg | |
| | | WFM | Fort William | |
| | | WFM | Haverfordwest | |
| | | WFM | Holme Moss | |
| | | WFM | Ilchester Cresent | |
| | | WFM | Keelylang Hill | |
| | | WFM | Rhymney | |
| | | WFM | South Khapdale | |
| 91.600 | | WFM | Brougher Mountain | |
| | | WFM | Durris | |
| | | WFM | Hutton | |
| | | WFM | Kikeel | |
| | | WFM | Limerick City | RTE Radio 1 |
| | | WFM | Llamdecwyn | |
| | | WFM | Machynlleth | |

| Base | Mobile | Mode | Location | User and Notes |
|---|---|---|---|---|
| 91.600 | | WFM | Newton | |
| | | WFM | Ventnor | |
| 91.700 | | WFM | Axe Valley | |
| | | WFM | Cahirciveen | RTE Radio 1 |
| | | WFM | Darvel | |
| | | WFM | Darwen | |
| | | WFM | Glengorm | |
| | | WFM | Innerleithin | |
| | | WFM | Kilvey Hill | |
| | | WFM | Oxford | |
| | | WFM | Pennar | |
| | | WFM | Salcombe | |
| 91.800 | | WFM | Fermdale | |
| | | WFM | Hastings | |
| | | WFM | Keswick Forest | |
| | | WFM | Limavady | |
| | | WFM | Llyswen | |
| | | WFM | Long Mountain | |
| | | WFM | Ludlow | |
| | | WFM | Mount Leinster | RTE Radio 1 |
| | | WFM | Rosemarkie | |
| | | WFM | Whalley | |
| | | WFM | Whitby | |
| 91.900 | | WFM | Barnoldswick | |
| | | WFM | Caterham | |
| | | WFM | Cornholme | |
| | | WFM | Eyemouth | |
| | | WFM | Kinlochleven | |
| | | WFM | Lyme Regis | |
| | | WFM | Mynydd Pencarreg | |
| | | WFM | Newhaven | |
| | | WFM | Redruth | |
| 91.900 | | WFM | Stranraer | |
| | | WFM | Tacolneston | |
| | | WFM | Wearsdale | |
| | | WFM | Whitehaven | |
| 92.000 | | WFM | Beecroft Hill | |
| | | WFM | Croaghmoyle, Mayo | RTE Radio 1 |
| | | WFM | Eitshal | |
| | | WFM | Fanad | RTE Radio 1 |
| | | WFM | Fendale | |
| | | WFM | Grantown | |
| | | WFM | Hemdean | |
| | | WFM | Kingswear | |
| | | WFM | Llanddona | |
| | | WFM | Llanrhaeadr-ym-M | |
| | | WFM | Saddleworth | |
| | | WFM | Salisbury | |
| | | WFM | Stanton Moor | |
| 92.100 | | WFM | Black Hill | |
| | | WFM | County Mayo | RTE Radio 1 |
| | | WFM | Haslingden | |
| | | WFM | Ivybridge | |
| | | WFM | Oliver's Mount | |
| | | WFM | Sheffield | |
| | | WFM | Wenvoe | |

| Base | Mobile | Mode | Location | User and Notes |
|------|--------|------|----------|----------------|
| 92.200 | | WFM | Bexhill | |
| | | WFM | Buxton | |
| | | WFM | High Wycombe | |
| | | WFM | Morecambe Bay | |
| | | WFM | Mullaghanish | RTE Radio 1 |
| | | WFM | Weymouth | |
| | | WFM | Woolmoor | |
| 92.300 | | WFM | Basingstoke | |
| | | WFM | Brighton | |
| | | WFM | Chatton | |
| | | WFM | Divis | |
| | | WFM | Dolgellau | |
| | | WFM | Llandinam | |
| | | WFM | Llandtfriog | |
| | | WFM | Marlborough | |
| | | WFM | Peterborough | |
| | | WFM | Rumster Forest | |
| | | WFM | Tullich | |

**92.4000 - 94.6000 MHz**    NATIONWIDE BBC RADIO 4, RTE AND LOCAL RADIO

| Base | Mobile | Mode | Location | User and Notes |
|------|--------|------|----------|----------------|
| 92.400 | | WFM | Clyro | BBC Radio Cymru |
| | | WFM | Holme Moss | BBC Radio Leeds |
| | | WFM | Swingate | BBC Radio 3 |
| 92.500 | | WFM | Ballachulish | BBC Radio Scotland |
| | | WFM | Bowmore | BBC Radio Scotland |
| | | WFM | Cirencester | |
| | | WFM | Clettral | BBC Radio Scotland |
| | | WFM | Deiniolen | BBC Radio Cymru |
| 92.500 | | WFM | Ffestiniog | BBC Radio Cymru |
| | | WFM | Grantham | |
| | | WFM | Guildford | |
| | | WFM | Llanidloes | BBC Radio Cymru |
| | | WFM | Mallaig | BBC Radio Scotland |
| | | WFM | Manningtree | |
| | | WFM | North Hessary Tor | |
| | | WFM | Penifiler | BBC Radio Scotland |
| | | WFM | Sundale | |
| 92.600 | | WFM | Betws-y-Coed | BBC Radio Cymru |
| | | WFM | Calne | |
| | | WFM | County Mayo | RTE Radio 3 |
| | | WFM | Galway | RTE Radio 3 |
| | | WFM | Knock More | BBC Radio Scotland |
| | | WFM | Nailsworth | |
| | | WFM | Newbury | |
| | | WFM | Rheola | BBC Radio Cymru |
| | | WFM | Truskmore | Raidio Na Gaeltachta |
| 92.700 | | WFM | Castletownbere | Raidio Na Gaeltachta |
| | | WMF | Edinburgh | BBC Radio Scotland |
| | | WFM | Forfar | BBC Radio Scotland |
| | | WFM | Kilmarnock | BBC Radio Scotland |
| | | WFM | Leicestershire | |
| | | WFM | Leven & Renton | BBC Radio Scotland |
| | | WFM | Lochgilphead | BBC Radio Scotland |
| | | WFM | Midland Counties | |

| Base | Mobile | Mode | Location | User and Notes |
|------|--------|------|----------|----------------|
| 92.700 | | WFM | Ness of Lewis | BBC Radio Scotland |
| | | WFM | Nottinghamshire | |
| | | WFM | Shetland Isl | BBC Radio Scotland |
| | | WFM | Staffordshire & Shorpshire | |
| | | WFM | Trowbridge | |
| | | WFM | Wensleydale | |
| | | WFM | Westwood | |
| | | WFM | Windermere | |
| 92.800 | | WFM | Campbeltown | BBC Radio Scotland |
| | | WFM | Clwyd | BBC Radio Cymru |
| | | WFM | Eastbourne | |
| | | WFM | Ebbw Vale | |
| | | WFM | Hebden Bridge | |
| | | WFM | Isle Of Man | |
| | | WFM | Mid Glamorgan | |
| | | WFM | Peebles | BBC Radio Scotland |
| | | WFM | South London | |
| | | WFM | Surrey | |
| | | WFM | Walsden | |
| | | WFM | Wharfdale | |
| 92.900 | | WFM | Central South of England | |
| | | WFM | Cowal Peninsular | BBC Radio Scotland |
| | | WFM | Croaghmoyle, Mayo | Raidio Na Gaeltachta |
| | | WFM | Devon | |
| | | WFM | Gwent | |
| | | WFM | Isle of Wight | |
| | | WFM | Moville | Raidio Na Gaeltachta |
| 92.900 | | WFM | North Eastern Counties | |
| | | WFM | Three Rock | Raidio Na Gaeltachta |
| | | WFM | West Glamorgan | |
| | | WFM | West Skye | BBC Radio Scotland |
| | | WFM | West Yorkshire | |
| 93.000 | | WFM | Bedford | |
| | | WFM | Berwick | |
| | | WFM | Hereford & Welsh Borders | |
| | | WFM | Inveraray | BBC Radio Scotland |
| | | WFM | Mid Glamorgan | |
| | | WFM | North West Lancashire | |
| | | WFM | Ross On Wye | |
| | | WFM | Warrenpoint | Radio Ulster |
| 93.100 | | WFM | Aberystwyth | BBC Radio Cymru |
| | | WFM | Ayr | BBC Radio Scotland |
| | | WFM | Cambridgeshire | |
| | | WFM | Edinburgh | BBC Radio Scotland |
| | | WFM | Folkestone | |
| | | WFM | Grampian | BBC Radio Scotland |
| | | WFM | Gwent | |
| | | WFM | Kirkconnel | BBC Radio Scotland |
| | | WFM | Lincolnshire | |
| | | WFM | Londonderry | Radio Foyle |
| | | WFM | Newark | |
| | | WFM | Okehampton | |
| 93.200 | | WFM | Ballycastle | |
| | | WFM | Chippenham | |
| | | WFM | Co Antrim | |
| | | WFM | Cornwall | |

| Base | Mobile | Mode | Location | User and Notes |
|------|--------|------|----------|----------------|
| 93.200 | | WFM | County Mayo | RTE Radio 3 |
| | | WFM | Crystal Palace | |
| | | WFM | Galway | RTE Radio 3 |
| | | WFM | Guernsey | BBC Radio Guernsey |
| | | WFM | Isles of Scilly | |
| | | WFM | Maghera | Raidio Na Gaeltachta |
| | | WFM | Penaligon Downs | |
| | | WFM | Ton Petre | BBC Radio Cymru |
| 93.300 | | WFM | Brecon | BBC Radio Cymru |
| | | WFM | Cambridge | |
| | | WFM | Carmarthen | BBC Radio Cymru |
| | | WFM | Chard | |
| | | WFM | Girvan | BBC Radio Scotland |
| | | WFM | Gwent | BBC Radio Cymru |
| | | WFM | Keighley | |
| | | WFM | Kinross | BBC Radio Scotland |
| | | WFM | Llangollen | |
| | | WFM | Northampton | |
| | | WFM | Oban | BBC Radio Scotland |
| | | WFM | Todmorden | |
| 93.400 | | WFM | Abertillery | |
| | | WFM | Bath City | |
| | | WFM | Chesterfield | |
| | | WFM | Dungarvan | Raidio Na Gaeltachta |
| 93.400 | | WFM | Exeter | |
| | | WFM | Kendal | |
| | | WFM | Minehead | |
| | | WFM | North Gloucestershire | |
| | | WFM | Perth | BBC Radio Scotland |
| | | WFM | South Glamorgan | BBC Radio Cymru |
| | | WFM | South Islay | BBC Radio Scotland |
| | | WFM | Swindon | |
| 93.500 | | WFM | Border Counties | BBC Radio Scotland |
| | | WFM | Brigport | |
| | | WFM | Bristol City | |
| | | WFM | Conwy | BBC Radio Cymru |
| | | WFM | Devon | |
| | | WFM | Dorset | |
| | | WFM | Home Counties | |
| | | WFM | Kent | |
| | | WFM | Kingussie | BBC Radio Scotland |
| | | WFM | Kippure | Raidio Na Gaeltachta |
| | | WFM | Llandrindod Wells | BBC Radio Cymru |
| | | WFM | London | |
| | | WFM | Poseys | |
| | | WFM | Radio Ulster Larne | |
| | | WFM | Somerset | |
| | | WFM | Ullapool & Lewis | BBC Radio Scotland |
| | | WFM | West Kilbride | BBC Radio Scotland |
| 93.600 | | WFM | Aberdare | BBC Radio Cymru |
| | | WFM | Cork City | Raidio Na Gaeltachta |
| | | WFM | Holywell Hill | Raidio Na Gaeltachta |
| | | WFM | Mid Glamorgan | |
| | | WFM | Pitlochry | BBC Radio Scotland |
| | | WFM | Pontypool | BBC Radio Cymru |
| | | WFM | Rosneath | BBC Radio Scotland |

| Base | Mobile | Mode | Location | User and Notes |
|------|--------|------|----------|----------------|
| 93.600 | | WFM | Stroud | |
| 93.700 | | WFM | Achill | Raidio Na Gaeltachta |
| | | WFM | Alderney | Island FM |
| | | WFM | Bristol | BBC Radio 4 |
| | | WFM | Bristol | BBC Radio 4 |
| | | WFM | Cheshire | |
| | | WFM | County Galway | RTE Radio 3 |
| | | WFM | Daliburgh | BBC Radio Scotland/Highland |
| | | WFM | Derbyshire | |
| | | WFM | Fort William | BBC Radio Scotland |
| | | WFM | Galway | RTE Radio 3 |
| | | WFM | Greater Manchester | |
| | | WFM | Gwent | |
| | | WFM | Humberside | |
| | | WFM | Lancashire | |
| | | WFM | Merseyside | |
| | | WFM | Nottinghamshire | |
| | | WFM | Orkney Isl | BBC Radio Scotland |
| | | WFM | Perthshire | BBC Radio Scotland |
| | | WFM | South Knapdale | BBC Radio Scotland |
| | | WFM | Wrexham & Deeside | |
| 93.700 | | WFM | Yorkshire | |
| 93.800 | | WFM | Avon | |
| | | WFM | Enniskillen | Radio Ulster |
| | | WFM | Gwynedd | |
| | | WFM | Kincardine | BBC Radio Scotland |
| | | WFM | London | Vibes FM |
| | | WFM | Newry | BBC Radio Ulster |
| | | WFM | Northumberland | |
| | | WFM | Poseys | BBC Radio Cymru |
| | | WFM | Ventnor | |
| 93.900 | | WFM | Cahirciveen | Raidio Na Gaeltachta |
| | | WFM | Devon | |
| | | WFM | East Skye | BBC Radio Scotland |
| | | WFM | Grantham | |
| | | WFM | Greenholm & Darvel | BBC Radio Scotland |
| | | WFM | Innerleithen | BBC Radio Scotland |
| | | WFM | Oxfordshire & Wiltshire | |
| | | WFM | Pennar | |
| | | WFM | Swansea | BBC Radio Cymru |
| | | WFM | Tobermoray & Mull | BBC Radio Scotland |
| | | WFM | Todmorden | |
| | | WFM | Welshpool | |
| 94.000 | | WFM | Fermdale | |
| | | WFM | Inverness | BBC Radio Scotland |
| | | WFM | Keswick Forest | |
| | | WFM | Lancashire | |
| | | WFM | Limavady | |
| | | WFM | Ludlow | |
| | | WFM | Mid Glamorgan | |
| | | WFM | Mount Leinster | Raidio Na Gaeltachta |
| | | WFM | North East Scotland | BBC Radio Scotland |
| | | WFM | W. Midlands | Black County Sounds |
| | | WFM | Whitby | |

| Base | Mobile | Mode | Location | User and Notes |
|------|--------|------|----------|----------------|
| 94.100 | | WFM | Berwickshire | BBC Radio Scotland |
| | | WFM | Cornholme | |
| | | WFM | Kinlochleven | BBC Radio Scotland |
| | | WFM | Lyme Regis | |
| | | WFM | Newhaven | |
| | | WFM | Norfolk | |
| | | WFM | Redruth | |
| | | WFM | Saddleworth | |
| | | WFM | South East London | |
| | | WFM | Stranraer | BBC Radio Scotland |
| | | WFM | Suffolk | |
| | | WFM | Surrey | |
| | | WFM | Wearsdale | |
| | | WFM | West Cornwall | |
| | | WFM | Whitehaven | |
| 94.200 | | WFM | Anglesey | BBC Radio Cymru |
| | | WFM | Caversham | |
| | | WFM | Clwyd | |
| | | WFM | County Mayo | RTE Radio 3 |
| | | WFM | Derby | BBC Radio Derby |
| 94.200 | | WFM | Fanad | Raidio Na Gaeltachta |
| | | WFM | Galway | RTE Radio 3 |
| | | WFM | Hastings | |
| | | WFM | Matlock | |
| | | WFM | Newcastle | |
| | | WFM | Pudsey | |
| | | WFM | Salisbury | |
| | | WFM | South Devon | |
| | | WFM | Stornaway | BBC Radio Scotland |
| 94.300 | | WFM | Bristol | |
| | | WFM | Edinburgh | BBC Radio Scotland |
| | | WFM | Forth Valley | BBC Radio Scotland |
| | | WFM | Gloucester & Somerset | |
| | | WFM | Haslingden | |
| | | WFM | High Wycombe | |
| | | WFM | Lowland Scotland | BBC Radio Scotland |
| | | WFM | Scarborough | |
| | | WFM | Sheffield | |
| | | WFM | Somerset & North Devon | |
| | | WFM | South & East Wales | |
| 94.400 | | WFM | Buxton | |
| | | WFM | High Wycombe | |
| | | WFM | Morecambe Bay | |
| | | WFM | Mullaghanish | Raidio Na Gaeltachta |
| | | WFM | North Yorkshire | |
| | | WFM | South Cumbria | |
| | | WFM | South East Kent | |
| | | WFM | Weymouth | |
| 94.500 | | WFM | Basingstoke | |
| | | WFM | Belfast & East Counties | Radio Ulster |
| | | WFM | Berwick & Borders | |
| | | WFM | Brighton | |
| | | WFM | Chatton | |
| | | WFM | Deeside | BBC Radio Scotland |
| | | WFM | Dolgellau | BBC Radio Cymru |
| | | WFM | Llandyfriod | BBC Radio Cymru |

| Base | Mobile | Mode | Location | User and Notes |
|------|--------|------|----------|----------------|
| 94.500 | | WFM | Marlborough | |
| | | WFM | Peterborough | |
| | | WFM | Poseys | |
| | | WFM | Wick | BBC Radio Scotland |

**94.6000 -97.5000 MHz** NATIONWIDE BBC, INDEPENDENT RADIO RTE AND LOCAL RADIO

| Base | Mobile | Mode | Location | User and Notes |
|------|--------|------|----------|----------------|
| 94.600 | | WFM | Bexhill | BBC Radio 4 |
| | | WFM | Cheshire | BBC Radio Stoke On Trent |
| | | WFM | Granton | BBC Radio Scotland |
| | | WFM | Henley | BBC Thames Valley FM |
| | | WFM | Pendle Forest | BBC Radio 4 |
| 94.700 | | WFM | Argyll | BBC Radio 4 |
| | | WFM | Chesterfield | BBC Radio Sheffield |
| | | WFM | Glasgow | BBC Radio Scotland |
| | | WFM | Hereford | BBC Radio Hereford & Worc's |
| | | WFM | Invernessshire | BBC Radio 4 |
| | | WFM | Isle of Islay | BBC Radio 4 |
| | | WFM | Solway | BBC Radio Solway |
| 94.800 | | WFM | Huntshaw Cross | BBC Radio Devon |
| | | WFM | Isle of Skye | BBC Radio 4 |
| | | WFM | Jersey | BBC Radio 4 |
| | | WFM | Knock More | BBC Radio 4 |
| | | WFM | Meridan | BBC CWR |
| 94.900 | | WFM | Ayrshire | BBC Radio 4 |
| | | WFM | Bristol City | BBC Radio Bristol |
| | | WFM | Crystal Palace | BBC GLR |
| | | WFM | Edinburgh | BBC Radio 4 |
| | | WFM | Forfar | BBC Radio 4 |
| | | WFM | Lincolnshire | BBC Radio Lincolnshire |
| | | WFM | Londonderry | BBC Radio 4 |
| | | WFM | Perth | BBC Radio Scotland |
| | | WFM | Shetland | BBC Radio 4 |
| 95.000 | | WFM | Leicester | BBC Radio Leicestershire |
| | | WFM | Ludlow | BBC Radio Shropshire |
| | | WFM | Newhaven | BBC Radio Sussex |
| | | WFM | Newhaven | BBC SCR |
| | | WFM | Peebles | BBC Radio 4 |
| | | WFM | Stroud | BBC Radio Gloucestershire |
| | | WFM | Teesside | BBC Radio Cleveland |
| 95.100 | | WFM | Argyll | BBC Radio 4 |
| | | WFM | Ballycastle | Radio Ulster |
| | | WFM | Gwent | BBC Radio Wales |
| | | WFM | Holme Moss | BBC GMR |
| | | WFM | Horsham | BBC Radio Sussex |
| | | WFM | Horsham | BBC SCR |
| | | WFM | Isle of Lewis | BBC Radio 4 |
| | | WFM | Norfolk | BBC Radio Norfolk |
| | | WFM | South Wales | BBC Radio Gwent |
| | | WFM | Western Isles | BBC Radio 4 |
| 95.200 | | WFM | Argyll | BBC Radio 4 |
| | | WFM | Clermont Carn | RTE Radio 1 |
| | | WFM | E Cornwall | BBC Radio Cornwall |
| | | WFM | Kendal | BBC Radio Cumbria |
| | | WFM | Oxfordshire | BBC Thames Valley FM |

| Base | Mobile | Mode | Location | User and Notes |
|---|---|---|---|---|
| 95.300 | | WFM | Aberdeenshire | BBC Radio 4 |
| | | WFM | Argyll | BBC Radio 4 |
| | | WFM | Ayrshire | BBC Radio 4 |
| 95.300 | | WFM | Brighton | BBC Radio Sussex |
| | | WFM | Dumfriesshire | BBC Radio 4 |
| | | WFM | Kirkcudbrightshire | BBC Radio 4 |
| | | WFM | Matlock | BBC Radio Derby |
| | | WFM | Perthshire | BBC Radio 4 |
| | | WFM | Southend | BBC Radio Essex |
| | | WFM | Wharfdale | BBC Radio Leeds |
| | | WFM | Whitehawk Hill | BBC SCR |
| 95.400 | | WFM | Limavady | Radio Ulster |
| | | WFM | Tyneside | BBC Radio Newcastle |
| | | WFM | Windsor | BBC Thames Valley FM |
| 95.500 | | WFM | Bedford | BBC Radio Bedfordshire |
| | | WFM | Bristol | BBC Radio Bristol |
| | | WFM | Carmarthen | BBC Radio 4 |
| | | WFM | E Lancashire | BBC Radio Lancashire |
| | | WFM | Lowestoft | BBC Suffolk |
| | | WFM | Mansfield | BBC Radio Nottingham |
| | | WFM | Sandy Heath | BBC 3CR |
| | | WFM | Scarborough | BBC Radio York |
| | | WFM | Somerset | Somerset Sound |
| | | WFM | Taunton | BBC Radio Bristol |
| | | WFM | Tayside | BBC Radio 4 |
| 95.600 | | WFM | Argyll | BBC Radio 4 |
| | | WFM | Co Fermanagh | BBC Radio 4 |
| | | WFM | Cumbria | BBC Radio Cumbria |
| | | WFM | W Midlands | BBC Radio West Midlands |
| 95.700 | | WFM | Dorset | BBC Radio Dorset |
| | | WFM | Invernessshire | BBC Radio 4 |
| | | WFM | Isle of Islay | BBC Radio 4 |
| | | WFM | Peterborough | BBC Radio Cambridge |
| 95.800 | | WFM | Cirencester | BBC Radio Gloucestershire |
| | | WFM | Edinburgh | BBC Radio 4 |
| | | WFM | Exeter | BBC Radio Devon |
| | | WFM | Glasgow | BBC Radio 4 |
| | | WFM | Lanarkshire | BBC Radio 4 |
| | | WFM | London | 95.8 Capital FM |
| | | WFM | Merseyside | BBC Radio Merseyside |
| | | WFM | Whitby | BBC Radio Cleveland |
| 95.900 | | WFM | Aberdeenshire | BBC Radio 4 |
| | | WFM | Borders | BBC Radio Newcastle |
| | | WFM | Fort William | BBC Radio 4 |
| | | WFM | Orkney | BBC Radio 4 |
| | | WFM | SW Wales | BBC Radio 4 |
| | | WFM | South Wales | BBC Radio Gwent |
| | | WFM | Thanet | Invicta FM |
| | | WFM | Western Isles | BBC Radio 4 |
| | | WFM | Yorkshire | BBC Radio Humberside |
| 96.000 | | WFM | Belfast | BBC Radio 4 |
| | | WFM | Belfast | Radio Ulster |
| | | WFM | Cambridgeshire | BBC Radio Cambridge |
| | | WFM | Chatton | BBC Radio Newcastle |
| | | WFM | Okehampton | BBC Radio Devon |
| | | WFM | Scillies | BBC Radio Cornwall |

| Base | Mobile | Mode | Location | User and Notes |
|------|--------|------|----------|----------------|
| 96.000 | | WFM | Shropshire | BBC Radio Shropshire |
| | | WFM | Weymouth | Wessex FM |
| 96.100 | | WFM | Ashford | Invicta FM |
| | | WFM | Colchester | SGR Colchester |
| | | WFM | County Mayo | MWR FM |
| | | WFM | Innerleithen | BBC Radio 4 |
| | | WFM | Isle of Mull | BBC Radio 4 |
| | | WFM | Isle of Skye | BBC Radio 4 |
| | | WFM | Isle of Lewis | BBC Radio 4 |
| | | WFM | Morecambe Bay | BBC Radio Cumbria |
| | | WFM | Poseys | BBC Radio Cymru |
| | | WFM | S Hampshire | BBC Radio Solent |
| | | WFM | SW Cumbria | BBC Radio Furness |
| | | WFM | Ullapool | BBC Radio 4 |
| 96.200 | | WFM | Aylesbury | Mix 96 |
| | | WFM | Coventry | Kix 96 |
| | | WFM | North Devon | Lantern FM |
| | | WFM | Nottingham | Trent FM |
| | | WFM | Scarborough | Yorkshire Coast Radio |
| | | WFM | Shetland | SIBC |
| | | WFM | Tonbridge | KFM |
| | | WFM | Tyneside | Century Radio |
| 96.300 | | WFM | Bristol | GWR FM |
| | | WFM | Leeds | 96.3 Aire FM |
| | | WFM | North Wales | Coast FM |
| | | WFM | Paisley | 96.3 QFM |
| | | WFM | Southend | Essex FM |
| 96.400 | | WFM | Birmingham | 96.4 FM BRMB |
| | | WFM | Bury St Edmonds | SGR-FM |
| | | WFM | Congleton | Signal Cheshire |
| | | WFM | County Mayo | RTE 3 |
| | | WFM | Galway | County Clare Radio |
| | | WFM | Guildford | 96.4 The Eagle |
| | | WFM | Haslemere | Delta Radio 97.1 FM |
| | | WFM | Limavady | Downtown Radio |
| | | WFM | Newton | Century Radio |
| | | WFM | Penrith | CFM |
| | | WFM | Perth | Tay FM |
| | | WFM | Swansea | Sound Wave |
| | | WFM | Torbay | Gemini FM |
| 96.500 | | WFM | Blackpool | Radio Wave |
| | | WFM | Nottingham | Trent FM |
| 96.600 | | WFM | Aberystwyth | Radio Ceredigion |
| | | WFM | Chichester | Spirit FM |
| | | WFM | Enniskillen | Downtown Radio |
| | | WFM | Fort William | Nevis Radio |
| | | WFM | Inverness | Moray Firth Radio |
| | | WFM | Northampton | Northants Radio |
| | | WFM | Plymouth | Plymouth Sound FM |
| | | WFM | St Albans | 96.6 FM Classic Hits |
| | | WFM | Teesside | TFM |
| 96.700 | | WFM | Ayrshire | West Sound FM |
| | | WFM | Belfast | BCR |
| 96.700 | | WFM | Grantham | Lincs FM |
| | | WFM | Kidderminster | Wyvern FM |
| | | WFM | Kings Lynn | KL.FM 96.7 |

| Base | Mobile | Mode | Location | User and Notes |
|------|--------|------|----------|----------------|
| 96.700 | | WFM | Merseyside | City FM |
| | | WFM | North Kent | BBC Radio Kent |
| | | WFM | South Hampshire | Ocean FM |
| 96.800 | | WFM | Bristol | BBC Radio Cymru |
| | | WFM | County Mayo | Galway Bay Radio |
| | | WFM | Selkirk | Radio Borders |
| | | WFM | Wenvoe | BBC Radio Cymru |
| 96.900 | | WFM | Aberdeen | NorthSound One |
| | | WFM | Bedford | B97 |
| | | WFM | Brixton | Choice FM London |
| | | WFM | Humberside | Viking FM |
| | | WFM | Isle of Man | Manx Radio |
| | | WFM | Morecambe Bay | The Bay |
| | | WFM | Newhaven | Southern FM |
| | | WFM | Stafford | Signal One |
| 97.000 | | WFM | Coventry | Mercia Sound |
| | | WFM | Dover | Invicta FM |
| | | WFM | Exeter | Gemini FM |
| | | WFM | Glasgow | Clyde 1 FM |
| | | WFM | Ireland | RTE 2 |
| | | WFM | Plymouth | Plymouth Sound FM |
| | | WFM | Reading | 2-TEN FM |
| | | WFM | SW Scotland | South West Sound |
| 97.100 | | WFM | Galway | MWR FM |
| | | WFM | Haslemere | Delta Radio |
| | | WFM | Ipswich | SGR-FM |
| | | WFM | Jersey | BBC Radio 1 |
| | | WFM | Tyneside | Metro FM |
| | | WFM | Wrexham | MFM |
| | | WFM | Yeovil | Orchard FM |
| 97.200 | | WFM | Bristol | Galaxy Radio |
| | | WFM | Dorchester | Wessex FM |
| | | WFM | Harrogate | 97.2 Stray FM |
| | | WFM | Isle of Man | Manx Radio |
| | | WFM | Swindon | GWR FM |
| | | WFM | Wolverhampton | Beacon Radio |
| 97.300 | | WFM | Edinburgh | Radio Forth FM |
| | | WFM | London | London News 97.3 FM |
| 97.400 | | WFM | Banbury | Fox FM |
| | | WFM | Belfast | Cool FM |
| | | WFM | Cambridge | Q103 FM |
| | | WFM | Inverness | Moray Firth Radio |
| | | WFM | Newport | Red Dragon Radio |
| | | WFM | Preston | Red Rose Rock FM |
| | | WFM | Shaftesbury | Gold Radio |
| | | WFM | Sheffield | Hallam FM |
| 97.500 | | WFM | Ayr | West Sound FM |
| | | WFM | Berwick | Radio Borders |
| | | WFM | Bradford | The Pulse |
| | | WFM | Pitlochry | Heartland FM |
| 97.500 | | WFM | South Hampshire | Ocean FM |

| Base | Mobile | Mode | Location | User and Notes |
|------|--------|------|----------|----------------|

**97.6000 -108.000 MHz** Nationwide BBC Radio , Independent Radio, RTE and Local Radio

| Base | Mobile | Mode | Location | User and Notes |
|------|--------|------|----------|----------------|
| 97.600 | | WFM | Aberdeen | NorthSound One |
| | | WFM | Edinburgh | Forth FM |
| | | WFM | Folkestone | BBC Radio Kent |
| | | WFM | Hereford | Wyvern FM |
| | | WFM | Kent | BBC Kent |
| | | WFM | Luton | Chiltern FM |
| 97.700 | | WFM | Ballachulish | |
| | | WFM | Bowmore | |
| | | WFM | Cirencester | |
| | | WFM | Clettraval | |
| | | WFM | Clyro | |
| | | WFM | Deiniolen | |
| | | WFM | Ffestiniog | |
| | | WFM | Grantham | |
| | | WFM | Guildford | |
| | | WFM | Llanidloes | |
| | | WFM | Mallaig | |
| | | WFM | Manningtree | |
| | | WFM | North Hessary Tor | |
| | | WFM | Penifiler | |
| | | WFM | Sundale | |
| 97.800 | | WFM | Betws-y-Coed | |
| | | WFM | Bexhill | |
| | | WFM | Calne | |
| | | WFM | Knock More | |
| | | WFM | Nailsworth | |
| | | WFM | Newbury | |
| | | WFM | Rheola | |
| | | WFM | Truskmore | RTE Radio 1 |
| 97.900 | | WFM | Bressay | |
| | | WFM | Castletownbere | RTE Radio 1 |
| | | WFM | Forfar | |
| | | WFM | Lethanhill | |
| | | WFM | Llwyn-Onn | |
| | | WFM | Lochgilphead | |
| | | WFM | Millburn Muir | |
| | | WFM | Moville | RTE Radio 1 |
| | | WFM | Ness of Lewis | |
| | | WFM | Rostrevor Forest | |
| | | WFM | Sutton Coldfield | |
| | | WFM | Ullapool | |
| | | WFM | Wensleydale | |
| | | WFM | Westwood | |
| | | WFM | Windermere | |
| 98.000 | | WFM | Campbeltown | |
| | | WFM | Carmel | |
| | | WFM | Douglas, Isle Of Man | |
| | | WFM | Ebbw Vale | |
| | | WFM | Folkestone | |
| 98.00 | | WFM | Hebden Bridge | |
| | | WFM | Kenley | |
| | | WFM | London | Unity FM |
| | | WFM | Peebles | |
| | | WFM | Penmaen Rhos | |

| Base | Mobile | Mode | Location | User and Notes |
|------|--------|------|----------|----------------|
| 98.000 | | WFM | Porth | |
| | | WFM | Walsden South | |
| | | WFM | Wharfdale | |
| 98.100 | | WFM | Barnstaple | |
| | | WFM | Blaenavon | |
| | | WFM | Cwmafan | |
| | | WFM | Dublin | 98 FM Dublin |
| | | WFM | Dungarvan | RTE Radio 1 |
| | | WFM | Idle | |
| | | WFM | Plympton | |
| | | WFM | Pontop Pike | |
| | | WFM | Rothesay | |
| | | WFM | Rowbridge | |
| | | WFM | Skraig | |
| | | WFM | Three Rock | RTE Radio 1 |
| 98.200 | | WFM | Berwick On Tweed | |
| | | WFM | Bow Brickhall | |
| | | WFM | Llangeinor | |
| | | WFM | Ridge Hill | |
| | | WFM | Strachur | |
| | | WFM | Upperton | |
| | | WFM | Winter Hill | |
| 98.300 | | WFM | Abergavenny | |
| | | WFM | Ardgour | |
| | | WFM | Beacon Hill | |
| | | WFM | Ben Gullipen | |
| | | WFM | Cambret Hill | |
| | | WFM | Camlough | |
| | | WFM | Kirkconnel | |
| | | WFM | Londonderry | |
| | | WFM | Luddenden | |
| | | WFM | Meldrum | |
| | | WFM | Okehampton | |
| 98.400 | | WFM | Ballycastle | |
| | | WFM | Belmont | |
| | | WFM | Carnmoney Hill | |
| | | WFM | Chippenham | |
| | | WFM | County Mayo | RTE Radio 1 |
| | | WFM | Crystal Palace | |
| | | WFM | Isles of Scilly | |
| | | WFM | Maghera | RTE Radio 1 |
| | | WFM | Penaligon Downs | |
| | | WFM | Ton Pentre | |
| 98.500 | | WFM | Brecon | |
| | | WFM | Cambridge | |
| | | WFM | Carmarthen | |
| | | WFM | Chard | |
| | | WFM | Crystal Palace | |
| | | WFM | Girvan | |
| | | WFM | Gwent | |
| | | WFM | Keighley | |
| | | WFM | Llangollen | |
| | | WFM | Northampton | |
| | | WFM | Oban | |
| | | WFM | Todmorden | |

| Base | Mobile | Mode | Location | User and Notes |
|------|--------|------|----------|----------------|
| 98.600 | | WFM | Abertillery | |
| | | WFM | Bath City | |
| | | WFM | Blunsdon | |
| | | WFM | Chesterfield | |
| | | WFM | Churchdown Hill | |
| | | WFM | Croeserw | |
| | | WFM | Isle of Man | Manx Radio |
| | | WFM | Kendal | |
| | | WFM | Kirkton Mailer | |
| | | WFM | Minehead | |
| | | WFM | Port Ellen | |
| | | WFM | St Thomas | |
| 98.700 | | WFM | Ashkirk | |
| | | WFM | Brigport | |
| | | WFM | Combe Martin | |
| | | WFM | Conwy | |
| | | WFM | Egford Hill | |
| | | WFM | Kingussie | |
| | | WFM | Kippure | RTE Radio 1 |
| | | WFM | Larne | |
| | | WFM | Llandrindod Wells | |
| | | WFM | Llanfyllin | |
| | | WFM | Melvaig | |
| | | WFM | West Kilbride | |
| 98.800 | | WFM | Aberdare | |
| | | WFM | Chalford | |
| | | WFM | Holywell Hill | RTE Radio 1 |
| | | WFM | Ogmore Vale | |
| | | WFM | Pitlochry | |
| | | WFM | Pontypool | |
| | | WFM | Rosneath | |
| 98.900 | | WFM | County Galway | RTE Radio 1 |
| | | WFM | Crieff | |
| | | WFM | Daliburg | |
| | | WFM | Fort William | |
| | | WFM | Haverfordwest | |
| | | WFM | Holme Moss | |
| | | WFM | Ilchester Crescent | |
| | | WFM | Keelylang Hill | |
| | | WFM | Rhymney | |
| | | WFM | South Khapdale | |
| 99.000 | | WFM | Brougher Mountain | |
| | | WFM | Durris | |
| | | WFM | Hutton | |
| | | WFM | Kikeel | |
| | | WFM | Limerick City | RTE Radio 1 |
| | | WFM | Llamdecwyn | |
| | | WFM | Machynlleth | |
| | | WFM | Newton | |
| | | WFM | Ventnor | |
| 99.100 | | WFM | Axe Valley | |
| | | WFM | Cahirciveen | RTE Radio 1 |
| | | WFM | Darvel | |
| | | WFM | Darwen | |
| | | WFM | Glengorm | |
| | | WFM | Innerleithen | |

| Base | Mobile | Mode | Location | User and Notes |
|------|--------|------|----------|----------------|
| 99.100 | | WFM | Kilvey Hill | |
| | | WFM | Oxford | |
| | | WFM | Pennar | |
| | | WFM | Salcombe | |
| 99.200 | | WFM | Bexhill | |
| | | WFM | Fermdale | |
| | | WFM | Hastings | |
| | | WFM | Keswick Forest | |
| | | WFM | Limavady | |
| | | WFM | Llyswen | |
| | | WFM | Long Mountain | |
| | | WFM | Ludlow | |
| | | WFM | Mount Leinster | RTE Radio 1 |
| | | WFM | Rosemarkie | |
| | | WFM | Whalley | |
| | | WFM | Whitby | |
| 99.300 | | WFM | Barnoldswick | |
| | | WFM | Caterham | |
| | | WFM | Cornholme | |
| | | WFM | Eyemouth | |
| | | WFM | Kinlochleven | |
| | | WFM | Lyme Regis | |
| | | WFM | Mynydd Pencarreg | |
| | | WFM | Newhaven | |
| | | WFM | Redruth | |
| | | WFM | Stranraer | |
| | | WFM | Tacolneston | |
| | | WFM | Wearsdale | |
| | | WFM | Whitehaven | |
| 99.400 | | WFM | Beecroft Hill | |
| | | WFM | Eitshal | |
| | | WFM | Fendale | |
| | | WFM | Grantown | |
| | | WFM | Hemdean | |
| | | WFM | Kingswear | |
| | | WFM | Llanddona | |
| | | WFM | Llanrhaeadr-ym-M | |
| | | WFM | Saddleworth | |
| | | WFM | Salisbury | |
| | | WFM | Stanton Moor | |
| 99.500 | | WFM | Black Hill | |
| | | WFM | County Mayo | RTE Radio 1 |
| | | WFM | Haslingden | |
| 98.500 | | WFM | Ivybridge | |
| | | WFM | Oliver's Mount | |
| | | WFM | Sheffield | |
| | | WFM | Wenvoe | |
| 99.600 | | WFM | Buxton | |
| | | WFM | High Wycombe | |
| | | WFM | Morecambe Bay | |
| | | WFM | Mullaghanish | RTE Radio 1 |
| | | WFM | Swingate | |
| | | WFM | Weymonth | |
| | | WFM | Woolmoor | |

| Base | Mobile | Mode | Location | User and Notes |
|---|---|---|---|---|
| 99.700 | | WFM | Basingstoke | |
| | | WFM | Brighton | |
| | | WFM | Chatton | |
| | | WFM | Divis | |
| | | WFM | Dolgellau | |
| | | WFM | Llandinam | |
| | | WFM | Llandtfriog | |
| | | WFM | Marlborough | |
| | | WFM | Peterborough | |
| | | WFM | Rumster Forest | |
| | | WFM | Tullich | |
| 99.800 | | WFM | Clyro | |
| 100.000 | | WFM | London | Kiss FM |
| | | WFM | North Hessary Tor | Classic FM |
| 100.100 | | WFM | Angus | Classic FM |
| | | WFM | Manchester | Classic FM |
| | | WFM | Sutton Coldfield | Classic FM |
| 100.200 | | WFM | London | Jazz FM 102.2 |
| 100.300 | | WFM | Central Scotland | Scot FM |
| | | WFM | Gosport | Classic FM |
| | | WFM | Isle of Wight | Classic FM |
| | | WFM | Tyneside | Classic FM |
| 100.400 | | WFM | London | Pressure FM |
| | | WFM | North West England | Jazz FM 100.4 |
| 100.500 | | WFM | Lincolnshire | Classic FM |
| | | WFM | Londonderry | Classic FM |
| | | WFM | Meldrum | Classic FM |
| | | WFM | Nationwide | RSL 28 Day stations |
| 100.600 | | WFM | Crystal Palace | Classic FM |
| 100.700 | | WFM | Gwynedd | Classic FM |
| | | WFM | North East | Century FM |
| | | WFM | West Midlands | 100.7 Heart FM |
| 100.800 | | WFM | Berkshire | Classic FM |
| | | WFM | Buckinghamshire | Classic FM |
| | | WFM | Oxfordshire | Classic FM |
| 100.900 | | WFM | Kent | Classic FM |
| | | WFM | London | Classic FM |
| 101.000 | | WFM | Calne | Galaxy 101 |
| 101.100 | | WFM | Edinburgh | Scot FM |
| | | WFM | Holme Moss | Classic FM |
| 101.300 | | WFM | Ayrshire | Classic FM |
| | | WFM | Oxford | Classic FM |
| | | WFM | Swansea | Classic FM |
| 101.500 | | WFM | Norwich | Classic FM |
| | | WFM | Alton | Wey Valley Radio |
| | | WFM | Anglesey | Classic FM |
| | | WFM | Gwynedd | Classic FM |
| | | WFM | London | Star FM |
| | | WFM | Tonbridge | KFM |
| 101.700 | | WFM | Bristol | Classic FM |
| | | WFM | Central Scotland | Classic FM |
| | | WFM | Harlow | Ten 17 |
| | | WFM | Sheffield | Classic FM |
| | | WFM | Wenvoe | Classic FM |
| 101.800 | | WFM | Dover | Classic FM |
| | | WFM | North East | Century FM |

| Base | Mobile | Mode | Location | User and Notes |
|------|--------|------|----------|----------------|
| 101.900 | | WFM | Belfast | Classic FM |
| | | WFM | Peterborough | Classic FM |
| 102.000 | | WFM | Alton | Wey Valley Radio |
| | | WFM | Hastings | Southern FM |
| | | WFM | Hastings | Southern FM |
| | | WFM | Manchester | Kiss 102 |
| | | WFM | Salisbury | Spire FM |
| | | WFM | Stratford Upon Avon | FM 102-The Bear |
| 102.100 | | WFM | Inverurie | North East Community Radio |
| 102.200 | | WFM | Birmingham | Choice FM Birmingham |
| | | WFM | East Cornwall | Pirate FM |
| | | WFM | Lincoln | Lincs FM |
| | | WFM | London | Jazz FM |
| | | WFM | Shetland | SIBC |
| | | WFM | Wiltshire | GWR FM |
| 102.300 | | WFM | Bournemouth | 2CR FM |
| | | WFM | Littlehampton | Spirit FM |
| | | WFM | Windermere | The Bay |
| 102.400 | | WFM | Cheltenham | Severn Sound |
| | | WFM | Eastbourne | Southern FM |
| | | WFM | Londonderry | Downtown Radio |
| | | WFM | Norwich | Broadland 102 |
| | | WFM | Wigan | Wish 102.4 FM |
| 102.500 | | WFM | Carlisle | CFM |
| | | WFM | County Mayo | MWR FM |
| | | WFM | Glasgow | Clyde 1 FM |
| | | WFM | Huddersfield | The Pulse |
| | | WFM | Penrith | CFM Radio |
| 102.600 | | WFM | Chelmsford | Essex FM |
| | | WFM | Northumberland | Metro FM |
| | | WFM | Oxford | Fox FM |
| | | WFM | Somerset | Orchard FM |
| | | WFM | Staffordshire | Signal One |
| 102.700 | | WFM | Clermont Carn | Raidio Na Gaeltachta |
| | | WFM | Keighley | BBC Radio Leeds |
| | | WFM | Peterborough | 102.7 Hereward FM |
| | | WFM | Reigate | Mercury FM |
| 102.800 | | WFM | Canterbury | Invicta FM |
| | | WFM | Derby | Ram FM |
| 102.800 | | WFM | Dundee | Tay FM |
| | | WFM | West Cornwall | Pirate FM |
| | | WFM | Worcester | Wyvern FM |
| 102.900 | | WFM | Barnsley | Hallam FM |
| | | WFM | Basingstoke | 2-TEN FM |
| | | WFM | Leamington Spa | Mercia FM |
| | | WFM | Londonderry | Q102.9 FM |
| | | WFM | Rotherham | Hallam FM |
| 103.000 | | WFM | Bath | GWR FM |
| | | WFM | Cambridge | Q103 FM |
| | | WFM | East Devon | Gemini FM |
| | | WFM | Isle of Wight | Classic FM |
| | | WFM | Manchester | Key 103 |
| | | WFM | Manchester | Key 103 |
| | | WFM | Newcastle upon Tyne | Metro FM |
| | | WFM | Peterhead | NorthSound One |
| | | WFM | Stroud | Severn Sound |

| Base | Mobile | Mode | Location | User and Notes |
|------|--------|------|----------|----------------|
| 103.100 | | WFM | Maidstone | Invicta FM |
| | | WFM | Peebles | Radio Borders |
| | | WFM | Scarborough | Yorkshire Coast Radio |
| | | WFM | Shrewsbury | Beacon Radio |
| | | WFM | Stirling | Central FM |
| 103.200 | | WFM | Bradford | Sunrise FM |
| | | WFM | Cardiff | Red Dragon Radio |
| | | WFM | Darlington | A1 FM |
| | | WFM | Kendal | The Bay |
| | | WFM | Leicester | Leicester Sound |
| | | WFM | Solent | Power FM |
| | | WFM | Tyne Valley | Metro FM |
| 103.300 | | WFM | Aberystwyth | Radio Ceredigion |
| | | WFM | Donegal | Hi-Land Radio |
| | | WFM | Haringay | London Greek Radio |
| | | WFM | Milton Keynes | FM 103 Horizon |
| | | WFM | Oban | Oban FM |
| | | WFM | Rosneath | Clyde 1 FM |
| 103.400 | | WFM | Devon | BBC Radio Devon |
| | | WFM | Doncaster | Hallam FM |
| | | WFM | Eyemouth | Radio Borders |
| | | WFM | Great Yarmouth | The Beach |
| | | WFM | Sunderland | Sun City 103.4 |
| | | WFM | Wrexham | MFM |
| 103.500 | | WFM | Abergavenny | Radio Cymru |
| | | WFM | Brighton | Southern FM |
| | | WFM | Ffestiniog | BBC Radio 4 |
| | | WFM | Great Bransted | BBC Radio Essex |
| | | WFM | Isle of Mull | BBC Radio Nan Gaidheal |
| | | WFM | Larne | BBC Radio 4 |
| | | WFM | Newton Barrow | BBC Wiltshire Sounds |
| | | WFM | Verteg Hill | BBC Radio 4 |
| | | WFM | West Kilbride | BBC Radio 4 |
| 103.600 | | WFM | Bowmore | BBC Radio Nan Gaidheal |
| | | WFM | Croeserw | BBC Radio 4 |
| | | WFM | Dolgellau | BBC Radio 4 |
| 103.600 | | WFM | Geddington | BBC Radio Northampton |
| | | WFM | Llanddona | BBC Radio 4 |
| | | WFM | Long Mountain | BBC Radio Cymru |
| | | WFM | Machynlleth | BBC Radio 4 |
| | | WFM | Rosemarkie | BBC Radio 4 |
| | | WFM | Stranraer | BBC Radio 4 |
| 103.700 | | WFM | Aklam Wold | BBC Radio York |
| | | WFM | Ballachulish | BBC Radio Nan Gaidheal |
| | | WFM | Clettraval | BBC Radio Nan Gaidheal |
| | | WFM | Jersey | Channel 103 |
| | | WFM | Jurby | Manx Radio |
| | | WFM | Lark Stoke | BBC CWR |
| | | WFM | Mynydd Pencarreg | BBC Radio Cymru |
| | | WFM | Ogmore Vale | BBC Radio Cymru |
| | | WFM | Pennar | BBC Radio Cymru |
| 103.800 | | WFM | Bincombe Hill | BBC Dorset FM |
| | | WFM | Donegal | North Atlantic Radio |
| | | WFM | Llandrindod Wells | BBC Radio 4 |
| | | WFM | Llanrhaeadr-ym-M | BBC Radio Cymru |
| | | WFM | Mapperley Ridge | BBC Radio Nottingham |

| Base | Mobile | Mode | Location | User and Notes |
|---|---|---|---|---|
| 103.800 | | WFM | Rosneath | BBC Radio 4 |
| | | WFM | Zouches Farm | BBC 3CR |
| 103.900 | | WFM | Ashkirk | BBC Radio 4 |
| | | WFM | Beecroft Hill | BBC Radio Leeds |
| | | WFM | Blunsdon | BBC Wiltshire Sounds |
| | | WFM | Kilkeel | BBC Radio 4 |
| | | WFM | Mannongtree | BBC Radio Suffolk |
| | | WFM | Melvaig | BBC Radio Nan Gaidheal |
| | | WFM | Pitlochry | BBC Radio 4 |
| | | WFM | Redruth | BBC Radio Cornwall |
| | | WFM | Rostrevor Forest | BBC Radio 4 |
| | | WFM | Winter Hill | BBC Radio Lancashire |
| 104.000 | | WFM | Blaenavon | BBC Radio Cymru |
| | | WFM | Blaenplwyf | BBC Radio 4 |
| | | WFM | Great Malvern | BBC Hereford & Worcester |
| | | WFM | Nuneaton | BBC CWR |
| | | WFM | Reigate | BBC SCR |
| 104.100 | | WFM | Deiniolen | BBC Radio 4 |
| | | WFM | Edinburgh | BBC Gaelic |
| | | WFM | Hannington | BBC Thames Valley FM |
| | | WFM | Holme Moss | BBC Radio Sheffield |
| | | WFM | Millburn Muir | BBC Radio 4 |
| | | WFM | Stafford | BBC Radio Stoke |
| 104.200 | | WFM | Daliburgh | BBC Radio Nan Gaidheal |
| | | WFM | Fort William | BBC Radio Nan Gaidheal |
| | | WFM | Grantown | BBC Radio 4 |
| | | WFM | Kilvey Hill | BBC Radio 4 |
| | | WFM | Northampton | BBC Radio Northampton |
| | | WFM | Strachur | BBC Radio Nan Gaidheal |
| | | WFM | Swingate | BBC Radio Kent |
| | | WFM | Windermere | BBC Radio Cumbria |
| 104.300 | | WFM | Abertillery | BBC Radio Cymru |
| | | WFM | Darvel | BBC Radio 4 |
| | | WFM | Eitshal | BBC Radio Nan Gaidheal |
| | | WFM | Llangollen | BBC Radio Cymru |
| | | WFM | Mallaig | BBC Radio Nan Gaidheal |
| | | WFM | Naish Hill | BBC Wiltshire Sound |
| | | WFM | Penifiler | BBC Radio Nan Gaidheal |
| | | WFM | Ton Petre | BBC Radio 4 |
| | | WFM | Woolmoor | BBC Radio York |
| 104.400 | | WFM | Conwy | BBC Radio 4 |
| | | WFM | Fenham | BBC Radio Newcastle |
| | | WFM | Great Massingham | BBC Radio Norfolk |
| | | WFM | Kinlochleven | BBC Radio Nan Gaidheal |
| | | WFM | Llandyfriog | BBC Radio 4 |
| | | WFM | Llyswen | BBC Radio 4 |
| | | WFM | Reading | BBC Thames Valley FM |
| 104.500 | | WFM | Bow Brickhill | BBC 3CR |
| | | WFM | Cwmafan | BBC Radio Cymru |
| | | WFM | Heathfield | BBC Southern Counties Radio |
| | | WFM | Kirkton Mailer | BBC Radio 4 |
| | | WFM | Lancaster | BBC Radio Lancashire |
| | | WFM | Porth | BBC Radio Cymru |
| | | WFM | Rumster Forest | BBC Radio 4 |
| | | WFM | Sutton Coldfield | BBC Radio Derby |
| | | WFM | Tullich | BBC Radio 4 |

| Base | Mobile | Mode | Location | User and Notes |
|---|---|---|---|---|
| 104.600 | | WFM | Bath | BBC Radio Bristol |
| | | WFM | Camlough | BBC Radio 4 |
| | | WFM | Carmel | BBC Radio 4 |
| | | WFM | Ebbw Vale | BBC Radio Cymru |
| | | WFM | Eyemouth | BBC Radio 4 |
| | | WFM | Great Barton | BBC Radio Suffolk |
| | | WFM | Guildford | BBC Southern Counties Radio |
| | | WFM | Kidderminster | BBC Hereford & Worcester |
| | | WFM | Llangeinor | BBC Radio Cymru |
| | | WFM | Oban | BBC Radio Nan Gaidheal |
| | | WFM | Penmaen Rhos | BBC Radio 4 |
| | | WFM | Saddleworth | BBC GMR |
| 104.700 | | WFM | Aberdare | BBC Radio 4 |
| | | WFM | Brecon | BBC Radio 4 |
| | | WFM | Churchdown Hill | BBC Radio Gloucestershire |
| | | WFM | Edinburgh | BBC Gaelic |
| | | WFM | Grantham | BBC Radio Lincoinshire |
| | | WFM | Guernsey | Island FM |
| | | WFM | Skraig | BBC Radio Nan Gaidheal |
| | | WFM | York | Minster FM |
| 104.800 | | WFM | Burton Down | BBC Southern Counties Radio |
| | | WFM | Llanidloes | BBC Radio 4 |
| | | WFM | Llwyn-Onn | BBC Radio 4 |
| | | WFM | Pontypool | BBC Radio 4 |
| | | WFM | Rheola | BBC Radio 4 |
| | | WFM | South Knapdale | BBC Radio Nan Gaidheal |
| 104.900 | | WFM | Ardgour | BBC Radio Nan Gaidheal |
| | | WFM | Ben Gullipen | BBC Radio 4 |
| | | WFM | Betws-y-Coed | BBC Radio 4 |
| | | WFM | Clyro | BBC Radio 4 |
| | | WFM | Copt Oak | BBC Radio Leicestershire |
| | | WFM | Edinburgh | BBC Radio 4 |
| | | WFM | Ferndale | BBC Radio Cymru |
| | | WFM | Haverfordwest | BBC Radio 4 |
| | | WFM | Llandecwyn | BBC Radio Cymru |
| | | WFM | Marlborough | BBC Wiltshire Sound |
| | | WFM | Ness of Lewis | BBC Radio Nan Gaidheal |
| | | WFM | Port Ellen | BBC Radio Nan Gaidheal |
| | | WFM | Rhymney | BBC Radio Cymru |
| | | WFM | Rosemarkie | BBC Radio Nan Gaidheal |
| | | WFM | Stockport | Signal Cheshire |
| | | WFM | Ullapool | BBC Radio Nan Gaidheal |
| 105.100 | | WFM | Leeds | Kiss 105 |
| 105.200 | | WFM | Nationwide | RSL 28 Day stations |
| 105.400 | | NFM | Campbeltown | Kintyre Commiunity Radio (weekends only) |
| | | WFM | London | Melody FM |
| | | WFM | Nationwide | RSL 28 Day stations |
| 105.600 | | WFM | Bradford | Kiss 105 |
| | | WFM | Nationwide | RSL 28 Day stations |
| 105.800 | | WFM | Hull | Kiss 105 |
| | | WFM | London | Virgin Radio London |
| | | WFM | Nationwide | RSL 28 Day stations |
| 106.000 | | WFM | Nationwide | RSL 28 Day stations |
| 106.200 | | WFM | London | Heart 106.2 |
| | | WFM | Nationwide | RSL 28 Day stations |

| Base | Mobile | Mode | Location | User and Notes |
|------|--------|------|----------|----------------|
| 104.500 | | WFM | Windsor | Star FM |
| 106.600 | | WFM | Nationwide | RSL 28 Day stations |
| 106.800 | | WFM | Thamesmead | Melenium FM |
| 107.000 | | WFM | Nationwide | RSL 28 Day stations |
| 107.400 | | WFM | Nationwide | RSL 28 Day stations |
| 107.600 | | WFM | M20/Channel Ports | Channel Travel Radio |
| 107.800 | | WFM | Nationwide | RSL 28 Day stations |

An indepentent outside broadcasting unit working off Hyde Park,
London, and linking to its studios at Southwark.

## 108.0000 - 112.0000MHz TACAN and DME Idents, ILS Localisers and ILS Localisers

| Base | Mode | Location | User and Notes |
| --- | --- | --- | --- |
| 108.10000 | AM | Belfast | DME (I-BFH) |
| | AM | Dundee Airport | DME Ident (DDE) |
| | AM | Guernsey | ILS Localiser Runway 09 (I-UY) |
| | AM | Guernsey | ILS Localiser Runway 27 (I-GH) |
| | AM | RAF Chivenor | ILS Localiser Runway 28 (CV) |
| | AM | RAF Cottesmore | TACAN Ident (CTM) |
| | AM | USAF Mildenhall | ILS Localiser Runway 11 (I-MIL) |
| | AM | USAF Mildenhall | ILS Localiser Runway 29 (I-MLD) |
| 108.15000 | AM | Blackpool | DME Ident |
| | AM | Blackpool | ILS Localiser Runway 28 (I-BPL) |
| | AM | Lydd Airport | DME Ident |
| | AM | Lydd Airport | ILS Localiser Runway 22 (I-LYX) |
| 108.20000 | AM | Boscombe Down (MoD) | TACAN Ident (BDN) |
| 108.30000 | AM | Londonderry | ILS/DME Rwy 26 (EGT) |
| | AM | USAF Lakenheath | ILS Localiser Runway 24 (I-LKH) |
| 108.40000 | AM | RAF Valley | TACAN Ident (VYL) |
| | AM | RAF Benson | ILS Localiser Runway 19 (BO) |
| | AM | Sumburgh Airport | DME Ident |
| | AM | Sumburgh Airport | ILS Localiser Runway 09 (SUB) |
| | AM | Sumburgh Airport | ILS Localiser Runway 27 (I-SG) |
| | AM | Teesside Airport | DME Ident |
| | AM | Teesside Airport | ILS Localiser Runway 05 (I-TSE) |
| | AM | Teesside Airport | ILS Localiser Runway 23 (I-TD) |
| 108.60000 | AM | Kirkwall Airport | VOR/DME Ident (KWL) |
| 108.70000 | AM | Newton Point | TACAN Ident (NTP) |
| | AM | RAF Leuchars | ILS Localiser Runway 27 (LU) |
| | AM | RAF Shawbury | ILS Localiser Runway 19 (SY) |
| | AM | RAF St Mawgan | ILS Localiser Runway 31 (SM) |
| 108.75000 | AM | Humberside Airport | DME Ident |
| | AM | Humberside Airport | ILS Localiser Runway 21 (I-HS) |
| 108.80000 | AM | Weathersfield | TACAN Ident (WET) |
| 108.90000 | AM | Cranfield | ILS Localiser Runway 22 (I-CR) |
| | AM | Dublin | ILS/DME Rwy 10 |
| | AM | Dublin | ILS/DME Rwy 28 |
| | AM | Edinburgh Airport | DME Ident |
| | AM | Edinburgh Airport | ILS Localiser Runway 07 (I-VG) |
| | AM | Edinburgh Airport | ILS Localiser Runway 25 (I-TH) |
| | AM | Kerry | DME/ILS R25 KER |
| | AM | Ventnor | TACAN Ident (VNR) |
| 108.95000 | AM | Woodford | DME Ident (I-WU) |
| | AM | Woodford | ILS Localiser Runway 25 (I-WU) |
| 109.05000 | AM | Yeovil Aerodrome | DME Ident (YVL) |
| 109.10000 | AM | Southampton Airport | ILS Localiser Runway 20 (I-SN) |
| 109.15000 | AM | Luton Airport | DME Ident |
| | AM | Luton Airport | ILS Localiser Runway 26 (I-LJ) |
| | AM | Luton Airport | ILS Localiser Rwy 08 (I-LTN) |
| 109.20000 | AM | Inverness Airport | VOR/DME Ident (INS) |
| | AM | Swansea Aerodrome | DME Ident (SWZ) |
| 109.30000 | AM | Glasgow | ILS Localiser Runway 23 (I-OO) |
| 109.35000 | AM | Biggin Hill | ILS Localiser Runway 21 (I-BGH) |
| | AM | East Midlands | ILS Localiser Runway 09 (I-EMW) |
| 109.35000 | AM | East Midlands | ILS Localiser Runway 27 (I-EME) |
| 109.40000 | AM | Barrow Airport | DME Ident (WL) |
| | AM | Guernsey | VOR/ATIS (GUR) |

| Base | Mobile | Mode | Location | User and Notes |
|---|---|---|---|---|
| 109.50000 | | AM | London (Heathrow) | DME Ident |
| | | AM | London (Heathrow) | ILS Localiser Runway 09R (I-BB) |
| | | AM | London (Heathrow) | ILS Localiser Runway 27L (I-LL) |
| | | AM | Manchester Airport | DME Ident |
| | | AM | Manchester Airport | ILS Localiser Runway 06 (I-MM) |
| | | AM | Manchester Airport | ILS Localiser Runway 24 (I-NN) |
| | | AM | Plymouth Airport | DME Ident |
| | | AM | Plymouth Airport | ILS Localiser Runway 31 (I-PLY) |
| | | AM | Shannon Airport | ILS Runway 24 (SA) |
| 109.60000 | | AM | RAF Linton-on-Ouse | TACAN Ident (LOZ) |
| | | AM | RAF Odiham | TACAN Ident (ODH) |
| 109.70000 | | AM | Belfast (Aldergrove) | ILS Localiser Runway 25 (I-AG) |
| | | AM | RAF Cranwell | ILS Localiser Runway 26 (CW) |
| | | AM | RAF Kinloss | ILS Localiser Runway 26 (KS) |
| | | AM | RAF Lyneham | ILS Localiser Runway (LA) |
| | | AM | RAF Valley | ILS Localiser Runway 14 (VY) |
| 109.75000 | | AM | Coventry Airport | ILS Localiser Runway 23 (I-CT) |
| 109.80000 | | AM | RAF Kinloss | TACAN Ident (KSS) |
| | | AM | RAF Lyneham | TACAN (LYE) |
| 109.85000 | | AM | Fair Oaks Aerodrome | DME Ident (FRK) |
| 109.90000 | | AM | Aberdeen (Dyce Airport) | ILS Localiser Runway 16 (I-AX) |
| | | AM | Aberdeen (Dyce Airport) | ILS Localiser Runway 34 (I-ABD) |
| | | AM | Cork Airport | ILS Runway 17 (ICA) |
| | | AM | Cork Airport | ILS Runway 35 (ICN) |
| | | AM | East Midlands Airport | ILS Localiser Runway 09 (I-EMW) |
| | | AM | East Midlands Airport | ILS Localsier Runway 27 (I-EME) |
| | | AM | Exeter Airport | ILS Localiser Runway 26 (I-XR) |
| | | AM | Stornoway Airport | ILS Localiser Runway 18 (I-SV) |
| | | AM | Warton (MoD) | DME Ident |
| | | AM | Warton (MoD) | ILS Localiser Runway 26 (WQ) |
| 110.00000 | | AM | Galway | DME (CRN) |
| 110.10000 | | AM | Birmingham International | DME Ident |
| | | AM | Birmingham International | ILS Localiser Runway 15 (I-BIR) |
| | | AM | Birmingham International | ILS Localiser Runway 33 (I-BM) |
| | | AM | Glasgow | ILS Localiser Runway 05 (I-UU) |
| | | AM | RAF Marham | ILS Localiser Runway 24 (MR) |
| 110.15000 | | AM | Bristol Airport | ILS Localiser Runway 09 (I-BON) |
| | | AM | Bristol Airport | ILS Localiser Runway 27 (I-BTS) |
| 110.20000 | | AM | USAF Lakenheath | TACAN Ident (LKH) |
| 110.30000 | | AM | Jersey Airport | ILS Localiser Runway 27 (I-DD) |
| | | AM | London (Heathrow) | DME Ident |
| | | AM | London (Heathrow) | ILS Localiser Runway 09L (I-AA) |
| | | AM | London (Heathrow) | ILS Localiser Runway 27R (I-RR) |
| | | AM | Prestwick Airport | ILS Localiser Runway 13 (I-PP) |
| | | AM | Prestwick Airport | ILS Localiser Runway 31 (I-KK) |
| | | AM | RAF Cottesmore | ILS Localiser Runway 23 (CM) |
| | | AM | RAF Leeming | ILS Localiser Runway 16 (LI) |
| 110.40000 | | AM | Perth Aerodrome | VOR (PTH) |
| 110.50000 | | AM | Bournemouth (Hurn) | DME Ident |
| | | AM | Bournemouth (Hurn) | ILS Localiser Runway 08 (I-BMH) |
| | | AM | Bournemouth (Hurn) | ILS Localiser Runway 26 (I-BH) |
| | | AM | RAF Leuchars | TACAN Ident (LUK) |
| | | AM | Stansted | DME Ident |
| | | AM | Stansted | ILS Localiser Runway 05 (I-SED) |
| | | AM | Stansted | ILS Localiser Runway 23 (I-SX) |

| Base | Mobile | Mode | Location | User and Notes |
|------|--------|------|----------|----------------|
| 110.55000 | | AM | Filton (BAe), Bristol | ILS Localiser Runway 10 (I-BRF) |
| | | AM | Filton (BAe), Bristol | ILS Localiser Runway 28 (I-FB) |
| 110.70000 | | AM | Cardiff Airport | DME Ident |
| 110.70000 | | AM | Cardiff Airport | ILS Localiser Runway 12 (I-CDF |
| | | AM | Cardiff Airport | ILS Localiser Runway 30 (I-CWA) |
| | | AM | Carlisle Airport | DME Ident (CO) |
| | | AM | Connaught (Knock) | ILS Localsier Rwy 27 (I-CK) |
| | | AM | London (Heathrow) | DME Ident (HHT) |
| | | AM | London (Heathrow) | ILS Localiser Runway 23 (I-CC) |
| | | AM | RAF Coningsby | ILS Localiser Runway 26 (CY) |
| | | AM | RAF Linton-on-Ouse | ILS Localsier Runway 22 (LO) |
| 110.90000 | | AM | Belfast (Aldergrove) | ILS Runway 17 (I-FT) |
| | | AM | Jersey Airport | DME Ident (I-JJ) |
| | | AM | Jersey Airport | ILS Localiser Runway 09 (I-JJ) |
| | | AM | Leeds/Bradford Airport | ILS Localiser Runway 09 (I-LBF) |
| | | AM | Leeds/Bradford Airport | ILS Localiser Runway 32 (I-LF) |
| | | AM | London (Gatwick) | DME Ident |
| | | AM | London (Gatwick) | ILS Localiser Runway 08R (I-GG) |
| | | AM | London (Gatwick) | ILS Localiser Runway 26L (I-WW) |
| | | AM | Norwich Airport | ILS Localiser Runway 14 (I-NH) |
| | | AM | Ronaldsway, Isle of Man | DME Ident |
| | | AM | Ronaldsway, Isle of Man | ILS Localiser Runway 27 (I-RY) |
| 111.00000 | | AM | RNAS Yeovilton | TACAN Ident (VLN) |
| 111.10000 | | AM | RAF Coningsby | TACAN Ident (CGY) |
| | | AM | RAF Lossiemouth | ILS Localiser Runway 23 (LM) |
| | | AM | RAF Waddington | ILS Localiser Runway 21 (WA) |
| | | AM | USAF Fairford | ILS Localiser Runway 09 (I-FFA) |
| | | AM | USAF Fairford | ILS Localiser Runway 27 (I-FFD) |
| 111.20000 | 111.200 | NFM | Nationwide | Illegal Bugging Device |
| 111.30000 | | AM | Hatfield Aerodrome | ILS Localiser Runway 24 (I-HD) |
| 111.35000 | | AM | Southend Airport | DME Ident |
| | | AM | Southend Airport | ILS Localiser Runway 24 (I-ND) |
| 111.50000 | | AM | Dublin | ILS/DME Rwy 16 |
| | | AM | London (City Airport) | DME Ident |
| | | AM | London (City Airport) | ILS Localiser Runway 10 (LST) |
| | | AM | London (City Airport) | ILS Localiser Runway 28 (LST) |
| | | AM | Newcastle Airport | DME Ident |
| | | AM | Newcastle Airport | ILS Localiser Runway 07 (I-NC) |
| | | AM | Newcastle Airport | ILS Localiser Runway 25 (I-NWC) |
| | | AM | RAF Coltishall | ILS Localiser Runway 22 (CS) |
| | | AM | USAF Fairford | TACAN Ident (FFA) |
| 111.60000 | | AM | RAF Chivenor | TACAN Ident (CVR) |
| 111.70000 | | AM | Boscombe Down (MoD) | ILS Localiser Runway 24 (BD) |
| 111.75000 | | AM | Liverpool Airport | DME Ident |
| | | AM | Liverpool Airport | ILS Localiser Runway 09 (LVR) |
| | | AM | Liverpool Airport | ILS Localiser Runway 27 (I-LQ) |
| 111.90000 | | AM | RAF Brize Norton | ILS Localiser Runway 08 (BZA) |
| | | AM | RAF Brize Norton | ILS Localiser Runway 26 (BZB) |
| | | AM | RAF Brize Norton | TACAN Ident (BZN) |
| | | AM | RAF Honington | ILS Localiser Runway 27 (HT) |

## 112.0000 - 117.9750 MHz TACAN and DME Idents, ATIS and VOR Aero

| Base | Mobile | Mode | Location | User and Notes |
| --- | --- | --- | --- | --- |
| 112.10000 | | AM | Pole Hill | VOR/DME Ident (POL) |
| 112.20000 | | AM | Jersey Airport | VOR/ATIS (JSY) |
| | | AM | Ronaldsway, Isle of Man | VOR/DME Ident (IOM) |
| 112.50000 | | AM | St Abbs | VOR/DME Ident (SAB) |
| 112.60000 | | AM | RAF St Mawgan | TACAN Ident (SMG) |
| 112.70000 | | AM | Berry Head | VOR/DME Ident (BHD) |
| | | AM | Donegal Aerodrome | DME Ident (CFN) |
| 112.80000 | | AM | Gamston Aerodrome | VOR/DME Ident (GAM) |
| 113.10000 | | AM | Strumble | VOR/DME Ident (STU) |
| 113.20000 | | AM | Warton (MoD) | TACAN Ident (WTN) |
| 113.30000 | | AM | Shannon Airport | DVOR/DME (SHA) |
| 113.35000 | | AM | Southampton Airport | VOR/ATIS (SAM) |
| 113.55000 | | AM | Manchester Airport | VOR/DME Ident (MCT) |
| 113.60000 | | AM | London (Heathrow) | VOR/DME Ident (LON) |
| | | AM | Wick Aerodrome | TACAN Ident (WIZ) |
| | | AM | Wick Aerodrome | VOR (WIK) |
| 113.65000 | | AM | Honiley | VOR/DME Ident (HON) |
| 113.75000 | | AM | Bovingdon | VOR/DME Ident (BNN) |
| 113.90000 | | AM | Ottringham | VOR/DME Ident (OTR) |
| 114.00000 | | AM | Midhurst | VOR/DME Ident (MID) |
| 114.05000 | | AM | Lydd Airport | VOR (LYD) |
| 114.10000 | | AM | Wallasey | VOR/DME Ident (WAL) |
| 114.20000 | | AM | Land's End Airport | VOR/DME Ident (LND) |
| 114.25000 | | AM | Newcastle Airport | VOR/ATIS (NEW) |
| 114.30000 | | AM | Aberdeen (Dyce Airport) | ATIS |
| | | AM | Aberdeen (Dyce Airport) | VOR/DME Ident (ADN) |
| 114.35000 | | AM | Compton | VOR/DME Ident (CPT) |
| 114.40000 | | AM | Benbecula Airport | TACAN Ident (BEZ) |
| | | AM | Benbecula Airport | VOR (BEN) |
| 114.55000 | | AM | Clacton Aerodrome | VOR/DME Ident (CLN) |
| 114.60000 | | AM | Cork Airport | DVOR/DME Ident (CRK) |
| 114.75000 | | AM | Chichester/Goodwood | VOR (GWC) |
| 114.90000 | | AM | Dublin | VOR/DME (DUB) |
| | | AM | Dublin | VOR/DME Ident (DUB) |
| | | AM | Vallafield | TACAN Ident (VFD) |
| 114.95000 | | AM | Dover | VOR/DME Ident (DVR) |
| 115.10000 | | AM | Biggin Hill | VOR/DME Ident (BIG) |
| | | AM | Stornoway Airport | TACAN Ident (STZ) |
| | | AM | Stornoway Airport | VOR (STN) |
| 115.20000 | | AM | Dean Cross | VOR/DME Ident (DCS) |
| 115.30000 | | AM | Ockham | VOR/DME Ident (OCK) |
| 115.40000 | | AM | Glasgow | VOR/ATIS/DME Ident (GOW) |
| 115.55000 | | AM | Gloucestershire Airport | DME Ident (GOS) |
| 115.60000 | | AM | Lambourne | VOR/DME Ident (LAM) |
| 115.70000 | | AM | Stoke on Trent | VOR/DME Ident (TNT) |
| 115.80000 | | AM | Balldonnel, Eire | VOR Ident (BAL) |
| 115.90000 | | AM | USAF Mildenhall | TACAN Ident (MLD) |
| 116.00000 | | AM | RAF Machrihanish | DVOR (MAC) |
| 116.20000 | | AM | Blackbushe | DME Ident (BLC) |
| 116.25000 | | AM | Barkway | VOR/DME Ident (BKY) |
| 116.40000 | | AM | Daventry | VOR/DME Ident (DTY) |
| 116.50000 | | AM | Cranfield | VOR Ident (CFD) |
| 116.50000 | | AM | RAF Coltishall | TACAN Ident (CSL) |
| 116.75000 | | AM | Cambridge Airport | DME Ident (CAB) |

| Base | Mobile | Mode | Location | User and Notes |
|------|--------|------|----------|----------------|
| 117.00000 | | AM | Seaford | VOR/DME Ident (SFD) |
| 117.10000 | | AM | Burnham | VOR (BUR) |
| 117.20000 | | AM | Belfast | VOR/DME Ident (BEL) |
| 117.30000 | | AM | Detling | VOR/DME Ident (DET) |
| 117.35000 | | AM | Sumburgh Airport | VOR/DME Ident (SUM) |
| 117.40000 | | AM | Connaught (Knock) | VOR/DME Ident (CON) |
| | | AM | RAF Cranwell | TACAN Ident (CWZ) |
| 117.45000 | | AM | Brecon | VOR/DME Ident (BCN) |
| 117.50000 | | AM | Brookmans Park | VOR/DME Ident (BPK) |
| | | AM | Turnberry | VOR/DME Ident (TRN) |
| 117.60000 | | AM | RAF Wittering | TACAN Ident (WIT) |
| 117.70000 | | AM | Oxford/Kidlington Airport | DME Ident (OX) |
| | | AM | Tiree | VOR/DME Ident (TIR) |
| 117.90000 | | AM | Mayfield | VOR/DME Ident (MAY) |

**117.9750 - 136.9750 MHz    International Civil Aviation Band 50 kHz**

| Base | Mobile | Mode | Location | User and Notes |
|------|--------|------|----------|----------------|
| 118.00000 | | AM | Nationwide | Air-Air Display Coordination |
| | | AM | Nationwide | Marlboro Aerobatic Display |
| | | AM | Natiownide | Civilian Air-Air |
| | | AM | Yeovil | Westland Helicopter Tests |
| 118.02500 | | AM | Leeds/Bradford Airport | ATIS |
| 118.05000 | | AM | Birmingham International | Radar/Approach |
| | | AM | North Sea | Frigg Oil Field deck |
| 118.07500 | | AM | Barra, Scotland | AFIS |
| | | AM | London (City Airport) | Tower |
| 118.10000 | | AM | Aberdeen (Dyce Airport) | Tower |
| | | AM | Farnborough | Air Show Tower |
| | | AM | Liverpool Airport | Tower |
| | | AM | Penzance Heliport | Tower |
| 118.15000 | | AM | Prestwick Airport | Tower |
| 118.20000 | | AM | Ronaldsway, Isle of Man | Radar |
| | | AM | Southampton Airport | Tower |
| 118.25000 | | AM | Brittas Bay, Eire | Air/Ground (Brittas Bay Radio) |
| | | AM | Sumburgh Airport | Tower |
| 118.27500 | | AM | Fishburn | Air/Ground |
| 118.30000 | | AM | Belfast (Aldergrove) | Tower |
| | | AM | Birmingham International | Tower |
| | | AM | Kirkwall Airport | Tower/Approach |
| 118.32500 | | AM | Ipswich Airport | AFIS |
| 118.35000 | | AM | Derby | Air/Ground |
| 118.37500 | | AM | RAF West Drayton | Air Traffic Control |
| 118.40000 | | AM | Blackpool | Tower |
| 118.42500 | | AM | RAF Lyneham | Approach/Radar (Director) |
| | | AM | Wroughton | Approach |
| 118.45000 | | AM | Liverpool Airport | Radar |
| 118.47500 | | AM | West Drayton | London ATC |
| 118.50000 | | AM | Dublin Airport | Director |
| | | AM | London (Heathrow) | Tower |
| | | AM | Newcastle Airport | Radar |
| 118.55000 | | AM | Humberside Airport | Tower |
| | | AM | Jersey | Approach |
| | | AM | Jersey Airport | Radar |
| 118.57500 | | AM | Manchester | ATC arrivals |
| | | AM | Manchester Airport | Radar standby |
| 118.60000 | | AM | Dublin Airport | Tower |
| | | AM | London (Gatwick) | Radar |

| Base | Mobile | Mode | Location | User and Notes |
|---|---|---|---|---|
| 118.62500 | | AM | Manchester Airport | Tower |
| 118.65000 | | AM | Bournemouth (Hurn) | Radar |
| 118.70000 | | AM | Edinburgh Airport | Tower |
| | | AM | London (Heathrow) | Tower |
| | | AM | Shannon Airport | Tower |
| 118.80000 | | AM | Cork Airport | Radar |
| | | AM | Glasgow | Tower |
| 118.82500 | | AM | West Drayton | London Control ACC |
| 118.85000 | | AM | Teesside Airport | Approach/Radar |
| 118.87500 | | AM | Oxford (Kidlington Airport) | Tower/AFIS |
| 118.90000 | | AM | Guernsey | Radar |
| | | AM | Kemble | Air/Ground |
| | | AM | RAF Lossiemouth | Tower |
| | | AM | Ronaldsway, Isle of Man | Tower |
| 118.92500 | | AM | RAF Cosford | Approach/Tower |
| 118.95000 | | AM | London (Gatwick) | Radar |
| 119.00000 | | AM | Nationwide | RAF Common |
| | | AM | RAF Brize Norton | Zone |
| | | AM | Shetlands | East Shetland Information |
| | | AM | USAF Fairford | Approach |
| 119.05000 | | AM | Exeter Airport | Radar |
| 119.10000 | | AM | Glasgow | Approach/Radar |
| 119.12000 | | AM | Newton | Approach/Tower |
| 119.12500 | | AM | RAF Newton | Tower |
| 119.15000 | | AM | USAF Fairford | Tower |
| 119.20000 | | AM | Benbecula | Approach/Tower and FIS |
| 119.22500 | | AM | RAF Lyneham | Tower |
| 119.25000 | | AM | Coventry Airport | Approach |
| 119.27500 | | AM | RAF Manston | Tower |
| 119.30000 | | AM | Cork Airport | Tower |
| | | AM | Glasgow | Radar |
| | | AM | Hatfield Aerodrome | Radar |
| 119.35000 | | AM | Dornoch Aerodrome | Approach (Lossiemouth) |
| | | AM | Norwich Airport | Approach/Radar |
| | | AM | RAF Kinloss | Approach |
| | | AM | RAF Lossiemouth | Approach (LARS/MATZ) |
| 119.37500 | | AM | RAF Cranwell | Approach |
| 119.40000 | | AM | Haydock Park | Approach |
| | | AM | Manchester Airport | Approach/Radar (Director) |
| 119.42500 | | AM | Stubton Park | Air/Ground |
| 119.45000 | | AM | Hinton in the Hedges | Air/Ground |
| 119.45000 | | AM | Jersey Airport | Tower |
| | | AM | Prestwick Airport | Radar |
| 119.47500 | | AM | Cardiff Airport | ATIS |
| 119.47500 | | AM | RAF St Athan | Cardiff Information |
| 119.55000 | | AM | Dublin Airport | Radar |
| | | AM | Shipdam | Air/Ground and AFIS |
| 119.60000 | | AM | London (Gatwick) | Radar |
| 119.62500 | | AM | Bournemouth (Hurn) | Approach/Radar |
| 119.65000 | | AM | Derby | Approach (East Midlands) |
| | | AM | East Midlands Airport | Approach |
| 119.70000 | | AM | Newcastle Airport | Tower |
| | | AM | Swansea | Air/Ground |
| | | AM | Wick | Air/Ground |
| 119.72500 | | AM | London (Heathrow) | Approach (Director) |

| Base | Mobile | Mode | Location | User and Notes |
|---|---|---|---|---|
| 119.75000 | | AM | Perranporth | Air/Ground |
| | | AM | RAF Woodvale | Tower |
| 119.77500 | | AM | West Drayton | London Control |
| 119.80000 | | AM | Exeter | Tower |
| | | AM | London (Gatwick) | Police Helicopter Ops |
| | | AM | Perth (Scone) | Air/Ground and AFIS |
| | | AM | Teesside Airport | Tower |
| 119.85000 | | AM | Burtonwood | US Army Helicopter Ops |
| | | AM | Liverpool Airport | Approach/Radar |
| 119.87500 | | AM | Prestwick | Scottish ACC (Information) |
| 119.90000 | | AM | Cork Airport | Approach |
| | | AM | London (Heathrow) | Radar |
| | | AM | RAF Odiham | Helicopter Ops |
| 119.92500 | | AM | RAF Manston | Radar |
| 119.95000 | | AM | Blackpool | Approach |
| | | AM | Guernsey | Tower |
| 119.97500 | | AM | RAF Coningsby | Tower |
| 120.00000 | | AM | Belfast (Aldergrove) | Radar |
| 120.02500 | | AM | West Drayton | London Control |
| 120.07500 | | AM | North Sea | Pickerill Oil Field deck |
| | | AM | North Sea | Trent Oil Field deck |
| | | AM | North Sea | Tyne Oil Field deck |
| | | AM | North Sea | Viking Oil Field log |
| 120.12500 | | AM | East Midlands Airport | Radar |
| 120.15000 | | AM | North Coates | Air/Ground |
| 120.17500 | | AM | West Drayton | London Control Inbound |
| 120.20000 | | AM | Shannon Airport | Approach |
| 120.22500 | | AM | Southampton Airport | Approach Solent |
| 120.25000 | | AM | Panshanger | Air/Ground |
| 120.25500 | | AM | Solent | Interial contact frequency |
| 120.27500 | | AM | Redhill Aerodrome | Tower/AFIS |
| 120.30000 | | AM | Jersey Airport | Approach/Radar |
| | | AM | Leeds/Bradford Airport | Tower |
| 120.32500 | | AM | RAF Northolt | Departure |
| 120.40000 | | AM | Aberdeen (Dyce Airport) | Approach/Radar |
| | | AM | London (Heathrow) | Approach |
| 120.42500 | | AM | RAF Barkston Heath | Tower |
| 120.45000 | | AM | Jersey Airport | Air Traffic Control (Zone)/Radar |
| 120.45000 | | AM | North Sea | Oil Rig Heliport Common |
| 120.47500 | | AM | West Drayton | London Control SIDs |
| 120.50000 | | AM | RAF Leeming | Tower |
| 120.52500 | | AM | Biggin Hill | Speedbird Ops |
| | | AM | West Drayton | London Control ACC |
| 120.55000 | | AM | Prestwick Airport | Approach/Radar |
| 120.57500 | | AM | Luton Airport | ATIS |
| 120.60000 | | AM | Cumbernauld Airport | AFIS |
| 120.62500 | | AM | Andrewsfield | Radar (Stansted) |
| | | AM | High Easter Aerodrome | Approach (Stansted) |
| | | AM | Stansted | Approach/Radar |
| 120.70000 | | AM | Lydd Airport | AFIS |
| 120.77500 | | AM | RAF Shawbury | Approach/Tower (LARS and MATZ) |
| | | AM | RAF Ternhill | Approach |
| 120.80000 | | AM | Nationwide | Battle Of Britain Flight |
| | | AM | RAF Coningsby | Approach (LARS and MATZ) |
| 120.85000 | | AM | Ronaldsway, Isle of Man | Approach/Radar |

| Base | Mobile | Mode | Location | User and Notes |
|------|--------|------|----------|----------------|
| 120.90000 | | AM | Belfast (Aldergrove) | Approach/Radar |
| | | AM | RAF Benson | Zone |
| 120.92500 | | AM | Cork Airport | ATIS |
| | | AM | Fowlemere | Air/Ground |
| 120.97500 | | AM | Gloucestershire Airport | Radar |
| 121.00000 | | AM | RAF Woodvale | Approach |
| | | AM | Sligo | Tower/AFIS |
| 121.02500 | | AM | London (Gatwick) | ATIS |
| 121.05000 | | AM | Leeds/Bradford Airport | Radar |
| 121.07500 | | AM | Cheltenham Racecourse | Heliport |
| | | AM | Duxford | Air Display Channel |
| | | AM | North Weald | Fighter Grouping meet |
| 121.07500 | | AM | Silverstone | Air/Ground |
| 121.10000 | | AM | Dublin Airport | Approach |
| | | AM | Henlow | Air/Ground |
| | | AM | RAF Odiham | Odiham Information |
| 121.17500 | | AM | North Weald | Display frequency |
| 121.20000 | | AM | Edinburgh Airport | Approach/Radar |
| 121.22500 | | AM | West Drayton | London Control |
| 121.25000 | | AM | Aberdeen (Dyce Airport) | Radar |
| 121.27500 | | AM | West Drayton | London Control |
| 121.30000 | | AM | Glasgow | Radar |
| | | AM | Lochaber | Air Ambulance |
| 121.32500 | | AM | West Drayton | London Control TMA |
| 121.35000 | | AM | Manchester Airport | Radar |
| 121.40000 | | AM | Shannon Airport | Approach |
| 121.50000 | | AM | Nationwide | Civil Aviation Distress Channel |
| | | AM | Nationwide | Distress & Emergency |
| 121.60000 | | AM | Aberdeen (Dyce Airport) | Fire Channel |
| | | AM | Birmingham International | Fire Service |
| | | AM | East Midlands Airport | Fire Service |
| | | AM | Kerry | Ground |
| | | AM | Manchester | Fire Service |
| | | AM | Nationwide | Airfield Fire & Rescue |
| 121.70000 | | AM | Aberdeen (Dyce Airport) | Ground |
| | | AM | Bournemouth (Hurn) | Ground |
| | | AM | Cork Airport | Tower |
| | | AM | Coventry Airport | Ground |
| | | AM | Glasgow | Ground |
| | | AM | Manchester Airport | Delivery/Ground |
| | | AM | Shannon | Clearance Delivery |
| 121.72500 | | AM | Stansted | Ground |
| 121.75000 | | AM | Belfast (Aldergrove) | Ground |
| | | AM | Blackpool | ATIS |
| | | AM | Edinburgh Airport | Ground |
| | | AM | Luton Airport | Ground |
| | | AM | Oxford (Kidlington Airport) | ATIS |
| | | NFM | Space | Soyuz Space Station/Mir |
| 121.77500 | | AM | Wycombe Air Park (Booker) | Ground |
| 121.80000 | | AM | Birmingham International | Ground |
| | | AM | Cork Airport | Ground |
| | | AM | Dublin Airport | Ground |
| | | AM | Guernsey | Ground |
| | | AM | London (Gatwick) | Ground |
| | | AM | Prestwick Airport | Ground |
| | | AM | Shannon Airport | Ground |

| Base | Mobile | Mode | Location | User and Notes |
|---|---|---|---|---|
| 121.80000 | | AM | Southend Airport | ATIS |
| 121.85000 | | AM | Aberdeen (Dyce Airport) | ATIS |
| | | AM | Manchester Airport | Ground |
| | | AM | Wroughton | PFA Delivery |
| 121.87500 | | AM | Biggin Hill | ATIS |
| | | AM | Cranfield | Approach/ATIS |
| | | AM | Dublin Airport | Delivery |
| 121.90000 | | AM | Connaught (Knock) Airport | Ground |
| | | AM | East Midlands Airport | Ground |
| | | AM | Jersey Airport | Ground |
| | | AM | London (Heathrow) | Ground |
| 121.92500 | | AM | Redhill | Ground (Airshows only) |
| 121.92500 | | AM | Wroughton | PFA Ground |
| 121.95000 | | AM | Bournemouth (Hurn) | ATIS |
| | | AM | London (Gatwick) | Delivery |
| | | AM | Oxford (Kidlington Airport) | Ground |
| | | AM | RAF Cosford | Ground |
| 121.97500 | | AM | London (Heathrow) | Delivery |
| 122.00000 | | AM | Baldonnel, Eire | Approach |
| | | AM | Coventry Airport | Radar |
| | | AM | Lashenden (Headcorn) | Air/Ground |
| | | AM | North Sea | BP Buchan Field |
| | | AM | North Sea | BP Cyprus Field |
| | | AM | North Sea | BP Forties Field |
| | | AM | North Sea | BP Gyda Field |
| | | AM | North Sea | Caister Oil Field deck |
| | | AM | North Sea | Unity Oil Field deck |
| | | AM | RAF Mona | Air/Ground (weekends only) |
| 122.02500 | | AM | North Sea | Murdoch Oil Field deck |
| 122.05000 | | AM | Aberdeen (Dyce Airport) | British Airways |
| | | AM | Liverpool | Keenair Ops |
| | | AM | London | Jersey Air Ops |
| | | AM | Nationwide | Brymon Airways |
| | | AM | North Sea | Chevron Ninian Field log |
| | | AM | North Sea | Conoco Murchison Field deck |
| | | AM | North Sea | Ninian Field |
| | | AM | North Sea | Shell/Esso Auk Field |
| | | AM | North Sea | Shell/Esso Fulmar Field |
| | | AM | North Sea | Shell/Esso Kittiwake Field |
| | | AM | North Sea | Thistle Field deck |
| | | AM | Nottingham Aerodrome | Hutchins Crop Sprayers |
| | | AM | Southend | Heavilift Ops |
| | | AM | Stapleford | Aeromega Ops. (Helicopter ops) |
| 122.07500 | | AM | Duxford | Information |
| | | AM | Whitchurch (Tilstock) | Air/Ground |
| 122.10000 | | AM | Middle Wallop Army | Tower/Approach |
| | | AM | N of 56N | Fisheries Protection |
| | | AM | Nationwide | Military Tower Common |
| | | AM | RAF Benson | Approach |
| | | AM | RAF Church Fenton | Tower/Ground |
| | | AM | RAF Colerne | Approach/Tower |
| | | AM | RAF Coltishall | Approach/Tower |
| | | AM | RAF Coningsby | Approach/Tower and Ground |
| | | AM | RAF Cottesmore | Tower/Ground |
| | | AM | RAF Cranwell | Tower |
| | | AM | RAF Dishforth (also Army) | Approach/Tower and Ground |

| Base | Mobile | Mode | Location | User and Notes |
|------|--------|------|----------|----------------|
| 122.10000 | | AM | RAF Kinloss | Tower |
| | | AM | RAF Leeming | Tower |
| | | AM | RAF Leuchars | Tower/Ground |
| | | AM | RAF Linton-on-Ouse | Tower/Ground |
| | | AM | RAF Lossiemouth | Tower |
| | | AM | RAF Lyneham | Tower/Ground |
| | | AM | RAF Manston | Tower |
| | | AM | RAF Marham | Tower |
| | | AM | RAF Newton | Tower |
| | | AM | RAF Odiham | Tower |
| | | AM | RAF Shawbury | Tower |
| | | AM | RAF Spadeadam | SRE |
| | | AM | RAF St Athan | Tower |
| | | AM | RAF St Mawgan | Approach/Tower |
| | | AM | RAF Ternhill | Approach |
| | | AM | RAF Topcliffe | Approach/Tower |
| | | AM | RAF Valley | Tower |
| | | AM | RAF Wittering | Tower |
| | | AM | RNAS Culdrose | Tower |
| | | AM | RNAS Merryfield | Tower |
| | | AM | RNAS Portland | Tower |
| | | AM | RNAS Predannack | Tower |
| | | AM | RNAS Yeovilton | Tower |
| | | AM | USAF Fairford | Approach |
| | | AM | USAF Lakenheath | Tower |
| | | AM | Wattisham (Army Airfield) | Tower |
| 122.12500 | | AM | Aberporth (MoD) | AFIS |
| | | AM | Flotta Airfield | Tower |
| | | AM | Leicester Aerodrome | Air/Ground |
| | | AM | North Sea | Hamilton Argyll Field |
| 122.15000 | | AM | Aberporth | AFIS |
| 122.17500 | | AM | North Sea | Mobil Beryl Field |
| 122.17500 | | AM | Turweston Aerodrome | Air/Ground |
| 122.20000 | | AM | Cambridge Airport | Tower |
| | | AM | Gormanston, Eire | IAC Military Approach |
| | | AM | Haverfordwest Aerodrome | Air/Ground |
| | | AM | Huddersfield (Crossland Moor) | Air/Ground |
| 122.25000 | | AM | Caernarfon Aerodrome | Tower |
| | | AM | North Sea | Shell/Esso Brent Field |
| | | AM | Rochester Aerodrome | AFIS |
| 122.27500 | | AM | Nationwide | CAA Calibrator Aircraft |
| 122.30000 | | AM | Alderney | Aurigny Airlines |
| | | AM | Baldonnel, Eire | IAC Military Radar |
| | | AM | Blackbushe | AFIS and Air/Ground |
| | | AM | Nationwide | Aircraft Exercise frequency |
| | | AM | Peterborough (Sibson) | Approach/Radar |
| 122.32500 | | AM | North Sea | Hamilton Esmond Field |
| | | AM | North Sea | Hamilton Forbes Field |
| | | AM | North Sea | Hamilton Gordon Field |
| 122.35000 | | AM | Audley End | Air/Ground |
| | | AM | Brooklands | Air/Ground |
| | | AM | Cardiff Airport | Operations |
| | | AM | East Midlands Airport | Air Bridge Carriers Ops |
| | | AM | Edinburgh Airport | Execair Operations |
| | | AM | Glasgow | Execair |
| | | AM | Grimsby (Cuxwold) | Air/Ground |

| Base Mobile | Mode | Location | User and Notes |
|---|---|---|---|
| 122.35000 | AM | Guernsey | Aurigny Air Services |
| | AM | Hethel | Air/Ground |
| | AM | Hitchin (Rush Green) | Air/Ground |
| | AM | Liverpool | Cheshire Air Training Ops |
| | NFM | Lochaber | PLM Helicopters |
| | AM | London (Heathrow) | Gulf Air Terminal 3 |
| | AM | Luton Airport | Reed Aviation |
| | AM | Manchester | Air Kilroe Ops |
| | AM | North Sea | Total Alwyn Field |
| | AM | Teesside Airport | Air Cam |
| 122.37500 | AM | Humberside | Bond Helicopters |
| | AM | Morecambe Bay BP Field | Helicopters |
| | AM | North Sea | BP Magnus Field Deck |
| | AM | Peterhead/Longside | Air/Ground Bond Helicopters |
| | AM | Plockton Airfield | Air/Ground |
| | AM | Strubby Heliport | Air/Ground |
| 122.39500 | AM | North Sea | Magnus BP |
| 122.40000 | AM | Bantry, Eire | Air/Ground |
| | AM | Dounreay Aerodrome | Tower |
| | AM | Elstree Aerodrome | Air/Ground/AFIS |
| | AM | Scatsa Aerodrome | Radar |
| | AM | Weston (Dublin) | Air/Ground |
| 122.42500 | AM | Earls Colne | Air/Ground |
| 122.45000 | AM | Chichester | Military Police Helicopter Ops |
| | AM | Chichester (Goodwood) | AFIS |
| | AM | North Sea | Claymore & Tartan |
| | AM | North Sea | Occidental Claymore Field |
| | AM | North Sea | Piper Oil Field deck |
| | AM | North Sea | Saltire Oil Field deck |
| | AM | North Sea | Texaco Tartan Field |
| | AM | Sleap Aerodrome | Air/Ground |
| | AM | Wickenby Aerodrome | Air/Ground |
| 122.47500 | AM | Nationwide | Hot Air Ballooning |
| 122.50000 | AM | Bitteswell Aerodrome | Air/Ground |
| | AM | Farnborough (RAE Airfield) | Tower |
| | AM | Galway | Air/Ground and AFIS |
| | AM | Llanbedr (MoD) | Tower/Radar |
| | AM | Weston-super-Mare | Tower |
| 122.52500 | AM | Ashcroft Farm | Air/Ground |
| | AM | North Sea | Hamilton Pipe Field |
| | AM | North Sea | Judy Oil Field deck |
| | AM | North Sea | Clyde Oil Field deck |
| 122.55000 | AM | Dunsfold Aerodrome | Radar |
| | AM | USAF Mildenhall | Tower |
| | AM | West Freugh (MoD) | Tower |
| 122.60000 | AM | Abbeyshrule, Eire | Air/Ground |
| | AM | Castlebar, Eire | Air/Ground |
| | AM | Inverness Airport | Approach/Tower |
| | AM | Lerwick (Tingwall) | Air/Ground and Air Ambulance |
| | AM | Plymouth City Airport | Tower |
| | AM | Seething Aerodrome | Air/Ground |
| | AM | Sherburn-in-Elmet | Tower |
| | AM | White Waltham | Air/Ground |
| 122.62500 | AM | North Sea | Conoco Viking Field |

| Base | Mobile | Mode | Location | User and Notes |
|------|--------|------|----------|----------------|
| 122.65000 | | AM | North Sea | Nelson Oil Field deck |
| | | AM | Duxford | Ops |
| | | AM | Scotland | Bonzai Sqn Air-Air |
| 122.70000 | | AM | Barton Aerodrome | Air/Ground |
| | | AM | Bodmin | Tower |
| | | AM | Compton Abbas | Air/Ground |
| | | AM | Gormanston, Eire | IAC Military Tower |
| | | AM | Northampton (Sywell) | AFIS |
| | | AM | Silverstone | Tower |
| | | AM | Tiree | AFIS |
| 122.72500 | | AM | Filton (BAe), Bristol | Approach/Radar |
| 122.75000 | | AM | Cowden Range | Range Control |
| | | AM | Netheravon (Army) | Air/Ground (Salisbury Plain) |
| | | AM | North Coates | Air/Ground Donna Nook Range |
| | | AM | Salisbury Plain (Army) | Ops |
| 122.77500 | | AM | Crowfield Aerodrome | Air/Ground |
| | | AM | North Sea | Scott Oil Field deck |
| | | AM | Oaksey Park | Air/Ground |
| 122.80000 | | AM | Baldonnel, Eire | Area Control |
| | | AM | North Sea | Unionoil Heather Field |
| | | AM | Nottingham Aerodrome | Air/Ground |
| | | AM | Stapleford | Air/Ground |
| 122.82500 | | AM | Bruntingthorpe | Air/Ground |
| 122.85000 | | AM | Cranfield | Approach |
| 122.87500 | | AM | North Sea | Excalibur Oil Field deck |
| | | AM | North Sea | Galahad Oil Field deck |
| | | AM | North Sea | Guinevere Oil Field deck |
| | | AM | North Sea | Lancelot Oil Field deck |
| | | AM | North Sea | Phillips Hewett Field |
| 122.90000 | | AM | Dundee | Approach Tower |
| | | AM | Gloucestershire Airport | Tower |
| | | AM | Kilkenny | Air/Ground |
| | | AM | London, Westland Heliport | Tower (Battersea) |
| | | AM | Long Marston Aerodrome | Tower |
| 122.92500 | | AM | Fenland | Air/Ground and AFIS |
| | | AM | North Sea | Phillip Ekofisk Field |
| 122.95000 | | AM | Aberdeen (Dyce Airport) | Bristow Helicopters |
| | | AM | Birr Aerodrome, Eire | Air/Ground (Birr Radio) |
| | | AM | London | Air Ambulance Ops |
| | | AM | Nationwide | Freemans Aviation |
| | | AM | North Sea | Eko/Tees Pip Oil Field deck |
| | | AM | North Sea | Kotter Oil Field deck |
| | | AM | North Sea | Logger Oil Field deck |
| | | AM | North Sea | Nam Nam Field |
| | | AM | North Sea | Nam Noordwinning |
| | | AM | North Sea | Penzoil Noordwinning |
| | | AM | North Sea | Petroland Petroland Field |
| | | AM | North Sea | Placid Placid Field |
| | | AM | North Sea | Zanddijk |
| 122.97500 | | AM | Marston Moor Aerodrome | Tower |
| 123.00000 | | AM | Connemara, Eire | Air/Ground |
| | | AM | Eaglescott | Air/Ground |
| | | AM | Halfpenny Green Aerodrome | FIS |
| | | AM | Inisheer, Eire | Air/Ground |
| | | AM | Inishman, Eire | Air/Ground |
| | | AM | Inishmore, Eire | Air/Ground |

| Base | Mobile | Mode | Location | User and Notes |
|------|--------|------|----------|----------------|
| 123.00000 | | AM | North Sea | Ivanhoe Oil Field deck |
| 123.02500 | | AM | North Sea | Hamilton Ravenspurnn North |
| | | AM | North sea | Gryphon Oil Field deck |
| 123.05000 | | AM | Beverley (Linley Hill) | Tower |
| | | AM | North Sea | Brent Oil Field log |
| | | AM | North Sea | North Cormorant log |
| | | AM | North Sea | Shell/Esso Eider Field log |
| | | AM | North Sea | Shell/Esso Tern Field log |
| | | AM | North Sea | South Cormorant log |
| | | AM | Nuthampstead, Royston | Air/Ground |
| | | AM | Old Warden (Biggleswade) | Tower (Display days only) |
| | | AM | RAF Leconfield | Leconfield Rescue |
| | | AM | Stevenage Aerodrome | British Aerospace |
| | | AM | Wigtown | Tower |
| 123.10000 | | AM | Baldonnel, Eire | Ground |
| | | AM | Nationwide | Search and Rescue |
| | | AM | RAF Boulmer | Boulmer Rescue |
| | | AM | Scotland | Air Mountain Rescue |
| 123.15000 | | AM | Fair Isle | Approach (Sumburgh) |
| | | AM | Humberside Airport | Radar |
| | | AM | Islay Airport | AFIS |
| | | AM | Scilly Isles (St. Marys) | Approach/Tower |
| | | AM | Shoreham Aerodrome | Approach/Tower |
| | | AM | Sumburgh Airport | Approach/Radar |
| 123.17500 | | AM | Badminton | Air/Ground |
| 123.20000 | | AM | Barrow (Walney Island) | Air/Ground |
| | | AM | Enniskillen (St. Angelo) | FIS |
| | | AM | Old Sarum | Air/Ground |
| | | AM | St Angelo | Tower |
| | | AM | Fadmoor Aerodrome | Air/Ground |
| 123.22500 | | AM | North Sea | Arco Thames Field |
| | | AM | North Sea | Bruce Oil Field deck |
| 123.25000 | | AM | Bagby (Thirsk) | Air/Ground |
| | | AM | Bembridge, Isle of Wight | AFIS and Air/Ground |
| | | AM | Welshpool | Air/Ground |
| 123.27500 | | AM | Netherthorpe | Air/Ground |
| 123.30000 | | AM | Dublin Airport | Dublin Military ATC |
| | | AM | Manchester | ATC |
| | | AM | Nationwide | Military Airfield Radar |
| | | AM | RAF Benson | Radar |
| | | AM | RAF Brize Norton | Brize Talkdown |
| | | AM | RAF Church Fenton | Talkdown |
| | | AM | RAF Coltishall | Radar |
| | | AM | RAF Coningsby | Radar |
| | | AM | RAF Cottesmore | Talkdown |
| | | AM | RAF Cranwell | Talkdown |
| | | AM | RAF Honington | Approach |
| | | AM | RAF Kinloss | Radar |
| | | AM | RAF Leuchars | Tower/Radar |
| | | AM | RAF Linton-on-Ouse | Radar |
| | | AM | RAF Lyneham | Talkdown |
| | | AM | RAF Manston | Talkdown |
| | | AM | RAF Marham | Radar |
| | | AM | RAF Odiham | Talkdown |
| | | AM | RAF Shawbury | Talkdown |
| | | AM | RAF St Athan | Talkdown |

| Base | Mobile | Mode | Location | User and Notes |
|------|--------|------|----------|----------------|
| 123.30000 | | AM | RAF St Mawgan | Radar |
| | | AM | RAF Topcliffe | Talkdown |
| | | AM | RAF Valley | Director/Talkdown |
| | | AM | RAF Waddington | Radar |
| | | AM | RAF Wittering | Radar |
| | | AM | RNAS Culdrose | Tower/Talkdown |
| | | AM | RNAS Portland | Tower |
| | | AM | RNAS Yeovilton | Director/Talkdown |
| | | AM | Spanish Point, Eire | Air/Ground |
| | | AM | Trim, Eire | Air/Ground |
| | | AM | USAF Lakenheath | Radar |
| | | AM | Wattishan (Army Airfield) | Approach |
| 123.35000 | | AM | Hatfield Aerodrome | Approach |
| | | AM | Hawarden Aerodrome | Approach |
| 123.37500 | | AM | Morecambe Bay | British Gas Helicopters |
| | | AM | Prestwick | Scottish Control TMA |
| 123.40000 | | AM | Gt Yarmouth (N. Denes) | Approach, Tower and Air/Ground |
| | | AM | North Sea | Dab Duc Skjold Field |
| | | AM | RAF Lyneham | Radar (Zone) |
| | | AM | RAF St Mawgan | Tower |
| 123.42500 | | AM | Fairoaks | Tower and AFIS |
| 123.45000 | | AM | Cark | Cark Radio |
| | | AM | Errol Aerodrome | Drop Zone Control |
| | | AM | Mull | Mull Traffic |
| | | AM | Nationwide | Air-Air Common |
| | | AM | North Sea | Amoco Indefatigable Field |
| | | AM | North Sea | Marathon East Kinsale |
| | | AM | North Sea | Marathon West Kinsale |
| | | AM | North Sea | Rolf Oil Field deck |
| | | AM | Unst (Saxavord) | Ops |
| 123.47500 | | AM | Dunkeswell Aerodrome | Air/Ground |
| 123.50000 | | AM | Baldonnel, Eire | Tower |
| | | AM | Berwick-on-Tweed (Winfield) | Winfield Radio |
| | | AM | Eggesford Aerodrome | Tower |
| | | AM | Felthorpe Aerodrome | Tower |
| | | AM | Newtownards | Air/Ground |
| | | AM | Sandown, Isle of Wight | Air/Ground |
| | | AM | Shobdon Aerodrome | Air/Ground |
| | | AM | Stornoway Airport | Approach/Tower and AFIS |
| | | AM | Swanton Morley | Air/Ground |
| 123.52500 | | AM | North Weald | Air/Ground |
| 123.55000 | | AM | North Sea | Captian Oil Field deck |
| | | AM | North Sea | Sun Balmoral Field |
| 123.57500 | | AM | North Sea | Tiffany Oil Field deck |
| 123.60000 | | AM | Belmullet, Eire | AFIS and Air/Ground |
| | | AM | Cambridge Airport | Approach |
| | | AM | Carlisle Airport | Approach/Tower and Air/Ground |
| | | AM | Rathkenny | Air/Ground (Rathkenny Radio) |
| | | AM | Scatsa Aerodrome | Approach/Tower |
| 123.62500 | | AM | Ballykelly | Approach (Eglinton)ATZ |
| | | AM | Londonderry | Approach |
| | | AM | North Sea | Amoco Indefatigable Field |
| | | AM | North Sea | Amoco Leman Field |
| | | AM | North Sea | Bessemer Oil Field deck |
| | | AM | North Sea | Camelott Oil Field deck |
| | | AM | North Sea | Davey Oil Field deck |

| Base | Mobile | Mode | Location | User and Notes |
|------|--------|------|----------|----------------|
| 123.62500 | | AM | North Sea | Shell/Esso Indefatigable |
| | | AM | North Sea | Shell/Esso Leman Field |
| | | AM | North Sea | Shell/Esso Sean Field |
| | | AM | North Sea | Thames Oil Field deck |
| | | AM | Walton Wood | Air/Ground |
| 123.65000 | | AM | Hatfield Aerodrome | Hatair Ops |
| | | AM | Hayes Heliport | Air/Ground (Macline Hayes) |
| | | AM | London (Heathrow) | British Airways |
| | | AM | Nationwide | Brymon Airways |
| | | AM | North Sea | Beatrice Field deck |
| | | AM | North Sea | Brae Oil Field deck |
| | | AM | North Sea | East Brae Oil Field deck |
| | | AM | S of 56N | Fisheries Protection |
| 123.72500 | | AM | Epson Aerodrome | Tower |
| 123.75000 | | AM | Leeds/Bradford Airport | Approach |
| 123.77500 | | AM | Prestwick | Scottish Control |
| 123.80000 | | AM | Stansted | Tower |
| 123.87500 | | AM | North Sea | Maureen Oil Field deck |
| 123.90000 | | AM | London (Heathrow) | ATIS |
| 123.92500 | | AM | Little Staughton | Air/Ground |
| 123.95000 | | AM | Shannon | Shanwick Oceanic ACC |
| 124.00000 | | AM | East Midlands Airport | Tower |
| 124.02500 | | AM | Wellesbourne Mountford | Air/Ground |
| 124.05000 | | AM | Prestwick | Scottish Control |
| 124.07500 | | AM | Tatenhill Aerodrome | Air/Ground |
| 124.10000 | | AM | Cardiff Airport | Radar |
| | | AM | Kerry | Tower |
| 124.12500 | | AM | Humberside Airport | ATIS |
| 124.15000 | | AM | Little Snoring Aerodrome | Air/Ground |
| | | AM | Nationwide | Army Helicopter Common |
| | | AM | RAF Marham | Approach |
| | | AM | RAF Ternhill | Army Approach |
| | | AM | RNAS Portland | Approach (LARS and MATZ) |
| 124.20000 | | AM | Manchester Airport | Manchester Air Traffic Control |
| 124.22500 | | AM | London (Gatwick) | Tower |
| 124.25000 | | AM | Norwich Airport | Tower |
| 124.27500 | | AM | West Drayton | London Control |
| 124.32500 | | AM | Dunsfold Aerodrome | Tower |
| 124.35000 | | AM | Bristol Airport | Radar |
| 124.37500 | | AM | Newcastle | Approach/Radar |
| 124.45000 | | AM | North Sea | Tyra Oil Field deck |
| | | AM | Warton (BAe) | Radar |
| 124.47500 | | AM | London (Heathrow) | Stand-by Ground |
| 124.50000 | | AM | Guernsey | Radar |
| | | AM | Prestwick | Scottish Control |
| 124.52500 | | AM | Dublin | ATIS |
| 124.60000 | | AM | West Drayton | London Control FIR Information |
| 124.65000 | | AM | Dublin Airport | Area Control Centre (South Sector)/Radar |
| 124.67000 | | AM | Hull (Mount Airy) | Approach (Humberside) |
| 124.67500 | | AM | Humberside Airport | Approach/Radar |
| 124.70000 | | AM | Shannon | Shannon Control |
| 124.75000 | | AM | West Drayton | London Control Information |
| 124.80000 | | AM | Coventry Airport | Tower |
| 124.82500 | | AM | Prestwick | Scottish Control (0700-2145 Hrs) |
| 124.95000 | | AM | Chester Garrison | Army Helicopter |

| Base | Mobile | Mode | Location | User and Notes |
|------|--------|------|----------|----------------|
| 124.95000 | | AM | Hawarden Aerodrome | Tower |
| 124.97500 | | AM | RAF Northolt | Radar/Tower |
| 125.00000 | | AM | Cardiff Airport | Tower |
| 125.00000 | | AM | Dishforth | Approach |
| | | AM | RAF Topcliffe | Director |
| 125.10000 | | AM | Manchester Airport | Manchester Air Traffic Control |
| 125.17500 | | AM | North Sea | Markham Oil Field deck |
| | | AM | North Sea | Noordwinning Oil Field deck |
| | | AM | North Sea | Nordwinning/Zanddijk Oil Field deck |
| | | AM | North Sea | Petroland Oil Field deck |
| | | AM | North Sea | Placid Oil Field deck |
| 125.20000 | | AM | Jersey Airport | Air Traffic Control (Zone)/Radar |
| | | AM | Lasham | Approach (Farnborough) |
| | | AM | RAE Farnborough | Radar |
| | | AM | RAF Odiham | Approach |
| 125.30000 | | AM | Ronaldsway, Isle of Man | Radar |
| 125.32500 | | AM | Oxford (Kidlington Airport) | Approach |
| 125.35000 | | AM | Alderney | Tower |
| 125.35000 | | AM | RAF Waddington | Zone |
| 125.40000 | | AM | Shoreham Aerodrome | Tower (when directed) |
| | | AM | Yeovil (Westland) | Tower & Air/Ground (Judwin Radio) |
| 125.47500 | | AM | West Drayton | London Control Information |
| 125.50000 | | AM | RAF Faiford | International Air Tattoo Base Ops |
| 125.55000 | | AM | RAF St Mawgan | Approach |
| | | AM | Stansted | Tower |
| 125.60000 | | AM | Bournemouth (Hurn) | Tower |
| 125.62500 | | AM | London (Heathrow) | Radar |
| 125.65000 | | AM | Gloucestershire Airport | Approach |
| 125.67500 | | AM | Prestwick | Scottish Control |
| 125.72500 | | AM | Aberdeen (Dyce Airport) | Scottish VOLMET |
| | | AM | Belfast (Aldergrove) | Scottish VOLMET |
| | | AM | Edinburgh Airport | Scottish VOLMET |
| | | AM | Inverness Airport | Scottish VOLMET |
| | | AM | London (Heathrow) | Scottish VOLMET |
| | | AM | Prestwick Airport | Scottish VOLMET |
| | | AM | Stornoway Airport | Scottish VOLMET |
| | | AM | Sumburgh | Scottish VOLMET |
| 125.80000 | | AM | Wattisham (Army Airfield) | Approach |
| | | AM | West Drayton | London Control Radar Departure |
| 125.85000 | | AM | Cardiff Airport | Approach/Radar |
| | | AM | RAF St Athan | Approach |
| | | AM | Sumburgh Airport | ATIS |
| 125.87500 | | AM | London (Gatwick) | Radar |
| | | AM | RAF Northolt | Talkdown |
| 125.90000 | | AM | Campbeltown | Flight Information |
| | | AM | RAF Coltishall | Director |
| 125.95000 | | AM | Manchester Airport | Manchester Air Traffic Control |
| 126.02500 | | AM | Bristol Airport | ATIS |
| 126.05000 | | AM | Coventry | ATIS |
| 126.07500 | | AM | West Drayton | London Control |
| 126.10000 | | AM | Prestwick | Highland Radar |
| 126.15000 | | AM | Nationwide | RAF Flight Checker |
| 126.25000 | | AM | Prestwick | Scottish Control (Information) |
| 126.27500 | | AM | Birmingham International | ATIS |

| Base | Mobile | Mode | Location | User and Notes |
|------|--------|------|----------|----------------|
| 126.30000 | | AM | Prestwick | Scottish Control (2145-0700 Hrs) |
| | | AM | West Drayton | London Control Inbound |
| 126.35000 | | AM | Canterbury | Traffic information (Manston) |
| | | AM | RAF Manston | Approach/Radar (LARS/MATZ) |
| 126.45000 | | AM | RAF Northolt | Approach |
| 126.50000 | | AM | RAF Brize Norton | Tower/Ground |
| | | AM | RAF Church Fenton | Approach (MATZ) |
| | | AM | RAF Leuchars | Approach (LARS and MATZ) |
| | | AM | RAF St Mawgan | Approach (LARS and MATZ) |
| | | AM | USAF Fairford | Tower (Airshows Only) |
| 126.55000 | | AM | Wycombe Air Park | Tower/AFIS |
| 126.60000 | | AM | Blackpool | London VOLMET (North) |
| | | AM | East Midlands Airport | London VOLMET (North) |
| | | AM | Leeds/Bradford Airport | London VOLMET (North) |
| | | AM | Liverpool Airport | London VOLMET (North) |
| | | AM | London (Gatwick) | London VOLMET (North) |
| | | AM | Manchester Airport | London VOLMET (North) |
| | | AM | Newcastle Airport | London VOLMET (North) |
| | | AM | RAF West Drayton | London VOLMET (North) |
| | | AM | Ronaldsway, Isle of Man | London VOLMET (North) |
| | | AM | Teeside Airport | London VOLMET (North) |
| 126.65000 | | AM | Manchester Airport | Manchester Air Traffic Control |
| 126.70000 | | AM | Boscombe Down (MoD) | Radar |
| | | AM | Middle Wallop Army Airfield | Army Air/Ground |
| | | AM | Netheravon (Army) | Approach (ATZ) |
| 126.72500 | | AM | Luton Airport | Approach/Radar |
| 126.82500 | | AM | London (Gatwick) | Approach (Director) |
| 126.85000 | | AM | Prestwick | Scottish Control |
| 126.87500 | | AM | West Drayton | London Control Inbound |
| 126.92500 | | AM | Woodford | Approach/Tower |
| 126.95000 | | AM | Stansted | Radar |
| 127.00000 | | AM | Belfast (Aldergrove) | Dublin VOLMET |
| | | AM | Cork Airport | Dublin VOLMET |
| | | AM | Dublin Airport | Dublin VOLMET |
| | | AM | London (Gatwick) | Dublin VOLMET |
| | | AM | London (Heathrow) | Dublin VOLMET |
| | | AM | Manchester Airport | Dublin VOLMET |
| 127.05000 | | AM | Nationwide | CAA Test Flights |
| 127.10000 | | AM | West Drayton | London Control |
| 127.12500 | | AM | Prestwick Airport | ATIS (Information) |
| 127.15000 | | AM | RAF Benson | Approach |
| 127.17500 | | AM | Stansted | ATIS |
| 127.27500 | | AM | Prestwick | Scottish ACC (Information) |
| 127.35000 | | AM | RAF Waddington | Radar (LARS and MATZ) |
| | | AM | RNAS Yeovilton | Approach/Radar |
| | | AM | Yeovil | Radar (LAKS) |
| 127.42500 | | AM | West Drayton | London Control Upper Sector East |
| 127.45000 | | AM | West Drayton | London Military Northwest |
| 127.47500 | | AM | Gloucestershire Airport | ATIS |
| 127.50000 | | AM | Shannon Airport | ACC |
| 127.52500 | | AM | London (Heathrow) | Approach |
| 127.55000 | | AM | London (Heathrow) | Approach |
| 127.57500 | | AM | Deanethorpe | Approach |
| 127.62500 | | AM | London (Heathrow) | Approach |
| 127.65000 | | AM | Shannon Airport | Shanwick Oceanic ACC |
| | | AM | West Drayton | Oceanic Clearance (E of 30_W) |

| Base | Mobile | Mode | Location | User and Notes |
|---|---|---|---|---|
| 127.70000 | | AM | West Drayton | London Control |
| 127.72500 | | AM | Southend Airport | Approach/Tower |
| 127.75000 | | AM | Nationwide | Air UK Company Channel |
| | | AM | RAF Leeming | Approach/Director |
| 127.87500 | | AM | West Drayton | London Control |
| 127.90000 | | AM | Shannon | Shanwick Oceanic ACC (Shanwick Radio) |
| 127.95000 | | AM | London (City Airport) | Tower/ATIS |
| 127.97500 | | AM | Filton (BAe), Bristol | Approach/Radar |
| | | AM | Warton (BAe) | Ops |
| 128.02500 | | AM | London (City Airport) | Radar/City Radar |
| 128.10000 | | AM | St Kilda | Tower |
| 128.12500 | | AM | West Drayton | London Control North Sea |
| 128.15000 | | AM | Exeter Airport | Approach/Radar |
| 128.17500 | | AM | Manchester | ATIS |
| 128.20000 | | AM | Belfast (Aldergrove) | ATIS |
| 128.22500 | | AM | East Midlands Airport | ATIS |
| 128.25000 | | AM | West Drayton | London Military |
| 128.30000 | | AM | Aberdeen (Dyce Airport) | Radar |
| | | AM | Netheravon (Army) | Drop Zone Radio |
| | | AM | Netheravon (Army) | Tower |
| 128.32500 | | AM | Norwich Airport | Radar |
| 128.35000 | | AM | Newcastle Airport | Army Tower |
| 128.42500 | | AM | West Drayton | London Control |
| 128.50000 | | AM | Duxford | Air Display Channel |
| | | AM | Prestwick | Scottish Control (TMA) |
| 128.52500 | | AM | Sheffield City | AFIS |
| 128.55000 | | AM | Bristol Airport | Approach |
| | | AM | Clonbullogue, Eire | Air/Ground |
| 128.58750 | | AM | RAF West Drayton | London VOLMET (South) |
| 128.60000 | | AM | Birmingham International | London VOLMET (South) |
| | | AM | Bournemouth (Hurn) | London VOLMET (South) |
| | | AM | Bristol Airport | London VOLMET (South) |
| | | AM | Cardiff | London VOLMET (South) |
| | | AM | Jerset Airport | London VOLMET (South) |
| | | AM | Luton Airport | London VOLMET (South) |
| | | AM | Norwich Airport | London VOLMET (South) |
| | | AM | West Drayton | London VOLMET (South) |
| 128.65000 | | AM | Alderney | Approach (Guernsey) |
| 128.67500 | | AM | Manchester Airport | Pennine Radar |
| 128.70000 | | AM | West Drayton | London Military Radar |
| 128.75000 | | AM | Luton Airport | Approach/Radar |
| 128.77500 | | AM | RAF Manston | Tower |
| 128.85000 | | AM | Nationwide | Eastern Airlines Packet Ch |
| | | AM | Southampton Airport | Approach (as directed)/Radar |
| | | AM | Teesside Airport | Radar |
| 128.90000 | | AM | USAF Lakenheath | MATZ |
| 128.95000 | | AM | Southend Airport | Approach/Radar |
| 128.97500 | | AM | Edinburgh Airport | Radar |
| 129.00000 | | AM | Nationwide | Hang Gliders & Ballons |
| 129.02500 | | AM | London (Gatwick) | Radar Standby |
| 129.02500 | | AM | Nationwide | Air France Company Channel |
| 129.07500 | | AM | West Drayton | London Control |
| 129.10000 | | AM | West Drayton | London Control |
| 129.12500 | | AM | RAF Linton-on-Ouse | Approach (LARS and MATZ) |
| 129.15000 | | AM | RAF Linton-On-Ouse | Director/Radar and Departures |

| Base | Mobile | Mode | Location | User and Notes |
|------|--------|------|----------|----------------|
| 129.17500 | | AM | Dublin | Area Control Centre (North Sector) |
| 129.20000 | | AM | Nationwide | American Airlines Packet |
| | | AM | West Drayton | London Control |
| 129.22500 | | AM | Prestwick | Scottish Control |
| | | AM | Wroughton | PFA Circuit |
| 129.25000 | | AM | Nationwide | CAA Special Events |
| | | AM | USAF Fairford | Tower (Airshows Only) |
| 129.37500 | | AM | West Drayton | London Control |
| 129.40000 | | AM | Biggin Hill | Approach |
| 129.42500 | | AM | West Drayton | London Control |
| 129.47500 | | AM | RAF Lyneham | Ground |
| 129.50000 | | AM | Nationwide | Delta Airlines Packet Channel |
| 129.55000 | | AM | Luton Airport | Approach/Radar |
| 129.60000 | | AM | Nationwide | Delta Airlines Packet Channel |
| | | AM | West Drayton | London Control |
| 129.62500 | | AM | Nationwide | TWA Packet Frequency |
| 129.65000 | | AM | North Sea | Statfjord Oil Field deck |
| 129.70000 | | AM | Alderney | Trinity Lightship Heliport |
| | | AM | Baldonnel, Eire | IAC Military Radar |
| | | AM | Baldonnel, Eire | Radar |
| | | AM | Blackbushe | A.T.S. |
| | | AM | English Channel | Bishops Rock Trinity Lightship |
| | | AM | English Channel | Casquets Trinity Lightship |
| | | AM | English Channel | Flatholm Trinity Lightship |
| | | AM | English Channel | Hanois Trinity Lightship |
| | | AM | English Channel | Inner Dowsing Trinity L.ship |
| | | AM | English Channel | Longships Trinity Lightship |
| | | AM | English Channel | Lundy South Trinity Lightship |
| | | AM | English Channel | Round Island Trinity Lightship |
| | | AM | English Channel | Royal Sovereign Trinity Lightship |
| | | AM | English Channel | Skerries Trinity Lightship |
| | | AM | English Channel | Skokholm Trinity Lightship |
| | | AM | English Channel | Smalls Trinity Lightship |
| | | AM | English Channel | South Bishop Trinity Lightship |
| | | AM | English Channel | St Anns Head Trinity Lightship |
| | | AM | Glasgow | Northwest |
| | | AM | Jersey | Aviation Beauport Ops |
| | | AM | London (Heathrow) | Mam Aviation |
| | | AM | Nationwide | Britannia Ops |
| | | AM | Nationwide | Trinity House Helicopters |
| | | AM | North Sea | Amoco Arbroath Field |
| | | AM | North Sea | Amoco Montrose Field |
| | | AM | North Sea | Everest Oil Field deck |
| | | AM | North Sea | Gannet Oil Field deck |
| | | AM | North Sea | Lomond Oil Field deck |
| | | AM | Prestwick Airport | Ogden Aviation |
| | | AM | Southend | Express Flight |
| 129.72500 | | AM | Lewes (Deanland) | Air/Ground |
| | | AM | Peterborough (Conington) | Air/Ground |
| | | AM | Warton (BAe) | Radar |
| 129.75000 | | AM | Filton (BAe), Bristol | Rolls Royce Ops |
| | | AM | Nationwide | Air Express Ops |
| | | AM | Nationwide | BMA Ops |
| | | AM | Nationwide | Brymon Airways |
| | | AM | Nationwide | Loganair Ops |

| Base | Mobile | Mode | Location | User and Notes |
|------|--------|------|----------|----------------|
| 129.75000 | | AM | Nationwide | Manx Ops |
| | | AM | North Sea | Elf Aquataine Norge Frigg |
| | | AM | North Sea | Kewanee Nordsee Field |
| | | AM | North Sea | Total/Elf Frigg Field |
| | | AM | Norwich Airport | Air UK Ops |
| | | AM | Stansted | Servisair Ops |
| 129.77500 | | AM | North Sea | Lennox Oil Field deck |
| | | AM | North Sea | North Hamiton Oil Field deck |
| 129.80000 | | AM | Bourn Aerodrome | Air/Ground |
| | | AM | Breighton | Air/Ground |
| | | AM | Donegal (Carrickfinn),Eire | Tower/AFIS |
| | | AM | Popham Aerodrome | Popham Radio |
| | | AM | Truro Aerodrome | Air/Ground |
| 129.82000 | | AM | Esholt | Air/Ground (Esholt Radio Weekends) |
| 129.82500 | | AM | Cromer (Northrepps) | Air/Ground (Micro) |
| | | AM | Insch Airfield | Air/Ground |
| | | AM | Nationwide | Microlight Common |
| | | AM | Swindon (Draycott) | Air/Ground |
| 129.85000 | | AM | Chester Garrison | Army Helicopter Tower |
| | | AM | Waterford | Tower and AFIS |
| 129.87500 | | AM | Enstone Aerodrome | Air/Ground |
| | | AM | Hethersett Aerodrome | Hethersett Radio |
| | | AM | North Sea | Amethyst Field deck |
| | | AM | North Sea | BP Cleeton Field deck |
| | | AM | North Sea | BP Ravenspurn North Field deck |
| | | AM | North Sea | BP West Sole Field deck |
| | | AM | North Sea | British Gas Rough Field deck |
| | | AM | North Sea | West Sole Oil Field deck |
| 129.90000 | | AM | Cardiff | Tremorfa Heliport |
| | | NFM | Cockerham | Parachuting |
| | | AM | Coonagh, Eire | Air/Ground |
| | | AM | Langar Airfield | Drop Zone |
| | | AM | Lasham Aerodrome | Glider Ops |
| | | AM | Limerick (Coonagh) | Air/Ground |
| | | AM | Liskeard | Civil Heliport |
| | | AM | Nationwide | Air Ambulance |
| | | AM | Nationwide | Hang Gliding |
| | | AM | Nationwide | Hot Air Ballooning |
| | | NFM | Nationwide | RAC Network Q Medivac Helo |
| | | AM | Nationwide | RAF Formation Air to Air |
| | | AM | North Sea | Eider Oil Field deck |
| | | AM | North Sea | Phillips Eko/EMB Pipe Oil Field deck |
| | | AM | Pocklington | Base |
| | | AM | Strathallan Aerodrome | Air/Ground |
| 129.95000 | | AM | North Sea | North Cormorant Deck |
| | | AM | North Sea | Shell/Esso Dunlin Field deck |
| | | AM | North Sea | Shell/Esso Tern Field deck |
| | | AM | North Sea | South Cormorant Oil Field deck |
| | | AM | Shetland Basin | Viking Approach |
| | | AM | Sumburgh Airport | Helicopter Information |
| 129.97000 | | AM | Tibenham | Air/Ground |
| 129.97500 | | AM | Nationwide | Gliding |
| | | AM | North Sea | Helicopter Common |
| | | AM | North Weald | Gliders |
| | | AM | Rufforth, York | Air/Ground |

| Base Mobile | Mode | Location | User and Notes |
|---|---|---|---|
| 129.97500 | AM | Swansea Airport | ATC Glider Training |
| 130.00000 | AM | Boscombe Down (MoD) | Radar |
| 130.02500 | AM | Biggin Hill | Srikair |
| | AM | London | Capital Radio Flying Eye Ops |
| | AM | Nationwide | Dollar Air Metro |
| | AM | Southend | British World ops |
| | AM | Woodford | BAe Ops |
| 130.05000 | AM | Aberdeen (Dyce Airport) | Ground Staff |
| | AM | Farnborough (RAE Airfield) | Precision Approach Radar |
| | AM | Sumburgh | Radar |
| | AM | West Freugh (MoD) | Approach |
| | AM | Woodford | Tower |
| 130.07500 | AM | London (Gatwick) | Servisair Ops |
| | AM | London (Heathrow) | Air Malta Ops |
| | AM | RAF Brize Norton | Brize Ops |
| 130.10000 | AM | Bellarena | Air/Ground Gliders |
| | AM | Dishforth | Air/Ground Gliders |
| | AM | Long Marston Aerodrome | Tower |
| | AM | Nationwide | Gliders |
| | AM | Netheravon (Army) | Tower |
| | AM | Oban | Air/Ground |
| | AM | Perranporth | Glider Ops |
| | AM | Pocklington | Air/Ground glider ops |
| | AM | Spalding (Crowland) | Tower |
| | AM | Strubby Aerodrome | Air/Ground (Strubby Base) gliders |
| | AM | Tibenham | Air/Ground (Gliders) |
| 130.12500 | AM | Nationwide | Glider Training |
| | AM | Scarborough | Air/Ground Glider Ops |
| 130.15000 | AM | London (Heathrow) | Emirates Ops |
| | AM | Netheravon (Army) | Salisbury Plain Tower |
| 130.16250 | NFM | Space | Mir |
| 130.17500 | AM | Blackbushe | Air Lynton Ops |
| | AM | Blackpool | Janes Ops |
| | AM | Blackpool | Lynton Ops |
| | AM | Cambridge | Suckling Ops |
| | AM | Cambridge Airport | Magnet Air |
| | AM | Exeter | Markair Ops |
| | AM | Exeter Airport | Handling |
| | AM | Liverpool Airport | Emerald Ops |
| | AM | Liverpool Airport | Royal Mail Ops |
| | AM | London (Heathrow) | Ambassador Ops |
| | AM | London (Heathrow) | Corporate Jet Ops |
| | AM | London (Heathrow) | Gama Ops |
| | AM | Luton Airport | Magec Ops |
| | AM | Manchester | Ryan Air Ops |
| | AM | North Weald | Aceair Company Channel |
| 130.20000 | AM | Cottesmore | Approach (LARS and MATZ) |
| | AM | Langar Airfield | Approach |
| | AM | North Sea | Alwyn North Oil Field log |
| | AM | North Sea | Dunbar Oil Field deck |
| | AM | Peterborough (Sibson) | MATZ and LARS |
| | AM | RAF Chivenor | Air/Ground |
| | AM | RAF Cottesmore | Approach/Director |
| | AM | RAF Wittering | Radar |
| 130.25000 | AM | East Midlands | Donington Aviation |
| | AM | Hawarden Aerodrome | Radar |

| Base | Mobile | Mode | Location | User and Notes |
|------|--------|------|----------|----------------|
| 130.25000 | | AM | Henstridge | Tower |
| | | AM | Nationwide | American Airlines Packet |
| | | AM | RAF Benson | Tower/Zone |
| | | AM | Tresco | Civil Heliport |
| 130.30000 | | AM | Sturgate Aerodrome | Air/Ground |
| 130.35000 | | AM | RAF Northolt | Radar (Director) |
| | | AM | Unst (Saxavord) | Air/Ground |
| 130.37000 | | AM | Blackbushe | Air Hanson Ops |
| | | AM | Wick | Air/Ground (Far North) |
| 130.37500 | | AM | Farnborough | Executive Ops |
| | | AM | Manchester | FLS Engineering Ops |
| 130.40000 | | AM | Edinburgh Airport | Approach (gliders) |
| | | AM | Kilkenny | Air/Ground (Weekends) |
| | | AM | Nationwide | Gliders Channel |
| | | AM | Punchestown | Air/Ground (Parachute & Gliders) |
| | | AM | Spalding (Crowland) | Tower (gliders) |
| | | AM | Thirsk (Sutton Bank) | Air/Ground (gliders) |
| 130.42500 | | AM | Elmsett | Air/Ground (Elmsett Radio) |
| | | AM | Halton Aerodrome | Air/Ground |
| | | AM | Nationwide | SAR Incident |
| | | AM | Sandtoft Aerodrome | Tower |
| 130.45000 | | AM | Glenrothes | Air/Ground |
| | | AM | Skegness Aerodrome | Tower |
| | | AM | Thruxton Aerodrome | Air/Ground |
| 130.47500 | | AM | Retford | Air/Ground |
| 130.50000 | | AM | Castleforbes, Eire | Air/Ground |
| | | AM | Nationwide | Aquilla Spanish air display team Air-to-Air |
| 130.55000 | | AM | Andrewsfield | Air/Ground |
| | | AM | Brough Aerodrome | Tower and Air/Ground |
| | | AM | North Sea | Amoco Vauxhall Field |
| | | AM | North Sea | Phillips Albuskjell Field |
| | | AM | North Sea | Phillips Cod Field |
| | | AM | North Sea | Phillips Edda Field |
| | | AM | North Sea | Phillips Ekofisk Field |
| | | AM | North Sea | Phillips Eldfisk Field |
| | | AM | North Sea | Phillips Tor Field |
| | | AM | North Sea | Valhall Oil Field deck |
| 130.57500 | | AM | London (Gatwick) | Interflight Ops |
| | | AM | London (Heathrow) | Shell Ops |
| | | FM | Nationwide | Philips Airship Air to Ground |
| | | AM | Stansted | Universal Air Handling |
| 130.60000 | | AM | Aberdeen (Dyce Airport) | Air UK |
| | | AM | Aberdeen (Dyce Airport) | Servisair |
| | | AM | Belfast (Aldergrove) | Servisair |
| | | AM | Birmingham International | Servisair |
| | | AM | Blackpool | Servisair |
| | | AM | Bournemouth (Hurn) | Channel Express |
| | | AM | Bristol Airport | Servisair |
| | | AM | Cardiff Airport | Servisair |
| | | AM | Edinburgh Airport | Servisair |
| | | AM | Guernsey | Servisair |
| | | AM | Jersey | Servisair |
| | | AM | London (Gatwick) | British Caledonian |
| | | AM | London (Heathrow) | Fields Aviation Ops |
| | | AM | London (Heathrow) | Huntair |

| Base | Mobile | Mode | Location | User and Notes |
| --- | --- | --- | --- | --- |
| 130.60000 | | AM | Manchester | Servisair |
| | | AM | Nationwide | Brymon Airways Ops |
| | | AM | Nationwide | Delta Airlines Ops |
| | | AM | Nationwide | Servisair |
| | | AM | Newcastle | Servisair |
| | | AM | RAF Manston | KIA Ops |
| | | AM | Stansted | Air UK Leisure Ops |
| 130.62000 | | AM | Stapleford | Stapleford Ops |
| 130.62500 | | AM | Aberdeen (Dyce Airport) | Granite Ops |
| | | AM | Bristol Airport | Clifton Ops |
| | | AM | East Midlands Airport | Donington Aviation Ops |
| | | AM | Ronaldsway, Isle of Man | Island Aviation |
| | | AM | Southend Airport | British Air Ferries Ops |
| 130.65000 | | AM | Bournemouth (Hurn) | Services |
| | | AM | Foulsham Aerodrome | Tower |
| | | AM | Glasgow | Loganair Ops |
| | | AM | Glasgow | Maersk Ops |
| | | AM | Jersey | Company Ops |
| | | AM | Kyle of Lochalsh | Royal Navy Heliport |
| | | AM | London (Gatwick) | American Airlines |
| | | AM | London (Gatwick) | China Airlines |
| | | AM | London (Gatwick) | Handling |
| | | AM | London (Gatwick) | Korean Airlines |
| | | AM | London (Gatwick) | Northwest Orient |
| | | AM | Manchester | Aer Lingus Ops |
| | | AM | Manchester | Handling |
| | | AM | Manchester | LTU Ops |
| | | AM | Manchester | Northern Executive |
| | | AM | Newcastle | Samson Ops |
| | | AM | Skye | Tower |
| | | AM | Southampton Airport | Ops |
| 130.67500 | | AM | Duxford | Air Display Channel |
| 130.70000 | | AM | Connaught (Knock) Airport | Tower |
| | | AM | Land's End (St Just) | Tower/Approach and Air/Ground |
| | | AM | Wroughton | Tower |
| 130.72500 | | AM | Denham | Air/Ground and AFIS |
| | | AM | North Sea | FRG/STFS Pipe |
| | | AM | West Freugh (MoD) | Radar |
| 130.75000 | | AM | Belfast (City) | Tower |
| | | AM | Boscombe Down (MoD) | Tower/Ground |
| | | AM | Cambridge Airport | Radar |
| | | AM | Manchester | Aer Lingus Ops |
| | | AM | Woodford | Approach |
| 130.77500 | | AM | Braintree Airfield | Air/Ground |
| 130.80000 | | AM | English Channel | Fisheries Protection |
| | | AM | Hatfield Aerodrome | Tower |
| | | AM | Hucknall Aerodrome | Air/Ground |
| | | AM | North Sea | Amoco NW Hutton Deck |
| | | AM | North Sea | Conoco Hutton Deck |
| | | AM | Warton (BAe) | Tower |
| | | AM | Yeovil (Westland) | Approach/Radar (Judwin) |
| 130.85000 | | AM | Belfast (City) | Approach/Radar |
| | | AM | Little Gransden Aerodrome | Air/Ground |
| 130.87000 | | AM | North Sea | Kittiwake Oil Field deck |
| 130.87500 | | AM | North Sea | Alba Oil Field deck |
| | | AM | North Sea | Andrew Oil Field deck |

| Base | Mobile | Mode | Location | User and Notes |
|---|---|---|---|---|
| 130.92500 | | AM | West Drayton | London Control TMA |
| 130.95000 | | AM | Shannon Airport | ATIS |
| 131.00000 | | AM | Southampton Airport | Approach Southampton |
| 131.05000 | | AM | West Drayton | London Control Nort East UIR |
| 131.07500 | | AM | London (Gatwick) | Servisair |
| 131.10000 | | AM | Nationwide | British Airways Packet |
| 131.12500 | | AM | West Drayton | London Control |
| 131.15000 | | AM | Shannon | Shannon Control ACC (Cork sector) |
| 131.30000 | | AM | Prestwick | Scottish Control (Stornoway) |
| | | AM | Sumburgh Airport | Radar (N. Sea Offshore Advisory) |
| 131.37500 | | AM | Glasgow | Air Canada |
| 131.40000 | | AM | London (Heathrow) | Bangladesh Biman |
| | | AM | London (Heathrow) | CSA |
| | | AM | London (Heathrow) | Kenya Airways |
| | | AM | London (Heathrow) | Trans Mediterranean |
| | | AM | London (Heathrow) | Zambian Airlines |
| 131.42500 | | AM | Birmingham International | Allied |
| | | AM | Birmingham International | Ogden Aviation |
| | | AM | Dublin | British Midlands Ops |
| | | AM | London (Gatwick) | Air New Zealand Ops |
| | | AM | London (Gatwick) | Ogden Aviation Ops |
| | | AM | London (Gatwick) | Virgin Ops |
| | | AM | London (Heathrow) | British Midlands Ops |
| | | AM | London (Heathrow) | Royal Jordanian Ops |
| | | AM | London (Heathrow) | Saudia Ops |
| | | AM | Manchester | Cathay Pacific Ops |
| 131.45000 | | AM | London (Heathrow) | Aer Lingus Ops |
| | | AM | London (Heathrow) | Air Canada Ops |
| | | AM | London (Heathrow) | Air Malta Ops |
| | | AM | London (Heathrow) | Alitalia Ops |
| | | AM | London (Heathrow) | BWIA Ops |
| | | AM | London (Heathrow) | Cathay Pacific Ops |
| | | AM | London (Heathrow) | KLM Ops |
| | | AM | London (Heathrow) | Pakistan International Ops |
| | | AM | London (Heathrow) | Thai Airways Ops |
| | | AM | Prestwick Airport | Air Canada Ops |
| | | AM | Shannon | Servisair |
| 131.47500 | | AM | Dublin | Translift Ops |
| | | AM | London (Gatwick) | British Airways Maintence. |
| | | AM | London (Gatwick) | Caledonian Ops |
| | | AM | London (Heathrow) | All Nippon Ops |
| | | AM | London (Heathrow) | GB Airways Ops |
| | | AM | London (Heathrow) | Maersk Ops |
| | | AM | London (Heathrow) | Sabena |
| | | AM | London (Heathrow) | Speedbird Control North |
| | | AM | London (Heathrow) | TAT Ops |
| | | AM | Nationwide | Canadian Armed Forces |
| 131.50000 | | AM | Cork Airport | Aer Lingus Ops |
| | | AM | Dublin Airport | Aer Lingus |
| | | AM | London (Heathrow) | Air France Ops |
| | | AM | London (Heathrow) | British Airways Ops |
| | | AM | London (Heathrow) | Kuwait Airways Ops |
| 131.52500 | | AM | Luton Airport | London European Airways |
| | | AM | Luton Airport | Monarch Airlines |
| | | AM | Luton Airport | Ryan Air |
| | | AM | Manchester | American Ops |

| Base Mobile | Mode | Location | User and Notes |
|-------------|------|----------|----------------|
| 131.55000 | AM | Dublin | Ryanair Ops |
| | AM | London (Heathrow) | British Airways Parking |
| | AM | London (Heathrow) | Luxair Ops |
| | AM | London (Heathrow) | Ryanair Ops |
| | AM | London (Heathrow) | Springbok Ops |
| 131.57500 | AM | Belfast (Aldergrove) | British Midland |
| | AM | Birmingham International | Loganair |
| | AM | Birmingham International | TEA Operations |
| | AM | East Midlands Airport | British Midland |
| | AM | East Midlands Airport | Excalibur Ops |
| | AM | Edinburgh Airport | British Midland |
| | AM | Guernsey | British Midland Ops |
| | AM | Jersey | British Midland Jersey Ops |
| | AM | London (Heathrow) | Channnel Express Ops |
| | AM | London (Heathrow) | El Al |
| | AM | London (Heathrow) | Iran Air Ops |
| | AM | London (Heathrow) | Manx Ops |
| | AM | Plymouth City Airport | Brymon |
| 131.60000 | AM | East Midlands | UPS Ops |
| | AM | London (Gatwick) | City Flyer Ops |
| | AM | London (Gatwick) | TWA Ops |
| | AM | London (Heathrow) | Air Lines Ops |
| | AM | London (Heathrow) | Fields Ops |
| | AM | London (Heathrow) | TWA Ops |
| 131.62500 | AM | London (Gatwick) | British Caledonian |
| | AM | London (Gatwick) | Canadian Pacific Ops |
| | AM | London (Gatwick) (S. Terminal) | British Airways |
| | AM | London (Heathrow) | Royal Jordanian Ops |
| | AM | London (Heathrow) | Sabena |
| | AM | Portishead | Aero Radio Telephones |
| | AM | Shannon | Aerofolt Ops |
| 131.65000 | AM | London (Heathrow) | Air Malta Ops |
| | AM | London (Heathrow) | Japan Airlines Ops |
| | AM | London (Heathrow) | KLM Ops Terminal 4 |
| 131.67500 | AM | Luton Airport | Britannia Airways |
| 131.70000 | AM | Birmingham International | Air 2000 Ops |
| | AM | Glasgow | Air 2000 Ops |
| | AM | London (Gatwick) | Jetset Ops |
| | AM | London (Heathrow) | Air 2000 Ops |
| | AM | London (Heathrow) | Crossair Ops |
| | AM | London (Heathrow) | Delta Ops |
| | AM | London (Heathrow) | KLM |
| | AM | London (Heathrow) | SAS Ops |
| | AM | London (Heathrow) | Sabena |
| | AM | London (Heathrow) | Swissair Ops |
| | AM | Manchester | Air 2000 Ops |
| | AM | Manchester | SAS Ops |
| | AM | Manchester | Swissair Ops |
| 131.72500 | AM | Nationwide | ACARS Frequency |
| 131.75000 | AM | London (Gatwick) | Continental |
| | AM | London (Heathrow) | Aer Lingus Ops |
| | AM | London (Heathrow) | Air UK |
| | AM | London (Heathrow) | Kenya Airways |
| | AM | London (Heathrow) | Lufthansa Ops |
| | AM | London (Heathrow) | TAP Air Portugal |
| | AM | Manchester | Aer Lingus Ops |

| Base | Mobile | Mode | Location | User and Notes |
|------|--------|------|----------|----------------|
| 131.77500 | | AM | Birmingham International | Air Foyle |
| 131.77500 | | AM | London (Heathrow) | Aeroflot |
| | | AM | London (Heathrow) | British Airways Ops |
| | | AM | London (Heathrow) | CSA |
| | | AM | London (Heathrow) | Icelandair |
| | | AM | London (Heathrow) | JAT |
| | | AM | London (Heathrow) | Korean Air Ops |
| | | AM | London (Heathrow) | LOT |
| | | AM | London (Heathrow) | Malev |
| | | AM | London (Heathrow) | Olympic |
| | | AM | London (Heathrow) | Sabena |
| | | AM | Luton Airport | Air Foyle |
| | | AM | Luton Airport | BA Maintence |
| | | AM | Stansted | Air Foyle |
| 131.80000 | | AM | Edinburgh Airport | British Airways |
| | | AM | London (Heathrow) | British Airways |
| | | AM | Nationwide | Air to Air Common |
| | | AM | Nationwide | Fisheries Protection |
| 131.82500 | | AM | Dublin | Park Aviation |
| | | AM | Jersey | Company Ops |
| | | AM | London (Heathrow) | Cathay Pacific Ops |
| | | AM | London (Heathrow) | Federal Express Ops |
| | | AM | London (Heathrow) | Gibair Ops |
| 131.85000 | | AM | Aberdeen (Dyce Airport) | British Airways Ops |
| | | AM | Belfast (Aldergrove) | British Airways Ops |
| | | AM | Benbecula | British Airways Ops |
| | | AM | Birmingham International | Birmingham Executive |
| | | AM | Birmingham International | British Airways Ops |
| | | AM | Cork Airport | Aer Lingus Company Chan. |
| | | AM | Inverness Airport | British Airways Ops |
| | | AM | Jersey | British Airways Jersey Ops |
| | | AM | London (Heathrow) | Emirates Ops |
| | | AM | London (Heathrow) | Malaysian Airlines |
| | | AM | London (Heathrow) | United Ops |
| | | AM | London (Heathrow) | Zambian Airlines |
| | | AM | Manchester | British Airways Ops |
| | | AM | Nationwide | British Airways Ops |
| 131.87500 | | AM | London (Heathrow) | Quantas Ops |
| | | AM | Manchester | Euro Manx Ops |
| 131.90000 | | AM | London (Gatwick) | Air 2000 |
| | | AM | London (Heathrow) | British Airways Speedbird Ops |
| | | AM | London (Heathrow) | Conair Ops |
| | | AM | London (Heathrow) | South African Airlines |
| | | AM | London (Heathrow) | TAT Ops |
| | | AM | Prestwick Airport | Eastern Airlines Ops |
| 131.92500 | | AM | Birmingham International | Lufthansa |
| | | AM | London (Gatwick) | American Airlines |
| | | AM | London (Heathrow) | Air India Ops |
| | | AM | London (Heathrow) | American Airlines Maintence |
| | | AM | London (Heathrow) | American Ops |
| | | AM | London (Heathrow) | Lufthansa |
| | | AM | Manchester | Lufthansa |
| 131.95000 | | AM | Dublin | Aer Turas Ops |
| | | AM | London (Heathrow) | El Al |
| | | AM | London (Heathrow) | Federal Express |
| | | AM | London (Heathrow) | Iberia Airlines Ops |

| Base Mobile | Mode | Location | User and Notes |
| --- | --- | --- | --- |
| 131.95000 | AM | London (Heathrow) | MEA Ops |
| | AM | London (Heathrow) | Nigerian Airlines Ops |
| | AM | London (Heathrow) | Olympic Airways Ops |
| | AM | London (Heathrow) | Singapore Airlines Ops |
| | AM | London (Heathrow) | Viva Ops |
| | AM | Manchester | Federal Express |
| | AM | Nationwide | AAC Eagles Air to Air Secondary |
| | AM | Nationwide | Air France Company Channel |
| 131.97500 | AM | Glasgow | British Airways |
| | AM | London (Heathrow) | El Al |
| | AM | London (Heathrow) | Nigerian Airlines Ops |
| | AM | London (Heathrow) | United Ops |
| 132.05000 | AM | London (Heathrow) | Departure/TMA |
| 132.07500 | AM | Edinburgh Airport | ATIS |
| 132.15000 | AM | Shannon | Shannon Control ACC |
| 132.17500 | AM | Glasgow | ATIS |
| 132.20000 | AM | Prestwick | Reykjavik Oceanic (Polar Track) |
| | AM | West Drayton | Reykjavik Oceanic (Polar Tracks) |
| 132.32500 | AM | Full Sutton | Air/Ground |
| 132.35000 | AM | Filton (BAe), Bristol | Tower |
| 132.40000 | AM | Shoreham | ATIS |
| 132.45000 | AM | West Drayton | London Control |
| 132.55000 | AM | Luton Airport | Tower |
| 132.60000 | AM | West Drayton | London Control SW Approach |
| 132.65000 | AM | London (Heathrow) | Medivac |
| | AM | Nationwide | Royal Flights |
| | AM | RAF Northolt | Queen's Flight Ops |
| | AM | Swansea | Air Sea Rescue |
| 132.70000 | AM | London (City Airport) | Approach/Thames Radar |
| | AM | London (Heathrow) | Thames Radar |
| 132.72500 | AM | Prestwick | Scottish Control |
| 132.75000 | AM | Biggin Hill | Radar (Thames) |
| 132.80000 | AM | West Drayton | London Control (Bristol) |
| 132.90000 | AM | Manchester | Pennine Radar |
| | AM | RNAS Yeovilton | Display director |
| | AM | Wroughton | PFA Arrivals |
| 132.95000 | AM | West Drayton | London Control |
| 133.05000 | AM | Manchester Airport | Manchester Air Traffic Control |
| 133.07500 | AM | London (Heathrow) | ATIS |
| 133.17500 | AM | West Drayton | London Control |
| 133.20000 | AM | Prestwick | Scottish Information |
| 133.30000 | AM | West Drayton | London Military Radar |
| 133.40000 | AM | Manchester Airport | Manchester Air Traffic Control |
| 133.45000 | AM | West Drayton | London Control |
| 133.52500 | AM | West Drayton | London Control North Sea |
| 133.55000 | AM | Plymouth City Airport | Approach |
| 133.57500 | AM | North Sea | Clipper Oil Field deck |
| | AM | North Sea | Galleon Oil Field deck |
| 133.60000 | AM | West Drayton | London Control |
| 133.65000 | AM | Weston on the Green | Weston Radio |
| | AM | Wroughton | Tower |
| 133.67500 | AM | Prestwick | Scottish ACC (Entire Route) |
| 133.70000 | AM | West Drayton | London Control |
| 133.75000 | AM | RAF Brize Norton | Brize Director |
| 133.80000 | AM | Shannon Airport | North Altantic Track Broadcasts |
| | AM | West Drayton | Oceanic Track Broadcasts |

| Base | Mobile | Mode | Location | User and Notes |
|------|--------|------|----------|----------------|
| 133.85000 | | AM | Bristol Airport | Tower |
| 133.87500 | | AM | North Sea | Barque Oil Field deck |
| 133.90000 | | AM | West Drayton | London Military Brize Radar |
| 134.05000 | | AM | RNAS Culdrose | Approach/Radar |
| | | AM | RNAS Predannack | Culdrose Approach |
| 134.10000 | | AM | Aberdeen (Dyce) | Radar |
| | | AM | Prestwick | Highland Radar |
| 134.12500 | | AM | West Drayton | London Control |
| 134.15000 | | AM | Londonderry | Tower |
| | | AM | Shetland | Radar |
| 134.22500 | | AM | London (Gatwick) | Aproach/Radar |
| 134.25000 | | AM | West Drayton | London Control North Sea |
| 134.27500 | | AM | Shannon | ACC |
| 134.30000 | | AM | Kemble | Radar (Brize) |
| | | AM | Prestwick Airport | Scottish Military |
| | | AM | RAF Benson | Centralised Approach Control |
| | | AM | RAF Brize Norton | Brize Radar |
| | | AM | RAF Lyneham | Radar (Brize) |
| | | AM | USAF Fairford | Centralised Approach Control |
| 134.35000 | | AM | Farnborough (RAE Airfield) | Approach |
| | | AM | RAF Mona | Radar |
| | | AM | RAF Valley | Radar (LARS and MATZ) |
| 134.42500 | | AM | West Drayton | London Control Irish Sea |
| 134.45000 | | AM | London (Heathrow) | London Zone |
| | | AM | West Drayton | London Control (Hurn) |
| 134.47500 | | AM | Prestwick Airport | Scottish Military |
| 134.50000 | | AM | Filton (BAe), Bristol | Filton Ops |
| 134.60000 | | AM | Beccles Heliport | Air/Ground |
| 134.65000 | | AM | Nationwide | RAF Flight Checker |
| 134.75000 | | AM | West Drayton | London Control Upper Sector West |
| 134.77500 | | AM | Prestwick | Scottish Control |
| 134.80000 | | AM | Belfast (City) | Radar |
| | | AM | Biggin Hill | Tower |
| 134.85000 | | AM | Duxford | Air Display Channel |
| | | AM | Prestwick Airport | Scottish Air Traffic Control |
| 134.90000 | | AM | West Drayton | London Control |
| 134.92500 | | AM | Cranfield | Tower |
| 134.97500 | | AM | London (Heathrow) | Approach |
| | | AM | Nationwide | CAA Tests Flight |
| 135.00000 | | AM | Nationwide | CAA Tests Flight |
| 135.05000 | | AM | West Drayton | London Control |
| 135.15000 | | AM | RAF West Drayton | London Military Radar |
| 135.17500 | | AM | Aberdeen (Dyce Airport) | Information |
| | | AM | Dunsfold | Approach/Radar |
| 135.22500 | | AM | Shannon | Shannon Control Southern Sector |
| 135.25000 | | AM | West Drayton | London Control (Cardiff) |
| 135.27500 | | AM | RAF West Drayton | London Military Radar |
| 135.32500 | | AM | West Drayton | London Control (Cardiff) |
| 135.37500 | | AM | Dublin Airport | London VOLMET (Main) |
| | | AM | London (Gatwick) | London VOLMET (Main) |
| | | AM | London (Heathrow) | London VOLMET (Main) |
| | | AM | Manchester Airport | London VOLMET (Main) |
| | | AM | Stansted | London VOLMET (Main) |
| | | AM | West Drayton | London VOLMET (Main) |
| 135.40000 | | AM | Clacton Aerodrome | Air/Ground |
| 135.42500 | | AM | West Drayton | London Control |

| Base | Mobile | Mode | Location | User and Notes |
|---|---|---|---|---|
| 135.47500 | | AM | Nationwide | CAA Tests Flight |
| 135.52500 | | AM | Prestwick | Shanwick Oceanic (Clearances) |
| | | AM | Shannon Airport | Shanwick Oceanic ACC (Clearences) |
| 135.57500 | | AM | London (Gatwick) | Radar Standby |
| 135.60000 | | AM | Shannon Airport | ACC |
| 135.67500 | | AM | Prestwick Airport | Scottish Air Traffic Control |
| 135.70000 | | AM | Lee-on-Solent | Tower (Fleatlands) |
| 135.75000 | | AM | Farnborough | Air Show Approach |
| 135.75000 | | AM | Nationwide | CAA Tests Flight |
| 135.85000 | | AM | Prestwick | Scottish Control UIR |
| 135.95000 | | AM | Blackpool | Radar |
| 135.97500 | | AM | Liverpool Airport | Mail Flights (Air-Air) |
| | | AM | Nationwide | Army Air-Air |
| | | AM | Nationwide | Ryanair (Air-Air) |
| | | NFM | USAF Fairford | Silver Eagles Display Team |

### 136.0000 - 136.9750 MHz National & International Air Traffic Control Centres 25 kHz, Space Operations and Research, Meteorologictes

| Base | Mobile | Mode | Location | User and Notes |
|---|---|---|---|---|
| 136.05000 | | NFM | Nongeostationary | Canada Isis 1 |
| 136.08000 | | NFM | Nongeostationary | Canada Isis 2 |
| 136.10000 | | NFM | Nongeostationary | NASA Explorer 15 |
| 136.11000 | | NFM | Nongeostationary | NASA Explorer 35 |
| 136.11100 | | NFM | Nongeostationary | NASA Explorer 18 |
| 136.11200 | | NFM | Nongeostationary | France/US Ayame 2 |
| | | NFM | Nongeostationary | Japan MOS-1 |
| 136.12500 | | NFM | Nongeostationary | NASA Explorer 28 |
| 136.14100 | | NFM | Nongeostationary | NASA Explorer 34 |
| 136.14200 | | NFM | Nongeostationary | NASA Explorer 21 |
| 136.14500 | | NFM | Nongeostationary | NASA Explorer Series |
| 136.15900 | | NFM | Nongeostationary | Japan Ohsumi 1 |
| 136.16000 | | NFM | Nongeostationary | ESRO Aurorae |
| 136.17000 | | NFM | Nongeostationary | NASA Explorer 42 |
| | | NFM | Nationstationary | US Echo 2 |
| 136.17100 | | NFM | Nongeostationary | NASA Explorer 22 |
| 136.17500 | | NFM | USAF Fairford | Chilean Air Force Display Team |
| 136.20000 | | NFM | Nongeostationary | US Cameo 1 |
| | | NFM | Nongeostationary | US ERS 20 |
| | | NFM | Nongeostationary | US Injun SR3 |
| | | NFM | Nongeostationary | US Nimbus 2 |
| | | NFM | Nongeostationary | US SERT 2 |
| 136.22000 | | NFM | Nongeostationary | US OAO 1 |
| 136.23000 | | NFM | Nongeostationary | US ESSA 1 |
| 136.23100 | | NFM | Nongeostationary | US Tiros 9 |
| 136.23300 | | NFM | Nongeostationary | US Tiros 8 |
| 136.23400 | | NFM | Nongeostationary | US Tiros 7 |
| 136.25000 | | NFM | Nongeostationary | France Castor |
| 136.26000 | | NFM | Nongeostationary | NASA OV5-3 |
| 136.27300 | | NFM | Nongeostationary | NASA Explorer Series |
| 136.27500 | | NFM | Nongeostationary | NASA Explorer 26 |
| 136.29000 | | NFM | Nongeostationary | NASA Explorer 40 |
| | | NFM | Nongeostationary | NASA Hawkeye |
| 136.29300 | | NFM | Nongeostationary | NASA Explorer 25 |
| 136.30000 | | NFM | Nongeostationary | NASA SMS 1 |
| 136.31900 | | NFM | Nongeostationary | USAF GGSE 1 |

| Base | Mobile | Mode | Location | User and Notes |
|---|---|---|---|---|
| 136.32000 | | NFM | Nongeostationary | NASA GEOS 3 |
| | | NFM | Nongeostationary | USAF Ferret |
| 136.34820 | | NFM | Nongeostationary | Australia WRESAT 1 |
| 136.35000 | | NFM | Nongeostationary | France EOLE 1 |
| | | NFM | Nongeostationary | France FR 1 |
| | | NFM | Nongeostationary | USAF SR 11B |
| 136.38000 | | NFM | Nongeostationary | US ERS 27 |
| 136.41000 | | NFM | Nongeostationary | Canada Isis 1 |
| | | NFM | Nongeostationary | ITSO Intelsat |
| 136.41500 | | NFM | Nongeostationary | USAF ERS 6 |
| 136.43000 | | NFM | Nongeostationary | India Bhaskara |
| 136.44000 | | NFM | Nongeostationary | USAF ERS 15 |
| 136.46800 | | NFM | Nongeostationary | NASA SYNCOM 2 |
| 136.50000 | | NFM | Nongeostationary | NASA ATS Series |
| | | NFM | Nongeostationary | NASA Injun |
| | | NFM | Nongeostationary | NASA SR 3 |
| | | NFM | Nongeostationary | US NOAA 10 |
| 136.51000 | | NFM | Nongeostationary | NASA OVS 9 |
| 136.52100 | | NFM | Nongeostationary | US SOLRAD 11B |
| 136.53000 | | NFM | Nongeostationary | US OV 5-9 |
| | | NFM | Nongeostationary | US SOLRAD 11B |
| | | NFM | Nongeostationary | US Vela Hotel 8 |
| 136.56000 | | NFM | Nongeostationary | Germany GRS-A |
| 136.56300 | | NFM | Nongeostationary | US RADSAT 43 |
| 136.59000 | | NFM | Nongeostationary | Canada Alouette 1 |
| | | NFM | Nongeostationary | Canada Isis 1 & 2 |
| 136.60000 | | AM | West Drayton | London Ait Traffic Control (standby) |
| 136.61000 | | NFM | Nongeostationary | ESA Arian LO3 |
| | | NFM | Nongeostationary | ESA CAT 1 |
| 136.62000 | | NFM | Nongeostationary | Italy Sirio 1 |
| | | NFM | Nongeostationary | USAF OV 5 |
| 136.63000 | | NFM | Nongeostationary | France Signe 3 |
| 136.65000 | | AM | Manchester | Ringway Handling |
| | | NFM | Nongeostationary | US TRAAC |
| | | NFM | Nongeostationary | US Transit 5B5 |
| | | NFM | Nongeostationary | USAF OV 5-5 |
| 136.65100 | | NFM | Nongeostationary | USAF SN-43 |
| 136.67800 | | NFM | Nongeostationary | US SMS |
| 136.69400 | | NFM | Nongeostationary | Japan Shinsei |
| 136.69500 | | NFM | Nongeostationary | Japan Jiki'ken |
| 136.71000 | | NFM | Nongeostationary | US OSO-4 |
| 136.71200 | | NFM | Nongeostationary | US OGO-2 |
| 136.71300 | | NFM | Nongeostationary | Japan Tansei |
| | | NFM | Nongeostationary | NASA OSO-2 |
| 136.72500 | | NFM | Nongeostationary | Japan CORSA B |
| 136.74000 | | NFM | Nongeostationary | France ERS-A |
| 136.76800 | | NFM | Nongeostationary | ESA ERS-17 ORS3 |
| 136.77000 | | NFM | Nongeostationary | US NOAA 6 |
| | | NFM | Nongeostationary | US NOAA 8 |
| | | NFM | Nongeostationary | US NOAA 9 |
| 136.77100 | | NFM | Nongeostationary | USAF ERS-13 TRS6 |

| Base | Mobile | Mode | Location | User and Notes |
|---|---|---|---|---|

**136.8000 - 136.9750 MHz   INTERNATIONAL OPERATIONS & DATALINKS**
**25 kHz (SIMPLEX)**

| Base | Mode | Location | User and Notes |
|---|---|---|---|
| 136.80000 | AM | Manchester Airport | Airtours Ops |
| | AM | Manchester Airport | Tourjet Ops |
| | AM | Nationwide | Kestrel Ops |
| 136.80100 | NFM | Nongeostationary | USAF SOLRAD 7B |
| 136.80400 | NFM | Nongeostationary | US EGRS SECOR |
| 136.80970 | NFM | Nongeostationary | Japan UME 1 & 2 |
| 136.81000 | NFM | Nongeostationary | Japan ETS-1 KIKU |
| 136.82500 | AM | Dublin | City Jet Ops |
| | AM | London (City Airport) | City Jet Ops |
| | AM | Manchester | American Airlines Ops |
| | AM | Nationwide | Dutch Ops |
| 136.83000 | NFM | Nongeostationary | USAF EGRS 8 |
| | NFM | Nongeostationary | USAF ERS 28 |
| 136.84000 | NFM | Nongeostationary | USAF EGRS 9 |
| | NFM | Nongeostationary | USAF TOPO 1 |
| 136.85000 | AM | East Midlands Airport | UPS Ops |
| 136.86000 | NFM | Nongeostationary | NASA IUE TETR 2 |
| | NFM | Nongeostationary | NASA RMS |
| | NFM | Nongeostationary | US ERS 21 |
| | NFM | Nongeostationary | USA Landsat 2 |
| | NFM | Nongeostationary | USAF Cannonball 2 |
| | NFM | Nongeostationary | USAF OV5-4 |
| 136.87000 | NFM | Nongeostationary | US Injun 3 |
| 136.87500 | AM | London (Gatwick) | Monarch Airlines Ops |
| | AM | Luton Airport | Monarch Airlines Ops |
| | AM | Manchester | Monarch Airlines Ops |
| | AM | Nationwide | Monarch Airlines Ops |
| 136.88700 | NFM | Nongeostationary | USAF SOLRAD 7A |
| 136.89000 | NFM | Nongeostationary | NASA Explorer 47 |
| | NFM | Nongeostationary | USAF ERS 9 TRS4 |
| | NFM | Nongeostationary | USAF SOLRAD 6 |
| 136.89100 | NFM | Nongeostationary | USAF ERS 9 |
| 136.89200 | NFM | Nongeostationary | USAF ERS 5 |
| 136.91900 | NFM | Nongeostationary | US Tiros 9 |
| 136.92000 | NFM | Nongeostationary | USAF OSO 8 |
| | NFM | Nongeostationary | USAF SERT 28 |
| 136.95000 | NFM | Nongeostationary | ESA COS B1 |
| 136.97500 | AM | London (Heathrow) | British Airways Speedbird Ops |
| | AM | London (Heathrow) | Conair Ops |
| | AM | London (Heathrow) | South African Airlines |
| | AM | London (Heathrow) | TAT Ops |
| | AM | Nationwide | Sharks Helicopter Displays |
| 137.04000 | NFM | Nongeostationary | USAF Ferret |
| 137.08000 | NFM | Nongeostationary | ESA Meteorsat 1/2 |
| 137.11000 | NFM | Nongeostationary | US ATS 6 |
| 137.14000 | NFM | Nongeostationary | ERS ECS 2 |
| 137.15000 | NFM | Nongeostationary | USSR Meteor |
| 137.17000 | NFM | Nongeostationary | ERS MARECS A |
| | NFM | Nongeostationary | France MAROTS |
| 137.19000 | NFM | Nongeostationary | US GEOS 3 |
| 137.20000 | NFM | Nongeostationary | USSR Meteor |
| | AM | USAF Lakenheath | Dep Con |
| 137.23000 | NFM | Nongeostationary | India/USSR Bhaskara 2 |

| Base | Mobile | Mode | Location | User and Notes |
|------|--------|------|----------|----------------|
| 137.23000 | | NFM | Nongeostationary | US NOAA 61 |
| 137.26000 | | NFM | Nongeostationary | US OAO-A2 |
| 137.30000 | | NFM | Nongeostationary | US Meteor 2-17 |
| | | NFM | Nongeostationary | US Meteor 3-2 |
| | | NFM | Nongeostationary | US Timation 2 |
| | | NFM | Nongeostationary | USSR Meteor 2-18 |
| | | NFM | Nongeostationary | USSR Meteor 2-5 |
| 137.38000 | | NFM | Nongeostationary | USAF OVS 3 |
| 137.40000 | | NFM | Nongeostationary | USAF SMS-2 |
| | | NFM | Nongeostationary | USSR Meteor 2-16/17 |
| 137.41000 | | NFM | Nongeostationary | USAF Explorer 30 |
| | | NFM | Nongeostationary | USSR Meteor 3-1 |
| 137.42000 | | NFM | Nongeostationary | India Rohini |
| 137.44000 | | NFM | Nongeostationary | India Aryabhata |
| | | NFM | Nongeostationary | India Bhaskari 3 |
| 137.50000 | | NFM | Nongeostationary | US NOAA 10 |
| | | NFM | Nongeostationary | US NOAA 6 |
| | | NFM | Nongeostationary | USSR Meteor 3-1 |
| 137.56000 | | NFM | Nongeostationary | UK UK 6 |
| 137.57000 | | NFM | Nongeostationary | NASA Explorer Series |
| 137.62000 | | NFM | Nongeostationary | NASA NOAA 11 |
| | | NFM | Nongeostationary | NASA NOAA 9 |
| 137.67600 | | NFM | Nongeostationary | US P76-5 |
| 137.77000 | | NFM | Nongeostationary | US NOAA 9 |
| 137.80000 | | NFM | Nongeostationary | USAF SOLRAD 11 |
| 137.85000 | | NFM | Nongeostationary | USSR Intercosmos 18 |
| | | NFM | Nongeostationary | USSR Meteor 2-15 |
| | | NFM | Nongeostationary | USSR Meteor 2-16 |
| | | NFM | Nongeostationary | USSR Meteor 2-19 |
| | | NFM | Nongeostationary | USSR Meteor 3-3 |
| 137.86000 | | NFM | Nongeostationary | US Landsat 2 |
| 137.89000 | | NFM | Nongeostationary | NASA RMS |
| | | NFM | Nongeostationary | US ANS-1 |
| 137.95000 | | NFM | Nongeostationary | Canada Isis |
| | | NFM | Nongeostationary | NASA Explorer 45 |
| 137.98000 | | NFM | Nongeostationary | NASA Explorer 50 |
| 138.00000 | | NFM | Nongeostationary | USAF Hilat 1 |

## 138.000 - 138.2125 MHz   Wide Area Paging 12.5 kHz

| Base | Mobile | Mode | Location | User and Notes |
|------|--------|------|----------|----------------|
| 137.97500 | | NFM | Nationwide | Paging |
| 138.07500 | | NFM | Nationwide | Vodapage |
| | | FM | Newmarket | Hospital Paging (LCD Pagers) |
| 138.15000 | | NFM | Nationwide | Vodafone Paging |
| 138.16125 | | NFM | Windermere | Data Link |
| 138.17500 | | NFM | Nationwide | Mercury Personal Pagers |

## 138.01675 - 138.30625 MHz      Police Air to Ground

| Base | Mobile | Mode | Location | User and Notes |
|------|--------|------|----------|----------------|
| 138.01625 | | NFM | London | Police helicopter |
| 138.09375 | | NFM | England & Wales | Police Heli-Teli Channel 1 |
| 138.09375 | | NFM | Merseyside | Police Air Support Grp (M1) |
| 138.09380 | | NFM | Nationwide | Police Chopper Hellitel |
| 138.10000 | | NFM | London | Police Metropolitan Helicopter |
| 138.10500 | | NFM | Great Lippits Hill | Police Heli-Teli Chan 40 |
| | | NFM | Manchester | Police Air Support Unit (I99) |
| | | NFM | Merseyside | Police Air Support Unit (I99) |

| Base | Mobile | Mode | Location | User and Notes |
|------|--------|------|----------|----------------|
| 138.10625 | | NFM | England & Wales | Police Heli-Teli Channel 2 |
| | | NFM | London | Police Helicopter |
| | | NFM | Manchester | Police Helicopter |
| | | NFM | West Midlands | Police Helicopter Downlink |
| 138.29375 | | NFM | Cheshire | Police Helicopter |
| | | NFM | England & Wales | Police Heli-Teli Channel 3 |
| 138.30625 | | NFM | England & Wales | Police Heli-Teli Channel 4 |
| | | NFM | Lancashire | Police Helicopter |

**138.00625 - 140.96875 MHz   VHF HIGH BAND PUBLIC UTILITIES AND TRANSPORT 12.5 kHz**

| Base | Mobile | Mode | Location | User and Notes |
|------|--------|------|----------|----------------|
| 138.02500 | | AM | Kent | Southern Gas |
| | | AM | York | North East Gas |
| 138.03125 | | NFM | Westerfield | Train Link |
| 138.04375 | | NFM | English Channel | Train Link |
| 138.06000 | | NFM | London | Calling Points |
| 138.06875 | | NFM | Ipswich | Train Link |
| 138.20000 | | AM | Gloucester | British Gas |
| 138.24375 | | NFM | Brampton | Train Link |
| | | NFM | Darsham | Train Link |
| | | NFM | Halesworth | Train Link |
| | | NFM | Ipswich | Train Link |
| | | NFM | Lowestoft | Train Link |
| | | NFM | Saxmundham | Train Link |
| | | NFM | Woodbridge | Train Link |
| 138.25625 | | NFM | Perth | Data Link |
| 138.30000 | | AM | Nationwide | USAF Air to Air |
| 138.32500 | | NFM | Nationwide | British Rail RETD |
| | | NFM | Woodbridge | East Suffolk Line RETB |
| 138.33000 | | NFM | London | Railtrack Link |
| 138.33125 | | NFM | London | Railtrack Link |
| | | NFM | Tayside | Data Link |
| 138.33750 | | NFM | Newmarket | Data Link |
| 138.34375 | | NFM | Norfolk | Railway Data Link |
| | | NFM | Suffolk | Railway Data Link |
| 138.35000 | | NFM | Nationwide | Train Radiophone |
| 138.35625 | | NFM | Nationwide | Train Radiophone |
| | | NFM | Nationwide | Train Radiophone |
| 138.36550 | | NFM | Nationwide | Train Radiophone |
| 138.36875 | | NFM | Nationwide | Train Radiophone |
| | | NFM | Norfolk | Data Link |
| | | NFM | Suffolk | Data Link |
| 138.38750 | | AM | Halifax | North East Gas |
| 138.39375 | | AM | Holdengate, Keighley | British Gas |
| | | AM | Southowram, Halifax | British Gas |
| 138.40000 | | AM | Bradford | British Gas |
| 138.40625 | | AM | Holdengate, Keighley | British Gas |
| | | AM | Southowram, Halifax | British Gas |
| 138.41250 | | AM | Keighley | British Gas |
| 138.41875 | | AM | Tingley, Leeds | British Gas |
| | | AM | Wetherby | British Gas |
| 138.43125 | | AM | Moortop, Horsforth | British Gas |
| 138.44000 | | AM | Swindon | British Gas |
| 138.44375 | | AM | Queensbury, Bradford | British Gas |

| Base | Mobile | Mode | Location | User and Notes |
|---|---|---|---|---|
| 138.45625 | | AM | Moortop, Leeds | British Gas |
| | | AM | Tingley, Leeds | British Gas |
| | | AM | Wetherby | British Gas |
| 138.46250 | | AM | Skipton | British Gas |
| 138.46875 | | AM | Brighouse, Halifax | British Gas |
| | | AM | Heyshaw, Harrogate | British Gas |
| | | AM | Moortop, Ilkley | British Gas |
| | | AM | Nappa, Keighley | British Gas |
| | | AM | Todmorden, Halifax | British Gas |
| 138.47500 | | AM | Otley | British Gas |
| 138.48125 | | AM | Moortop, Horseforth | British Gas |
| | | AM | Tingley, Leeds | British Gas |
| 138.50000 | | AM | Nationwide | Military Test Flights |
| | | NFM | Nationwide | Train Radiophone |
| 138.54375 | | AM | Essex | Eastern Gas |
| 138.63135 | | AM | Luton | British Gas Ch 2 |
| 138.66250 | | NFM | Barrow in Furness | Norweb Electricity |
| 138.70000 | | AM | Nationwide | Search and Rescue |
| 138.75625 | | AM | Brecon | Welsh Gas |
| 138.75625 | | AM | Suffolk | British Gas |
| 138.82000 | | AM | Manchester | British Gas |
| 138.83125 | | AM | Brecknock East | Welsh Gas |
| | | AM | Bury St Edmonds | British Gas |
| | | AM | Luton | British Gas |
| 138.84000 | | AM | Falkirk | Scottish Gas |
| 138.84375 | | AM | Peterborough | British Gas Ch 1 |
| 138.85200 | | AM | Yorkshire | British Gas |
| 138.85625 | | AM | Brecon | Welsh Gas |
| | | AM | Norfolk | Eastern Gas |
| | | AM | Suffolk | Eastern Gas |
| 138.86635 | | AM | Norwich | British Gas Ch 2 |
| 138.86875 | | AM | Norwich | British Gas |
| 138.88755 | | NFM | Belfast | Data Link |
| 138.95625 | | AM | Nationwide | PLC Plant Hire |
| 138.96875 | 148.46875 | NFM | Yorkshire | British Coal Security |
| 138.97500 | | AM | Glasgow | Scottish Power |
| 138.98000 | | AM | Aberdeen | British Gas |
| | | AM | Edinburgh | British Gas |
| 138.98125 | | AM | Brecon | Welsh Gas |
| | | AM | Keighly | British Gas |
| | | AM | Peterborough | British Gas Ch 2 |
| 138.99375 | | AM | Brecknock East | Welsh Gas |
| | | AM | Lincolnshire | British Gas |
| | | AM | Luton | British Gas Ch 1 |
| 139.00000 | | AM | Glasgow | Scottish Power |
| | | AM | Hull | Eastern British Gas |
| | | NFM | Nationwide | Illegal Bugging Devices |
| 139.00625 | | AM | Derbyshire | British Gas |
| | | AM | Humberside | North East Gas |
| | | AM | Ipswich | British Gas |
| | | AM | Norwich | British Gas |
| 139.01250 | | AM | Barrow | British Gas |
| | | AM | Cumbria | British Gas |
| | | AM | Oxford | British Gas |
| | | AM | Truro | British Gas |

| Base | Mobile | Mode | Location | User and Notes |
|---|---|---|---|---|
| 139.01875 | | AM | Oxfordshire | British Gas |
| 139.03125 | | AM | Bradford | British Gas |
| | | NFM | Lancaster | British Gas |
| | | AM | Luton | British Gas |
| | | NFM | Morecambe | British Gas |
| | | AM | Norwich | British Gas |
| | | AM | Peterborough | British Gas |
| 139.03375 | | AM | Kent | Southern Gas |
| 139.04375 | | AM | Bradford | North East Gas |
| 139.05626 | | AM | Bradford | North East Gas |
| 139.06250 | | AM | Bradford | British Gas |
| | | AM | Edinburgh | British Gas |
| 139.06875 | | NFM | Nationwide | Press Construction Ltd |
| | | AM | Suffolk | British Gas |
| 139.08125 | | AM | Essex | Essex Gas |
| | | AM | Radnor | Welsh Gas Channel 3 |
| | | AM | Reading | British Gas |
| 139.10000 | | AM | Oxford | British Gas |
| 139.10625 | | AM | Balshall | British Gas |
| | | AM | Grimsby | British Gas |
| | | AM | Ipswich | British Gas |
| | | AM | Kings Heath | British Gas |
| 139.11575 | | AM | Kent | Southern Gas |
| 139.11875 | | AM | Oxford | British Gas |
| 139.12250 | | AM | Bath | British Gas |
| 139.12500 | | AM | Kent | British Gas |
| 139.13000 | | AM | Milton Keynes | British Gas |
| 139.13125 | | AM | Bath | British Gas |
| | | AM | Brecon | South Wales Electric |
| | | AM | Milton Keynes | British Gas |
| 139.13750 | | AM | East Sussex | British Gas |
| | | AM | London | British Gas |
| 139.14000 | | AM | Truro | British Gas |
| 139.14375 | | AM | Kent | Southern Gas |
| 139.15000 | | AM | Leicester | British Gas |
| | | AM | Manchester | British Gas |
| 139.15500 | | AM | Crewe | British Gas |
| 139.16250 | | AM | Surrey | British Gas |
| | | AM | Yorkshire | Yorkshire Electric |
| 139.16275 | | NFM | Essex | North Thames Gas |
| 139.17000 | | AM | Farnborough | British Gas |
| | | NFM | Scarborough | British Gas |
| 139.17500 | | AM | Halifax | British Gas |
| 139.17625 | | AM | Essex | Seeboard |
| 139.18130 | | AM | Hull | British Gas |
| 139.19375 | | NFM | Essex | North Thames Gas |
| 139.19500 | | NFM | Lancaster | British Gas |
| | | NFM | Morecambe | British Gas |
| | | AM | South Yorkshire | British Gas |
| | | AM | Swindon | British Gas |
| 139.20000 | | AM | Yorkshire | Emergency Gas Call Outs |
| 139.20625 | | AM | Kent | Southern Gas |
| 139.21000 | | AM | London | British Gas |
| 139.24375 | 147.74375 | AM | Nationwide | New Power and Fuel Ch |
| 139.25000 | | AM | Leeds | British Gas |

| Base | Mobile | Mode | Location | User and Notes |
|------|--------|------|----------|----------------|
| 139.25625 | 147.75625 | AM | Clacton | British Gas |
| | | AM | Clacton-on-Sea | British Gas |
| | | AM | Nationwide | New Power and Fuel Ch 1 |
| | | AM | Oxford | Western Gas |
| 139.26250 | | AM | Yorkshire | British Gas |
| 139.26575 | | NFM | Kent | Southern Gas |
| 139.26875 | 147.76875 | AM | Nationwide | New Power and Fuel Ch 2 |
| | | AM | West Midlands | MEB |
| 139.27500 | | AM | London | British Gas |
| 139.28125 | 147.78125 | AM | Kent | Southern Gas |
| | | AM | Nationwide | New Power and Fuel Ch 3 |
| 139.28750 | | AM | London | British Gas |
| 139.29375 | 147.79375 | AM | Kent | Southern Gas |
| | | AM | Nationwide | New Power and Fuel Ch |
| 139.30000 | | NFM | Space | Shuttle to Mix link |
| 139.30625 | 147.80625 | AM | Essex | Seeboard |
| | | AM | Nationwide | New Power and Fuel Ch 5 |
| 139.31250 | 147.81250 | AM | Staines | North Thames Gas |
| | | AM | Wakefield | British Gas |
| 139.31875 | 147.81875 | AM | Brecon | SWALEC |
| | | AM | Nationwide | New Power and Fuel Ch 6 |
| 139.33125 | 147.83125 | AM | Kent | Southern Gas |
| | | AM | Manchester | British Gas |
| | | AM | Nationwide | New Power and Fuel Ch 7 |
| 139.34375 | 147.84375 | AM | Kent | Southern Gas |
| | | AM | Nationwide | New Power and Fuel Ch 8 |
| 139.35000 | | AM | London | British Gas |
| 139.35625 | 147.85625 | AM | Nationwide | New Power and Fuel Ch 9 |
| | | AM | Walton-on-Thames | Southern Gas |
| 139.35875 | | AM | Walton-on-Thames | Southern Gas |
| 139.36250 | | AM | Surrey | British Gas |
| 139.36875 | 147.86875 | AM | Nationwide | New Power and Fuel Ch 10 |
| | | AM | Woodbridge | British Gas |
| 139.38125 | 147.88125 | AM | Nationwide | New Power and Fuel Ch 11 |
| 139.39375 | 147.89375 | AM | Nationwide | New Power and Fuel Ch 12 |
| | | AM | Norfolk | Eastern Gas |
| | | AM | Suffolk | British Gas |
| 139.40625 | 147.90625 | AM | Nationwide | New Power and Fuel Ch 13 |
| 139.41675 | 147.91875 | AM | Nationwide | New Power and Fuel Ch 14 |
| 139.42500 | | AM | Barrow | British Gas |
| | | AM | Cumbria | British Gas |
| 139.43125 | | AM | Kent | Southern Gas |
| 139.43125 | 147.93125 | AM | Nationwide | New Power and Fuel Ch 15 |
| 139.43750 | | AM | Shipley | Yorkshire Electricity |
| 139.44375 | 147.94375 | AM | Nationwide | New Power and Fuel Ch 16 |
| 139.45500 | | AM | Swindon | British Gas |
| 139.45625 | 147.95625 | AM | Nationwide | New Power and Fuel Ch 17 |
| 139.46875 | | AM | Oxford | Southern Electricity |
| 139.51250 | 148.01250 | NFM | Newport | British Gas |
| 139.51875 | 148.01875 | AM | Kent | Seeboard |
| | | NFM | Nationwide | Electricity Ch J22 |
| 139.52500 | | AM | Cumbria | Norweb |
| 139.52500 | | NFM | Shrewsbury | East Midlands Electricity |
| 139.53000 | | NFM | Manchester | Norweb |
| 139.53125 | 148.03125 | NFM | Nationwide | Electricity Ch J23 |

| Base | Mobile | Mode | Location | User and Notes |
|------|--------|------|----------|----------------|
| 139.53125 | | NFM | West Midlands | East Midlands Electricity |
| 139.54375 | 148.04375 | AM | Highlands | Scottish Hydro Electric |
| | | NFM | Nationwide | Electricity Ch J24 |
| | | AM | Windsor | Eastern Electric |
| 139.55000 | 148.05500 | NFM | Leeds | Yorkshire Electricity |
| | | NFM | Plymouth | Parcel Delivery |
| | | NFM | Somerset | SWEB |
| | | AM | Tunbridge Wells | Seeboard Power Care (Tango) |
| 139.55625 | 148.05625 | AM | Abingdon | Seeboard |
| | | NFM | Nationwide | Electricity Ch J25 |
| | | NFM | West Sussex | Seeboard |
| 139.56250 | 139.56250 | NFM | Arnside | Voice Link |
| | | AM | Hampshire | Southern Electric |
| | | AM | Hull | Yorkshire Electricity |
| | | AM | Milton Keynes | Eastern Electric |
| | | NFM | Newmarket | Data Link [Multi-Station] |
| | | AM | Tunbridge Wells | Seeboard Power Care (Tango) |
| 139.56875 | 148.06875 | AM | Argyll | Scottish Hydro Electric |
| | | NFM | Nationwide | Electricity Ch J26 |
| | | AM | Perth | Scottish Hydro Electric |
| | | NFM | West Midlands | MEB |
| 139.57000 | | NFM | Lancaster | ManWeb |
| | | NFM | Morecambe | Northern Electric |
| | | NFM | Newmarket | Data Link |
| 139.57500 | | AM | Bradford | Yorkshire Electricity |
| | | NFM | Cheshire | MEB |
| | | NFM | Jersey | Electricity |
| 139.58000 | 148.01250 | NFM | Burnley | Norweb |
| | | AM | Cornwall | South West Electricity |
| | | NFM | Glenrothes | Scottish Hydro Electric |
| 139.58000 | 148.08000 | NFM | Somerset | SWEB |
| 139.58000 | 139.58000 | NFM | Staffs | East Midland Electricity |
| 139.58125 | 148.08125 | NFM | Ipswich | Eastern Electricity |
| | | NFM | Nationwide | Electricity Ch J27 |
| | | AM | Thames Valley | Eastern Electric |
| 139.58500 | | NFM | Glenrothes | Scottish Hydro Electric |
| 139.58750 | | NFM | Glasgow | Data Link |
| 139.59375 | 148.09375 | NFM | Nationwide | Electricity Ch J28 |
| 139.60000 | | NFM | Lauder | Data Link |
| | | NFM | Nationwide | Illegal Bugging Devices |
| 139.60500 | | NFM | Manchester | Manweb |
| 139.60625 | 148.10625 | NFM | Nationwide | Electricity Ch J29 |
| 139.61250 | | AM | Morecambe | North West Electricity |
| 139.61375 | | NFM | Stirling | Data Link |
| 139.61875 | 148.11875 | NFM | Nationwide | Electricity Ch J30 |
| 139.62375 | | AM | Stirling | Scottish Hydro Electric |
| 139.62500 | 148.12500 | NFM | Alnwick | Data Link |
| | | NFM | Newport | SWALAC |
| | | AM | Perth | Scottish Hydro Electric |
| 139.63000 | | AM | Rayleigh | Eastern Electricity |
| 139.63125 | 148.13125 | AM | Harold Hill | Eastern Electric |
| | | NFM | Nationwide | Electricity Ch J31 |
| | | AM | Thames Valley | Eastern Electric |
| | | NFM | West Midlands | Midlands Electricity |
| | | NFM | West Sussex | Southern Electric |

| Base | Mobile | Mode | Location | User and Notes |
|------|--------|------|----------|----------------|
| 139.63750 | | AM | Aberdeen | Scottish Hydro Electric |
| | | AM | Kent | Seeboard |
| | | AM | Morecambe | North West Electricity |
| | | AM | Newmarket | Eastern Electricity |
| | | AM | Portsmouth | Southern Electric |
| 139.64375 | 148.14375 | AM | Cambridge | Eastern Electricity |
| | | NFM | Chesterfield | East Midlands Electricity |
| | | AM | Highlands | Scottish Hydro Electric |
| | | NFM | Nationwide | Electricity Ch J32 |
| | | NFM | West Midlands | Midlands Electricity |
| 139.64500 | | NFM | Burnley | Norweb |
| | | NFM | Manchester | Norweb |
| 139.65000 | | NFM | Harlow | Eastern Electricity |
| | | AM | Immingham | Yorkshire Electricity |
| | | NFM | Manchester | Norweb |
| 139.65625 | 148.15625 | AM | Kent | Southern Electric |
| | | NFM | Nationwide | Electricity Ch J33 |
| | | AM | Norwich | Eastern Electric |
| 139.66875 | 148.16875 | AM | Clacton-on-Sea | Eastern Electricity |
| | | NFM | Nationwide | Electricity Ch J34 |
| | | NFM | West Sussex | Southern Electric |
| 139.67500 | | NFM | Dyfed | SWEB |
| | | AM | Newmarket | Eastern Electricity |
| | | AM | Perth | Scottish Hydro Electric |
| | | AM | Surrey | Seeboard |
| 139.68000 | | AM | Aberdeen | Scottish Hydro Electric |
| 139.68125 | 148.18125 | NFM | Nationwide | Electricity Ch J35 |
| | | AM | Norfolk | Eastern Electric |
| 139.68200 | | AM | Perth | Scottish Hydro Electric |
| 139.68500 | | AM | Aberdeen | Scottish Hydro Electric |
| 139.68750 | | AM | East Sussex | Seeboard |
| 139.69000 | | NFM | Burnley | Norweb |
| 139.69375 | 148.19375 | NFM | Ayr | Scottish Power |
| | | AM | Highlands | Scottish Hydro Electric |
| | | NFM | Nationwide | Electricity Ch J36 |
| | | AM | Norwich | Eastern Electric |
| | | NFM | West Midlands | East Midlands Electricity |
| 139.69500 | | NFM | Glenrothes | Scottish Hydro Electric |
| | | NFM | Tyne & Wear | Northern Electricty |
| 139.70000 | | AM | Kent | Seeboard |
| | | NFM | Lothian & Borders | Scottish Power |
| 139.70500 | | NFM | Bolton | Eastern Electricity |
| | | NFM | Norfolk | Street Lighting |
| 139.70625 | 148.20625 | AM | Chelmsford | Seeboard |
| | | AM | Dundee | Scottish Hydro Electric |
| | | NFM | Ipswich | Eastern Electricity |
| | | NFM | Nationwide | Electricity Ch J37 |
| 139.71250 | | AM | Aberdeen | Scottish Hydro Electric |
| | | NFM | Glasgow | Scottish Power |
| 139.71625 | | AM | Perth | Scottish Hydro Electric |
| 139.71875 | 148.21875 | AM | Harlow | Southern Electric |
| | | NFM | Nationwide | Electricity Ch J38 |
| 139.72000 | | AM | Glasgow | Scottish Power |
| | | AM | Swindon | Southern Electricity |
| 139.72375 | | AM | Stirling | Scottish Hydro Electric |

| Base | Mobile | Mode | Location | User and Notes |
|------|--------|------|----------|----------------|
| 139.72500 | | AM | Hampshire | Southern Electricity |
| | | AM | London | London Electricity |
| 139.73000 | | NFM | Blackpool | Norweb |
| | | AM | Folkestone | Seeboard |
| | | AM | South Yorkshire | Yorkshire Electricity |
| 139.73125 | 148.23125 | AM | Andover | Electric Line Faults |
| | | AM | Essex | Eastern Electric |
| | | AM | Highlands | Scottish Hydro Electric |
| | | AM | Kings Lynn | Eastern Electricity |
| | | NFM | Nationwide | Electricity Ch J39 |
| | | NFM | Whitehaven | Norweb |
| 139.73750 | 148.23750 | AM | Leeds | Yorkshire Electricity |
| | | AM | Portsmouth | Southern Electric |
| | | AM | Slough | Southern Electric |
| | | AM | Surrey | Seeboard |
| 139.74375 | 148.24375 | AM | Essex | Eastern Electric |
| | | NFM | Nationwide | Electricity Ch J40 |
| | | NFM | West Midlands | East Midlands Electricity |
| | | NFM | West Sussex | Southern Electric |
| | | AM | West Yorkshire | Yorkshire Electricity |
| 139.74500 | | NFM | Glossop | East Midlands Electricity |
| 139.75000 | | AM | Hertfordshire | East Midlands Electricity |
| 139.75500 | | AM | Rayleigh | Eastern Electricity |
| 139.75625 | 148.26625 | AM | Essex | Eastern Electric |
| | | NFM | Nationwide | Electricity Ch J41 |
| 139.76250 | 148.25000 | NFM | Cardiff | S Wales Electricity |
| | | AM | Edinburgh | Scottish Power |
| | | AM | Perth | Scottish Hydro Electric |
| | | AM | Shepway | Seeboard |
| 139.76875 | 148.26875 | AM | Humberside | Northern Electric |
| | | NFM | Lancaster | Norweb |
| | | NFM | Morecambe | Northern Electricity |
| | | NFM | Nationwide | Electricity Ch J42 |
| 139.77500 | | NFM | Cardiff | SWALEC |
| | | AM | Halifax | Yorkshire Electricity |
| | | NFM | Harlow | Eastern Electricity |
| | | NFM | Huddersfield | Yorkshire Electricity |
| 139.78125 | 148.28125 | NFM | Nationwide | Electricity Ch J43 |
| | | AM | Reading | Reading Electricity |
| | | NFM | West Midlands | MEB |
| | | NFM | West Sussex | Southern Electric |
| 139.78500 | | AM | Leicester | Seeboard |
| | | AM | Aberdeen | Scottish Hydro Electric |
| | | AM | Keighley | Yorkshire Electricity |
| | | AM | Loughborough | Eastern Electricity |
| | | NFM | Manchester | Manweb |
| 139.79000 | 148.29000 | NFM | Peterborough | Eastern Electricity |
| 139.79375 | 148.29375 | AM | Aldershot | Seeboard |
| | | AM | Argyll | Scottish Hydro Electric |
| | | AM | Buckinghamshire | Eastern Electricity |
| | | AM | Montgomery | Manweb |
| | | NFM | Nationwide | Electricity Ch J44 |
| | | AM | Salisbury | Southern Electric |
| | | NFM | West Midlands | Manweb |
| 139.79500 | | NFM | Barrow in Furness | Norweb |
| 139.79775 | | AM | Thames | Eastern Electric |

| Base | Mobile | Mode | Location | User and Notes |
|---|---|---|---|---|
| 139.80000 | | AM | Ipswich | Eastern Electricity |
| | | NFM | Nationwide | Illegal Bugging Devices |
| 139.80500 | | NFM | Glenrothes | Scottish Hydro Electric |
| | | NFM | Stoke-on-Trent | MEB |
| 139.80625 | 148.30625 | NFM | Nationwide | Electricity Ch J45 |
| | | NFM | West Midlands | MEB |
| 139.81250 | | AM | Newmarket | Eastern Electricity |
| | | AM | Tunbridge Wells | Seeboard |
| 139.81500 | 139.81500 | NFM | Scarborough | Northern Electric |
| 139.81825 | 148.31825 | NFM | Nationwide | Electricity Ch J46 |
| | | AM | Buckinghamshire | Eastern Electricity |
| 139.82000 | | NFM | Manchester | Norweb |
| | | NFM | Southampton | Southern Electric |
| | | NFM | Wigan | Norweb |
| 139.82500 | | NFM | Glasgow | Scottish Power |
| | | AM | Swindon | MEB |
| | | NFM | W Yorkshire | Yorkshire Electricity |
| 139.83125 | 148.33125 | AM | Humberside | East Midlands Electricity |
| | | NFM | Nationwide | Electricity Ch J47 |
| 139.83625 | | AM | London | London Electric |
| 139.83750 | | AM | East Sussex | Seeboard |
| 139.84375 | 148.34375 | AM | Bury St. Edmunds | Eastern Electricity |
| | | NFM | Carlisle | Norweb |
| | | AM | London | London Electric |
| | | NFM | Nationwide | Electricity Ch J48 |
| | | NFM | Sheffield | Yorkshire Electricity |
| | | AM | Surrey | Southern Electric |
| 139.84500 | | NFM | Central Scotland | Scottish Power |
| | | AM | Cornwall | SWEB |
| | | NFM | Glossop | East Midlands Electricity |
| 139.85000 | | AM | Gwynedd | Manweb |
| | | AM | Kent | Seeboard |
| | | AM | Leicester | East Midlands Electricity |
| | | NFM | Merseyside | Manweb |
| | | AM | Plymouth | SWEB |
| 139.85500 | | NFM | Maidstone | Maidstone Power Care (Mike) |
| | | NFM | Newcastle | Northern Electric |
| 139.85625 | 148.35625 | NFM | Nationwide | Electricity Ch J49 |
| | | NFM | West Sussex | Southern Electric |
| 139.86375 | | AM | Stirling | Scottish Hydro Electric |
| 139.86500 | | NFM | Manchester | Manweb |
| 139.86875 | 148.36875 | AM | Argyll | Scottish Hydro Electric |
| | | AM | Kings Lynn | Eastern Electric |
| | | NFM | Lancaster | Norweb |
| | | NFM | Morecambe | Northern Electricity |
| | | NFM | Nationwide | Electricity Ch J50 |
| | | AM | Perth | Scottish Hydro Electric |
| | | NFM | West Midlands | MEB |
| 139.87000 | 139.87000 | NFM | Cheshire | East Midland Electricity |
| 139.87250 | 139.87250 | AM | Nationwide | USAF Air-Air |
| 139.87500 | | AM | Bradford | Yorkshire Electricity |
| 139.88125 | 148.38125 | AM | Essex | Eastern Electric |
| | | NFM | Nationwide | Electricity Ch 51 |
| 139.88250 | | NFM | Essex | Eastern Electric |
| 139.88750 | | NFM | Lauder | Data Link |

| Base | Mobile | Mode | Location | User and Notes |
|---|---|---|---|---|
| 139.89375 | 148.39375 | NFM | Nationwide | Electricity Ch J52 |
| | | AM | West Midlands | MEB |
| 139.90125 | | NFM | Ferrybridge | Data Link |
| | | NFM | Lauder | Data Link |
| | | NFM | Stirling | Data Link |
| 139.90625 | 148.40625 | NFM | Nationwide | Electricity Ch J53 |
| 139.91875 | 148.41875 | NFM | Nationwide | Electricity Ch J54 |
| 139.92000 | 148.42000 | NFM | Somerset | SWEB |
| 139.93000 | 148.43000 | NFM | Norfolk | Eastern Electricity |
| 139.93125 | 148.43125 | AM | Essex | Eastern Electric |
| | | AM | Hertfordshire | Eastern Electric |
| | | NFM | Nationwide | Electricity Ch J55 |
| | | NFM | West Midlands | MEB |
| 139.93750 | | NFM | Cheshire | Electricity Co. Data Link |
| | | AM | Glasgow | Scottish Power |
| 139.94375 | 148.44375 | NFM | London | North Thames Gas |
| | | NFM | Nationwide | Electricity Ch J56 |
| | | NFM | West Midlands | MEB |
| 139.95000 | | NFM | Manchester | Norweb |
| | | NFM | Sussex | Seeboard Electricity |
| 139.95500 | | NFM | Preston | Electricity Board |
| 139.95600 | | AM | Berkshire | Southern Electricity |
| 139.95625 | 148.45625 | AM | Henley-on-Thames | Southern Electric |
| | | NFM | Nationwide | Electricity Ch J57 |
| | | NFM | Sheffield | Yorkshire Electricity |
| | | NFM | West Midlands | MEB |
| 139.96875 | 148.96875 | NFM | Nationwide | Electricity Ch J58 |
| 139.97500 | | NFM | Newmarket | Data Link |
| | | AM | Sheffield | Yorkshire Electricity |
| 139.98125 | 148.48125 | NFM | Nationwide | Electricity Ch J59 |
| | | AM | Perth | Scottish Hydro Electric Data Link |
| 139.98750 | | NFM | Swansea | SWALEC |
| 139.99000 | | NFM | Somerset | British Gas |
| 139.99375 | 148.49375 | NFM | Ayr | Scottish Power |
| | | NFM | Nationwide | Electricity Ch J60 |
| 140.00000 | | NFM | Alnwick | Data Link |
| | | NFM | Nationwide | Illegal Bugging Devices |
| | | AM | Nationwide | USAF Air-Air |
| 140.00625 | 148.50625 | NFM | Nationwide | Electricity Ch J61 |
| 140.01250 | | NFM | Cumbria | Data Link |
| | | NFM | Lancashire | Data Link |
| 140.01875 | 148.51875 | NFM | Nationwide | Electricity Ch J62 |
| 140.02000 | | NFM | Durham | Data Link |
| 140.02500 | | NFM | Alnwick | Data Link |
| 140.03125 | 148.53125 | NFM | Nationwide | Electricity Ch J63 |
| 140.03750 | | NFM | Leeds | British Gas |
| 140.04375 | 148.54375 | NFM | Nationwide | Electricity Ch J64 |
| 140.04400 | | AM | Perth | Data Link |
| 140.05000 | | NFM | Bradford | British Gas |
| | | NFM | Cumbria | Data Link |
| | | NFM | Dundee | Data Link |
| | | NFM | Lancashire | Data Link |
| | | NFM | Lauder | Data Link |
| | | NFM | Nationwide | Mine Rescue Channel |
| | | NFM | Lancaster | Red Rose Radio Link |

| Base | Mobile | Mode | Location | User and Notes |
|------|--------|------|----------|----------------|
| 140.05625 | 148.55625 | NFM | Braintree | Eastern Gas |
| | | NFM | Nationwide | Electricity Ch J65 |
| | | AM | Nationwide | Coal Mine Rescue |
| 140.06250 | | NFM | Glasgow | Data Link |
| 140.07500 | | AM | County Durham | British Gas |
| | | NFM | Newmarket | Data Link |
| 140.08125 | 148.58125 | NFM | West Sussex | British Gas Southern |
| 140.10000 | | NFM | Haggerston | Data Link |
| | | NFM | W Yorkshire | British Gas |
| 140.10625 | 148.60625 | NFM | Ferrybridge | British Gas |
| | | NFM | Nationwide | British Gas Trunked System |
| | | NFM | West Midlands | British Gas |
| 140.11250 | | NFM | Cheshire | British Gas |
| | | AM | County Durham | British Gas |
| | | AM | Selby | North East Gas |
| 140.11875 | 148.61875 | NFM | Nationwide | British Gas Trunked System |
| | | NFM | Stirling | Data Link |
| | | NFM | West Midlands | British Gas |
| 140.12000 | 148.61875 | NFM | Burnley | British Gas |
| | | NFM | Stockport | British Gas |
| 140.12500 | 140.12500 | NFM | Eastham | British Gas |
| | | NFM | Glasgow | British Gas |
| 140.13125 | 148.63125 | NFM | Nationwide | British Gas Trunked System |
| | | NFM | West Midlands | British Gas |
| 140.13750 | | AM | Leeds | North East Gas |
| 140.13875 | | NFM | Stirling | Data Link |
| 140.14375 | 148.64375 | NFM | Colchester | Eastern Gas |
| | | AM | London | London Electric |
| | | NFM | Nationwide | British Gas Trunked System |
| | | NFM | Nationwide | Coal Mine Ambulance Channel |
| | | NFM | West Midlands | British Gas |
| 140.15000 | | AM | County Durham | British Gas |
| 140.15625 | | AM | Cleveland | British Gas |
| | | AM | West Midlands | Bus Company |
| 140.16500 | | NFM | Bradford | British Gas |
| 140.16875 | 148.66875 | NFM | Nationwide | British Gas Trunked System |
| 140.16875 | 140.10625 | AM | Perth | Scottish Hydro Electric |
| | | NFM | West Midlands | British Gas |
| | | NFM | West Sussex | British Gas Southern |
| 140.17500 | | AM | Bolton | British Gas |
| | | NFM | Glasgow | British Gas |
| | | AM | Manchester | British Gas |
| 140.19500 | | AM | Hull | British Gas |
| 140.20000 | | NFM | Dundee | Data Link |
| | | NFM | Leeds | British Gas |
| 140.20500 | | NFM | London, south east | Council schools |
| 140.20500 | 148.70500 | NFM | Portsmouth | Wessex Water |
| | | NFM | Somerset | British Gas |
| 140.20625 | | NFM | Clacton | Eastern Electric |
| 140.21125 | 148.71125 | NFM | London | British Gas |
| 140.21250 | | AM | Fareham | Southern Gas |
| | | AM | Gosport | Southern Gas |
| | | AM | Portsmouth | Southern Gas |
| 140.21875 | | AM | Surrey | Southern Electric |

| Base | Mobile | Mode | Location | User and Notes |
|------|--------|------|----------|----------------|
| 140.22000 | 148.72000 | NFM | Glossop | British Gas |
| | | AM | Rainham | Seeboard Power Care |
| | | NFM | Somerset | SWEB |
| 140.22500 | | AM | Tayside | Scottish Hydro Electric |
| | | NFM | Wakefield | British Gas |
| 140.23125 | | NFM | Lancaster | British Gas |
| 140.23750 | | AM | Newcastle | British Gas Repairs |
| 140.24375 | 148.74375 | AM | Colchester | Eastern Gas |
| | | NFM | Nationwide | British Gas Trunked System |
| | | NFM | West Midlands | British Gas |
| 140.24500 | 148.70000 | NFM | Avon | British Gas |
| | | NFM | Burnley | British Gas |
| 140.25000 | | NFM | Leeds | British Gas |
| 140.25625 | 148.75625 | AM | Ipswich | British Gas Repairs |
| | | NFM | Nationwide | British Gas Trunked System |
| | | NFM | West Midlands | British Gas |
| 140.26125 | | NFM | Stirling | Data Link |
| 140.26250 | 140.26250 | NFM | Neston | British Gas |
| 140.26875 | 148.76875 | NFM | Nationwide | British Gas Trunked System |
| | | NFM | West Midlands | British Gas |
| 140.27000 | | NFM | Runcorn | British Gas |
| 140.28750 | | NFM | Manchester | British Gas |
| 140.29375 | 148.79375 | NFM | Nationwide | British Gas Trunked System |
| | | NFM | West Midlands | British Gas |
| | | NFM | West Sussex | British Gas Southern |
| 140.29500 | | AM | Manchester | Manchester Buses |
| 140.30000 | | NFM | Glasgow | British Gas |
| | | NFM | Keighley | British Gas |
| 140.30625 | 148.80625 | NFM | Nationwide | British Gas Trunked System |
| | | NFM | West Midlands | British Gas |
| 140.31250 | | NFM | Dewsbury | British Gas |
| 140.32125 | | NFM | London | London Transport |
| 140.32500 | | NFM | Glasgow | British Gas |
| | | NFM | London (South) | British Gas |
| 140.33125 | 148.83125 | NFM | Surrey | Southern Gas |
| | | NFM | West Sussex | British Gas Southern |
| 140.33750 | | AM | Fareham | Southern Gas |
| | | AM | Gosport | Southern Gas |
| | | AM | Portmouth | Southern Gas |
| 140.34500 | | NFM | Darlington | BT Buses |
| | | NFM | West Midlands | British Gas |
| | | NFM | Wolverhampton | Bus Company |
| 140.35000 | | NFM | Ferrybridge | British Gas |
| | | NFM | Lancaster | British Gas |
| | | AM | Plymouth | SWEB |
| | | NFM | Pontefract | British Gas |
| | | AM | West Midlands | Bus Company |
| 140.35125 | | NFM | Surrey | Southern Gas |
| 140.35625 | 140.10625 | AM | Perth | Scottish Hydro Electric |
| 140.36250 | | AM | Pontefract | North East Gas |
| 140.37500 | | NFM | Wiltshire | Electricity |
| 140.38000 | | AM | Manchester | Manchester Buses |
| 140.38750 | | AM | County Durham | Northern Electric |
| | | NFM | Tyne & Wear | Metro Controller |
| 140.39375 | 148.89375 | NFM | Nationwide | British Gas Trunked System |
| 140.39375 | | NFM | West Midlands | British Gas |

| Base | Mobile | Mode | Location | User and Notes |
|------|--------|------|----------|----------------|
| 140.40000 | 148.80000 | AM | London, Croydon | British Gas |
| | | NFM | North West | British Gas |
| 140.40625 | | AM | South Yorkshire | Greenland Bus Company |
| 140.41250 | 140.41250 | NFM | Edinburgh | British Gas |
| | | NFM | Swansea | British Gas |
| 140.41875 | 148.91875 | NFM | Nationwide | British Gas Trunked System |
| | | NFM | Surrey | Southern Gas |
| | | NFM | West Midlands | British Gas |
| 140.42500 | 148.82500 | NFM | Bradford | British Gas |
| | | NFM | Lauder | Data Link |
| | | AM | Newcastle | British Gas |
| 140.43125 | 148.93125 | NFM | Nationwide | British Gas Trunked System |
| | | NFM | West Midlands | British Gas |
| 140.43750 | | AM | Fife | British Gas |
| 140.44000 | | NFM | Manchester | Electricity |
| 140.44375 | | NFM | London | London Transport |
| 140.44500 | | NFM | Newcastle | Buses |
| 140.45000 | | NFM | London (SW) | British Gas |
| | | AM | Newmarket | Telephone Link |
| | | AM | Plymouth | SWEB |
| | | AM | West Midlands | Bus Company |
| 140.45600 | 148.45000 | NFM | Tamworth | British Gas |
| 140.45625 | 148.95625 | NFM | Nationwide | British Gas Trunked System |
| 140.46250 | | AM | Glasgow | Scottish Power |
| 140.46875 | 148.96875 | NFM | Manchester | Manchester Buses |
| | | NFM | Nationwide | British Gas Trunked System |
| | | NFM | West Midlands | British Gas |
| 140.47500 | | NFM | Glasgow | British Gas |
| 140.48000 | 148.88000 | NFM | Barrow | British Gas |
| 140.48125 | 148.98125 | NFM | Barrow in Furness | British Gas |
| | | NFM | Nationwide | British Gas Trunked System |
| | | NFM | Surrey | British Gas |
| | | NFM | West Midlands | British Gas |
| 140.48750 | | NFM | London | London Transport |
| 140.50000 | | NFM | London | London Transport |
| 140.50625 | | NFM | London | London Transport |
| | | NFM | Nationwide | National Bus Company |
| 140.52500 | | NFM | Birmingham | Buses |
| | | NFM | Bradford | City Buses |
| 140.53125 | | NFM | Manchester | Manchester Buses |
| 140.54375 | | NFM | Manchester | Manchester Buses |
| 140.58175 | | AM | London | London Electricity |
| 140.63125 | | NFM | Newcastle | City Transport |
| 140.67500 | | NFM | North London | North Thames Gas |
| 140.70625 | | NFM | South Yorkshire | South Yorkshire Bus Company |
| 140.71875 | | NFM | Newcastle | City Transport |
| 140.73750 | | NFM | London | London Transport |
| 140.74375 | | NFM | London | London Transport |
| 140.76250 | | AM | Goole | North East Gas |
| | | NFM | London | London Transport |
| 140.76875 | | NFM | London | London Transport |
| 140.83000 | | NFM | Burnley | British Gas |
| 140.83125 | | NFM | London | London Transport |
| 140.83750 | | AM | Pontefract | North East Gas |
| 140.84375 | | NFM | London | London Transport |
| 140.85625 | | NFM | South Yorkshire | South Yorkshire Bus Company |

| Base | Mobile | Mode | Location | User and Notes |
|------|--------|------|----------|----------------|
| 140.87500 | | AM | Hull | British Gas |
| | | NFM | Isle of Man | Manx Electricity |
| 140.90500 | | NFM | Burnley | British Gas |
| 140.90625 | | NFM | South London | North Thames Gas |
| 140.93125 | | NFM | Kent | Southern Gas |
| 140.94375 | | NFM | Bognor Regis | Brighton & Hove Bus Co. |
| | | NFM | Brighton | Brighton & Hove Bus Co |
| | | NFM | Nationwide | NCT Bus Channel |
| 140.96875 | | NFM | Nationwide | DTI Short Term 28 Day Hire |

**141.0000 - 141.9000 MHz      ILR, BBC AND LOCAL RADIO TALKBACK**

| Base | Mobile | Mode | Location | User and Notes |
|------|--------|------|----------|----------------|
| 140.94375 | | NFM | Nationwide | TV Engineering Talkback |
| 140.99375 | | NFM | London | ITN 6 O'Clock News |
| | | NFM | London | LWT TV O/B |
| 140.99500 | | NFM | Leeds | ITV Studio Maintenance |
| | | NFM | London | GMTV studio direction |
| 140.99575 | | NFM | London | ITV Studio relay for "London Today" |
| 141.01250 | | NFM | Nationwide | ILR Talkback Channel 1 |
| 141.01875 | | NFM | Inverness | Moray Firth Radio O/B |
| 141.02500 | | NFM | Humberside | Viking Radio Links |
| | | NFM | Nationwide | ILR Common Talkback Ch 5 |
| 141.03125 | | NFM | Stoke on Trent | Signal Radio |
| 141.03750 | | NFM | Nationwide | Ch4 TV Engineering /News |
| | | NFM | Nationwide | ILR Engineering Ch 4 |
| | | NFM | Nationwide | ILR Primary O/B Channel 2 |
| 141.04375 | | NFM | Berkshire | Radio 210 |
| | | NFM | Hampshire | Radio 210 |
| | | NFM | Wolverhampton | Beacon Radio O/B |
| 141.05000 | 141.18750 | NFM | Andover | Independent Local Radio |
| | | NFM | Basingstoke | Independent Local Radio |
| | | NFM | Bristol | Independent Local Radio |
| | | NFM | Chelmsford | Independent Local Radio |
| | | NFM | Cornwall | Independent Local Radio |
| | | NFM | Hereward | Independent Local Radio |
| | | NFM | Inverness | Independent Local Radio |
| | | NFM | Liverpool | Independent Local Radio |
| | | NFM | Newcastle | Independent Local Radio |
| | | NFM | Oxford | Independent Local Radio |
| | | NFM | Peterborough | Independent Local Radio |
| | | NFM | Reigate | Independent Local Radio |
| | | NFM | Sheffield | Independent Local Radio |
| | | NFM | Wolverhampton | Independent Local Radio |
| 141.05500 | 141.05500 | NFM | Leeds | Radio Air Talk Back |
| 141.05600 | | NFM | Nongeostationary | US ATS 6 |
| 141.05625 | | NFM | Preston | Red Rose Radio |
| 141.06250 | 141.11250 | NFM | Exeter | Independent Local Radio |
| | | NFM | Gloucester | Independent Local Radio |
| | | NFM | Great Yarmouth | Independent Local Radio |
| | | NFM | Gwynedd | Independent Local Radio |
| | | NFM | Hereford | Independent Local Radio |
| | | NFM | Huddersfield | Independent Local Radio |
| | | NFM | Leicester | Independent Local Radio |
| | | NFM | Maidstone | Independent Local Radio |
| | | NFM | Nationwide | 2CR Eye in the Sky |
| | | NFM | Reading | Independent Local Radio |

| Base | Mobile | Mode | Location | User and Notes |
|------|--------|------|----------|----------------|
| 141.06250 | 141.11250 | NFM | Shrewsbury | Independent Local Radio |
| 141.06875 | | NFM | Liverpool | Radio City |
| 141.07500 | | NFM | Aberdeen | Independent Local Radio |
| | | NFM | Barnsley | Independent Local Radio |
| | | NFM | Berwick-upon-Tweed | Independent Local Radio |
| | | NFM | Cardiff | Independent Local Radio |
| | | NFM | Coventry | Independent Local Radio |
| | | NFM | Glasgow | Independent Local Radio |
| 140.07500 | | NFM | London | Independent Local Radio |
| | | NFM | Manchester | Independent Local Radio |
| | | NFM | Portsmouth | Independent Local Radio |
| | | NFM | Stoke on Trent | Independent Local Radio |
| | | NFM | Swindon | Independent Local Radio |
| 141.08125 | | NFM | Manchester | Piccadilly Radio |
| 141.08750 | 141.15000 | NFM | Bedford | Independent Local Radio |
| | | NFM | Bournemouth | Independent Local Radio |
| | | NFM | Eastbourne | Independent Local Radio |
| | | NFM | Edinburgh | Independent Local Radio |
| | | NFM | Guildford | Independent Local Radio |
| | | NFM | Hereford | Independent Local Radio |
| | | NFM | Humberside | Independent Local Radio |
| | | NFM | Ipswich | Independent Local Radio |
| | | NFM | Manchester | Independent Local Radio |
| | | NFM | Nottingham | Independent Local Radio |
| | | NFM | Plymouth | Independent Local Radio |
| | | NFM | Swansea | Independent Local Radio |
| | | NFM | Trent | Independent Local Radio |
| | | NFM | Whitehaven | Independent Local Radio |
| 141.10000 | 141.20000 | NFM | Aylesbury | Independent Local Radio |
| | | NFM | Belfast | Independent Local Radio |
| | | NFM | Birmingham | Independent Local Radio |
| | | NFM | Blackpool | Independent Local Radio |
| | | NFM | Bognor Regis | Independent Local Radio |
| | | NFM | Bradford | Independent Local Radio |
| | | NFM | Bury St Edmunds | Independent Local Radio |
| | | NFM | Cambridge | Independent Local Radio |
| | | NFM | Canterbury | Independent Local Radio |
| | | NFM | Derby | Independent Local Radio |
| | | NFM | Dorchester | Independent Local Radio |
| | | NFM | Dover | Independent Local Radio |
| | | NFM | Dumfries | Independent Local Radio |
| | | NFM | Dundee | Independent Local Radio |
| | | NFM | Gwent | Independent Local Radio |
| | | NFM | Leeds | Independent Local Radio |
| | | NFM | London | Capitol Radio Link |
| | | NFM | London | Independent Local Radio |
| | | NFM | Londonderry | Independent Local Radio |
| | | NFM | Middlesborough | Independent Local Radio |
| | | NFM | Milton Keynes | Independent Local Radio |
| | | NFM | Newmarket | Independent Local Radio |
| | | NFM | Newport | Independent Local Radio |
| | | NFM | Northampton | Independent Local Radio |
| | | NFM | Perth | Independent Local Radio |
| | | NFM | Preston | Independent Local Radio |
| | | NFM | Southampton | Independent Local Radio |
| | | NFM | Stranraer | Independent Local Radio |

| Base | Mobile | Mode | Location | User and Notes |
|---|---|---|---|---|
| 141.10000 | 141.20000 | NFM | Taunton | BBC |
| | | NFM | Weymouth | Independent Local Radio |
| | | NFM | Wrexham | Independent Local Radio |
| | | NFM | Yeovil | Independent Local Radio |
| 141.11875 | 468.84375 | NFM | Derby | GEM AM 945/.999 |
| | | NFM | Derby | Trent FM 96.2 |
| 141.12500 | 141.17500 | NFM | Birmingham | 96.4 FM BRMB Radio Talkback |
| 141.13125 | | NFM | Manchester | BBC GMR |
| 141.13750 | | NFM | Nationwide | IBA Local Radio Engineers |
| | | NFM | West of England | HTV Clean Feed |
| 141.14375 | | NFM | Kent | Invicta FM |
| 141.15000 | | NFM | Humberside | Viking Radio O/B |
| | | NFM | Nationwide | ITC Local Radio Engineers |
| | | NFM | Trent | Independent Local Radio Talkback |
| | | NFM | Birmingham | Birmingham O/B |
| 141.15625 | 469.26250 | NFM | London | LBC Radio Flying Eye |
| 141.16250 | | NFM | Dorset | 2CR Studio Talkback |
| 141.16875 | | NFM | Coventry | Mercia Sound |
| 141.18000 | | NFM | Leicester | Sunrise Radio O/B |
| | | NFM | Manchester | Piccadilly Radio Studio Link |
| 141.18125 | | NFM | London | Independent Radio O/B |
| 141.18750 | 469.46250 | NFM | Cowley | Fox FM Flying Eye Uplink |
| | | NFM | Humberside | Viking Radio O/B |
| 141.19375 | | NFM | Birmingham | Railtrack MB/Xtra AM |
| | | NFM | London | LBC |
| 141.19500 | | NFM | London | LBC Production/Control Room |
| | | NFM | London | Radio Piccadilly Studio Link |
| 141.20000 | | NFM | Hampshire | BBC Radio Solent |
| 141.20500 | 141.20500 | NFM | York | BBC Radio York Talkback |
| 141.20625 | 224.11875 | NFM | Birmingham | BBC Radio West Midlands |
| | | NFM | Northamptonshire | BBC Radio Northants |
| 141.21750 | | NFM | Derby | BBC Radio Derby |
| 141.21875 | | NFM | Hereford & Worcester | BBC Radio Worcester |
| | | NFM | London | BBC Radio Car O/B |
| 141.22000 | 141.22000 | NFM | Lincoln | BBC Radio Lincs Talkback |
| 141.22500 | | NFM | Leicester | BBC O/B Cricket Commentary |
| 141.23125 | | NFM | Surrey | BBC Radio Surrey |
| 141.23750 | | NFM | Taunton | BBC Talkback |
| 141.24300 | | NFM | Berkshire | BBC Radio Berkshire |
| 141.24375 | 224.01875 | NFM | Berkshire | BBC Radio Surrey & Berkshire |
| | | NFM | Channel Islands | ITN |
| 141.24375 | 224.10625 | NFM | Cornwall | ITN |
| 141.24375 | 224.16875 | NFM | Coventry | BBC CWR |
| | | NFM | London | BBC Radio Car O/B |
| | | NFM | Norfolk | ITN |
| 141.25000 | | NFM | London | ITN Music Link |
| 141.25500 | | NFM | Stoke on Trent | Radio Stoke Engineering |
| 141.25625 | 224.10625 | NFM | London | BBC Radio Car O/B |
| | | NFM | Stoke on Trent | BBC Radio Stoke |
| | | NFM | West Sussex | BBC Radio Sussex |
| 141.25630 | 224.10875 | NFM | Cambridge | ITN |
| | | NFM | Devon | ITN |
| 141.25630 | 224.09375 | NFM | Leeds | ITN |
| 141.25630 | 224.10625 | NFM | Stoke | ITN |
| 141.25630 | 213.73750 | NFM | Sussex | ITN |
| | | NFM | Wiltshire | ITN |

| Base | Mobile | Mode | Location | User and Notes |
|------|--------|------|----------|----------------|
| 141.25680 | 224.16750 | NFM | Channel Islands | ITN |
| 141.28750 | | NFM | London Ealing | Five Line O/B |
| 141.29000 | 141.29000 | NFM | Hull | BBC Radio Humberside Talkback |
| 141.29350 | 224.15625 | NFM | Shropshire | ITN |
| 141.29375 | | NFM | London | BBC Radio Car O/B |
| 141.29375 | 224.15625 | NFM | Shrewsbury | BBC Radio Shrewsbury |
| 141.29380 | 224.13125 | NFM | Humberside | ITN |
| 141.29380 | 224.10875 | NFM | Newcastle | ITN |
| 141.29500 | | NFM | London | BBC Radio news studio |
| 141.29750 | | NFM | York | Radio York O/B |
| 141.30625 | 224.13125 | NFM | Leicester | BBC Radio Leicester |
| 141.30630 | 213.76250 | NFM | Bedfordshire | ITN |
| 141.30630 | 224.11875 | NFM | Cleveland | ITN |
| 141.30630 | 224.14375 | NFM | Gloucester | ITN |
| 141.30630 | 224.13125 | NFM | Leicester | ITN |
| 141.31825 | | NFM | London | BBC Radio Car O/B |
| 141.32000 | | NFM | Nationwide | BBC O/B Link |
| 141.35000 | | NFM | Belfast | Data Link |
| | | NFM | London | BBC1 Clean Feed |
| | | NFM | London | ITN Music Links |
| | | NFM | Nationwide | BBC Radio 2 Engineering |
| | | NFM | Yorkshire | IBC Talkback |
| 141.37500 | 224.23350 | FM | Ayr | Racecourse BBC Outside Broadcvase |
| | | NFM | Bristol | BBC Points West Talkback |
| | | NFM | Ipswich | Local Radio |
| | | NFM | London | BBC1 TV Studio Sound Link |
| | | NFM | Nationwide | BBC O/B Talkback |
| 141.38000 | | WFM | West Midlands | BBC Pebblemill Studios |
| 141.38750 | 468.13750 | NFM | Manchester | Key 103 O/B |
| 141.42650 | | NFM | Newbury | BBC South Talkback |
| | | NFM | Southampton | BBC South Talkback |
| 141.44500 | | NFM | London | BBC2 TV Studio Sound Link |
| 141.45000 | | NFM | London | ITN Music Link |
| 141.46250 | | NFM | Leicester | BBC1 West Midlands Link |
| | | NFM | London | BBC TV O/B |
| | | NFM | London | BBC1 Link |
| | | NFM | Manchester | BBC TV |
| | | NFM | Nottingham | BBC1 Nottingham Clean Feed |
| 141.47500 | | WFM | Southampton | BBC TV South Feed to OB |
| 141.55000 | | NFM | Nationwide | BBC Radio 2 O/B |
| 141.61875 | | NFM | Cornwall | BBC |
| | | NFM | Essex | BBC |
| | | NFM | Nottingham | BBC |
| | | NFM | Surrey | BBC |
| | | NFM | Trent | BBC Radio Trent O/B |
| 141.63125 | | NFM | Bedford | BBC |
| | | NFM | Shrewsbury | BBC |
| | | NFM | Norfolk | BBC |
| 141.64375 | | NFM | Nationwide | BBC Outside Broadcasts |
| 141.65625 | | NFM | Brighton | BBC |
| | | NFM | Northampton | BBC |
| | | NFM | York | BBC |
| 141.66825 | | NFM | Sussex | BBC |

| Base | Mobile | Mode | Location | User and Notes |
|------|--------|------|----------|----------------|
| 141.66875 | | NFM | Hereford | BBC |
| | | NFM | Lancashire | BBC |
| | | NFM | London | Electronic News Gathering |
| | | NFM | Nationwide | BBC Engineering Talkback |
| 141.67000 | | NFM | Lancaster | Radio Lancashire |
| | | NFM | Nationwide | TV News ENG |
| 141.67500 | | NFM | London | Breakfast Time News |
| 141.68125 | | NFM | Bedford | BBC |
| | | NFM | Lincolnshire | BBC TV O/B |
| 141.69375 | | NFM | Bangor | BBC |
| | | NFM | Gloucester | BBC |
| | | NFM | Nationwide | GLR Talkback |
| 141.69790 | | NFM | London | Radio London. |
| 141.70625 | | NFM | Devon | BBC |
| | | NFM | Leicesier | BBC |
| 141.71350 | | NFM | Merseyside | BBC |
| 141.71625 | | NFM | Glasgow | BBC |
| 141.71875 | | NFM | Solent | BBC |
| 141.72500 | | NFM | Northampton | BBC |
| | | NFM | Sheffield | BBC |
| | | NFM | Sheffield | BBC Radio Sheffield O/B |
| 141.73125 | | NFM | Cambridge | BBC |
| | | NFM | Newcastle | BBC |
| | | NFM | Sheffield | BBC |
| | | NFM | West Midlands | BBC |
| | | NFM | Wiltshire | BBC |
| 141.74375 | | NFM | London | Radio News |
| | | NFM | Nationwide | BBC Radio Cue |
| 141.75500 | | NFM | Stoke on Trent | Radio Stoke Engineering |
| 141.75625 | | NFM | Cardiff | BBC |
| | | NFM | Humberside | BBC |
| | | NFM | Stoke-on-Trent | BBC |
| | | NFM | Suffolk | BBC |
| 141.76625 | | NFM | Foyle | BBC |
| 141.76875 | | NFM | Crystal Palace | BBC Radio News |
| | | NFM | Edinburgh | BBC |
| | | NFM | Nationwide | BBC Radio Cue |
| 141.77500 | | NFM | Nationwide | BBC Radio OB (20kHz Audio Ch) |
| | | NFM | Sheffield | BBC Radio Sheffield O/B |
| 141.78125 | | NFM | Bristol | BBC |
| | | NFM | Cumbria | BBC |
| | | NFM | Derby | BBC |
| | | NFM | Leeds | BBC |
| 141.78750 | | NFM | Manchester | Radio Manchester O/B |
| 141.79375 | | NFM | Cambridge | BBC |
| | | NFM | Cleveland | BBC |
| | | NFM | Kent | BBC |
| | | NFM | Manchester | BBC |
| | | AM | Thames Valley | BBC |
| | | NFM | Warwickshire | BBC |
| 141.79500 | | NFM | Manchester | Radio Manchester O/B |
| 141.80000 | | NFM | Lincolnshire | BBC TV O/B |
| 141.81875 | | NFM | Nationwide | BBC News ENG |
| 141.82500 | | NFM | Nationwide | BBC News DB Link |
| | | AM | Nationwide | Patroulle de Francais air display team |

| Base | Mobile | Mode | Location | User and Notes |
|------|--------|------|----------|----------------|
| 141.83875 | | NFM | Nationwide | BBC O/B Camera Data |
| | | NFM | Nationwide | BBC TV O/B's Data |
| 141.85750 | | NFM | Brookman Park | BBC TX Group |
| | | NFM | Nationwide | BBC Transmitter Group |
| 141.86000 | | NFM | Holme Moss | BBC Maintenance |
| 141.86250 | | NFM | Crystal Palace | BBC ENG |
| | | NFM | Dorset | 2CR Eye-In-The-Sky |
| 141.87500 | 141.87500 | AM | Nationwide | BBC TV O/B's Data |
| 141.88750 | 141.88750 | AM | Nationwide | BBC TV Air-Ground |
| 141.89250 | 141.89250 | AM | Nationwide | BBC TFS Air-Ground |

### 141.9000 - 142.0000 MHz   GOVERNMENT AGENCIES NFM

| Base | Mobile | Mode | Location | User and Notes |
|------|--------|------|----------|----------------|
| 141.91250 | | NFM | Nationwide | Army |
| | | NFM | Swansea | Government Surveillance Teams |
| | | NFM | Swansea | Teritorial Army (DELTA) |
| 141.93750 | | NFM | Winter Hill-Isle of Man | Mould Link |
| 141.96250 | | NFM | Nationwide | Army |
| 141.98750 | | NFM | London | Police Wembley Relay Transmitter |
| | | NFM | Swansea | Government Surveillance Teams |
| | | NFM | Swansea | Teritorial Army (ALPHA) |
| 142.02500 | 142.02500 | AM | Nationwide | MoD Aircraft |

### 142.0000 - 142.9750 MHz  MOD, USAF & SOVIET SPACE COMMUNICATIONS

| Base | Mobile | Mode | Location | User and Notes |
|------|--------|------|----------|----------------|
| 142.02500 | | AM | Nationwide | USAF Air-Air |
| 142.05000 | | AM | Nationwide | USAF Air-Air |
| | | NFM | Thetford | Army Stanford exercise area |
| 142.07500 | | AM | Nationwide | USAF Air-Air |
| | | AM | USAF Mildenhall | Dep Con |
| 142.08750 | | NFM | North Yorkshire | Army |
| | | NFM | South Wales | Mould |
| | | NFM | Strathclyde | Mould |
| 142.10000 | | AM | Nationwide | USAF Air to Air |
| 142.11250 | | NFM | South Wales | Mould |
| 142.12500 | | NFM | London | Police Wembley Relay Transmitter |
| 142.15000 | | NFM | Humberside | USAF |
| 142.17500 | | NFM | London | Police Wembley Relay Transmitter |
| 142.21250 | | NFM | London | Police Wembley Relay Transmitter |
| 142.22500 | | AM | USAF Fairford | Tower |
| | | AM | RAF Manston | Ground |
| 142.27500 | | AM | USAF Mildenhall | ATIS |
| 142.28750 | | NFM | London | Police Wembley Relay Transmitter |
| 142.29500 | | AM | RAF Coltishall | Tower/Approach |
| | | AM | RAF Wittering | Approach |
| 142.31250 | | NFM | London | Police Wembley Relay Transmitter |
| 142.33750 | | NFM | Humberside | USAF |
| 142.36875 | | NFM | London Ealing | Police (XD) |
| 142.37500 | | NFM | Chepstow | Mould |
| | | AM | Coningsby | RAF 56 (R) 5QN |
| 142.40000 | | NFM | Space | Soviet Mir Space Station |
| 142.41250 | | NFM | Nationwide | Mould |
| | | NFM | South Wales | Mould |
| 142.41700 | | NFM | Space | Soviet Mir/Salyut 7 Space Station |
| 142.42000 | | NFM | Space | Soviet Mir Space Station |
| 142.42500 | | NFM | Dover | Government surveillance |
| | | NFM | Gosport | Fort Monkton Camp |
| | | NFM | Stanford | Army |
| | | NFM | Sussex | Royal Sigs Excerices |

| Base | Mobile | Mode | Location | User and Notes |
|---|---|---|---|---|
| 142.42500 | | NFM | Thetford | Army Stanford exercise area |
| 142.47500 | | AM | USAF Lakenheath | Approach |
| 142.48750 | | NFM | Strathclyde | Mould |
| 142.50000 | | NFM | Brighton | Lancer Minicabs Encrypted |
| | | NFM | Coulport | MoD Police |
| | | NFM | London | High Speed Computer Link |
| | | NFM | London | Lancer Minicabs Encrypted |
| 142.60000 | | NFM | Space | Soviet Mir Space Station |
| | | NFM | Stanford | Army |
| | | NFM | Thetford | Army Stanford exercise area |
| 142.61250 | 149.86750 | NFM | Cranmore | Mould |
| 142.61250 | 149.61250 | NFM | Dorset | Mould HF Links |
| 142.61250 | | NFM | Salisbury | Mould |
| 142.67500 | 149.82500 | NFM | Nationwide | MoD Paging |
| | | NFM | Nationwide | National MoD Radiopaging |
| 142.70000 | 142.70000 | AM | Nationwide | USAF Air-Air |
| 142.70500 | | NFM | Nationwide | BBC Radio 1 Roadshow Talkback |
| 142.72000 | | AM | Nationwide | USAF Air to Air |
| 142.72500 | | AM | Nationwide | USAF Air to Air |
| | | AM | RAF Brize Norton | 101 Sqn Air-Air |
| 142.77500 | | AM | Doncaster | RAF |
| 142.78750 | 149.71250 | NFM | Dorset | Mould HF Links |
| | | NFM | Newton/Morgans | Mould |
| 142.80000 | 142.80000 | AM | Nationwide | Backup NATO UFR |
| | | NFM | Stanford | Army |
| | | NFM | Thetford | Army Stanford exercise area |
| 142.82500 | | AM | Nationwide | USAF Air to Air |
| 142.83750 | | NFM | Lochaber | Fire Brigade |
| 142.85000 | | AM | USAF Mildenhall | Command Post |
| 142.87500 | | AM | Coningsby | RAF 56 (R) 5QN |
| 142.89750 | | NFM | Nationwide | Mould |
| 142.90000 | | AM | RAF Coltishall | Ops |
| 142.91250 | | NFM | Leicester | Mould |
| | | NFM | Strathclyde | Mould |
| 142.93750 | | NFM | Cornwall | Mould |
| | | NFM | Dorset | Mould |
| | | NFM | Suffolk | Mould |
| 142.95000 | | AM | Nationwide | USAF Air to Air |
| 142.97500 | 142.85000 | AM | USAF Mildenhall | US Navy Duty Air to Ground |
| 143.00000 | | AM | Nationwide | USAF Air to Air |

### 143.0000 - 144.0000 MHz METROPOLITAN AND SW SCOTTISH POLICE MOBILES (SIMPLEX)

| Base | Mobile | Mode | Location | User and Notes |
|---|---|---|---|---|
| 143.01250 | | NFM | Strathclyde | Police |
| 143.07500 | | NFM | Strathclyde | Police |
| 143.11250 | | NFM | Strathclyde | Police |
| 143.12500 | | NFM | Dumfries and Galloway | Police |
| 143.14400 | | NFM | Nongeostationary | Soviet Voice Channel |
| 143.15000 | | NFM | Strathclyde | Police |
| 143.16000 | | NFM | Dumfries and Galloway | Police |
| 143.21250 | | NFM | Strathclyde | Police |
| 143.25000 | | NFM | Dumfries and Galloway | Police |
| 143.27500 | | AM | Midlands | USAF |
| 143.30000 | | NFM | Strathclyde | Police |
| 143.35000 | | NFM | Strathclyde | Police |
| 143.37500 | | NFM | Dumfries and Galloway | Police |

| Base | Mobile | Mode | Location | User and Notes |
|------|--------|------|----------|----------------|
| 143.39000 | | NFM | Dumfries and Galloway | Police |
| 143.42500 | | NFM | Strathclyde | Police |
| 143.45000 | | AM | RAF West Drayton | London Military |
| 143.55000 | | NFM | Strathclyde | Police |
| 143.56250 | | NFM | Strathclyde | Police |
| 143.60000 | | AM | Nationwide | USAF Air-Air |
| | | NFM | Space | Shuttle to Mix link |
| 143.61250 | | NFM | Strathclyde | Police |
| 143.62500 | | NFM | Nongeostationary | Soviet Voice Channel (Mir) |
| | | NFM | Strathclyde | Police |
| 143.63750 | | NFM | Strathclyde | Police |
| 143.80000 | | AM | Nationwide | USAF Air-Air |
| 143.82500 | | NFM | Nongeostationary | Soviet Military Coded Ch |
| 143.88750 | | NFM | Belfast | Data Link |
| 143.90000 | | AM | Nationwide | USAF Air to Air |

### 144.0000 - 146.0000 MHz     2M AMATEUR RADIO

| Base | Mobile | Mode | Location | User and Notes |
|------|--------|------|----------|----------------|
| 144.05000 | | CW | Nationwide | CW calling frequency |
| 144.26000 | | NFM | Nationwide | Raynet |
| 144.30000 | | SSB | Nationwide | SSB calling frequency |
| 144.50000 | | NFM | Nationwide | SSTV Calling |
| | | CW | Nongeostationary | OSCAR 5 Telemetry beacon |
| 144.60000 | | NFM | Nationwide | RTTY calling |
| 144.67500 | | NFM | Nationwide | Packet radio |
| 144.70000 | | NFM | Nationwide | FAX calling |
| 144.75000 | | NFM | Nationwide | FSTV calling and talkback |
| 144.77500 | | NFM | Nationwide | Raynet |
| 144.91500 | | CW | St Austell | Beacon (GB3MCB) |
| 144.92500 | | CW | Wrotham | Beacon (GB3VHF) |
| 144.94200 | | CW | Ballymena | Repeater (GB3NGI) |
| 144.96500 | | CW | Lerwick | Beacon (GB3LER) |
| 144.97500 | | CW | Dundee | Beacon (GB3ANG) |
| 144.98300 | | CW | Nongeostationary | OSCAR 1 & 2 Beacon |
| 145.20000 | | NFM | Nationwide | Raynet S08 |
| 145.22500 | | NFM | Nationwide | Raynet S09 |
| 145.25000 | | NFM | Nationwide | Channel S10 |
| 145.27500 | | NFM | Nationwide | Channel S11 |
| 145.30000 | | NFM | Nationwide | Channel S12 |
| 145.32500 | | NFM | Nationwide | Channel S13 |
| 145.35000 | | NFM | Nationwide | Channel S14 |
| 145.37500 | | NFM | Nationwide | Channel S15 |
| 145.40000 | | NFM | Nationwide | Channel S16 |
| 145.42500 | | NFM | Nationwide | Channel S17 |
| 145.45000 | | NFM | Nationwide | Channel S18 |
| 145.47500 | | NFM | Nationwide | Channel S19 |
| 145.50000 | | NFM | Nationwide | Channel S20 |
| 145.52500 | | NFM | Nationwide | Channel S21 |
| 145.55000 | | NFM | Nationwide | Channel S22 |
| 145.57500 | | NFM | Nationwide | Channel S23 |
| 145.60000 | 145.00000 | NFM | Brighton | Amateur Radio Repeater (GB3SR) |
| | | NFM | Burntisland | Amateur Radio Repeater (GB3FF) |
| | | NFM | Bury | Amateur Radio Repeater (GB3MB) |
| | | NFM | Carlisle | Amateur Radio Repeater (GB3AS) |
| | | NFM | Charnwood Forest | Amateur Radio Repeater (GB3CF) |
| | | NFM | Driffield | Amateur Radio Repeater (GB3YC) |
| | | NFM | Elgin | Amateur Radio Repeater (GB3SS) |

| Base | Mobile | Mode | Location | User and Notes |
|---|---|---|---|---|
| 146.60000 | 145.00000 | NFM | Leicester | Amateur Radio Repeater (GB3CF) |
| | | NFM | Limavady | Amateur Radio Repeater (GB3LY) |
| | | NFM | London | Amateur Radio Repeater (GB3EL) |
| | | NFM | Mendips | Amateur Radio Repeater (GN3WR) |
| | | NFM | Wells | Amateur Radio Repeater (GB3WR) |
| 145.62500 | 145.02500 | NFM | Bournemouth | Amateur Radio Repeater (GB3SC) |
| | | NFM | Dalry | Amateur Radio Repeater (GB3AY) |
| | | NFM | Douglas | Amateur Radio Repeater (GB3GD) |
| | | NFM | Dover | Amateur Radio Repeater (GB3KS) |
| | | NFM | Fraserburgh | Amateur Radio Repeater (GB3NG) |
| 145.62500 | | NFM | Isle of Man | Amateur Radio Repeater (GB3GD) |
| | | NFM | London, Uxbridge | Amateur Radio Repeater (GB3WL) |
| | | NFM | Malvern | Amateur Radio Repeater (GB3MH) |
| | | NFM | Northallerton | Amateur Radio Repeater (GB3HG) |
| | | NFM | Norwich | Amateur Radio Repeater (GB3NB) |
| | | NFM | Paisley | Amateur Radio Repeater (GB3PA) |
| | | NFM | St Ives | Amateur Radio Repeater (GB3SI) |
| 145.65000 | 145.05000 | NFM | Bedford | Amateur Radio Repeater (GB3BF) |
| | | NFM | Birmingham | Amateur Radio Repeater (GB3WM) |
| | | NFM | Hull | Amateur Radio Repeater (GB3HS) |
| | | NFM | Ipswich | Amateur Radio Repeater (GB3PO) |
| | | NFM | Kirkwall | Amateur Radio Repeater (GB3OC) |
| | | NFM | London | Amateur Radio Repeater (GB3SL) |
| | | NFM | Selkirk | Amateur Radio Repeater (GB3SB) |
| | | NFM | St. Hellier, Jersey | Amateur Radio Repeater (GB3GJ) |
| | | NFM | Stockport | Amateur Radio Repeater (GB3MN) |
| | | NFM | Swindon | Amateur Radio Repeater (GB3WH) |
| | | NFM | Torquay | Amateur Radio Repeater (GB3TR) |
| 145.67500 | 145.07500 | NFM | Barnsley | Amateur Radio Repeater (GB3NA) |
| | | NFM | Barrow in Burness | Amateur Radio Repeater (GB3LD) |
| | | NFM | Hastings | Amateur Radio Repeater (GB3ES) |
| | | NFM | Lerwick | Amateur Radio Repeater (GB3LU) |
| | | NFM | Lochgilphead | Amateur Radio Repeater (GB3LG) |
| | | NFM | Perth | Amateur Radio Repeater (GB3PR) |
| | | NFM | Peterborough | Amateur Radio Repeater (GB3PE) |
| | | NFM | Reading | Amateur Radio Repeater (GB3RD) |
| | | NFM | Swansea | Amateur Radio Repeater (GB3SA) |
| | | NFM | Wolverhampton | Amateur Radio Repeater (GB3BX) |
| 145.70000 | 145.10000 | NFM | Appleby | Amateur Radio Repeater (GB3EV) |
| | | NFM | Aylesbury | Amateur Radio Repeater (GB3VA) |
| | | NFM | Berwick on Tweed | Amateur Radio Repeater (GB3BT) |
| | | NFM | Brecon | Amateur Radio Repeater (GB3BB) |
| | | NFM | Buxton | Amateur Radio Repeater (GB3HH) |
| | | NFM | Maidstone | Amateur Radio Repeater (GB3KN) |
| | | NFM | Oban | Amateur Radio Repeater (GB3HI) |
| | | NFM | Plymouth | Amateur Radio Repeater (GB3WD) |
| 145.72500 | 145.12500 | NFM | Alton | Amateur Radio Repeater (GB3SN) |
| | | NFM | Belfast | Amateur Radio Repeater (GB3NI) |
| | | NFM | Durham | Amateur Radio Repeater (GB3TW) |
| | | NFM | Forfar, Angus | Amateur Radio Repeater (GB3AG) |
| | | NFM | Inverness | Amateur Radio Repeater (GB3BI) |
| | | NFM | Keighley | Amateur Radio Repeater (GB3TP) |
| | | NFM | Lincoln | Amateur Radio Repeater (GB3LM) |
| | | NFM | St Austell | Amateur Radio Repeater (GB3NC) |
| | | NFM | Stoke on Trent | Amateur Radio Repeater (GB3VT) |

| Base | Mobile | Mode | Location | User and Notes |
|------|--------|------|----------|----------------|
| 145.75000 | 145.15000 | NFM | Crawley | Amateur Radio Repeater (GB3WS) |
| | | NFM | Denbigh | Amateur Radio Repeater (GB3MP) |
| | | NFM | Mansfield | Amateur Radio Repeater (GB3MX) |
| | | NFM | Newport | Amateur Radio Repeater (GB3BC) |
| | | NFM | Royston | Amateur Radio Repeater (GB3PI) |
| | | NFM | Salsburgh | Amateur Radio Repeater (GB3CS) |
| 145.77500 | 145.17500 | NFM | Aberdeen | Amateur Radio Repeater (GB3GN) |
| | | NFM | Burnley | Amateur Radio Repeater (GB3RF) |
| | | NFM | Clacton-on-Sea | Amateur Radio Repeater (GB3TE) |
| | | NFM | Crosshands | Amateur RadioRepeater (GB3WW) |
| | | NFM | Gatehouse of Fleet | Amateur Radio Repeater (GB3DG) |
| 145.77500 | | NFM | Leamington Spa | Amateur Radio Repeater (GB3WK) |
| | | NFM | Newtown | Amateur Radio Repeater (GB3PW) |
| | | NFM | Omagh | Amateur Radio Repeater (GB3WT) |
| | | NFM | Portsmouth | Amateur Radio Repeater (GB3PC) |
| | | NFM | Stornoway | Amateur Radio Repeater (GB3IG) |
| 145.78500 | 145.18500 | NFM | Buxton | Amateur Radio Repeater (GB3SF) |
| 145.80000 | | NFM | Nationwide | Raynet |
| 145.81000 | | CW | Nongeostationary | OSCAR 10 Beacon |
| 145.81750 | | CW | Nongeostationary | OSCAR 21 Beacon |
| 145.82500 | | CW | Nongeostationary | OSCAR 9 & 11 Telemetry |
| 145.95000 | | CW | Nongeostationary | OSCAR Beacons |
| 145.97500 | | CW | Nongeostationary | OSCAR 7 Telemetry Bcn |
| 145.98700 | | NFM | Nongeostationary | OSCAR 10 Engineering |
| 145.98750 | | NFM | Nongeostationary | OSCAR 21 Calling Channel |

Forfar Police Station showing the radio mast on the top
of the building

| Base | Mobile | Mode | Location | User and Notes |
|------|--------|------|----------|----------------|

**146.0000 - 148.0000 MHz**    GOVERNMENT AND POLICE

(REPEATERS + 8.0 MHz)

| Base | Mobile | Mode | Location | User and Notes |
|------|--------|------|----------|----------------|
| 146.0125 | | NFM | Newcastle | Police |
| 146.0125 | 154.9500 | NFM | Gwent | Fire Brigade (WR) |
| | | NFM | Thames Valley | Police |
| 146.0250 | | NFM | Darlington | Police |
| | | AM | Surrey | Fire Brigade (HF) |
| | | NFM | Tyne & Wear | Fire Brigade (LP) |
| | | NFM | West Mercia | Police (YK) |
| | | AM | West Sussex | Police (M2KB) |
| 146.0250 | 146.0250 | NFM | Dyfed & Powys | Police (WH) |
| | | NFM | North Wales | Police (WA) Channel 2 |
| 146.0375 | | NFM | Gerrards Cross | Police |
| 146.0375 | 154.8750 | NFM | Gwent | Fire Brigade (WP) |
| | | NFM | Thames Valley | Police |
| 146.0500 | | NFM | Derby | Fire Service ND |
| | | NFM | Essex | Police |
| | | NFM | Newport | Police |
| | | NFM | Yorkshire | Fire Brigade |
| 146.0625 | 154.9250 | NFM | Thames Valley | Police (HB) |
| 146.0750 | 154.9625 | NFM | South Wales | Police (WS) |
| | | NFM | Warwickshire | Police (YJ) |
| 146.0750 | 155.1500 | NFM | Manchester | Police (CK) |
| 146.0875 | | NFM | North Wales | Police Channel 4 |
| 146.1000 | | AM | Stockport | Police Mobile |
| 146.1000 | 146.1000 | NFM | Gloucester | Police (QL) Channel 1 |
| 146.1000 | 146.9000 | NFM | Suffolk | Police (VL) Channel 1 |
| 146.1000 | 154.7000 | NFM | Suffolk | Police (VL) Channel 3 |
| 146.1000 | 154.8625 | NFM | Suffolk | Police (VL) Channel 1 |
| 146.1000 | 155.0875 | NFM | Manchester | Police (CK) |
| 146.1000 | 155.8750 | NFM | Dorset | Police (OC) |
| 146.1125 | 155.6375 | NFM | Cumbria | Police (CC) |
| | | NFM | Warwickshire | Police (YJ) |
| 146.1250 | 146.1250 | NFM | Wiltshire | Police (QM) |
| 146.1250 | 154.0125 | NFM | Lancashire | Police (BB) |
| | | NFM | North M25 | Police (SM) |
| 146.1250 | 154.8875 | NFM | South Wales | Police (WL) |
| 146.1250 | | NFM | Cardiff | Police (WY) |
| 146.1375 | | NFM | North Wales | Police Channel 1 |
| 146.1375 | 154.0500 | NFM | West Mercia | Police (K) |
| 146.1375 | 154.1000 | NFM | Thames Valley | Police (HB) |
| 146.1500 | 146.1500 | NFM | Dyfed & Powys | Police (WH) |
| | | NFM | Loansdean | Police (M2LB) |
| 146.1500 | 154.8875 | NFM | South Wales | Police (WY) |
| 146.1625 | 154.0875 | NFM | South M25 | Police (SM) |
| 146.1750 | | NFM | Cambridgeshire | Fire Brigade |
| | | NFM | West Mercia | Police (YK) |
| 146.1750 | 154.0750 | NFM | Berkshire | Fire Brigade (G) |
| | | NFM | Devon/Cornwall | Fire Brigade (OA) |
| | | NFM | Lancashire | Police (BD) |
| | | NFM | Thames Valley | Fire Brigade (Q) |
| 146.1750 | 154.1250 | NFM | Cambridgeshire | Fire Brigade (VP) |
| | | NFM | London | Fire Brigade (FN) |
| | | NFM | Staffordshire | Fire Brigade (YG) |
| | | NFM | West Mercia | Police (YK) |
| | | NFM | Wiltshire | Fire Brigade (GM) |

| Base | Mobile | Mode | Location | User and Notes |
|------|--------|------|----------|----------------|
| 146.1750 | 154.4750 | NFM | Kent | Fire Brigade (HO) |
| | | NFM | Staffordshire | Fire Brigade (YG) |
| | | NFM | Wiltshire | Fire Brigade (GM) |
| 146.1750 | 154.9375 | NFM | South Wales | Police (WX) |
| 146.1875 | | AM | West Sussex | Police (M2KB) |
| 146.1875 | 154.9000 | NFM | Dorset | Police (OC) |
| 146.2000 | 146.2000 | NFM | Essex | Police (VB) Channel 2 |
| | | NFM | Jersey | EmerServices On-Site Comms |
| 146.2000 | 155.8000 | NFM | Surrey | Police (HJ) |
| 146.2000 | 155.8875 | NFM | Cumbria | Police (BB) |
| 146.2125 | | NFM | Essex | Police |
| 146.2125 | 146.2125 | NFM | West Haverford | Police (WL) |
| 146.2125 | 155.0125 | NFM | Manchester | Police (CK) |
| 146.2125 | 155.4625 | NFM | Devon & Cornwall | Police (GB) |
| 146.2250 | 146.2250 | NFM | Devon & Cornwall | Police (QD) |
| | | NFM | Staffordshire | Police (YB) |
| | | NFM | Staffs | Fire Service YT |
| | | NFM | Thames Valley | Police (HU) |
| 146.2250 | 155.6375 | NFM | Surrey | Police (HJ) |
| 146.2375 | 155.0625 | NFM | Manchester | Police (CK) |
| 146.2375 | 155.3250 | NFM | Devon & Cornwall | Police (GB) |
| 146.2500 | 155.5875 | NFM | Cumbria | Police (BB) |
| 146.2500 | 155.8625 | NFM | Surrey | Police (HJ) |
| 146.2625 | 155.3625 | NFM | Devon & Cornwall | Police (DB) |
| 146.2625 | 155.6500 | NFM | Derbyshire | Police (NA) |
| 146.2750 | | NFM | Lancashire | Police Helicopter |
| 146.2750 | 154.6750 | NFM | London | Fire Brigade (FE) |
| | | NFM | Nottinghamshire | Fire Brigade (NZ) |
| 146.2750 | 154.8375 | NFM | Thames Valley | Police (HB) |
| 146.2750 | 154.9375 | NFM | Lancashire | Police (BB) |
| 146.2875 | 146.2875 | NFM | Jersey | Ambulance Ch 3 |
| 146.2875 | 155.5750 | NFM | Cheshire | Fire Brigade (CF) |
| | | NFM | Devon & Cornwall | Police |
| 146.2875 | 155.8375 | NFM | Derbyshire | Police (NA) |
| 146.3000 | 146.3000 | NFM | Jersey | Fire Brigade Ch 3 |
| | | NFM | Jersey | Ambulance Ch 8 |
| 146.3000 | 155.4625 | NFM | Lancshire | Police |
| 146.3000 | 154.7750 | NFM | Thames Valley | Police |
| 146.3125 | | NFM | Sussex | Police |
| 146.3125 | 146.3125 | NFM | Jersey | Ambulance Ch 4 |
| 146.3125 | 155.2625 | NFM | Cheshire | Police |
| 146.3250 | 154.6250 | NFM | West Midlands | Police |
| 146.3250 | | NFM | Avon | Police (QP) |
| | | NFM | Bristol | Police (QP) |
| | | NFM | Dyfed | Police (WH) |
| | | AM | West Sussex | Police (M2KB) |
| 146.3375 | 155.2250 | NFM | Sussex | Police |
| 146.3375 | 155.4875 | NFM | Cheshire | Police |
| 146.3500 | | NFM | Newport | Police |
| 146.3500 | 146.3500 | NFM | Gwent | Police (WO/WE) |
| | | NFM | Jersey | Fire Brigade Ch 4 |
| | | NFM | Jersey | Ambulance Ch 9 |
| 146.3500 | 154.4500 | NFM | West Midlands | Police |
| 146.3500 | 154.1750 | NFM | London Area | Fire Brigade |
| 146.3625 | 155.0500 | NFM | Sussex | Police |
| 146.3625 | 155.3875 | NFM | Cheshire | Police |

| Base | Mobile | Mode | Location | User and Notes |
|------|--------|------|----------|----------------|
| 146.3625 | 154.1375 | NFM | Cambridge | Police |
| 146.3750 | 154.7000 | NFM | West Midlands | Police |
| 146.3875 | | AM | West Sussex | Police Mobile |
| 146.3875 | 155.4250 | NFM | Manchester | Police |
| 146.3875 | 155.1875 | NFM | Sussex | Police (KB) |
| 146.4000 | | NFM | Cleveland | Police |
| | | NFM | Lincoln | Police |
| 146.4000 | 146.4000 | NFM | Northamptonshire | Police (NB) Channel 2 |
| 146.4000 | 155.0875 | AM | Hampshire | Police |
| 146.4125 | | AM | Kent | Fire Brigade (KF) |
| | | AM | Stockport | Police Mobile |
| | | NFM | Wetherby | Police Repeater (GS) |
| 146.4125 | 155.6125 | NFM | Manchester | Police |
| 146.4125 | 155.2875 | NFM | Sussex | Police |
| 146.4250 | 154.9750 | NFM | West Midlands | Police |
| 146.4250 | 146.4250 | NFM | North Wales | Police (WA) Channel 1 |
| 146.4250 | | NFM | Staffs | Fire Service YM |
| 146.4375 | 155.1000 | NFM | North Wales | Police |
| 146.4375 | 155.1125 | NFM | Hampshire | Police |
| 146.4500 | | NFM | Essex | Fire Brigade (VD) |
| 146.4500 | 146.4500 | NFM | Northamptonshire | Police (NB) |
| 146.4500 | 146.4500 | NFM | Devon | Police (QB) |
| 146.4500 | 155.6375 | NFM | Cumbria | Police |
| 146.4500 | 154.3125 | NFM | West Midlands | Police |
| 146.4625 | 154.4255 | NFM | North Wales | Police |
| 146.4625 | 155.1625 | NFM | Hampshire | Police |
| 146.4625 | 155.5375 | NFM | West Midlands | Police |
| 146.4750 | | NFM | Darlington | Police |
| | | NFM | Lewes | Police |
| | | AM | West Sussex | Police (M2KB) |
| 146.4750 | 154.2625 | NFM | West Midlands | Police |
| 146.4875 | 154.1000 | NFM | North Wales | Police |
| 146.4875 | 154.9125 | NFM | Norfolk | Police |
| 146.4875 | 155.2625 | NFM | Hampshire | Police |
| 146.5000 | | NFM | Durham | Fire Brigade (M2LF) |
| 146.5000 | 154.5000 | NFM | Jersey | Police |
| 146.5125 | 154.0250 | NFM | West Mercia | Police |
| 146.5250 | | NFM | Hertfordshire | Police |
| 146.5250 | 154.5500 | NFM | Suffolk | Fire Brigade |
| 146.5375 | 154.0500 | NFM | Derbyshire | Fire Brigade |
| | | NFM | West Mercia | Fire Brigade |
| | | NFM | Yorkshire | Fire Brigade (XK) |
| 146.5500 | 146.5500 | AM | Cardiff | Police (WY) |
| | | NFM | Jersey | Police (M2GS) Ch 5 |
| | | NFM | Loansdean | Fire Brigade (M2LJ) |
| 146.5500 | | AM | South Glamorgan | Police (WY) |
| | | AM | South Wales | Police (WJ) |
| 146.5675 | 154.1125 | NFM | West Mercia | Fire Brigade |
| | | NFM | Suffolk | Police (VL) Channel 1 |
| 146.5750 | 155.1500 | NFM | Avon & Somerset | Police |
| 146.5750 | 155.8125 | NFM | Suffolk | Police (154.8625) |
| 146.5750 | 146.9250 | NFM | Suffolk | Police (154.8875, 152.8375) |
| | | NFM | Suffolk | Police (154.8875, 154.2750) |
| 146.5875 | 154.2000 | NFM | Staffordshire | Police |
| 146.5875 | 155.1000 | NFM | Kent | Police |
| 146.6000 | | AM | Newcastle | Police |

| Base | Mobile | Mode | Location | User and Notes |
|---|---|---|---|---|
| 146.6000 | 155.2000 | NFM | Hertfordshire | Police |
| 146.6000 | 155.4750 | NFM | Dyfed, Powys | Police |
| 146.6075 | 154.0250 | NFM | Cambridge | Police (VB) |
| 146.6125 | 154.0250 | NFM | East Sussex | Fire Brigade |
| 146.6125 | 154.5500 | NFM | Staffordshire | Police |
| 146.6125 | 154.9375 | NFM | Kent | Police |
| 146.6175 | 154.9625 | NFM | Kent | Police |
| 146.6250 | 154.6250 | NFM | Jersey | Police |
| 146.6250 | 155.1250 | NFM | Hertfordshire | Police |
| 146.6250 | 155.1625 | NFM | Warwickshire | Police |
| 146.6250 | 155.2750 | NFM | Powys | Police |
| 146.6250 | 155.4125 | NFM | Dyfed & Wales | Police |
| 146.6375 | | AM | Newcastle | Police |
| 146.6450 | | NFM | Hutton | Police Link |
| 146.6500 | 155.2375 | NFM | Hertfordshire | Police (VH) |
| 146.6500 | 155.2000 | NFM | Dyfed | Police (WH) |
| 146.6600 | | NFM | West Midlands | Fire Brigade |
| 146.6625 | 155.0500 | NFM | South Wales | Police (WA) |
| 146.6625 | 155.1375 | NFM | Kent | Police (KA) |
| 146.6625 | | NFM | Staffs | Fire Service SE) |
| 146.6750 | 154.1500 | NFM | Gloucester | Police (OL) |
| 146.6750 | 154.9875 | NFM | Norfolk | Police (VK) |
| 146.6875 | 154.9750 | NFM | Hampshire | Police (HK) |
| 146.7000 | 154.2250 | NFM | Gloucester | Fire Brigade (GL) |
| | | NFM | Staffordshire | Fire Brigade (YG) |
| 146.7000 | 154.8250 | NFM | Humberside | Fire Brigade (XT) |
| 146.7125 | | NFM | Gwynedd | Fire Brigade (WC) |
| 146.7250 | | NFM | Norfolk | Fire Brigade |
| 146.7250 | 154.3625 | NFM | Gloucester | Fire Brigade (GL) |
| 146.7250 | 154.8000 | NFM | Lancashire | Police |
| | | NFM | Leicester | Police |
| | | NFM | Sussex | Fire Brigade (KV) |
| 146.7375 | | AM | Hungerford | Police (HU) |
| 146.7375 | 154.3375 | NFM | Haverfordwest | Police (WH) |
| | | NFM | Thames Valley, Hungerford | Police |
| 146.7500 | | NFM | Leicester | Police |
| 146.7625 | 155.0625 | NFM | Avon & Somerset | Police |
| | | AM | Newport | Police Helicopter |
| 146.7750 | 145.1750 | NFM | Gatehouse of Fleet | Repeater (GB3DG) |
| 146.7750 | 154.9125 | NFM | Gwent | Police |
| | | NFM | Kent Motorways | Police (TD) |
| 146.7875 | 155.0375 | NFM | Avon & Somerset | Police |
| 146.8000 | 154.7875 | NFM | Gwent | Police |
| 146.8125 | 155.0125 | NFM | Avon & Somerset | Police |
| 146.8250 | | NFM | Lewes | Fire Brigade |
| | | AM | West Sussex | Police (M2KB) |
| 146.8250 | 154.0625 | NFM | Merseyside | Police |
| 146.8375 | 154.9000 | NFM | Bedfordshire | Police |
| | | NFM | Merseyside | Police |
| 146.8500 | 154.9875 | NFM | Avon & Somerset | Police |
| | | NFM | Norfolk | Police |
| 146.8625 | 154.7375 | NFM | Bedfordshire | Police |
| 146.8626 | | NFM | London | Rimington Minicabs Encrypted |
| 146.8750 | 154.8125 | NFM | Gwent | Police |
| 146.8750 | | AM | West Hoathly | Police Link (M2KB) |

| Base | Mobile | Mode | Location | User and Notes |
|------|--------|------|----------|----------------|
| 146.8750 | | NFM | Lewes | Police |
| | | NFM | Nottinghamshire | Fire Brigade |
| 146.8875 | 155.9375 | NFM | Thames Valley | Police |
| 146.9000 | | NFM | Merseyside | Police |
| 146.9000 | 146.9000 | NFM | Loansdean | Police (M2LB) |
| 146.9000 | 154.8625 | NFM | Suffolk | Police (VK) |
| 146.9000 | 154.9250 | NFM | Devon & Cornwall | Police |
| | | NFM | Merseyside | Police (CM) |
| 146.9125 | | NFM | West Midlands | Police (MA) |
| 146.9125 | 155.0125 | NFM | Wiltshire | Police |
| 146.9250 | | NFM | Merseyside | Police |
| 146.9250 | 146.5750 | NFM | Suffolk | Police (VL) Channel 1 |
| 146.9250 | 154.8875 | NFM | Suffolk | Police (VL) |
| 146.9250 | 155.1750 | NFM | Merseyside | Police |
| 146.9250 | 155.5125 | NFM | Devon & Cornwall | Police |
| 146.9375 | 155.8500 | NFM | Wiltshire | Police |
| 146.9500 | | NFM | Lewes | Police |
| | | AM | West Sussex | Police (M2KB) |
| 146.9500 | 155.2250 | NFM | Merseyside | Police |
| 146.9500 | 155.3875 | NFM | Devon & Cornwall | Police |
| 146.9625 | 155.9000 | NFM | Wiltshire | Police |
| 146.9750 | 155.3250 | NFM | Merseyside | Police |
| 146.9750 | 155.3000 | NFM | Devon & Cornwall | Police |
| 147.0000 | 154.5750 | NFM | Hampshire | Fire Brigade |
| 147.0000 | 155.3375 | NFM | Hampshire | Fire Brigade |
| 147.0000 | 155.4000 | NFM | Hereford/Worcester | Fire Brigade |
| 147.0000 | 155.4500 | NFM | West Midlands | Fire Brigade |
| 147.0000 | 155.6000 | NFM | Staffordshire | Fire Brigade |
| 147.0100 | | NFM | Thames Valley | Police |
| 147.0125 | | NFM | London | Diplomatic Protection (Ranger) |
| | | NFM | London, Ealing | Police, Kingston (VK) |
| 147.0125 | 147.0125 | NFM | Crickhowel | Army |
| | | AM | Wiltshire | Fire Brigade |
| 147.0125 | 155.9250 | NFM | Dorset | Police |
| 147.0250 | 154.7875 | NFM | Cambridge | Police |
| 147.0375 | | NFM | Newcastle | Police |
| 147.0500 | | AM | Newcastle | Data Link |
| 147.0500 | 146.5750 | NFM | Shropshire | Fire Brigade (YU) |
| 147.0600 | | AM | West Sussex | Police (M2KB) |
| 147.0625 | | NFM | Lewes | Police |
| | | NFM | Northampton | Police |
| | | AM | West Sussex | Police (M2KB) |
| 147.0750 | 154.6125 | NFM | Wiltshire | Police |
| 147.0875 | 155.2125 | NFM | Avon & Somerset | Police |
| 147.1000 | | AM | West Sussex | Police (M2KB) |
| 147.1000 | | NFM | Nuneaton, Warks | Fire Service YJ |
| 147.1250 | | AM | West Sussex | Police (M2KB) |
| 147.1250 | 147.1250 | NFM | London Heathrow | Airport Police (India Hunter) |
| 147.1250 | | NFM | Bambury Oxon | Fire Service Ch 2 |
| | | NFM | Leamington Spa, Warks | Fire Service (YK) |
| 147.1500 | | NFM | London, Barkingside | Police (JB) |
| 147.1625 | | NFM | Warwickshire | Fire Service (YS) |
| 147.2000 | | NFM | London | Diplomatic Protection (Ranger) Ch 25 |

| Base | Mobile | Mode | Location | User and Notes |
|------|--------|------|----------|----------------|
| 147.2125 | 155.3125 | NFM | Brockley | Police (PK) |
| | | NFM | London, Bethnal Green | Police (HB) Channel 26 |
| | | NFM | London, Brick Lane | Police (HR) |
| | | NFM | London, Harrow Road | Police (DR) |
| | | NFM | London, Kings Cross | Police (HD) |
| 147.2250 | 155.3250 | NFM | Banstead | Police (ZB) Channel 27 |
| | | NFM | Barkingside | Police (JB) |
| | | NFM | Beckenham | Police (PB) |
| | | NFM | Edinburgh | Police (K) |
| | | NFM | Hainault | Police (JT) |
| | | NFM | Hendon | Police (HO) |
| | | NFM | London, Loughton | Police (JO) |
| | | NFM | London, Stoneleigh | Police (ZS) |
| | | NFM | London, Whitechapel | Police (HT) |
| | | NFM | London, Woodford Green | Police (JF) |
| | | NFM | Sutton | Police (ZT) |
| | | NFM | Wallington | Police (ZW) |
| | | NFM | Waltham Abbey | Police (JA) |
| 147.2300 | | NFM | London | Police Loughton |
| 147.2375 | | AM | Stockport | Police Mobile |
| 147.2375 | 155.3375 | NFM | Camberwell | Police (MC) |
| | | NFM | Hackney | Police (GH) |
| | | NFM | Norbury | Police (ZN) |
| | | NFM | London, Dalston | Police (GA) Channel 28 |
| | | NFM | Stoke Newington | Police (GN) |
| 147.2500 | 155.3500 | NFM | Bedfordshire | Police Ch 29 |
| | | NFM | Borehamwood | Police (SD) Channel 29 |
| | | NFM | Bushey | Police (SU) |
| | | NFM | City Road | Police (GD) |
| | | NFM | Dalston | Police (GA) |
| | | NFM | London, Barnet | Police (SA) |
| | | NFM | London, Hackney | Police (GH) |
| | | NFM | London, Potter's Bar | Police (SP) |
| | | NFM | London, Rochester Row | Police (AR) |
| | | NFM | London, Shenley | Police (SY) |
| | | NFM | London, South Mimms | Police (SM) |
| | | NFM | London, Whetstone | Police (ST) |
| | | NFM | London, South Norwood | Police (ZS) CTCSS Tones |
| | | NFM | Nationwide | Police Ch 29 |
| | | NFM | Radlett | Police (SE) |
| | | NFM | Stoneleigh | Police (ZL) |
| 147.2625 | 155.3625 | NFM | Beckenham | Police (PB) |
| | | NFM | Canterbury | Police |
| | | NFM | Debden | Police (JE) |
| | | NFM | Lewisham | Police (PL) |
| | | NFM | London, Chigwell | Police (JD) |
| | | NFM | London, Chingford | Police (JC) |
| | | NFM | London, Hampstead | Police (EH) |
| | | NFM | London, Waltham Abbey | Police (JA) |
| | | NFM | London, Walthamstow | Police (JW) |
| | | NFM | London, West Hampstead | Police (EW) |
| | | NFM | Waltham Abbey | Police (JA) Channel 30 |

| Base | Mobile | Mode | Location | User and Notes |
|------|--------|------|----------|----------------|
| 147.2750 | 155.3750 | NFM | Barnet | Police (SA) |
| | | NFM | Borenhamwood | Police (SD) |
| | | NFM | Bow Street | Police (CB) |
| | | NFM | Bushey | Police (SC) |
| | | NFM | Harold Hill | Police (KA) |
| | | NFM | London, Forest Gate | Police (KF) |
| | | NFM | London, Sydenham | Police (PS) CTCSS Tones |
| | | NFM | London, West Ham | Police (KW) |
| | | NFM | Plaistow | Police (KO) |
| | | NFM | Potters Bar | Police (SP) |
| | | NFM | Radlett | Police (SE) |
| | | NFM | Shenley | Police (SY) |
| | | NFM | Vine Street | Police (CV) Channel 31 |
| | | NFM | West End Central | Police (CD) |
| | | NFM | Whetstone | Police (ST) |
| 147.2875 | 155.3875 | NFM | Chingford | Police (JC) |
| | | NFM | Croydon | Police (ZD) |
| | | NFM | Kingsbury | Police (RK) |
| | | NFM | London, Battersea | Police (WA) |
| | | NFM | London, Belvedere | Police (RB) |
| | | NFM | London, Feltham | Police (TF) |
| | | NFM | London, Hounslow | Police (TD) |
| | | NFM | London, Tooting | Police (WD) |
| | | NFM | London, Trinity Road | Police (WT) |
| | | NFM | Waltham Abbey | Police (JA) |
| | | NFM | Walthamstow | Police (JW) |
| 147.3000 | 155.4000 | NFM | London, Brixton | Police (LD) |
| | | NFM | London, Edgware | Police (QE) |
| | | NFM | London, Hampton | Police (TM) Channel 33 |
| | | NFM | London, Harlesden | Police (QH) |
| | | NFM | London, Kilburn | Police (OK) |
| | | NFM | London, St Anne's Road | Police (YA) |
| | | NFM | London, Sunbury | Police (TY) |
| | | NFM | London, Teddington | Police (TT) |
| | | NFM | London, Tottenham | Police (YT) |
| | | NFM | London, Twickenham | Police (TW) |
| | | NFM | London, Willesden Green | Police (QL) |
| | | NFM | London, Wood Green | Police (YD) |
| | | NFM | Shepperton | Police (TG) |
| | | NFM | Staines | Police (TG) |
| | | NFM | Staines | Police (TW) |
| 147.3125 | 155.4125 | NFM | London, Chelsea | Police (BC) |
| | | NFM | London, East Molesey | Police (VE) |
| | | NFM | London, Greenwich | Police (RG) |
| | | NFM | London, Kingsbury | Police (QY) |
| | | NFM | London, Lewisham | Police (PL) |
| | | NFM | London, Surbiton | Police (VS) |
| | | NFM | London, Wembley | Police (QD) |
| | | NFM | Norfolk | Police (VK) |
| | | NFM | Shooters Hill | Police (RH) |
| | | NFM | Thamesmead | Police (RT) |
| | | NFM | West Hendon | Police (SW) |
| | | NFM | Westcombe Park | Police (QY) |

| Base | Mobile | Mode | Location | User and Notes |
|------|--------|------|----------|----------------|
| 147.3250 | 155.4250 | AM | Cheshunt | Police (YC) Channel 35 |
| | | NFM | Earlsfield | Police (WF) |
| | | NFM | Harlesden | Police (QH) |
| | | NFM | London, Collier Row | Police (KL) |
| | | NFM | London, Edmonton | Police |
| | | NFM | London, Enfield | Police (YF) |
| | | NFM | London, Goffs Oak | Police (YG) |
| | | NFM | London, Harold Hill | Police (KA) |
| | | NFM | London, Hornchurch | Police (KC) |
| | | NFM | London, Ponders End | Police (YP) |
| | | NFM | London, Putney | Police (WP) |
| | | NFM | London, Romford | Police (KD) |
| | | NFM | London, Tooting | Police (WD) |
| | | NFM | London, Tower Bridge | Police (MT) |
| | | NFM | London, Upminster | Police (KU) |
| | | AM | Rainham | Police (KM) |
| | | NFM | Staines | Police (TS) |
| 147.3375 | 155.4375 | NFM | London | Police (GT) Channel 36 |
| 147.3500 | 155.4500 | NFM | Biggin Hill | Police (PH) |
| | | NFM | Chiselhurst | Police (PC) |
| | | NFM | Farnborough | Police (PF) |
| | | NFM | Harefield | Police (XF) Channel 37 |
| | | NFM | Highbury Vale | Police (NV) |
| | | NFM | London, Holloway | Police (NH) |
| | | NFM | London, Lewisham | Police (PL) |
| | | NFM | London, Northwood | Police (XN) |
| | | NFM | London, Orpington | Police (PN) |
| | | NFM | Ruislip | Police (XB) |
| | | NFM | St Mary Cray | Police (PM) |
| | | NFM | Uxbridge | Police (XU) |
| 147.3500 | 155.4750 | NFM | Northampton | Police Ch27 |
| 147.3625 | 155.4625 | NFM | Barking | Police (KB) Channel 38 |
| | | NFM | Dagenham | Police (KG) |
| | | NFM | Leytonstone | Police (JS) |
| | | NFM | London Golders Green | Police (SG) |
| | | NFM | London, Finchley | Police (SF) |
| | | NFM | London, Leyton | Police (JL) |
| 147.3750 | 155.4750 | NFM | Barking | Police (KB) |
| | | NFM | Hayes | Police (XY) |
| | | NFM | Kings Cross | Police (HD) |
| | | NFM | London Hendon | Police (SN) |
| | | NFM | London, Arbour Square | Police (HA) |
| | | NFM | London, City Road | Police (GD) |
| | | NFM | London, East Ham | Police (KE) |
| | | NFM | London, Harold Hill | Police (KA) |
| | | NFM | London, Mill Hill | Police (SH) |
| | | NFM | London, North Woolwich | Police (KN) |
| | | NFM | London, Plaistow | Police (KO) |
| | | NFM | London, West Ham | Police (KW) |
| | | NFM | Wellington | Police (AW) Channel 39 |
| | | NFM | West Drayton | Police (XW) |
| | | NFM | West Hendon | Police (SG) |

| Base | Mobile | Mode | Location | User and Notes |
|------|--------|------|----------|----------------|
| 147.3875 | 155.4875 | NFM | London, Belvedere | Police (RB) |
| | | NFM | London, Gerard Road | Police (AL) |
| | | NFM | London, Harrow Road | Police (DR) |
| | | NFM | London, Highgate | Police (YH) |
| | | NFM | London, Hornsey | Police (NR) |
| | | NFM | London, Marylebone Lane | Police (PM) |
| | | NFM | London, Muswell Hill | Police (YM) |
| | | NFM | London, Paddington Green | Police (DD) |
| | | NFM | London, St Annes Road | Police (YA) |
| | | NFM | London, Wood Green | Police (YD) |
| | | NFM | Hampton | Police (TM) |
| 147.4000 | 155.5000 | NFM | London, Barnes | Police (TN) Channel 41 |
| | | NFM | London, Holborn | Police (EO) |
| | | NFM | Streatham | Police (LS) |
| | | NFM | Twickenham | Police (TW) |
| | | NFM | London, West Ham | Police (TH) |
| 147.4125 | 155.5125 | NFM | London, Caledonian Road | Police (NC) |
| | | NFM | London, Chadwell Heath | Police (JH) |
| | | NFM | London, Chigwell | Police (JD) |
| | | NFM | London, Ilford | Police (JI) |
| | | NFM | London, Islington | Police (NI) |
| | | NFM | London, Kings Cross | Police (ND) |
| | | NFM | London, New Southgate | Police (YN) |
| | | NFM | London, Nine Elms | Police (WN) |
| | | NFM | London, Wanstead | Police (JN) |
| 147.4250 | 155.5250 | NFM | Acton | Police (XA) Channel 43 |
| | | NFM | Ealing | Police (XD) |
| | | NFM | Epsom | Police (ZP) |
| | | NFM | London Southgate | Police (YS) |
| | | NFM | London, Bow Street | Police (CB) |
| | | NFM | London, Edmonton | Police (YE) |
| | | NFM | London, Edmonton | Police (YE) |
| | | NFM | London, Wembley | Police (QD) |
| | | NFM | London, Winchmore Hill | Police (YW) |
| | | NFM | Stoneleigh | Police (ZL) |
| 147.4375 | 155.5375 | NFM | Barkingside | Police (JB) |
| | | NFM | Greenford | Police (XG) |
| | | NFM | London Southall | Police (XS) |
| | | NFM | London, Bow | Police (HW) Channel 44 |
| | | NFM | London, Brick Lane | Police (HR) |
| | | NFM | London, Isle of Dogs | Police (HI) |
| | | NFM | London, Kings Cross | Police (HD) |
| | | NFM | London, Limehouse | Police (HH) |
| | | NFM | London, Norwood Green | Police (XW) |
| | | NFM | London, Poplar | Police (HP) |
| | | NFM | Loughton | Police (JO) |
| | | NFM | Waltham Abbey | Police (JA) |
| 147.4500 | 155.5500 | NFM | Brentwood | Police (TB) Channel 45 |
| | | NFM | Chiswick | Police (TC) |
| | | NFM | Hammersmith | Police (FH) |
| | | NFM | Harrow | Police (QA) |
| | | NFM | London, Camberwell | Police (MC) |
| | | NFM | London, Carter Street | Police (MS) |
| | | NFM | London, Edgware | Police (QE) |
| | | NFM | London, Harrow Road | Police (DR) |
| | | NFM | London, Kentish Town | Police (EK) |

| Base | Mobile | Mode | Location | User and Notes |
|---|---|---|---|---|
| 147.4500 | 155.5500 | NFM | London, Marylebone | Police (DM) |
| | | NFM | London, St Johns Wood | Police (DS) |
| | | NFM | Pinner | Police (QP) |
| | | NFM | Richmond | Police (TR) |
| | | NFM | Wealdstone | Police (QW) |
| 147.4625 | 155.5625 | NFM | London | Met Police (GT) |
| 147.4750 | 155.5750 | NFM | Harlesden | Police (QH) |
| | | NFM | Harrow | Police (QA) |
| | | NFM | London, Albany Street | Police (ED) Channel 47 |
| | | NFM | London, Edgeware | Police (QE) |
| | | NFM | London, Hammersmith | Police (FD) F Div HQ |
| | | NFM | London, Kentish Town | Police (EK) |
| | | NFM | London, Marylebone | Police (DM) |
| | | NFM | London, Pinner | Police |
| | | NFM | London, Shephards Bush | Police (FH) |
| | | NFM | London, Southwark | Police (MD) |
| | | NFM | London, Tottenham Ct Rd | Police (ET) |
| | | NFM | London, Wealdstone | Police (QW) |
| | | NFM | Westcombe Park | Police (QY) |
| 147.4875 | 155.5875 | NFM | London | TSG Special Events |
| | | NFM | London | Police (GT) Channel 48 |
| 147.5000 | | NFM | Enniskillen | Military Data Link |
| 147.5000 | 155.6000 | NFM | London | Police (GT) Channel 49 |
| 147.5125 | 155.6125 | NFM | London | Police Engineers (GT) |
| | | NFM | London | Police (GT) Channel 50 |
| 147.5250 | 155.6250 | NFM | Bonnyrigg | Police |
| | | NFM | London | Police Control Ch 57 |
| | | NFM | London | Police Engineers (GT) |
| | | NFM | London | Police (GT) Channel 51 |
| 147.5375 | 154.0625 | NFM | Chichester | Fire Brigade |
| 147.5375 | 155.6375 | NFM | London | Police Engineers (GT) |
| 147.5500 | 155.6500 | NFM | London | Police Control Ch 53 |
| | | NFM | London | Police Engineers (GT) |
| | | NFM | London | Police (GT) Channel 53 |
| 147.5625 | | NFM | Derby | Police |
| 147.5750 | | NFM | Eastleigh | Fire Brigade |
| | | NFM | Northampton | Police data |
| 147.5800 | | NFM | London | Police Ch 29 |
| 147.5875 | 155.6875 | NFM | Norfolk | Police (VK1) |
| | | NFM | London | Police Inter-County Channel |
| 147.6000 | | NFM | Hereford & Worcester | Fire Brigade (YB) |
| 147.6000 | 155.7000 | NFM | Nationwide | RCS Channel 57 |
| | | NFM | Sussex | RCS |
| 147.6250 | 155.7250 | NFM | West Midlands | Police (YM) Channel 58 |
| | | NFM | Nationwide | RCS Channel 59 |
| 147.6500 | | NFM | Lewes | Police |
| | | NFM | Lincolnshire | Police (NC) Channel 1 |
| | | NFM | West Mercia | Police (YK) |
| 147.6500 | 155.7500 | NFM | Nationwide | RCS Surveillance Channel 61 |
| | | AM | West Sussex | Police (M2KB) |
| 147.6625 | 147.6625 | NFM | Bolton | Police Motorcycle Instructors |
| | | AM | Lancashire | Police (Car-Car) |
| | | NFM | Workington | Motor Cycle Training |
| 147.6750 | | NFM | Eastleigh | Fire Brigade |
| 147.6750 | 155.7500 | NFM | London Whitechapel | Police (HT) |
| 147.7000 | 168.7000 | NFM | Nationwide | RCS Secure Cougar System |

| Base | Mobile | Mode | Location | User and Notes |
|------|--------|------|----------|----------------|
| 147.7250 | 168.8000 | NFM | Nationwide | RCS Secure Cougar System |
| | | NFM | Nationwide | RCS Channel 71 |
| 147.7750 | 147.7750 | NFM | London | Police (MP) Ch 18 |
| 147.7750 | 155.8750 | NFM | Nationwide | RCS Channel 71 |
| 147.8000 | 155.9000 | NFM | Jersey | Fire Paging |
| | | AM | Nationwide | Fire Alert |
| 147.8125 | 147.8125 | NFM | Strathclyde | Police |
| 147.8500 | | NFM | Lincolnshire | Police (NC) Channel 2 |
| 147.8500 | 147.8500 | NFM | Dumfries and Galloway | Police |
| | | AM | Newcastle | MoD Police |
| | | NFM | Strathclyde | Fire Brigade (GX) |
| | | AM | Wiltshire | Police |
| 147.8500 | 147.9500 | NFM | London | Police Dartford Tunnel |
| 147.8625 | 147.8625 | NFM | London | Police Engineers Channel 78 |
| 147.8750 | 147.8750 | NFM | England & Wales | Police Mobiles Channel 21 |
| | | NFM | Kent | Police (Tour De France) |
| | | AM | London | Police (MP) Ch 16 |
| | | AM | M25 | Police Speed Traps |
| 147.8875 | | NFM | Kent Motorways | Police (TD) |
| | | NFM | Nottingham | Police Ch 3 |
| 147.9000 | | NFM | England | Fire Brigade Pagers |
| | | NFM | Newport | Fire Brigade |
| | | NFM | Strathclyde | Fire Brigade (GX) |
| 147.9125 | 147.9125 | NFM | England & Wales | Police Mobiles Channel 22 |
| | | NFM | London | Police (MP) Ch 17 |
| | | NFM | Nationwide | RCS Car-to-Car Channel 82 |
| | | AM | Sheerness | Police |
| 147.9250 | 147.9250 | NFM | London | Police Engineers Channel 83 |
| | | NFM | Nottingham | Police Ch 1 |
| | | NFM | Strathclyde | Fire Brigade (GX) |
| 147.9375 | 147.9375 | NFM | London | Police (MP) Ch 19 |
| | | NFM | Nationwide | RCS Channel 84 |
| 147.9500 | 147.9500 | NFM | London | Police Metropolitan CID |
| | | NFM | Nationwide | RCS Channel 00 |
| 147.9750 | 149.9750 | NFM | London | Police Metropolitan CID |
| | | NFM | Nationwide | RCS Channel 00 |
| | | NFM | Nottingham | Police Ch 2 |

## 148.00000 - 148.99875 MHz    NATIONAL POWER COMPANIES

| Base | Mobile | Mode | Location | User and Notes |
|------|--------|------|----------|----------------|
| 148.0000 | 139.5688 | NFM | Nationwide | Electricity Channel J21 |
| 148.0188 | 139.5188 | NFM | Nationwide | Electricity Channel J22 |
| 148.0313 | 139.5113 | NFM | Nationwide | Electricity Channel J23 |
| 148.0433 | 139.5439 | NFM | Nationwide | Electricity Channel J24 |
| 148.0563 | 139.5563 | NFM | Nationwide | Electricity Channel J25 |
| 148.0811 | | NFM | Luton | Electricity |
| 148.0811 | 139.5813 | NFM | Nationwide | Electricity Channel J27 |
| 148.0938 | 139.5938 | NFM | Nationwide | Electricity Channel J28 |
| 148.1063 | 139.6063 | NFM | Nationwide | Electricity Channel J29 |
| 148.1188 | 139.6188 | NFM | Nationwide | Electricity Channel J30 |
| 148.1313 | 139.6313 | NFM | Nationwide | Electricity Channel J31 |
| 148.1438 | | NFM | Cambridge | Electricity |
| 148.1438 | 139.6438 | NFM | Nationwide | Electricity Channel J32 |
| 148.1563 | 139.6563 | NFM | Nationwide | Electricity Channel J33 |
| 148.1563 | | NFM | Norfolk | Electricity |
| 148.1688 | | NFM | Clacton | Electricity |
| 148.1688 | 139.6688 | NFM | Nationwide | Electricity Channel J34 |

| Base | Mobile | Mode | Location | User and Notes |
|------|--------|------|----------|----------------|
| 148.1688 | | NFM | Peterborough | Electricity |
| 148.1813 | 139.6813 | NFM | Nationwide | Electricity Channel J35 |
| 148.1813 | | NFM | Suffolk | Electricity |
| 148.1938 | 139.6938 | NFM | Nationwide | Electricity Channel J36 |
| 148.1938 | | NFM | Norwich | Electricity |
| 148.2063 | | NFM | Chelmsford | Electricity |
| | | NFM | Clacton | Electricity |
| | | NFM | Ipswich | Electricity |
| 148.2063 | 139.7063 | NFM | Nationwide | Electricity Channel J37 |
| 148.2188 | | NFM | Harrow | Electricity |
| 148.2188 | 139.7188 | NFM | Nationwide | Electricity Channel J38 |
| 148.2313 | | NFM | Enfield | Electricity |
| | | NFM | Ipswich | Electricity |
| | | NFM | Kings Lynn | Electricity |
| 148.2313 | 139.7313 | NFM | Nationwide | Electricity Channel J39 |
| 148.2438 | 139.7438 | NFM | Nationwide | Electricity Channel J40 |
| 148.2563 | | NFM | Nationwide | Electricity Channel J41 |
| 148.2563 | 139.7563 | NFM | Nationwide | Electricity Channel J41 |
| 148.2688 | 139.7688 | NFM | Nationwide | Electricity Channel J42 |
| 148.2813 | 139.7813 | NFM | Nationwide | Electricity Channel J43 |
| 148.2938 | 139.7938 | NFM | Nationwide | Electricity Channel J44 |
| | | NFM | Nationwide | Electricity Channel J44 |
| 148.3063 | 139.8063 | NFM | Nationwide | Electricity Channel J45 |
| 148.3183 | | NFM | Nationwide | Electricity Channel J46 |
| 148.3183 | 139.8183 | NFM | Nationwide | Electricity Channel J46 |
| 148.3250 | | NFM | Bolton | Norweb |
| 148.3313 | 139.8313 | NFM | Nationwide | Electricity Channel J47 |
| 148.3438 | 139.8436 | NFM | Nationwide | Electricity Channel J48 |
| 148.3563 | 139.6563 | NFM | Nationwide | Electricity Channel J49 |
| 148.3688 | 139.8688 | NFM | Nationwide | Electricity Channel J50 |
| 148.3813 | 139.8813 | NFM | Nationwide | Electricity Channel J52 |
| 148.4063 | | NFM | Nationwide | Electricity Channel J53 |
| 148.4188 | 139.9188 | NFM | Nationwide | Electricity Channel J54 |
| 148.4311 | 139.9313 | NFM | Nationwide | Electricity Channel J55 |
| 148.4438 | 139.9438 | NFM | Nationwide | Electricity Channel J56 |
| 148.4563 | 139.9563 | NFM | Nationwide | Electricity Channel J57 |
| 148.4688 | 139.9668 | NFM | Nationwide | Electricity Channel J58 |
| 148.4750 | 147.9687 | NFM | Burnley | British Gas |
| 148.4813 | 139.9813 | NFM | Nationwide | Electricity Channel J59 |
| 148.4938 | 139.9938 | NFM | Nationwide | Electricity Channel J60 |
| 148.5063 | 140.0063 | NFM | Nationwide | Electricity Channel J61 |
| 148.5188 | 140.0188 | NFM | Nationwide | Electricity Channel J62 |
| 148.5313 | 140.0313 | NFM | Nationwide | Electricity Channel J63 |
| 148.5438 | 140.0438 | NFM | Nationwide | Electricity Channel J64 |
| 148.5563 | 140.0563 | NFM | Nationwide | Electricity Channel J65 |
| 148.5688 | 140.0688 | NFM | Nationwide | Electricity Channel J66 |
| 148.5813 | 140.0813 | NFM | Nationwide | Electricity Channel J67 |
| 148.5938 | 140.0938 | NFM | Nationwide | Electricity Channel J68 |
| 148.6063 | 140.1063 | NFM | Nationwide | Electricity Channel J69 |
| 148.6163 | 140.1188 | NFM | Nationwide | Electricity Channel J70 |
| 148.6313 | 140.1313 | NFM | Nationwide | Electricity Channel J71 |
| 148.6438 | 140.1438 | NFM | Nationwide | Electricity Channel J72 |
| 148.6563 | 140.1563 | NFM | Nationwide | Electricity Channel J73 |
| 148.6688 | 140.1688 | NFM | Nationwide | Electricity Channel J74 |
| 148.6813 | 140.1813 | NFM | Nationwide | Electricity Channel J75 |
| 148.6938 | 140.1938 | NFM | Nationwide | Electricity Channel J76 |

| Base | Mobile | Mode | Location | User and Notes |
|------|--------|------|----------|----------------|
| 148.7063 | 140.2043 | NFM | Nationwide | Electricity Channel J77 |
| 148.7188 | 140.2188 | NFM | Nationwide | Electricity Channel J78 |
| 148.7250 | | NFM | Jersey | BBC SAB mobile unit |
| 148.7313 | 140.2313 | NFM | Nationwide | Electricity Channel J79 |
| 148.7438 | 140.2438 | NFM | Nationwide | Electricity Channel J80 |
| 148.7563 | 140.2563 | NFM | Nationwide | Electricity Channel J81 |
| 148.7625 | | NFM | Newcastle | Link |
| 148.7688 | 140.2688 | NFM | Nationwide | Electricity Channel J82 |
| 148.7813 | 140.2813 | NFM | Nationwide | Electricity Channel J83 |
| 148.7938 | 140.2938 | NFM | Nationwide | Electricity Channel J84 |
| 148.8063 | 140.3063 | NFM | Nationwide | Electricity Channel J85 |
| 148.8188 | 140.3188 | NFM | Nationwide | Electricity Channel J86 |
| 148.8200 | | NFM | Durham | British Gas |
| 148.8313 | 140.3313 | NFM | Nationwide | Electricity Channel J87 |
| 148.8436 | 140.3438 | NFM | Nationwide | Electricity Channel J88 |
| 148.8563 | 140.3563 | NFM | Nationwide | Electricity Channel J89 |
| 148.8688 | 140.3689 | NFM | Nationwide | Electricity Channel J90 |
| 148.8813 | 140.3813 | NFM | Nationwide | Electricity Channel J91 |
| 148.8938 | 140.3938 | NFM | Nationwide | Electricity Channel J92 |
| 148.9063 | 140.4063 | NFM | Nationwide | Electricity Channel J93 |
| 148.9188 | 140.4188 | NFM | Nationwide | Electricity Channel J94 |
| 148.9313 | 140.4313 | NFM | Nationwide | Electricity Channel J95 |
| 148.9438 | 140.4438 | NFM | Nationwide | Electricity Channel J96 |
| 148.9500 | 148.9500 | AM | Nationwide | USAF General |
| 148.9563 | 140.4563 | NFM | Nationwide | Electricity Channel J97 |
| 148.9688 | 140.4688 | NFM | Nationwide | Electricity Channel J98 |
| 148.9813 | 140.4813 | NFM | Nationwide | Electricity Channel J99 |

### 149.0000 - 149.9000 MHz    GOVERNMENT & MoD MOULD REPEATERS

| Base | Mobile | Mode | Location | User and Notes |
|------|--------|------|----------|----------------|
| 149.00000 | | NFM | Nationwide | MoD Repeaters |
| 149.01250 | | NFM | Leicester | Mould |
| | | NFM | South Wales | Mould |
| 149.03750 | 149.03750 | NFM | Aberfield | MoD Police |
| 149.03750 | 153.83750 | NFM | Aldershop | Army range wardens cntrl (BEAVER) |
| 149.06250 | | NFM | S Wales | Mould |
| 149.07500 | | NFM | Cornwall | Mould |
| | | AM | Nationwide | ATC Channel V5 |
| | | NFM | S Wales | Mould |
| 149.08750 | 142.41250 | NFM | Cornwall | Mould |
| 149.10000 | 149.10000 | AM | Nationwide | USAF Rescue Helicopter to AART |
| 149.12500 | | NFM | RAF Carewent | Store Security |
| 149.17500 | | NFM | S Wales | Mould |
| 149.23750 | | NFM | Nationwide | MoD Establishments |
| 149.25000 | | NFM | S Wales | Mould |
| 149.26250 | | NFM | Cornwall | Mould |
| 149.27500 | | AM | Nationwide | ATC Channel V6 |
| 149.27500 | 149.27500 | NFM | Nationwide | RAF Cadets Channel V6 |
| 149.27500 | | NFM | RAF Spadeadam | Forward Air Controller |
| 149.28750 | | NFM | Tayside | Mould |
| 149.32500 | | NFM | MoD Aberporth | Ops |
| 149.36250 | | NFM | Nationwide | MoD Establishments |
| 149.38750 | | NFM | MoD Aberporth | Ops |
| | | NFM | Nationwide | MoD Establishments |
| 149.38750 | 142.06250 | NFM | Shoeburyness | Mould |
| 149.40000 | | AM | Nationwide | ATC Channel V2 |
| 149.40000 | 149.40000 | NFM | Nationwide | RAF ATC Channel V2 |

| Base | Mobile | Mode | Location | User and Notes |
|------|--------|------|----------|----------------|
| 149.40000 | | NFM | Porton Down | MoD Police |
| 149.41250 | | NFM | Boscombe Down | MoD Police |
| | | NFM | Nationwide | MoD Establishments |
| | | NFM | Porton Down | MoD Police |
| 149.41250 | 142.11250 | NFM | S Wales | Mould |
| 149.41750 | | NFM | S Wales | Mould Channel 4 |
| 149.42500 | | NFM | Nationwide | Sea Cadets |
| 149.42750 | | NFM | S Wales | Mould |
| 149.46250 | | NFM | S Wales | Mould |
| 149.48750 | | NFM | London | Warner Bros Store |
| 149.50000 | | NFM | S Wales | Mould |
| 149.53750 | | NFM | Manchester | Mould |
| | | NFM | Midlands | Mould |
| 149.62500 | | NFM | Cornwall | Mould |
| 149.63750 | | NFM | MoD Porton Down | Range |
| 149.65000 | 149.65000 | NFM | Nationwide | USAF Air-Air |
| | | NFM | RAF Midenhall | US Navy |
| | | NFM | USAF Lakenheath | Radar |
| 149.68750 | | NFM | Mod Porton Down | Link to Middle Wallop |
| 149.70000 | 149.72150 | NFM | Leicester | Mould |
| | | NFM | South Wales | Mould |
| 149.73750 | | NFM | Brecon Beacons | Mould |
| | | NFM | Caerwent | MoD Ops |
| | | NFM | Manchester | Mould |
| | | NFM | Tayside | Mould |
| 149.76250 | | NFM | Nationwide | MoD Establishments |
| | | NFM | Salisbury Plain | Army bio warfare firing |
| 149.77500 | 149.77500 | NFM | Nationwide | MoD Police Helicopters |
| | | NFM | Nationwide | MoD Regional Police Channel 1 |
| | | NFM | Nationwide | USAF Air-Air |
| 149.80000 | | NFM | S Wales | Mould |
| 149.81250 | 149.83750 | NFM | S Wales | Mould |
| | | NFM | Salisbury Plain | Army |
| 149.82500 | 149.82500 | NFM | London | MoD Police |
| | | NFM | Portsmouth | Whale Island MoD Police (PD) |
| 149.85000 | 149.85000 | NFM | Aldershot Barracks | MoD Police |
| | | NFM | Colchester | MoD Police |
| | | NFM | DRA Farnborough | MoD Police (FP) |
| | | NFM | Hadleigh | MoD Police |
| | | NFM | Nationwide | MoD Police Channel 3 |
| | | NFM | Portsmouth Naval Dks | Whale Island MoD Police (PD) |
| 149.86750 | | NFM | South Wales | Mould |
| | | NFM | Tayside | Mould |
| 149.90000 | | NFM | Caerleon | ATC Channel 2 |
| 149.90000 | 149.90000 | NFM | Nationwide | RAF Air Training Corps Chan2 |
| 149.91250 | | NFM | Salisbury | Army RTTY link |

## 149.9500 - 150.0500 MHz    SOVIET SATELLITE BEACONS

| Base | Mobile | Mode | Location | User and Notes |
|------|--------|------|----------|----------------|
| 149.97000 | | NFM | Space | Polar Bear 8688A |
| 149.98000 | | NFM | Space | Soviet Cosmos Satellites |

## 150.0500 - 152.0000 MHz    RADIO ASTRONOMY, PAGING AND MOD

| Base | Mobile | Mode | Location | User and Notes |
|------|--------|------|----------|----------------|
| 150.00000 | | CW | Woodbridge | Army Morse Code |
| 150.05000 | | NFM | London | MoD Procurement Executive Ch 1 |
| 150.07500 | | NFM | London | MoD Procurement Executive Ch 2 |
| 150.30000 | | NFM | Non-Geostationary | Russian Cosmos Geodetic |

| Base | Mobile | Mode | Location | User and Notes |
|---|---|---|---|---|
| 150.50000 | | NFM | Nationwide | Nissan Racing Team |
| 150.56250 | | NFM | Enniskillen | Military Data Link |
| 151.32500 | | NFM | Nationwide | Army Bomb Squad |
| 151.60000 | 156.60000 | NFM | Essex | Colchester Docks |
| | | NFM | Gravesend | Pool Control |
| | | NFM | London | Tower Bridge Control |
| 151.67500 | | NFM | Newmarket | Paging |
| 151.77500 | | NFM | Galway | University Hospital Paging |

### 150.5000 - 150.5500 MHz   Oil Slick Markers

| Base | Mobile | Mode | Location | User and Notes |
|---|---|---|---|---|
| 150.11000 | | NFM | Nationwide | Oil Slick Markers |
| 150.18500 | | NFM | Nationwide | Oil Slick Markers |

### 152.0000 - 152.9875 MHz   Police & Fire PMR 12.5 kHz

| Base | Mobile | Mode | Location | User and Notes |
|---|---|---|---|---|
| 152.0000 | 143.0750 | NFM | Leicester | Police (NL) Channel 1 |
| 152.0000 | 143.2625 | NFM | London | Police (MP) Channel 11 |
| 152.0125 | 143.1625 | NFM | Dumfries & Galloway | Police (AJ) |
| | | AM | Isle of Man | Police (MX) Channel 1 |
| | | NFM | Strathclyde | Police Data Channel |
| 152.0125 | 143.5625 | AM | West Yorkshire | Police (XW) Channel 3 |
| 152.0200 | | NFM | Glasgow | Police Channel 1 |
| 152.0250 | 143.0625 | NFM | London | Police Area Crime Squad (MP) Ch 3 |
| 152.0250 | 143.0250 | NFM | Strathclyde | Police Channel 1 |
| 152.0375 | 143.0750 | NFM | Dumfries & Galloway | Police (AJ) |
| | | AM | Leicester | Police (NL) Channel 1 |
| 152.0500 | 143.5875 | NFM | Co. Durham | Police |
| | | NFM | Dumfries & Galloway | Police (AJ) |
| 152.0500 | 143.0500 | NFM | Glasgow | Police (AS) Channel 2 |
| 152.0500 | | NFM | London | Police car to car (MP) Channel 5 |
| 152.0500 | 143.5850 | AM | West Yorkshire | Police (XW) Channel 5 |
| 152.0625 | 143.3125 | NFM | Mosspaul | Police |
| | | AM | North Yorkshire | Police (XN) Channel 2 |
| | | AM | Scarborough | Police 'D' Division |
| 152.0750 | 152.0750 | NFM | Dumfries and Galloway | Police |
| | | NFM | Langholm | Police |
| 152.0750 | 152.6750 | NFM | Ottercops | Police (M2LB) |
| 152.0750 | 143.4375 | NFM | Strathclyde | Police Channel 32 |
| | | NFM | Yorkshire | Fire Brigade Control |
| 152.0875 | 143.0875 | NFM | Berwick | Police |
| | | NFM | Edinburgh | Police (Fringe Festival) |
| | | NFM | Lincolnshire | Police (NC) |
| 152.0875 | 143.0750 | AM | Northumberland | Police (M2LB) Channel 1 |
| | | NFM | Strathclyde | Fire Brigade (GX) Channel 11 |
| | | NFM | Wisham | Fire Brigade |
| 152.1000 | 143.2625 | NFM | London | Police Channel 11 (MP) OSCAR |
| 152.1000 | 143.4375 | NFM | Strathclyde | Police Channel 31 |
| 152.1250 | | NFM | Ayr | Police (R) |
| 152.1250 | 146.9500 | NFM | Beacon Lough | Police (M2LB) |
| 152.1250 | 152.7250 | NFM | Quarry House | Police (M2LB) |
| 152.1250 | 143.0250 | NFM | Strathclyde | Police Channel 4 |
| 152.1375 | 143.5125 | NFM | Dumfries and Galloway | Police (AJ) |
| 152.1375 | 143.3125 | NFM | London | Police (MP) Channel 13 OSCAR |
| 152.1500 | | FM | Glasgow | Traffic Management |
| 152.1500 | 143.3625 | AM | North Yorkshire | Police (XN) Channel 4 |
| 152.1500 | 143.2000 | NFM | Strathclyde | Police Channel 1 |

| Base | Mobile | Mode | Location | User and Notes |
|------|--------|------|----------|----------------|
| 152.1625 | 143.2125 | NFM | London | Police (MP) Channel 9 |
| 152.1625 | 143.4250 | NFM | South Yorkshire | Police (XS) Channel 5 |
| 152.1625 | 143.3750 | NFM | Strathclyde | Fire Brigade (GX) Channel 5 |
|  |  | NFM | Strathclyde | Police Channel 3 |
| 152.1750 | 143.1000 | AM | Leicester | Police (NL) Channel 3 |
| 152.1750 | 143.2000 | NFM | Strathclyde | Police Channel 12 |
| 152.1750 |  | NFM | Teeside | Police |
| 152.1875 | 143.1375 | NFM | Bovington | Police |
|  |  | NFM | Brockely | Police |
|  |  | NFM | Dumfries & Galloway | Fire Brigade Channel 15 |
|  |  | NFM | Sandwich | Police |
| 152.1875 | 143.0375 | NFM | Strathclyde | Fire Brigade (GX) Channel 2 |
| 152.1880 | 143.1000 | AM | Northumberland | Police (M2LB) Channel 2 |
| 152.2000 |  | NFM | Dumfries and Galloway | Police (AJ) |
| 152.2000 | 143.5875 | NFM | Staffordshire | Police (YF) Channel 1 |
| 152.2000 | 143.2000 | NFM | Strathclyde | Police Channel 09 |
| 152.2125 |  | NFM | Dumfries and Galloway | Police (AJ) |
| 152.2125 | 143.4125 | NFM | Strathclyde | Police Channel 36 |
| 152.2250 | 152.2250 | NFM | Dumfries and Galloway | Police |
|  |  | NFM | London | Police Channel 6 (MP) |
| 152.2250 | 146.1500 | NFM | Quarry House | Police (M2LB) |
| 152.2250 | 143.2750 | NFM | Strathclyde | Police Channel 18 |
|  |  | NFM | Wigton | Police (W) |
|  |  | NFM | Nottingham | Police |
| 152.2375 | 143.4625 | NFM | Strathclyde | Fire Brigade (GX) Channel 2 |
| 152.2375 | 143.0375 | NFM | Strathclyde | Fire Brigade (GX) Channel 23 |
| 152.2375 | 143.7125 | NFM | Strathclyde | Fire Brigade (GX) Channel 35 |
| 152.2375 | 143.6625 | NFM | Strathclyde | Fire Brigade (GX) Channel 7 |
| 152.2500 | 143.5125 | NFM | Dumfries and Galloway | Police (AJ) |
| 152.2500 | 143.2750 | NFM | Strathclyde | Police Channel 5 |
| 152.2600 |  | NFM | London | Police Channel 8 (MP) |
| 152.2625 |  | NFM | Bridge of Orchy | Police |
|  |  | NFM | Kirkcudbright | Police |
|  |  | NFM | London | Police diplomatic and royalty protection |
|  |  | NFM | London | Police special movements |
| 152.2625 | 143.3875 | AM | North Yorkshire | Police (XN) Channel 5 |
| 152.2625 | 143.4125 | NFM | Strathclyde | Police Channel 37 |
| 152.2625 | 143.2625 | NFM | Strathclyde | Police Channel 45 |
| 152.2750 | 143.4000 | NFM | Dumfries and Galloway | Police (AJ) |
| 152.2750 | 152.6625 | NFM | Ottercops | Police (M2LB) |
| 152.2750 | 143.4500 | NFM | Strathclyde | Police Channel 26 |
| 152.2875 | 143.7250 | NFM | Dumfries and Galloway | Fire Brigade (Control) Channel 16 |
| 152.2875 | 143.1375 | NFM | Strathclyde | Fire Brigade (GX) Channel 11 |
| 152.2875 | 143.7125 | NFM | Strathclyde | Fire Brigade (GX) Channel 36 |
| 152.2875 | 143.2875 | NFM | Strathclyde | Fire Brigade (GX) Channel 48 |
| 152.2875 | 143.0375 | NFM | Strathclyde | Fire Brigade (GX) Channel 56 |
| 152.2875 | 143.4625 | NFM | Strathclyde | Fire Brigade (GX) Channel 7 |
| 152.2875 | 143.6625 | NFM | Strathclyde | Fire Brigade (GX) Channel 9 |
| 152.3000 | 153.0000 | NFM | Dumfries and Galloway | Police |
| 152.3000 | 143.2375 | NFM | London | Police Area Traffic Channel 10 (GT) |
| 152.3000 | 143.2000 | NFM | Strathclyde | Police Channel 14 |
| 152.3125 | 143.1500 | NFM | Dumfries and Galloway | Fire Brigade (Fire Control) |
| 152.3125 | 143.1625 | AM | Humberside | Police (XH) |
| 152.3125 | 143.2875 | NFM | Strathclyde | Fire Brigade (GX) |
| 152.3125 | 143.1375 | NFM | Strathclyde | Fire Brigade (GX) Channel 11 |

| Base | Mobile | Mode | Location | User and Notes |
|---|---|---|---|---|
| 152.3125 | 143.0375 | NFM | Strathclyde | Fire Brigade Channel 2 |
| 152.3250 | 143.2750 | NFM | Ayr | Police |
| | | NFM | London | Police Channel 7 (MP) |
| 152.3250 | 152.8500 | NFM | Quarry House | Police (M2LB) |
| | | NFM | Strathclyde | Police |
| 152.3375 | 143.0625 | NFM | Strathclyde | Fire Brigade (GX) |
| 152.3375 | 143.3375 | NFM | Strathclyde | Fire Brigade (GX) |
| 152.3375 | 143.3750 | NFM | Strathclyde | Fire Brigade (GX) |
| 152.3375 | 143.4625 | NFM | Strathclyde | Fire Brigade (GX) |
| | | NFM | Strathclyde | Police Channel 26 |
| 152.3375 | 143.0375 | AM | West Yorkshire | Police (XW) Channel 1 |
| 152.3500 | 143.3250 | NFM | Dumfries and Galloway | Police (AJ) |
| 152.3500 | 143.1250 | AM | Leicester | Police (NL) Channel 4 |
| | | AM | Leicestershire | Police Leicestershire Force HQ |
| 152.3500 | 143.2000 | NFM | Strathclyde | Police Channel 10 |
| 152.3500 | 143.6375 | NFM | Strathclyde | Police Channel 30 |
| 152.3500 | 143.3125 | NFM | Strathclyde | Police Channel 50 |
| 152.3600 | | NFM | London | Police Channel 2 (MP) |
| 152.3625 | 143.3625 | NFM | Strathclyde | Fire Brigade (GX) |
| 152.3750 | 143.4500 | NFM | Ayr | Police |
| | | NFM | Dumfries and Galloway | Police (AJ) |
| 152.3750 | 146.9000 | NFM | Round Meadows | Police (M2LB) |
| 152.3750 | 143.3875 | NFM | Strathclyde | Police Channel 19 |
| | | NFM | Strathclyde | Police Channel 27 |
| 152.3850 | | NFM | London | Police Channel 1 (MP) |
| 152.3875 | 143.2375 | AM | Cleveland | Police (LZ) Channel 1 |
| 152.3875 | 143.3875 | NFM | Strathclyde | Fire Brigade (GX) |
| 152.4000 | 152.4000 | NFM | Dumfries and Galloway | Police |
| 152.4000 | 143.2000 | AM | Nottinghamshire | Police (NH) Channel 1 |
| 152.4000 | 143.2750 | NFM | Strathclyde | Police Channel 16 |
| 152.4125 | 143.1250 | NFM | London | Police City of London |
| | | AM | Northumberland | Police (M2LB) |
| | | NFM | Strathclyde | Police Channel 33 |
| 152.4250 | 143.2375 | NFM | Isle of Man | Fire Brigade |
| | | AM | Manchester | Police |
| 152.4250 | 143.2250 | AM | Nottinghamshire | Police (NH) Channel 2 |
| 152.4250 | 143.6500 | NFM | Strathclyde | Police Channel 20 |
| 152.4250 | 143.2625 | NFM | Strathclyde | Police Channel 48 |
| 152.4375 | 143.5125 | NFM | Dumfries and Galloway | Police (AJ) |
| | | NFM | London | Police City of London |
| 152.4375 | 143.4500 | NFM | Strathclyde | Police Channel 29 |
| 152.4400 | | FM | Kilmarnock | Police U Division Control Room |
| 152.4500 | 143.5125 | NFM | Dumfries and Galloway | Police (AJ) |
| | | NFM | Ferrybridge | Police |
| 152.4500 | 143.1875 | AM | Humberside | Police (XH) |
| 152.4500 | 143.4500 | NFM | Strathclyde | Police Channel 28 |
| 152.4600 | | NFM | London | Police Channel 4 (MP) |
| 152.4625 | 143.0875 | NFM | London | Police (MN) |
| 152.4625 | 143.2875 | NFM | Strathclyde | Fire Brigade (GX) |
| 152.4625 | 143.5250 | NFM | Strathclyde | Fire Brigade (GX) |
| 152.4625 | 143.3750 | NFM | Strathclyde | Police Channel 40 |
| 152.4750 | 143.7750 | NFM | Coatbridge | Fire Brigade |
| | | NFM | Dumfries & Galloway | Police Channel 17 |
| | | NFM | Paisley | Fire Brigade |
| 152.4750 | 143.0625 | NFM | Strathclyde | Fire Brigade (GX) |
| 152.4750 | 143.3375 | NFM | Strathclyde | Fire Brigade (GX) |

| Base | Mobile | Mode | Location | User and Notes |
|------|--------|------|----------|----------------|
| 152.4875 | 143.2625 | AM | Cleveland | Police (LZ) |
| 152.4875 | 143.6500 | NFM | Strathclyde | Police Channel 19 |
| 152.4875 | 143.3125 | NFM | Strathclyde | Police Channel 51 |
| 152.5000 | 143.2500 | AM | Nottinghamshire | Police (NH) Channel 3 |
| 152.5000 | 143.5375 | NFM | Strathclyde | Police Channel 23 |
| 152.5125 | | AM | Manchester | Police |
| 152.5125 | 143.6625 | NFM | Strathclyde | Fire Brigade (GX) |
| 152.5125 | 143.7125 | NFM | Strathclyde | Fire Brigade (GX) |
| 152.5125 | 143.7125 | NFM | Strathclyde | Police Channel 25 |
| 152.5125 | 143.0875 | AM | West Yorkshire | Police (XW) Channel 3 |
| 152.5250 | | NFM | Lothian and Borders | Police (E) East Lothian |
| 152.5250 | 143.0375 | NFM | Strathclyde | Fire Brigade (GX) |
| 152.5250 | 143.4625 | NFM | Strathclyde | Fire Brigade (GX) |
| 152.5375 | 143.5375 | NFM | Strathclyde | Police Channel 22 |
| 152.5500 | 143.2875 | NFM | London | Police Channel 12 (MP) OSCAR |
| 152.5500 | 143.1500 | AM | Northumberland | Police (M2LB) |
| 152.5500 | 143.6625 | NFM | Strathclyde | Fire Brigade (GX) |
| 152.5500 | 143.7125 | NFM | Strathclyde | Fire Brigade (GX) |
| 152.5600 | | NFM | Glasgow | Police Ch6 (ES) |
| 152.5625 | 143.6500 | NFM | Strathclyde | Police Channel 21 |
| 152.5750 | 143.0250 | AM | Northamptonshire | Police (NG) |
| | | NFM | Strathclyde | Police (AS) Channel 3 |
| 152.5875 | | NFM | London | Police Royal Palaces |
| 152.5875 | 143.5375 | NFM | Strathclyde | Police Channel 24 |
| 152.5875 | 143.1125 | AM | West Yorkshire | Police (XW) Channel 4 |
| 152.6000 | 143.1750 | NFM | Dumfries and Galloway | Fire Brigade (Fire Control) |
| | | AM | Northumberland | Police (M2LB) |
| 152.6000 | 143.0625 | NFM | Strathclyde | Fire Brigade (GX) |
| 152.6000 | 143.3375 | NFM | Strathclyde | Fire Brigade (GX) |
| 152.6000 | 143.3750 | NFM | Strathclyde | Fire Brigade (GX) |
| 152.6000 | 143.5250 | NFM | Strathclyde | Fire Brigade (GX) |
| 152.6000 | 143.2875 | NFM | Strathclyde | Police Channel 46 |
| 152.6125 | 143.9000 | AM | Humberside | Police |
| | | NFM | Strathclyde | Police Channel 42 |
| 152.6250 | 143.7000 | NFM | Dumbarton | Police L Div Control Room |
| 152.6250 | 152.6250 | NFM | Dumfries and Galloway | Police |
| 152.6250 | 143.7000 | NFM | Strathclyde | Police Channel 38 |
| 152.6250 | 143.2625 | NFM | Strathclyde | Police Channel 46 |
| 152.6375 | 152.6375 | NFM | Northern Ireland | Fire Brigade Handhelds |
| 152.6375 | 143.6625 | NFM | Strathclyde | Fire Brigade (GX) |
| 152.6375 | 143.7125 | NFM | Strathclyde | Fire Brigade (GX) |
| 152.6500 | 143.9000 | NFM | Strathclyde | Police Channel 41 |
| 152.6625 | 146.5500 | NFM | Quarry House | Fire Brigade (M2LJ) |
| 152.6625 | 143.9000 | NFM | Strathclyde | Police Channel 44 |
| 152.6875 | 143.5125 | NFM | Dumfries and Galloway | Police Lowther Hills (AJ) |
| 152.6875 | | NFM | Ferrybridge | Police |
| 152.6875 | | AM | Humberside | Police (XH) Channel 3 |
| 152.7000 | 143.0500 | NFM | Dumfries and Galloway | Police (AJ) |
| | | AM | Northamptonshire | Police (NG) Channel 2 |
| 152.7000 | 143.7000 | NFM | Strathclyde | Police |
| 152.7125 | 143.7750 | NFM | Dumfries and Galloway | Fire Brigade (Fire Control) |
| 152.7125 | 143.3750 | NFM | Strathclyde | Fire Brigade (GX) |
| 152.7125 | 143.5250 | NFM | Strathclyde | Fire Brigade (GX) |
| 152.7125 | 143.0625 | AM | West Yorkshire | Police (XW) Channel 2 |
| 152.7250 | 143.3750 | AM | Lincolnshire | Police (NC) Channel 1 |
| 152.7400 | 152.7400 | NFM | Dumfries and Galloway | Police |

| Base | Mobile | Mode | Location | User and Notes |
|---|---|---|---|---|
| 152.7500 | 152.7500 | NFM | Dumfries and Galloway | Police |
| 152.7500 | 143.5375 | NFM | Strathclyde | Police Channel 25 |
| 152.7625 | | NFM | Arrochar | Police (L) |
| | | NFM | Machrihanish | Police (L) |
| | | NFM | Oban | Police (L) |
| 152.7625 | 146.9000 | NFM | Quarry House | Police (M2LB) |
| 152.7625 | 143.6375 | NFM | Strathclyde | Police Channel 30 |
| 152.7625 | 143.3125 | NFM | Strathclyde | Police Channel 52 |
| 152.7750 | 152.7750 | NFM | Dumfries and Galloway | Police |
| 152.7750 | 143.4625 | AM | Lincolnshire | Police (NC) Channel 2 |
| 152.7750 | 146.9000 | NFM | Ottercops | Police (M2LB) |
| 152.7875 | 143.2750 | AM | South Yorkshire | Police (XS) Channel 1 |
| 152.7875 | 143.6625 | NFM | Strathclyde | Fire Brigade (GX) |
| 152.7875 | 143.7125 | NFM | Strathclyde | Police |
| 152.7900 | 152.7900 | NFM | Dumfries and Galloway | Police |
| 152.8000 | | AM | County Durham | Police (LA) Channel 1 |
| | | NFM | Girvan | Police (R) |
| | | AM | Newcastle | Police |
| 152.8000 | 143.0250 | NFM | Strathclyde | Police Data Channel |
| 152.8050 | 143.4500 | NFM | Ayr | Police As control from Glasgow for R&R Divisions Channel 8 |
| 152.8125 | | AM | Manchester | Police |
| 152.8125 | 143.4375 | NFM | Strathclyde | Police Channel 30 |
| 152.8125 | 143.1375 | AM | West Yorkshire | Police (XW) Channel 6 |
| 152.8250 | 152.8250 | NFM | Castlebar | Paging |
| | | NFM | Dumfries and Galloway | Police |
| | | NFM | Galway | Garda |
| 152.8250 | 143.7000 | NFM | Strathclyde | Police Channel 39 |
| 152.8375 | 143.0500 | NFM | Ayr | Fire Brigade (D) |
| | | AM | Durham | Police (LA) Channel 2 |
| 152.8375 | 146.5750 | NFM | Ipswich | Police (VL) |
| 152.8375 | 143.6625 | NFM | Strathclyde | Fire Brigade (GX) |
| 152.8375 | 143.7125 | NFM | Strathclyde | Police |
| 152.8500 | 143.3250 | AM | South Yorkshire | Police (XS) Channel 3 |
| 152.8600 | 152.8600 | NFM | Dumfries and Galloway | Police |
| 152.8750 | 143.7750 | NFM | Dumfries & Galloway | Fire Brigade Channel 17 |
| 152.8750 | 143.1375 | NFM | Strathclyde | Fire Brigade (GX) |
| 152.8750 | 143.2875 | NFM | Strathclyde | Fire Brigade (GX) |
| 152.8850 | 152.8850 | NFM | Dumfries and Galloway | Police |
| | | NFM | Glasgow | Police Hampden Football Club |
| 152.8875 | | NFM | Co. Durham | Police (LA) |
| 152.8875 | 143.1875 | NFM | Isle of Man | Police (MX) Channel 2 |
| 152.9000 | 143.3000 | AM | Doncaster | Police |
| | | NFM | Dumfries and Galloway | Police (K) |
| | | AM | South Yorkshire | Police (XS) Channel 2 |
| 152.9000 | 143.9000 | NFM | Strathclyde | Police Channel 43 |
| 152.9100 | 152.9100 | NFM | Dumfries and Galloway | Police |
| 152.9200 | 143.1250 | NFM | Ayr | Police R Division Control covering RB Div Cumnock Channel 10 |
| 152.9250 | | NFM | Ayr | Police (R) |
| | | NFM | Dumfries and Galloway | Police (AJ) |
| 152.9250 | 146.1500 | NFM | Ottercops | Police (M2LB) |
| 152.9250 | 143.3500 | AM | South Yorkshire | Police (XS) Channel 4 |
| 152.9375 | 146.5500 | NFM | Round Meadows | Fire Brigade (M2LJ) |
| 152.9500 | 143.2875 | AM | North Yorkshire | Police (XN) |

| Base | Mobile | Mode | Location | User and Notes |
|------|--------|------|----------|----------------|
| 152.9500 | 143.1375 | NFM | Strathclyde | Fire Brigade (GX) |
| 152.9625 | 143.2125 | AM | Isle of Man | Police (MX) Channel 3 |
| | | NFM | Lincolnshire | Police Channel 2 |
| 152.9750 | 152.9750 | NFM | Dumfries and Galloway | Police |
| | | NFM | Ferrybridge | Police (WM) |
| | | AM | Ingleton | Police (M2XN) |
| 152.9750 | 143.3375 | AM | North Yorkshire | Police (XN) |
| 152.9800 | 152.9800 | NFM | Dumfries and Galloway | Police |
| 152.9875 | | NFM | Lincolnshire | Police Channel 1 |
| 152.9875 | 146.5500 | NFM | Ottercops | Fire Brigade (M2LJ) |

## 153.0125  153.500 MHz     NATIONAL PAGING

| Base | Mobile | Mode | Location | User and Notes |
|------|--------|------|----------|----------------|
| 153.0250 | | NFM | Nationwide | National Paging Channel 1 |
| 153.0500 | | NFM | Nationwide | National Paging Channel 2 |
| 153.0750 | | NFM | Nationwide | National Paging Channel 3 |
| 153.1250 | | NFM | Nationwide | BT Paging Channel 5 |
| 153.1500 | | NFM | Manchester | Paging |
| | | NFM | Nationwide | Redifon Paging Channel 6 |
| 153.1750 | | NFM | Nationwide | BT Paging Channel 7 |
| 153.2000 | | NFM | Nationwide | National Paging Channel 8 |
| | | NFM | Nationwide | UK Paging Test & Developmt |
| 153.2250 | | NFM | Nationwide | Redifon Paging Channel 9 |
| 153.2375 | | NFM | Nationwide | Paging |
| 153.2500 | | NFM | Nationwide | National Paging Channel 10 |
| 153.2750 | | NFM | Nationwide | Air Call Paging Channel 11 |
| 153.3000 | | NFM | Galway | University Hospital Paging |
| | | NFM | Nationwide | National Paging Channel 12 |
| 153.3250 | | NFM | Nationwide | Air Call Paging Channel 13 |
| 153.3375 | | NFM | Nationwide | Paging |
| 153.3450 | | NFM | Lincoln | Paging |
| 153.3500 | | NFM | Nationwide | Inter City Pagers Channel 14 |
| 153.3625 | | NFM | Nationwide | Paging |
| 153.3750 | | NFM | Jersey | Paging |
| | | NFM | Nationwide | National Paging Channel 15 |
| 153.4000 | | NFM | Nationwide | UKAEA Paging Channel 16 |
| 153.4250 | | NFM | Guernsey | Paging |
| 153.4250 | | NFM | Nationwide | National Paging Channel 17 |
| | | NFM | Tayside | Voice Paging |
| 153.4500 | | NFM | Guernsey | Life Boat Pagers |
| | | NFM | Nationwide | National Paging Channel 18 |
| | | NFM | Nationwide | Paging |
| 153.4750 | | NFM | Cambridge | City Council Paging |
| | | NFM | Nationwide | National Paging Channel 19 |
| 153.5000 | | NFM | Nationwide | National Paging Channel 20 |

## 153.5000 - 154.0000 MHz    MoD TACTICAL COMMUNICATIONS 25 kHz
### SIMPLEX

| Base | Mobile | Mode | Location | User and Notes |
|------|--------|------|----------|----------------|
| 153.5375 | | NFM | S Wales | MoD Paging |
| 153.5875 | | NFM | Bristol | MoD Link |
| 153.7125 | | NFM | Nationwide | Red Cross |
| 153.8250 | | NFM | Co Mayo | Paging |
| | | NFM | Galway | Garda Paging |
| | | NFM | Nationwide | RAF Cadets Channel V4 |

| Base | Mobile | Mode | Location | User and Notes |
|------|--------|------|----------|----------------|

154.0000 - 155.9875 MHx   POLICE BASE REPEATERS 12.5 KHZ

| Base | Mobile | Mode | Location | User and Notes |
|------|--------|------|----------|----------------|
| 154.0000 | 146.1000 | NFM | Kirkaldy | Police (Encrypted) |
| 154.0050 | 154.0050 | NFM | Dumfries and Galloway | Police |
| 154.0125 | 146.1250 | NFM | Fife | Fire Brigade |
|  |  | NFM | Lancashire | Police (BD) Channel 3 |
|  |  | NFM | London | Police M25 North (SM) Ch1 |
| 154.0125 | 154.0125 | NFM | London | Police Met Surveillance |
| 154.0125 | 146.1250 | NFM | Preston | Police |
| 154.0250 | 146.0500 | NFM | Fife | Police Traffic Division (ZT) |
| 154.0250 | 146.0250 | NFM | Glenrothes | Police |
| 154.0250 | 154.0250 | NFM | Inverness | Fire Brigade |
| 154.0250 | 146.1375 | NFM | Inverness | Police (UR) |
|  |  | NFM | Shropshire | Police (YK) |
| 154.0250 | 146.5125 | AM | West Mercia | Police (YK1) |
|  |  | AM | Worcester | Police (M2YK) |
| 154.0375 | 146.9000 | NFM | Beacon Lough | Police (M2LB) |
|  |  | NFM | Newcastle | Police |
| 154.0500 | 146.5375 | NFM | Derbyshire | Fire Brigade (M2ND) |
|  |  | NFM | Edinburgh | Police (T) |
| 154.0500 | 146.0500 | NFM | Fife | Police Traffic Division (ZT) |
|  |  | AM | Perry Bar | Police Motorway Channel 1 |
|  |  | NFM | Shropshire | Police (YK) |
|  |  | NFM | West Mercia | Police (YK2) |
| 154.0625 | 147.5375 | NFM | Burton Down | Fire Brigade |
| 154.0625 | 146.9000 | NFM | Dumfermline | Fire Brigade (F) |
|  |  | NFM | Edinburgh | Fire Brigade (F) |
|  |  | NFM | High Spen | Police (M2LB) |
| 154.0625 | 146.2125 | NFM | Inverness | Fire Brigade (UF) |
| 154.0750 | 146.1750 | NFM | Berkshire | Fire Brigade (HD) |
|  |  | NFM | Devon | Fire Brigade (QA) |
| 154.0750 | 154.9750 | NFM | Inverness | Fire Brigade |
| 154.0750 | 146.1375 | NFM | Inverness | Police (UR) |
| 154.0750 | 146.1750 | NFM | Lancashire | Police (BD) Channel 4 |
|  |  | NFM | Leven | Police (L) |
|  |  | AM | M6/M52/M62 | Police |
|  |  | AM | Manchester | Police traffic |
| 154.0750 | 146.8750 | NFM | Truleigh Hill | Police |
| 154.0850 |  | NFM | Fife | Fire Brigade |
| 154.0875 | 146.1500 | NFM | High Spen | Police (M2LB) |
| 154.0875 | 146.1625 | NFM | London | Police M25 South (SM) Channel.2 |
| 154.1000 | 146.0000 | NFM | Hereford/Worcs | Fire Brigade (YB) |
| 154.1000 |  | NFM | Kirkaldy | Police (E) Scambled |
| 154.1000 | 146.4875 | NFM | North Wales | Police (WA) Channel 4 |
| 154.1000 |  | AM | Oxford | Police |
| 154.1000 | 146.1375 | AM | Thames Valley | Police (HB) Channel 2 |
| 154.1125 |  | NFM | Aberdeen | Fire Control |
|  |  | NFM | Dumfermline | Fire Brigade (F) |
|  |  | NFM | Norfolk | Police Channel 1 |
| 154.1125 | 146.9500 | NFM | Truleigh Hill | Police |
| 154.1125 | 146.5625 | AM | West Mercia | Police (YK3) |
| 154.1250 | 147.6500 | NFM | Beddingham | Police |
| 154.1250 | 146.1375 | NFM | Cambridge | Fire Brigade (VF) |
|  |  | NFM | Edinburgh | Police (T) |
| 154.1250 | 146.0500 | NFM | Fife | Police Traffic Division (ZT) |

| Base | Mobile | Mode | Location | User and Notes |
|------|--------|------|----------|----------------|
| 154.1250 | 146.1375 | NFM | Inverness | Police (UR) |
| | | NFM | London | Fire Brigade (FN) |
| | | NFM | Staffordshire | Fire Brigade (M2YG) |
| | | NFM | West Mercia | Police (YK) Channel 2 |
| 154.1375 | 146.3625 | AM | Cambridge | Police (VB) Channel 3 |
| 154.1375 | 146.0500 | NFM | Fife | Police (ZT) |
| | | NFM | Southampton | Police |
| 154.1500 | 146.6750 | NFM | Glasgow | Police Drug Squad |
| | | AM | Gloucester | Police (QL) Channel 1 |
| 154.1500 | 146.5500 | NFM | High Spen | Fire Brigade (M2LJ) |
| 154.1500 | 146.4875 | NFM | Lothian and Borders | Police |
| 154.1500 | 146.6750 | NFM | Stirling | Fire Brigade (F) |
| | | AM | Stroud | Police |
| 154.1625 | 146.1625 | NFM | Fife | Police (B) |
| 154.1650 | 146.5250 | NFM | Beacon Lough | Police (M2LB) |
| 154.1750 | 154.1750 | FM | Cambridge | Police (VB) Car Return |
| 154.1750 | | NFM | Dumfermline | Police (D) |
| | | NFM | Stirling | Fire Brigade (F) |
| 154.1750 | 146.4750 | NFM | West Hoathly | Police |
| 154.1875 | 146.1500 | NFM | Beacon Lough | Police (M2LB) |
| 154.1875 | 146.8750 | NFM | Burton Down | Police |
| 154.1875 | 146.0500 | NFM | Fife | Police (ZT) |
| 154.1875 | 154.1875 | NFM | Inverness | Fire Brigade |
| 154.1875 | 146.4250 | NFM | Lochaber | Police (UR) |
| 154.1875 | 146.1000 | NFM | Newmarket | Police data |
| | | NFM | Rannoch Moor | Police |
| | | NFM | Sussex | Police |
| 154.2000 | | NFM | Bedfordshire | Police |
| | | AM | Cheshire | Police |
| 154.2000 | 147.6500 | NFM | Fairlight | Police |
| 154.2000 | | NFM | Fife | Police |
| 154.2000 | 146.5250 | NFM | High Spen | Police (M2LB) |
| 154.2000 | | AM | Perry Bar | Police Motorway Channel 2 |
| 154.2000 | 146.5875 | AM | Staffordshire | Police (YF) Channel 1 |
| 154.2125 | | NFM | Fife | Fire Brigade |
| 154.2250 | | AM | Bristol | Police |
| 154.2250 | 146.0000 | NFM | Cheshire | Fire Brigade (CF) |
| 154.2250 | | AM | East Sussex | Police (KB) |
| 154.2250 | 146.6500 | NFM | Fairlight | Police |
| 154.2250 | | AM | Gloucester | Police (QL) Channel 2 |
| | | NFM | Lanark | Police (ZS) |
| | | NFM | Norfolk | Police Channel 2 |
| 154.2250 | 146.7000 | NFM | Staffordshire | Fire Brigade (M2YG) |
| 154.2375 | 147.2375 | NFM | Bathgate | Police |
| | | NFM | Edinburgh | Police |
| | | NFM | Lanark | Police (ZS) |
| | | NFM | Lothian and Borders | Police (F and ZH) |
| 154.2375 | 147.2375 | NFM | West Lothian | Police |
| 154.2400 | | NFM | Edinburgh | Police Channel 1 (ZH) |
| 154.2500 | | NFM | Edinburgh | Police 'E' Div HQ |
| 154.2500 | 146.2500 | NFM | Lothian and Borders | Police (ZHE) East/Mid Lothian |
| 154.2500 | 146.0000 | NFM | West Midlands | Fire Brigade (FB) |
| 154.2600 | | AM | Worcester | Police (M2YK) |
| 154.2625 | 146.4750 | AM | Birmingham | Police (YM) |
| 154.2625 | | NFM | Edinburgh | Police (ZH) Special Events |
| 154.2625 | 147.0625 | NFM | Truleigh Hill | Police |

| Base | Mobile | Mode | Location | User and Notes |
|---|---|---|---|---|
| 154.2750 | 146.5750 | NFM | Ipswich | Police (VL) Channel 1 |
| 154.2750 | 146.1500 | NFM | Round Meadows | Police (M2LB) |
| 154.2850 | | NFM | Edinburgh | Police Channel 2 (T) |
| 154.2875 | | NFM | Edinburgh | Police (ZH) Channel 1 |
| 154.3000 | 146.3000 | NFM | Edinburgh, Fettes | Police (ZH) Channel 2 |
| 154.3125 | 146.4500 | AM | Birmingham | Police (YM) Channel 5 |
| 154.3125 | | NFM | Borders | Police (G and ZH) |
| | | NFM | Galashields | Police |
| 154.3125 | 146.0000 | NFM | Gloucester | Fire Brigade (OF) |
| 154.3250 | 147.8250 | NFM | Peebles | Police |
| 154.3350 | | AM | Thames Valley | Police |
| 154.3375 | 147.1750 | NFM | Greater Manchester | Police |
| | | NFM | Hungerford | Police (HB) Channel 1 |
| 154.3375 | 146.7375 | NFM | Thames Valley | Police (HB) Channel 1 |
| | | NFM | Wales | Police (WH) Channel 3 |
| 154.3500 | 146.3500 | NFM | Edinburgh, Fettes | Police (ZH) |
| 154.3500 | 146.4250 | NFM | Lochaber | Police (UR) |
| | | NFM | Onich | Police |
| 154.3675 | 146.7250 | AM | Gloucester | Police (QL) Channel 3 |
| 154.3750 | | NFM | Edinburgh | Police Radio Engineers |
| | | NFM | Livingstone | Police |
| | | NFM | Norfolk | Police Channel 3 |
| 154.3750 | 146.0000 | NFM | South Yorkshire | Fire Brigade (OS) |
| 154.3875 | | NFM | Edinburgh | Police 'E' Div HQ |
| 154.3875 | 146.2500 | NFM | Lothian and Borders | Police (ZHE) |
| 154.3875 | | NFM | West Mercia | Police (YK) |
| 154.4000 | 147.8250 | NFM | Meigle Hill | Police |
| 154.4000 | | NFM | Nationwide | M1 Low Volume |
| 154.4000 | 146.0000 | NFM | Norfolk | Fire Brigade (VF) |
| 154.4125 | 147.8250 | NFM | Hardens Hill | Police |
| 154.4125 | 147.6500 | NFM | Truleigh Hill | Police |
| 154.4125 | 146.0875 | NFM | Warwickshire | Police (YJ) Channel 1 |
| | | AM | West Mercia | Police (YK) |
| 154.4250 | | NFM | Galashields | Police (D) |
| 154.4250 | 146.4625 | NFM | North Wales | Police (WA) Channel 3 |
| | | NFM | Peebles | Police |
| 154.4375 | | NFM | Edinburgh | Police (T) Traffic Division |
| 154.4500 | 146.3500 | AM | Birmingham | Police (YM) |
| 154.4500 | 147.1875 | NFM | Perth | Police (W) |
| | | NFM | Pitlochry | Police (WP) |
| 154.4600 | | NFM | Lochaber | Police |
| 154.4625 | 146.4250 | NFM | Dalkeith | Police |
| | | NFM | Edinburgh | Police 'E' Div HQ |
| | | NFM | Fort William | Police (UR) |
| | | NFM | Galashiels | Police |
| | | NFM | Lochaber | Police (UR) |
| 154.4625 | 146.4875 | NFM | Lothian and Borders | Police |
| 154.4625 | 146.2500 | NFM | Lothian and Borders | Police (ZHE) East/Mid Lothian |
| 154.4625 | | AM | Preston | Police |
| 154.4750 | 146.6000 | AM | Dyfed | Police (WH) Channel. 1 |
| 154.4750 | 146.6250 | NFM | Edinburgh | Fire Brigade (F) |
| 154.4750 | 146.1750 | NFM | Kent | Fire Brigade (HO5) |
| 154.4875 | 147.0625 | NFM | Beddingham | Police |
| | | NFM | Central Scotland | Police |
| 154.4875 | 146.4875 | NFM | Lothian and Borders | Police |
| 154.4900 | | NFM | Stirling | Police HQ Channel 1 (AH) |

| Base | Mobile | Mode | Location | User and Notes |
|---|---|---|---|---|
| 154.5000 | 146.0000 | NFM | Avon/Somerset | Fire Brigade (QC) |
| 154.5000 | | NFM | Eyemouth | Police |
| 154.5000 | 146.5000 | NFM | Jersey | Police (M2GS) Channel 1 |
| 154.5000 | 147.6500 | NFM | West Hoathly | Police |
| 154.5125 | 146.4250 | NFM | Ballachulish | Police |
| 154.5125 | 146.8750 | NFM | Beddingham | Police |
| | | NFM | Dalkeith | Police |
| | | NFM | Edinburgh | Police 'E' Div HQ |
| 154.5125 | 146.2500 | NFM | Lothian and Borders | Police (ZHE) East/Mid Lothian |
| 154.5250 | 146.4875 | NFM | Central Scotland | Police Traffic Division (T) |
| 154.5250 | | AM | E Sussex | Police (KB) |
| 154.5250 | 146.8500 | NFM | Easter Ross | Police (UR) |
| 154.5250 | 147.8750 | NFM | Fairlight | Police |
| 154.5250 | 146.4875 | NFM | Galashiels | Police |
| | | NFM | Lothian and Borders | Police |
| 154.5250 | | NFM | West Mercia | Police (YK) |
| 154.5375 | 146.5375 | NFM | Edinburgh | Fire Brigade (F) |
| 154.5500 | 147.8250 | NFM | Ashkirk | Police |
| 154.5500 | 146.5500 | NFM | Channel Islands | Police harbour |
| 154.5500 | | NFM | Jersey | Fire Brigade Channel 5 |
| 154.5500 | 146.5500 | NFM | Jersey | Police (M2GS) Channel 5 |
| 154.5500 | 146.7125 | NFM | Kyle of Lochalsh | Police (UR) |
| 154.5500 | | AM | Merseyside | Police |
| 154.5500 | 146.0000 | NFM | Oxford | Fire Brigade (HI) |
| 154.5500 | 146.6125 | AM | Staffordshire | Police (YF) Channel 2 |
| 154.5625 | 146.5250 | NFM | Caithness | Police |
| 154.5625 | 146.8625 | NFM | Dingwall | Police (UR) |
| 154.5625 | 154.5625 | NFM | Inverness | Fire Brigade |
| 154.5625 | 146.4875 | NFM | Lothian and Borders | Police |
| 154.5750 | | NFM | Belfast | Military Tone Encryption |
| 154.5750 | 146.0000 | NFM | North Hampshire | Fire Brigade (ND) |
| 154.5750 | 146.6500 | NFM | Skye | Fire Brigade (UR) |
| 154.5875 | | NFM | Belfast | Military Tone Encryption |
| 154.5875 | 146.5250 | NFM | Caithness | Police |
| 154.5875 | | NFM | Galashiels | Police |
| | | NFM | West Mercia | Police (YK) |
| 154.6000 | | NFM | Belfast | Military Tone Encryption |
| | | NFM | Edinburgh | Police (ZH) Fettes |
| | | NFM | Enniskillen | Royal Ulster Constabulary |
| | | NFM | Essex | Police |
| | | AM | Guernsey Aiport | Fire Services |
| 154.6000 | 146.0000 | NFM | Humberside | Fire Brigade (XT) |
| 154.6000 | 147.2375 | NFM | Perth | Police (W) |
| 154.6125 | | AM | Bristol | Police |
| | | NFM | Edinburgh | Police |
| | | NFM | Galashiels | Police |
| 154.6125 | 147.8250 | NFM | Hardens Hill | Police |
| | | NFM | Lanark | Police (S) |
| | | NFM | Manchester | Police |
| | | AM | Melksham | Police |
| 154.6125 | 154.6125 | FM | Norfolk | Police (VK) Channel 4 |
| 154.6125 | 147.0750 | AM | Wiltshire | Police (QJ) Channel 4 |
| 154.6250 | 146.3250 | AM | Birmingham | Police (YM) Channel 1 |

| Base | Mobile | Mode | Location | User and Notes |
|------|--------|------|----------|----------------|
| 154.6250 | 146.6250 | NFM | Central Scotland | Fire Brigade (AYS) |
| | | NFM | Edinburgh | Fire Brigade (F) |
| | | NFM | Jersey | Police (M2GS) Channel 2 |
| | | AM | Perry Bar | Police Motorway Channel 3 |
| 154.6250 | 146.4750 | NFM | Truleigh Hill | Police |
| 154.6375 | | NFM | Aberdeen | Police |
| 154.6375 | 146.5250 | NFM | Caithness | Police |
| 154.6375 | 146.8625 | NFM | Dingwall | Police (UR) |
| 154.6375 | 154.6375 | NFM | Inverness | Fire Brigade |
| 154.6375 | 146.2875 | AM | Kent | Police (KA) Channel 5 |
| 154.6375 | | NFM | Poolewe | Police (UR) |
| 154.6500 | | NFM | Cheshire | Fire Brigade (CF) |
| | | NFM | Edinburgh | Fire Brigade (F) |
| | | NFM | Jersey | Ambulance Service Channel.1 |
| 154.6500 | 146.6500 | NFM | Skye | Fire Brigade |
| 154.6500 | 146.1125 | NFM | Warwickshire | Police (YJ) Channel 2 |
| 154.6500 | 146.9500 | NFM | West Hoathly | Police |
| 154.6500 | 146.1125 | AM | West Mercia | Police (YK) |
| 154.6625 | 146.6625 | NFM | Perth | Fire Brigade (Fire Control) |
| 154.6625 | 146.8750 | NFM | West Hoathly | Police |
| 154.6750 | 146.2750 | NFM | Nottinghamshire | Fire Brigade (M2NZ) |
| 154.6875 | 146.8750 | NFM | Caithness | Fire Brigade (UF) |
| 154.6875 | 154.6875 | NFM | Northern Ireland | Fire Brigade Handhelds Channel 3 |
| 154.6875 | 146.6500 | NFM | Skye | Fire Brigade |
| 154.7000 | 146.3750 | AM | Birmingham | Police (YM) |
| 154.7000 | 146.9500 | NFM | Burton Down | Police |
| 154.7000 | 147.8250 | NFM | Dunion Hill | Police |
| 154.7000 | 146.1000 | NFM | Suffolk | Police (VL) Channel 3 |
| 154.7000 | 146.8000 | NFM | Sutherland | Police (UR) |
| 154.7125 | 146.5250 | NFM | Caithness | Police |
| 154.7125 | 146.7125 | NFM | Kyle of Lochalsh | Police (UR) |
| 154.7125 | 146.9625 | NFM | Perth | Police (W) |
| 154.7250 | | NFM | Eire, Castlebar | Garda |
| 154.7250 | 146.7125 | NFM | Kyle of Lochalsh | Police Applecross (UR) |
| 154.7250 | 146.7250 | NFM | Norfolk | Fire Brigade (VF) |
| 154.7375 | 146.8625 | AM | Bedfordshire | Police (M2VA) Channel 2 |
| 154.7500 | 146.1375 | NFM | Inverness | Police (UR) |
| 154.7500 | 146.2250 | NFM | Jersey | Ambulance Service Ch2 |
| 154.7500 | 146.0000 | NFM | Kent | Fire Brigade (KA) |
| 154.7500 | 147.0625 | NFM | West Hoathly | Police |
| 154.7625 | 146.0000 | NFM | Hampshire | Fire Brigade (H) |
| 154.7625 | 147.2375 | NFM | Perth | Police (W) |
| 154.7625 | 146.8000 | NFM | Sutherland | Police (UR) |
| 154.7750 | 146.3000 | AM | Berkshire | Police (Motoway Patrols) |
| 154.7750 | 146.0000 | NFM | North Humberside | Fire Brigade (XT) |
| 154.7750 | 146.3000 | AM | Thames Valley | Police (HB) Channel 8 |
| 154.7875 | | NFM | Aberdeen | Fire Brigade (Fire Control) |
| 154.7875 | 146.0250 | AM | Cambridge | Police (VB) Channel 1 |
| 154.7875 | 146.8625 | NFM | Dingwall | Police (UR) |
| 154.7875 | 146.8000 | AM | Gwent | Police (WE) Channel 2 |
| 154.7875 | 154.7875 | NFM | Inverness | Fire Brigade |
| 154.7875 | | NFM | Lanark | Police (ZS) |
| 154.7875 | 146.0250 | AM | Newmarket | Police |
| 154.7875 | 146.9500 | NFM | Perth | Fire Brigade (Fire Control) |
| 154.7875 | 146.8625 | NFM | Ullapool | Police (UR) |

| Base | Mobile | Mode | Location | User and Notes |
|------|--------|------|----------|----------------|
| 154.8000 | 146.1875 | NFM | Bournemouth | Police |
|  |  | AM | Dorset | Police (QC) Channel 3 |
| 154.8000 | 146.7250 | AM | Lancashire | Police (BD) Channel 5 |
|  |  | NFM | Leicestershire | Police (NL) Channel 1 |
| 154.8000 | 146.8000 | NFM | Sutherland | Police (UR) |
| 154.8125 | 146.8750 | AM | Gwent | Police (WN) Channel 3 |
| 154.8125 | 146.8000 | NFM | Helmsdale | Police (UR) |
|  |  | NFM | North Wales | Police Channel 1 |
|  |  | NFM | Sutherland | Police (UR) |
| 154.8250 | 146.6875 | AM | Cambridge | Police (VB) Channel 2 |
| 154.8250 | 146.7000 | AM | Cheshire | Police (BA) |
|  |  | NFM | Hull | Fire Brigade (XT) |
| 154.8375 |  | NFM | Bicester | Police (SD) |
| 154.8375 | 146.8500 | NFM | Easter Ross | Police (UR) |
| 154.8375 | 146.9625 | NFM | Perth | Police (W) |
| 154.8375 | 146.2750 | AM | Thames Valley | Police (HB) Channel 4 |
| 154.8500 | 147.0625 | NFM | Burton Down | Police |
| 154.8500 | 146.8500 | NFM | Easter Ross | Police (UR) |
| 154.8500 |  | AM | Lakenheath | Police |
| 154.8500 | 146.0000 | NFM | Norfolk | Fire Brigade (VF) |
| 154.8625 | 146.1250 | AM | Brecon | Police (WL) |
| 154.8625 |  | AM | Bristol | Police |
|  |  | AM | Cheshire | Police traffic |
| 154.8625 | 146.8625 | NFM | Dingwall | Police (UR) |
| 154.8625 |  | AM | Haverfordwest | Police (WH) |
|  |  | NFM | Inverness | Fire Brigade |
|  |  | NFM | Ipswich | Police (VL) |
| 154.8625 | 146.8250 | AM | Merseyside | Police (CH) Channel 1 |
| 154.8625 |  | AM | Newmarket | Police |
| 154.8625 | 146.9000 | AM | Suffolk | Police (VL) Channel 1 |
| 154.8625 |  | AM | Swansea, Severn Bridge | Police (BQ) |
| 154.8750 | 146.6625 | NFM | Perth | Fire Brigade (Fire Control) |
| 154.8750 | 146.0375 | AM | Thames Valley | Police (HB) Channel 6 |
| 154.8875 |  | NFM | Aberfeldy | Police (W) |
| 154.8875 | 146.1500 | AM | Brecon | Police (WL) |
| 154.8875 | 146.4750 | NFM | Burton Down | Police |
| 154.8875 |  | NFM | Ipswich | Police (VL) Channel 2 |
|  |  | NFM | Isle Of Man | Police |
| 154.8875 | 146.7125 | NFM | Kyle of Lochalsh | Police (UR) |
| 154.8875 | 146.9250 | AM | Newmarket | Police (VL) Channel 2 |
| 154.8875 | 147.2375 | NFM | Perth | Police (W) |
| 154.8875 |  | NFM | South Wales | Police (WY) Channel 2 |
| 154.8875 | 146.9250 | NFM | Suffolk | Police (VL) Channel 2 |
| 154.8875 |  | NFM | Sussex | Police |
| 154.9000 | 146.8375 | AM | Bedfordshire | Police (M2VA) Channel 1 |
| 154.9000 |  | NFM | Merseyside | Police (A) |
| 154.9000 | 146.8500 | AM | Merseyside | Police (CH) Channel 2 |
| 154.9125 | 147.0500 | NFM | Blairgowrie | Police (WB) |
| 154.9125 | 146.7750 | AM | Gwent | Police (WO) Channel 1 |
| 154.9125 |  | NFM | Lochaber | Fire Brigade |
| 154.9125 | 146.4875 | AM | Norfolk | Police (VK) Channel 1 |
| 154.9125 |  | NFM | Perth | Police (W) |
| 154.9250 |  | NFM | Grampian | Police |
| 154.9250 | 146.9000 | AM | Merseyside | Police (CH) Channel 3 |
| 154.9250 | 146.0625 | AM | Thames Valley | Police (HB) Channel 5 |
| 154.9375 | 146.1750 | AM | Brecon | Police (WL) |

| Base | Mobile | Mode | Location | User and Notes |
|---|---|---|---|---|
| 154.9375 | 146.6125 | AM | Kent | Police (KA) Channel 2 |
| 154.9375 | | NFM | Lancashire | Police (BD) Channel 2 |
| 154.9375 | 146.2750 | AM | Oxford | Police |
| 154.9375 | 146.9375 | NFM | Perth | Fire Brigade (Fire Control) |
| 154.9375 | | NFM | South Wales | Police (WX) Channel 4 |
| 154.9500 | | NFM | Aberdeen | Fire Brigade (Fire Control) |
| 154.9500 | 146.8500 | AM | Birkenhead | Police (M53) |
| 154.9500 | | AM | Hampshire | Police (Motorway Patrols) |
| | | AM | Motoways M4/M40/M25 | Police |
| 154.9500 | 146.0125 | AM | Thames Valley | Police (HB) Channel 7 |
| 154.9600 | | AM | Kent | Police (KB) |
| 154.9600 | | NFM | London | Police (MP) |
| 154.9625 | 146.0750 | NFM | Brecon | Police (WL) |
| 154.9625 | 146.6375 | AM | Kent | Police (KA) |
| 154.9625 | | NFM | Kent Motorways | Police (TD) |
| 154.9625 | 146.9625 | NFM | Perth | Police (W) |
| 154.9625 | 146.0750 | NFM | South Wales | Police (WS) Channel 3 |
| 154.9750 | 147.0500 | NFM | Aberdeen | Fire Brigade (Fire Control) |
| 154.9750 | 146.4250 | AM | Birmingham | Police (YM) Channel 4 |
| 154.9750 | 147.0500 | NFM | Blairgowrie | Police (WB) |
| 154.9750 | 146.6875 | AM | Hampshire | Police (HC) Channel 5 |
| 154.9750 | 147.0500 | NFM | Perth | Police (W) |
| 154.9850 | | NFM | Norfolk | Police (VK) |
| 154.9875 | 146.8500 | AM | Avon | Police (M2QP) Channel 3 |
| 154.9875 | | NFM | Grampian | Police |
| 154.9875 | 146.6750 | AM | Norfolk | Police (VK) |
| | | NFM | Norfolk | Police Channel 5 |
| 154.9875 | | AM | Somerset | Police (QP) Channel 3 |
| 155.0000 | | NFM | Jersey | Ambulance Channel 5 |
| | | NFM | Jersey | Civil Defence |
| 155.0000 | 147.0000 | NFM | Jersey | Police (M2GS) Channel 4 |
| 155.0000 | | NFM | Kirkcaldy | Police (Special Events) |
| 155.0000 | 154.7000 | AM | Sussex | Police (M2KB) Channel 1 |
| 155.0000 | 146.3125 | AM | West Sussex | Police (M2KB1) Ctrl & Traffic |
| 155.0125 | 146.8125 | AM | Avon | Police (M2QP) Channel 7 |
| | | NFM | Chorlton-cum-Hardy | Police |
| 155.0125 | 147.5625 | NFM | Grampian | Police (UBE) |
| 155.0125 | 146.2125 | AM | Manchester | Police (CK) Channel 1 |
| 155.0125 | | AM | Somerset | Police (QP) Channel 7 |
| 155.0250 | 147.0250 | NFM | Dundee | Police (ZS) |
| 155.0250 | 146.2125 | AM | Essex | Police (VG) Channel 1 |
| 155.0250 | | NFM | Hereford & Worcester | Fire Brigade (YB) |
| 155.0250 | 147.1375 | AM | Manchester | Police (Traffic) |
| 155.0250 | | AM | Newmarket | Police |
| 155.0375 | 146.7875 | AM | Avon | Police (M2QP) Channel 6 |
| 155.0375 | 147.1875 | NFM | Enniskillen | Fire Brigade |
| 155.0375 | 147.0625 | NFM | Perth | Fire Brigade (Fire Control) |
| 155.0375 | 146.7875 | AM | Somerset | Police (QP) Channel 6 |
| 155.0500 | 147.0500 | NFM | Blairgowrie | Police (WB) |
| 155.0500 | 146.3625 | AM | Llandudno | Police |
| 155.0500 | 147.0500 | NFM | Perth | Police (W) |
| 155.0500 | 146.6625 | AM | Powys | Police (WA) Channel 1 |
| 155.0500 | 146.3625 | AM | West Sussex | Police (M2KB) Channel 3 |
| 155.0625 | 146.7625 | AM | Avon | Police (M2QP) Channel 5 |
| | | AM | Bristol | Police |

| Base | Mobile | Mode | Location | User and Notes |
|------|--------|------|----------|----------------|
| 155.0625 | 147.2375 | AM | Manchester | Police (CK) Channel 4 |
| | | AM | Merseyside | Police |
| 155.0625 | 147.0625 | NFM | Perth | Fire Brigade (Fire Control) |
| 155.0625 | 146.7625 | AM | Salisbury | Police |
| | | AM | Somerset | Police (QP) Channel 5 |
| 155.0750 | | NFM | Aberdeen | Fire Brigade (Fire Control) |
| | | AM | Bristol | Police |
| 155.0750 | 147.1875 | AM | Essex | Police (VG) Channel 2 |
| | | AM | Manchester | Police Traffic (CK) Channel 5 |
| 155.0870 | 155.2300 | AM | Holland | Public Transport |
| 155.0875 | 146.1000 | AM | Hampshire | Police (HC) Channel 1 |
| 155.0875 | | NFM | Holyhead | Police |
| 155.0875 | 146.1000 | AM | Manchester | Police Channel 5 (CK) |
| 155.1000 | 146.4375 | AM | Anglesey | Police (WA) |
| 155.1000 | 147.1875 | AM | Colwyn Bay | Police HQ |
| 155.1000 | 146.5875 | AM | Kent | Police (KA) Channel 1 |
| 155.1000 | | NFM | North Wales | Police |
| 155.1000 | 147.1875 | NFM | Perth | Police (W) |
| | | NFM | Pitlochry | Police (WP) |
| | | AM | Powys | Police (WA) Channel 2 |
| | | NFM | RAF Leuchars | Police |
| | | AM | Southport | Police |
| | | NFM | St Andrews | Police |
| | | NFM | Wrexham | Police (WA) |
| 155.1125 | 147.0625 | NFM | County Down | Fire Brigade |
| 155.1125 | 146.4375 | AM | Hampshire | Police (HC) Channel 2 |
| 155.1250 | 147.4875 | NFM | Crumhaugh Hill | Fire Brigade |
| 155.1250 | 146.6250 | AM | Hertfordshire | Police (VH) Channel 2 |
| 155.1250 | 147.4875 | NFM | Lothian and Borders | Fire Brigade (ZF) |
| 155.1375 | 147.0875 | NFM | County Armagh | Fire Brigade |
| 155.1375 | 146.6625 | AM | Kent | Police (KA) Channel 4 |
| 155.1375 | 147.1375 | NFM | Perth | Fire Brigade (Fire Control) |
| 155.1500 | 146.5750 | AM | Avon | Police (M2QP) Channel 4 |
| | | AM | Bristol | Police |
| 155.1500 | 146.0750 | AM | Manchester | Police (CK) Channel 6 |
| 155.1500 | 147.2250 | NFM | Perth | Police (W) |
| 155.1500 | | AM | Somerset | Police (QP) Channel 4 |
| 155.1600 | | NFM | Isle of Wight | Police |
| 155.1625 | | NFM | Blairgowrie | Police (WB) |
| 155.1625 | 147.1125 | NFM | County Tyrone | Fire Brigade |
| 155.1625 | 146.4625 | AM | Hampshire | Police (HC) Channel 4 |
| 155.1625 | | NFM | Newmarket | Police |
| | | NFM | North Wales | Police Repeater Channel 2 |
| 155.1625 | 147.6125 | AM | Warwickshire | Police (YJ) Channel 3 |
| 155.1650 | | NFM | Isle of Wight | Police |
| 155.1750 | 146.1625 | AM | Essex | Police (VG) Channel 3 |
| 155.1750 | 147.4875 | NFM | Lothian and Borders | Fire Brigade (ZF) |
| 155.1750 | 146.9250 | AM | Merseyside | Police (CH) Channel 4 |
| 155.1750 | | AM | Newmarket | Police |
| 155.1875 | 146.3875 | AM | Essex | Police (VG) |
| 155.1875 | | NFM | Kent | Police |
| 155.1875 | 147.4875 | NFM | Lothian and Borders | Fire Brigade (ZF) |
| 155.1875 | 146.3875 | AM | Manchester | Police (Traffic) |
| | | NFM | North Wales | Police |
| 155.1875 | 147.1875 | NFM | Perth | Police (W) |
| 155.1875 | 154.4125 | AM | West Sussex | Police (M2KB) Channel 4 |

| Base | Mobile | Mode | Location | User and Notes |
|------|--------|------|----------|----------------|
| 155.2000 | 146.6500 | NFM | Dyfed | Police (WH) Channel 2 |
| 155.2000 | 146.6000 | AM | Hertfordshire | Police (VH) Channel 1 |
| | | AM | Manchester | Police |
| 155.2000 | 147.0625 | NFM | Perth | Fire Brigade (Fire Control) |
| 155.2000 | 146.6500 | NFM | Skye | Fire Brigade |
| 155.2125 | 146.5000 | AM | Avon | Police (M2QP) Channel 1 |
| 155.2125 | | AM | Manchester | Police |
| 155.2125 | 147.2250 | NFM | Perth | Police (W) |
| 155.2125 | | AM | Somerset | Police (QP) Channel 1 |
| 155.2250 | 146.0000 | NFM | Leamington | Fire Brigade (YS) |
| 155.2250 | 146.9500 | AM | Merseyside | Police (CH) Channel 5 |
| 155.2250 | 147.2250 | NFM | Perth | Police (W) |
| 155.2250 | 146.3375 | AM | West Sussex | Police (M2KB2) Ctrl & Traffic Ch 2 |
| 155.2375 | 146.6500 | AM | Hertfordshire | Police (VH) Channel 3 |
| 155.2375 | 147.0375 | NFM | Londonderry | Fire Brigade |
| 155.2375 | 147.2375 | NFM | Perth | Police (W) |
| 155.2500 | 146.5250 | AM | Avon | Police (M2QP) Channel 2 |
| 155.2500 | | AM | Cheltenham | Police (QL) |
| | | NFM | Glasgow | Fire Brigade (ZF) |
| | | AM | Gloucester | Police (QL) |
| 155.2500 | 146.2750 | AM | Lancashire | Police (BD) |
| 155.2500 | 147.1500 | NFM | London | Police (GT) Channel 51 |
| 155.2500 | 147.4875 | NFM | Lothian and Borders | Fire Brigade (ZF) |
| 155.2500 | 146.5250 | AM | Manchester | Police |
| 155.2500 | | NFM | Newmarket | Police |
| | | AM | Somerset | Police (QP) |
| 155.2625 | 146.3125 | AM | Cheshire | Police (BA 03) Channel 2 |
| 155.2625 | | NFM | Fife | Police |
| 155.2625 | 146.4875 | AM | Hampshire | Police (HC) Channel 3 |
| 155.2625 | | AM | Manchester | Police traffic |
| 155.2650 | 155.2650 | NFM | Leeds | Police traffic |
| 155.2750 | 146.9000 | AM | Cornwall | Police (QB) Channel 2 |
| 155.2750 | | AM | Devon | Police (QB) Channel 2 |
| 155.2750 | 146.6250 | AM | Powys | Police (WH) Channel 4 |
| 155.2875 | | NFM | Aberdeen | Police |
| | | NFM | Grampian | Police (UBG) |
| 155.2875 | 147.2250 | NFM | Perth | Police (W) |
| 155.2875 | 146.4125 | AM | West Sussex | Police (M2KB) Channel 5 |
| 155.2900 | 47.23750 | NFM | Perth | Police (W) |
| 155.3000 | | NFM | Banchory | Police (UBK) |
| | | NFM | Braemar | Police (UBH) |
| 155.3000 | 146.9750 | AM | Cornwall | Police (QB) Channel 7 |
| 155.3000 | | AM | Devon | Police (QB) Channel 7 |
| 155.3000 | 147.2000 | NFM | London | Diplomatic Prot(Ranger) |
| 155.3000 | 147.1375 | NFM | Londonderry | Fire Brigade (North) |
| 155.3125 | 147.2375 | NFM | Perth | Police (W) |
| 155.3250 | 146.2375 | AM | Cornwall | Police (QB) Channel 4 |
| 155.3250 | 146.2375 | AM | Devon | Police (QB) Channel 4 |
| 155.3250 | 146.9750 | AM | Merseyside | Police (CH) Channel 6 |
| 155.3250 | | NFM | Merseyside | Police (D) |
| 155.3375 | 147.1875 | NFM | Perth | Police (W) |
| | | NFM | Pitlochry | Police (WP) |
| 155.3500 | | NFM | Cannock, Staffs | Fire Service YG |
| 155.3500 | 147.5625 | NFM | Grampian | Police (UBE) |
| 155.3625 | 146.2625 | AM | Cornwall | Police (QB) Channel 5 |
| | | AM | Devon | Police (QB) Channel 5 |

| Base | Mobile | Mode | Location | User and Notes |
|---|---|---|---|---|
| 155.3750 | | NFM | Grampian | Police (UBG) |
| 155.3750 | 147.1625 | NFM | Londonderry | Fire Brigade (South) |
| 155.3875 | 146.9500 | AM | Cornwall | Police (QB) Channel 6 |
| | | AM | Devon | Police (QB) Channel 6 |
| 155.3875 | 146.3625 | AM | West Cheshire | Police (BA 01) Channel 1 |
| 155.4000 | | NFM | Edinburgh | Fire Brigade (F) |
| | | NFM | Perth | Fire Brigade (Fire Control) |
| 155.4125 | | NFM | Ballachulish | Fire |
| 155.4125 | 146.6250 | AM | Dyfed | Police (WH) Channel 2 |
| 155.4125 | | NFM | Hampshire | Police |
| 155.4125 | 147.0375 | NFM | Highlands and Islands | Fire Brigade |
| 155.4125 | | NFM | Lochaber | Fire Brigade (UF) |
| 155.4250 | | NFM | Aberdeen | Police |
| 155.4250 | | AM | Cheshire | Police Channel 3 |
| 155.4250 | 146.3875 | AM | Manchester | Police (CK) Channel 2 |
| 155.4250 | 147.5750 | NFM | Northern Ireland | Royal Ulster Constabulary |
| 155.4250 | 147.2375 | NFM | Perth | Police (W) |
| 155.4375 | 146.6000 | AM | Dyfed | Police (WH) |
| 155.4375 | | NFM | Perth | Fire Brigade (Fire Control) |
| 155.4500 | 147.5625 | NFM | Grampian | Police (UBE) |
| 155.4500 | 146.4500 | NFM | Jersey | Airport Fire Service Ch1 |
| 155.4625 | 146.2125 | AM | Cornwall | Police (QB) Channel 1 |
| | | AM | Devon | Police (QB) Channel 1 |
| 155.4625 | 147.5625 | NFM | Grampian | Police (UBE) |
| 155.4625 | 146.3000 | NFM | Lancashire | Police (BD) Channel 1 |
| 155.4750 | 146.6000 | NFM | Dyfed & Powys | Police (WH) Channel 1 |
| 155.4750 | 147.5625 | NFM | Grampian | Police (UBE) |
| 155.4750 | 147.4500 | NFM | Northern Ireland | Royal Ulster Constabulary |
| 155.4750 | 146.1250 | NFM | West Mercia | Police (YK) Channel 2 |
| 155.4875 | 146.3375 | AM | Cheshire | Police (BA 02) Channel 3 |
| 155.4875 | 147.4875 | NFM | Lothian and Borders | Fire Brigade (ZF) |
| 155.5000 | 146.6500 | AM | Dyfed | Police (WH) |
| 155.5000 | 147.5625 | NFM | Grampian | Police (UBE) |
| 155.5000 | | NFM | Shrewsbury | Police |
| 155.5125 | | NFM | Belfast | RUC Voice Encryption |
| 155.5125 | 146.9250 | AM | Cornwall | Police (QB) Channel 3 |
| | | AM | Devon | Police (QB) Channel 3 |
| 155.5125 | 147.4875 | NFM | Peebles | Fire Brigade |
| 155.5250 | 147.7000 | NFM | Northern Ireland | Royal Ulster Constabulary |
| 155.5375 | 147.5625 | NFM | Aberdeen | Police |
| | | NFM | Grampian | Police (UBE) |
| 155.5375 | 146.4625 | AM | Powys | Police (WA) |
| | | NFM | West Midlands | Police (YH) Channel 6 |
| 155.5500 | | NFM | Aberdeen | Police |
| 155.5500 | 147.5500 | NFM | Northern Ireland | Royal Ulster Constabulary |
| 155.5625 | 147.0125 | NFM | Belfast | Fire Brigade |
| 155.5625 | | NFM | Belfast | Royal Ulster Constabulary |
| 155.5625 | 147.4875 | NFM | Edinburgh | Police (ZS) |
| | | NFM | Galashiels | Fire Brigade |
| 155.5625 | | NFM | London | Police Tactical Support Group |
| 155.5625 | 147.4875 | NFM | Lothian and Borders | Fire Brigade (ZF) |
| 155.5625 | | NFM | Perth | Police (W) |
| 155.5750 | 146.2875 | AM | Cornwall | Police (QB) Channel 8 |
| 155.5750 | | AM | Devon | Police (QB) Channel 8 |
| | | NFM | Grampian | Police (UBG) |
| 155.5750 | 147.5250 | NFM | Northern Ireland | Royal Ulster Constabulary |

| Base | Mobile | Mode | Location | User and Notes |
|---|---|---|---|---|
| 155.5750 | | NFM | Perth | Police (W) |
| 155.5750 | | NFM | Stafford | Fire Service |
| 155.5875 | | NFM | Aberdeen | Police |
| 155.5875 | 146.2500 | AM | Cumbria | Police (BB3) M6 Motorway |
| 155.5875 | | NFM | Grampian | Police |
| | | NFM | Preston | Police |
| 155.6000 | | AM | Derbyshire | Police (NA) |
| 155.6000 | 147.7500 | NFM | Northern Ireland | Royal Ulster Constabulary |
| 155.6125 | | NFM | Hartside Hill | Fire Brigade |
| 155.6125 | 147.0375 | NFM | Highlands and Islands | Fire Brigade |
| 155.6125 | | NFM | Lochaber | Fire Brigade (UF) |
| 155.6125 | 147.4875 | NFM | Lothian and Borders | Fire Brigade (ZF) |
| 155.6125 | 146.4125 | AM | Manchester | Police (CK) Channel 3 |
| 155.6250 | | NFM | Aberdeen | Police |
| 155.6250 | | AM | Colwyn Bay | Police (WA) Traffic |
| 155.6250 | 147.6250 | NFM | Grampian | Police (UB) |
| 155.6250 | | NFM | North Wales | Police |
| 155.6250 | 147.7750 | NFM | Northern Ireland | Royal Ulster Constabulary |
| 155.6250 | 146.4875 | AM | Powys | Police (WA) |
| 155.6375 | 146.4500 | AM | Cumbria | Police (BB) Channel 2 |
| 155.6375 | 147.9375 | NFM | Jersey | Fire Brigade Channel 1 |
| 155.6500 | 146.2625 | AM | Derbyshire | Police (NA) Channel 1 |
| 155.6500 | 147.9000 | NFM | Northern Ireland | Royal Ulster Constabulary |
| 155.6500 | | NFM | Penicuik | Police |
| 155.6625 | 146.2000 | AM | Cumbria | Police (BB) |
| 155.6625 | 147.9500 | AM | Guernsey | Fire Brigade Channel 1 |
| 155.6625 | 147.8875 | NFM | Northern Ireland | Royal Ulster Constabulary |
| 155.6750 | 147.9625 | NFM | Jersey | Fire Brigade Channel 2 |
| 155.6750 | 147.8750 | NFM | Northern Ireland | Royal Ulster Constabulary |
| 155.6750 | | NFM | Suffolk | Police Regional Crime Squads |
| 155.7000 | | NFM | Jersey | Police CID Encrypted (M2GS) Ch 6 and Police Drug Squad |
| | | NFM | London | Police Regional Crime Squad (CS) |
| 155.7000 | 155.7000 | AM | Manchester | Police |
| 155.7000 | | NFM | Nationwide | Police Regional Crime Squad Ch 2 |
| | | NFM | Suffolk | Police Regional Crime Squads |
| | | NFM | Wiltshire | Police CID |
| 155.7250 | 155.7250 | NFM | London | Police Regional Crime Squad (CS) |
| 155.7250 | | AM | Manchester | Police Surveillance Squad |
| | | NFM | Nationwide | Police Regional Crime Squad Ch 3 |
| | | NFM | Suffolk | Police Regional Crime Squads |
| 155.7375 | | NFM | Grampian | Fire Brigade (Fire Control) |
| 155.7375 | 147.0375 | NFM | Highlands and Islands | Fire Brigade |
| 155.7500 | | AM | Chester | Police |
| | | NFM | Jersey | Police Drug Squad |
| | | NFM | London | Police Regional Crime Squad (CS) |
| 155.7500 | 155.7500 | AM | Manchester | Police |
| 155.7500 | | NFM | Nationwide | Police Regional Crime Squad Ch 1 |
| 155.7750 | 155.7750 | NFM | London | Police Regional Crime Squad (CS) |
| 155.7750 | 147.9500 | NFM | Northern Ireland | Royal Ulster Constabulary |
| 155.7750 | | NFM | Suffolk | Police Regional Crime Squads |
| 155.7875 | | NFM | Grampian | Fire Brigade (Fire Control) |
| 155.7875 | 147.9375 | NFM | Northern Ireland | Royal Ulster Constabulary |
| 155.7875 | | NFM | Northern Ireland | Security Forces |
| 155.8000 | | NFM | Aberdeen | Police |

| Base | Mobile | Mode | Location | User and Notes |
|------|--------|------|----------|----------------|
| 155.8000 | 147.9250 | NFM | Bangor | Royal Ulster Constabulary |
| | | NFM | Belfast | Royal Ulster Constabulary (U) |
| 155.8000 | | AM | Durham | Police |
| | | NFM | Grampian | Police (UBG) |
| 155.8000 | 147.7625 | AM | Guernsey | Police (QY) Channel 1 |
| 155.8000 | 147.9250 | NFM | Larne | Royal Ulster Constabulary |
| | | NFM | Northern Ireland | Royal Ulster Constabulary |
| 155.8000 | 146.2000 | AM | Surrey | Police (HJ) Channel 1 |
| 155.8125 | | AM | Gloucester | Police (QL) |
| | | NFM | Grampian | Police |
| 155.8125 | 146.5750 | NFM | Ipswich | Police |
| 155.8125 | 146.5750 | NFM | Suffolk | Police (VL) Channel 3 |
| 155.8125 | 146.9125 | AM | Wiltshire | Police (QJ) Channel 1 |
| 155.8250 | 147.4000 | NFM | Belfast | Royal Ulster Constabulary |
| 155.8250 | 147.9750 | AM | Guernsey | Fire Brigade Channel 2 |
| 155.8250 | 147.4000 | NFM | Larne | Royal Ulster Constabulary |
| 155.8250 | 147.4000 | NFM | Northern Ireland | Royal Ulster Constabulary |
| 155.8375 | 146.2875 | AM | Derbyshire | Police (NA) Channel 2 |
| 155.8375 | 146.2250 | AM | Surrey | Police (HJ) Channel 2 |
| 155.8500 | | AM | Bristol | Police |
| 155.8500 | 147.4250 | NFM | Northern Ireland | Royal Ulster Constabulary |
| 155.8500 | | AM | Swindon | Police |
| 155.8500 | 146.9375 | AM | Wiltshire | Police (QJ) Channel 2 |
| 155.8625 | 147.7500 | NFM | Jersey | Police (M2GS) Channel 3 |
| 155.8625 | | NFM | Merseyside | Police |
| 155.8625 | 146.2500 | AM | Surrey | Police (HJ) Channel 3 |
| 155.8750 | 146.1000 | AM | Dorset | Police (QC) Channel 1 |
| 155.8750 | | NFM | Dumfermline | Fire Brigade (F) |
| 155.8750 | 147.8500 | NFM | Belfast | Royal Ulster Constabulary |
| 155.8750 | | AM | Winforth | Police |
| 155.8875 | 146.2000 | AM | Cumbria | Police (BB1) South Lakes |
| 155.9000 | 147.4750 | NFM | Belfast | Royal Ulster Constabulary |
| | | AM | Bristol | Police |
| 155.9000 | 147.8500 | AM | Guernsey | Police (QY) Channel 2 |
| 155.9000 | | NFM | Norfolk | Police Channel 6 |
| 155.9000 | 147.4750 | NFM | Northern Ireland | Royal Ulster Constabulary |
| 155.9000 | | AM | Swindon | Police |
| 155.9000 | 146.9625 | AM | Wiltshire | Police (QJ) Channel 3 |
| 155.9125 | | NFM | Hertfordshire | Police (VH) |
| 155.9125 | | NFM | Newport | Police |
| 155.9250 | | NFM | Belfast | Royal Ulster Constabulary |
| 155.9250 | 147.0125 | AM | Dorset | Police (QC) Channel 2 |
| 155.9250 | | NFM | Norfolk | Police Channel 7 |
| 155.9250 | 147.6250 | NFM | Northern Ireland | Royal Ulster Constabulary |
| 155.9375 | | NFM | Bournemouth | Police |
| 155.9375 | 147.9625 | NFM | Northern Ireland | Royal Ulster Constabulary |
| 155.9375 | | AM | Slough | Police |
| 155.9375 | 146.8875 | AM | Thames Valley | Police (HB) Channel 3 |
| 155.9500 | 147.9750 | NFM | Belfast | Royal Ulster Constabulary |
| | | NFM | Larne | Royal Ulster Constabulary |
| | | NFM | Northern Ireland | Royal Ulster Constabulary |
| 155.9625 | 146.2375 | AM | Essex | Police (VG) Channel 4 |
| 155.9625 | 155.9625 | NFM | Jersey | All Services Channel 7 |

| Base | Mobile | Mode | Location | User and Notes |
|------|--------|------|----------|----------------|
| 155.9625 | 147.9875 | NFM | Jersey | Ambulances Channel 6 |
| | | NFM | Jersey | Fire Brigade Channel 8 |
| | | NFM | Jersey | Police (M2GS) Channel 6 |
| | | NFM | Jersey | Police Speed Traps |
| 155.9625 | | NFM | Newmarket | Police |
| 155.9750 | 147.6750 | AM | Devon | Police (QB) Channel 7 |
| | | NFM | Northern Ireland | Royal Ulster Constabulary |

**156.0000 - 162.5000 MHz    MARITIME BAND 25 KHZ (SHIP TX/SHORE TX)**

**INTERNATIONAL MARITIME VHF CHANNELS**

| Base | Mobile | Mode | Location | User and Notes |
|------|--------|------|----------|----------------|
| 156.00000 | 156.00000 | NFM | Nationwide | Channel 0 Coastguard/Lifeboat Primary Airborne Rescue Coordination |
| 156.0250 | 160.6250 | NFM | Nationwide | Channel 60 |
| 156.0500 | 160.6500 | NFM | Nationwide | Channel 01 |
| 156.0750 | 160.6750 | NFM | Nationwide | Channel 61 |
| 156.1000 | 160.7000 | NFM | Nationwide | Channel 02 |
| 156.1250 | 160.7250 | NFM | Nationwide | Channel 62 - Port operations |
| 156.1500 | 160.7500 | NFM | Nationwide | Channel 03 - Port operations |
| 156.1750 | 160.7750 | NFM | Nationwide | Channel 63 |
| 156.2000 | 160.8000 | NFM | Nationwide | Channel 04 |
| 156.2250 | 160.8250 | NFM | Nationwide | Channel 64 |
| 156.2500 | 160.8500 | NFM | Nationwide | Channel 05 |
| 156.2750 | 160.8750 | NFM | Nationwide | Channel 65 |
| 156.3000 | 156.3000 | NFM | Nationwide | Channel 06 - Intership |
| 156.3250 | 160.9250 | NFM | Nationwide | Channel 66 - Port operations |
| 156.3500 | 160.9500 | NFM | Nationwide | Channel 07 - Port operations |
| 156.3750 | 156.3750 | NFM | Nationwide | Channel 67 - Small UK boat safety |
| 156.4000 | 156.4000 | NFM | Nationwide | Channel 08 - Intership |
| 156.4250 | 156.4250 | NFM | Nationwide | Channel 68 - Port operations |
| 156.4500 | 156.4500 | NFM | Nationwide | Channel 09 |
| 156.4750 | 156.4750 | NFM | Nationwide | Channel 69 - Intership and port operations |
| 156.5000 | 156.5000 | NFM | Nationwide | Channel 10 - Pollution |
| 156.5250 | 156.5250 | NFM | Nationwide | Channel 70 - Digital selective calling |
| 156.5500 | 156.5500 | NFM | Nationwide | Channel 11 |
| 156.5750 | 156.5750 | NFM | Nationwide | Channel 71 - Port operations |
| 156.6000 | 156.6000 | NFM | Nationwide | Channel 12 |
| 156.6250 | 156.6250 | NFM | Nationwide | Channel 72 - Intership |
| 156.6500 | 156.6500 | NFM | Nationwide | Channel 13 |
| 156.6750 | 156.6750 | NFM | Nationwide | Channel 73 |
| 156.7000 | 156.7000 | NFM | Nationwide | Channel 14 |
| 156.7250 | 156.7250 | NFM | Nationwide | Channel 74 |
| 156.7500 | 156.7500 | NFM | Nationwide | Channel 15 - On-board Handhelds and port operations |
| 156.7625 | 156.7875 | NFM | Nationwide | Channel 75 Guard Band |
| 156.8000 | 156.8000 | NFM | Nationwide | Channel 16 Distress & Calling |
| 156.8125 | 156.8375 | NFM | Nationwide | Channel 76 Guard Band |
| 156.8500 | 156.8500 | NFM | Nationwide | Channel 17 - On-board Handhelds and port operations |
| 156.8750 | 156.8750 | NFM | Nationwide | Channel 77- Intership |
| 156.9000 | 161.5000 | NFM | Nationwide | Channel 18 - Port operations |
| 156.9250 | 161.5250 | NFM | Nationwide | Channel 78 - Port operations |
| 156.9500 | 161.5500 | NFM | Nationwide | Channel 19 |
| 156.9750 | 161.5750 | NFM | Nationwide | Channel 79 |

| Base | Mobile | Mode | Location | User and Notes |
|------|--------|------|----------|----------------|
| 157.0000 | 161.6000 | NFM | Nationwide | Channel 20 - Port operations |
| 157.0250 | 161.6250 | NFM | Nationwide | Channel 80 |
| 157.0500 | 161.6500 | NFM | Nationwide | Channel 21 |
| 157.0750 | 161.6750 | NFM | Nationwide | Channel 81 - Port operations |
| 157.1000 | 161.7000 | NFM | Nationwide | Channel 22 - Port operations |
| 157.1250 | 161.7250 | NFM | Nationwide | Channel 82 |
| 157.1500 | 161.7500 | NFM | Nationwide | Channel 23 |
| 157.1750 | 161.7750 | NFM | Nationwide | Channel 83 |
| 157.2000 | 161.8000 | NFM | Nationwide | Channel 24 |
| 157.2250 | 161.8250 | NFM | Nationwide | Channel 84 - Port operations |
| 157.2500 | 161.8500 | NFM | Nationwide | Channel 25 |
| 157.2750 | 161.8750 | NFM | Nationwide | Channel 85 |
| 157.3000 | 161.9000 | NFM | Nationwide | Channel 26 |
| 157.3250 | 161.9250 | NFM | Nationwide | Channel 86 |
| 157.3500 | 161.9500 | NFM | Nationwide | Channel 27 |
| 157.3750 | 161.9750 | NFM | Nationwide | Channel 87 |
| 157.4000 | 162.0000 | NFM | Nationwide | Channel 28 |
| 157.4250 | 162.0250 | NFM | Nationwide | Channel 88 Lighthouse Channel |

The above international channel are used in all countries. Not all ports and harbours use all these channels but have selected ones allocated to them. There are a vast number and all of them are listed in *Scanning the Maritime Bands* which enables you to monitor not only the ones in the UK but the whole of Western Europe. Details of the book are given on page 487. The following maritime frequencies are some of the specialized ones.

| Base | Mobile | Mode | Location | User and Notes |
|------|--------|------|----------|----------------|
| 156.1000 | 160.7000 | NFM | Runcorn | Ship Canal Maintenance |
| 156.1250 | | NFM | Forth | Working Channel |
| | | NFM | Thames Navigation | Working Channel |
| 156.1500 | | NFM | Pembroke | Pembroke Ferry |
| 156.2500 | | NFM | Birkenhead | Alfred Docks |
| | | NFM | Liverpool | Gladstone Docks |
| 156.3000 | | NFM | Barrow | Port Ops |
| | | NFM | Browshill | Chasewater National Powerboat rescue control |
| | | NFM | Milford Haven | Patrol & Pilot Launch |
| | | NFM | Nationwide | Comms Primary. Used by Coastguard vessels during SAR |
| | | NFM | Nationwide | Intership |
| | | NFM | Liverpool | In Bound Ships |
| 156.35000 | | NFM | Manchester Canal | Eastham Locks |
| | | NFM | River Severn | Weather Reports |
| 156.37500 | | NFM | Edinburgh | Marine Weather |
| | | NFM | Hull | Saltend Jetty |
| | | NFM | Milford Haven | Patrol & Pilot Launch |
| | | NFM | Nationwide | Coastguard Secondary |
| 156.40000 | | NFM | Lancaster | Port of Glasson Dock |
| | | NFM | Liverpool | In Bound Ships |
| | | NFM | Manchester Canal | Inbound Tugs |
| | | NFM | Milford Haven | Patrol & Pilot Launch |
| 156.42500 | 156.4250 | NFM | Port of Heysham | Fishers Shipping |
| | | NFM | Runcorn | Shipping Agent |
| 156.45000 | | NFM | Felixstowe | Pilot Arrangements |
| | | NFM | Harwich | Pilot |
| | | NFM | Hull | King George V Docks |

| Base | Mobile | Mode | Location | User and Notes |
|---|---|---|---|---|
| 156.45000 | | NFM | Kent | Medway Control |
| | | NFM | Liverpool | Mersey Radio (2) |
| | | NFM | Manchester Canal | Alfred Docks |
| | | NFM | Milford Haven | Milford Haven Docks |
| 156.47500 | | NFM | Lancaster | Port of Glasson Dock |
| | | NFM | Nationwide | HM Customs & Excise |
| 156.50000 | | AM | Edinburgh, Leith Heliport | Air/Ground (Leith Radio) |
| | | NFM | Liverpool | Mersey Ship to Tugs |
| | | NFM | Liverpool | Out Bound Ships |
| | | NFM | Manchester Canal | Outbound Tugs |
| 156.55000 | | NFM | Fleetwood | Fish Quay |
| | | NFM | Liverpool | Pilot |
| | | NFM | Milford Haven | Patrol & Pilot Launch |
| | | NFM | Portsmouth | Queens Harbour Master |
| | | NFM | Spurn Point | Pilot's Channel |
| 156.57500 | | NFM | Manchester Canal | Weather Navigation |
| 156.57500 | | NFM | RNAS Portland | Royal Navy |
| 156.60000 | | NFM | Humber | Vessel Traffic System |
| | | NFM | Liverpool | Mersey Radio (1) |
| | | NFM | Milford Haven | Milford Haven Docks |
| | | NFM | Milford Haven | Patrol & Pilot Launch |
| | | NFM | Portsmouth | Royal Navy Marine Traffic |
| | | NFM | Solent | Vessel Traffic System |
| | | NFM | Southampton | VTS |
| 156.70000 | | NFM | Eastham | Manchester Ship Canal |
| | | NFM | Glensanda | Super Quarry |
| | | NFM | Grangemouth | Grangemouth Locks |
| | | NFM | Humber | Pilot |
| | | NFM | Liverpool | Out Bound Ships |
| | | NFM | Manchester | Ship Canal |
| | | NFM | Manchester Canal | Eastham Control |
| | | NFM | Milford Haven | Elf & Gulf Oil Terminals |
| | | NFM | Milford Haven | Milford Haven Docks |
| | | NFM | Milford Haven | Patrol & Pilot Launch |
| | | NFM | Milford Haven | Texaco Oil Terminal |
| | | NFM | Teeside | Tees Harbour Radio |
| | | NFM | Woolwich | Thames Pilot |
| 156.7250 | | NFM | Kent | Medway Radio |
| | | NFM | Lochaber | Caledonian Canal |
| 156.7500 | 156.7400 | NFM | Liverpool Bay | Offshore gas rig supply vessels |
| 156.8000 | | NFM | Milford Haven | Elf & Gulf Oil Terminals |
| | | NFM | Milford Haven | Milford Haven Docks |
| | | NFM | Milford Haven | Patrol & Pilot Launch |
| | | NFM | Milford Haven | Texaco Oil Terminal |
| 156.8500 | | NFM | English Channel | BCIF |
| 156.8750 | | NFM | Swansea Docks | Swansea-Cork Ferry |
| 156.9000 | | NFM | Manchester Canal | Barton and Irlam Docks |
| | | NFM | Milford Haven | Elf & Gulf Oil Terminals |
| 156.9500 | 161.5500 | NFM | Tranmere | Shell Oil Terminal |
| 157.0000 | 161.6000 | NFM | Liverpool | Garston Docks |
| | | NFM | Manchester Canal | Stanlow Docks |
| | | NFM | Stanlow | Shell Refinery |
| 157.0250 | 161.6250 | NFM | Brighton | Marina Ops |
| | | NFM | Dover | Coastguard |
| | | NFM | Hull | Hull Marina |

| Base | Mobile | Mode | Location | User and Notes |
|---|---|---|---|---|
| 157.0500 | 161.6500 | NFM | Liverpool | Manchester Canal, Langton Docks |
|  |  | NFM | Milford Haven | Texaco Oil Terminal |
| 157.1750 | 161.7750 | NFM | Thames | Working Channel |
| 157.2500 | 161.8500 | NFM | Minehead | Severn Radio |
|  |  | NFM | Portishead | Severn Radio |
| 157.3000 | 161.9000 | NFM | Illfracombe | Severn Radio |
| 157.4250 | 162.0250 | NFM | Anvil Point | Lighthouse |
|  |  | NFM | North Foreland | Lighthouse |
|  |  | NFM | Pillar Rock Pt | Lighthouse |
| 157.4500 | 162.0500 | NFM | Channel Island | British Ferries Channel 29 |
| 157.4500 | 157.4500 | NFM | Jersey | Local Fishing Boats |
|  |  | NFM | Nationwide | Channel 29 |
|  |  | NFM | Plymouth | Torpoint Ferries |
|  |  | NFM | Torpoint Ferry | Operations |
| 157.4750 | 162.0750 | NFM | Nationwide | Channel 89 |
| 157.5000 | 162.1000 | NFM | English Channel | Herm Seaway Channel 30 |
|  |  | NFM | Swansea Docks | Trinity Lighthouse Crews |
| 157.5250 | 162.1250 | NFM | Nationwide | Patrol Boats Channel 90 |
| 157.5500 | 162.1500 | NFM | Nationwide | Fisheries Protection Channel 31 |
|  |  | NFM | Nationwide | RNLI Private Channel |
|  |  | NFM | Sark | Working Channel 31 |
| 157.5750 | 162.1750 | NFM | Nationwide | Channel 91 |
| 157.6000 | 162.2000 | NFM | Nationwide | Channel 32 |
| 157.6250 | 162.2250 | NFM | Nationwide | Channel 92 |
| 157.6500 | 162.2500 | NFM | English Channel | Fishermens Cooperative Ch 33 |
|  |  | NFM | English Channel | Hovercraft Channel 33 |
| 157.6750 | 162.2750 | NFM | Greencastle | Fishermens Cooperative Ch 93 |
|  |  | NFM | Nationwide | Channel 93 |
| 157.7000 | 162.3000 | NFM | English Channel | Herm Channel 34 |
|  |  | NFM | Nationwide | RNLI Private Channel |
| 157.7250 | 157.7250 | NFM | Jersey | Local Fishing Boats |
| 157.7250 | 162.3250 | NFM | Nationwide | Channel 94 |
|  |  | NFM | Dover | Hovercraft Channel 35 |
| 157.7500 | 157.7500 | NFM | Jersey | Local Fishing Boats |
| 157.7750 | 162.3750 | NFM | Nationwide | Channel 95 |
| 157.7875 |  | NFM | Thames | Pilot to Tug |
| 157.8000 | 162.4000 | NFM | Brighton | Marina Security Channel 36 |
|  |  | NFM | Nationwide | Channel 36 |
|  |  | NFM | Scilly Isles | St Mary's Boatmans Association |
| 157.8250 | 162.4250 | NFM | Nationwide | Channel 96 |
| 157.8500 | 157.8500 | NFM | Brighton | Mariner |
|  |  | NFM | Hartlepool | Yacht Marina |
|  |  | NFM | Jersey | St Catherines Yacht Club |
|  |  | NFM | Milford Haven | Marine & Yacht Station |
|  |  | NFM | Nationwide | Marinas Channel M1 |
|  |  | NFM | Plymouth | Queen Anne's Battery |
| 157.8750 | 162.4750 | NFM | Nationwide | Channel 97 |
| 157.9000 | 162.5000 | NFM | English Channel | British Ferries Channel 38 |
|  |  | NFM | Isle of Man | Steam Packet Ferries |
|  |  | NFM | London | Police Thames |
| 157.9250 | 162.5250 | NFM | Nationwide | Channel 98 |
| 157.9500 | 162.5500 | NFM | Nationwide | Channel 39 |
|  |  | NFM | Runcorn | Shipping Company |
| 157.9750 | 157.9750 | NFM | Montrose Docks | Cam Shipping |
| 157.9750 | 162.5750 | NFM | Nationwide | Channel 99 |
| 158.0000 | 162.6000 | NFM | Nationwide | Channel 40 |

| Base | Mobile | Mode | Location | User and Notes |
|---|---|---|---|---|
| 158.0250 | 162.6250 | NFM | Nationwide | Channel 100 |
| 158.0500 | 162.6500 | NFM | English Channel | Battricks Channel 41 |
| 158.0500 | 158.0500 | NFM | Jersey | Local Fishing Boats |
| 158.0750 | 162.6750 | NFM | Nationwide | Channel 101 |
| 158.1000 | 158.1000 | NFM | Jersey | Local Fishing Boats |
| 158.1000 | 162.7000 | NFM | Nationwide | Channel 42 |
| 158.1250 | 162.7250 | NFM | Nationwide | Channel 102 |
| 158.1500 | 162.7500 | NFM | Nationwide | Channel 43 |
| 158.1500 | 162.7500 | NFM | Swansea | Shipping Pilots for Docks Pilot HQ |
| 158.1750 | 162.7750 | NFM | Nationwide | Channel 103 |
| 158.2000 | 162.8000 | NFM | Moray Firth | Beatrice Alpha/Bravo Platform |
| 158.2125 | 158.2125 | NFM | Jersey | Marine FAX |
|  |  | NFM | Nationwide | Channel 104 |
| 158.2250 | 158.2250 | NFM | Nationwide | Marine FAX Channel 104B |
| 158.2500 | 158.2500 | NFM | Jersey | Local Fishing Boats |
| 158.2500 | 162.8500 | NFM | Moray Firth | Beatrice Alpha/Bravo Platform |
| 158.2750 | 162.8750 | NFM | Nationwide | Channel 105 |
| 158.3000 | 158.3000 | NFM | Jersey | Local Fishing Boats |
| 158.3000 | 162.9000 | NFM | Moray Firth | Beatrice Alpha/Bravo Platform |
| 158.3125 | 162.9125 | NFM | Nationwide | Channel 106 |
| 158.3500 | 162.9250 | NFM | Moray Firth | Beatrice Alpha/Bravo Platform |
| 158.3750 | 162.9750 | NFM | Nationwide | Channel 107 |
| 158.4000 | 163.0000 | NFM | Aberdeen | Dockside Channel 48 |
| 158.4250 | 163.0250 | NFM | English Channel | Condor Hydrofoils |
|  |  | NFM | Nationwide | Channel 108 |
|  |  | NFM | Nationwide | Coast Guards |
| 158.4500 | 163.0500 | NFM | Bowness | Lake Windermere Steamers |
|  |  | NFM | Isle Of Rhum | Scottish National Heritage |
|  |  | NFM | Jersey | Channel Islands Yacht Services |
|  |  | NFM | Moray Firth | Beatrice Alpha/Bravo Platform |
|  |  | NFM | Nigg Bay | Oil Tanker Ldg Channel 49 |
| 158.4750 | 163.0750 | NFM | Aberdeen | Shipping Info Channel 109 |
|  |  | NFM | Jersey | Ag & Fisheries |
| 158.5000 | 163.1000 | NFM | English Channel | Emeraude Line Channel 50 |
|  |  | NFM | Nationwide | Private Shipping Channel 50 |
|  |  | NFM | Nigg Bay | Oil Tanker Ldg Channel 50 |
|  |  | NFM | Solent | Solent Sea Rescue Org. |
| 158.5125 | 159.9125 | NFM | Nationwide | British Telecom Radiophone |
| 158.5500 | 163.0500 | NFM | Nationwide | Private Shipping Channel 51 |
| 158.6000 | 163.1000 | NFM | Nationwide | Private Shipping Channel 52 |

## 158.53125 - 160.54375 MHz    PMR AND DATA 12.5 KHZ NFM

| Base | Mobile | Mode | Location | User and Notes |
|---|---|---|---|---|
| 158.53750 | 163.03750 | NFM | Nationwide | Channel 1 |
| 158.63750 | 163.13750 | NFM | Nationwide | Channel 2 |
| 158.65000 | 158.65000 | NFM | Fort William | Police Rescue Services |
| 158.65000 |  | NFM | Nationwide | Private Shipping Channel 53 |
|  |  | NFM | Nationwide | RAF Mountain Rescue |
|  |  | NFM | Scotland | National Mountain Rescue |
| 158.70000 | 163.30000 | NFM | Nationwide | Private Shipping Channel 54 |
| 158.73750 | 163.23750 | NFM | Nationwide | Channel 3 |
| 158.75000 | 163.35000 | NFM | Nationwide | Private Shipping Channel 55 |
| 158.83750 | 163.33750 | NFM | Nationwide | Channel 4 |
| 158.85000 | 163.35000 | NFM | Nationwide | British Telecom |
| 158.93750 | 163.43750 | NFM | Nationwide | Channel 5 |
| 159.00000 | 159.00000 | NFM | Nationwide | Shipping Rescue |
| 159.01250 | 159.01250 | NFM | Tamworth | Alfred McAlpine Construction |

| Base | Mobile | Mode | Location | User and Notes |
|---|---|---|---|---|
| 159.03750 | 163.53750 | NFM | Nationwide | Channel 6 |
| 159.13750 | 163.63750 | NFM | Nationwide | Channel 7 |
| 159.18750 | | NFM | Jersey | Surveyors |
| 159.23750 | 163.73750 | NFM | Nationwide | Channel 8 |
| 159.25000 | | NFM | North Weald Airfield | Security Channel 3 |
| 159.33750 | 163.83750 | NFM | Nationwide | Channel 9 |
| 159.40000 | 163.90000 | NFM | Nationwide | Short Term Hire |
| 159.42500 | 163.92500 | NFM | Nationwide | Short Term Hire |
| 159.43750 | 163.93750 | NFM | Nationwide | Channel 10 |
| 159.45000 | 163.95000 | NFM | Swansea | Jinks Taxis |
| 159.48750 | | NFM | Exeter | Imperial Hotel doorman |
| 159.48750 | 163.98750 | NFM | Kent | Tour De France Forward Convoy |
| 159.48750 | | NFM | London | Arsenal Football Club Box Office |
| | | NFM | London | Plaza Shopping Centre Oxford St |
| | | NFM | London | Shorrocks Ltd. |
| | | NFM | Mildenhall | Service Provider |
| | | NFM | Nationwide | RAC Network Q Rally |
| | | NFM | Nationwide | Short Term Hire |
| 159.50000 | 164.00000 | NFM | Carlisle | B+Q |
| | | NFM | Llanelli | Trostre Tinplate Works |
| | | NFM | London | Brent Cross Shopping Centre |
| | | NFM | London, Oxford St | Plaza Shopping Centre security |
| | | NFM | Nationwide | Short Term Hire |
| 159.52500 | 164.03750 | NFM | London (Heathrow) | Pink Elephant Parking |
| | | NFM | Nationwide | Channel 11 |
| | | NFM | Bristol | Balloon Festival |
| 159.58750 | 164.08750 | NFM | Kent | Tour De France Marshalls & Security |
| 159.58750 | 164.03750 | NFM | London, Stratford | Shopping Centre security |
| | | NFM | Nationwide | Short Term Hire |
| | | NFM | Stoneleigh | Royal Show |
| 159.62500 | 164.12500 | NFM | Kent | Tour De France Channel 4 TV |
| 159.62500 | 159.62500 | NFM | Llanelli | Trostre Tinplate Works |
| | | NFM | Nationwide | Short Term Hire |
| 159.63750 | 164.13750 | NFM | Nationwide | Channel 12 |
| 159.68750 | 164.18750 | NFM | Kent | Tour De France Start/Finish |
| 159.68750 | 164.13750 | NFM | Nationwide | Short Term Hire |
| 159.73750 | 164.23750 | NFM | Nationwide | Channel 13 |
| 159.83750 | 164.33750 | NFM | Nationwide | Channel 14 |
| 159.87500 | 164.37500 | NFM | Space | Mir |
| 160.06000 | | NFM | Southampton | Healthcall Services (Doctors) |
| 160.06250 | 164.56250 | NFM | Bolton | Doctors Service |
| 160.12500 | 164.62500 | NFM | Kent | Tour De France (Italian) |
| 160.12500 | | NFM | Space | Soviet Mir Space Station |
| 160.15000 | 160.15000 | NFM | Blackpool | Doctors Messages |
| 160.30000 | | NFM | Eastbourne | Doctors on call |
| 160.54000 | | NFM | Gateshead | Council Housing |

**160.5500 - 160.5750 MHz   LOCAL AUTHORITY EMERGENCY ALARMS**

| Base | Mobile | Mode | Location | User and Notes |
|---|---|---|---|---|
| 160.55000 | | NFM | Nationwide | OAP Alarm System |
| 160.56250 | | NFM | Nationwide | OAP Alarm System |
| 160.57500 | | NFM | Nationwide | OAP Alarm System |

**160.6000 - 160.9750 MHz   INTERNATIONAL MARITIME SHORE TRANSMIT**

| Base | Mobile | Mode | Location | User and Notes |
|---|---|---|---|---|
| 160.6000 | | NFM | Aberdeen | Aberdeen Coastguard |
| 160.6000 | | NFM | Brixham | Brixham Coastguard |
| 160.6000 | | NFM | Crail | Crail Coastguard |

| Base | Mobile | Mode | Location | User and Notes |
|------|--------|------|----------|----------------|
| 160.6000 | | NFM | Falmouth | Falmouth Coastguard |
| 160.6000 | | NFM | Great Yarmouth | Lifeboat |
| 160.6000 | 160.6000 | NFM | Nationwide | HM Coastguard Channel 99 |
| 160.6000 | | NFM | Redcar | Redcar Coastguard |
| 160.8500 | | NFM | Liverpool | Alfred Dock Ops |
| 160.8500 | 156.2500 | NFM | Liverpool | Gladstone Dock Ops |
| 160.9500 | 156.3500 | NFM | Eastham | Manchester Ship Canal |
| 160.9500 | 156.3500 | NFM | Ilfracombe | Marine Ship to Shore |
| 160.9500 | | NFM | North Foreland | Working Channel |
| 160.9750 | | NFM | Eastbourne | Lifeguards |

**160.9750 - 161.4750 MHz**  PAGING ACKNOWLEDGEMENT CHANNELS & INTERNATIONAL MARITIME SERVICE BUSINESS MARINE RADIO AND LOCAL COMMUNITY SERVICES  25 kHz NFM SIMPLEX

| Base | Mobile | Mode | Location | User and Notes |
|------|--------|------|----------|----------------|
| 161.00000 | 31.725000 | NFM | Nationwide | Hospital Paging |
| 161.01250 | | NFM | Windsor Castle | PSA |
| 161.02500 | 31.750000 | NFM | Nationwide | Hospital Paging |
| 161.27500 | | NFM | Nationwide | Radio alarms |
| 161.03750 | 459.37500 | NFM | Ipswich | B.H.S Paging |
| 161.05000 | 31.775000 | NFM | Eastbourne | Hospital paging |
| | | NFM | London | LWTV Park Royal Channel 2 |
| | | NFM | Nationwide | Hospital Paging |
| 161.07500 | 459.43750 | NFM | Swansea City | Royal Mail |
| 161.08500 | 164.51000 | NFM | Newcastle-under-Lyme | Homebase Paging |
| 161.13000 | | NFM | Manchester | Norweb |
| 161.15000 | | NFM | Nationwide | Paging Returns |
| | | NFM | Port of Heysham | British Gas |
| 161.19500 | | NFM | Leicester | Electricity |
| 161.20000 | 161.20000 | NFM | Bacton | Philips Petroleum |
| 161.20500 | | NFM | Manchester | Norweb |
| 161.23000 | | NFM | Northampton | Electricity Repairs |
| 161.24500 | 161.20000 | NFM | Manchester | Norweb |
| | | NFM | Pembroke | Taxi |
| | | NFM | Preston | Electric Board Meter Changes |
| 161.27500 | | NFM | Nationwide | Small Boats Alarms |
| 161.30000 | | NFM | Cardiff | Haulage Firm |
| 161.30000 | 161.30000 | NFM | English Channel | British Channel. Island Ferries |
| | | NFM | Felixstowe | Alexandra Towing Tugs |
| | | NFM | Nationwide | On-Board Handhelds |
| | | NFM | Swansea Docks | AB Ports |
| 161.32500 | | NFM | Newmarket | Turners of Soham Ltd |
| 161.34500 | | NFM | Northampton | Company Radio |
| 161.35000 | 161.35000 | NFM | English Channel | BCIF 'Pride of Portsmouth' |
| | | NFM | Europort | Townsend Torisson Ferry Loadg |
| | | NFM | Fleetwood | Pandora Loading |
| | | NFM | Jersey | BCIF 'Pride of Portsmouth' |
| | | NFM | Manchester | Norweb |
| | | NFM | Nationwide | On-Board Handhelds |
| 161.38750 | 161.38750 | NFM | Croydon | ITV Thames TV Channel 2 |
| 161.42500 | 161.42500 | NFM | Jersey | Local Fishing Boats |
| | | NFM | Jersey | Marina |
| | | NFM | Marina & Yachts | Channel M2 |
| 161.44500 | 161.44500 | NFM | Machynlleth | Marina |

| Base | Mobile | Mode | Location | User and Notes |
|------|--------|------|----------|----------------|
| 161.45000 | 161.45000 | NFM | Croydon | ITV Thames TV Channel 3 |
| | | NFM | London | LWT Park Royal |
| | | NFM | Nationwide | On-Board Handhelds |
| | | NFM | Northampton | Works Radio |
| 161.47000 | | NFM | Manchester | Norweb |

**161.4750 - 162.0500 MHz    INTERNATIONAL MARITIME SHORE TRANSMIT**

| Base | Mobile | Mode | Location | User and Notes |
|------|--------|------|----------|----------------|
| 161.5000 | 156.9000 | NFM | Liverpool | Mersey Radio Radar |
| 161.5250 | | NFM | Hartlepool | Security Firm |
| 161.5500 | | NFM | Blyth | Harbour |
| 161.5500 | 156.9500 | NFM | Liverpool | Merset Radio Radar |
| 161.5800 | | NFM | Lancashire | Preston Gas Servicers |
| 161.6000 | 157.0000 | NFM | Garston | Garston Dock Ops |
| 161.6500 | 157.0500 | NFM | Liverpool | Langton Dock Ops |
| 161.6750 | | NFM | Nationwide | Marinas & Yacht Clubs Channel M2 |
| | | NFM | Port of Heysham | British Gas |
| 161.6800 | | NFM | Lancashire | Leyland Gas Servicers |
| 161.7000 | 157.1000 | NFM | Liverpool | Mersey Radio Radar |
| 161.8000 | | NFM | Edinburgh | International Marine |

**162.0500 - 163.03125 MHz  PRIVATE MARINE ALLOCATION AND PMR**
**25 KHZ NFM**

| Base | Mobile | Mode | Location | User and Notes |
|------|--------|------|----------|----------------|
| 162.0500 | 157.4500 | NFM | Jersey | BCIF Channel 29 |
| 162.0750 | 157.4750 | NFM | London | Contract dustcarts |
| | | NFM | London | Fortnum and Mason |
| | | NFM | London | Target Couriers |
| | | NFM | Nationwide | Motorola UK Channel 1 |
| | | NFM | Teeside | Harbour Pilot |
| 162.0875 | 157.4875 | NFM | London | Target Couriers |
| | | NFM | Walsall | All-Points Couriers |
| 162.1000 | 157.5000 | NFM | Jersey | Herm Seaway Channel 30 |
| 162.1250 | | NFM | Brent C | Shell PMR |
| 162.1375 | 157.5375 | NFM | Brighton | British Gas |
| | | NFM | Nationwide | RAC Network Q Rally-Subaru |
| 162.1500 | 157.5500 | NFM | Edinburgh Airport | PMR Channel 16 |
| | | NFM | Isle of Sark | Shipping Channel 31 |
| 162.1750 | 157.5750 | NFM | Driffield | J.R. Hood |
| | | NFM | London | Securicor Trunks |
| | | NFM | Nationwide | Motorola UK Channel 2 |
| 162.2000 | 157.6000 | NFM | London | Target Couriers |
| | | NFM | Merry Hill | Drinks Machines Company |
| | | NFM | Nationwide | Motorola UK Channel 3 |
| 162.2125 | | NFM | West Midlands | Coaches |
| 162.2250 | 157.6250 | NFM | Bristol | Security Company |
| | | NFM | Cheshire | Delivery Company |
| | | NFM | Lincoln | Taxi Service |
| | | NFM | Nationwide | Motorola UK Channel 4 |
| 162.2450 | | NFM | Machynlleth | British Gas |
| 162.2500 | 157.6500 | NFM | Jersey | Fishermans Co-Op |
| 162.2750 | 157.6750 | NFM | Blackpool | Builders |
| | | NFM | Hull | Container Terminal |
| | | NFM | Manchester | Delivery Company |
| 162.3000 | 157.7000 | NFM | Felixstowe | Shipping Company |
| | | NFM | Jersey | Shipping Company |

| Base | Mobile | Mode | Location | User and Notes |
|---|---|---|---|---|
| 162.3250 | 157.7250 | NFM | Boston | Fossitt & Thorne Tyres Ltd |
| | | NFM | Felixstowe | Shipping Company |
| | | NFM | London | Contract Buses |
| 162.3250 | 157.7250 | NFM | London | Courier |
| | | NFM | London | Securicor Trunks |
| | | NFM | Nationwide | Motorola UK Channel 5 |
| 162.3500 | 157.7500 | NFM | Bournemouth | Off-Shore Drilling Channel 35 |
| 162.3600 | | NFM | Droitwich | Securicor Base |
| 162.3625 | 157.7625 | NFM | Nationwide | Motorola UK Channel 6 |
| | | NFM | Solihull | Courier |
| 162.3750 | 157.7750 | NFM | London | Securicor Trunks |
| | | NFM | Nationwide | Motorola UK Channel 7 |
| | | NFM | Swindon | Skip Company |
| 162.4000 | 157.8000 | NFM | Hull | Humber Tugs |
| | | NFM | Space | NOAA Satellite |
| | | AM | Wigan | Toyota Emergency Repairs |
| 162.4250 | 157.8250 | NFM | Blackpool | Hospital Cleaners |
| | | NFM | Liverpool | Engineers |
| | | NFM | London, north | Taxis |
| | | NFM | Nationwide | Motorola UK Channel 8 |
| | | NFM | Space | NOAA Satellite |
| 162.4500 | | NFM | Nationwide | Differential GPS |
| 162.4750 | 157.8750 | NFM | Bristol | Contractor |
| | | NFM | London | Buses |
| | | NFM | London | Securicor Trunks |
| | | NFM | Manchester | Delivery Company |
| | | NFM | Nationwide | Motorola UK Channel 9 |
| 162.4750 | | NFM | Space | NOAA Satellite |
| 162.5000 | 157.9000 | NFM | Dieppe | Ferry Co. Channel 38 |
| | | NFM | Harwich | Pilots |
| | | NFM | Isle of Man | Steam Packet Ferries |
| | | NFM | London | Police Thames boats |
| | | NFM | Newhaven | Sealink Channel 38 |
| 162.5250 | 162.5250 | NFM | Staffs | Haulage |
| 162.5375 | 157.9375 | NFM | Nationwide | Network Q Rally - Toyota |
| 162.5500 | 157.9500 | NFM | Nationwide | Townsend Thorenson Channel 39 |
| 162.5500 | | NFM | Space | NOAA Satellite |
| 162.5750 | 157.9750 | NFM | Nationwide | Motorola UK Channel 10 |
| | | NFM | Ninian North Chevron | Back-up to Ninian S |
| 162.6500 | 158.0250 | NFM | Liverpool | Shipping Agents |
| | | NFM | Wallesey | Mersey Ferries |
| 162.6800 | | NFM | Manchester | Piccadilly Radio |
| 162.7000 | 158.1000 | NFM | Bristol | Dock Tugs Channel 42 |
| 162.8500 | 162.8500 | NFM | Liverpool | Ship Ops |
| 162.8750 | | NFM | Manchester | Building Firm |
| | | NFM | Manchester | Delivery Company |
| 162.9250 | 158.3250 | NFM | Boston | Fossitt & Thorne Tyres Ltd |
| | | NFM | London | Securicor Trunks |
| | | NFM | London (Wembley) | Bus Hoppas |
| | | NFM | Manchester | Delivery Company |
| 162.9375 | 158.3375 | NFM | Bristol | Coast Guard |
| 162.9750 | 158.3750 | NFM | Boston | Fossitt & Thorne Tyres Ltd |
| | | NFM | Oldham | Service Engineers |
| 163.0000 | 158.4000 | NFM | London | BB Securities Ltd. |
| | | NFM | Southampton | MediCall Channel 1 |

| Base | Mobile | Mode | Location | User and Notes |
|---|---|---|---|---|
| 163.0250 | | NFM | Isle of Man | Calf of Man Telephone Link |
| | | NFM | Nationwide | Differential GPS |

**163.03125 - 165.0000 MHz      PMR BAND**

| Base | Mobile | Mode | Location | User and Notes |
|---|---|---|---|---|
| 163.05000 | 158.55000 | NFM | Cumnock | Gibson Whyte, heating engineers |
| | | NFM | Hampshire | Bus Company |
| | | NFM | Jersey | Amal-grow |
| | | NFM | Jersey | Besco |
| | | NFM | Jersey | Cable TV |
| | | NFM | Jersey | Dynarod |
| | | NFM | Jersey | Gorey Cabs |
| | | NFM | Jersey | Securicor |
| | | NFM | Peterborough | Hector |
| 163.06000 | | NFM | Irvine | Parcel Force |
| 163.06250 | 158.56250 | NFM | Peterborough | Various Users |
| 163.07500 | 158.57500 | NFM | Brighton | Construction Company |
| | | NFM | Colchester | Pub and club link to police |
| | | NFM | Manchester | Bus Inspectors |
| 163.08750 | 158.58750 | NFM | Nationwide | Road Construction Engineers |
| 163.11250 | 158.61250 | NFM | Dublin | District Police Surveillance |
| 163.13750 | 158.63750 | NFM | Dublin | District Police Surveillance |
| | | NFM | London | Wembley Stadium contract cleaners |
| 163.15000 | 163.15000 | NFM | London | Police Royal Parks Ch 2 (RZ) |
| | | NFM | Swansea | Council Warden Channel 2 |
| 163.16250 | 158.66250 | NFM | Dublin | District Police Surveillance |
| 163.18750 | | NFM | London | Dept. of Environment |
| 163.20000 | 158.70000 | NFM | Bangor | DSS |
| | | NFM | Birmingham | City Hospital medical engineers |
| | | NFM | Jersey | Amal-grow |
| | | NFM | Jersey | Besco |
| | | NFM | Jersey | Cable TV |
| | | NFM | Jersey | Dynarod |
| | | NFM | Jersey | Gorey Cabs |
| | | NFM | Jersey | Securicor |
| | | NFM | Peterborough | CBS Repeater |
| | | NFM | Preston | Lowe's Plant Hire |
| 163.21250 | 158.71250 | NFM | London | Doctors & Medics |
| | | NFM | Perthshire | Electricians |
| | | NFM | Peterborough | CBS Repeater |
| | | NFM | Tayside | Heating Engineers |
| 163.22500 | 158.72500 | NFM | Handcross | Comrep |
| | | NFM | Manchester Gorton | Steves Bakery |
| | | NFM | Oldham | Emergency Doctor |
| | | NFM | Peterborough | Community Repeater |
| 163.30000 | 158.70000 | NFM | Derby | Civil Engineers |
| | | NFM | Fleetwood | Golf Club |
| | | NFM | Lea Valley | Hoddesdon & Herts Buses |
| | | NFM | Nationwide | Contractor |
| | | NFM | West Yorkshire | Haulage Firm |
| 163.32500 | 158.82500 | NFM | London | Islington Refuse |

| Base | Mobile | Mode | Location | User and Notes |
|---|---|---|---|---|
| 163.35000 | 158.85000 | NFM | Co Durham | Waste Disposal |
| | | NFM | Cornwall | Repeater |
| | | NFM | Devon | Associated Leisure |
| | | NFM | Jersey | Amal-grow |
| | | NFM | Jersey | Besco |
| | | NFM | Jersey | Cable TV |
| | | NFM | Jersey | Dynarod |
| | | NFM | Jersey | Gorey Cabs |
| | | NFM | Jersey | Securicor |
| | | NFM | Newton Abbot | Amtrack |
| | | NFM | Oakhampton | Target Express |
| | | NFM | Peterborough | Octane |
| | | NFM | Plymouth | Granada TV |
| 163.36250 | 158.86250 | FM | Cambridge | Vehicle Towaway |
| | | NFM | Cirencester | By Pass Construction |
| | | NFM | Cleveland | Private Message |
| | | NFM | Manchester Lees | Battery Deliveries |
| | | NFM | Newcastle | Security Firm |
| | | NFM | Peterborough | CBS Repeater |
| 163.37500 | 158.87500 | NFM | Nationwide | Contractor |
| | | NFM | Preston | Taxis |
| 163.38750 | | NFM | Newport | Community Repeater |
| | | NFM | West Perthshire | Data Link |
| 163.42500 | 163.42500 | FM | Cambridge | ACA Test Frequency |
| 163.43750 | 158.93750 | NFM | Aberdeen | Message Handling |
| 163.51250 | 159.12500 | NFM | Coventry | Mowlem Construction |
| 163.51250 | | NFM | Lichfield | Tarmac |
| | | NFM | M6 | Motorway Maintenance |
| | | NFM | Nationwide | Contractor |
| | | NFM | Stoke on Trent | Civil Engineers |
| 163.51500 | | NFM | Leicester | Emergency Doctor |
| 163.60000 | 159.10000 | NFM | Tyneside | UK Security |
| 163.61250 | 159.11250 | NFM | M25 | Engineers |
| 163.68750 | 159.18750 | NFM | London | Community Repeater |
| 163.90000 | 163.90000 | NFM | Dudley | Construction Company |
| 163.90000 | 159.40000 | NFM | Grimsby | Murphy Construction |
| | | NFM | Kent | Tour De France Race Direction |
| | | NFM | Lichfield | Tarmac |
| | | NFM | London | Notting Hill Carnival |
| | | NFM | Nationwide | RAC Network Q Rally |
| | | NFM | Nationwide | Short Term Hire |
| | | NFM | Newport, Gwent | Newport Hospital Security (RGH) |
| | | NFM | Peterborough | Viscount Buses |
| | | NFM | Warwickshire | Tarmac |
| 163.91250 | 163.91250 | FM | Cambridge | Data Link |
| 163.91250 | 159.41250 | NFM | Jersey | Island Cabs |
| 163.92500 | 159.42500 | NFM | Kent | Tour De France Tour & Press |
| | | NFM | London | Oval Cricket Ground Stewards |
| | | NFM | Nationwide | Short Term Hire |
| | | NFM | Sheffield | Gleason Builders |
| 163.95000 | | NFM | Chesterfield | Hospital Porters |
| 163.96250 | 159.46250 | NFM | Birmingham | School Maintenance |
| | | NFM | Fleetwood | Pharmacy Agency |
| | | NFM | Peterborough | CBS Repeater |
| 163.97500 | 159.47500 | NFM | Lichfield | Taxi |
| | | NFM | Peterborough | Various Users |

| Base | Mobile | Mode | Location | User and Notes |
|------|--------|------|----------|----------------|
| 163.98000 | 163.98000 | NFM | Bedford | Repeater |
| 163.98750 | 159.48750 | NFM | Nationwide | Short Term Hire |
| 164.00000 | 159.50000 | NFM | Bletchley Park | Securicor guards |
| | | NFM | Jersey | Motor Tarffic Dept Channel 3 |
| | | NFM | London, Oxford St. | Plaza Shopping Centre |
| | | NFM | Nationwide | Short Term Hire |
| 164.01250 | 164.01250 | NFM | Guernsey | Aurigny Airlines |
| 164.01500 | | NFM | England (Southern) | O'Rourke Construction Channel 4 |
| 164.02500 | 159.52500 | NFM | Dublin | District Police (E) |
| | | NFM | Edinburgh | Police (Easter Road Match Control) |
| | | NFM | London | Chelsea Footbal Club stewards |
| 164.03750 | 159.53750 | NFM | Dublin | District Police (N) |
| | | NFM | Hendon | RAF Museum (BLUE CONTROL) |
| | | NFM | Jersey | Aurigny Airlines Handhelds |
| 164.05000 | 159.55000 | NFM | City of London | Bus Company |
| | | NFM | Dublin | District Police (R) |
| | | NFM | Edinburgh | Sheriff Court Security |
| | | NFM | Humberside | Boy Scouts Channel 1 |
| | | NFM | Jersey | European Golf Championships |
| | | NFM | London, Oxford St. | HMV Shop Security |
| | | NFM | Nationwide | National Scout Association |
| | | NFM | Nationwide | Short Term Hire |
| | | NFM | Nationwide | St John's Ambulance Channel 4 |
| | | NFM | Newmarket | Security Company |
| | | NFM | Northampton | Golf Club |
| 164.06100 | | NFM | Birmingham, Aston Villa | St John's Ambulance Ch 3 |
| 164.06250 | 159.56250 | NFM | Carnforth | Tarmac |
| | | NFM | Dublin | District Police (K) |
| | | NFM | Jersey | European Golf Championships |
| | | NFM | Jersey | Tilbury Douglas |
| | | NFM | Morecambe | Sea Scout |
| | | NFM | Nationwide | National Scout Association |
| | | NFM | Nationwide | St John's Ambulances Channel 3 |
| | | NFM | Stevenage | British Home Stores net |
| 164.07500 | 159.57500 | NFM | Dublin | District Police (C) |
| 164.08750 | 159.58750 | NFM | Dublin | District Police (L) |
| | | NFM | Glasgow | Taxis |
| | | NFM | Kent | Tour De France TV Cameras |
| | | NFM | Nationwide | RAC Network Q Rally |
| | | NFM | Nationwide | Short Term Hire |
| | | NFM | Nationwide | Whitby Davison Production (films) |
| | | NFM | Stevanage | Multiplx cimema staff net |
| 164.10000 | 159.60000 | NFM | Dublin | District Police (W) |
| 164.11250 | 159.61250 | NFM | Dublin | District Police (J) |
| 164.12500 | 159.62500 | NFM | Ashford | Council (Tour De France) |
| | | NFM | Dublin | District Police (F) |
| | | NFM | England (Southern) | O'Rourke Construction Channel 1 |
| | | NFM | Humberside Airport | Security |
| | | NFM | London, Soho | Village pub doorman |
| | | FM | Nationwide | Orourke Construction |
| | | NFM | Nationwide | Short Term Hire |
| | | NFM | Southampton | Taxis |
| 164.13750 | 159.63750 | NFM | Dublin | District Police (A) |
| | | NFM | Edinburgh | Data Link |
| | | NFM | Jersey | Jersey Telecom Cable Laying |
| | | FM | Newmarket | Security (OB) |

| Base | Mobile | Mode | Location | User and Notes |
|------|--------|------|----------|----------------|
| 164.14500 | | NFM | England (Southern) | O'Rourke Construction Channel 2 |
| 164.16250 | 159.66250 | NFM | Dublin | District Police (H) |
| 164.17500 | 159.67500 | NFM | Dublin | District Police (M) |
| 164.18500 | 164.18500 | FM | Newmarket | Abbey Security |
| 164.18750 | 159.68750 | NFM | London | Alexandra Palace security |
| | | NFM | Nationwide | RAC Network Q Rally-Toyota |
| | | NFM | Nationwide | Short Term Hire |
| 164.19500 | | NFM | England (Southern) | O'Rourke Construction Ch3 |
| 164.20000 | 159.70000 | NFM | Dublin | District Police (D) |
| | | NFM | Nationwide | Paging Speech Return |
| 164.21250 | 159.71250 | NFM | Dublin | District Police (G) |
| 164.22500 | 159.72500 | NFM | Dublin | District Police (P) |
| | | NFM | Galway | Community Repeater |
| | | NFM | Nationwide | Pacnet Data |
| 164.23750 | 159.73750 | NFM | Nationwide | Pacnet Data |
| | | NFM | Tayside | Data Link |
| 164.25000 | 159.75000 | NFM | Glasgow | Data Link |
| 164.25000 | | NFM | Nationwide | Pacnet |
| 164.26250 | 159.76250 | NFM | Newcastle | Data Link |
| | | NFM | Tayside | Data Link |
| 164.27500 | 159.77500 | NFM | Ashton under Lyme | Tyre Co. Deliveries |
| | | NFM | Nationwide | Pacnet Data |
| 164.28750 | 159.78750 | NFM | Nationwide | Pacnet Data |
| | 159.80000 | NFM | Blackburn | DMC Private Hire |
| | | NFM | Glasgow | Data Link |
| | | NFM | Nationwide | Pacnet |
| | | NFM | Newport | Community Repeater |
| 164.31250 | 159.81250 | NFM | Nationwide | Pacnet Data |
| 164.32500 | 159.82500 | NFM | Nationwide | Pacnet Data |
| | | NFM | Newcastle | Data Link |
| | | NFM | Tayside | Data Link |
| 164.33750 | 159.83750 | NFM | Glasgow | Data Link |
| | | NFM | Nationwide | Pacnet |
| 164.35000 | 159.85000 | NFM | Nationwide | Pacnet |
| | | NFM | Tayside | Data Link |
| 164.36250 | 159.86250 | NFM | Glasgow | Data Link |
| | | NFM | Nationwide | Pacnet Data |
| 164.37500 | 159.87500 | NFM | Blackburn | Chippy's Private Hire |
| | | NFM | Nationwide | Pacnet Data |
| | | NFM | Newmarket | Security |
| 164.38750 | 159.88750 | NFM | Manchester Hyde | Lewis Food Co |
| | | NFM | Nationwide | Airport Duty Officer Channel 2 |
| | | NFM | Nationwide | Pacnet |
| 164.40000 | 159.90000 | NFM | Blackburn | C&M Private Hire |
| | | NFM | Manchester | Service Engineers |
| | | NFM | Nationwide | BT Selcal to Mobiles |
| 164.42740 | 160.17350 | NFM | Nottingham | Medics |
| 164.43750 | 159.93750 | NFM | Nationwide | Mobile Phone Link |
| | | NFM | Peterborough | Various Users |
| | | NFM | Queensbury | Calderdale Council |
| 164.44500 | 159.94500 | AM | Bedfordshire | Repeater |
| | | NFM | London | Vehicle Recovery |

| Base | Mobile | Mode | Location | User and Notes |
|---|---|---|---|---|
| 164.45000 | 159.95000 | NFM | Cleveland | Security Firm |
| | | NFM | Dyfed | Riverlea Tractors |
| | | NFM | Haverfordwest | Coin Machines |
| | | NFM | Manchester | Security |
| | | NFM | Newmarket | Taxis |
| | | NFM | Pembrokeshire | Riverlea Tractors |
| | | NFM | Peterborough | Beeline |
| | | NFM | Peterborough | Ranger |
| | | NFM | Worcester | A W Taxis |
| 164.46250 | 159.96250 | NFM | Glasgow | Community Repeater |
| | | NFM | Gloucester | Security Firm |
| | | NFM | Horsham | Comrep |
| | | NFM | Penrith | County Taxis |
| | | NFM | Peterborough | Various Users |
| | | NFM | Southampton | Aircall |
| 164.47500 | 159.97500 | NFM | Brighton | Aircall (Doctors) |
| 164.47500 | 164.47500 | FM | Cambridge | White Sec Security |
| | | NFM | Nationwide | Aircall Channel 10 |
| | | NFM | Peterborough | Optic |
| | | NFM | Warick | Council boarding-up service |
| 164.48750 | 159.98750 | NFM | Bishop Stortford | Taxis |
| | | NFM | Crewe | Recovery Vehicles |
| | | NFM | Poole | Repeater |
| | | NFM | Southampton | Taxis |
| 164.50000 | 160.00000 | NFM | Bolton | Transport Service |
| | | NFM | Bournemouth | Medicare |
| | | NFM | Cardiff | Emergency Doctors |
| | | NFM | Cheshire | Haulage |
| | | NFM | Glasgow | Strathclyde Medicall |
| | | NFM | London | Parcel Deliveries |
| | | NFM | Manchester Hyde | Security Firm |
| | | NFM | Nationwide | Doctors Common |
| | | NFM | Poole | Paramedics |
| | | NFM | Sheffield | Medicare |
| | | NFM | Southampion | Skip Hire Co |
| | | NFM | Wakefield | Doctor's DepService |
| | | NFM | Warrington | Garden Centre |
| 164.51250 | 160.01250 | NFM | Nationwide | Aircall |
| | | NFM | Newport | Parcel Company |
| | | NFM | Peterborough | Various Users |
| | | NFM | Portsmouth | Nynex |
| 164.52500 | 160.02500 | NFM | Kent | Amtrak |
| | | NFM | Kent | Drainage Engineers (MD) |
| | | NFM | Kent | Gold Taxis |
| | | NFM | Worthing | Taxi |
| 164.53750 | 160.03750 | NFM | East Durham | Doctors On Call |
| | | NFM | Galway | Community Repeater |
| | | NFM | Nottingham | Emergency doctors |
| | | NFM | West Midlands | All Waist |

| Base | Mobile | Mode | Location | User and Notes |
|------|--------|------|----------|----------------|
| 164.55000 | 160.05000 | NFM | Blackburn | CRM Private Hire |
| | | NFM | Cardiff | Emergency Doctors |
| | | NFM | Co Durham | Alarm Engineers |
| | | AM | Grimsby | Aircall |
| | | NFM | Hull | Dynarod Ltd |
| | | NFM | Hull | East Yorkshire Buses |
| | | NFM | Manchester Hyde | Builders Yard |
| | | NFM | Nationwide | Aircall Channel 5 |
| | | NFM | Peterborough | Castor |
| 164.55000 | 160.05000 | NFM | Swansea | BT Security |
| 164.56250 | 160.06250 | NFM | Bournemouth | Emergency Services |
| | | NFM | Coventry | Healthcall |
| | | NFM | Coventry | Medics |
| | | NFM | Edinburgh | Doctors Service |
| | | NFM | Manchester | Doctors Dep Service |
| | | NFM | Nationwide | Aircall |
| | | NFM | Peterborough | Various Users |
| | | NFM | South Yorkshire | Aircall Medical |
| | | NFM | Southampton | MediCall Channel 2 |
| | | NFM | Tyne & Wear | Doctors On Call |
| 164.57500 | 160.07500 | NFM | Maidstone | Scan Electronics |
| | | NFM | Nationwide | Aircall |
| | | NFM | Peterborough | Various Users |
| 164.58750 | 160.08750 | NFM | Bury | Emergency Doctor |
| | | NFM | Croydon | Minicab Firm |
| | | NFM | Hull | Emergency Doctors |
| | | NFM | Manchester | Emergency Doctors |
| | | NFM | Peterborough | CBS Repeater |
| 164.59000 | | NFM | Gateshead | Security |
| 164.60000 | 160.10000 | NFM | Nationwide | Aircall |
| | | NFM | Newcastle | UK Waste Skip Hire |
| | | NFM | Poole | Repeater |
| | | NFM | Sheffield | Community Repeater |
| | | NFM | Sheffield | Forge Alert security |
| 164.61250 | 160.11250 | NFM | Bournemouth | Council Road Gangs |
| | | NFM | Nationwide | Aircall Channel 2 |
| | | NFM | Poole | Repeater |
| 164.62500 | 160.12500 | NFM | Bournemouth | St John's |
| | | NFM | Bristol | Hospital Transport |
| | | NFM | Hampshire | Aircall |
| | | NFM | London | Medic Pager |
| | | NFM | Nationwide | Aircall Channel 5 |
| | | NFM | Parkstone | Aristoview |
| | | NFM | Peterborough | Tango |
| | | NFM | Plymouth | Emergency Doctors Service |
| | | NFM | Poole | Repeater |
| | | NFM | Staffordshire | Emergency Doctor |
| 164.63750 | 160.13750 | NFM | Glasgow | Doctors Service |
| | | NFM | Newport | Paramedic Doctors Service |
| | | NFM | Portsmouth | MediCall Channel 1 |
| | | NFM | Southampton | Taxis |
| | | NFM | Swansea City | Doctors on Call |
| | | NFM | Tyne & Wear | Taxis |
| | | NFM | Wolverhampton | Doctors Service |

| Base | Mobile | Mode | Location | User and Notes |
|------|--------|------|----------|----------------|
| 164.65000 | 160.15000 | NFM | Birmingham | Doctors Service |
| | | NFM | Bristol | Healthcare Services Ltd. |
| | | NFM | Newcastle | Doctors on Call |
| 164.66250 | 160.16250 | NFM | Poole | Repeater |
| 164.67500 | 160.17500 | NFM | Severn Bridge | Toll Booths |
| 164.68750 | 160.18750 | NFM | County Durham | Doctor's Medicall |
| | | NFM | Newcastle | Security Firm |
| | | NFM | Tyneside | Security |
| 164.70000 | 160.20000 | NFM | Nationwide | Teleacoustic |
| | | NFM | Newcastle | Council |
| | | NFM | Tyneside | Plumbing Repairs |
| | | NFM | West Midlands | Burglar Alarms |
| 164.71250 | 160.21250 | NFM | Gloucester | Repeater |
| | | NFM | London | Medical & Rescue Services |
| | | NFM | Peterborough | Various Users |
| 164.72500 | 160.22500 | NFM | Crewe | Taxis |
| | | NFM | Gravesend | Doctors |
| | | NFM | London | Bermondsey Council |
| | | NFM | London | Security Company |
| | | NFM | Newmarket | Trunked Network |
| | | NFM | Peterborough | Spark |
| | | NFM | Poole | Repeater |
| 164.73750 | 160.23750 | NFM | Cleveland | Doctors On Call |
| | | NFM | Nationwide | Lodge Radio Service |
| 164.75000 | 160.25000 | NFM | Ely | Taxis |
| | | NFM | London | St John's Ambulance |
| | | NFM | Oxford | Hospital Services |
| | | NFM | Southern England | Saxon Security |
| | | NFM | Wrexham | Haulage Contractor |
| 164.76250 | 160.26250 | NFM | Cambridge | John Hendry & Son |
| | | NFM | Kent | Eurotunnel |
| | | AM | Leeds | Taxis |
| | | NFM | London | Medicall South London |
| | | NFM | Lothian & Borders | Lothian Regional Council |
| | | NFM | Newmarket | Transport Firm |
| | | NFM | Perthshire | Delivery company |
| | | NFM | Portsmouth | Taxis |
| 164.78750 | 160.28750 | NFM | Blackpool | Haulage Contractors |
| | | NFM | Bournemouth | Council Lighting |
| | | NFM | Nationwide | Teleacoustic |
| 164.80000 | 160.30000 | NFM | Bodmin | Vet Services |
| | | NFM | Bournemouth | Aircall Radio |
| | | NFM | Nationwide | Teleacoustic |
| | | NFM | Newcastle | Council |
| | | NFM | Norfolk | Red Star Parcels |
| 164.81250 | 160.01250 | NFM | Bath | Strode Sound CBS |
| | | NFM | Bristol | Taxis |
| | | NFM | Leicester | Council office Security |
| | | NFM | Poole | Repeater |
| 164.82500 | 160.32500 | NFM | Central London | Motor Rescue Service |
| | | NFM | London | Auto Breakdown Service |
| | | NFM | London | National Rescue |
| | | NFM | London | St Mary's Hospital Ambulances |
| | | NFM | Poole | Repeater |
| | | NFM | Tamworth | Bluebell Taxi |
| | | NFM | West Sussex | Recovery Firm |

| Base | Mobile | Mode | Location | User and Notes |
|------|--------|------|----------|----------------|
| 164.82500 | 160.32500 | NFM | Worcester | Delta Sierra Base |
| 164.83750 | 160.33750 | NFM | Birmingham | Glaziers |
| | | NFM | Bournemouth | Express Carriers |
| | | NFM | Poole | Repeater |
| 164.85000 | 160.35000 | NFM | Colwyn Bay | BR Station |
| | | NFM | Nationwide | Message Handling |
| | | NFM | Wadesbridge | Builder's Merchants |
| 164.86250 | 160.36250 | NFM | Manchester | Bouncey Castle Hire |
| | | NFM | Manchester | Plant Firm |
| | | NFM | South West Wales | DSS Fraud Teams |
| 164.86250 | 160.86250 | NFM | Swansea | Council Warden Channel 1 |
| 164.87500 | 160.37500 | NFM | Nationwide | Mobile Phone Link |
| | | NFM | Newcastle | British Gas |
| | | NFM | Norfolk | Alpha Drains |
| | | NFM | Northen Ireland | NCF Milk Tankers |
| | | NFM | Poole | Repeater |
| | | NFM | Sussex Coast | Coastway Hospital Radio |
| 164.88750 | 160.38750 | AM | Bedfordshire | Vehicle Recovery |
| | | NFM | Burton, Staffs | Skips |
| | | NFM | London | Security Company |
| | | NFM | Nationwide | Mobile Phone Link Channel 2B |
| | | NFM | Newcastle | Data Link |
| 164.90000 | 160.40000 | AM | Bedfordshire | Repeater |
| | | NFM | Cheshire | Tyre Services |
| | | NFM | Lincoln | Gas Suppliers |
| | | NFM | Manchester | Delivery Company |
| | | NFM | Wirral | Data Link |
| 164.91250 | 160.41250 | NFM | Bournemouth | Taxi Hire Co. |
| | | NFM | Ipswich | Garage |
| | | NFM | Newport | Central Heating Company |
| 164.92500 | 160.42500 | NFM | Brighton | RCS Comrep Channel 8 |
| | | NFM | Kent | Tour De France (French) |
| | | NFM | Norfolk | ANC Parcels |
| | | NFM | Peterborough | Anglo |
| | | NFM | Suffolk | Morlings TV Rentals |
| 164.93750 | 160.43750 | NFM | Bristol | Security Co |
| | | NFM | Poole | Repeater |
| 164.95000 | 160.45000 | NFM | Glasgow | Taxi |
| | | NFM | Gloucester | Group 4 Static Guards |
| | | NFM | Grangetown | Private Message |
| | | NFM | London | Ambulance Service |
| | | NFM | Nottingham | Taxi |
| 164.96250 | 160.46250 | NFM | Birmingham | Leisure Services Security |
| | | NFM | Jersey | Links CBS 4 |
| 164.97500 | 160.47500 | NFM | Merseyside | Surveyors |
| 164.98750 | 172.12500 | NFM | Cambridge | Car Breakdown Recovery Firm |
| 164.98750 | 160.48750 | NFM | Kent | Tour de France (French) |
| 165.00000 | 169.81250 | NFM | Aberdeen | Northern Garage |
| 165.00000 | 160.50000 | NFM | Bath | Bath University Research |
| | | NFM | Blackburn | City Private Hire |
| | | NFM | Cornwall | Repeater |
| | | NFM | Dorking | RCS Comrep Channel 3 |
| | | NFM | Felixstowe | Paging |
| | | NFM | Ipswich | Paging |
| | | NFM | Kent | Doctors On Call |
| | | NFM | London | ODRATS Channel 5 |

| Base | Mobile | Mode | Location | User and Notes |
|------|--------|------|----------|----------------|
| 165.00000 | 160.50000 | NFM | Manchester | Plant hire company |
| | | NFM | Manchester | Security |
| | | NFM | Morecambe | Security Vans |
| | | NFM | New Malden | North West Cars |
| | | NFM | Newmarket | Medical |
| | | NFM | Poole | Taxi |

**165.0125- 168.2250 MHz    VHF HIGH BAND PMR BASE/REPEATERS (MOBILE SPLIT + 4.8 MHz) AMBULANCE SERVICES (ENGLAND & WALES)**

| Base | Mobile | Mode | Location | User and Notes |
|------|--------|------|----------|----------------|
| 165.0125 | 169.8125 | NFM | Jersey | Trinity Farm |
| | | | Tamworth, Staffs | Quarry |
| 165.0250 | 169.8250 | NFM | Bath | Bath University Research |
| | | NFM | Blackpool | First Aid Council Post |
| | | NFM | Bristol | City Link Parcel Express |
| | | NFM | Burnley | Delivery Service |
| | | NFM | Cardiff | Commercial Rigging |
| | | NFM | Dover | Castle Comms |
| | | NFM | Guernsey | Links CBS 3 |
| | | NFM | Newcastle | Housing Repairs |
| | | NFM | North Yorkshire | Doctor Service |
| 165.0250 | 160.5250 | NFM | Staffs | Forestry Rangers |
| 165.0350 | | NFM | Cardiff Area | Delivery Company |
| 165.0375 | 169.8375 | NFM | Bristol | Bristol Dogs Home |
| | | NFM | Jersey | Eurocar Hire |
| | | NFM | London | City of Westminster Cleansing |
| | | NFM | Newcastle | Site Delivery |
| | | NFM | Newport | Community Repeater |
| | | NFM | Nottingham | Taxis |
| | | NFM | Poole | Repeater |
| | | NFM | Preston | Farm Suppliers |
| | | NFM | Tyne & Wear | British Gas |
| 165.0500 | 169.8500 | NFM | Bathgate | Taxi |
| | | NFM | Birmingham | Ambulance Service |
| | | NFM | Blackburn | B&B Private Hire |
| | | NFM | Bournemouth | Critax Taxis |
| | | NFM | Cheetham | Ekko Private Hire |
| | | NFM | Dumfries | Taxis |
| | | NFM | Guernsey | Circuit Skips |
| | | NFM | Hull | Taxis |
| | | NFM | Jersey | SGB Scaffolding Erectors |
| | | NFM | Lincoln | A2B Taxis |
| | | NFM | Manchester | Taxi |
| | | NFM | Newtown | Newtown Taxis |
| | | NFM | Peterborough | Osbourne Plumbing |
| | | NFM | Plymouth | AA Taxis |
| | | NFM | Swindon | Inta-Car Taxis |
| 165.0625 | 169.8625 | NFM | Aberdeen | ANC |
| | | NFM | Bristol | Auto Glass |
| | | NFM | Carlisle | Biffa |
| | | NFM | Crewe | Garage |
| | | NFM | Cromer | Tylers Waste Management |
| | | NFM | Essex | Warrior Skips |
| | | NFM | Guernsey | Links Community Repeater 1 |
| | | NFM | Indian Queens | Interlink Parcels |
| | | NFM | Ipswich | Keiths Co |

| Base | Mobile | Mode | Location | User and Notes |
|---|---|---|---|---|
| 165.0625 | 169.8625 | NFM | Perth | King Contractors (King Base) |
| | | NFM | Perth | Perth Council Investigators |
| | | NFM | Pocklington | Town Travel Taxis |
| | | NFM | Poole | Repeater |
| | | NFM | Rillington | H Atkinson Slaughter House |
| | | NFM | Scarborough | TWDB |
| | | NFM | Suffolk | Garage Supplies |
| 165.0650 | 169.8650 | NFM | Haverfordwest | Taxi |
| 165.0750 | 169.8750 | NFM | Coventry | Security |
| | | NFM | Dover Castle | Security/Works Dept |
| | | NFM | Fife | Council |
| | | NFM | London | Central Government |
| | | NFM | M1 | Associated Asphalt |
| | | NFM | Nationwide | Road Engineers |
| | | NFM | Newport | R.E. |
| | | NFM | Norfolk | May Gurney |
| | | NFM | Perth | Community Repeater |
| | | NFM | Suffolk | May Gurney & Co |
| 165.0875 | 169.8875 | NFM | Biggleswade | Jordans Cereals |
| | | NFM | Blackpool | C Cabs |
| | | NFM | Chestwood | Chestwood Mushrooms |
| | | NFM | Hatfield | Tarmac Construction |
| | | NFM | Ipswich | Motorways Recovery M5 |
| | | NFM | Jersey | Normans Ltd Channel 1 |
| | | NFM | Jersey | Securicor |
| | | NFM | Liverpool | Local Authority Security |
| | | NFM | London | Minicab Firm Penge |
| | | NFM | Plymouth | University Security |
| | | NFM | Portsmouth | Bus Service |
| 165.1000 | 169.9000 | NFM | Blackpool | C Cabs |
| | | NFM | Bournemouth | Wade's Taxis |
| | | NFM | Bristol | Durston Plant |
| | | NFM | Carlisle | Abbey Skip Hire |
| | | NFM | Clacton | Clacton Taxis |
| | | NFM | Coventry | Taxi |
| | | NFM | Edinburgh | Taxis |
| | | NFM | Fordham | D Jenkins TV |
| | | NFM | Glasgow | Drumchaple Taxis |
| | | NFM | Gorleston-on-Sea | Ace Day & Night Taxis |
| | | NFM | Guernsey | Transfer Taxis |
| | | NFM | Havant | Taxis |
| | | NFM | Hazelgrove | Lynx Private Hire |
| | | NFM | Kings Lynn | Geoff's Taxis |
| | | NFM | Kirkcaldy | Taxis |
| | | NFM | Korleston | Ace Day and Night |
| | | NFM | Leigh | Swift Next Day |
| | | NFM | Lincoln | City Taxis |
| | | NFM | Little Downham | Mott Farmers |
| | | NFM | London | SEB Scaffold |
| | | NFM | London, Acton | Minicab Firm |
| | | NFM | London, Croydon | Minicab Firm |
| | | NFM | Manchester | Bishop's security Company |
| | | NFM | Manchester, Gorton | Taxi |
| | | NFM | Montrose | Taxis |
| | | NFM | Newcastle | Taxis |
| | | NFM | Newtown | Police |

| Base | Mobile | Mode | Location | User and Notes |
|---|---|---|---|---|
| 165.1000 | 169.9000 | NFM | Peterborough | Evening Telegraph |
| | | NFM | Poole | Rapid Lads |
| | | NFM | Saxmundham | Fishwick Vets |
| | | NFM | Seaforth | Dale's Taxis |
| | | NFM | St Austell | Davis Automatics |
| | | NFM | Stockport | Taxi |
| | | NFM | Stoke-on-Trent | Taxis |
| | | NFM | Wickford | Taxis |
| | | NFM | Woodbridge | TV Repairs |
| 165.1100 | 169.9100 | NFM | Kilmarnock | Taxi |
| 165.1125 | 169.9125 | AM | Barrow | Taxis |
| | | NFM | Bournemouth | Brown Motors |
| | | NFM | Cambridge | Inter-City Cabs |
| | | NFM | Carlisle | Borders Cabs |
| | | NFM | Dyfed | J Lawrence Tractors |
| | | NFM | Dymchurch | Dymchurch Light Railway |
| | | NFM | Glasgow | Taxi |
| | | NFM | Guernsey | Fuel Supplies |
| | | NFM | Jersey | Beeline Taxis Ch1 |
| | | NFM | London | Minicab Firm North London |
| | | NFM | Pembrokeshire | J Lawrence Tractors |
| | | NFM | Sandy | Ariston Group Service |
| | | NFM | Sheffield | Network Taxis |
| | | NFM | Swansea | Abba Taxis |
| | | NFM | Walton-on-Thames | Vending Machine Company |
| 165.1250 | 169.9250 | AM | Aberdeen | Amtrak |
| | | NFM | Burnley | Taxis |
| | | NFM | Cosham | Taxis |
| | | NFM | Dalkeith | Police |
| | | NFM | Edinburgh | Taxis |
| | | NFM | Failsworth | Embassy Cars |
| | | NFM | Glasgow | Taxis |
| | | NFM | Guernsey | C. Richard Vehicle Recovery |
| | | NFM | Hadleigh | Wilsons Corn & Milling |
| | | NFM | Huntingdon | Mercury Bluebird Taxis |
| | | NFM | Immingham | Taxis |
| | | NFM | Jersey | Farm |
| | | NFM | London | Minicab Firm Croydon |
| | | NFM | Manchester Gorton | Security |
| | | NFM | Oldham | Embassy Cars |
| | | NFM | Perth | Taxis |
| | | NFM | Portsmouth | Taxis |
| | | NFM | Slough | Topcars |
| | | NFM | Sudbury | Wilsons Corn & Milling Co |
| | | NFM | Sudbury | Woods Taxis |
| | | NFM | Waltham | Ariston Group Service |
| | | NFM | Weymouth | Taxi Co |
| 165.1375 | 169.9375 | NFM | Aberystwyth | County Council Highways |
| | | NFM | Guernsey | Stan Brouard Ltd |
| | | NFM | Hull | Reckitts Security |
| | | NFM | Isle of Man | Manx Electricity |
| | | NFM | London | Lambeth Council |
| | | NFM | London | Police Royal Parks |
| | | NFM | London | Redbridge Council |
| | | NFM | Manchester | Motorway Maintenance |
| | | NFM | Poole | Repeater |

| Base | Mobile | Mode | Location | User and Notes |
|------|--------|------|----------|----------------|
| 165.1375 | 169.9375 | NFM | RAF Cardingdon | MoD |
| | | NFM | Swaffham | Reed & Mikik Ltd |
| 165.1500 | 169.9500 | NFM | Anglesey | Council Bin men |
| | | NFM | Brighton | Group 4 |
| | | NFM | Coventry | Walsgrave Hospital Porters |
| | | NFM | Glasgow | Taxi |
| | | NFM | Grimsby | Doctors Night Call Service |
| | | NFM | Guernsey | Norman Piette |
| | | NFM | Jersey | R.G. Romeril Plant Hire |
| | | NFM | Merry Hill | Centre Maintenance |
| | | NFM | Nationwide | Group Four Security Ch1 |
| | | NFM | Telford | Wrekin District Council |
| | | NFM | Walsgrove on Stowe | Hospital Porters |
| 165.1600 | | NFM | Bonnybridge | United Distillers Security |
| 165.1625 | 169.9625 | NFM | Bedfordshire | Repeater |
| | | NFM | Bournemouth | Beach Patrol |
| | | NFM | Doncaster | Transline |
| | | NFM | Guernsey | Vehicle Recovery Service |
| | | NFM | Hull | Reckitts Security |
| | | NFM | Ipswich | Spotcheck Security |
| | | NFM | Nottingham | Nottingham University |
| | | NFM | Perth Royal Infirmary | Security & Maintenance |
| | | NFM | Wakefield | The Riding Centre |
| 165.1750 | 169.9750 | NFM | Bristol | Group 4 Security |
| | | NFM | Cleveland | Group 4 Security |
| | | NFM | Nationwide | Group 4 Security Channel 2 |
| 165.1875 | 169.9875 | NFM | Aberdeen | Security |
| | | NFM | Ayr | Butlins Mat |
| | | NFM | Birmingham | Selly Oak Hospital porters |
| | | NFM | Bournemouth | Securitas Security |
| | | NFM | Bristol | Store Detectives |
| | | NFM | Burnley | CCTV System |
| | | NFM | Exeter | Store Watch scheme |
| | | NFM | Hull | Security Firm |
| | | NFM | Manchester | Man. City FC Stewards |
| | | NFM | Norfolk | Pritchard Security |
| | | NFM | Perth | Taxi |
| 165.2000 | 170.0000 | NFM | Aberdeen | Aberdeen Vets |
| | | NFM | Cheshire | Alternative Taxis |
| | | NFM | Edinburgh | Taxi |
| | | NFM | Guernsey | States Works |
| | | NFM | Isle of Man | Manx Electricity |
| | | NFM | London | Cabetel Installation Ltd |
| | | NFM | Newmarket | Cambridge Cable |
| | | NFM | Newport, Gwent | Maintenance Repair Company |
| | | NFM | Norwich | Esso Heating |
| | | NFM | Peterborough | CBS Repeater |
| | | NFM | Poole | Repeater |
| | | NFM | Swansea | Group 4 Security |
| 165.2100 | 170.0100 | NFM | Merry Hill | Centre Cleaners |
| 165.2125 | 170.0125 | NFM | Bolton | College Security |
| | | NFM | Cambridge | Grafton Centre |
| | | NFM | Coventry | GEC Security |
| | | NFM | Edinburgh | Scottish & Newcastle Brewers |
| | | NFM | Exeter | University security and porters |
| | | NFM | Grafton | Grosvenor Estates |

| Base | Mobile | Mode | Location | User and Notes |
|---|---|---|---|---|
| 165.2125 | 170.0125 | NFM | Hull | Security Firm |
| | | NFM | Ipswich | Dock Security |
| | | NFM | London | US Embassy Secret Service |
| | | NFM | Milton Keynes | Milton Keynes Taxis |
| | | NFM | Nationwide | British Coal Security |
| | | NFM | Sheffield | Group 4 Security |
| | | NFM | Swansea | Quadrant Shopping Centre Security |
| 165.2250 | 170.0250 | NFM | Blackburn | Arcade Private Hire |
| | | NFM | Frome | Blue Taxis |
| | | NFM | Halifax | 4 Ways Taxis |
| | | NFM | Jersey | Flying Dragon Cabs |
| | | NFM | Langley | Station Minicabs |
| | | NFM | Leicester | LCL Cable Comms |
| | | NFM | London | Minicab Firm Woodford |
| | | NFM | London (Heathrow) | Interlink |
| | | NFM | Nottingham | Taxi |
| | | NFM | Oldham | ATS |
| | | NFM | Portishead | Esso Fuels Docks |
| | | NFM | Slough | Minicab Firm |
| | | NFM | Southampton | Taxis |
| | | NFM | Tamworth | Taxis |
| | | NFM | Weymouth | Dorset Alarms |
| 165.2375 | 170.0375 | NFM | Anglesey | Benji's Taxis |
| | | AM | Barrow | Taxis |
| | | NFM | Birmingham | Castle Taxi |
| | | NFM | Cardiff | Amber Taxis Channel 2 |
| | | NFM | Carlisle | Taxis |
| | | NFM | Crewe | Taxi |
| | | NFM | Glasgow | Taxi |
| | | NFM | Glossop | Thameside Council |
| | | NFM | Guernsey | Access Skips |
| | | NFM | Leighton Buzzard | Choake Billington |
| | | NFM | London | Minicab Firm Ealing |
| | | NFM | Plymouth | Taxis |
| | | NFM | Poole | Repeater |
| | | NFM | Torpoint | Taxis |
| | | NFM | Wales | Black and White Taxis |
| 165.2500 | 170.0500 | AM | Aberdeen | Lucas |
| | | NFM | Airdrie | Monkland Independent Taxis |
| | | NFM | Birmingham Northfield | Taxi |
| | | NFM | Coventry | Taxi |
| | | NFM | Elvington | Warter Estate Farms |
| | | NFM | Glasgow | Taxi |
| | | NFM | Guernsey | Island Taxis |
| | | NFM | Lancing | Taxis |
| | | NFM | Manchester | Taxi |
| | | NFM | March | Middle Level Commissioner |
| | | NFM | Milton Keynes | Ace Cars |
| | | NFM | Montrose | Radio TV Company |
| | | NFM | Newcastle | Taxi |
| | | NFM | Slough | Compass Cars |
| | | NFM | Southend | Taxis |
| | | NFM | Wirral | Taxi |

| Base | Mobile | Mode | Location | User and Notes |
|---|---|---|---|---|
| 165.2625 | 170.0625 | NFM | Ashington | Heating Repairs |
| | | AM | Bedfordshire | Parcels Service |
| | | AM | Buckinghamshire | Parcels Service |
| | | NFM | Cheltenham | Bus Engineers |
| | | NFM | Dudley | TV Repairs |
| | | NFM | Ipswich | Security |
| | | NFM | Jersey | J P Mauger |
| | | NFM | Jersey | Trinity Home Improvements |
| | | NFM | Lancashire | Barkley Council |
| | | NFM | Neath | Port Talbot Council |
| | | NFM | Newcastle | Council Housing |
| | | NFM | Poole | Repeater |
| | | NFM | Preston | Council Dog Warden |
| | | NFM | Reading | Centurian Security |
| | | NFM | Sheffield | Crystal Peaks Security |
| | | NFM | Snaefell, Isle of Man | Repeater |
| | | NFM | Southampton | B & K Security |
| | | NFM | Southampton | Ravenscroft Motors |
| | | NFM | Walsall | GB Engineering |
| 165.2700 | 170.0700 | NFM | West Sussex | Berkshire Recovery Services |
| 165.2740 | 170.0740 | NFM | West Sussex | Taxi |
| 165.2750 | 170.0750 | NFM | Ashington | Ashington Taxi |
| | | NFM | Bath | Orange Grove Taxis |
| | | NFM | Benfleet | Wheel's Taxis |
| | | NFM | Brierley Hill | Lady Cabs |
| | | NFM | Dover | A2B Cars |
| | | AM | Exeter | City Minibus Co. |
| | | NFM | Felling | Taxi |
| | | NFM | Fletwood | Doctors |
| | | AM | Glasgow | Taxi |
| | | NFM | Guernsey | H.F. Gaudion |
| | | NFM | Halstead | Gosling Bros |
| | | NFM | Ipswich | Comm Repeater |
| | | NFM | Kingston | Minicab Firm |
| | | NFM | London | Minicab Firm Holloway |
| | | NFM | Manchester | Taxi |
| | | NFM | Mansfield | Ace Taxis |
| | | NFM | Montrose | Taxis |
| | | NFM | Newport | Show Taxis |
| | | NFM | Perth | Data |
| | | NFM | Poole | Repeater |
| | | NFM | Portsmouth | Taxis |
| | | NFM | Shire Oaks | Shire Oaks Colliery Security |
| | | NFM | Swindon | Swindon Taxis |
| 165.2865 | 170.0865 | NFM | Louth | Allied Mills |
| 165.2875 | 170.0875 | NFM | Chestercord | Park Research |
| | | NFM | Cleveland | Boro Taxis |
| | | NFM | Colchester | Taxis |
| | | NFM | Cumbria | South Lakes District Council |
| | | NFM | Downham Market | Lindsay Smith |
| | | NFM | Falkirk | Taxi |
| | | NFM | Ferndown | Taxis |
| | | NFM | Jersey | Polar Car Hire |
| | | NFM | Lincoln | Imp Taxis |
| | | NFM | London, Beckenham | Minicab Firm |

| Base | Mobile | Mode | Location | User and Notes |
|------|--------|------|----------|----------------|
| 165.2875 | 170.0875 | NFM | London, Bromley | Minicab Firm |
| | | NFM | Macclesfield | Silvertown Taxis |
| 165.2875 | 170.0875 | NFM | Montrose | Taxis |
| | | NFM | New Quay | New Quay Taxis |
| | | NFM | Rochdale | Streamline Taxis |
| | | NFM | Rochester | Marconi Avionics security |
| | | NFM | Spalding | Baytree Nurseries |
| | | NFM | Woolwich | Taxis |
| 165.3000 | 170.1000 | NFM | Colwyn Bay | Taxis |
| | | NFM | East Dereham | Dereham Taxis |
| | | NFM | Edinburgh | Taxis |
| | | NFM | Guernsey | Links Community Repeater 2 |
| | | NFM | Lichfield | Taxi |
| | | NFM | Midlands | Delta Delivery |
| | | NFM | Midlands | Target Delivery |
| | | NFM | Newcastle | Plumbers |
| | | NFM | Oxfordshire | Security Firm |
| | | NFM | Worcester | Security Company |
| 165.3125 | 170.1125 | NFM | Christchurch | Taxis |
| | | AM | Cleethorpes | Taxis |
| | | NFM | Ely | Garrett |
| | | NFM | Glasgow | Taxis |
| | | NFM | Glossop | Padtax Taxis |
| | | NFM | Jersey | Harbour Dept |
| | | NFM | Launceston | Roscar Electronics |
| | | NFM | Leigh | Avacab |
| | | NFM | London | Minicab Firm Putney |
| | | NFM | Manchester | Taxis |
| | | NFM | Merseyside | Taxis |
| | | NFM | Morecambe | Taxis |
| | | NFM | Northampton | Taxis |
| | | NFM | Nottingham | Taxis |
| | | NFM | Peterborough | Euro Cabs |
| | | NFM | Plymouth | Council Security |
| | | NFM | Southampton | Taxis |
| | | NFM | Stansted | Aircars |
| | | NFM | Swindon | Ace Taxis |
| | | NFM | Tamworth | Acorn Cabs |
| | | NFM | Taunton | Alpha/Apex Taxis |
| | | NFM | Newcastle | Taxi |
| 165.3240 | 165.3250 | NFM | Runcorn | Parcel Delivery |
| 165.3250 | 170.1250 | NFM | Bristol | Paramedics |
| | | NFM | Coventry | Linkline Parcels |
| | | NFM | Edinburgh | Taxis |
| | | NFM | Humberside | Haulage Co |
| | | NFM | Lincoln | Council |
| | | NFM | London | Diplomatic Transport |
| | | NFM | Peterborough | CBS Repeater |
| | | NFM | Plymouth | City Security (Papa Control) |
| | | NFM | Poole | Repeater |
| | | NFM | Sheffield | Kay & Hodgkinson plant hire |
| | | NFM | Southampton | Taxis |
| | | NFM | Swansea | A & M Parcel Delivery Service |
| | | NFM | Warwickshire | Farmers |

| Base | Mobile | Mode | Location | User and Notes |
|------|--------|------|----------|----------------|
| 165.3350 | 170.1350 | NFM | Glasgow | Taxi |
| 165.3375 | 170.1375 | NFM | Calne | Taxis |
| | | NFM | Carlisle | Auto Recoveries |
| | | NFM | Clacton-on-Sea | Bernies Taxis |
| | | NFM | Cleethropes | AA Car Taxis |
| | | NFM | Coventry | Linkline Parcels |
| | | NFM | East London | Traffic Wardens |
| | | NFM | Eccles | Minicars Ltd |
| | | NFM | Glasgow | Clydeside Taxi |
| | | NFM | Kings Lynn | Simons |
| | | NFM | Letchwood | John's Taxis |
| | | NFM | London | Minicab Firm Campden |
| | | NFM | Lytham | Lytham Taxis |
| | | NFM | Manchester | Taxis |
| | | NFM | Nationwide | MoD Police |
| | | NFM | Southampton | Taxis |
| | | NFM | Stoke On Trent | Z Carz Taxis |
| | | NFM | Stowmarket | ICI Paint Depot |
| | | NFM | Swindon | Taxis |
| | | NFM | Winchester | Taxis |
| | | NFM | Wrexham | Atax Taxis |
| 165.3400 | 170.1400 | NFM | Newcastle | Taxi |
| 165.3500 | 170.1500 | NFM | Bath | Twerton Taxis |
| | | NFM | Bury | Star Taxis |
| | | NFM | Dumfries | Diamond Taxis |
| | | NFM | Felling | Taxi |
| | | NFM | Glasgow | Taxis |
| | | NFM | Great Melton | Downham Farm Services |
| | | NFM | Lichfield | Taxi |
| | | NFM | Lincoln | Security |
| | | NFM | London | Minicab Firm Lewisham |
| | | NFM | Luton | Victor Taxis |
| | | NFM | Manchester | Taxis |
| | | NFM | Newcastle | Northumbria University |
| | | NFM | Nottingham | Doctors Service |
| | | NFM | Peterborough | ABC Taxis |
| 165.3625 | 170.1625 | NFM | Birkenhead | Car Breakdown Recovery |
| | | NFM | Bournemouth | CBS Lynx Carriers |
| | | NFM | Derby | Community Repeater |
| | | NFM | Dundee | Car Hire Service |
| | | NFM | Edinburgh | Community Repeater |
| | | NFM | Gosport | Taxis |
| | | NFM | Greenham | Council |
| | | NFM | Isle of Wight | Plant Hire |
| | | NFM | Kent | Thanet Bus Company |
| | | NFM | Leicester | Taxis |
| | | NFM | Liverpool | Taxis |
| | | NFM | London | Streetwise Bus |
| | | NFM | London | Tosca skips |
| | | NFM | London | West London skips |
| | | NFM | Matlock | Haulage Company |

| Base | Mobile | Mode | Location | User and Notes |
|------|--------|------|----------|----------------|
| 165.3625 | 170.1625 | NFM | Mendlesham | Norcon Sky |
| | | NFM | Milford Haven | Skip Lorries |
| | | NFM | Oxfordshire | Security Firm |
| | | NFM | Perth | Community Repeater |
| | | NFM | Plymouth | Devro Security |
| | | NFM | Poole | Repeater |
| 165.3625 | 170.1625 | NFM | Southampton | Security |
| | | NFM | St. Monans | Bass Rock Oil Co. Ltd |
| | | NFM | Worcester | Double Glazing Company |
| 165.3750 | 170.1750 | NFM | Bath | Rainbow Taxis |
| | | NFM | Cambridge | Able Cars |
| | | NFM | Chelmsford | Taxis |
| | | NFM | Dumfries | Bee Hive Taxis |
| | | NFM | Glasgow | Taxis |
| | | NFM | Harlow | Regency Cars |
| | | NFM | London | Minicab Firm Nine Elms |
| | | NFM | London | US Embassy Secret Service |
| | | NFM | Plymouth | Olympic Taxis |
| | | NFM | Ramsbottom | Snobs Private Hire |
| | | NFM | Reading | Checkers Cars |
| | | NFM | Warrington | Warrington Borough County |
| 165.3875 | 170.1875 | NFM | Cambridge | Alf Bucks |
| | | NFM | Carlisle | Taxis |
| | | NFM | Clacton-on-Sea | Apollo Taxis |
| | | NFM | Cumbria | Community Repeater S. Lakes |
| | | NFM | Fakenham | Selective Fertilisers |
| | | NFM | Glasgow | Taxis |
| | | NFM | Grampian | Farm Workers |
| | | NFM | Hoylake | Hoylake Radio Station Taxis |
| | | NFM | Jersey | F. Brown Recovery |
| | | NFM | Louth | Community Repeater |
| | | NFM | Luton Airport | Lep Transport |
| | | NFM | Medway | Kingsferry Coaches |
| | | NFM | Morecambe | Joe's Taxis |
| | | NFM | Motherwell | United Taxis |
| | | NFM | Newport | Red Dragon Taxis Channel 1 |
| | | NFM | Peterlee | Yellow Cabs |
| | | NFM | Portsmouth | Taxis |
| | | NFM | Retford | Malcolm's Taxis |
| | | NFM | Sheffield | City Cars |
| | | NFM | Soham | Tompsett |
| | | NFM | Tayside | Farm Workers |
| 165.4000 | 170.2000 | NFM | Aberdeen | Oil Fabricators |
| | | NFM | Bedford | Community Repeater |
| | | NFM | Cambourne | Vending Firm |
| | | NFM | Cornwall | Houpers Haulage |
| | | NFM | Cumbria | Community Repeater South Lakes |
| | | NFM | East Durham | Private Message |
| | | NFM | Haverfordwest | Jewsons |
| | | NFM | Ipswich | Repeater |
| | | NFM | Lancashire | Andersons Pumps |
| | | NFM | London | IBA Maintenance |
| | | NFM | London | Underground, Baker Street |
| | | NFM | London | Underground, Balham |
| | | NFM | London | Underground, Clapham Common |
| | | NFM | London | Underground, Clapham North |

| Base | Mobile | Mode | Location | User and Notes |
|---|---|---|---|---|
| 165.4000 | 170.2000 | NFM | London | Underground, Clapham South |
| | | NFM | London | Underground, Monument |
| | | NFM | London | Underground, Neasden |
| | | NFM | London | Underground, Oxford Circus |
| | | NFM | London | Underground, Spare Channel |
| | | NFM | London | Underground, Tooting Bec |
| 165.4000 | 170.2000 | NFM | London | Underground, Tooting Broadway |
| | | NFM | Milton Keynes | Repeater |
| | | NFM | Morecambe | Delivery Service |
| | | NFM | Morpeth | Garden Centre |
| | | NFM | Nottingham | Taxis |
| | | NFM | Peterborough | CBS Repeater |
| | | NFM | Worthing | Transport Co. |
| 165.4125 | 170.2125 | NFM | Brighton | Dyke Golf Club |
| | | NFM | Bristol | Avon Alpha Control |
| | | NFM | Cornwall | Kay Base |
| | | NFM | Ellesmere Port | Ellesmore Port Council |
| | | NFM | Fife | Fife Regional Council |
| | | NFM | Leeds | Motor Factors |
| | | NFM | London | Underground, Bakerloo line |
| | | NFM | London | Underground, Circle line |
| | | NFM | London | Underground, District line |
| | | NFM | London | Underground, Northern line |
| | | NFM | Newcastle | Plumbers |
| | | NFM | Perth | King Contractors |
| | | NFM | Plymouth | Ranger Base |
| | | NFM | Shrewsbury | Flower Show Officals |
| 165.4250 | 170.2250 | NFM | Birmingham Sparkhill | Taxi |
| | | NFM | Calne | Taxis |
| | | NFM | Chatteris | W Barnes |
| | | AM | Cleethorpes | Beavers Cars |
| | | NFM | Falkirk | Bruce Taxis |
| | | NFM | Hitchin | DER Television |
| | | NFM | Hull | Taxis |
| | | NFM | Lichfield | Taxi |
| | | NFM | Milford Haven | Taxi |
| | | NFM | Newcastle | Taxi |
| | | NFM | Plymouth | Night Watch Security |
| | | NFM | Pontypridd | Regal Taxis |
| | | NFM | Sheffield | EMI Homeserve |
| | | NFM | Wakefield | Taxis |
| 165.4375 | 170.2375 | NFM | Barrow in Furness | CAW Skip Hire & Haulage |
| | | NFM | Birmingham | Castle Security |
| | | NFM | Brecon | Mountain Rescue (S) |
| | | NFM | Bristol | Taxis |
| | | NFM | Carlisle | H & E Trotter |
| | | NFM | Carnforth | Council Roads Department |
| | | NFM | Haverfordwest | Taxis |
| | | NFM | Humberside | Cash Register Co |
| | | NFM | London | Underground, City line |
| | | NFM | London | Underground, Metropolitan line |
| | | NFM | London | Underground, Piccaddilly line |
| | | NFM | Manchester | Taxis |
| | | NFM | Mansfield | Doctors Service |
| | | NFM | Merthyr | Mountain Rescue (S) |
| | | NFM | Peterborough | City Aerials Ltd |

| Base | Mobile | Mode | Location | User and Notes |
|------|--------|------|----------|----------------|
| 165.4375 | 170.2375 | NFM | Truro | Pellows Waste |
| | | NFM | West Midlands | Castle Security |
| 165.4500 | 170.2500 | NFM | Edinburgh | Central Taxis |
| | | NFM | Frome | Taxis |
| | | NFM | Hastings | Conquest Hospital Porters |
| | | NFM | London | Minicab Firm Greenford |
| 165.4500 | 170.2500 | NFM | Milton Keynes | Municipal Cleaning Services |
| | | NFM | Nationwide | ITC Maintenance |
| | | NFM | Newport | Alfa Taxis |
| | | NFM | Poole | Repeater |
| | | NFM | West Midlands | Meridian Delivery |
| 165.4625 | 170.2625 | AM | Belfast | Water Board |
| | | NFM | Bristol | Community Repeater |
| | | NFM | Eye, Suffolk | T G Asher, agric haulage |
| | | NFM | Gloucester | Repeater |
| | | NFM | Ipswich | Kengrove Aggregates (K-Base) |
| | | NFM | Ipswich | Nightfreight (East) Ltd (B) |
| | | NFM | Ipswich | Polar Base Freezers |
| | | NFM | London | Underground, Central line |
| | | NFM | London | Underground, Jubilee line |
| | | NFM | London | Underground, Victoria line |
| | | NFM | Poole | Repeater |
| | | NFM | Tayside | Vets |
| | | NFM | Worthing | Nynex Cable Comms |
| 165.4750 | 170.2750 | NFM | Fort Regent, Jersey | Honorary Police Channel 1 |
| | | NFM | Newport | Community Repeater |
| | | NFM | Norfolk | Carphones |
| | | NFM | Peterborough | CBS Repeater |
| | | NFM | Plymouth | Red Lightning Dispatch |
| | | NFM | Poole | Repeater |
| | | NFM | Scunthorpe | Courier Service |
| | | NFM | Southampton | MediCall Channel 3 |
| | | NFM | Suffolk | Carphones |
| 165.4857 | 170.2875 | NFM | Millom | Pete's Taxis |
| | | NFM | Ashton-under-Lyne | Stamford Private Hire |
| | | NFM | Barry | Flat Holm Maintenance |
| | | NFM | Birmingham | Taxis |
| | | NFM | Bristol | Seven Bridge Maintenance (JASMINE) |
| | | NFM | Carlisle | Taxis |
| | | NFM | Exeter | Maxi Taxis |
| | | NFM | Little Hulton | Radio Cars Ltd Taxis |
| | | NFM | London | ODRATS |
| | | NFM | Manchester | Taxi |
| | | NFM | Milton Keynes | Quicker Cars |
| | | NFM | Montrose | Taxis |
| | | NFM | Oldham | Delta Cars |
| | | NFM | Runcorn | Taxi |
| | | NFM | West Midlands | Arrow Taxi |
| 165.5000 | 170.3000 | NFM | Bournemouth | Token Amusements Ltd |
| | | NFM | Cambridge | DER Television |
| | | NFM | Cleethorpes | Fon-a-Car |
| | | NFM | Dover | P&O Ferries Bus System |
| | | NFM | Glasgow | Taxi |
| | | NFM | Gorton | Beue Vue Cars |
| | | NFM | Holyhead | Taxis |

| Base | Mobile | Mode | Location | User and Notes |
|------|--------|------|----------|----------------|
| 165.5000 | 170.3000 | NFM | Letchwood | G Folly Builders |
| | | NFM | Paisley | Taxis |
| | | NFM | Plymouth | Tower Cabs |
| 165.5121 | 170.3121 | NFM | Aberdeen | Taxi |
| | | NFM | Aberystwyth | Aber Cars |
| | | NFM | Bishop Stortford | Taxis |
| | | NFM | Bolton | Halliwell Taxis |
| | | NFM | Cambridge | Browns Taxis |
| | | NFM | Gloucester | TV Repairs |
| | | NFM | Jersey | States |
| | | NFM | Liverpool | Taxi |
| | | NFM | London (Gatwick) | Airport Parking |
| | | NFM | Manchester | Taxi |
| | | NFM | Poole | Repeater |
| | | NFM | Stockport | Taxi |
| | | NFM | Swansea | Lakes Taxis |
| | | NFM | Worthing | Taxis |
| | | NFM | Wrexham | Club Taxis |
| 165.5125 | 170.3125 | NFM | Ashton under Lyme | Courier Service |
| | | NFM | Nottingham, Hucknall | Apex Taxis |
| | | NFM | Sheffield | Bradwell Skips Services |
| 165.5250 | 170.3250 | NFM | Bristol | Community Repeater |
| | | NFM | Dudley | Merry Hill Security |
| | | NFM | Halifax | ABC TAxis |
| | | NFM | London | Embassy Cars |
| | | NFM | Manchester | Taxi |
| | | NFM | Peterborough | DER Television |
| | | NFM | Reading | 1st Yellow Cars |
| | | NFM | Urmston | Phoenix Taxis |
| | | NFM | Wiltshire | TV Repairs |
| 165.5375 | 170.3375 | NFM | Abingdon | Eagle Security Co |
| | | NFM | Askam in Furness | Furness Car & Commercial Recovery Service |
| | | NFM | Heathfield | Comrep |
| | | NFM | North Yorkshire | Doctor Service |
| | | NFM | Oxford | Community Repeater |
| | | NFM | Scunthorpe | British Steel Emergency |
| | | NFM | Wolverhampton | Skip Hire |
| 165.5500 | 170.3500 | NFM | Blackburn | Intack Private Hire |
| | | NFM | Edinburgh | Tarmac Roadstone |
| | | NFM | London | Dry Cleaning Company |
| | | NFM | London | Vehicle wheel clamping |
| | | NFM | London, Camden | Council Traffic Wardens |
| | | NFM | Plymouth | Military Security (RM) |
| | | NFM | Southampton | Taxis |
| | | NFM | Warwickshire South | Farmers |
| 165.5625 | 170.3625 | NFM | Brighton | Security Company |
| | | NFM | Bristol | Community Repeater |
| | | NFM | Cheltenham | Bus Inspectors |
| | | NFM | Edinburgh | Carpet Fitting Co. |
| | | NFM | Edinburgh | Castle Security |
| | | NFM | Edinburgh | Trinity Roofing |
| | | NFM | Glasgow | Taxis |
| | | NFM | Gloucester | Fruit Machine Engineers Channel 1 |
| | | NFM | Gloucester | Monarch Security |
| | | NFM | Lancaster | City Council |

| Base | Mobile | Mode | Location | User and Notes |
|------|--------|------|----------|----------------|
| 165.5625 | 170.3625 | NFM | Norwich | Blueline Taxis |
| | | NFM | Poole | Fernside Recovery |
| | | NFM | Portsmouth | Bus Co |
| 165.5625 | 170.3625 | NFM | Starford | Tree surgeons |
| | | NFM | Suffolk | East Counties Farmers Channel 2 |
| | | NFM | Swindon | Games Machines |
| | | NFM | Tyne & Wear | Healthcall Service |
| | | NFM | Wirral | Brombourgh Cabs |
| | | NFM | Yorkshire | Yorkshire Water |
| 165.5750 | 170.3750 | NFM | Accrington | D-Line Cars |
| | | NFM | Cambridge | H Robinson |
| | | NFM | Edinburgh | Eden Aerial Riggers |
| | | NFM | Felixstowe | Taxis |
| | | AM | Grimsby | Taxis |
| | | NFM | Haverhill | Jennings Transport |
| | | NFM | Kings Lynn | DER Television |
| | | AM | Manchester | New United Taxis |
| | | NFM | Montrose | Farm Workers |
| | | NFM | Newport | Star Taxis |
| | | NFM | Sheffield | Star Cars |
| | | NFM | Woodbridge | KTuckwell Engineers |
| 165.5800 | 170.3875 | NFM | Newhaven | Taxi |
| | | NFM | Blackburn | A&B Private Hire |
| | | NFM | Coventry | Builders Suppliers |
| | | NFM | Harpenden | DER Television |
| | | NFM | Hewhaven | Taxis |
| | | NFM | Hull | Rediffusion TV Rental |
| | | NFM | Luton | DER Television |
| | | NFM | Macclesfield | Taxis |
| | | NFM | Manchester | Taxis |
| | | NFM | Stockport | Taxis |
| | | NFM | Swinton | Radio Cars Ltd |
| 165.5876 | | NFM | Sheffield | FW Collins Ltd. skips |
| 165.6000 | 170.4000 | NFM | Aldridge | Alpha Taxis |
| | | NFM | Bridlington | Coastline Cabs |
| | | NFM | Bury | Taxis |
| | | NFM | Cornwall | English China Clay |
| | | NFM | Glasgow | Taxis |
| | | NFM | Glossop | Shadow Taxis |
| | | NFM | London | Carreras Rothams Displays |
| | | NFM | Manchester | Taxis |
| | | NFM | Paddington | Z Car hire |
| | | NFM | Paisley | Taxis |
| | | NFM | Stockport | Taxis |
| | | NFM | Strathclyde | British Transport Police (D) |
| | | NFM | Swansea Docks | Train Signal Box |
| 165.6100 | 170.4100 | NFM | Bury St Edmunds | Taxis |
| 165.6125 | 170.4125 | NFM | Castleton | Castleton Cars |
| | | NFM | Dunstable | Hunter Taxis |
| | | NFM | Grimsby | Council Maintenance |
| | | NFM | Jersey Airport | Airport Duty Officer Ch1 |
| | | NFM | Kirkham | Taxis |
| | | NFM | Lakenheath | Base Taxis |
| | | NFM | Linlithgow | Taxi |
| | | NFM | Newcastle | Buses |
| | | NFM | Perth | Council Plumbers |

| Base | Mobile | Mode | Location | User and Notes |
|---|---|---|---|---|
| 165.6125 | 170.4125 | NFM | Scunthorpe | Steel Works Maintenance |
| | | NFM | Sheffield | Indoor Market Security |
| | | NFM | St Austell | ECC Pits |
| 165.6125 | 170.4125 | NFM | Stanstead | Taxis |
| 165.6250 | 170.4250 | NFM | Bolton | Tonge Moor Private Hire |
| | | NFM | Bridlington | Star Cars |
| | | NFM | Brighton | British Rail Transport Police |
| | | AM | Bristol | Bond Delivery |
| | | NFM | Co. Durham | Haulage Coal Wagons |
| | | NFM | East Dereham | Acab Taxis |
| | | NFM | Edinburgh | Special Events |
| | | NFM | Glasgow | Taxis |
| | | NFM | Leicester | City Buses |
| | | NFM | London | Transport Police |
| | | NFM | Nationwide | Transport Police Channel 3 |
| | | NFM | Newcastle | Taxi |
| | | NFM | Oxford | Royal Taxis |
| | | NFM | Plymouth | Central Taxis |
| | | NFM | Sheffield | Sheffield United FC stewards |
| | | NFM | Southampton | Buses |
| | | NFM | Worcester | Take-Away Delivery Service |
| 165.6375 | 170.4375 | NFM | Birmingham | British Transport Police |
| | | NFM | Bristol | British Transport Police |
| | | NFM | Chester | British Transport Police |
| | | NFM | Crewe | British Transport Police |
| | | NFM | Liverpool | British Transport Police |
| | | NFM | London | British Transport Police (Victoria) |
| | | NFM | London | Police Royal Parks Channel 2 |
| | | NFM | Manchester | British Transport Police |
| | | NFM | Nationwide | British Transport Police Channel 2 |
| | | NFM | Newport | British Transport Police |
| | | NFM | Swansea | British Transport Police |
| 165.6400 | 170.4400 | NFM | Newcastle | British Transport Police |
| 165.6500 | 170.4500 | NFM | Brighton | British Transport Police |
| | | NFM | Glasgow | Railway Workmen |
| | | NFM | London | Underground Transport Police |
| | | NFM | Lothian & Borders | Transport Police (DA) |
| | | NFM | Nationwide | Transport Police Channel 1 |
| 165.6625 | 170.4625 | NFM | Bristol | City Line Buses |
| | | NFM | Consett | Taxis |
| | | NFM | Cornwall | English China Clay (Clay Control) |
| | | NFM | Jersey | Public Services |
| | | NFM | Llandudno | Taxi Service |
| | | NFM | London | Auto Car Repair |
| | | NFM | Macclesfield | Macc Radio Cars |
| | | NFM | Manchester | Taxi |
| | | NFM | Rochdale | Strand Private Hire |
| | | AM | Scarborough | Laker Taxis |
| 165.6750 | 170.4750 | NFM | Bolton | Taxis |
| | | NFM | Dunstable | E. J Allan |
| | | NFM | Hull | Railtrack |
| | | AM | Ipswich | Crown Taxi |
| | | NFM | Manchester | Taxi |
| | | NFM | Reading | ABC Cars |
| | | AM | Scarborough | Laker Taxis |
| | | NFM | Scunthorpe | British Steel Transport |

| Base | Mobile | Mode | Location | User and Notes |
|---|---|---|---|---|
| 165.6750 | 170.4750 | NFM | Sheffield | Taxis |
| | | NFM | St Annes | West Star Taxis |
| | | NFM | Stanwell | TNT Carriers |
| 165.6875 | 170.4875 | NFM | Cheshire | Bell Fruit Machines |
| | | NFM | Edinburgh | Bell Fruit Machines |
| | | NFM | Ipswich | Bell Fruit Machines |
| | | NFM | Lincoln | Bell Fruit Machines |
| | | NFM | London | Bell Fruit Machines |
| | | NFM | Peterborough | Bell Fruit Machines |
| | | NFM | Sheffield | Paymaster Ltd. |
| 165.7000 | 170.5000 | NFM | Brighton | Taxis |
| | | NFM | Chatteris | Catwood Potatoes |
| | | AM | Christchurch | Critax Taxis |
| | | NFM | Glasgow | Taxis |
| | | NFM | Guernsey | T & D Services |
| | | NFM | Hamilton | Cadzow Cars |
| | | NFM | Humberside | Transport Co |
| | | NFM | Ipswich | Clarke Demolition |
| | | NFM | Ipswich | Thompson & Morgan |
| | | NFM | Jersey | T & D Services |
| | | NFM | Kings Lynn | Ambassador Taxis |
| | | NFM | Portsmouth | Aqua Taxis |
| | | NFM | Saffron Walden | Crusader Cars |
| | | NFM | Southampton | Taxis |
| 165.7125 | 170.5125 | NFM | Aldershot | Taxis |
| | | NFM | Basildon | Taxis |
| | | NFM | Bognor Regis | Taxis |
| | | NFM | Bristol | Blue Iris Coaches |
| | | NFM | Cambridge | Four Four Taxis |
| | | NFM | Carnforth | PR Taxis |
| | | NFM | Crewe | Taxis |
| | | NFM | Edinburgh | Taxis |
| | | NFM | Folkestone | Folkestone City Buses |
| | | NFM | Headham | Gower Ltd |
| | | NFM | Ipswich | E H Roberts |
| | | NFM | Newcastle | Castle Cars |
| | | NFM | Tamworth | Acorn Taxis |
| 165.7250 | 170.5250 | NFM | Ayr | Railway Workmen |
| | | NFM | Blackburn | Manhattan Private Hire |
| | | NFM | Bolton | MacArthur Private Hire |
| | | NFM | Bournemouth | Southern Dispatch Couriers |
| | | NFM | Hatfield | Tarmac Construction |
| | | NFM | Hockwold Cum Wilton | Bob's Taxis |
| | | NFM | Ipswich | DER |
| | | NFM | Nationwide | Tarmac Construction Co |
| | | NFM | Scunthorpe | British Steel Trains |
| | | NFM | Truro | Hospital Services |
| 165.7375 | 170.5375 | NFM | Belfast | TNT Carriers |
| | | NFM | Bury | Royal Taxis |
| | | NFM | Coventry | Lion Taxis |
| | | NFM | Runcorn | Taxi |
| | | NFM | Stockton-on-Tees | Taxi Service |
| | | NFM | Sudbury | Amey Roadstones |
| | | NFM | Swindon | Tramps Radio Cars |
| | | NFM | Widnes | Taxis |

| Base | Mobile | Mode | Location | User and Notes |
|------|--------|------|----------|----------------|
| 165.7500 | 170.5500 | NFM | Bournemouth | Dust vans |
| | | NFM | Cambridge | Cambus |
| | | NFM | Carlisle | Council Highways |
| | | NFM | Dundee | Taxis |
| | | NFM | Fylde | Town Council |
| | | NFM | Halifax | Binmen FOCSA |
| | | NFM | Hove | Council |
| | | NFM | Lancaster | City Council |
| | | NFM | Leamington | Council |
| | | NFM | London | Enfield Borough Council |
| | | NFM | Luton | Luton Borough Council |
| | | NFM | Machynlleth | Hendre Quarry |
| | | NFM | Newark | Taxis |
| | | NFM | Norfolk | Bus Company |
| | | NFM | Norwich | ECOC |
| | | NFM | Perth | Taxis |
| | | NFM | Peterborough | Viscount Travel |
| | | NFM | Reading | Council |
| | | NFM | Stoke-on-Trent | Council |
| | | NFM | Swindon | Town Council |
| | | NFM | Wiltshire | Thamesdown Council |
| | | NFM | Wirral, Woodchurch | A-Z Private Hire |
| 165.7600 | 170.5600 | FM | Ayr | Council Services |
| | | NFM | Stoke on Trent | Town Council |
| 165.7625 | 170.5625 | NFM | Aberdeen | Waste Masters |
| | | NFM | Bedfordshire | District Council |
| | | NFM | Bolton | District Council |
| | | NFM | Bournemouth | Public Transport Channel 1 |
| | | NFM | Brierley Hill | Council |
| | | NFM | Cunninghame | SRC Local Council Services |
| | | NFM | Dundee | City Council Dog Catcher |
| | | NFM | Edinburgh | Lothian Regional Council |
| | | NFM | Ipswich | Housing Department |
| | | NFM | Llanelli | Council |
| | | AM | London | Southall Council |
| | | NFM | Luton | Contractor |
| | | NFM | Norfolk | Norfolk County Council |
| | | NFM | Poole | Repeater |
| | | NFM | Preston | District Council |
| | | NFM | St Saviour Parish, Jersey | Honorary Police Channel 5 |
| | | NFM | Gateshead | Council |
| 165.7750 | 170.5750 | NFM | Congleton | Taxi |
| | | NFM | Cwnbran | Cwnbran Plumbing Plc |
| | | NFM | Dudley | Council |
| | | NFM | Glasgow | Strathkelvin District Council |
| | | NFM | Havant | Council |
| | | NFM | Hayling Island | Council |
| | | NFM | High Wycombe | Council Parks Dept |
| | | NFM | Huntingdon | County Council |
| | | NFM | Ipswich | Brough Transport |
| | | NFM | Jersey | States of Jersey Repeater |
| | | AM | London | Croydon Council |
| | | NFM | North Yorkshire | Doctor Service |
| | | NFM | Norwich | Norwich City Council |
| | | NFM | Portsmouth | City Council |
| | | NFM | Somerset | County Council |

| Base | Mobile | Mode | Location | User and Notes |
|---|---|---|---|---|
| 165.7750 | 170.5750 | NFM | Southend on Sea | District Council |
| | | NFM | Stoke-on-Trent | Council Parks Dept. |
| | | NFM | Taunton | Parking inspectors |
| | | NFM | Wiltshire | Wilts County Council |
| 165.7875 | 170.5875 | NFM | Boston | Organic Lincolnshire Growers Assc |
| | | NFM | Bournemouth | Council |
| | | NFM | Carlisle | County Contracting North |
| | | NFM | Coventry | West Midlands Gas |
| | | NFM | Fawley | Power Station |
| | | NFM | Hyndburn | Accrington Bus Control |
| | | NFM | London | US Embassy Secret Service |
| | | NFM | Manchester | Motorway Maintenance |
| | | NFM | Peterborough | Betta Cars Amalgamated |
| | | NFM | Poole | Repeater |
| | | NFM | Stoke-on-Trent | Skip Hire |
| | | NFM | Suffolk | Mid Suffolk District Council |
| | | NFM | Swindon | Thamesdown Council |
| | | NFM | Ayr | North of Scotland Water Authority |
| 165.8000 | 170.6000 | NFM | Brighton | Streamline Taxis |
| | | NFM | Bristol | RSPCA |
| | | NFM | Derby Langley Mill | Taxi |
| | | NFM | Dudley | Five Star Taxis |
| | | NFM | Dundee | Taxis |
| | | NFM | Exeter | Castle Cars |
| | | NFM | Felixstowe | Peewit Caravans |
| | | NFM | Jersey | Normans Channel 2 |
| | | NFM | Kent | Tour De France (French) |
| | | NFM | Kilmarnock | Taxi |
| | | NFM | London | Taxis |
| | | NFM | Luton | C.J. Private Hire |
| | | NFM | Newcastle | RSPCA |
| | | NFM | Sheffield | Taxis |
| | | NFM | Swansea | Hooper Taxis |
| 165.8125 | 170.6125 | NFM | Bath | Abbey Taxis Channel 2 |
| | | NFM | Cambridge | Panther Cars |
| | | NFM | Cleethorpes | Bob's Cars |
| | | NFM | Coventry | Godiva Taxis |
| | | NFM | Coventry | Lewis Taxis |
| | | NFM | London | ODRATS |
| | | NFM | Preston | Cabtax Taxis |
| | | NFM | St Austell | Taxis |
| 165.8250 | 170.6250 | NFM | Bath | Abbey Taxis Channel 1 |
| | | NFM | Bolton | ABA Private Hire |
| | | NFM | Dudley | Midland Taxis |
| | | NFM | Glasgow | Taxi Company |
| | | NFM | Ipswich | Wilding & Smith |
| | | NFM | March | Worrall Potatoes |
| | | NFM | Oxford | ABC Taxis |
| 165.8375 | 170.6375 | NFM | Caistor | Hurdiss Quarries |
| | | NFM | Cardiff | Transport Firm |
| | | NFM | Ely | A.E. Lee Farms |
| | | NFM | Glasgow | Taxis |
| | | NFM | Halifax | Vinneys Taxis |
| | | NFM | Liverpool, Garston | Allerton Taxis |
| | | NFM | London | ODRATS |
| | | NFM | Macclesfield | Taxis |

| Base | Mobile | Mode | Location | User and Notes |
|---|---|---|---|---|
| 165.8375 | 170.6375 | NFM | Oldham | Limeline Private Hire |
| | | NFM | Peterborough | Hereward Ace Taxis |
| | | NFM | Plymouth | Taxis |
| | | NFM | Sheffield | Airport Express (TEX) |
| | | NFM | St. Osyth | Tudor Taxis |
| 165.8400 | 170.6400 | NFM | Newcastle | Taxi |
| | | NFM | Falkirk | Taxis |
| 165.8500 | 170.6500 | NFM | Bristol | RSPCA |
| | | NFM | Carlisle | Carlisle Drivers |
| | | NFM | Falkirk | Blue Star Taxis (Star) |
| | | NFM | Gt. Manchester | Avacabs |
| | | NFM | Haddenham | A.F. Buck |
| | | NFM | Leigh | Avacabs |
| | | NFM | Liverpool | City Cars |
| | | NFM | London | ODRATS |
| | | NFM | Newport, Gwent | Royal Cars |
| | | NFM | Plymouth | Estate Security |
| | | NFM | Three Holes | Hallsworth Framing Co. |
| 165.8600 | 170.6600 | NFM | Ayr | Taxi |
| 165.8625 | 170.6625 | NFM | Cambridge | Securicor |
| | | NFM | Coventry | Security |
| | | NFM | Hythe | Hythe Ferry and Pier |
| | | NFM | Jersey | Pony Express Delivery |
| | | NFM | Leeds | Courier Service |
| | | NFM | Nationwide | Securicor Channel 6 |
| 165.8750 | 170.6750 | NFM | Birmingham | Black Cabs |
| | | NFM | Coventry | Security |
| | | NFM | Edinburgh | Pony Express Couriers |
| | | NFM | Fleetwood | Nightwatchmen |
| | | NFM | Guernsey | Securicor |
| | | NFM | Nationwide | Securicor Channel 2 |
| | | NFM | Space | Mir Space Station |
| 165.8875 | 170.6875 | NFM | Bournemouth | Council Tarmac Gang |
| | | NFM | Horwich | Duval Security |
| | | NFM | Nationwide | Securicor Channel 3 |
| | | NFM | Preston | Builders |
| 165.9000 | 170.7000 | NFM | Airdrie | Twin Cabs |
| | | NFM | Dartford | Abba Dart Taxis |
| | | NFM | Dundee | Taxis |
| | | NFM | Gt. Manchester | Atherton Cab Co. |
| | | NFM | Hitchin | Duggan's Taxis |
| | | NFM | Ipswich | Taxis |
| | | NFM | London | US Embassy Secret Service |
| | | NFM | Rochdale | Norden Cars |
| | | NFM | Sevenoaks | Beeling Radio Taxis |
| | | NFM | Sheffield | Amusement Machine Servicing |
| | | NFM | Sheffield | Paymaster Ltd. |
| | | NFM | Swansea | Lloyds Taxis |
| | | AM | Swindon | Viking Taxis |
| | | NFM | Wantage | Robert's Taxis |
| | | NFM | West Drayton | LHR Express Cars |

| Base | Mobile | Mode | Location | User and Notes |
|------|--------|------|----------|----------------|
| 165.9125 | 170.7125 | NFM | Devizes | Community Repeater |
| | | NFM | Jersey | A1 Double Glazing |
| | | NFM | Nationwide | Securicor Channel 7 |
| | | NFM | Walsall | MFI Deliveries |
| | | NFM | Aberdeen | Oil Industry |
| | | NFM | Brighton | Car Mechanics Channel 1 |
| | | NFM | Cirencester | Gerry's Cars |
| | | NFM | Cleveland | 6767 Taxis |
| | | NFM | Jersey | Hire Cars |
| | | NFM | Manchester | Taxis |
| | | NFM | Middleton | Middleton Radio Cars |
| | | NFM | Newcastle | Taxi |
| | | NFM | Nottingham, Hucknall | Bells Taxis |
| | | NFM | Poole | Data Repeater |
| | | NFM | Portsmouth | Aqua Cabs |
| | | NFM | Sheffield | Arc Taxis (AZTEC) |
| | | NFM | Sheffield | Valley Taxis |
| | | NFM | Stockton-on-Tees | Taxi Service |
| 165.9375 | 170.7375 | NFM | Liverpool | Gas Fitters |
| | | NFM | Nationwide | Securicor Channel 8 |
| | | NFM | Newcastle | Central Heating Co. |
| | | AM | Portsmouth | American News |
| | | NFM | Swansea | Thorn Homeserve |
| 165.9500 | 170.7500 | NFM | Brighton | Car Mechanics Channel 2 |
| | | NFM | Cumbria | South Lakes Refuse Collection |
| | | NFM | Dundee | Taxis |
| | | AM | Grimsby | Fletchers Taxis |
| | | NFM | Jersey | Collas & Le Sueur |
| | | NFM | Kendal | District Council |
| | | NFM | London | Minicab Firm Southall |
| | | NFM | March | Guy Morton |
| | | NFM | Norfolk | Norfolk Farm Produce |
| | | NFM | Northampton | Taxis |
| | | NFM | Norwich | Taxis |
| 165.9625 | 170.7625 | NFM | Birmingham | Gas Contractors |
| | | NFM | Bournemouth | Council Parks Division |
| | | NFM | Isle of Wight | Landscaping Service |
| | | NFM | Liverpool | Taxis |
| | | NFM | Nationwide | Securicor Channel 4 |
| 165.9750 | 170.7750 | NFM | Brighton | Securicor |
| | | NFM | Bristol | Video Company |
| | | NFM | Haverfordwest | Securicor |
| | | NFM | Nationwide | Securicor Channel 1 Emergency |
| | | NFM | St Annes | Night Security |
| 165.9875 | 170.7875 | NFM | Jersey | Securicor |
| | | NFM | Nationwide | Securicor Channel 5 |
| 166.0000 | 170.8000 | NFM | Barrow in Furness | Z-Cars Taxis |
| | | NFM | Cannock, Staffs | Taxi |
| | | NFM | Chelmsford | Farmers Supplies |
| | | NFM | Glasgow | Taxis |
| | | NFM | Guernsey | Vaudins Taxi |
| | | NFM | Hull | Taxis |
| | | NFM | Linlithgow | Taxis |
| | | NFM | Martham | Fleggmart |
| | | NFM | Perth | Taxis |

| Base | Mobile | Mode | Location | User and Notes |
|------|--------|------|----------|----------------|
| 166.0000 | 170.8000 | NFM | Prestatyn | Robert's Taxis |
| | | NFM | Sheffield | Ace Taxis |
| | | NFM | South Shields | Taxi |
| | | NFM | Space | Soviet Satellite (Mir) |
| | | NFM | Stevenage | Parker Cars |
| | | NFM | Swansea | Taxi Shop |
| | | NFM | Tollerton | Gadd's Farm |
| | | NFM | Torpoint | Taxis |
| | | NFM | West Drayton | Station Cars |
| | | NFM | Winton | M&G Electronics |
| 166.0100 | 170.8100 | NFM | Cwmbran, Gwent | Tiger Cars |
| 166.0125 | 170.8125 | NFM | Aberdeen | Taxis |
| | | NFM | Cardiff | Roath Taxis |
| | | NFM | Glasgow | Taxis |
| | | NFM | Hamilton | Taxi Owners Association |
| | | NFM | Kings Lynn | Baconpac Co |
| | | NFM | Peterborough | On Site Tyres |
| | | NFM | Sheffield | Swallownest Taxis |
| 166.0150 | 170.8100 | NFM | Newcastle | Taxi |
| 166.0250 | 170.8250 | AM | Aberdeen | Oil Industry |
| | | NFM | Birmingham, Sheldon | Taxi |
| | | NFM | Bolton | Taxis |
| | | NFM | Cornwall | English China Clay |
| | | NFM | Doncaster | Mucks Taxis |
| | | NFM | Hillingdon | Civic Centre Security |
| | | NFM | Kennyhill | J.A Butcher |
| | | NFM | Manchester | Taxis |
| | | NFM | Newcastle | Taxis |
| | | NFM | Oldham | Taxis |
| | | NFM | Peterborough | Hotpoint |
| | | NFM | Woodbridge | Council Vans |
| 166.0300 | 170.8300 | NFM | Ayr | Taxi |
| 166.0375 | 170.8375 | AM | Aberdeen | Taxis |
| | | FM | Cambridge | Taxis |
| | | NFM | Cromer | Biffa Ltd |
| | | AM | Grimsby | Taxis |
| | | NFM | Jersey | Pentagon Ltd |
| | | NFM | London | Biffa Waste Disposal |
| | | NFM | London (East) | Taxis |
| | | NFM | Macclesfield | Atax |
| | | NFM | Motherwell | Forgewood Security |
| | | NFM | Newport | A1 Ship Hire |
| | | NFM | Peterborough | A2B Taxis |
| | | NFM | Redruth | Amtrack Deliveries |
| 166.0500 | 170.8500 | AM | Belfast | Water Board |
| | | NFM | Cardiff | Council |
| | | NFM | Chelmsford | Borough Council |
| | | NFM | Doncaster | Council Manual Workers |
| | | NFM | Dover | District Council |
| | | NFM | Glasgow | City Council |
| | | NFM | Gloucester | County Council |
| | | NFM | Hawick | Roxburg |
| | | NFM | Lake Windermere | Rangers & Wardens |
| | | NFM | Lancashire | Road Repairs |
| | | NFM | Liverpool | Bruno Security |
| | | NFM | London | Hillingdon Council |

| Base | Mobile | Mode | Location | User and Notes |
|---|---|---|---|---|
| 166.0500 | 170.8500 | NFM | Manchester | Security |
| | | NFM | Motherwell | District Council |
| | | NFM | Oxford | Oxford City Council |
| | | NFM | Powys | Ambulance |
| | | NFM | Preston | Council |
| | | NFM | Southampton | Council Engineering |
| | | NFM | Suffolk | Suffolk Coastal Council |
| | | NFM | Walsall | Environmental Health |
| | | NFM | Wokinghan | Council Berks |
| 166.0600 | 170.8600 | NFM | Crewe | Heating Engineers |
| 166.0625 | 170.8625 | NFM | Barrow in Furness | District Council |
| | | NFM | Barrow in Furness | SITA Cleansing Department |
| | | NFM | Blackburn | Silverline Private Hire |
| | | AM | Brent | Council |
| | | NFM | Cleethorpes | Borough Council |
| | | NFM | Colchester | Borough Council |
| | | NFM | Deeside | Deeside Council |
| | | NFM | Dundee | City Council Workshop |
| | | NFM | Eakering | BP Depot |
| | | NFM | Hertfordshire | County Council |
| | | NFM | Luton | Repeater |
| | | NFM | Manchester | City Council |
| | | NFM | Newbury | Council |
| | | NFM | Newcastle | City Council |
| | | NFM | Sheffield | Council Housing Dept Area 5 |
| | | NFM | Slough | Borough Council |
| | | NFM | Taunton | Taunton Borough Council |
| | | NFM | Tonbridge | Tonbridge & Malling Council |
| 166.0750 | 170.8750 | NFM | Cannock, Staffs | Council |
| | | NFM | Carlisle | County Contracting East |
| | | NFM | Chelmsford | Council Dustcart |
| | | NFM | Cleveland | Gritters |
| | | NFM | Edinburgh | Lothian Regional Council |
| | | NFM | Hertfordshire | District Council |
| | | NFM | Ipswich | Borough Council (Parks) |
| | | NFM | Jersey | Elizabeth Castle |
| | | NFM | London, Harringay | Council Floods Control |
| | | NFM | Luton | Repeater |
| | | NFM | Manchester | Trafford Council |
| | | NFM | Nationwide | Securicor |
| | | NFM | Southampton | MediCall Channel 4 |
| | | NFM | Wirral | Community Patrol Channel 2 |
| | | NFM | Wirral | Council Parks and Gardens |
| 166.0850 | 170.8850 | NFM | Wirral | Community Patrol Channel 1 |
| 166.0875 | 170.8875 | NFM | Berkshire | Council Channel 1 |
| | | NFM | Bolton | District Council |
| | | NFM | Bristol | Ambulance Service |
| | | NFM | Burton, Staffs | Council |
| | | NFM | Cleethorpes | G.C. Transport |
| | | NFM | Edinburgh | Lothian Regional Council |
| | | NFM | Essex | Havering Council |
| | | NFM | Fleetwood | Wyre Council |
| | | NFM | Grimsby | Stagecoach Buses |
| | | NFM | Halifax | Council |
| | | NFM | London | Westminster Council |
| | | NFM | Oldham | Council Rubbish Men |

| Base | Mobile | Mode | Location | User and Notes |
|---|---|---|---|---|
| 166.0875 | 170.8875 | NFM | Perth | Council Leisure & Recreation |
| | | NFM | Poulton | Council |
| | | NFM | Southampton | City Buses |
| | | NFM | Surrey | Surrey Council (callsign zulu) |
| | | NFM | Wirral | Education Security |
| 166.1000 | 170.9000 | NFM | Bristol | Ambulance Service |
| | | NFM | Chester | Ambulance Service |
| | | NFM | Devizes | Council |
| | | NFM | Halifax | A Star Taxis |
| | | NFM | Jersey | Turner/Bluebird Cabs |
| | | NFM | Merseyside | Ambulance Service |
| | | NFM | Norfolk | Ambulance Service |
| | | NFM | North Yorkshire | Ambulance Service |
| | | NFM | Northumberland | Ambulance Service |
| | | NFM | Nottinghamshire | Ambulance Service |
| | | NFM | Oxfordshire | Ambulance Service |
| | | NFM | Sandwell | Medicall |
| | | NFM | Tyne and Wear | Ambulance Service |
| | | NFM | Ashington | Wansbeck District Council |
| 166.1125 | 170.9125 | NFM | Doncaster | Council Metro Clean |
| | | NFM | Douglas, Isle of Man | Douglas Gas |
| | | NFM | Grimsby | Town Council |
| | | NFM | Isle of Man | Local Government |
| | | NFM | London | Camden Council |
| | | NFM | London | Tower Hamlets Council |
| | | NFM | Newcastle | Council |
| | | NFM | Newmarket | British Legion Security |
| | | NFM | Poole | Repeater |
| | | NFM | Wakefield | District Council. |
| 166.1250 | 170.9250 | NFM | Atherstone, Warks | Council |
| | | NFM | Aylesbury | District Council |
| | | NFM | Bexley Heath | Council |
| | | NFM | Buckinghamshire | Council |
| | | NFM | Carlisle | County Contracting West |
| | | NFM | Doncaster | Council Emergency Callout |
| | | NFM | Hounslow | Traffic Wardens |
| | | NFM | London | Bexley Council |
| | | NFM | Newcastle | Housing Repairs |
| | | NFM | Newport | Neighbourhood Watch |
| | | NFM | Peterborough | Holland Farms |
| | | NFM | Poole | Repeater |
| | | NFM | Scarborough | Council |
| | | NFM | Space | Soviet Mir Telemetry |
| | | NFM | Swansea City | Roads Department |
| 166.1375 | 170.9375 | NFM | Basildon | District Council |
| | | NFM | Brent | Council |
| | | NFM | Chippenham | Council |
| | | NFM | Doncaster | Roads Dept. |
| | | NFM | Glasgow | Taxis |
| | | NFM | Hertfordshire | District Council |
| | | NFM | Jersey | Agriculture & Fisheries Dept |
| | | NFM | London | Harrow Council Maintenance |
| | | NFM | Merseyside | Ambulance Service |
| | | NFM | Newmarket | McCourts Channel 9 |
| | | NFM | Newport | Refuse Skip Control |
| | | NFM | Oxford | Bus Company |

| Base | Mobile | Mode | Location | User and Notes |
|------|--------|------|----------|----------------|
| 166.1375 | 170.9375 | NFM | Sheffield | Brown Construction |
| 166.1375 | 170.9375 | NFM | Surrey | Council |
| 166.1500 | 170.9500 | NFM | Aberdeen | Dee Van Hire |
| | | NFM | Berkshire | Council Channel 2 |
| | | NFM | Brighton | Brough Council |
| | | NFM | Bromley | Council |
| | | NFM | Doncaster | City Council |
| | | NFM | Litchfield | Council |
| | | NFM | Liverpool | City Council |
| | | NFM | Llandudno | Flood Planning |
| | | NFM | London | Bromley Council |
| | | NFM | London | Enfield Council |
| | | NFM | London | Epping Forest Council |
| | | NFM | London | Southwark Council |
| | | NFM | Newport | Council Channel 1 |
| | | NFM | Oakengates, Salop | Council |
| | | NFM | Poole | Repeater |
| | | NFM | Windsor | Council |
| | | NFM | Wirral | Community Patrol Channel 3 |
| | | NFM | Wirral | Council Housing |
| 166.1600 | 170.9600 | NFM | Kilmarnock | Doctor on Call |
| 166.1625 | 170.9625 | NFM | Bracknell | District Council |
| | | NFM | Eastbourne | Community Transport |
| | | NFM | Forest Heath | Council |
| | | NFM | London | Hammersmith Council |
| | | NFM | Salford | District Council |
| | | NFM | Sheffield | Parks Security |
| | | NFM | Solihull | Council |
| | | NFM | Winboune | Council |
| 166.1750 | 170.9750 | NFM | Abingdon | Council |
| | | NFM | Belfast | NI Railways |
| | | NFM | Birmingham Sheldon | Severn Trent Water |
| | | NFM | Brighton | Local Authority |
| | | NFM | Burnley | Council Inspectors |
| | | NFM | Burton Staffs | Council |
| | | NFM | Cambridge | District Council |
| | | NFM | Christchurch | Council |
| | | NFM | Cumbria | Lake District National Park |
| | | NFM | Gateshead | Council |
| | | NFM | Grays | District Council |
| | | NFM | Grimsby | Council |
| | | NFM | Harrow | Council |
| | | NFM | Heysham | Power Station |
| | | NFM | Ipswich | Jewsons Builders Merchants |
| | | NFM | Kings Lynn | District Council |
| | | NFM | Lanark | Council Repairs |
| | | NFM | Lancaster | Council |
| | | NFM | London | Lewisham Council |
| | | NFM | London | Thames Ditton Council |
| | | NFM | Macclesfield | Taxis |
| | | NFM | Manchester | City Council |
| | | NFM | Morecambe | Council |
| | | NFM | Newcastle | Council Housing Repairs |
| | | NFM | Newport | Council Dustbins |
| | | NFM | Norfolk | District Council |
| | | NFM | St Albans | Council Maintenance |

| Base | Mobile | Mode | Location | User and Notes |
|---|---|---|---|---|
| 166.1750 | 170.9750 | NFM | Stirling | Stirling Council |
| 166.1750 | 170.9750 | NFM | Thanet | District Council |
| | | NFM | Vale of White Horse | District Council |
| | | NFM | Viewpark | Council Repairs |
| | | NFM | Welwyn Garden City | Welwyn & Hatfield Council |
| | | NFM | West Norfolk | Council |
| 166.1875 | 170.9875 | NFM | Aberdeen | Council Roads Department |
| | | NFM | Carlisle | City Council |
| | | NFM | Dudley | Ambulance Service |
| | | NFM | Folkestone | District Council |
| | | NFM | Hull | City Council |
| | | NFM | Ipswich | Doctor's Call Out |
| | | NFM | London | Ealing Borough Maintenance |
| | | NFM | Manchester | North West Water |
| | | NFM | Nottingham | County Council |
| | | NFM | Poole | Repeater |
| | | NFM | Spelthorth | Council |
| | | NFM | Tandridge | Council |
| | | NFM | Tedford | Council |
| | | NFM | West Midlands | Environmental Health |
| 166.2000 | 171.0000 | NFM | Cheshire | Ambulance Service |
| | | NFM | Chichester | St Richards Hospital |
| | | NFM | Cleveland | Ambulance Service |
| | | NFM | Dudley | Ambulance Service |
| | | NFM | Dyfed | Ambulance Service |
| | | NFM | Hampshire | Ambulance Service |
| | | NFM | Lancashire | Ambulance Service |
| | | NFM | Leeds Centre | Security |
| | | NFM | Lincolnshire | Ambulance Service |
| | | NFM | London | Ambulance (Orange) South East |
| | | NFM | Merseyside | Ambulance Service |
| | | NFM | Mid Glamorgan | Ambulance Service |
| | | NFM | Nationwide | Manpower Services Commission |
| | | NFM | Perth | Community Data Repeater |
| | | NFM | Wakefield | Hospital Services |
| | | NFM | Warrington | Ambulance Service |
| | | NFM | West Midlands | Ambulance Service |
| | | NFM | West Yorkshire | Ambulance Service |
| | | NFM | Worthing | Hospital Services |
| 166.2100 | 170.0100 | NFM | Worcester | Gritters and snowploughs |
| 166.2125 | 170.0125 | NFM | Cardiff | Bunnon |
| | | NFM | Castle Point | Borough Council |
| | | NFM | Buckinghamshire | Amersham Council |
| | | NFM | Crawley | Crawley Council |
| | | NFM | Essex | Council |
| | | NFM | Glasgow | Taxis |
| | | NFM | Greenwich | Council |
| | | NFM | Hampshire | Council |
| | | NFM | Hinchley | Council |
| | | NFM | Hinchley | Council Repairs |
| | | NFM | London | US Embassy Secret Service |
| | | NFM | Manchester | District Council |
| | | NFM | Newport | Gwent Council Decorators |
| | | NFM | Norfolk | ICL |
| | | NFM | Swindon | Cooper's Metals |
| | | NFM | Woking | Council |

| Base | Mobile | Mode | Location | User and Notes |
|---|---|---|---|---|
| 166.2150 | 171.0150 | NFM | Gateshead | Council |
| | | NFM | Worcester | City Council Depot |
| 166.2250 | 171.0250 | NFM | Aberdeen | Fish Market |
| | | NFM | Ashford | District Council |
| | | FM | Ayr | Sewer Maintenance |
| | | NFM | Birmingham | Park Patrol Central Control |
| | | NFM | Bridgnorth | Bridgnorth District Council |
| | | NFM | Cambridge | Council |
| | | NFM | Coventry | Council Environmental Dept. Abatement Notice |
| | | NFM | Eastlelgh | Council |
| | | NFM | Guildford | Council |
| | | NFM | Gwent | Blaena Gwent Council |
| | | NFM | Jersey | Jersey Gas |
| | | NFM | Kilmarnock | Parks Department |
| | | NFM | Lewisham | Council |
| | | NFM | Lincoln | Local Authority |
| | | NFM | Livingstone | West Lothian District Council |
| | | NFM | London | Kensington Council |
| | | NFM | London | Newham Council |
| | | NFM | Nationwide | Local Authorities |
| | | NFM | Newham | Council |
| | | NFM | Nottingham | Taxis |
| | | NFM | Plymouth | City Bus Company |
| | | NFM | Preston | Council Maintenance |
| | | NFM | Reigate & Banstead | Council |
| | | NFM | Sunderland | Council |
| 166.2375 | 171.0375 | NFM | Aberdeen | TV Repairs |
| | | NFM | Bathgate | Streamline Taxis (Streamline) |
| | | NFM | Chichester | Council |
| | | NFM | Coventry, Stoneleigh | National Agricultural Centre |
| | | NFM | Cwnbran | Council |
| | | NFM | Manchester | Thameside Council |
| | | NFM | Norfolk | Haller's Skip Hire |
| | | NFM | Oldham | Halroyd Skips |
| 166.2500 | 171.0500 | NFM | Basingstoke | Council. |
| | | NFM | Birmingham | Traffic lights maintenancde |
| | | NFM | Brighton | Brighton Council |
| | | NFM | Bury St Edmunds | Bury Council |
| | | NFM | Chandlers Ford | Taxis |
| | | NFM | Dundee | Electrical Repairs |
| | | NFM | Elmbridge | Council |
| | | NFM | Harlow | Council |
| | | NFM | Hertfordshire | District Council |
| | | NFM | Humberside | Beverly Council |
| | | NFM | Jersey | Tantivy Holiday Coaches |
| | | NFM | Kingston | Council |
| | | NFM | Lambeth | Council |
| | | NFM | Manchester | House Calls |
| | | NFM | Poole | Repeater |
| | | NFM | Trowbridge | Builders |
| | | NFM | Tyneside | Tyne Tunnel |

| Base | Mobile | Mode | Location | User and Notes |
|------|--------|------|----------|----------------|
| 166.2625 | 171.0625 | NFM | Bolton | Dog Warden |
| | | NFM | Braintree | Borough Council |
| | | NFM | Chesterfield | Bus Company |
| | | NFM | Dundee | Data Link |
| | | NFM | Edinburgh | Citadel Couriers (City) |
| | | NFM | Essex | Council Channel 2 |
| | | NFM | Leicester | Dustmen |
| | | NFM | Leven | DCL Security |
| | | NFM | London | Bus & Coach Co. |
| | | NFM | Nuneaton & Bedworth | Council |
| | | NFM | Preston | Preston Buses |
| | | NFM | Richmond | Council |
| | | NFM | Rochford | Council |
| | | NFM | Thetford | Broadland Council |
| 166.2650 | 171.0650 | NFM | Newcastle | Taxi |
| 166.2750 | 171.0750 | NFM | Grangemouth | Central Taxis (Central) |
| | | NFM | Lancashire | Ambulance Service |
| | | NFM | Lincolnshire | Ambulance Service |
| | | NFM | London | Ambulance (Orange) South West |
| | | NFM | Somerset | Ambulance Service |
| | | NFM | South Cumbria | Ambulance Service |
| | | NFM | Sussex | Ambulance Service |
| | | NFM | West Midlands | Ambulance Service |
| 166.2875 | 171.0875 | NFM | Belfast | Ambulance Service |
| | | NFM | Buckinghamshire | Ambulance Service |
| | | NFM | Cornwall | Ambulance Service |
| | | NFM | Kent | Ambulance Service |
| | | NFM | Manchester | Ambulance Service |
| | | NFM | Northumberland | Ambulance Service |
| | | NFM | Nottinghamshire | Ambulance Service |
| | | NFM | Tyne and Wear | Ambulance Service |
| | | AM | Withenshaw | Paramedics |
| 166.2900 | 171.0900 | NFM | Gateshead | Ambulance |
| 166.3000 | 171.1000 | NFM | Carlisle | Ambulance Service |
| | | NFM | Cumbria | Ambulance Service |
| | | NFM | Dorset | Ambulance Service |
| | | NFM | Humberside | Ambulance Service |
| | | NFM | Leicestershire | Ambulance Service |
| | | NFM | London | Ambulance (Gold) North East |
| | | NFM | Manchester | Ambulance Service |
| | | NFM | Pontypridd | Doctors Service |
| | | NFM | South Glamorgan | Ambulance Service |
| | | NFM | West Yorkshire | Ambulance Service |
| 166.3125 | 171.1125 | NFM | Belfast | Ambulance Service |
| | | NFM | Cambridgeshire | Ambulance Service |
| | | NFM | Derbyshire | Ambulance Service |
| | | NFM | Dyfed | Doctor's Radio |
| | | NFM | Gwynedd | Ambulance Service |
| | | NFM | London | Ambulance (Red) East |
| | | NFM | Plymouth | Devon Ambulance Service |
| | | NFM | Powys | Ambulance Service |
| | | NFM | Preston | District Nurses |
| | | NFM | Salop | Ambulance Service Channel 3 |
| 166.3215 | 171.1215 | NFM | Merthyr, Powys | Mountain Rescue Air Ambulance |

| Base | Mobile | Mode | Location | User and Notes |
|------|--------|------|----------|----------------|
| 166.3250 | 171.1250 | NFM | Belfast | Ambulance Service |
| | | NFM | Humberside | Ambulance Service |
| | | NFM | Lincolnshire | Ambulance Service |
| | | NFM | London | Ambulance (Orange) S. West |
| | | NFM | Merseyside | Ambulance Service |
| | | NFM | Mid Glamorgan | Ambulance Service |
| | | NFM | Nuneaton | Private Ambulance |
| | | NFM | Rhymney Valley | Ambulance Service |
| | | NFM | Warickshire | Ambulance service |
| 166.3375 | 171.1375 | NFM | Bedfordshire | Ambulance Service |
| | | NFM | Belfast | Ambulance Service |
| | | NFM | Dundee | City Council Data Link |
| | | NFM | Hertfordshire | Ambulance Service |
| | | NFM | Kent | Ambulance Service |
| | | NFM | Merseyside | Ambulance Service |
| | | NFM | North Yorkshire | Ambulance Service |
| | | NFM | Portsmouth | Health Service |
| | | NFM | Somerset | Ambulance Service |
| | | NFM | Suffolk | Ambulance Service |
| 166.3500 | 171.1500 | NFM | Cambridgeshire | Ambulance Service |
| | | NFM | Cleveland | Ambulance Service |
| | | NFM | Cumbria | Ambulance Service |
| | | NFM | London | Ambulance (Red) East |
| | | NFM | Manchester | Satellite Installers |
| | | NFM | Nuneaton | Council |
| | | NFM | Peterborough | MAGPAS |
| | | NFM | Sheffield | Health Centre |
| | | NFM | Sheffield | Mobile nurse |
| | | NFM | Swansea | Ambulance Service |
| | | NFM | West Glamorgan | Ambulance Service |
| | | NFM | West Midlands | Ambulance Service |
| | | NFM | Whittlesey | Luxicabs |
| 166.3600 | 171.1600 | NFM | Merseyside | Ambulance |
| 166.3625 | 171.1625 | NFM | Channel Tunnel | Maintenance |
| | | NFM | Cheshire | Ambulance Service |
| | | NFM | Chester | Ambulance |
| | | NFM | Crewe | Ambulance Service |
| | | NFM | Dyfed | Ambulance Service |
| | | NFM | Essex | Ambulance Service |
| | | NFM | Gloucester | Ambulance Service |
| | | NFM | Hampshire | Ambulance Service |
| | | NFM | Lincolnshire | Ambulance Service |
| | | NFM | Liverpool | Ambulance Service |
| | | NFM | Pembroke | Ambulance Service |
| 166.3750 | 171.1350 | NFM | Barrow in Furness | Ambulance |
| | | NFM | Cumbria | Ambulance Service |
| | | NFM | Derbyshire | Ambulance Service |
| | | NFM | Dundee | Taxis |
| | | NFM | Fleetwood | Medicall |
| | | NFM | Hereford & Worcester | Ambulance Service |
| | | NFM | Isle of Wight | Ambulance Service |
| | | NFM | London South East | Ambulance (Green) |
| | | NFM | Stockport | Ambulance Service |
| | | NFM | Sussex | Ambulance Service |
| | | NFM | Whittlesey | Jenner Health Centre |

| Base | Mobile | Mode | Location | User and Notes |
|------|--------|------|----------|----------------|
| 166.3825 | 171.1825 | NFM | East Sussex | Ambulance Service |
| 166.3875 | 171.1875 | NFM | Berkshire | Ambulance Service |
| | | NFM | Cambridgeshire | Ambulance Service |
| | | NFM | Kent | Ambulance Service |
| | | NFM | Lancashire | Ambulance Service |
| | | NFM | North Yorkshire | Ambulance Service |
| | | NFM | Peterborough | Ambulance Service |
| | | NFM | Preston | Ambulance |
| | | NFM | Staffordshire | Ambulance Service |
| | | NFM | Warrington | Ambulance |
| | | NFM | West Yorkshire | Ambulance Service |
| 166.4000 | 171.2000 | NFM | Belfast | NI Ambulance Service |
| | | NFM | Blackburn | Ambulance Service |
| | | NFM | Derbyshire | Ambulance Service |
| | | NFM | East Sussex | Ambulance Service |
| | | NFM | Gwent | Ambulance Service |
| | | NFM | Humberside | Ambulance Service |
| | | NFM | Lincolnshire | Ambulance Service |
| | | NFM | London | US Embassy Secret Service |
| | | NFM | Northumberland | Ambulance Service |
| | | NFM | Tyne and Wear | Ambulance Service (Red) |
| | | NFM | West Yorkshire | Ambulance Service |
| 166.4125 | 171.2125 | NFM | Dalton in Furness | Taxi |
| | | NFM | Dyfed | Doctor's Radio |
| | | NFM | Leicestershire | Ambulance Service |
| | | NFM | Lincoln | Ambulance Service |
| | | NFM | London | Ambulance (Red) South Channel 3. |
| | | NFM | Nottinghamshire | Ambulance Service |
| | | NFM | Rhyl | Dee's Taxis |
| | | NFM | Shropshire | Ambulance Service |
| | | NFM | Swindon | Ambulance Service |
| | | NFM | West Yorkshire | Ambulance Service |
| | | NFM | Wiltshire | Ambulance Service |
| 166.4250 | 171.2250 | NFM | Birmingham | Locums Service |
| | | NFM | Bradford | Doctors On Call |
| | | NFM | Cambridge | Dr Lankester |
| | | NFM | Glasgow | Taxis |
| | | NFM | Kilmarnock | Johnnie Walker Distillery |
| | | NFM | Kings Lynn | Dr Ewlett |
| | | NFM | Liverpool | Emergency Doctors |
| | | NFM | London | Ambulance (Gold) North East |
| | | NFM | Norfolk | Doctors On Call |
| | | NFM | Norfolk | Emergency Doctor Service |
| | | NFM | Salop | Midwives Channel 4 |
| | | NFM | Shropshire | Ambulance Service |
| | | AM | Stoke on Trent | Emergency Doctor |
| | | NFM | W Yorkshire | Deputising Service |
| | | NFM | West Midlands | Doctors on Call |
| 166.4350 | 171.2350 | NFM | Chester | Ambulance |
| 166.4375 | 171.2375 | NFM | Bedfordshire | Ambulance Emergency Relay |
| | | NFM | Berkshire | Ambulance Emergency Relay |
| | | NFM | Buckinghamshire | Ambulance Emergency Relay |
| | | NFM | Cambridgeshire | Ambulance Emergency Relay |
| | | NFM | Cheshire | Ambulance Emergency Relay |
| | | NFM | Cleveland | Ambulance Emergency Relay |
| | | NFM | Devon | Air Ambulance |

| Base | Mobile | Mode | Location | User and Notes |
|------|--------|------|----------|----------------|
| 166.4375 | 171.2375 | NFM | East Sussex | Ambulance Emergency Relay |
| | | NFM | Essex | Ambulance Emergency Relay |
| | | NFM | Hampshire | Ambulance Emergency Relay |
| | | NFM | Humberside | Ambulance Emergency Relay |
| | | NFM | Leicestershire | Ambulance Emergency Relay |
| | | NFM | Lincolnshire | Ambulance Emergency Relay |
| | | NFM | London | Air Ambulance |
| | | NFM | Manchester Airport | Ambulance |
| | | NFM | Merseyside | Ambulance Emergency Relay |
| | | NFM | Nationwide | Emergency Ambulance Channel |
| | | NFM | Norfolk | Ambulance Emergency Relay |
| | | NFM | North Yorkshire | Ambulance Emergency Relay |
| | | NFM | Northamptonshire | Ambulance Emergency Relay |
| | | NFM | Suffolk | Ambulance Emergency Relay |
| | | NFM | Surrey | Ambulance Emergency Relay |
| | | NFM | Tyne and Wear | Ambulance Emergency Relay |
| | | NFM | Warickshire | Ambulance service relay |
| | | NFM | West Midlands | Ambulance Emergency Relay |
| | | NFM | West Sussex | Ambulance Emergency Relay |
| | | NFM | West Yorkshire | Ambulance Emergency Relay |
| 166.4500 | 171.2500 | NFM | Blackburn | Blackburn Health Authority |
| | | NFM | Bradford | Doctor Dep Service |
| | | NFM | Bristol | Roman Taxis |
| | | NFM | Derby | District Nurses |
| | | NFM | Jersey | Honorary Police St Ouen Channel 2 |
| | | NFM | London | Ambulance (Blue) North West |
| | | NFM | Manchester | Ambulance Service |
| | | NFM | Newport, Gwent | Breakdown Recovery Company |
| | | NFM | Poole | East Dorset Health Authority |
| | | NFM | W Yorkshire | Lexicon Deputising Service |
| | | NFM | Wantage | Doctors |
| | | NFM | Wisbeach | Clarkson Health Centre |
| 166.4625 | 171.2625 | NFM | Bedfordshire | Ambulance Service |
| | | NFM | Cheltenham | Metro Buses |
| | | NFM | Clwyd | Ambulance Service |
| | | NFM | Coventry | Ambulance Service |
| | | NFM | East Sussex | Ambulance Service |
| | | NFM | London | US Embassy Secret Service |
| | | NFM | North Yorkshire | Ambulance Service |
| | | NFM | Ravenglass | Steam Railway |
| | | NFM | Rhyl (Clwyd) | Emergency Ambulances |
| | | NFM | Swindon | Metro Buses |
| | | NFM | West Midlands | Ambulance Service |
| | | NFM | West Yorkshire | Ambulance Service |
| 166.4750 | 171.2750 | NFM | Gwynedd | Ambulance Service |
| | | NFM | Hampshire | Ambulance Service |
| | | NFM | Hereford & Worcester | Ambulance Service |
| | | NFM | Jersey | Honorary Police Channel 4 |
| | | NFM | London | Ambulance (Blue) North West |
| | | NFM | Merseyside | Ambulance Service |
| | | NFM | North Yorkshire | Ambulance Service |
| | | NFM | Scarborough | Ambulance Service |

| Base | Mobile | Mode | Location | User and Notes |
|---|---|---|---|---|
| 166.4875 | 171.2875 | NFM | Blackburn | Ambulance Service |
| | | NFM | Dorset | Ambulance Service |
| | | NFM | Essex | Ambulance Service |
| | | NFM | Jersey | Honorary Police Channel 3 |
| | | NFM | London | US Embassy Secret Service |
| | | NFM | Manchester | Ambulance Service |
| | | NFM | Northumberland | Ambulance Service |
| | | NFM | Oxfordshire | Ambulance Service |
| | | NFM | South Yorkshire | Ambulance Service |
| | | NFM | Tyne and Wear | Ambulance Service |
| 166.5000 | 171.3000 | NFM | Blackpool | Ambulance |
| | | NFM | Bolton | Ambulance |
| | | NFM | Bury | Medical |
| | | NFM | Cambridgeshire | Ambulance Service |
| | | NFM | Cornwall | Ambulance Service |
| | | NFM | London | Ambulance (Gold) North East |
| | | NFM | Manchester | Ambulance Service |
| | | NFM | North Yorkshire | Ambulance Service |
| | | NFM | Northumberland | Ambulance Service |
| | | NFM | Northwich | Ambulance |
| | | NFM | Staffordshire | Ambulance Service |
| | | NFM | Warwickshire | Ambulance Service |
| | | NFM | West Midlands | Ambulance Service |
| 166.5125 | 171.3125 | NFM | Cambridge | Ambulance Service |
| | | NFM | County Durham | Ambulance Service (DC) |
| | | NFM | Lancashire | Ambulance Service |
| | | NFM | Leeds | Wymas to Hospital |
| | | NFM | London | US Embassy Secret Service |
| | | NFM | Manchester | Ambulance Service |
| | | NFM | Northumberland | Ambulance Service |
| | | NFM | Oldham | Ambulance Service |
| | | NFM | Peterborough | Ambulance Service |
| | | NFM | Shropshire | Ambulance PTS |
| | | NFM | Surrey | Ambulance Service |
| | | NFM | Warwickshire | Ambulance Service |
| 166.5250 | 171.3250 | NFM | East Ridding | Ambulance Service |
| | | NFM | Humberside | Ambulance Service |
| | | NFM | Lancashire | Ambulance Service |
| | | NFM | London | Ambulance (Red) South |
| | | NFM | Mid Glamorgan | Ambulance Service |
| | | NFM | North Yorkshire | Ambulance Service |
| | | NFM | Suffolk | Ambulance Service |
| | | NFM | Warwickshire | Ambulance Service |
| | | NFM | West Sussex | Ambulance Service |
| 166.5375 | 171.3375 | NFM | Blackburn | Ambulance Service |
| | | NFM | Halifax | Ambulance |
| | | NFM | Leeds | Doctors Service |
| | | NFM | Leicestershire | Ambulance Service |
| | | NFM | North Yorkshire | Ambulance Service |
| | | NFM | Surrey | Ambulance Service |
| | | NFM | West Yorkshire | Ambulance Service |

| Base | Mobile | Mode | Location | User and Notes |
|------|--------|------|----------|----------------|
| 166.5500 | 171.3500 | NFM | Cirencester | Hospital Doctors |
| | | NFM | Devon | Patient Ambulance Service |
| | | NFM | Doncaster | Doctors On Call |
| | | NFM | Essex | Ambulance Service |
| | | NFM | Hampshire | Ambulance Service |
| | | NFM | Humberside | Ambulance Service |
| | | NFM | Lancashire | Ambulance Service |
| | | NFM | Northamptonshire | Ambulance Service |
| | | NFM | Portsmouth | Ambulance Service |
| | | NFM | Sheffield | Ambulance Emergency |
| | | NFM | South Yorkshire | Ambulance Service |
| | | NFM | West Midlands | Ambulance Service |
| | | NFM | West Yorkshire | Ambulance Service |
| 166.5625 | 171.3625 | NFM | Barnsley | Hospitial services. |
| | | NFM | Bournemouth | Hospital Minibus |
| | | NFM | Buckinghamshire | Ambulance Service |
| | | NFM | Clwyd | Ambulance Service |
| | | NFM | Devon | Ambulance Service |
| | | NFM | Dundee | National Carriers |
| | | NFM | Hereford & Worcester | Ambulance Service |
| | | NFM | Mold (Clwyd) | Ambulance Service |
| | | NFM | Norfolk | Ambulance Service |
| | | NFM | Perth | Ready Mixed Concrete |
| | | NFM | Sheffield | Ambulance Out-Patients |
| | | NFM | South Yorkshire | Ambulance Service |
| | | NFM | West Sussex | Ambulance Service |
| 166.5750 | 171.3750 | NFM | Abram | Medical Centre |
| | | NFM | Bolton | Doctors On Call |
| | | NFM | Gwent | Ambulance Service |
| | | NFM | Gwynedd | Ambulance Service |
| | | NFM | Hampshire | Ambulance Service |
| | | NFM | Hereford & Worcester | Ambulance Service |
| | | NFM | Humberside | Ambulance Service |
| | | NFM | Leeds | Ambulance Service |
| | | NFM | London | Ambulance (White) Inner London |
| | | NFM | London, south east | Ambulance Service |
| | | NFM | Merseyshire | Ambulance Service |
| | | NFM | North Yorkshire | Ambulance Service |
| | | NFM | Northamptonshire | Ambulance Service |
| | | NFM | Northumberland | Ambulance Service |
| | | NFM | West Glamorgan | Ambulance Service |
| 166.5875 | 171.3875 | NFM | Aberdeen | Surveyors |
| | | NFM | Durham | Ambulance Service |
| | | NFM | Hampshire | Ambulance Service |
| | | NFM | Hertfordshire | Ambulance Service |
| | | NFM | Merseyside | Ambulance Service |
| | | NFM | South Glamorgan | Ambulance Service |
| | | NFM | South Yorkshire | Ambulance Service |
| | | NFM | Staffordshire | Ambulance Service |
| 166.6000 | 171.4000 | NFM | Doncaster | Midwives |
| | | AM | England & Wales | Doctors Special Services |
| | | NFM | Ipswich | Doctor's Surgery |
| | | NFM | Manchester | Ambulance Service |
| | | NFM | Northumberland | Ambulance Service |
| | | NFM | Peterborough | Dr. Gray |
| | | NFM | Preston | Electricians |

| Base | Mobile | Mode | Location | User and Notes |
|------|--------|------|----------|----------------|
| 166.6000 | 171.4000 | AM | Saffron Walden | Accident Group |
| | | AM | Swaffham | Dr. Pilkington |
| | | NFM | Tyne and Wear | Ambulance Service |
| | | NFM | West Midlands | Ambulance Service |
| 166.6100 | 171.4100 | NFM | Stoke on trent | Ambulance |
| 166.6125 | 171.4125 | NFM | Barking | Council |
| | | NFM | Berkshire | Ambulance Service |
| | | NFM | Havant | Dixies Taxis |
| | | NFM | Hertfordshire | Ambulance |
| | | NFM | Humberside | Ambulance Service |
| | | NFM | North Yorkshire | Ambulance Service |
| | | NFM | Oxfordshire | Ambulance Service |
| | | NFM | Perthshire | Electricians |
| | | NFM | Staffordshire | Ambulance Service |
| | | NFM | Wiltshire | Ambulance Service |
| 166.6250 | 171.4250 | AM | Aberdeen | Retail Park |
| | | NFM | Bath | Francis Plant Hire |
| | | NFM | Bolton | Cobra Taxis |
| | | NFM | Bournemouth | Breakdown Recovery |
| | | NFM | Bristol | Red Taxis |
| | | NFM | Cambridge | Cambridge Growers |
| | | NFM | Cardiff | City Taxis |
| | | NFM | Dundee | Taxis |
| | | NFM | Eltham | Taxis |
| | | NFM | Hampshire | Streamline Cabs |
| | | NFM | Ipswich | DHSS |
| | | NFM | Lytham | Whitesides Taxis |
| | | NFM | Manchester | Taxi |
| | | AM | Nationwide | Ambulance-to-Hospital Link |
| | | NFM | Poole | Repeater |
| | | NFM | Stirling | Thistle Centre |
| | | NFM | Worcester | Delta Taxis |
| 166.6375 | 171.43750 | NFM | Aberdeen | Radio Specialists |
| | | NFM | Ashington | Toward Taxis |
| | | NFM | Bolton | Taxis |
| | | NFM | Collyhurst | Taxis |
| | | NFM | Coventry | Lewis Taxis |
| | | NFM | Drayton | Draytax Taxis |
| | | NFM | Isle of Wight | Grange Taxis |
| | | NFM | Lancing | Access Cars |
| | | NFM | London | Taxis |
| | | NFM | Manchester | Crestra Car Hire |
| | | NFM | Nationwide | Rediffussion Comms |
| | | NFM | Oldham | Taxis |
| | | NFM | Peacehaven | Dave's Taxis |
| | | NFM | Royston | Farmers Fertilisers |
| | | NFM | Whittlesey | S & S Tractors |
| | | NFM | Woodbridge | Greenwell Farms |
| 166.6500 | 171.4500 | NFM | Bedfordshire | Bedfordshire Growers |
| | | NFM | Belfast | Ferguson Flowers |
| | | NFM | Bury | Byford Taxis |
| | | NFM | Cardiff | ICL Computers |
| | | NFM | Central London | Taxis |
| | | NFM | Flixton | Beaumont's Private Hire |
| | | NFM | Glasgow | Taxis |
| | | NFM | Halifax | Crossleys Taxis |

| Base | Mobile | Mode | Location | User and Notes |
|---|---|---|---|---|
| 166.6500 | 171.4500 | NFM | Hampshire | Wessex Plant Hire |
| | | NFM | Huntingdon | R. O'Connell |
| | | NFM | Ipswich | Taxi Association |
| | | NFM | London | ODRATS |
| 166.6550 | 171.4550 | NFM | Woodingdean | Taxis |
| 166.6625 | 171.4625 | NFM | Baldock | Butts Taxis |
| | | NFM | Barkway | British Sugar |
| | | NFM | Bristol | Aerial Riggers |
| | | NFM | Bury | British Sugar |
| | | NFM | Cantley | British Sugar |
| | | NFM | Cheltenham | Celtax Couriers |
| | | NFM | Dullingham | P.B Taylor |
| | | NFM | Grimsby | Peter Sheffield Buses |
| | | NFM | London | Scorpio Cars |
| | | NFM | Manchester | Taxis |
| | | NFM | Methil | Taxis |
| | | NFM | Nationwide | ICL Channel 1 |
| | | NFM | Perth | Tay Taxis |
| | | NFM | Sudbury | A Line Taxis |
| | | NFM | Sussex | Tarmac Contractors |
| | | NFM | Swinton | Skytax |
| 166.6750 | 171.4750 | NFM | Alconbury | Steve's Taxis |
| | | NFM | Alderney | Alderney Taxis |
| | | NFM | Bolton | Best Way Taxis |
| | | NFM | Ealing | Taxis |
| | | NFM | Elvington | Rolawn Turf Suppliers |
| | | NFM | Glasgow | Taxi Company |
| | | NFM | Hampshire | Ace Taxis |
| | | NFM | Hounslow | Minicab Co |
| | | NFM | Hull | Security Co |
| | | NFM | Ipswich | Taxis |
| | | NFM | Lancaster | District Nurse |
| | | NFM | London, Wimbledon | Minicab Firm |
| | | NFM | Morecambe | District Nurse |
| | | NFM | Mostyn | Dave's Taxis |
| | | NFM | Nationwide | ICL Channel 2 |
| | | NFM | North London | Taxis |
| | | NFM | Northampton | Taxis |
| | | NFM | Radcliffe | Harvey's Taxis |
| | | NFM | Southampton | A2B Taxis |
| | | NFM | Southhall | Taxis |
| | | NFM | West Midlands | Cashmore's Steel |
| | | NFM | Winbourne | Skiphire |
| 166.6875 | 171.4875 | NFM | Berinsfield | Star Cars |
| | | NFM | Bury St Edmonds | British Sugar |
| | | NFM | Buxton | Crane & Son |
| | | NFM | Chatteris | Whitworth Produce |
| | | NFM | East Kilbride | Kelvin Kabs |
| | | NFM | Glasgow | Taxis |
| | | NFM | Guernsey | AC Heating |
| | | NFM | Guernsey | Cobo Building |
| | | NFM | Ipswich | Ransomes |
| | | NFM | Kings Lynn | British Sugar |
| | | NFM | Newport | Town Taxis |
| | | NFM | Norfolk | Crane & Son |
| | | NFM | Northampton | Taxis |

| Base | Mobile | Mode | Location | User and Notes |
|---|---|---|---|---|
| 166.6875 | 171.4875 | NFM | Peterborough | Co-Op TV Services |
| | | NFM | Portsmouth | CTE Television |
| | | NFM | Swindon | Starlight Taxis |
| 166.6900 | 171.4900 | NFM | Newport, Gwent | ABC Taxis |
| 166.7000 | 171.5000 | NFM | Bestway | Taxis |
| | | NFM | Birmingham Shard End | Taxi |
| | | NFM | Cirencester | Radio Cars |
| | | NFM | Guernsey | Central Transfers |
| | | NFM | Hampshire | Haverson Electronics |
| | | NFM | Hull | Parks Department |
| | | NFM | London | US Embassy Secret Service |
| | | NFM | Methwold | Darby Bros Farms |
| | | NFM | Montrose | Taxis |
| | | NFM | Northampton | Taxis |
| | | NFM | Norwich | Bestway Taxis |
| | | NFM | Nottingham, Hucknall | Phoenix Cars |
| | | NFM | Sheffield | Taxis |
| | | NFM | Southampton | RMS Motors |
| 166.7125 | 171.5125 | NFM | Abingdon | JMB Plant Hire |
| | | NFM | Canvey Island | Taxis |
| | | NFM | Coventry | Taxi |
| | | NFM | Edinburgh | Festival Cars |
| | | NFM | Grimsby | Taxis |
| | | NFM | Havant | Jacks Taxis |
| | | NFM | Morecambe | Taxis |
| | | NFM | Norwich | Knight Benjamin |
| | | NFM | Sheffield | RD Cars |
| | | NFM | Southampton | Taxis |
| | | NFM | Wispington | British Sugar |
| 166.7250 | 171.5250 | NFM | Alderney | Alderney Emergency Service |
| | | NFM | Gt. Yarmouth | Birds Eye Vans |
| | | NFM | Lowestoft | Birds Eye |
| | | NFM | Sharnbrook | Unilever |
| 166.7375 | 171.5375 | NFM | Bolton | Cross Private Hire |
| | | AM | Colchester | Rainbow Taxis |
| | | NFM | Essex | Taxis |
| | | NFM | Grampian | Transport Company |
| | | NFM | London | National Radio Cars |
| | | NFM | Manchester | Taxis |
| | | NFM | Nationwide | ICL Channel 3 |
| | | NFM | Norwich | Knight Benjamin |
| | | NFM | Pitsea | Taxis |
| | | NFM | Poulton | Poulton Cabs |
| | | NFM | Rochdale | Globe Taxis |
| | | NFM | Widnes | Kay Cabs |
| 166.7400 | 166.7400 | NFM | West Midlands | JRs Taxis |
| 166.7500 | 171.5500 | NFM | Banchory | Taxis |
| | | NFM | Co Durham | Emergency Doctors Service |
| | | NFM | Crewe | Ambulance |
| | | NFM | Eastbourne | Ambulance Service |
| | | NFM | Lancaster | Council |
| | | NFM | Morecambe | Council |
| | | NFM | Nationwide | DSS Dole Fraud Teams |
| | | NFM | Portsmouth | Ambulance Service |
| | | NFM | Surrey | Ambulance Service |

| Base | Mobile | Mode | Location | User and Notes |
|------|--------|------|----------|----------------|
| 166.7625 | 171.5625 | NFM | Bournemouth | Traffic Wardens |
| | | NFM | Castle Donington | Race Control |
| | | NFM | Coventry | Coventry University Maintenance |
| | | NFM | Dudley | Delivery Company |
| | | NFM | Dumfries | District Council |
| | | NFM | Finchley | Medics |
| | | NFM | Ipswich | Taxis |
| | | NFM | Irvine | Shopping Centre Security |
| | | NFM | Kirkcaldy | Mercat Shopping Centre Security |
| | | NFM | Nationwide | DSS Dole Fraud Teams |
| | | NFM | Poole | Guardforce Security |
| | | NFM | Rother Valley | Sports Centre |
| | | NFM | Rugby | Shops Radio Link to Police |
| | | NFM | Swindon | Oasis Leisure Centre |
| 166.7650 | 171.5650 | NFM | Harlow | Harvey Centre Security |
| 166.7750 | 171.5750 | NFM | Abingdon | Abingdon Hospital |
| | | NFM | Bedfordshire | Midwives |
| | | NFM | Birmingham | Doctors |
| | | NFM | Burnley | Doctors Call Out |
| | | NFM | Cardiff | Health Service |
| | | NFM | Dover | Council |
| | | NFM | Hampshire | Health Service |
| | | NFM | Ipswich | Midwives |
| | | NFM | Lancaster | District Nurse |
| | | NFM | Manchester | Taxis |
| | | NFM | Morecambe | District Nurse |
| | | NFM | Nationwide | DSS Dole Fraud Teams |
| | | NFM | Warwickshire | Ambulance Service |
| 166.7850 | 171.5875 | NFM | Stoke on Trent | TV Aerials |
| | | AM | Aberdeen | Oil Servicing |
| | | NFM | Bournemouth | Castle Recovery |
| | | NFM | Caterham Hill | RCS Comrep Channel 5 |
| | | NFM | Cornwall | Vetco Base |
| | | NFM | Dorking | Car Recovery (King Babe) |
| | | NFM | Dumfries | District Council |
| | | NFM | Edinburgh | Diamond Security |
| | | NFM | Grimsby | Lincs Vending |
| | | NFM | Grimsby | Mariner Gas |
| | | NFM | Hampshire | Council |
| | | NFM | Ipswich | Taxis |
| | | NFM | Lancaster | District Nurse |
| | | NFM | Linconshire | Comunity Repeater |
| | | NFM | Morecambe | District Nurse |
| | | NFM | Plymouth | Co-Op Store Detectives |
| | | NFM | Tyneside/Tyne & Wear | Recovery Service |
| 166.7900 | 171.5900 | NFM | Newcastle | Auto Breakdowns |
| 166.8000 | 171.6000 | NFM | Doncaster | Royal Infirmary |
| | | NFM | Glossop | District Nurses |
| | | NFM | Gloucester | Ambulance Service Ch2 |
| | | NFM | Manchester | Hospital Porters |
| | | NFM | Mansfield | Kings Mill Hospital |
| | | NFM | Poole | General Hospital |
| | | NFM | Winsford | Doctors Base |

| Base | Mobile | Mode | Location | User and Notes |
|------|--------|------|----------|----------------|
| 166.8125 | 171.6125 | NFM | Berkshire | Common Doctors Freq. |
| | | NFM | Chapmanslade | Barters Farm |
| | | NFM | Doncaster | Emergency Doctors &Health Centre |
| | | NFM | Essex | Havering Council |
| | | NFM | Haverfordwest | E Williams Transport |
| | | NFM | Hertfordshire | Doctors Channel |
| | | NFM | Isle of Man | Ambulance Service |
| | | NFM | Llanelli | Doctors on Call |
| | | NFM | Nationwide | Doctors Channel 1 |
| | | NFM | North Lancashire | Doctors On Call |
| | | NFM | Northampton | Emergency Doctors |
| | | NFM | Oxfordshire | Common Doctors Freq. |
| | | NFM | Runcorn | Doctor Channel |
| | | NFM | Stoke-on-Trent | Doctors Service |
| | | NFM | Sussex | Brighton Council |
| | | NFM | Swindon | Ambulance Service |
| | | NFM | Upwell | Health Centre |
| | | NFM | Welwyn & Hatfield | Accident Services |
| | | NFM | Yorkshire | Medic Service |
| 166.8250 | 171.6250 | NFM | Bournemouth | Emergency Services |
| | | NFM | Burnley | Council Security Patrols |
| | | NFM | Clare | Dr Carter |
| | | NFM | Hastings | Council |
| | | NFM | Ipswich | Wilding & Smith |
| | | NFM | Jersey | Yellow Cabs |
| | | NFM | Kent | Ambulance Service |
| | | NFM | London, Islington | Flood Control |
| | | NFM | Nationwide | DSS Dole Fraud Teams |
| | | NFM | Swansea City | Ambulance Service |
| | | AM | Thanet | Ambulance |
| | | NFM | Wirral | District Nurses |
| 166.8375 | 171.6375 | NFM | Castle Donington | Medic Control |
| | | NFM | Dorset | Health Service |
| | | NFM | Emsworth | John's Cabs |
| | | NFM | Hampshire | District Nurse |
| | | NFM | Hockley | Doctors |
| | | NFM | Kent | Health Service |
| | | NFM | Leeds | Telephone Engineers |
| | | NFM | Leeds, Seacroft | Ball cable media |
| | | NFM | Peterborough | Doctors Service |
| | | NFM | S Essex | Mobile Doctors Channel 1 |
| 166.8400 | 171.6400 | NFM | Gateshead | Doctor on Call Interlink |
| 166.8500 | 171.6500 | NFM | Bristol | Washing Machine Engineers |
| | | NFM | Cambridgeshire | Community Nurses |
| | | NFM | Dundee | Christian Salvensen |
| | | NFM | East Sussex | Doctors On Call |
| | | NFM | Edinburgh | Taxis |
| | | NFM | Haverfordwest | Gillmans Quarry |
| | | NFM | Kent | Health Service |
| | | NFM | Medway | Doctors on Call |
| | | NFM | North Humberside | Transport |
| | | NFM | Poole | Taxis |
| | | NFM | Swansea | Brisco Skip Hire Waste Disposal |
| | | NFM | Tower Hill | Doctors |
| 166.8600 | 171.6600 | NFM | Crewe | Town Council |

| Base | Mobile | Mode | Location | User and Notes |
|------|--------|------|----------|----------------|
| 166.8625 | 171.6625 | AM | Aberdeen | Rig Servicing |
| | | NFM | Coventry | Mayfair Security Channel 1 |
| | | NFM | Crewe | City Council |
| | | NFM | Edinburgh | Housing Dept. |
| | | NFM | Hillingdon | Emergency Radio System |
| | | NFM | Jersey | Pioneer Coaches |
| | | NFM | Newcastle | Taxi |
| | | NFM | Swindon | Thamesdown Buses |
| | | NFM | Wigan | Highways Department |
| | | NFM | Yorkshire | Wimpey Homes |
| 166.8735 | 171.6375 | NFM | Portsmouth | MediCall Channel 2 |
| | | NFM | St Helens | Emergency Doctors |
| 166.8750 | 171.6750 | NFM | Aberdeen | Community Repeater |
| 166.8750 | | NFM | Ayr | Carriers |
| 166.8750 | | NFM | Dundee | Doctors |
| 166.8750 | | NFM | Freethorpe | Aitchison Bros |
| 166.8750 | | NFM | Gateshead | Security |
| 166.8750 | | NFM | Grimsby | GY Buses |
| 166.8750 | | NFM | Herefordshire | Farmers |
| 166.8750 | | NFM | Irvine | Parcel Force |
| 166.8750 | | NFM | Manchester | Porter's Dairies |
| 166.8750 | | NFM | Morpeth | Council |
| 166.8750 | | NFM | Norfolk | Auto Windscreens |
| 166.8750 | | NFM | Northumberland | Farm Workers |
| 166.8750 | | NFM | Oxford | Rascal |
| 166.8750 | | NFM | Peterborough | CBS Repeater |
| 166.8750 | | NFM | Poole | Taxis |
| 166.8750 | | NFM | Preston | Dynarod |
| 166.8750 | | NFM | Rhymney Valley | Hotpoint Service Engineers |
| 166.8750 | | NFM | Worcester | Gaming Machine Repairs |
| 166.8875 | 171.6875 | NFM | Benson | A Cabs |
| | | NFM | Birmingham | Taxis |
| | | NFM | Blackpool | Council Transport |
| | | NFM | Bolton | Express Taxis |
| | | NFM | Dorset | Nightguard Security |
| | | NFM | Fleetwood | Works Department |
| | | NFM | Gateshead | Taxis |
| | | NFM | Halifax | Whitehill Taxis |
| | | NFM | Hampshire | PDSA |
| | | NFM | Lancaster | Council |
| | | NFM | Morecambe | Council |
| | | NFM | Nationwide | Community Repeater |
| | | NFM | Poole | Repeater |
| 166.8900 | 171.6900 | NFM | Heworth | Leam Taxis |
| 166.9000 | 171.7000 | NFM | Aberdeen | Aberdeen Vets |
| | | NFM | Brighton | Nynex Cablecomms |
| | | NFM | Cannock | Mr Sparks Garage |
| | | NFM | Cardiff | TNT Deliveries Channel 2 |
| | | NFM | Colchester | A.E Arnold |
| | | NFM | Doncaster | Fone-A-Car |
| | | NFM | Ely | Vets |
| | | NFM | Gloucester | Community Repeater |
| | | NFM | Jersey | Hurricaine Despatch |
| | | NFM | Oldham | Council |
| | | NFM | Worthing | Nynex Cable |

| Base | Mobile | Mode | Location | User and Notes |
|---|---|---|---|---|
| 166.9125 | 171.7125 | NFM | Bolton | Zodiac Taxis |
| | | NFM | Durham | TNT Carriers |
| | | NFM | Edinburgh | Scottish & Newcastle Security |
| | | NFM | Guernsey | States Electricity |
| | | NFM | Ipswich | British Sugar |
| | | NFM | Maidenhead | Taxis |
| | | NFM | Nationwide | TNT Transport |
| | | NFM | Newark | Taxis |
| | | NFM | Nottingham | Taxis |
| | | NFM | Peterborough | British Sugar |
| | | NFD | Sheffield | Tri-Star Security Ltd. (BULLDOG) |
| | | NFM | Stretham | N Rose Builders |
| 166.9250 | 171.7250 | NFM | Bootle | Taxis |
| | | NFM | Central Manchester | Lion Private Hire |
| | | NFM | Edinburgh | Community Repeater |
| | | NFM | Enfield | Taxis |
| | | NFM | Finchley | Taxis |
| | | NFM | Frome | Taxis |
| | | NFM | Great Yarmouth | Birds Eye Vans |
| | | NFM | Guernsey | States Electricity |
| | | NFM | Littleport | J.H.Martin |
| | | NFM | Lowestoft | Birds Eye |
| | | NFM | Newcastle | Taxi |
| | | NFM | Oldham | Roller's Private Hire |
| | | NFM | Peterborough | 3 Star Taxis |
| | | NFM | Slough | Viking Radio Cars |
| 166.9375 | 171.7375 | NFM | Aberdeen | Retail Park Security |
| | | NFM | Greenhan County | Council |
| | | NFM | Hindley | Anrich Vets |
| | | NFM | Portsmouth | Harbour Security |
| | | NFM | Trowbridge | Alpha Taxis |
| 166.9400 | 171.7400 | NFM | Newcastle | Highway Maintenance |
| 166.9500 | 171.7500 | NFM | Accrington | Doctors callout service |
| | | NFM | East Dereham | Taxis |
| | | NFM | Isle of Man | Harris Electricity |
| | | NFM | Jersey | PS Car Parks |
| | | NFM | Nationwide | BBC TV O/B Crews |
| | | NFM | Sheffield | Vending Machine Company |
| | | NFM | Surrey | Amey Roadstone M3 maintenance |
| 166.9600 | 171.7600 | NFM | Worthing | Taxi |
| 166.9625 | 171.7625 | NFM | Ashford | Invecta Taxis |
| | | NFM | Glasgow | Taxis |
| | | NFM | Hull | Taxis |
| | | NFM | Irvine | Taxi |
| | | NFM | London | Taxis |
| | | NFM | Prestwich | Taxis |
| | | NFM | Salford | Taxis |
| | | NFM | Whitefield | Blueline Private Hire |
| | | NFM | Winchester | Taxis |
| 166.9750 | 171.7750 | NFM | Barnsley | Taxis |
| | | NFM | Dyfed | Crane Hire |
| | | NFM | Edinburgh | Community Repeater |
| | | NFM | Guernsey | Channel TV Rent-a-Set |
| | | NFM | Harwich | Daves Taxis |
| | | NFM | Haverfordwest | Crane Hire |

| Base | Mobile | Mode | Location | User and Notes |
|---|---|---|---|---|
| 166.9750 | 171.7750 | NFM | Manchester | Taxis |
| | | NFM | Oxford | 001 Cars |
| 166.9750 | 171.7750 | NFM | Peterborough | Associated Adams Taxis |
| | | NFM | Poole | Knight |
| | | NFM | Portsmouth | Taxis |
| | | NFM | Sheffield | A1 Cars |
| | | NFM | Southampton | Taxis |
| 166.9875 | 171.7875 | NFM | Cambridgeshire | Haulage Co. |
| | | NFM | Dunstable | Jim & Jocks Taxis |
| | | NFM | Felixstowe | Road Haulage Co |
| | | NFM | Fleetwood | Wyre Borough Council |
| | | NFM | Glasgow | Taxis |
| | | NFM | Littleport | Sallis Bros |
| | | NFM | Luton | Silverline Taxis |
| | | NFM | Newmarket | E.F. Saltmarsh |
| | | NFM | Poole | Council |
| | | NFM | Portsmouth | Channel Satellites |
| 167.0000 | 171.8000 | NFM | Bedfordshire | Vet Service |
| | | NFM | Ellerker | F.S. & E.M. Wood Haulage |
| | | NFM | Hampshire | Dickson Bros. |
| | | NFM | Humberside | RSPCA |
| | | NFM | Leicester | Taxis |
| | | NFM | Newcastle | Delivery Firm |
| | | NFM | Newcastle | Road Maintenance |
| 167.0125 | 171.8125 | NFM | Binbrook | Nickersons Farmers |
| | | NFM | Burnley | General Hospital Security |
| | | NFM | Cardiff | Council |
| | | NFM | Cardiff | Security |
| | | NFM | Coventry | BFI Waste |
| | | NFM | Essex | Telecom Repeater |
| | | NFM | Humberside | Birds-Eye Foods |
| | | NFM | Ipswich | Yellow Taxis |
| | | NFM | Kenilworth | Brookshire Taxis |
| | | NFM | Newmarket | Suffolk Housing |
| | | NFM | Northampton | Taxis |
| | | NFM | Swindon | Swindon Bus Company |
| | | NFM | Wales | Council Contractors |
| 167.0250 | 171.8250 | NFM | Benfleet | Vehicle Recovery Co. |
| | | NFM | Birmingham Chelmsley Wd | Taxi |
| | | NFM | Bolton | Lyma Taxis |
| | | NFM | East Dereham | Fransham Farm Co. |
| | | NFM | Ely | Stopps Taxis |
| | | NFM | Glasgow | Taxis |
| | | NFM | Hull | Taxis |
| | | NFM | Leicester | Taxis |
| | | NFM | London | Kerri Cars |
| | | NFM | London | US Embassy Secret Service |
| | | NFM | Poulton | Poulton Cabs |
| | | NFM | Whiston | Britannia Taxis |
| | | NFM | Whitley Bay | Taxis |
| 167.0350 | 171.8350 | NFM | Merry Hill | Centre Traffic |
| 167.0375 | 171.8375 | NFM | Glasgow | Securiguard |
| | | NFM | Hull | Birds Eye Pea Vining |
| | | NFM | Hull | East Yorkshire Motor Services |
| | | NFM | Isle of Man | Manx Transport Services |
| | | NFM | Leicester | Security |

| Base | Mobile | Mode | Location | User and Notes |
|---|---|---|---|---|
| 167.0375 | 171.8375 | NFM | London | Burns Security |
| | | NFM | Lowestoft | Birds Eye |
| 167.0375 | 171.8375 | NFM | Newport | Hales TV Repairs |
| | | NFM | Norfolk | Council Car Parks |
| | | NFM | Swanage | Beach patrols |
| | | NFM | Wiltshire | Longleat House |
| 167.0500 | 171.8500 | NFM | Nottingham | TV Repairs |
| | | AM | Southamption | TVS |
| 167.0600 | 171.8600 | NFM | Halifax | Ziggys Taxis |
| 167.0625 | 171.8625 | NFM | Abbeywood | Taxis |
| | | AM | Bolton | Private Hire |
| | | NFM | Chelmsford | Car Recovery |
| | | AM | Humberside | Haulage Co |
| | | NFM | Kirkcaldy | Ellis Taxis |
| | | NFM | Leicester | University Security |
| | | NFM | London, south east | Taxis |
| | | NFM | Newark | Taxis |
| | | NFM | Salford | Publicans Warning/Security Net. |
| | | NFM | Sharnbrook | Associated Asphalt |
| | | NFM | Sheffield | A1 Cars Channel 2 |
| | | NFM | Sheffield | KC Cars |
| 167.0750 | 171.8750 | NFM | Chorley | Taxis |
| | | NFM | Cleveland | Peter Taxis |
| | | NFM | Forrest Hill | Taxis |
| | | NFM | Glasgow | Taxis |
| | | NFM | Guernsey | Bob Froome |
| | | NFM | Humberside | Haulage Co |
| | | NFM | Manchester | Taxi |
| | | NFM | Motherwell | Redline Cabs |
| | | NFM | North Walsham | Norfolk Cannaries |
| | | NFM | Peterborough | CBS Repeater |
| 167.0875 | 171.8875 | NFM | Birmingham | Taxi Company |
| | | NFM | Cwmbran | Aerial Riggers |
| | | NFM | Great Yarmouth | Botton Bros. |
| | | NFM | London, south west | Taxis |
| | | NFM | Perth | Taxis |
| | | NFM | Poole | Repeater |
| | | NFM | Portsmouth | Council |
| | | NFM | Somerset | Council Ops |
| | | NFM | South Humberside | Ross Foods |
| | | NFM | Swansea City | County Hall Ops |
| | | NFM | Torpoint | Taxis |
| | | NFM | Walsall | Metro Taxis |
| 167.1000 | 171.9000 | NFM | Birmingham 4 Oaks | Taxi |
| | | NFM | Brandon | F Hiam Farms |
| | | NFM | Cambridge | Ace Taxis |
| | | NFM | Cardiff | Capital Taxis |
| | | NFM | Carlisle | Cavrays Security |
| | | NFM | Eltham | Taxis |
| | | NFM | Glasgow | Taxis |
| | | NFM | Guernsey | Bluebird Taxis |
| | | NFM | Hampshire | Council |
| | | NFM | Hemel Hempsted | Minicab Co |
| | | NFM | Hempstead | R.DHaylock |
| | | NFM | Manchester | Taxis |
| | | NFM | Newcastle | Taxi |

| Base | Mobile | Mode | Location | User and Notes |
|---|---|---|---|---|
| 167.1000 | 171.9000 | NFM | Perth | Taxis |
| | | NFM | Stockton-on-Tees | Taxi Service |
| 167.1000 | 171.9000 | NFM | Thorley | M.S. Smith |
| 167.1125 | 171.9125 | NFM | Bristol | Peters Taxis |
| | | NFM | Coventry | Central Taxis |
| | | NFM | Dover | Invicta Cars |
| | | NFM | Farnham | Minicab Co |
| | | NFM | Glasgow | Taxi Company |
| | | NFM | Great Yarmouth | J & H Bunn |
| | | NFM | Guernsey | Guernsey Telecom CBS |
| | | NFM | Hull | Birds Eye |
| | | NFM | Manchester | Taxis |
| | | NFM | Rotherham | Crown Taxis |
| | | NFM | South London | National Rescue |
| | | NFM | Swansea | Taxis |
| 167.1250 | 171.9250 | NFM | Bristol | CableTel Channel 2 |
| | | NFM | Burnley | Bus Station Taxi Rank |
| | | NFM | Cardiff | Repair Company |
| | | NFM | Dudley | Skip Hire |
| | | NFM | Edinburgh | Taxis |
| | | NFM | Folkstone | Taxis |
| | | NFM | Gwent | CableTel Channel 2 |
| | | NFM | Hemel Hempsted | Minicab Co |
| | | NFM | Kings Lynn | Watlington Plant |
| | | NFM | Liverpool | Taxis |
| | | NFM | March | Ross-Produce |
| | | NFM | Milton Keynes | Pursell Taxis |
| | | NFM | Portsmouth | Dog Catcher |
| | | NFM | Scunthorpe | Transport Firm |
| | | NFM | Swansea | Brynamman Taxis |
| 167.1350 | 171.9375 | NFM | Eastbourne | Taxi |
| | | NFM | Blackburn | Golden Line Private Hire |
| | | NFM | Edinburgh | Eagle Couriers |
| | | NFM | Jersey | J H Michael Plant |
| | | NFM | Kings Lynn | Wheelers TV Services |
| | | NFM | Lancashire | Bulkers Commercial Refuse |
| | | NFM | Leicester | Taxis |
| | | NFM | Oxford | Streamline Taxis |
| | | NFM | Preston | South Ribble School Bus |
| | | NFM | Scunthorpe | Taxis |
| 167.1400 | 171.9400 | NFM | Tynemouth | Taxi |
| 167.1500 | 171.9500 | NFM | Aberdeen | Taxis |
| | | NFM | Aberystwyth | University Security |
| | | NFM | Barrow in Furness | JC Taxis |
| | | NFM | Bury | Bury Taxi Rank Ltd |
| | | NFM | Carlisle | Radio Taxis |
| | | NFM | Crewe | Taxis |
| | | NFM | Downham Market | THurlow |
| | | NFM | Guernsey | Ronez |
| | | NFM | Lancashire | South Ribble Refuse |
| | | NFM | Manchester | Taxis |
| | | NFM | Norwich | Taxis |
| | | NFM | Nottingham | Taxi |
| | | NFM | Oldham | Startex Cabs |
| | | NFM | Portsmouth | Repeater |
| | | NFM | St. Neots | T & R Taxis |

| Base | Mobile | Mode | Location | User and Notes |
|---|---|---|---|---|
| 167.1500 | 171.9500 | NFM | West Midlands | ABS Taxis |
| | | NFM | Wolverhampton | Taxi |
| 167.1500 | 171.9500 | NFM | Worlington | Tuckwell |
| 167.1600 | 171.9600 | NFM | Newport, Gwent | Servu Taxis |
| 167.1625 | 171.9625 | NFM | Central London | Couriers |
| | | NFM | Coventry | Skyline Taxis |
| | | NFM | Dover | Victory Cars |
| | | NFM | Ipswich | Taxis |
| | | NFM | Keswick | Ambulance |
| | | NFM | Newport | Newport Taxis |
| | | NFM | Norfolk | ICL |
| | | NFM | Sheffield | City Taxis |
| | | NFM | Swindon | Starlight Taxis |
| | | NFM | Wigan | Cable TV Engineers |
| | | NFM | Wrexham | Prostigo Taxis |
| | | NFM | Newcastle | Taxi |
| 167.1750 | 171.9750 | NFM | Bexley Heath | Taxis |
| | | FM | Cambridge | Taxi |
| | | NFM | Cheshire | Choice Taxis |
| | | NFM | Glasgow | Taxis |
| | | NFM | Guernsey | R. J. Le Huray |
| | | NFM | London (East) | Couriers |
| | | NFM | Manchester | Taxis |
| | | NFM | Norfolk | ICL |
| | | NFM | Rochdale | Tiger Cars |
| | | NFM | Sidcup | Taxis |
| 167.1850 | 171.9850 | NFM | Newport, Gwent | Dial-a-cab Taxis |
| 167.1875 | 171.9875 | NFM | Bolton | North West Cars |
| | | NFM | Brownhills | Bee-Jays Taxis |
| | | NFM | Colchester | A1 Taxis |
| | | NFM | Coventry | Taxi |
| | | NFM | Glasgow | Mac Cars |
| | | NFM | Great Yarmouth | Taxi |
| | | NFM | Immingham | Oaklands Taxis |
| | | NFM | Lancaster | Council Roads Dept |
| | | NFM | Macclesfield | Taxis |
| | | NFM | Manchester | Midway Taxis |
| | | NFM | Middleton | Swan Cars |
| | | NFM | Milton Keynes | Raffles Taxis |
| | | NFM | Scarborough | Taxis |
| | | NFM | Sheffield | A2B Car Hire |
| | | NFM | Swindon | Handy Gas Shop |
| 167.2000 | 172.0000 | NFM | Ashford | United Taxis |
| | | NFM | Barrow | Mobile Community Watch |
| | | NFM | Bristol | Festival of the Sea (Security) |
| | | NFM | Dunstable | Glider Taxis |
| | | NFM | Edinburgh | Burtons Security |
| | | NFM | Fleetwood | Taxis |
| | | NFM | Jersey | Home James |
| | | NFM | Lancaster | Security Service |
| | | NFM | Le-Mans | Halya Sport Team |
| | | NFM | Leicester | Taxis |
| | | NFM | Midland | Hutchings |
| | | NFM | Morecambe | Security Service |
| | | NFM | Nationwide | PMR Short Term Hire |
| | | NFM | Nottinghamshire | Ambulance Service |

| Base | Mobile | Mode | Location | User and Notes |
|------|--------|------|----------|----------------|
| 167.2000 | 172.0000 | NFM | Peterborough | Burghley-House Steeplechase |
| | | NFM | Thetford | Abbey Taxis |
| 167.2125 | 172.0125 | NFM | Belfast | CityCabs |
| | | NFM | Chelmsford | A1 Demolition |
| | | NFM | Chelmsford | Crest Dairies |
| | | NFM | Cumbernauld | Yellow Star Taxis (Yellow) |
| | | NFM | Edinburgh Airport | Stock Control |
| | | NFM | Glasgow | Taxis |
| | | NFM | Hull | Taxis |
| | | NFM | Jersey | Immigration Department |
| | | NFM | Manchester | Taxis |
| | | NFM | Newcastle | Silver Cars |
| | | NFM | Newmarket | McCourts |
| | | NFM | Norfolk | ICL |
| | | NFM | Oldham | Home James Taxis |
| | | NFM | Rayleigh | Taxis |
| 167.2250 | 172.0250 | NFM | Coventry | Taxi |
| | | NFM | Downham Market | B.W. Mack |
| | | NFM | Holbeach | Plant Hire |
| | | NFM | Hull | Taxis |
| | | NFM | Humberside | Haulage Co |
| | | NFM | Jersey | Waverley Coaches |
| | | NFM | Mendips | Business Post |
| | | NFM | Midlands | Yellow Cabs |
| | | NFM | Royston | Meltax |
| | | NFM | Stockton-on-Tees | Taxi Service |
| | | NFM | Thetford | Chips Taxis |
| | | NFM | Worksop | Bee Line Taxis |
| 167.2375 | 172.0375 | NFM | Aberdeen | Taxis |
| | | NFM | Ashton | Taxis |
| | | NFM | Chadderton | Chadderton Cars |
| | | NFM | Dartford | Black Cabs |
| | | NFM | Felixstowe | BW Mack |
| | | NFM | Glasgow | Taxis |
| | | NFM | Guernsey | Total Oil |
| | | NFM | Halifax | AA Taxis |
| | | NFM | Hampshire | Vets |
| | | NFM | Haverhill | Chequer Cabs |
| | | NFM | Huntingdon | Pete's Taxis |
| | | NFM | Leicester | Asda Security |
| | | NFM | Norfolk | ICL |
| | | NFM | Oxford | Black Cabs |
| | | NFM | Swansea | Diamond Cabs |
| 167.2500 | 172.0500 | NFM | Aberdeen | Taxis |
| | | NFM | Bolton | Pal Cars Taxis |
| | | NFM | Elvington | Garrowby Estate Farms |
| | | NFM | Guernsey | Post Office |
| | | NFM | Hull | Goldstar Taxis |
| | | NFM | Newtown | Taxis |
| | | NFM | Plymouth | Armada Taxis |
| | | NFM | Powys | Thomas Jones (Vet) |
| | | NFM | Slough | Interpoint Taxis |
| | | NFM | Swansea | Fishwicks Taxis |
| | | NFM | Upton | Road Runner Taxis |
| | | NFM | Whiston | Diamond Taxis Ltd |

| Base | Mobile | Mode | Location | User and Notes |
|------|--------|------|----------|----------------|
| 167.2600 | 172.0600 | NFM | Worcester | Central Taxis |
| 167.2625 | 172.0625 | NFM | Belfast | Belfast City Council |
| | | NFM | Blackpool | J Cabs |
| | | NFM | Guernsey | Guernsey Bus |
| | | NFM | Haverhill | Havtaxi |
| | | NFM | Milton Keynes | Embassy Cars |
| | | NFM | Portsmouth | Blue Light Cabs |
| | | NFM | Reading | 1st City Cars |
| | | NFM | Sheffield | Paymaster Ltd. |
| | | NFM | Stevenage | Freewheelers |
| | | NFM | West Midlands | Fruit Machine Repairs |
| 167.2750 | 172.0750 | NFM | Aberdeen | Office Security |
| | | NFM | Alloa | Taxis |
| | | NFM | Birmingham Moseley | Taxi |
| | | NFM | Bolton | Red Rose Taxis |
| | | NFM | Brighton | Southern Taxis |
| | | NFM | Gt. Stokely | H. Raby & Sons |
| | | NFM | Hockwold Cum Wilton | J. Denney Taxis |
| | | NFM | Hull | Taxis |
| | | NFM | Huntingdon | H. Raby & Sons |
| | | NFM | Jersey | States Motor Traffic Department |
| | | NFM | Nationwide | TNT Transport |
| | | NFM | Portsmouth | Taxis |
| | | NFM | Sheffield | Foundry maintenance |
| | | NFM | Southend on Sea | Associated Radio Cars |
| | | NFM | Sutton | Darby Plant |
| | | NFM | Weymouth | Taxi Co |
| 167.2875 | 172.0875 | NFM | Abingdon | Autotaxis |
| | | NFM | Burnley | AK Taxis |
| | | NFM | Cardiff | Taxis |
| | | NFM | Chesterfield | Central Taxis |
| | | NFM | Dalton in Furness | Taxi |
| | | NFM | East Dereham | Breckland Taxis |
| | | NFM | Eastleigh | Taxis |
| | | NFM | Falkirk | Police |
| | | NFM | Glasgow | Taxis |
| | | NFM | Hampshire | Taxis |
| | | NFM | Haverfordwest | Rocky's Taxis |
| | | NFM | Leicester | Taxis |
| | | NFM | London, south | Taxis |
| | | NFM | London, west | Couriers |
| | | NFM | Montrose | Taxis |
| | | NFM | Norfolk | ICL |
| | | NFM | Peterborough | CBS Repeater |
| | | NFM | Plymouth | Chequars Cabs |
| | | NFM | Wrexham | Ace Taxis |
| 167.3000 | 172.1000 | NFM | Blackburn | Super Line Private Hire |
| | | NFM | Gateshead | Builders Merchant |
| | | NFM | Kings Lynn | R.D. Carter |
| | | NFM | Luton | Black Cabs |
| | | NFM | Norfolk | ICL |
| | | NFM | Oxford | Radiotaxis |
| | | NFM | Sheffield | Toby Taxis |
| | | NFM | Swindon | Taxis |

| Base | Mobile | Mode | Location | User and Notes |
|---|---|---|---|---|
| 167.3125 | 172.1125 | NFM | Aberdeen | Office Security |
| | | NFM | Brownhills | Taxi |
| | | NFM | Doncaster | Race Course |
| | | NFM | Glasgow | Taxis |
| | | NFM | Newark | Taxis |
| | | NFM | Southampton | Taxis |
| 167.3250 | 172.1250 | NFM | Astley | Astley Van Hire |
| | | NFM | Barrow in Furness | Coastline Taxis |
| | | NFM | Bedford | Bedfordia Farms |
| | | NFM | Central London | Taxis/Couriers |
| | | NFM | Chatteris | Graves & Graves |
| | | NFM | Dartford | Taxis |
| | | NFM | Forest Hill | Taxi |
| | | NFM | Glasgow | Taxis |
| | | NFM | Ipswich | Robin Hood Taxis |
| | | NFM | Manchester | Astley Van Hire |
| | | AM | Shoreham | Shoreham Airport Taxis |
| | | NFM | Southend | Doctors night callout |
| | | NFM | Stirling | Police |
| | | NFM | Swansea | A and M Taxis |
| 167.3375 | 172.1375 | NFM | Biggleswade | Whitbread Farms |
| | | FM | Cambridge | Parcel Carriers |
| | | NFM | Cardiff | Taxis |
| | | NFM | Glasgow | Taxis |
| | | NFM | Heywood | Eagle Cars |
| | | NFM | Stowmarket | Taxi |
| | | NFM | Stretford | New Moon Private Hire |
| | | NFM | Warwickshire | Farmers |
| 167.3500 | 170.1500 | AM | Aberdeen | Taxi |
| | | NFM | Blackpool | R. Walker & Co |
| | | NFM | Burnham | Burnham Radio Cabs |
| | | NFM | Cornwall | English China Clay |
| | | NFM | Coventry | Coventry Aerial Services |
| | | NFM | Eccles | Taxis |
| | | NFM | Fareham | Taxis |
| | | NFM | Fordham | Allen Newport |
| | | NFM | Hampshire | Wayne Haverson |
| | | NFM | Hull | Taxis |
| | | NFM | Jersey | Regal Construction |
| | | NFM | Manchester | Taxis |
| | | NFM | Preston | Taxis |
| | | NFM | Rochdale | Central Taxis |
| | | NFM | Salford | Taxis |
| | | NFM | Stockport | Taxis |
| | | NFM | Stoke-on-Trent | Taxis |
| | | NFM | Tamworth | Taxis |
| | | NFM | Whiston | Diamond Taxis Ltd |
| | | NFM | Whittlesey | Luxicabs |
| 167.3600 | 172.1600 | NFM | Newport, Gwent | Caxton Taxis |
| 167.3625 | 172.1625 | NFM | Bolton | Murtax Taxis |
| | | NFM | Bristol | Paramedics |
| | | NFM | Coventry | City centre store detectives |
| | | NFM | Guernsey | Community Repeater 2 |
| | | NFM | Halifax | Beeline Taxis |
| | | NFM | Hull | Taxis |
| | | NFM | London, east | Taxis |

| Base | Mobile | Mode | Location | User and Notes |
|------|--------|------|----------|----------------|
| 167.3625 | 172.1625 | NFM | Plymouth | Taxis |
|          |          | NFM | Soham | Greens of Soham |
| 167.3750 | 172.1750 | NFM | Aberdeen | Tyre Service |
|          |          | NFM | Chippenham | Taxis |
|          |          | NFM | Eastbourne | Taxi |
|          |          | AM  | Manchester | Taxifone Taxis |
|          |          | NFM | Nationwide | Comet Television |
|          |          | NFM | Northumberland | Open Cast Site |
|          |          | NFM | Poole | Repeater |
|          |          | NFM | Southampton | Taxis |
|          |          | NFM | Winchester | Council |
|          |          | NFM | Wrexham | Regal Taxis |
| 167.3875 | 172.1875 | NFM | Aberdeen | Taxis |
|          |          | NFM | Cardiff | Plumbing Company |
|          |          | NFM | Derby | Taxi |
|          |          | NFM | Devizes | Devizes Taxis |
|          |          | NFM | Glasgow | Taxis |
|          |          | NFM | Hull | Taxis |
|          |          | NFM | Kettering | KLM Taxis |
|          |          | NFM | Manchester | Taxis |
|          |          | NFM | Newport | CableTel Channel 1 |
|          |          | NFM | Norfolk | ICL |
|          |          | NFM | Pontypool | Red Dragon Taxis |
|          |          | NFM | Salford | Swan Private Hire |
|          |          | NFM | Sheffield | TCS Taxis |
| 167.3900 | 167.3900 | NFM | Newport, Gwent | BT Engineers |
| 167.4000 | 172.2000 | NFM | Birmingham Erdington | Taxi |
|          |          | NFM | Colchester | Paxmans Diesels |
|          |          | NFM | Hampshire | Cascade Cars |
|          |          | NFM | Leicester | Taxis |
|          |          | NFM | Leigh on Sea | Kelly's Radio |
|          |          | NFM | Manchester | Taxis |
|          |          | NFM | Norfolk | Associated Leisure |
|          |          | NFM | Oldham | Bluebird Private Hire |
|          |          | NFM | Perth | Taxis |
| 167.4125 | 172.2125 | NFM | Aberdeen | Estate Security |
|          |          | NFM | Bury | Harvey's Taxis |
|          |          | NFM | Dalmellington | Open Cast Mining |
|          |          | NFM | Dalton | Marj's Cars |
|          |          | NFM | Edinburgh | Doctors Service |
|          |          | NFM | Glasgow | Taxis |
|          |          | NFM | Grimsby | M.D. Cars |
|          |          | NFM | Leicester | Taxis |
|          |          | NFM | Manchester | Taxis |
|          |          | NFM | Newark | Taxis |
|          |          | NFM | Norfolk | ICL |
|          |          | NFM | Oxford | City Taxis |
|          |          | NFM | Portsmouth | Taxis |
|          |          | NFM | Sheffield | Direct Taxis |
|          |          | NFM | Stoke on Trent | Haulage Company |
| 167.4200 | 172.2200 | NFM | Eastbourne | Taxi |

| Base | Mobile | Mode | Location | User and Notes |
|---|---|---|---|---|
| 167.4250 | 172.2250 | NFM | Aberdeen | Taxis |
| | | NFM | Bloxwich | Abba Taxis |
| | | NFM | Coventry | Trinity Street Taxis |
| | | NFM | Downham Market | B.W. Mack |
| | | NFM | Glasgow | Taxi Company |
| | | NFM | Huntingdon | R. Brading |
| | | NFM | Jersey | HM Prison  La Moye |
| | | NFM | Jersey | Jersey States Repeater |
| | | NFM | Jersey | Lucas Bros. Farm Shop |
| | | NFM | Jersey | Ransom Garden Centre |
| | | NFM | Jersey | States Electronics Dept. |
| | | NFM | Larbert | Plough Taxis |
| | | NFM | Norwich | J.B. Green |
| | | NFM | Nottingham | Taxis |
| | | NFM | Plymouth | Cotton's Taxis |
| | | NFM | Sheffield | Tram Works Construction |
| 167.4375 | 172.2375 | NFM | Airdrie | Taxis |
| | | NFM | Cleveland | City Taxis |
| | | NFM | Coventry | BFI Waste |
| | | NFM | Glasgow | Taxis |
| | | NFM | Montrose | Taxis |
| | | NFM | Newport | French's TV Repairs |
| | | NFM | Norwich | C Wace |
| | | NFM | Steeple Bumpstead | Shore Hall Estates |
| | | NFM | Tywyn, North Wales | Taxis |
| 167.4500 | 172.2500 | NFM | Abingdon | Newtop Taxis |
| | | NFM | Edinburgh | Taxis |
| | | NFM | Knebworth | Vendustrial Ltd |
| | | NFM | Manchester | White Line Taxis |
| | | NFM | Musselborough | Taxis |
| | | NFM | Newmarket | Chilcotts Taxis |
| | | NFM | Norfolk | ICL |
| | | NFM | Sheffield | Alpha Taxis |
| | | NFM | Southsea | Pier Security |
| 167.4625 | 172.2625 | NFM | Aberdeen | Crane Hire |
| | | NFM | Bristol | Works Dispatch |
| | | NFM | Eastbourne | TNT |
| | | NFM | Eastbourne | Taxi |
| | | NFM | Gt. Yarmouth | Birds Eye Vans |
| | | NFM | London (east) | Taxis/Couriers |
| | | NFM | Lowestoft | Birds Eye |
| | | NFM | Manchester | District Council |
| | | NFM | Nationwide | TNT |
| | | NFM | Nationwide | Tesco Supermarkets |
| | | NFM | Newport | TNT Deliveries Channel 1 |
| | | NFM | Oldham | Security |
| | | NFM | Peterborough | Tesco |
| | | NFM | Sheffield | Alpha Cars Channel 1 |
| | | NFM | Southampton | Taxis |
| | | NFM | Warminster | Taxis |
| 167.4750 | 172.2750 | NFM | Ancoats | Chariots |
| | | NFM | Bristol | Shell Gas Bottle Delivery |
| | | NFM | Burton, Staffs | Taxi |
| | | NFM | Liverpool | Car Breakdown Recovery |
| | | NFM | London | National Radio Cars |
| | | NFM | Nottingham, Hucknall | TC Taxis |

| Base | Mobile | Mode | Location | User and Notes |
|------|--------|------|----------|----------------|
| 167.4750 | 172.2750 | NFM | Poole | Repeater |
| | | NFM | Sheffield | Mercury Cars Channel 2 |
| 167.4800 | 172.2800 | NFM | Leeds Seacroft | Taxi |
| 167.4857 | 172.2875 | NFM | Eastbourne | Borough Council |
| | | NFM | Aberdeen | Taxis |
| | | NFM | Edinburgh | Taxis |
| | | NFM | Glasgow | Forge Shopping Mall Security |
| | | NFM | Grampian | Transport |
| | | NFM | Leicester | Taxis |
| | | NFM | Newport | Red Base Taxis |
| | | NFM | Portsmouth | Council |
| | | NFM | Ryton | A1 Taxis |
| | | NFM | Snaefell, Isle of Man | Repeater |
| 167.5000 | 172.3000 | NFM | Aberdeen | Farm |
| | | NFM | Barway | Shropshire Produce |
| | | NFM | Blackpool | Streamline Taxis |
| | | NFM | Brighton | John Jug Ltd |
| | | NFM | Charminster | Bee Cabs |
| | | NFM | Hemingbrough | AIS Brown Butlin Chemicals |
| | | NFM | Rochford | Taxis |
| | | NFM | Saltdean | Taxi |
| | | NFM | Shipham | William Moorfoot |
| | | NFM | Swindon | Link Taxis |
| 167.5100 | 172.3100 | NFM | Cwmbran, Gwent | Chauffeur Taxis |
| 167.5125 | 172.3125 | NFM | Blackley | Avenue Cars |
| | | NFM | Jersey | HM Customs & Excise Channel 5 |
| | | NFM | Manchester | Taxis |
| | | NFM | Newcastle | Taxi |
| | | NFM | Norfolk | ICL |
| | | NFM | Worthing | Nynex Cable |
| 167.5200 | 172.3200 | NFM | Birkenhead | Cavalier Taxis |
| 167.5250 | 172.3250 | NFM | Bradford | Taxi Blackcabs |
| | | NFM | Cambridge | Able Taxis |
| | | NFM | Edinburgh | Phone Line Banking |
| | | NFM | Harlow | Anglie Cable (Techs) |
| | | NFM | Huntingdon | A.E. Abraham |
| | | NFM | Jersey, Fort Regent | Leisure Complex Ch3 |
| | | NFM | Letchworth | Mick's Taxis |
| | | NFM | Norwich | Five Star Taxis |
| | | NFM | Nottingham | Taxis |
| | | NFM | Salford | Taxis |
| 167.5375 | 172.3375 | NFM | Aberdeen | Farm |
| | | NFM | Bury | Peel Cars |
| | | NFM | Cornwall | English China Clay |
| | | NFM | Walsall Wood | Barons Taxis |
| 167.5400 | 172.3400 | NFM | Newcastle | Taxi |
| 167.5500 | 172.3500 | NFM | Bradford-on-Avon | Taxis |
| | | NFM | Colchester | Abbeygate Taxis |
| | | NFM | Grimsby | "Evening Telegraph" |
| | | NFM | Jersey | Fort Regent Leisure Centre |
| | | NFM | London | Taxis |
| | | NFM | Portsmouth | City Wide Taxis |
| | | NFM | Salford | Briffin Cars |
| | | NFM | Weymouth | Taxis |

| Base | Mobile | Mode | Location | User and Notes |
|------|--------|------|----------|----------------|
| 167.5625 | 172.3625 | NFM | Aberdeen | Estate |
| | | NFM | Blackburn | Super B Private Hire |
| | | NFM | Cheshire | Station Cars |
| | | NFM | Gillingham | Taxis |
| | | NFM | Glasgow | Taxis |
| | | NFM | Grangemouth | Taxi Owners Association |
| | | NFM | Guernsey | Sunshine Cabs |
| | | NFM | Isle of Wight | Taxis |
| | | NFM | March | G.E. Tribe |
| | | AM | Nottingham | Taxis |
| | | NFM | Nottingham | Toton Plant Hire |
| | | NFM | Plymouth | Key Cab Taxis |
| | | NFM | Salford | Dolphin Cars |
| | | NFM | Worthing | Taxis |
| 167.5750 | 172.3750 | NFM | Coventry | Sky Blue Radio Taxis |
| | | NFM | Dumfries | Taxis |
| | | NFM | Erith | Taxis |
| | | NFM | Essex | Taxis |
| | | NFM | London | Courier |
| | | NFM | March | David Johnson Farms |
| | | NFM | Newcastle | Taxi |
| | | NFM | Peterborough | CBS Repeater |
| | | NFM | Salford | Taxis |
| | | NFM | Southampton | Taxis |
| | | NFM | Worthing | Taxis |
| 167.5875 | 172.3875 | NFM | Bedford | Riverside Taxis |
| | | NFM | Elvington | Inturf |
| | | NFM | Glasgow | Taxis |
| | | NFM | Leeds, Seacroft | Bell cable media installers |
| | | NFM | Leicester | Taxis |
| | | NFM | Sheffield | RSPCA |
| | | NFM | Swinton | Swintax |
| | | NFM | Wakefield | Bell |
| 167.6000 | 172.4000 | NFM | Cumbernauld | Central Cab Co. |
| | | NFM | East Dereham | Venture Taxis |
| | | NFM | Glasgow | Taxis |
| | | NFM | Ipswich | Peter Green |
| | | NFM | Manchester | Taxis |
| | | NFM | Salford | Central Private Hire |
| | | NFM | Telford | Car Repairs |
| 167.6125 | 172.4125 | NFM | Bedford | Windshield Enterprise |
| | | NFM | Blantyre | Mac Cars |
| | | NFM | Glasgow | Taxis |
| | | NFM | Grimsby | Skip Co |
| | | NFM | London | Taxis |
| | | NFM | Southampton | Security co for army property |
| | | NFM | Stevenage | Amber Cars |
| | | NFM | Warwickshire | Farmers |
| 167.6250 | 172.4250 | NFM | Aberdeen | Deeside Shop Fitters |
| | | NFM | Barway | Shropshire Produce |
| | | NFM | Blackburn | Blackburn's Taxi Ranks |
| | | NFM | Burton, Staffs | Taxi |
| | | NFM | Glasgow | Taxis |
| | | NFM | Ipswich | Surveyors |
| | | NFM | Isle of Wight | Newport Council |
| | | NFM | Lothian and Borders | East Lothian District Council |

| Base | Mobile | Mode | Location | User and Notes |
|---|---|---|---|---|
| 167.6250 | 172.4250 | NFM | Perth | Tayside Shopper Fitters |
| | | NFM | Rochford | Andrews Taxis |
| | | NFM | Shropshire | Barkway Ely |
| | | NFM | Shropshire | Shropshire Produce |
| | | NFM | Walton | Taxis |
| | | NFM | Warwickshire | Farmers |
| 167.6375 | 172.4375 | NFM | Breckland | Council House Repairs |
| | | NFM | Glasgow | Taxis |
| | | NFM | Lees | Cartax |
| | | NFM | Manchester | Taxis |
| | | NFM | Nottingham | Taxis |
| | | NFM | Suffolk | Rumbelows Television |
| | | NFM | Trowbridge | Ace's Taxis |
| 167.6500 | 172.4500 | NFM | Aldershot | Taxi Co |
| | | NFM | Bristol | Hemmings Waste |
| | | NFM | Edinburgh | Airport Taxis |
| | | NFM | Glasgow | Taxi Company |
| | | NFM | Humberside | Mechanics |
| | | NFM | London | Compass Curious |
| | | NFM | Preston | VIP Cabs |
| | | NFM | Southampton | Randals Taxis |
| | | NFM | Welwyn | Target Cars |
| | | NFM | Wickford | Carter & Ward |
| | | NFM | Wirral | Eastham Cabs |
| 167.6625 | 172.4625 | NFM | Colchester | Smythe Motors |
| | | NFM | Glasgow | Taxis |
| | | NFM | Leicester | Taxis |
| | | NFM | Widnes | Taxis |
| 167.6750 | 172.4750 | NFM | Guernsey | Central Cabs |
| | | AM | Ipswich | Taxis |
| | | NFM | Larbert | Taxis |
| | | NFM | Perth | Perth & Kinross Council |
| | | NFM | Pontypool | Real Gwent Taxis |
| | | NFM | Portsmouth | Taxis |
| | | NFM | Rochdale | Cozy Cars |
| | | NFM | Scunthorpe | British Steel |
| | | NFM | Stevenage | Rowleys Taxis |
| | | NFM | Warwickshire | Farmers |
| 167.6875 | 172.4875 | NFM | Aberdeen | Slatters |
| | | NFM | Buxton | Taxi |
| | | NFM | Cardiff | Taxis |
| | | NFM | Dunstable | Threeways Taxis |
| | | NFM | London, Geden Park | Koil Mine Cabs |
| | | NFM | Medway | Taxis |
| | | NFM | Sale | Trafford Private Hire |
| | | NFM | Trowbridge | Taxis |
| 167.7000 | 172.5000 | AM | Aberdeen | Security |
| | | NFM | Ancoats | Town Cars |
| | | NFM | Glasgow | East Kilbride Taxis |
| | | NFM | Hull | Willingham's Vehicle Recovery |
| | | NFM | Littleport | H Thompson |
| | | NFM | London | Olympic Cars |
| | | NFM | London, Finchley | Tally Ho Cars |
| | | NFM | Manchester | Taxis |
| | | NFM | Peacehaven | Taxi |
| | | NFM | Peterborough | Bell CableMedia |

| Base | Mobile | Mode | Location | User and Notes |
|------|--------|------|----------|----------------|
| 167.7000 | 172.5000 | NFM | Peterborough | Cablevision |
| | | NFM | Portsmouth | Taxis |
| | | NFM | Ramsgate | Kent Medical Services |
| | | NFM | Sheffield | Regency Cars |
| | | NFM | Southampton | Taxis |
| 167.7125 | 172.5125 | NFM | Attlebridge | Hales Containers |
| | | NFM | Cambridge | Jakubowski Builders |
| | | NFM | Chester | Doctors |
| | | NFM | London (Heathrow) | Heathrow Luxury Cars |
| | | NFM | Prestwich | Magnum Private Hire |
| 167.7250 | 172.5250 | NFM | Barton | Booth transport |
| | | NFM | Gt. Yarmouth | Birds Eye |
| | | NFM | Hampshire | Tesco |
| | | NFM | Kilburn | Taxis |
| | | NFM | Kirkcaldy | Taxis |
| | | NFM | Leicester | Taxis |
| | | NFM | Lowestoft | Birds Eye |
| | | NFM | Notingham | Co-Op TV Service |
| | | NFM | Poole | Repeater |
| | | NFM | Reading | ABC Taxis |
| | | NFM | Stockport | Taxis |
| | | NFM | Stourbridge | Taxis |
| | | NFM | Tamworth, Staffs | Taxi |
| 167.7274 | 172.5375 | NFM | Seaford | Taxi |
| 167.7300 | 172.5300 | NFM | Birkenhead | Park Taxis |
| 167.7350 | 172.7350 | NFM | Ayr | Taxi |
| 167.7370 | 172.5370 | NFM | Ashford | Binmen (EF) |
| 167.7375 | 172.5375 | NFM | Bournemouth | Council Electricians |
| | | NFM | Dover | Skips |
| | | NFM | Hull | Taxis |
| | | NFM | Manchester | Veterinary Surgeon |
| 167.7400 | 172.5400 | NFM | Newcastle | Grosvenor Taxis |
| 167.7500 | 172.5500 | NFM | Dundee | Taxis |
| | | NFM | Hull | Taxis |
| | | NFM | Lowestoft | Oulton Radio Taxis |
| | | NFM | Nottingham | Yellow Cabs |
| | | NFM | West Midlands | Wheelchair Cabs |
| | | NFM | Wirral | New Brighton Cabs |
| 167.7600 | 172.5600 | NFM | Cumbernauld | Taxis |
| 167.7625 | 172.5625 | NFM | Birmingham | Taxis |
| | | NFM | Bolton | Manor Taxis |
| | | NFM | Cumbernauld | Cita Taxis (Cita) |
| | | NFM | Dunstable | Cannon Cars |
| | | NFM | Gateshead | Council |
| | | NFM | Glasgow | Taxis |
| | | NFM | Halifax | Pennine Taxis |
| | | NFM | Southampton | Hospital Transport |
| | | NFM | Walsall | Taxis |
| 167.7750 | 172.5750 | AM | Boston | Star Taxis |
| | | NFM | Coventry | Bills Taxis |
| | | NFM | Exmouth | Discount Cars |
| | | NFM | Hull | Taxis |
| | | NFM | Manchester | Taxis |
| | | NFM | Norwich | Cablevision |
| | | NFM | Taplow | Burnham Couriers |
| | | NFM | Welwyn Garden City | Industrial Services |

| Base | Mobile | Mode | Location | User and Notes |
|------|--------|------|----------|----------------|
| 167.7750 | 172.5750 | NFM | Woburn | Speedwell Farms |
| | | NFM | York | Taxi |
| 167.7850 | 172.5985 | NFM | Ayr | Taxi |
| 167.7875 | 172.5875 | NFM | Basildon | Ace Taxi Group |
| | | NFM | Birmingham | Taxi |
| | | NFM | Eccles | New Lyle Cars |
| | | NFM | Edinburgh | Falcon Delivery |
| | | NFM | Jersey | Jersey States Housing Dept. |
| | | NFM | Lincoln | Taxis |
| | | NFM | Manchester | Taxis |
| | | NFM | Peterborough | ABBA Taxis |
| | | NFM | Rochdale | Town Cars |
| | | NFM | Saddleworth | Taxis |
| | | NFM | St Andrews | Jay Taxis |
| 167.8000 | 172.6000 | AM | Aberdeen | Security |
| | | NFM | Blackburn | Lancs Private Hire |
| | | NFM | Burnley | Taxis |
| | | NFM | Cambridge | United Taxis |
| | | NFM | Coventry | T White Skips |
| | | NFM | Cumbernauld | Taxi |
| | | NFM | Dovercourt | Starling Taxis |
| | | NFM | Glasgow | Taxis |
| | | AM | Grimsby | Revels Taxis |
| | | NFM | Leicester | Slot Machines |
| | | NFM | Manchester | Cresta Cars |
| | | NFM | Nottingham | Amusement Machine Servicing |
| | | NFM | Oldham | Britannia Cars |
| | | NFM | Portsmouth | Coop TV Service |
| | | NFM | Sheffield | Eagle Cars |
| | | NFM | Weymouth | Taxi Co |
| | | NFM | Wirral | 50-50 Cabs |
| 167.8100 | 172.6100 | NFM | Cwymbran, Gwent | Gwent Taxis |
| 167.8125 | 172.6125 | NFM | Alloa | Taxis |
| | | NFM | Bath | Abbey Taxis |
| | | NFM | Bedford | M.W. Ward |
| | | NFM | Bootle | Taxis |
| | | FM | Cambridge | BT Line Repair Team |
| | | NFM | Glasgow | Taxis |
| | | NFM | Manchester, Levenshulme | Kings Private Hire |
| | | NFM | Watlington | Watlington Plant Hire |
| | | NFM | Westmount, Jersey | CSL Repeater |
| | | NFM | Westmount, Jersey | De La Haye Plant Ltd |
| | | NFM | Westmount, Jersey | Fuel Supplies Ltd |
| | | NFM | Westmount, Jersey | Keith Prowse Tours |
| | | NFM | Westmount, Jersey | MacLead & Allan |
| | | NFM | Westmount, Jersey | Ronez Ltd |
| 167.8250 | 172.6250 | NFM | Bolton | Tele Taxis |
| | | NFM | Bristol | Downend Taxis |
| | | NFM | Edinburgh | Taxis |
| | | NFM | Grangemouth | Tartan Line Radio Cabs (Tartan) |
| | | NFM | Ipswich | Robin Hood Taxis |
| | | NFM | Liverpool | Cavalier Taxis |
| | | NFM | Tamworth | Polesworth Cars |

| Base | Mobile | Mode | Location | User and Notes |
|---|---|---|---|---|
| 167.8375 | 172.6375 | NFM | Manchester | Taxis |
| | | NFM | Polesworth | Polesworth Cabs |
| | | NFM | Rochdale | Milnrow Cars |
| | | NFM | Tynemouth | Taxis |
| 167.8400 | 172.6400 | NFM | Newcastle | Taxi |
| 167.8500 | 172.6500 | NFM | Bexley Heath | Taxis |
| | | AM | Blackpool | Ace Cabs |
| | | NFM | Bridlington | Q Cars |
| | | NFM | Cambridge | Clearaway |
| | | NFM | Cardiff | Amber Taxis |
| | | NFM | Cleveleys | Ace Cabs |
| | | AM | Ipswich | Taxis |
| | | NFM | Nottinghamshire | Clumber Park |
| 167.8625 | 172.6625 | NFM | Leicester | Taxis |
| | | NFM | Manchester | Taxis |
| | | NFM | Middleton | Star Taxis |
| | | NFM | Milton Keynes | City Bus Ltd |
| | | NFM | Ormskirk | Taxis |
| | | NFM | Sheffield | Mercury Taxis |
| | | NFM | Swansea | E and G Taxis |
| | | NFM | Wiltshire | Bus Inspectors & Mechanics |
| | | NFM | Worthing | Taxis |
| 167.8750 | 172.6750 | FM | Pampisford, Cambs | Solapark Building Yard |
| | | NFM | Plymouth | Taxis |
| | | NFM | Scunthorpe | Taxis |
| | | AM | Sheffield | DB Taxis |
| 167.8875 | 172.6875 | NFM | Atherton | J & K Taxis |
| | | NFM | Chelmsford | Trade Comms |
| | | NFM | Cheshire | Whites Taxis |
| | | NFM | Congleton | Taxi |
| | | NFM | Eastleigh | Taxis |
| | | NFM | Glasgow | Taxi Company |
| | | AM | Ipswich | Taxis |
| | | NFM | Liverpool | Dock Taxis |
| | | NFM | Oldham | Radio Cars |
| | | NFM | Sheffield | Airport Express |
| 167.9000 | 172.7000 | NFM | Heywood | Heywood Cars |
| | | NFM | Jersey | HM Customs & Excise Channel 1 |
| | | NFM | Leicester | Windscreen Repairs |
| | | NFM | Northampton | Taxis |
| | | NFM | Prescot | All Black Cabs Ltd |
| | | NFM | Welwyn Garden City | Garden City Taxis |
| | | NFM | Winton | Taxis |
| 167.9125 | 172.7125 | NFM | Dalton in Furness | Taxi |
| | | NFM | Grain | Geoffrey Clark |
| | | AM | Ipswich | Taxis |
| | | NFM | London | Skip Hire |
| | | NFM | Newport | Dragon Taxis Channel 1 |
| | | NFM | Royston | B & B Taxis |
| | | NFM | Sheffield | Blue Star Security |
| | | NFM | Woodbridge | Normans Transport |
| | | NFM | Wrexham | Cresta Taxis |

| Base | Mobile | Mode | Location | User and Notes |
|---|---|---|---|---|
| 167.9250 | 172.7250 | NFM | Ashford | Freightline Parcels |
| | | NFM | Chelmsford | Ace Mini Cabs |
| | | NFM | Cheltenham | Taxis |
| | | NFM | Hertsfordshire | Martini Cars |
| | | NFM | Leeds | Taxis |
| | | NFM | London | Bus Company |
| | | NFM | Newmarket | Sound City Cars |
| | | NFM | Radcliffe | United Private Hire |
| | | NFM | Sheffield | Sita (GB) Ltd., plant and skips |
| | | NFM | Stevenage | Sierra Taxis |
| 167.9375 | 172.7375 | NFM | Bracknell | Bracknell Radio Cars |
| | | NFM | Coatbridge | Town Taxis |
| | | NFM | Cumbernauld | Taxis |
| | | NFM | Glasgow | Taxis |
| | | NFM | Hemel Hempsted | Minicab Co |
| | | NFM | Luton | Harvey Plant Hire |
| | | NFM | Oldham | Red Cars |
| | | NFM | Tamworth | Taxi Firm |
| | | NFM | Taunton | Ace Taxis |
| 167.9500 | 172.7500 | NFM | Glasgow | Taxis |
| | | NFM | Ipswich | Taxis |
| | | NFM | Jersey | Clarendon Cabs |
| | | NFM | Lichfield | Taxi |
| | | NFM | Nationwide | Search and Rescue |
| | | NFM | Rochdale | Kings Private Hire |
| 167.9625 | 172.7625 | NFM | Birkenhead | Robo's Taxis |
| | | NFM | Bootle | Taxis |
| | | NFM | Brighton | Taxis |
| | | NFM | Jersey | Falles Hire Cars |
| | | NFM | Nottingham, Bulwell | Central Cars |
| | | NFM | Peterborough | Clover Cars |
| | | NFM | Peterborough | Horrells Dairies |
| | | NFM | Pocklington | Central Taxis |
| | | NFM | Sheffield | Moss Cabs |
| 167.9750 | 172.7750 | NFM | Edinburgh | Taxis |
| | | NFM | Glasgow | Croft Radio Cars |
| | | NFM | Ipswich | Hawk's Taxis |
| | | NFM | Ipswich | Tarmac Roadstones Ltd |
| | | NFM | Lincoln | Taxis |
| | | NFM | Liverpool | Taxis |
| | | NFM | London | Taxis |
| | | NFM | March | Coy & Manchett |
| | | NFM | Neath | Abbey Cabs |
| | | NFM | Peterborough | Crown Taxis |
| | | NFM | Portsmouth | Taxis |
| | | NFM | Royton | Royton Private Hire |
| 167.9875 | 172.7875 | NFM | Airdrie | M. Moffat Ccars |
| | | NFM | Cannock | TNT Carriers |
| | | NFM | Exeter | Taxis control |
| | | NFM | Glasgow | Taxis |
| | | NFM | Halifax | Railway Taxis |
| | | NFM | Jersey | HM Customs & Excise Channel 3 |
| | | NFM | Leicester | Taxis |
| | | NFM | Manchester | Taxis |
| | | NFM | Salford | Shopping City Security. |
| | | NFM | Seaford | Taxi |

| Base | Mobile | Mode | Location | User and Notes |
|---|---|---|---|---|
| 167.9875 | 172.7875 | NFM | Sussex | Brighton Marina Security |
| | | NFM | Swansea Docks | Crane Crews |
| | | NFM | Thanet | B.C. Taxis |
| | | NFM | Walkden | Star Private Hire |
| | | NFM | Wrexham | Gold Star Taxis |
| 168.0000 | 172.8000 | NFM | Bristol | Dail A Cab |
| | | NFM | Burnley | Day Rider Couriers |
| | | NFM | Cambridge | Camtax |
| | | NFM | Falkirk | Express Taxis (Express) |
| | | NFM | Glasgow | Eastwood Taxis |
| | | NFM | Jersey | Poineer Holiday Coaches |
| | | NFM | Manchester | Taxis |
| | | NFM | Preston | Buses |
| | | NFM | Salford | Taxis |
| | | NFM | Stoke On Trent | Abbey Taxis |
| | | NFM | West Glamorgan | S Wales Bus Co. |
| | | NFM | Weymouth | Brewers Quay Exhibition |
| 168.0125 | 172.8125 | NFM | Brighton | Taxis |
| | | NFM | Edinburgh | Capital Cabs Channel 1 |
| | | NFM | London | Taxis |
| | | NFM | Salford | Mainline Taxis |
| | | NFM | Sheffield | Taxis |
| | | NFM | Stoke on Trent | Fourstar Taxis |
| 168.0250 | 172.8250 | NFM | Glasgow | Taxis |
| | | NFM | Hitchin | Swan Garage |
| | | NFM | Ipswich | Robin Hood Taxis |
| | | NFM | Leamington | Binmen |
| | | NFM | Swansea | ABC Taxis |
| 168.0375 | 172.8375 | NFM | Edinburgh | Capital Cabs Channel 2 |
| | | NFM | Glasgow | Taxis |
| | | NFM | Guernsey | D.J. Machan Engineering |
| | | NFM | London | New Barnet Cars |
| | | NFM | March | Rowe |
| 168.0500 | 172.8500 | NFM | Bristol | Z Cars Taxis |
| | | NFM | Cambridge | A1 Taxis |
| | | NFM | Central London | Taxis |
| | | NFM | Colchester | AA Taxis |
| | | NFM | Cowley | Rover Plant Ambulance |
| | | NFM | London (Heathrow) | Airport Cars |
| | | NFM | Nationwide | Pretty Things Road Crew |
| | | NFM | Oldham | Delta Taxis |
| | | NFM | St Andrews | Golf City Taxis |
| | | NFM | Worksop | J.J & J.R. Jacksons |
| | | NFM | Worthing | Taxis |
| 168.0625 | 172.8625 | NFM | Birmingham | Taxi |
| | | NFM | Hull | Hull Daily Mail Paper |
| | | NFM | London, south east | Taxis |
| | | NFM | Manchester Reddish | Taxi |
| | | NFM | Manchester, Walkden | Taxis |
| | | NFM | Peterborough | ABC Taxis |
| 168.0750 | 172.8750 | NFM | Heywood | New Embassy Taxis |
| | | NFM | Liverpool | City Centre Taxis |
| | | NFM | London, central | Taxis |
| | | NFM | Newport | Reliance Taxis |
| | | NFM | West Bergholt | John Willsher |

| Base | Mobile | Mode | Location | User and Notes |
|------|--------|------|----------|----------------|
| 168.0875 | 172.8875 | NFM | Ascot | Cooper 24Hr Taxis |
| | | NFM | Barrow in Furness | Taxi |
| | | NFM | Birmingham | Taxi |
| | | NFM | Cardiff | Taxis |
| | | NFM | Glasgow | Taxis |
| | | NFM | Guernsey | Stan Brouard |
| | | NFM | Guernsey | Unigrow |
| | | NFM | Stevenage | W.G. Silverton |
| | | NFM | Walney | Avon Cars |
| 168.1000 | 172.9000 | NFM | Bristol | Streamline Taxis |
| | | NFM | Burnley | Taxis |
| | | NFM | Cardiff | Taxis |
| | | NFM | Co Durham | Taxis |
| | | NFM | Cumbernauld | Taxi |
| | | NFM | Edinburgh | Taxis |
| | | NFM | Edinburgh | United Artist Cable TV |
| | | NFM | Glasgow | Kingsway Taxis |
| | | NFM | Hamilton | Wellman Taxis |
| | | NFM | Newark | Taxis |
| | | NFM | Slough | A-2-B Taxis |
| | | NFM | Southampton | ESSO Fawley Security |
| | | NFM | Sussex | Palace Pier Security |
| | | NFM | Tottington | Tram Cars |
| | | NFM | Welwyn Garden City | 752 Taxis |
| 168.1125 | 172.9125 | NFM | Bath | Taxis |
| | | NFM | Bromley | Taxis |
| | | NFM | Caister | Avenue Taxis |
| | | NFM | Cardiff | Capital Taxis |
| | | NFM | Edinburgh | Taxis |
| | | NFM | Glasgow | Head End |
| | | NFM | Harlow | Buzz Bus |
| | | NFM | Heysham | Heysham Radio Taxis |
| | | NFM | London | Minicab Firm Woodford |
| | | NFM | Preston | Evening Gazette |
| | | NFM | Radcliffe | Centre Radio Cars |
| | | NFM | Sunderland | Star Taxis |
| 168.1250 | 172.9250 | NFM | Dundry | Brinks Mat Security |
| | | NFM | Edinburgh | Taxis |
| | | NFM | Ipswich | Ipswich Buses Ltd |
| | | NFM | Sheffield | Balfour Beaty Base |
| | | NFM | West Midlands | Blue Taxi |
| 168.1325 | 172.9375 | NFM | Aberdeen | Plant Hire |
| | | NFM | Arlesey | Station Cars |
| | | NFM | Bolton | Breightmet Taxis |
| | | NFM | Burton-On-Trent | Lift Maintenance |
| | | NFM | Edinburgh | Black Cabs |
| | | NFM | Glasgow | Taxis |
| | | NFM | Gosport | Taxis |
| | | NFM | Manchester Airport | Taxis |
| | | NFM | Mansfield | A Line Taxis |
| | | NFM | Stoke on Trent | Sid's Taxis |
| | | NFM | Langley, Kent | Farmers (Newshelf) |

| Base | Mobile | Mode | Location | User and Notes |
|------|--------|------|----------|----------------|
| 168.1500 | 172.9500 | NFM | Balthwalles | Royal Welsh Show Security |
| | | NFM | Benwick | Bank Farms |
| | | NFM | Dover | District Council |
| | | NFM | Dublin | Dublin Cablelink |
| | | NFM | Ely | Evans Taxis |
| | | NFM | Hull | Taxis |
| | | NFM | Manchester | Town Cars |
| | | AM | Scarborough | Beeline |
| | | NFM | Swansea | S and E Taxis |
| 168.1625 | 172.9625 | NFM | Aberdeen | Taxis |
| | | NFM | Birmingham 4 Oaks | Taxi |
| | | AM | Cleethorpes | Taxis |
| | | NFM | Essex | Minicab Firm |
| | | NFM | Glasgow | Taxi |
| | | NFM | Goodwood Race Course | Goodwood Control |
| | | NFM | London | Capital Cars |
| | | NFM | Manchester | Taxi |
| | | NFM | Wisbech | Ellis & Everard |
| 168.1750 | 172.9750 | NFM | Bedford | Key Cars |
| | | NFM | Birmingham Shirley | Taxi |
| | | AM | Grimsby | TV Repairs |
| | | NFM | Newmarket | Triax |
| | | NFM | Rochdale | Castle Private Hire |
| 168.1875 | 172.9875 | NFM | Abingdon | K-9 Security |
| | | NFM | Birmingham Shard End | Taxi |
| | | NFM | Blackpool | Black Tax Taxis |
| | | NFM | Eastbourne | East College |
| | | NFM | Manchester, Levenshulme | White Line Private Hire |
| | | NFM | Peterborough | DJ Taxis |
| | | NFM | Salisbury | Bros Sutton |
| | | NFM | Sutton | Salisbury Bros. |
| 168.2000 | 173.0000 | NFM | Ayr | Taxi |
| | | NFM | Beswick | UK Cars |
| | | NFM | Brentwood | TNT Carriers |
| | | NFM | Glasgow | Taxis |
| | | AM | Grimsby | Taxis |
| | | NFM | London | Taxis |
| | | NFM | Manchester | Taxis |
| | | NFM | Milton | TNT Carriers |
| | | NFM | Peterborough | Rivergate Security |
| | | NFM | Reading | 1A Cars |
| | | NFM | Shaftesbury | Alford Taxis |
| | | NFM | Shaftesbury | Hilltop Taxis |
| | | NFM | Sheffield | School security |
| 168.2100 | 173.0100 | NFM | Crewe | Taxi |
| 168.2125 | 173.0125 | NFM | Bettacars | Cambridge |
| | | NFM | Cambridge | Bettacars |
| | | NFM | Dukinfield | Taxis |
| | | NFM | Glasgow | Taxis |
| | | NFM | Manchester | Zip Dispatch |
| | | NFM | Norfolk | ICL |
| | | NFM | Norwich | Royal Taxis |
| | | NFM | Sheffield | Eagle Taxis |
| | | NFM | Stirling | D & M Taxis (D) |
| | | NFM | Swinton | Zip Dispatch |
| | | NFM | Trowbridge | Alpha Taxis |

| Base | Mobile | Mode | Location | User and Notes |
|------|--------|------|----------|----------------|
| 168.2200 | 173.0200 | NFM | Eastbourne | School Bus Service |
| 168.2250 | 173.0250 | NFM | Blackpool | Green Star Taxis |
| | | NFM | Glasgow | Taxis |
| | | NFM | Jersey | Interlink Delivery |
| | | NFM | London | AZ Couriers |
| | | NFM | Manchester | Taxis |
| | | NFM | March | Central Shopping Security |
| | | NFM | Nationwide | Radio Investigations Service |
| | | NFM | Oldham | Untied Private Hire |
| | | NFM | Peterborough | Rivergate Security |
| | | NFM | Swindon | A2B Taxis |
| | | NFM | West Midlands | Public House Repairs |
| 168.2375 | 173.0375 | NFM | Carlisle | City Taxis |
| | | NFM | Corsham | Taxis |
| | | NFM | Doncaster | Midwives and Home Helps |
| | | NFM | Felling | Taxis |
| | | NFM | Great Yarmouth | Halcyon Shipping |
| | | NFM | Llandudno | Taxi Service |
| | | NFM | Nottingham | Holme Pier Water Sports |
| | | NFM | Woodbridge | Taxis |

## Monitoring the PMR Bands with the New MPT1327 Decoder

Have you noticed recently more and more radio users such as airport ground staffs, buses, trains and security companies have stopped using the old radio systems which used only one frequency that you could easily monitor on your scanner? Many of these users now have a trunked radio system which means any time a radio makes a call it could use any one the 20 or so channels allocated to the system. So even if you programme all the frequencies into your scanner you are still very unlikely to hear the user you want because the system keeps on changing the frequencies. For more details on how the system operates see *Scanner Busters 2* on page 488.

This column lists the frequencies to tune into

Details frequencies logged

Now thanks to a new decoder from Australia, known as Ftrunk, you can now monitor the most commonly used tunked systems. By fitting the Ftrunk between a scanner and a PC computer you can not only find out the activity on the PMR bands but the frequencies to monitor. The scanner picks up signals sent to a mobile radio telling it which channel to use and this information and the frequency will be displayed on the computer screen. Tune the scanner into this frequency to hear the conversation. The latest version of Ftrunk lets you connect a second scanner which will automatically switches to the frequency with the conversation. It not only covers Band 3 PMR but Power Companies, RAC, Railtrack, Securicor, Water Companies and unknown systems plus networks in Australia, Netherlands, Norway and Uganda. The decoder also displays the growing number of text messages sent on trunked radios.

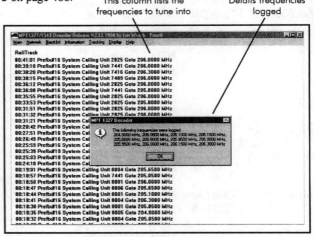

For further details contact Interproducts, 8 Abbot Street, Perth, PH2 0EB (tel. and fax 01738-441199) or the manufacturers Talkback Systems Australia, PO Box 8054, Northland Centre, Victoria, 3072, Australia (Email: mpt1327@tbsa.com.au).

| Base | Mobile | Mode | Location | User and Notes |
|------|--------|------|----------|----------------|

| Base | Mobile | Mode | Location | User and Notes |
|------|--------|------|----------|----------------|
| 168.2500 | | NFM | Dudley | Waterfront Security |
| | | NFM | Ferndown | E.G. Hoare |
| | | NFM | Nationwide | BT Linesmen |
| | | NFM | Nationwide | Radio Investigations |
| | | NFM | Swindon | Cooper's Metals |
| 168.2625 | | NFM | Alderney | Alderney Electricity |
| | | NFM | Nationwide | BT Cable Laying |
| 168.2750 | | NFM | Dorset | Radiocommunications Agency |
| | | NFM | Hampshire | Radiocommunications Agency |
| | | NFM | Lancashire | Radiocommunications Agency |
| | | NFM | Nationwide | Radiocommunications Agency |
| | | NFM | Worcester | Surveillance Unit |
| 168.2875 | | NFM | Burnley | Taxis |
| | | NFM | Edinburgh | Lothian & Borders Fire Brigade |
| | | NFM | Nationwide | Local authority alarms |
| 168.3000 | | NFM | Nationwide | BT & Post Office Investigators |
| | | NFM | Nationwide | Radio Investigation |
| 168.3200 | | NFM | Boston | Farmworkers |
| 168.3875 | | NFM | Melksham | Taxis |
| 168.4000 | | NFM | Formula One Racing | Williams Team Voice Link |
| 168.4375 | | NFM | Aberdeen | Security |
| 168.4750 | | NFM | Dudley | Hospital Security |
| | | NFM | Tamworth | Drayton Manor Park |
| 168.5375 | | NFM | High Wycombe | Council car park wardens |
| 168.6000 | | NFM | London | Diplomatic Protection (Ranger) |
| 168.7260 | | NFM | Doncaster | Royal Mail |
| 168.7500 | | NFM | Guernsey | Civil Defence Network |
| | | NFM | Jersey | Civil Defence Network |
| | | NFM | Swansea | DSS Fraud Teams |
| 168.7625 | | NFM | Bristol | Badgerline Buses |
| 168.8500 | | NFM | Swansea City | Royal Mail |
| 168.8625 | | NFM | Euro Tunnel, Dover | Shakespeare Clift |
| | | NFM | Glasgow | Taxi |
| | | NFM | Jersey Airport | Beauport Aviation Gnd Staff |
| | | NFM | Nationwide | National Seismic Studies |
| | | NFM | Suffolk | Police Regional Crime Squads |
| 168.8750 | | NFM | Cardiff | Cardiff Van Hire |
| | | NFM | Swansea | DSS Fraud Teams |
| | | NFM | Nationwide | BT Video Set Up Link |
| 168.9000 | | NFM | Guernsey | Lesbirel Agricultural Services |
| 168.9125 | | NFM | Newport | DHSS |
| 168.9200 | | NFM | Mossblown | Sheltered Housing Warden |
| 168.9250 | | NFM | Cardiff, Newport | Royal Mail |
| | | NFM | London | Bullion Movement Security |
| 168.9375 | | NFM | Nationwide | Local authority alarms |
| 168.9500 | | NFM | Jersey | Driving Tests Chase Vehicle |
| | | NFM | Nationwide | British Telecom |
| 168.9600 | | NFM | Barrow in Furness | VSEL Shopfloor & Onboard Comms |

| Base | Mobile | Mode | Location | User and Notes |
|------|--------|------|----------|----------------|
| 168.9625 | | NFM | Aberdeen | Docks security |
| | | NFM | Ayr | Butlins Security |
| | | NFM | Bury St Edmunds | Rushbrooke Farms |
| | | NFM | Jersey | Industrial (Motors) Ltd |
| | | NFM | Minehead | Butlins Security |
| | | NFM | Scarborough | Brurowick Pavillion Cent. Security |
| | | NFM | Sheffield City Centre | Bus Instectors |
| 168.9750 | | NFM | Barrow in Furness | VSEL |
| | | NFM | Caversham Park | BBC Monitoring Service |
| | | NFM | Jersey | Horse Racing Shows |
| | | NFM | Leighton Buzzard | Joseph Arnold |
| | | NFM | London | Hopton Holiday Village staff |
| | | NFM | London | Wembley Stadium Security |
| | | NFM | Nationwide | Ordinance Survey |
| | | NFM | Newcastle | British Telecom |
| 168.9875 | | NFM | Aberdeen | Docks security |
| | | NFM | Cambridge | Fitzwilliam College |
| | | NFM | Croydon | Crystal Palace Shopping Centre |
| | | NFM | Durham | TNT Carriers |
| | | NFM | Felixstowe | Docks |
| | | NFM | Guernsey | Condor Shipping |
| | | NFM | Haverfordwest | Farm |
| | | NFM | Jersey | Harbour (Condor) |
| | | NFM | London | Wembley Stadium Stewards |
| | | NFM | Nationwide | BBC Engineering Channel |
| | | NFM | Nationwide | ITC Riggers |
| | | NFM | Nationwide | Ordnance Survey teams |
| | | NFM | Newport | Steelworks Handhelds |
| | | NFM | Peterborough | Ferry Meadows Rangers |
| | | NFM | Preston | Moathouse Hotel |
| | | NFM | Prestwick Airport | British Aerospace |
| 169.0000 | | NFM | Bolton | Council Car Park Attendants |
| | | NFM | Bournemouth | Synagogue Security |
| | | NFM | Cambridge | Trinity College |
| | | NFM | Cheltenham | FMR Investigations |
| | | NFM | Crewe | Oakley Centre |
| | | NFM | Guernsey | PSS Security |
| | | NFM | Killwinning | Water Baliffs |
| | | NFM | Nationwide | RAC Rally |
| | | NFM | Sheffield | Shinecliffe College |
| | | NFM | Sheffield | Transport Interchange Security |
| | | NFM | Southampton | Dock Security |
| | | NFM | Southampton | TNT Carriers |
| | | NFM | Tilbury | Docks Freightliner Terminal |
| 169.0125 | | NFM | Burnley | York House Cabaret |
| | | NFM | Cornwall | T S Brent |
| | | NFM | Dundee | Tay Bridge Maintenance |
| | | NFM | Edinburgh | HMV Record Shop Security |
| | | NFM | Jersey | DHL Courier |
| | | NFM | London | Wembley Stadium Merchandise |
| | | NFM | London | Lords Cricket Ground stewards |
| | | NFM | Nationwide | Network Q Rally - Subaru |
| | | NFM | Nationwide | RAC Rally |
| | | NFM | Nationwide | Short Term Hire |
| | | NFM | Parkeston Quay | Harwich Transport |
| | | NFM | Sheffield | Sheffield Arena stewards |

| Base | Mobile | Mode | Location | User and Notes |
|------|--------|------|----------|----------------|
| 169.0125 | | NFM | St Austell | Scrap Car Yard |
| | | NFM | Weymouth | Guardforce Security |
| 169.0200 | | NFM | Enfield | Police |
| | | NFM | Brighton | Pier and Front |
| | | NFM | Bury St Edmonds | Council |
| | | NFM | Cambridge | Posthouse Forte Hotel |
| | | NFM | Chippenham | Shopping Centre Security |
| | | NFM | Guernsey | Mainland Market Deliveries |
| | | NFM | Hillingdon | Council |
| | | NFM | Humberside Airport | Servisair |
| | | NFM | Jersey | Deliveries |
| | | NFM | Liverpool | Marks & Spencer Security |
| | | NFM | London | Cazenove & Co Stockbrokers |
| | | NFM | Nationwide | RAC Rally |
| | | NFM | Nationwide | St Johns Ambulance Channel B |
| | | NFM | Perth | Security |
| | | NFM | Powys | Powys County Council |
| | | NFM | Prestatyn | Pontins Holiday Camp Security |
| | | NFM | Sheffield | Shinecliffe security (APPLE) |
| 169.0375 | | NFM | Bournemouth | International Centre Security |
| | | NFM | Bristol | Fruit Market |
| | | NFM | Cheltenham | FMR Investigations |
| | | NFM | Clacton | Pier Co |
| | | NFM | Eastbourne | Seafront train |
| | | NFM | Fort William | Nevis Range Ski Co. |
| | | NFM | Hull | Hull Rugby Stewards |
| | | NFM | Humberside Airport | Servisair Ops |
| | | NFM | Jersey | Jersey Zoo |
| | | NFM | Lochaber | Nevis Rescue Services |
| | | NFM | London | London Zoo staff |
| | | NFM | London, Wimbledon | Tennis Championship |
| | | NFM | Luton Airport | Britannia Ground |
| | | NFM | Maidstone | Leeds Castle Security Staff |
| | | NFM | Manchester | Freightliners Yard Staff |
| | | NFM | Penzance | Antenna Riggers |
| | | NFM | Plymouth | City Centre Shop Security |
| | | NFM | Scarborough | Core Security |
| | | NFM | Sellafield | Construction |
| | | NFM | Tendring | Southern Water |
| 169.0500 | | NFM | Bacton | British Gas Corp |
| | | NFM | Nationwide | RAC Rally |
| | | NFM | Newport | Tarmac Road Repairs |
| 169.0625 | | NFM | Brighton | Palace Pier |
| | | NFM | Carlisle | Portland Centre |
| | | NFM | Jersey | Commodore Shipping |
| | | NFM | London | Trocadero Security, Piccadilly |
| | | NFM | Lowestoft | Christian Salvesen |
| | | NFM | Nationwide | ICL Computers |
| 169.0750 | | NFM | Coventry | Park surveyors |
| | | NFM | Glen Coe | White Corries Ski Co. |
| | | NFM | Guernsey | Balfour Beatty Falla |
| | | NFM | Liverpool | Albert Dock Security |
| | | NFM | Llanelli | Pembury Country Park Rangers |
| | | NFM | London | Arsenal FC Security |
| | | NFM | London | Queens Park Ranges FC Security |
| | | NFM | London | West Ham FC Security |

| Base | Mobile | Mode | Location | User and Notes |
|------|--------|------|----------|----------------|
| 169.0750 | | NFM | Newquay | Hendra Caravan Park |
| | | NFM | Poole | Valiant Security |
| | | NFM | Turbury Derbyshire | Nestles |
| | | NFM | Tyneside | Five Star Security |
| 169.0850 | | NFM | Ayr | Water Bailiff Handhelds |
| 169.0875 | | NFM | Abergavenny | Mountain Rescue Team 1 |
| 169.0875 | | NFM | Blackpool | Social Security |
| | | NFM | Bolton | Peak Security |
| | | NFM | Crownhill | DSS Security Office |
| | | NFM | Guernsey | Allied Heating |
| | | NFM | Guernsey | Louis Dekker Bulbs |
| | | NFM | Jersey | European Golf Championships |
| | | NFM | London | Arsenal FC Security |
| | | NFM | Nationwide | Limited DSS use |
| | | NFM | Nationwide | Red Cross |
| | | NFM | Newmarket | Bookmakers |
| | | NFM | Plymouth | DSS Security Office |
| | | NFM | Plymouth | Plymouth Market Security |
| | | NFM | RAF St Mawgan | PSA Agency |
| | | NFM | Southampton | Docks |
| | | NFM | Southern England | Mowlen Civil Engineering |
| | | NFM | Sutton Coldfield | Belfry Golf Course |
| 169.1000 | | NFM | Cambridge | Medical Research Council |
| | | NFM | Fishguard | Stena Sealink |
| | | NFM | Folkestone | Stena Sealink |
| | | NFM | Isle Of Arran | National Trust for Scotland Rangers |
| | | NFM | Larne | Stena Sealink |
| | | NFM | Norwich | Football Stewards |
| | | NFM | Southampton | Stena Sealink |
| | | NFM | Stranraer | Stena Sealink |
| | | NFM | Ayr | Taxi |
| 169.1125 | | NFM | Bournemouth | International Centre Security |
| | | NFM | Doncaster | Steatley Quarry |
| | | NFM | Grimsby | Shopping Centre |
| | | NFM | Halesworth | K.W. Thomas |
| | | NFM | Kent | Camber Sands |
| | | NFM | Sheffield | Sheffield Arena ops |
| | | NFM | St Helier | Reclamation Site |
| | | NFM | Stanton | Marshalls Quarries |
| | | NFM | Swansea | AMEC Mining |
| | | NFM | Trowbridge | Garden Centre |
| | | NFM | University of Kent | Canterbury College |
| | | NFM | Weymouth | Hospital Security |
| | | NFM | Worksop | Fox Covert Scrap Yard |
| 169.1200 | | NFM | Greenock | Wilson Coaches |
| 169.1250 | | NFM | Birkenhead | Shopping Centre Security |
| | | NFM | Plymouth | Plymouth Hospital |
| | | NFM | Scarborough | Scarborough FC Stewards |
| | | NFM | Sheffield | Beacon Radio |
| | | NFM | Sheffield | Sheffield Arena ops |
| | | NFM | Worcester | White Arrow Delivery |
| 169.1300 | | NFM | Grand Prix Circuits | Williams Team Voice Link |
| 169.1375 | | NFM | Aberdeen | Bon Accord Centre Security |
| | | NFM | Durris | National Trust for Scotland Rangers |
| | | NFM | Hampshire | Council |
| | | NFM | London | Sega Mega World |

| Base | Mobile | Mode | Location | User and Notes |
|---|---|---|---|---|
| 169.1375 | | NFM | London | Wembley Stadium Security |
| | | NFM | Nationwide | Short Term Hire |
| | | NFM | Nationwide | St John's Ambulances |
| | | NFM | Scunthorpe | Balfour Beatty Construction |
| | | NFM | Sheffield | Dry ski slope |
| | | NFM | Weymouth | RSPB |
| 169.1500 | | NFM | Bournmouth | Beach Wardens |
| | | NFM | Jersey | Jersey Builders |
| | | NFM | Lancaster | Boots |
| | | NFM | London | Alexandra Palace Leisure Centre |
| | | NFM | Manchester | Pump Services |
| | | NFM | Nationwide | National Trust |
| | | NFM | Stanton | East Coast Slag |
| | | NFM | Whitland | Dairy Crest |
| | | NFM | Worksop | Bassetlaw Hospital |
| 169.1600 | | NFM | Luton Airport | Aircraft Cleaning |
| 169.1625 | | NFM | Ayr | Butlins Entertainment |
| | | NFM | Barrow in Furness | Shopping Centre |
| | | NFM | Bedford | Bedfordshire Festival 1994 |
| | | NFM | Bishop Strotford | Mears Construction |
| | | NFM | Cardigan | Cardi Cabs |
| | | NFM | Coventry | Mayfair Security Channel 2 |
| | | NFM | Coventry | Motorcycle theives with stolen radios |
| | | NFM | Edinburgh | City Surveyors |
| | | NFM | Essex | Top Guard International |
| | | NFM | Haverfordwest | Cardi Cabs |
| | | NFM | Jersey | Keith Rogers Building Renovation |
| | | NFM | Kirkcaldy | Boots Security |
| | | NFM | London | DSS Discreet |
| | | NFM | London | Planet Hollywood Security |
| | | NFM | London | Wembley Stadium Security |
| | | NFM | London, Wimbledon | Lawn Tennis Club groundsmen |
| | | NFM | Luton Airport | Baggage Handlers |
| | | NFM | Nationwide | Short Term Hire |
| | | NFM | Nationwide | St John's Ambulances Channel 5 |
| | | NFM | Surrey | Council County Engineer |
| | | NFM | Taplow | Cliveden House Hotel Security |
| | | NFM | Twickenham | Rugby Stewards |
| 169.1750 | | NFM | Ballachulish | Glencoe Mountain Rescue Team |
| | | NFM | Barrow in Furness | Tipper Trucks |
| | | NFM | Barrow in Furness | VSEL DDH Shopfloor Services |
| | | NFM | Boston | Organic Lincolnshire Growers Assoc |
| | | NFM | Cardiff | St Fagans Fock Museum |
| | | NFM | Guernsey | Ronez (Monmains) |
| | | NFM | Martlesham Heath | Department of Energy |
| | | NFM | Nationwide | Mountain Rescue Scotland |
| | | NFM | Perth | Landscape Gardens Ltd |
| | | NFM | Peterborough | East of England Show Ground |
| | | NFM | Snowdon | Mountain Railway |
| | | NFM | Three Holes | Frank Hartley |
| 169.1875 | | NFM | Biggleswade Airfield | Ops |
| | | NFM | Brighton | Marina Asda Supermarket |
| | | NFM | Burnley | Marks & Spencer Security |
| | | NFM | Garston | Freightliner terminal |
| | | NFM | Grand Prix Circuits | Lotus Team Channel 3 |
| | | NFM | Ingleston | Market Stewards |

| Base | Mobile | Mode | Location | User and Notes |
|---|---|---|---|---|
| 169.1875 | | NFM | Jersey | Lift Engineers |
| | | NFM | Killingholme | National Power Security |
| | | NFM | London | Public Health Labs |
| | | NFM | London | Sega Mega World |
| | | NFM | London | Wembley Stadium Catering |
| | | NFM | Morecambe | Trino's Taxis |
| | | NFM | Nationwide | NCB Emergencies |
| | | NFM | Nationwide | Short Term Hire |
| | | NFM | Nationwide | St John's Ambulances Channel 6 |
| | | NFM | Penrith | Market Security |
| | | NFM | Perth | Security |
| | | NFM | Peterlee | Five Star Taxis |
| | | NFM | Plymouth | Cascade Security |
| | | NFM | Redruth | Land Rover Racing |
| | | NFM | Wigan | Statesman Security |
| 169.2000 | | NFM | Aberdeen | Aberdeen Ice Rink |
| | | NFM | Ashford | Stour Leisure Centre |
| | | NFM | Belfast Airport | Ground Services |
| | | NFM | Bolton | Peak Security |
| | | NFM | Burnley | Potterton Production Lines Channel 1 |
| | | NFM | Edinburgh | Chamber St. Museum |
| | | NFM | Fort William | BSW Sawmill |
| | | NFM | Gateshead | Fewster Square Leisure Centre |
| | | NFM | Huyton | Ferraris Nighclub Security |
| | | NFM | Jersey | Wilson Vets & Animal Shelter |
| | | NFM | London | University College, London University |
| | | NFM | London | Westminster City Hall |
| | | NFM | London, Knightsbridge | Harvey Nichols security |
| | | NFM | Perth | Security |
| | | NFM | Peterborough | Peterborough Regional College |
| | | NFM | Sheffield | British Steel |
| | | NFM | Swansea | Construction |
| | | NFM | Swansea | F.R.F Motors |
| | | NFM | Thanet | Thanet Technical College |
| | | NFM | Ware | Glaxo Operations |
| 169.2125 | | NFM | Bournemouth | Malibu Club Doormen |
| | | NFM | Croydon | Water Palace |
| | | NFM | Dover | District Council |
| | | NFM | East Midlands Airport | Airport Security |
| | | NFM | Harwell | UK Atomic Energy Authority |
| | | NFM | Jersey | Beachguards |
| | | NFM | Stoke on Trent | Stoke City FC Security |
| | | NFM | Wigan | Car Park Security |
| 169.2250 | | NFM | Carlisle | Thomas Graham & Sons |
| | | NFM | Coventry | Apex Trust |
| | | NFM | Epping | North Weald Airfield Security & Fire |
| | | NFM | Gillingham, Dorset | School caretakers |
| | | NFM | Glasgow University | Security |
| | | NFM | Jersey | Hurricaine Despatch |
| | | NFM | Liverpool | Taxi-Taxi Channel |
| | | NFM | Nationwide | RAC Rallies |
| | | NFM | North Weald | Security & Crash Ops |
| | | NFM | Orton | Longueville School |
| | | NFM | Wigan | Rugby Ground Stewards |

| Base | Mobile | Mode | Location | User and Notes |
|---|---|---|---|---|
| 169.2375 | | NFM | Barnet | Spires Shopping Centre security |
| | | NFM | Chatham | Pentagon Centre security |
| | | NFM | England | Water Baliffs |
| | | NFM | Lancaster | WH Smiths |
| | | NFM | Liverpool | Dolcis Shop Co Ordering Dept |
| | | NFM | Liverpool | G.H. Lee Security |
| | | NFM | Stevenage | Westgate Shopping Centre |
| 169.2500 | | NFM | Brecon | Mountain Railway |
| | | NFM | Southampton | University Security |
| | | NFM | Trafford | Haulage Company |
| 169.2600 | | FM | Easbourne | Arndale Centre Security |
| 169.2625 | | NFM | Felixstowe | Repcon |
| | | NFM | Great Yarmouth | St.Nicholas Hospital |
| | | NFM | Guernsey | Harlequin Hire Cars |
| | | NFM | Hull | Prospect Shopping Cent. Security |
| | | NFM | Jersey | Builders |
| | | NFM | London | Hopton Holiday Village security |
| | | NFM | London, Brent Cross | John Lewis |
| | | NFM | Taunton | Musgrove Park Hospital |
| 169.2750 | | NFM | Isle of Man | Doctors On Call |
| | | NFM | London, Edmonton | Pickets Lock Centre |
| | | NFM | Shoreham Airport | Ground Vehicles |
| | | NFM | Southend-on-Sea | Technical College |
| | | NFM | Stansted | Maintenance |
| | | NFM | Woodbridge | Kemball |
| 169.2875 | | NFM | Croydon | Croydon Health |
| | | NFM | Felixstowe | Docks |
| | | NFM | Kettering | Metalforce Ltd |
| | | NFM | Southampton | Dock Stevadores |
| | | NFM | Woburn Sands | Plysu Plc |
| 169.3000 | | NFM | Birmingham | W. Bromwich Albion FC Stewards |
| | | NFM | Carlisle | H & H Auction Mart |
| | | NFM | Guernsey | Sarnia Hire Cars |
| | | NFM | Heathrow Airport | Passenger Services |
| | | NFM | London (Heathrow) | Airline Passenger Service |
| | | NFM | Morecambe | Pleasure Beach Security |
| | | NFM | Newport | Town Centre Security |
| | | NFM | Wirral | Community Patrol Channel 4 |
| 169.3125 | | NFM | Channel Tunnel | Group 4 Security |
| | | NFM | Doncaster | Motorcycle Tests |
| | | NFM | Epping | North Weald Airfield Car Park Stewards |
| | | NFM | Jersey | Commodore Shipping |
| | | NFM | Jersey | Otis Lifts |
| | | NFM | London | Wembley Stadium Car Parks |
| | | NFM | London, Embankment | Jubilee Line extension works |
| | | NFM | Nationwide | Network Q Rally - Nissan |
| | | NFM | Nationwide | Titan Fire Services |
| | | NFM | Wigan | British Waterways |
| 169.3250 | | NFM | Barton-on-Humber | Peter Birse Construction |
| | | NFM | Bath | Theatre Royal |
| | | NFM | Cannock | TNT Carriers |
| | | NFM | Clevedon | Passanger Traffic Control |
| | | NFM | Exeter | Exeter Cathedral |
| | | NFM | Hull | Hull FC Stewards |
| | | NFM | Luton Airport | Baggage Handlers |
| | | NFM | Newquay | Car Park Attendants |

| Base | Mobile | Mode | Location | User and Notes |
|------|--------|------|----------|----------------|
| 169.3250 | | NFM | Nottingham | American Adventure Theme Park |
| | | NFM | Pwllheli | Butlins Camp Security |
| 169.3260 | | NFM | Norwich | Fotball Stewards |
| 169.3375 | | NFM | Cambridge | Kings College |
| | | NFM | Cornwall | Tarmac |
| | | NFM | County Durham | Doctor's Medicall |
| | | NFM | Devon | Tamar Bridge Security |
| | | NFM | Halifax | St. Johns Ambulance |
| | | NFM | Halifax | Websters Brewery Security |
| | | NFM | Jersey | Island Sports Officials |
| | | NFM | Kings College | Cambridge University |
| | | NFM | London | Cazenove & Co Stockbrokers |
| | | NFM | Merry Hill | Centre Waterfront Security |
| | | NFM | Perth | St John's Centre Security |
| | | NFM | Sellafield | Construction |
| | | NFM | Silverstone | RAC General Use |
| | | NFM | Snetterton | British Auto Racing |
| 169.3500 | | NFM | Bournemouth | Weymouth House Security |
| | | NFM | Doncaster | Dome Centre |
| | | NFM | Hull | Humber Bridge Control |
| | | NFM | Lynmouth | Security |
| | | NFM | Powys | South Wales Electricity |
| | | NFM | Sussex | St John's Ambulance |
| | | AM | Swansea Airport | Runway & Ground Crews |
| 169.3625 | | NFM | Bolton | Bolton FC Stewards |
| | | NFM | Burnley | Shopping Centre |
| | | NFM | Deptford | Dispatch Company |
| | | NFM | Doncaster | Tesco Distribution Depot |
| | | NFM | Dorset | DADPC Blandford Camp |
| | | NFM | Glasgow | Woyka Timber Mill |
| | | NFM | Leighton Buzzard | George Garside Sand |
| | | NFM | Nationwide | Dept. of Trade & Industry |
| | | NFM | Nationwide | St Johns Ambulance Channel A/1 |
| | | NFM | Preston | Harris Museum |
| | | NFM | Swansea | DSS Fraud Teams |
| | | NFM | Whiston | Hexagon (HISS) Security Ltd |
| 169.3750 | | NFM | Bell College | Saffron Walden |
| | | NFM | Coventry | Tyre Fitters |
| | | NFM | London, Oxford St | Forbidden Planet Ltd |
| | | NFM | London, Southbank | National Theatre |
| | | NFM | Sheffield | Council Housing Department |
| | | NFM | South Walden | Bell College |
| 169.3875 | | NFM | Blackpool | Car Park Attendants |
| | | NFM | Humberside Airport | Tower-Ground |
| | | NFM | Kent | Prismo Road Surfacing |
| | | NFM | Nationwide | St Johns Ambulance Channel 2 |
| | | NFM | Nottingham | Technical Services |
| | | NFM | Preston | Council Car Parks |
| | | NFM | Sheffield | Makro car park control |
| | | NFM | Silverstone Airfield | Security & Crash Ops |
| | | NFM | Southwark | Crown Court Security |

| Base | Mobile | Mode | Location | User and Notes |
|------|--------|------|----------|----------------|

**169.39375 - 169.84375 MHz** NEW EUROPEAN MESSAGING SERVICE (ERMES) PMR SIMPLEX 12.5 KHz NFM

| Base | Mobile | Mode | Location | User and Notes |
|------|--------|------|----------|----------------|
| 169.4000 | | NFM | Gt Yarmouth | Palgrave Brown |
| | | NFM | Newmarket | Harry Wrass Ltd |
| 169.4250 | | NFM | Gt Yarmouth | Shipping Co |
| 169.4375 | | NFM | Eastleigh | Taxis |
| | | NFM | Jersey | Hotel de France Conferences |
| | | NFM | Norwich | TV servicing |
| | | NFM | South Midlands | Comms Ltd Demo Channel |
| | | NFM | Southampton | Event Control |
| 169.4500 | | NFM | Wisbech | J.D. Walker Ltd |
| 169.4625 | | NFM | London | Security |
| | | NFM | Tamworth | Road Works |
| 169.4750 | | NFM | Abergavenny | TV Antenna Riggers |
| | | NFM | Caister | Holiday Camp |
| | | NFM | Cambridge | Christ's College |
| | | NFM | Stowmarket | Helmingham Est Farms |
| 169.4875 | | NFM | Bournmouth | Centurian Security |
| | | NFM | Grand Prix Circuits | Benetton Voice |
| | | NFM | Grimsby | Burns Security |
| | | NFM | Nationwide | Red Cross Ambulance |
| 169.5000 | | NFM | Lochore | Lochore Meadows Park |
| | | NFM | Nationwide | Carlink Ferries |
| | | NFM | Norwich | British Rail |
| 169.5125 | | NFM | Brandon | F.Hiam Farms |
| 169.5250 | | NFM | Jersey | South Pier Shipyard |
| | | NFM | Luton | Vauxhall Motors |
| | | NFM | Woodbridge | Tubbs Building Supplies |
| 169.5375 | | NFM | Blackpool | R Smith Leisure Services |
| | | NFM | Burnley | Guardhall Security |
| | | NFM | Cambridge | Council |
| | | NFM | Epsom | Race Course |
| | | NFM | Jersey | Rob Thompson Electronics |
| | | NFM | Nationwide | Honda Williams Racing Team |
| | | NFM | Nationwide | Whitbread World Race Security |
| 169.5500 | | NFM | West Bergholt | Wicken Farm Co. |
| | | NFM | Canterbury | Cathedral security |
| | | NFM | Chatteris | Nongell Ltd |
| | | NFM | Dorset | Clearway Transport |
| | | NFM | Folkestone | SIS |
| | | NFM | Swansea | Private Detectives |
| | | NFM | Wisbech | J.D. Walker |
| 169.6125 | | NFM | Wanton | Morley Farms |
| | | NFM | Dereham | Crane Fruehauf |
| | | NFM | Hythe | Nicholls Quarry |
| | | NFM | Thetford | H. Fledger |
| 169.6375 | | NFM | Bournemouth | Farm Security |
| | | NFM | Cumbria | Community Repeater South Lakes |
| | | NFM | Newhaven Port | Shorrock Security |
| 169.6625 | | NFM | Nottingham | Sheriff Plant Hire |
| | | NFM | Woolverstone | A.W Mayhew Farms |
| 169.6750 | | NFM | Nationwide | DSS Snoopers Channel 01 |
| | | NFM | Nottingham | Claredon College |
| 169.7000 | | NFM | Glenshee | Glenshee Rescue Team |
| | | NFM | Nationwide | DSS Snoopers Channel 02 |

| Base | Mobile | Mode | Location | User and Notes |
|------|--------|------|----------|----------------|
| 169.7250 | | NFM | Bournemouth | Southern Despatch Bikes |
| | | NFM | Plymouth | St John's Ambulance |
| 169.7375 | | NFM | Birmingham | Bull Ring Security |
| | | NFM | London | Chelsea FC Link |
| 169.7625 | | NFM | Bedlinton | Taxis |
| | | NFM | Buckinghamshire | Bucks Council Channel 1 |
| | | NFM | London Picadilly | Tower Records Security |
| | | NFM | London, Piccadilly | The Rock Gardens Security |
| | | NFM | Sandwich | Royal St George Golf Club |
| | | NFM | South Midlands | South Midlands Comms Demo |
| 169.7750 | | NFM | Bedford | Smith & Co |
| | | NFM | Bishop Stortford | College |
| 169.7875 | | NFM | Cambridge | Roy Pett |
| | | NFM | Reading | Council |
| 169.8000 | | NFM | Bath | Bath University Research |
| | | NFM | Bristol | D.O.T. |
| | | NFM | Guernsey | Airport Services |
| 169.8125 | | NFM | Birmingham | Aston Villa FC Stewards |
| | | NFM | Glenshee | Glenshee Rescue Team |
| | | NFM | Guernsey | Aurigny Ground Services |
| | | NFM | Sheffield | Northern Gen. Hospital Security |
| 169.8250 | | NFM | Folkestone | Burstin Hotel |
| | | NFM | Jersey | Honorary Police Channel 6 |
| | | NFM | Leamington Spa, Warks | The Watch Security |
| | | NFM | Nationwide | DSS Snoopers Channel 03 |
| | | NFM | Nationwide | Inland Revenue Channel 03 |
| | | NFM | Perth | Maintenance |
| 169.8375 | | NFM | Burnley | Potterton ProdLines Channel 2 |
| | | NFM | Hull | Princes Quay Carpark Security |
| | | NFM | London | Wembley Stadium Stewards |
| | | NFM | Oxford | Oxford FC Stewards |
| | | NFM | Sheffield | Orchard Square Shopping Centre |
| | | NFM | St Austell | ECC Pits |
| | | NFM | Wisbech | British Road Services |
| | | NFM | Wisbech | Corbill Ltd |

### 169.8437 - 173.04375 MHz    PMR HIGH BAND MOBILES
### (BASE SPLIT - 4.8 MHz)

| Base | Mobile | Mode | Location | User and Notes |
|------|--------|------|----------|----------------|
| 169.8500 | 165.0500 | NFM | Kings Lynn | British Road Service |
| | | NFM | Lincoln | A2B Taxis |
| 169.8875 | | NFM | Portsmouth | Buses |
| 169.9125 | 165.1125 | NFM | Jersey | Beeline Taxis Channel 2 |
| 169.9250 | 165.1250 | NFM | Ulverston | McKenna's Taxis |
| 169.9375 | 169.9375 | NFM | Jersey | Land Surveyors & Architects |
| 169.9450 | | NFM | Bristol | South West Electric Company |
| 169.9625 | | NFM | East Durham | Private Message |
| | | NFM | Folkestone | Rotunda Park |
| 169.9625 | 169.9625 | NFM | London | Cazenove & Co Stockbrokers |
| 169.9625 | 170.7625 | NFM | Trowbridge | Driving Instructors |
| 169.9750 | | NFM | Felixstowe | Docks |
| 170.0000 | | NFM | Barrow | BNFL Security |
| 170.0375 | | NFM | Greater Manchester | Thameside Council |
| 170.0750 | | NFM | Fleetwood | Doctors Paging |
| 170.0875 | | NFM | Wrexham | Apollo Taxis |
| 170.2000 | 170.2000 | NFM | Bedford | Building Co. |
| 170.2250 | 170.2250 | NFM | Milford Haven | A2B Taxis |

**The UK Scanning Directory**

| Base | Mobile | Mode | Location | User and Notes |
|------|--------|------|----------|----------------|
| 170.2625 | | NFM | Worthing | Nynex Cable |
| 170.2875 | | NFM | Manchester | Taxis |
| 170.4000 | | NFM | Manchester | Taxis |
| 170.5000 | | NFM | Portsmouth | Taxis |
| 170.5175 | | NFM | Newmarket | La Hoge Farm |
| 170.6125 | | NFM | Perren Purth | Taxis |
| 170.7650 | | NFM | Newcastle | Security |
| 170.9750 | | NFM | Burnley | Corporation Base |
| 171.0600 | | NFM | Nuneaton | Council |
| 171.1000 | | NFM | Manchester | Private ambulance service |
| 171.4625 | | NFM | Barrow | Council Highways & Cleansing |
| 171.4750 | 166.6750 | NFM | Southampton | A2B Taxis |
| 171.5625 | | NFM | Liverpool | Panda Security |
| 171.6125 | | NFM | Isle of Man | Nobles Hospital |
| 171.6850 | | NFM | Heworth | Leam Taxis |
| 171.7000 | | NFM | Manchester | Refuse Collection |
| | | NFM | Nationwide | BBC O/B Link (OL-94) |
| 171.8500 | 171.8500 | NFM | Newport | Steelworks Paging |
| 171.9625 | | NFM | New Biggen | Taxis |
| 172.0000 | | NFM | Brechin | Builders |
| 172.0000 | 172.0000 | NFM | Jersey | Dock Crane Operators |
| 172.0000 | 167.2000 | NFM | Nationwide | PMR  Demo Chan |
| | | NFM | Scotland | Scottish Sports Council |
| | | NFM | Slough | Mars Factory |
| 172.0000 | 172.0000 | NFM | West Midlands | Short Term Hire |
| 172.1250 | | NFM | Grundon | Waste disposal |
| 172.1500 | 176.3500 | NFM | Haywards Heath | Census Taxis |
| 172.2125 | | NFM | Manchester | Taxis |
| 172.3125 | 172.3125 | NFM | Jersey | HM Customs & Excise Channel 6 |
| 172.3250 | 172.3250 | NFM | Jersey | Fort Regent Channel 4 |
| 172.3500 | 172.3500 | NFM | Jersey | Fort Regent Channel 2 |
| 172.3750 | | NFM | Cramlinton | Taxis |
| 172.4500 | | NFM | Walsall | Taxi |
| 172.5250 | | NFM | Carno | Laura Ashley Security |
| 172.6000 | | NFM | Nationwide | BBC O/B Link (OL-94) |
| 172.6625 | | NFM | Worthing | Taxis |
| 172.7000 | 172.7000 | NFM | Jersey | HM Customs & Excise Channel 2 |
| 172.7500 | 167.9450 | NFM | Ashington | Collier Taxi |
| 172.7875 | 172.7875 | NFM | Jersey | HM Customs & Excise Channel 4 |
| | | NFM | Swansea | Docks |
| 173.0000 | 172.8625 | NFM | Nationwide | Low Power Guitar Systems |
| 173.0250 | | NFM | Nationwide | DTI Channel 1 |

**173.04375 - 173.09375 MHz     PMR Simplex 12.5 kHz NFM**

| Base | Mobile | Mode | Location | User and Notes |
|------|--------|------|----------|----------------|
| 173.0500 | | NFM | Nationwide | DTI Channel 2 |
| 173.0625 | | NFM | Bristol | DHSS |
| | | NFM | Nationwide | RAC Network Q Rally |
| 173.0750 | | NFM | Nationwide | Stolen Car Detector Systems |
| | | NFM | Nationwide | DTI Channel 3 |
| 173.0875 | | NFM | Jersey | Surveyors |

**173.09375 - 173.9875 MHz  Low Power Devices, Radio Deaf Aids, Biological Telemetry, Garage Door Openers, and Police Usage and Indoor**

| Base | Mobile | Mode | Location | User and Notes |
|------|--------|------|----------|----------------|

RADIO MICROPHONES

| Base | Mobile | Mode | Location | User and Notes |
|------|--------|------|----------|----------------|
| 173.0875 | | NFM | Torridon | National Trust for Scotland Rangers |
| 173.1875 | | NFM | Nationwide | Mobile Alarm Paging |
| 173.2125 | | NFM | Llanelli | BSC Trostre Works |
| 173.2200 | | NFM | Scotland | Singing Kettle Entertainment Grp |
| 173.2250 | | NFM | Nationwide | Building Site Alarms |
| | | NFM | Nationwide | Radio Controled Garage Doors |
| | | NFM | Nationwide | Short Range Security Alarms |
| | | NFM | Nationwide | Suma Designs Bugging Devices |
| 173.3500 | | NFM | Jersey | School Deaf Aids |
| 173.3500 | | NFM | Llanelli | BSC Trostre Works |
| 173.4000 | | NFM | Jersey | School Deaf Aids |
| | | NFM | Nationwide | Deaf Aids |
| 173.4625 | | NFM | Jersey | School Deaf Aids |
| 173.4650 | | NFM | Nationwide | Deaf Aids |
| 173.5450 | | NFM | Nationwide | Deaf Aids |
| 173.6000 | | NFM | Nationwide | Yellow Channel |
| | | NFM | Worthing | Radio Mic Social Club |
| 173.6400 | | NFM | Jersey | School Deaf Aids |
| | | NFM | Nationwide | Deaf Aids |
| 173.8000 | | NFM | Nationwide | Theatre Radio Microphone |
| | | NFM | Nationwide | Yellow Channel |
| | | NFM | Perth | Church Radio Microphone |
| | | NFM | Swansea | Elim Pentecostal Church |
| | | NFM | Worcester | Swan Theatre Radio Mic |
| | | NFM | Worthing | Radio Mic Community Hall |
| 173.8250 | | NFM | Newport | Panic-Phone Alarms |
| 173.9500 | | NFM | Jersey | School Deaf Aids |
| 174.0000 | | NFM | London | Transport Co. |
| 174.0125 | | NFM | Nationwide | RAC Network Q Rally |
| 174.0250 | | NFM | Nationwide | RAC Network Q Rally |
| 174.0375 | | NFM | Nationwide | RAC Network Q Rally |
| 174.1000 | | NFM | Guernsey | Channel TV Radio Mics |
| | | NFM | Nationwide | Phil Collins Radio Mic (2) |
| | | NFM | Nationwide | Red Channel |
| | | NFM | Nationwide | Theatre Radio Microphone |
| 174.1100 | | NFM | Scotland | Singing Kettle Entertainment Grp |
| 174.1180 | | NFM | Scotland | Singing Kettle Entertainment Grp |
| 174.2875 | | NFM | Edinburgh | Edinburgh Castle Security |
| 174.3000 | | NFM | Nationwide | Church Radio Mics |
| 174.4250 | | NFM | London | Transport Co. |
| 174.5000 | | NFM | Glasgow | Baptist Church Mic |
| | | NFM | Leicester | Church Radio Mix |
| | | NFM | Nationwide | Blue Channel |
| | | NFM | Nationwide | Phil Collins Radio Mic (1) |
| | | NFM | Worcester | Worcester Cathdral Radio Mic |
| 174.5250 | | NFM | Nationwide | Low Power Guitar Systems |
| 174.6000 | | NFM | Nationwide | Channel Radio Mics |
| 174.6625 | | NFM | Aberdeen | ASD |
| 174.6625 | | NFM | Scarborough | Theatre Mic |
| 174.6750 | | NFM | Nationwide | Channel Radio Mics Green |
| 174.7000 | | WFM | Jersey | BBC Jersey Radio Mics |
| | | NFM | Nationwide | Channel Radio Mics |
| 174.8000 | | NFM | Blackpool | St Thomas Church Radio Mic |
| | | NFM | Nationwide | Green Channel |
| | | NFM | Nationwide | Theatre Radio Microphone |

| Base | Mobile | Mode | Location | User and Notes |
|------|--------|------|----------|----------------|
| 174.8000 | | NFM | Prescot | Leisure Centre Mics |
| | | NFM | Southampton | Mecca Bingo Radio Mic |
| 174.9750 | | NFM | Dorset | 2CR VHF Radio Microphones |
| 175.0000 | | NFM | Ambleside | Methodist Church Radio Mic |
| | | WFM | Jersey | BBC Jersey Radio Mics |
| | | NFM | Nationwide | Theatre Radio Microphone |
| | | NFM | Nationwide | White Channel |
| | | NFM | Scotland | Singing Kettle Entertainment Grp |
| | | NFM | St. Helier | Church Radio Microphone |
| 175.0875 | | NFM | Canvey Island | Trio Radio Cars |
| 175.5200 | | NFM | Nationwide | ITV Radio Microphone |
| 176.1625 | | NFM | Sheffield | City Cars |
| 176.1875 | | NFM | Basildon | Taxis |
| 176.4000 | | NFM | Nationwide | Theatre Radio Microphone |
| 176.6000 | | NFM | Nationwide | BBC Radio Microphone |
| 176.8000 | | NFM | Nationwide | BBC News Radio Mics |
| 177.0000 | | NFM | Nationwide | Theatre Radio Microphone |

**177.2000 - 181.7000 MHz   Trunked PMR Base Repeaters 12.5 kHz (Split + 8.0 kHz)**

| Base | Mobile | Mode | Location | User and Notes |
|------|--------|------|----------|----------------|
| 177.1250 | 185.1250 | NFM | London | Multi-Business Shared Repeater |
| 177.4625 | 185.4625 | NFM | London | Multi-Business Shared Repeater |
| 177.6125 | 185.6125 | NFM | London | Courier Service |
| | | NFM | London (Heathrow) | Ground Staff |
| 177.7625 | 185.7625 | NFM | London | RSPCA |
| 177.9125 | 185.9125 | NFM | London | London Bus Co. |
| 178.0625 | 186.0625 | NFM | London | RSPCA |
| 178.2375 | 186.2375 | NFM | Stirling | Data Link |
| 178.2625 | 186.2625 | NFM | London | Courier Service |
| 178.2875 | 186.2875 | NFM | London | Private ambulance service |
| 178.3250 | 186.3250 | NFM | London | Hammersmith Council |
| 178.3625 | 186.3625 | NFM | London | Courier Service |
| 178.4750 | 186.4750 | NFM | London | Thames Water |
| 178.5125 | 186.5125 | NFM | London | Multi-Business Shared Repeater |
| 178.6625 | 186.6625 | NFM | London | Multi-Business Shared Repeater |
| 178.7250 | 186.7250 | NFM | Tayside | Data Repeater |
| 178.8125 | 186.8125 | NFM | London | Multi-Business Shared Repeater |
| 178.9625 | 186.9625 | NFM | London | Multi-Business Shared Repeater |
| 179.0250 | 187.0250 | NFM | Tayside | Data Repeater |
| 179.1125 | 187.1125 | NFM | London | Multi-Business Shared Repeater |
| 179.1875 | 187.1875 | NFM | Glasgow | Data Link |
| 180.0000 | 188.0000 | NFM | Nationwide | Illegal Bugging Devices |
| | | NFM | Space | Cosmos 1870 Satellite |
| 180.0125 | 188.0125 | NFM | London | Multi-Business Shared Repeater |
| 180.1250 | 188.1250 | NFM | Space | Cosmos Satellite |
| 180.1500 | 188.1500 | NFM | Bedford | City Link |
| 180.1625 | 188.1625 | NFM | London | Big Bus tours |
| 180.4125 | 188.4125 | NFM | Warwickshire | Warwickshire Parcels Ltd |
| 180.4250 | 188.4250 | NFM | London | Multi-Business Shared Repeater |
| 180.5375 | 188.5375 | NFM | Manchester | HGV Haulage |
| 180.5750 | 188.5750 | NFM | London | Locksmith Ambulances |
| 180.7250 | 188.7250 | NFM | London | Multi-Business Shared Repeater |
| 180.9500 | 188.9500 | NFM | Tayside | Data Repeater |
| 181.0000 | 189.0000 | NFM | Birmingham | Hippodrome Theatre |
| 181.1375 | 189.1375 | NFM | Manchester | Transport Company |
| 181.2000 | 189.2000 | NFM | Pocklington | Orchard Taxis |

| Base | Mobile | Mode | Location | User and Notes |
|------|--------|------|----------|----------------|

| Base | Mobile | Mode | Location | User and Notes |
|------|--------|------|----------|----------------|
| 181.5000 | | NFM | London | BBC Lime Grove Feed to TS2 O/B Mobile |

**181.7000 - 181.8000 MHz   BROADCASTING LINKS**
This band coincides with French TV so is unsuitable for PMR.

**181.8000 - 183.5000 MHz   PMR 12.5 kHz NFM DUPLEX**

**183.5000 - 184.5000 MHz   METER READING**
This band also coincides with French TV so is unsuitable for PMR. It is allocated to future remote reading applications.

**184.5000 - 185.2000 MHz   RADIO MICROPHONES NFM**

| Base | Mobile | Mode | Location | User and Notes |
|------|--------|------|----------|----------------|
| 184.6000 | | NFM | Nationwide | BBC News Radio Mics |
| 184.8000 | | NFM | Jersey | Channel TV Radio Mics |
| | | NFM | Nationwide | ITV Radio Microphone |
| 185.0000 | | NFM | Nationwide | ITV Radio Microphone |
| | | NFM | Tayside | Radio Tay OB Mics |

**185.2000 - 189.7000 MHz   PMR MOBILES COVERING M1 12.5 kHz (SPLIT 8.0 kHz)**

| Base | Mobile | Mode | Location | User and Notes |
|------|--------|------|----------|----------------|
| 187.0100 | | WFM | London | Community Radio Feed to 100.6 MHz |

**189.7000 - 189.8000 MHz   BROADCASTING LINKS**

| Base | Mobile | Mode | Location | User and Notes |
|------|--------|------|----------|----------------|
| 188.0000 | | NFM | London | Police discrete PMG |
| 189.7025 | | NFM | Twickenham | BBC ITV Links Thames TV |
| 189.7813 | | NFM | Twickenham | Thames TV |
| 189.7938 | | NFM | Twickenham | BBC ITV Links Thames TV |

**189.8000 - 191.5000 MHz   PMR 12.5 kHz NFM DUPLEX**

| Base | Mobile | Mode | Location | User and Notes |
|------|--------|------|----------|----------------|
| 190.1500 | 206.1500 | NFM | Penygrain | Railway cab radio link |

**191.5000 - 193.2000 MHz   RADIO MICROPHONES AND LIMITRD PMR**

| Base | Mobile | Mode | Location | User and Notes |
|------|--------|------|----------|----------------|
| 191.9000 | | NFM | Scarborough | Theatre Microphone |
| 192.6000 | | NFM | Nationwide | BBC News Radio Mics |
| 192.8000 | | WFM | Nationwide | BBC Antiques Roadshow Mics |
| | | NFM | Nationwide | ITV Radio Microphone |
| 193.0000 | | NFM | Nationwide | BBC Radio Microphone |
| 193.1525 | | NFM | Glasgow | Strathclyde Buses |

**193.2000 - 199.5000 MHz   PMR MOBILES 12.5 kHz (BASE + 8.0 MHz)**

| Base | Mobile | Mode | Location | User and Notes |
|------|--------|------|----------|----------------|
| 193.4625 | 201.4625 | NFM | London | Transport Co. |
| 193.5625 | 201.5625 | NFM | London | Transport Co. |
| 193.6125 | 201.6125 | NFM | London | Transport Co. |
| 193.7125 | 201.7125 | NFM | London | Transport Co. |
| 193.7625 | 201.7625 | NFM | London | Transport Co. |
| 193.8625 | 201.8625 | NFM | London | Transport Co. |
| 193.9125 | 201.9125 | NFM | London | Transport Co. |
| 193.9250 | 201.9250 | NFM | Walsall | Council |
| 193.9625 | 201.9625 | NFM | London | Transport Co. |
| 194.0625 | 205.0625 | NFM | Manchester | Metro Link |
| 194.3125 | 202.3125 | NFM | London | Transport Co. |
| 194.4250 | 202.4250 | NFM | London | Transport Co. |
| 194.4750 | 202.4750 | NFM | Walsall | Trunked PMR |

| Base | Mobile | Mode | Location | User and Notes |
|---|---|---|---|---|
| 195.0125 | 203.0125 | NFM | London | Transport Co. |
| 195.2000 | 203.2000 | NFM | Walney Island | Mobile Coastguard |
| 196.1125 | 204.0000 | NFM | Mid Wales | Railway Repeaters |
| 196.8125 | 204.8125 | NFM | London | Transport Co. |
| 196.8500 | 204.8500 | NFM | Achanalt | Railway cab radio link |
| | | NFM | Garelochead | Railway cab radio link |
| | | NFM | Helensburgh Upper | Railway cab radio link |
| 196.8750 | 204.8750 | NFM | Walsall | Maintenance |
| 196.9625 | 204.9625 | NFM | London | Transport Co. |
| 197.0125 | 205.0125 | NFM | Garve | Railway cab radio link |
| | | NFM | London | Capitol Bus |
| 197.0500 | 205.0500 | NFM | Achasheen | Railway cab radio link |
| | | NFM | Achnasheallach | Railway cab radio link |
| | | NFM | Arrochar | Railway cab radio link |
| | | NFM | Attadale | Railway cab radio link |
| | | NFM | Duirinish | Railway cab radio link |
| | | NFM | Duncraig | Railway cab radio link |
| | | NFM | Glen Douglas (Loop) | Railway cab radio link |
| | | NFM | Glenfinnan | Railway cab radio link |
| | | NFM | Kyle of Lochalsh | Railway cab radio link |
| | | NFM | Locheilside | Railway cab radio link |
| | | NFM | Mallaig | Railway cab radio link |
| | | NFM | Plockton | Railway cab radio link |
| | | NFM | Strathcarron | Railway cab radio link |
| | | NFM | Stromferry | Railway cab radio link |
| 197.1000 | 205.1000 | NFM | Arisaig | Railway cab radio link |
| | | NFM | Beasdale | Railway cab radio link |
| | | NFM | Corrour | Railway cab radio link |
| | | NFM | Dingwall | Railway cab radio link |
| | | NFM | Inverness | Railway cab radio link |
| | | NFM | Morar | Railway cab radio link |
| | | NFM | Muir of Ord | Railway cab radio link |
| | | NFM | Roy Bridge | Railway cab radio link |
| | | NFM | Tulloch | Railway cab radio link |
| 197.1500 | 205.1500 | NFM | Bridge of Orchy | Railway cab radio link |
| | | NFM | Rannoch | Railway cab radio link |
| 197.4000 | 205.4000 | NFM | Ardlui | Railway cab radio link |
| | | NFM | Caersws | Railway cab radio link |
| | | NFM | Machynlleth | Railway cab radio link |
| | | NFM | Newtown | Railway cab radio link |
| | | NFM | Shrewsbury | Railway cab radio link |
| | | NFM | Sutton Bridge Junction | Railway cab radio link |
| | | NFM | Welshpool | Railway cab radio link |
| 197.6500 | 205.6500 | NFM | Darsham | Railway cab radio link |
| | | NFM | Saxmundham | Railway cab radio link |
| 197.7500 | 205.7500 | NFM | Dovey Junction | Railway cab radio link |
| 197.8000 | 205.8000 | NFM | Brampton | Railway cab radio link |
| | | NFM | Eccles | Railway cab radio link |
| 197.9000 | 205.9000 | NFM | Westerfield | Railway cab radio link |
| | | NFM | Woodbridge | Railway cab radio link |
| 197.9500 | 205.9500 | NFM | Banavie | Railway cab radio link |
| | | NFM | Barmouth | Railway cab radio link |
| | | NFM | Fort William | Railway cab radio link |
| | | NFM | Llanaber | Railway cab radio link |
| | | NFM | Loch Eil O/B | Railway cab radio link |
| | | NFM | Tywtn | Railway cab radio link |

| Base | Mobile | Mode | Location | User and Notes |
|---|---|---|---|---|
| 198.0000 | 206.1000 | NFM | Barmouth | Railway cab radio link |
| | | NFM | Braemar | Railway cab radio link |
| | | NFM | Oulton Broad South | Railway cab radio link |
| 198.1500 | 206.1500 | NFM | Harlech | Railway cab radio link |
| | | NFM | Penychain | Railway cab radio link |
| | | NFM | Portmadoc | Railway cab radio link |
| | | NFM | Pwllheli | Railway cab radio link |
| 198.1625 | 206.1625 | NFM | Bristol | Lawrence Hill Buses Control |
| 198.3500 | 206.3500 | NFM | Aberystwyth | Railway cab radio link |
| | | NFM | Bortu | Railway cab radio link |
| | | NFM | Dovey Junction | Railway cab radio link |
| 198.4500 | 206.4500 | NFM | Isle Of Sheppey | Railtrack |
| 198.7625 | 206.7625 | NFM | London | Medicall |

**199.5000 -00.5000MHz   BROADCASTING LINKS**

**200.5000 -01.2000 MHz   RADIO MICROPHONES**

| Base | Mobile | Mode | Location | User and Notes |
|---|---|---|---|---|
| 200.3000 | | NFM | Scarborough | Theatre Microphone |
| 200.5000 | | NFM | Nationwide | Radio Mics |
| 200.6000 | | WFM | Nationwide | BBC Antiques Roadshow Mics |
| 200.6000 | | NFM | Nationwide | BBC Radio Microphone |
| 200.8000 | | NFM | Nationwide | ITV News Radio Mics |
| 201.0000 | | NFM | Jersey | Channel TV Radio Mics |
| | | NFM | Nationwide | ITV Radio Microphone |

**201.2000 -07.5000 MHz   TRUNKED BASE PMR 12.5 kHz**
**(MOBILES -8.0 MHz)**

| Base | Mobile | Mode | Location | User and Notes |
|---|---|---|---|---|
| 201.2000 | 193.2000 | NFM | Nationwide | Trunked PMR |
| 201.2125 | 193.2125 | NFM | Nationwide | Trunked PMR |
| 201.2250 | 193.2250 | NFM | Nationwide | Trunked PMR |
| 201.2375 | 193.2375 | NFM | Nationwide | Trunked PMR |
| 201.2500 | 193.2500 | NFM | Perth | Trunked PMR |
| | | NFM | Rugby | Electricians |
| 201.2625 | 193.2625 | NFM | Nationwide | Trunked PMR |
| 201.2750 | 193.2750 | NFM | Nationwide | Trunked PMR |
| 201.2875 | 193.2875 | NFM | Nationwide | Trunked PMR |
| 201.3000 | 193.3000 | NFM | Nationwide | Trunked PMR |
| 201.3125 | 193.3125 | NFM | Central Scotland | Bus Company |
| | | NFM | Sheffield | S Yorkshire Transport (Lead Mill) |
| | | NFM | South Yorkshire | Bus Company |
| 201.3250 | 193.3250 | NFM | Nationwide | Trunked PMR |
| 201.3375 | | NFM | Nationwide | Trunked PMR |
| 201.3500 | 193.3500 | NFM | Nationwide | Trunked PMR |
| 201.3625 | 193.3625 | NFM | Central Scotland | Bus Company |
| | | NFM | London | Bus Company |
| | | NFM | Newport | Bus Company |
| | | NFM | South Yorkshire | Bus Company |
| 201.3750 | 193.3750 | NFM | Nationwide | Trunked PMR |
| 201.3875 | 193.3875 | NFM | Nationwide | Trunked PMR |
| 201.4000 | 193.4000 | NFM | Tayside | Trunked PMR |
| 201.4125 | 193.4125 | NFM | Alder Valley | Bus Company |
| | | NFM | Manchester | Bus Company |
| | | NFM | Strathclyde | Bus Company |
| 201.4175 | 193.4375 | NFM | Nationwide | Trunked PMR |
| 201.4250 | 193.4250 | NFM | Nationwide | Trunked PMR |

| Base | Mobile | Mode | Location | User and Notes |
|------|--------|------|----------|----------------|
| 201.4500 | 193.4500 | NFM | Nationwide | Trunked PMR |
| 201.4625 | 193.4625 | NFM | Glasgow | Bus Company |
| | | NFM | London | London Transport |
| 201.4750 | 193.4750 | NFM | Nationwide | Trunked PMR |
| 201.4875 | 193.4875 | NFM | Nationwide | Trunked PMR |
| 201.5000 | 193.5000 | NFM | London | Securiplan Plc Security |
| 201.5125 | 193.5125 | NFM | Cardiff | Bus Company |
| | | NFM | London | London Transport |
| | | NFM | West Midlands | Bus Company |
| | | NFM | West Yorkshire | Bus Company |
| 201.5250 | 193.5250 | NFM | Hull | Council Housing Repairs |
| | | NFM | Hull | Mobile Doctors Service |
| 201.5375 | 193.5375 | NFM | Nationwide | Trunked PMR |
| 201.5500 | 193.5500 | NFM | Tayside | Data Link/Trunked PMR |
| 201.5625 | 193.5625 | NFM | London | Bus Company |
| | | NFM | Manchester | Metrolink Control |
| | | NFM | Northampton | Bus Company |
| | | NFM | Scotland (West) | Bus Company |
| | | NFM | Yorkshire | Bus Company |
| 201.5750 | 193.5750 | NFM | Nationwide | Trunked PMR |
| 201.5875 | 193.5075 | NFM | Nationwide | Trunked PMR |
| 201.6000 | 193.6000 | NFM | Nationwide | Trunked PMR |
| 201.6125 | 193.6125 | NFM | Glasgow | Strathclyde Buses |
| | | NFM | London | London Transport |
| | | NFM | Manchester | Bus Company |
| | | NFM | Strathclyde | Bus Company |
| 201.6250 | 193.6250 | NFM | Nationwide | Trunked PMR |
| 201.6375 | 193.6375 | NFM | Nationwide | Trunked PMR |
| 201.6500 | 193.6500 | NFM | London | Doctors call out |
| 201.6625 | 193.6625 | NFM | Birmingham | West Midlands Bus Travel |
| | | NFM | Cardiff | Bus Company |
| | | NFM | Chester | Bus Company |
| | | NFM | Darlington | Bus Company |
| | | NFM | Lancashire | Squires Transport |
| | | NFM | London | London Transport |
| | | NFM | Manchester | Bus Company |
| | | NFM | Strathclyde | Bus Company |
| 201.6750 | 193.6750 | NFM | Nationwide | Trunked PMR |
| 201.6875 | 193.6875 | NFM | Manchester | Transport |
| 201.7000 | 193.7000 | NFM | Tayside | Data Link/Trunked PMR |
| 201.7125 | 193.7125 | NFM | Cardiff | Bus Company |
| | | NFM | London | London Transport |
| | | NFM | Tyne & Wear | Bus Company |
| 201.7250 | 193.7250 | NFM | Nationwide | Trunked PMR |
| 201.7375 | 193.7375 | NFM | Nationwide | Trunked PMR |
| 201.7500 | 193.7500 | NFM | Nationwide | Trunked PMR |
| 201.7600 | | NFM | Falkirk | Midland Bluebird Buses |
| 201.7625 | 193.7625 | NFM | London | London Transport |
| | | NFM | Rotherham | South Yorkshire Transport |
| | | NFM | Scotland | Midland Scottish |
| | | NFM | South Yorkshire | Bus Company |
| 201.7750 | 193.7750 | NFM | Nationwide | Trunked PMR |
| 201.7875 | 193.7875 | NFM | Nationwide | Trunked PMR |

| Base | Mobile | Mode | Location | User and Notes |
|------|--------|------|----------|----------------|
| 201.8000 | 193.8000 | NFM | London | Security Company |
| 201.8125 | | NFM | London | United |
| | | NFM | Manchester | United |
| 201.8125 | 193.8125 | NFM | Nationwide | Channel 42 |
| | | NFM | West Midlands | United |
| 201.8250 | 193.8250 | NFM | Nationwide | PMR Band III Channel |
| 201.8375 | 193.8375 | NFM | Nationwide | Trunked PMR |
| 201.8500 | 193.8500 | NFM | Nationwide | PMR Band III Channel |
| | | NFM | Tayside | Trunked PMR/Data |
| 201.8625 | 193.8625 | NFM | Glasgow | Strathclyde Buses |
| | | NFM | London | Buses |
| | | NFM | London | London Transport |
| | | NFM | Nationwide | PMR Band III Channel 40 |
| | | NFM | Strathclyde | Buses |
| 201.8750 | 193.8750 | NFM | Nationwide | Band III Channel |
| 201.8875 | 193.8875 | NFM | Manchester | Transport |
| | | NFM | Nationwide | Trunked PMR |
| 201.9000 | 193.9000 | NFM | Nationwide | Trunked PMR |
| 201.9125 | 193.9125 | NFM | London | Buses |
| | | NFM | London | London Transport |
| | | NFM | Nationwide | Band III Channel 30 |
| | | NFM | Warrington | Buses |
| | | NFM | West Yorkshire | Buses |
| 201.9250 | 193.9250 | NFM | Nationwide | Trunked PMR |
| 201.9375 | 193.9375 | NFM | Nationwide | Trunked PMR |
| 201.9500 | 193.9500 | NFM | Nationwide | Trunked PMR |
| 201.9625 | 193.9625 | NFM | Bristol | Buses |
| | | NFM | London | London Transport |
| | | NFM | Manchester | GM Buses |
| | | NFM | Yorkshire | Buses |
| 201.9750 | 193.9750 | NFM | Nationwide | Trunked PMR |
| 201.9875 | 193.9875 | NFM | Nationwide | Trunked PMR |
| 202.0000 | 194.0000 | NFM | Nationwide | Trunked PMR |
| 202.0125 | 194.0125 | NFM | Bristol | Buses |
| | | NFM | Derby | Buses |
| | | NFM | London | London Transport |
| | | NFM | Manchester | GM Buses |
| | | NFM | Tyne & Wear | Buses |
| 202.0250 | 194.0250 | NFM | Nationwide | PMR Band III Channel |
| 202.0375 | 194.0375 | NFM | Nationwide | PMR Band III Channel |
| 202.0500 | 194.0500 | NFM | Nationwide | PMR Band III Channel |
| 202.0625 | 194.0625 | NFM | London | London Transport |
| | | NFM | Manchester | Metrolink Control |
| | | NFM | Nationwide | PMR Band III Channel 59 |
| | | NFM | Sheffield | S. Yorkshire Transport (Herris) |
| | | NFM | Sheffield, Olive Grove | Mainline Bases Channel 58 |
| 202.0750 | 194.0750 | NFM | Nationwide | PMR Band III Channel |
| 202.0875 | 194.0875 | NFM | Nationwide | Trunked PMR |
| 202.1000 | 194.1000 | NFM | Nationwide | Trunked PMR |
| 202.1125 | 194.1125 | NFM | Nationwide | National Express Buses |
| 202.1250 | 194.1250 | NFM | Nationwide | Trunked PMR |
| 202.1375 | 194.1375 | NFM | Nationwide | Trunked PMR |
| 202.1500 | 194.1500 | NFM | Tayside | Data Link/Trunked PMR |

| Base | Mobile | Mode | Location | User and Notes |
|---|---|---|---|---|
| 202.1625 | 194.1625 | NFM | Birmingham | West Midlands Bus Travel |
| | | NFM | Manchester | GM Buses |
| | | NFM | Nationwide | National Express Buses |
| | | NFM | Nationwide | PMR Band III Channel 38 |
| 202.1750 | 194.1750 | NFM | Nationwide | PMR Band III Channel |
| 202.1875 | 194.1875 | NFM | Nationwide | Trunked PMR |
| 202.2000 | 194.2000 | NFM | Nationwide | Trunked PMR |
| 202.2125 | 194.2125 | NFM | Birmingham | West Midlands Bus Travel |
| | | NFM | Hull | Buses |
| | | NFM | London | London Transport |
| | | NFM | Scotland | East Scottish Buses |
| | | NFM | Sheffield | Trams |
| | | NFM | West Yorkshire | Buses |
| 202.2250 | 194.2250 | NFM | Nationwide | Trunked PMR |
| 202.2375 | 194.2375 | NFM | Nationwide | PMR Band III Channel |
| 202.2500 | 194.2500 | NFM | Nationwide | Trunked PMR |
| 202.2625 | 194.2625 | NFM | Ely | Buses |
| | | NFM | Maidstone | Buses |
| | | NFM | Manchester | GM Buses |
| | | NFM | West Yorkshire | Northern General |
| 202.2750 | 194.2750 | NFM | Nationwide | Trunked PMR |
| 202.2875 | 194.2875 | NFM | London | London Transport |
| 202.3000 | 194.3000 | NFM | Portsmouth | Taxis |
| 202.3125 | | NFM | London | London Transport |
| 202.3125 | 194.3125 | NFM | Manchester | GM Buses |
| 202.3125 | 194.3215 | NFM | Swindon | Bass |
| | | NFM | Tyne & Wear | Buses |
| 202.3175 | 194.3175 | NFM | London | London Transport |
| | | NFM | London | Revenue Protection Inspectors Ch 2 |
| 202.3250 | 194.3250 | NFM | Nationwide | Trunked PMR |
| 202.3375 | 194.3375 | NFM | Nationwide | Trunked PMR |
| 202.3500 | 194.3500 | NFM | Nationwide | Trunked PMR |
| | | NFM | London | London Transport |
| | | NFM | Manchester | GM Buses |
| | | NFM | Nationwide | PMR Band III Channel 32 |
| 202.3625 | 194.3625 | NFM | Sheffield | S. Yorkshire Transport (East Dark) |
| | | NFM | Tyne & Wear | Buses |
| 202.3750 | 194.3750 | NFM | Nationwide | Trunked PMR |
| 202.3875 | 194.3875 | NFM | Nationwide | Trunked PMR |
| 202.4000 | 194.4000 | NFM | Nationwide | Trunked PMR |
| 202.4125 | 194.4125 | NFM | Nationwide | PMR Band III Channel |
| 202.4250 | 194.4250 | NFM | Nationwide | PMR Band III Channel |
| 202.4375 | 194.4375 | NFM | Nationwide | Trunked PMR |
| 202.4500 | 194.4500 | NFM | Nationwide | Trunked PMR |
| 202.4625 | 194.4625 | NFM | London | London Transport |
| | | NFM | Manchester | GM Buses |
| | | NFM | Midlands | Buses |
| | | NFM | Nationwide | PMR Band III Channel 31 |
| 202.4750 | 194.4750 | NFM | Nationwide | Trunked PMR |
| 202.5000 | 194.5000 | NFM | Nationwide | Trunked PMR |
| 202.5125 | 194.5125 | NFM | East Kent | Buses |
| | | NFM | Merseyside | Buses |
| | | NFM | South Wales | Buses |
| | | NFM | Tayside | Buses |

| Base | Mobile | Mode | Location | User and Notes |
|---|---|---|---|---|
| 202.5250 | 194.5250 | NFM | Nationwide | Trunked PMR |
| 202.5375 | 194.5375 | NFM | Nationwide | Trunked PMR |
| 202.5500 | 194.5500 | NFM | Nationwide | Trunked PMR |
| 202.5625 | 194.5625 | NFM | Nationwide | Trunked PMR |
| 202.5750 | 194.5750 | NFM | Nationwide | Trunked PMR |
| 202.5875 | 194.5875 | NFM | Nationwide | Trunked PMR |
| 202.6000 | 194.6000 | NFM | Nationwide | Trunked PMR |
| 202.6125 | 194.6125 | NFM | Nationwide | Trunked PMR |
| 202.6175 | 194.6075 | NFM | Nationwide | Trunked PMR |
| 202.6250 | 194.6250 | NFM | Nationwide | Trunked PMR |
| 202.6500 | 154.6500 | NFM | Nationwide | Trunked PMR |
| 202.6625 | 194.6625 | NFM | Nationwide | Trunked PMR |
| 202.6750 | 194.6750 | NFM | Nationwide | Trunked PMR |
| 202.6875 | 194.6875 | NFM | Nationwide | Trunked PMR |
| 202.7000 | 194.7000 | NFM | Nationwide | Trunked PMR |
| 202.7125 | 194.7125 | NFM | Nationwide | Trunked PMR |
| 202.7250 | 194.7250 | NFM | Nationwide | Trunked PMR |
| 202.7375 | 194.7375 | NFM | Nationwide | Trunked PMR |
| 202.7500 | 194.7500 | NFM | Stockport | Breakdown Recovery |
| 202.7625 | 194.7625 | NFM | Nationwide | Trunked PMR |
| 202.7750 | 194.7750 | NFM | Nationwide | Trunked PMR |
| 202.7875 | 194.7875 | NFM | Nationwide | Trunked PMR |
| 202.8000 | 194.8000 | NFM | Nationwide | Trunked PMR |
| 202.8125 | 194.8125 | NFM | Nationwide | Trunked PMR |
| 202.8250 | 194.8250 | NFM | Nationwide | Trunked PMR |
| 202.8375 | 194.8375 | NFM | Nationwide | Trunked PMR |
| 202.8500 | 194.8500 | NFM | Nationwide | Trunked PMR |
| 202.8625 | 194.8625 | NFM | Nationwide | Trunked PMR |
| 202.8750 | 194.8750 | NFM | Nationwide | Trunked PMR |
| 202.8875 | 194.8875 | NFM | Nationwide | Trunked PMR |
| 202.9000 | 194.9000 | NFM | Nationwide | Trunked PMR |
| 202.9125 | 194.9125 | NFM | Nationwide | Trunked PMR |
| 202.9250 | 194.9250 | NFM | Nationwide | Trunked PMR |
| 202.9375 | 194.9375 | NFM | Nationwide | Trunked PMR |
| 202.9500 | 194.9500 | NFM | Nationwide | Trunked PMR |
| 202.9625 | 194.9625 | NFM | Devon | Buses |
| | | NFM | Fife | Buses |
| | | NFM | London | Buses |
| | | NFM | Nationwide | Trunked PMR |
| | | NFM | West Midlands | Buses |
| | | NFM | West Yorkshire | Buses |
| 202.9756 | 194.9750 | NFM | Nationwide | Trunked PMR |
| 202.9875 | 194.9875 | NFM | Nationwide | Trunked PMR |
| 203.0000 | 195.0000 | NFM | London | R & I Blue Buses |
| 203.0125 | 195.0125 | NFM | Hampshire | Buses |
| | | NFM | London | London Transport |
| | | NFM | Scotland | East Scottish Buses |
| | | NFM | Sheffield | Trams |
| | | NFM | West Yorkshire | Buses |
| 203.0250 | 195.0250 | NFM | Nationwide | Trunked PMR |
| 203.0375 | 195.0375 | NFM | Manchester | Rescue & Recovery |
| 203.0500 | 195.0500 | NFM | Nationwide | Trunked PMR |

| Base | Mobile | Mode | Location | User and Notes |
|---|---|---|---|---|
| 203.0625 | 195.0625 | NFM | Devon | Buses |
| | | NFM | London | Buses |
| | | NFM | Sheffield | Trains |
| | | NFM | Tyne & Wear | Buses |
| | | NFM | West Yorkshire | Buses |
| 203.0750 | 195.0750 | NFM | Nationwide | PMR Band III Channel |
| 203.0875 | 195.0875 | NFM | Nationwide | PMR Band III Channel |
| 203.1000 | 195.1000 | NFM | Nationwide | PMR Band III Channel |
| 203.1125 | 195.1125 | NFM | Devon | Buses |
| | | NFM | Gt. Manchester | Buses |
| | | NFM | Maidstone | Buses |
| | | NFM | Strathclyde | Buses |
| 203.1250 | 195.1250 | NFM | Nationwide | Trunked PMR |
| 203.1375 | 195.1375 | NFM | Nationwide | Trunked PMR |
| 203.1500 | 195.1500 | NFM | Nationwide | Trunked PMR |
| 203.1625 | 195.1625 | NFM | London | Buses |
| | | NFM | Plymouth | Western National Buses |
| | | NFM | Yorkshire | Yorkshire Traction |
| 203.1750 | 195.1750 | NFM | Nationwide | Trunked PMR |
| 203.1875 | 195.1875 | NFM | Nationwide | PMR Band III Channel |
| 203.2000 | 195.2000 | NFM | Nationwide | PMR Band III Channel |
| 203.2125 | 195.2125 | NFM | Sheffield | S. Yorkshire Transport (Greenland) |
| 203.2250 | 195.2250 | NFM | Nationwide | PMR Band III Channel |
| 203.2375 | 195.2375 | NFM | Manchester | Bus Company |
| 203.2500 | 195.2500 | NFM | Nationwide | PMR Band III Channel |
| 203.2575 | 195.2175 | NFM | Nationwide | Band III Channel |
| 203.2625 | 195.2625 | NFM | Chesterfield | Buses |
| | | NFM | Hartlepool | Buses |
| | | NFM | London | London Transport Emergency Channel |
| 203.2750 | 195.2750 | NFM | Nationwide | PMR Band III Channel |
| 203.2875 | 195.2875 | NFM | Nationwide | PMR Band III Channel |
| 203.3000 | 195.3000 | NFM | Nationwide | PMR Band III Channel |
| 203.3125 | 195.3125 | NFM | Lancaster | Buses |
| | | NFM | London | London Transport |
| | | NFM | Nationwide | PMR Band III Channel 37 |
| 203.3250 | 195.3250 | NFM | Nationwide | PMR Band III Channel |
| 203.3375 | 195.3375 | NFM | Nationwide | PMR Band III Channel |
| 203.3500 | 195.3500 | NFM | Nationwide | PMR Band III Channel |
| 203.3625 | 195.3625 | NFM | Burnley | Buses |
| | | NFM | London | London Transport |
| | | NFM | Nationwide | PMR Band III Channel 36 |
| 203.3675 | 195.3875 | NFM | Nationwide | Trunked PMR |
| 203.3750 | 195.3750 | NFM | Nationwide | PMR Band III Channel |
| 203.3750 | | NFM | Nationwide | Railtrack |
| 203.4000 | 195.4000 | NFM | Nationwide | Trunked PMR |
| 203.4125 | 195.4125 | NFM | Nationwide | Trunked PMR |
| 203.4250 | 195.4250 | NFM | Nationwide | Trunked PMR |
| 203.4375 | 195.4375 | NFM | Nationwide | Trunked PMR |
| 203.4500 | 195.4500 | NFM | Nationwide | Trunked PMR |
| 203.4625 | 195.4625 | NFM | Nationwide | Trunked PMR |
| 203.4750 | 195.4750 | NFM | Nationwide | Trunked PMR |
| 203.4875 | 195.4875 | NFM | Dover | Night Page Security |
| 203.5000 | 195.5000 | NFM | Nationwide | Trunked PMR |
| 203.5125 | 195.5125 | NFM | Nationwide | Trunked PMR |
| 203.5250 | 193.5250 | NFM | Nationwide | Trunked PMR |
| 203.5375 | 195.5375 | NFM | Nationwide | Trunked PMR |

| Base | Mobile | Mode | Location | User and Notes |
|------|--------|------|----------|----------------|
| 203.5500 | 195.5500 | NFM | Nationwide | Trunked PMR |
| 203.5625 | 195.5625 | NFM | Pocklington | Peter Winn Tyres |
| 203.5750 | 195.5750 | NFM | Nationwide | Trunked PMR |
| 203.5875 | 195.5875 | NFM | Nationwide | Trunked PMR |
| 203.6000 | 195.6000 | NFM | Nationwide | Trunked PMR |
| 203.6125 | 195.6125 | NFM | Nationwide | Trunked PMR |
| 203.6250 | 195.6250 | NFM | Nationwide | Trunked PMR |
| 203.6375 | 195.6375 | NFM | Dover | Night Page Security |
| 203.6500 | 195.6500 | NFM | Nationwide | Trunked PMR |
| 203.6625 | 195.6625 | NFM | Central Scotland | Buses |
| | | NFM | Cynon Valley | Buses |
| | | NFM | London | London Transport |
| | | NFM | Nationwide | PMR Band III Channel 60 |
| | | NFM | Sheffield | South Yorkshire Transport (Halfway) |
| | | NFM | South Yorkshire | Buses |
| 203.6750 | 195.6750 | NFM | Nationwide | Trunked PMR |
| 203.6875 | 195.6875 | NFM | Nationwide | Trunked PMR |
| 203.7000 | 195.7000 | NFM | Nationwide | Trunked PMR |
| 203.7125 | 195.7125 | NFM | London | London Transport |
| | | NFM | Manchester | Buses |
| | | NFM | Tyne & Wear | Buses |
| 203.7250 | 195.7250 | NFM | Nationwide | Trunked PMR |
| 203.7375 | 195.7375 | NFM | Nationwide | PMR Band III Channel |
| 203.7500 | 195.7500 | NFM | Nationwide | Trunked PMR |
| 203.7625 | 195.7625 | NFM | Midlands | Tec & Development |
| 203.7750 | 195.7750 | NFM | Nationwide | PMR Band III Channel |
| 203.7875 | 195.7875 | NFM | Nationwide | Trunked PMR |
| 203.8000 | 195.8000 | NFM | Nationwide | Trunked PMR |
| 203.8125 | 195.8125 | NFM | Cardiff | Buses |
| | | NFM | Ribble | Buses |
| | | NFM | Sheffield | Main line buses data Channel 49 |
| | | NFM | West Midlands | Buses |
| 203.8250 | 195.8250 | NFM | Manchester | Transport |
| 203.8375 | 195.6375 | NFM | Nationwide | PMR Band III Channel |
| 203.8500 | 195.8500 | NFM | Nationwide | Trunked PMR |
| 203.8625 | | NFM | Halton | Buses |
| | | NFM | Oxford | Buses |
| 203.8625 | 195.6625 | NFM | West Yorkshire | Buses |
| 203.8675 | 195.8875 | NFM | Nationwide | PMR Band III Channel |
| 203.8750 | 195.8750 | NFM | Nationwide | PMR Band III Channel |
| 203.9000 | 195.9000 | NFM | Nationwide | Trunked PMR |
| 203.9125 | 195.9125 | NFM | Reading | Buses |
| | | NFM | Scotland | Highland Scottish Buses |
| | | NFM | West Midlands | Buses |
| | | NFM | West Yorkshire | Buses |
| 203.9250 | 195.9250 | NFM | Nationwide | Trunked PMR |
| 203.9375 | 195.9375 | NFM | Hythe | Nightforce Security |
| 203.9500 | 195.9500 | NFM | Nationwide | Trunked PMR |
| 203.9625 | 195.9625 | NFM | Nationwide | PMR Band III Channel |
| 203.9750 | 195.9750 | NFM | London | Security Company |
| 203.9875 | 195.9875 | NFM | Nationwide | Trunked PMR |
| 204.0000 | 196.0000 | NFM | Nationwide | Trunked PMR |
| 204.0125 | 196.0125 | NFM | Nationwide | Trunked PMR |
| 204.0250 | 196.0250 | NFM | Nationwide | Trunked PMR |
| 204.0375 | 196.0375 | NFM | Nationwide | PMR Band III Channel |
| 204.0500 | 196.0500 | NFM | Nationwide | Trunked PMR |

| Base | Mobile | Mode | Location | User and Notes |
|------|--------|------|----------|----------------|
| 204.0625 | 196.0625 | NFM | Nationwide | Trunked PMR |
| 204.0750 | 196.0750 | NFM | Nationwide | PMR Band III Channel |
| 204.0875 | 196.0875 | NFM | Nationwide | Trunked PMR |
| 204.1000 | 196.1000 | NFM | Nationwide | Trunked PMR |
| 204.1125 | 196.1125 | NFM | Nationwide | Trunked PMR |
| 204.1250 | 196.1250 | NFM | Nationwide | Trunked PMR |
| 204.1375 | 196.1375 | NFM | Nationwide | Trunked PMR |
| 204.1500 | 196.1500 | NFM | Nationwide | Trunked PMR |
| 204.1625 | 196.1625 | NFM | Nationwide | Trunked PMR |
| 204.1750 | 196.1750 | NFM | Nationwide | PMR Band III Channel |
| 204.1875 | 196.1875 | NFM | Hythe | Nightforce Security |
| 204.2000 | 196.2000 | NFM | Nationwide | Trunked PMR |
| 204.2125 | 196.2125 | NFM | Nationwide | Trunked PMR |
| 204.2250 | 196.2250 | NFM | Hull | Council Repairs |
|  |  | NFM | Hull | Doctors On Call |
| 204.2375 | 196.2375 | NFM | Nationwide | Trunked PMR |
| 204.2500 | 196.2500 | NFM | Nationwide | PMR Band III Channel |
| 204.2625 | 196.2625 | NFM | Nationwide | PMR Band III Channel |
| 204.2750 | 196.2750 | NFM | Nationwide | Trunked PMR |
| 204.2875 | 196.2875 | NFM | Nationwide | Trunked PMR |
| 204.3000 | 196.3000 | NFM | Nationwide | Trunked PMR |
| 204.3125 | 196.3125 | NFM | Nationwide | PMR Band III Channel |
| 204.3250 | 196.3250 | NFM | Nationwide | Trunked PMR |
| 204.3375 | 196.3375 | NFM | Nationwide | Trunked PMR |
| 204.3500 | 196.3500 | NFM | Nationwide | Trunked PMR |
| 204.3625 | 196.3625 | NFM | Nationwide | Trunked PMR |
| 204.3750 | 196.3750 | NFM | Nationwide | Trunked PMR |
| 204.3875 | 196.3875 | NFM | Nationwide | Trunked PMR |
| 204.4000 | 196.4000 | NFM | Nationwide | Trunked PMR |
| 204.4125 | 196.4125 | NFM | Nationwide | Trunked PMR |
| 204.4250 | 196.4250 | NFM | Nationwide | Trunked PMR |
| 204.4375 | 196.4375 | NFM | Nationwide | Trunked PMR |
| 204.4500 | 196.4500 | NFM | Nationwide | Trunked PMR |
| 204.4625 | 196.4625 | NFM | Nationwide | Trunked PMR |
| 204.4750 | 196.4750 | NFM | Nationwide | Trunked PMR |
| 204.4875 | 196.4875 | NFM | Nationwide | Trunked PMR |
| 204.5000 | 196.5000 | NFM | Nationwide | Trunked PMR |
| 204.5125 | 196.5125 | NFM | Nationwide | Trunked PMR |
| 204.5250 | 196.5250 | NFM | Nationwide | Trunked PMR |
| 204.5375 | 196.5375 | NFM | Nationwide | Trunked PMR |
| 204.5500 | 196.5500 | NFM | Nationwide | Trunked PMR |
| 204.5625 | 196.5625 | NFM | Nationwide | Trunked PMR |
| 204.5750 | 196.5750 | NFM | Nationwide | Trunked PMR |
| 204.5875 | 196.5875 | NFM | Tayside | Data Link |
| 204.6000 | 196.6000 | NFM | Nationwide | Trunked PMR |
| 204.6125 | 196.6125 | NFM | Nationwide | Trunked PMR |
| 204.6250 | 196.6250 | NFM | Nationwide | Trunked PMR |
| 204.6375 | 196.6375 | NFM | Nationwide | Trunked PMR |
| 204.6500 | 196.6500 | NFM | Nationwide | Trunked PMR |
| 204.6625 | 196.6625 | NFM | Nationwide | Trunked PMR |
| 204.6750 | 196.6750 | NFM | Nationwide | Trunked PMR |
| 204.6875 | 196.6875 | NFM | Nationwide | Trunked PMR |
| 204.7000 | 196.7000 | NFM | Nationwide | Trunked PMR |
| 204.7125 | 196.7125 | NFM | Birmingham | West Midlands Bus Travel |
|  |  | NFM | Nationwide | PMR Band III Channel 55 |
|  |  | NFM | Scotland | Tec & Development |

| Base | Mobile | Mode | Location | User and Notes |
|---|---|---|---|---|
| 204.7250 | 196.7250 | NFM | Nationwide | Trunked PMR |
| 204.7375 | 196.7375 | NFM | Tayside | Data Link |
| 204.7500 | 196.7500 | NFM | Nationwide | Trunked PMR |
| 204.7625 | 196.7625 | NFM | Birmingham | West Midlands Bus Travel |
| | | NFM | Bristol | Buses |
| | | NFM | London | Buses |
| | | NFM | Manchester | Buses |
| | | NFM | Nationwide | PMR Band III Channel 26 |
| | | NFM | Tyne & Wear | Buses |
| 204.7750 | 196.7750 | NFM | Nationwide | Trunked PMR |
| 204.7875 | 196.7875 | NFM | Nationwide | Trunked PMR |
| 204.8000 | 196.8000 | NFM | Nationwide | Trunked PMR |
| 204.8125 | 196.8125 | NFM | Cleveland | Buses |
| | | NFM | London | London Transport |
| | | NFM | Manchester | GM Buses |
| | | NFM | Midlands | Buses |
| | | NFM | Nationwide | PMR Band III Channel 53 |
| | | NFM | Ribble | Buses |
| 204.8250 | 196.8250 | NFM | Nationwide | Trunked PMR |
| 204.8375 | 196.8375 | NFM | Blackpool | Vehicle Recovery |
| | | NFM | Nationwide | Trunked PMR |
| 204.8500 | 196.8500 | NFM | Merseyside | Merseyside Electric |
| | | NFM | Nationwide | Railtrack |
| 204.8625 | 196.8625 | NFM | London | London Transport |
| | | NFM | Nationwide | PMR Band III Channel |
| 204.8750 | 196.8750 | NFM | Nationwide | Trunked PMR |
| 204.8875 | 196.8875 | NFM | Nationwide | Trunked PMR |
| 204.9000 | 196.9000 | NFM | Caersws | Mid Wales Railway Line RETB |
| | | NFM | Nationwide | Railtrack Channel 353 |
| | | NFM | Newcastle | Metro Rail System |
| 204.9125 | 196.9125 | NFM | London | London Transport |
| | | NFM | Manchester | GM Buses |
| | | NFM | Nationwide | PMR Band III Channel 29 |
| | | NFM | Tyne & Wear | Buses |
| 204.9250 | 196.9250 | NFM | Nationwide | Trunked PMR |
| 204.9375 | 196.9375 | NFM | Nationwide | Trunked PMR |
| 204.9500 | 196.9500 | NFM | Nationwide | Railtrack Channel 357 |
| | | NFM | Tayside | Data Link |
| 204.9625 | 196.9625 | NFM | Birmingham | West Midlands Bus Travel |
| | | NFM | London | London Transport |
| | | NFM | Manchester | GM Buses |
| | | NFM | Nationwide | PMR Band III Channel 62 |
| | | NFM | Scotland | West Scottish Buses |
| | | NFM | West Riding | Buses |
| 204.9750 | 196.9750 | NFM | Nationwide | Trunked PMR |
| 204.9875 | 196.9875 | NFM | Blackpool | RAC |
| | | NFM | Nationwide | Trunked PMR |
| 205.0000 | 197.0000 | NFM | Nationwide | Railtrack Channel 361 |
| | | NFM | Newport | Railtrack |
| 205.0125 | 197.0125 | NFM | Birmingham | West Midlands Bus Travel |
| | | NFM | London | Buses |
| | | NFM | Nationwide | PMR Band III Channel 10 |
| | | NFM | Portsmouth | Blue Ankiral Buses |
| | | NFM | Sheffield | Don Valley Buses |
| | | NFM | Sheffield | S. Yorkshire Transport (Greenland) |
| 205.0250 | 197.0250 | NFM | Nationwide | Trunked PMR |

| Base | Mobile | Mode | Location | User and Notes |
|------|--------|------|----------|----------------|
| 205.0375 | 197.0375 | NFM | Tayside | Data Link |
| 205.0500 | 197.0500 | NFM | Fort William | Railtrack |
| | | NFM | London | Buses |
| | | NFM | Nationwide | Railtrack Channel 365 |
| 205.0625 | 197.0625 | NFM | Manchester | City Bus Inspectors |
| | | NFM | Nationwide | PMR Band III Channel 57 |
| | | NFM | Plymouth | City Buses |
| | | NFM | South | Tec & Development. |
| 205.0750 | 197.0750 | NFM | Nationwide | Trunked PMR |
| 205.0875 | 197.0875 | NFM | Nationwide | Trunked PMR |
| 205.1000 | 197.1000 | NFM | Nationwide | Railtrack Channel 369 |
| 205.1125 | 197.0125 | NFM | Nationwide | Bus National Emergency Chanl |
| 205.1250 | 197.1250 | NFM | Nationwide | Trunked PMR |
| 205.1375 | 197.1375 | NFM | Nationwide | Trunked PMR |
| 205.1500 | 197.1500 | NFM | Nationwide | Railtrack Cab Channel 373 |
| | | NFM | Newtown | Mid Wales Railway Line RETD |
| | | NFM | Shrewsbury | Mid Wales Railway Line RETD |
| | | NFM | Sutton Bridge Junction | MWL RETD |
| | | NFM | Welshpool | Mid Wales Railway Line RETD |
| | | NFM | Westbury | Mid Wales Railway Line RETD |
| 205.1625 | 197.1625 | NFM | Nationwide | Trunked PMR |
| 205.1750 | 197.1750 | NFM | Nationwide | Trunked PMR |
| 205.1875 | 197.1875 | NFM | Tayside | Data Link |
| 205.2000 | 197.2000 | NFM | Nationwide | Railtrack Channel 377 |
| | | NFM | Newport | Railtrack |
| 205.2125 | 197.2125 | NFM | Nationwide | Trunked PMR |
| 205.2250 | 197.2250 | NFM | Nationwide | Trunked PMR |
| 205.2315 | 197.2375 | NFM | Nationwide | Trunked PMR |
| 205.2500 | 197.2500 | NFM | Nationwide | Railtrack Cab Channel 381 |
| 205.2625 | 197.2625 | NFM | Nationwide | Trunked PMR |
| 205.2750 | 197.2750 | NFM | Nationwide | Trunked PMR |
| 205.2875 | 197.2875 | NFM | Nationwide | Trunked PMR |
| 205.3000 | 197.3000 | NFM | Nationwide | Railtrack Channel 385 |
| 205.3125 | 197.3125 | NFM | Nationwide | PMR Band III Channel |
| 205.3250 | 197.3250 | NFM | Nationwide | PMR Band III Channel |
| 205.3375 | 197.3375 | NFM | Nationwide | Trunked PMR |
| 205.3500 | 197.3500 | NFM | Aberyswyth | Mid Wales Railway Line RETD |
| | | NFM | Borth | Mid Wales Railway Line RETD |
| | | NFM | Dovey Junction | MWL RETD |
| | | NFM | Nationwide | Railtrack Cab Channel 389 |
| 205.3625 | 197.3625 | NFM | Manchester | Transport |
| 205.3750 | 197.3750 | NFM | Nationwide | Trunked PMR |
| 205.3875 | 197.3875 | NFM | Nationwide | Trunked PMR |
| 205.4000 | 197.4000 | NFM | Machynlleth | Mid Wales Railway Line RETD |
| | | NFM | Nationwide | Railtrack Channel 393 |
| | | NFM | Newtown | Mid Wales Railway Line RETD |
| | | NFM | Shrewsbury | Mid Wales Railway Line RETD |
| | | NFM | Sutton Bridge Junction | Mid Wales Railway Line RETD |
| | | NFM | Welshpool | Mid Wales Railway Line RETD |
| | | NFM | Westbury | Mid Wales Railway Line RETD |
| 205.4125 | 197.4125 | NFM | Nationwide | Trunked PMR |
| 205.4250 | 197.4250 | NFM | Nationwide | Trunked PMR |
| | | NFM | Weymouth | Heavy Breakdown Recovery |
| 205.4375 | 197.4375 | NFM | Nationwide | Trunked PMR |
| 205.4500 | 197.4500 | NFM | Nationwide | Railtrack Channel 397 |

| Base | Mobile | Mode | Location | User and Notes |
|---|---|---|---|---|
| 205.4625 | 197.4625 | NFM | Brighton | Buses |
| | | NFM | Crosville | Buses |
| | | NFM | Nationwide | Trunked PMR |
| | | NFM | Preston | Buses |
| | | NFM | Scotland | Midland Scottish Buses |
| | | NFM | Southdown | Buses |
| 205.4750 | 197.4750 | NFM | Nationwide | Trunked PMR |
| 205.4875 | 197.4875 | NFM | Nationwide | Trunked PMR |
| 205.5000 | 197.5000 | NFM | Nationwide | Railtrack Channel 401 |
| 205.5125 | 197.5125 | NFM | Central Scotland | Buses |
| | | NFM | Fareham | Buses |
| | | NFM | Gosport | Buses |
| | | NFM | Merseyside | Buses |
| 205.5250 | 197.5250 | NFM | Nationwide | Trunked PMR |
| 205.5375 | 197.5375 | NFM | Nationwide | Trunked PMR |
| 205.5500 | 197.5500 | NFM | Nationwide | Railtrack Channel 405 |
| 205.5625 | 197.5625 | NFM | Colchester | Buses |
| | | NFM | Crosville | Buses |
| | | NFM | Lothian | Buses |
| | | NFM | Manchester | GM Buses |
| 205.5750 | 197.5750 | NFM | Nationwide | Trunked PMR |
| 205.5875 | 197.5875 | NFM | Nationwide | Railtrack Channel |
| 205.6000 | 197.6000 | NFM | Nationwide | Railtrack Channel 409 |
| 205.6125 | 197.6125 | NFM | Crosville | Buses |
| | | NFM | Eastbourne | Buses |
| | | NFM | Ipswich | Buses |
| | | NFM | Manchester | GM Buses |
| | | NFM | Nationwide | PMR Band III Channel 9 |
| | | NFM | Ribble | Buses |
| 205.6250 | 197.6250 | NFM | Nationwide | Trunked PMR |
| 205.6375 | 197.6375 | NFM | Nationwide | Trunked PMR |
| 205.6500 | 197.6500 | NFM | Nationwide | Railtrack Channel 413 |
| 205.6625 | 197.6625 | NFM | Bournemouth | Buses |
| | | NFM | London | Buses |
| | | NFM | Merseyside | Buses |
| | | NFM | Scotland | East Scottish Buses |
| 205.6750 | 197.6750 | NFM | Nationwide | Railtrack Channel 415 |
| 205.6875 | 197.6875 | NFM | Nationwide | Trunked PMR |
| 205.7000 | 197.7000 | NFM | Nationwide | Railtrack Channel 417 |
| 205.7125 | 197.7125 | NFM | Crosville | Buses |
| | | NFM | Lothian | Buses |
| | | NFM | Manchester | GM Buses |
| | | NFM | Nationwide | PMR Band III Channel 17 |
| | | NFM | Portsmouth | Buses |
| 205.7250 | 197.7250 | NFM | Nationwide | Railtrack Channel 419 |
| 205.7375 | 197.7375 | NFM | Hythe | Nightforce Security |
| 205.7500 | 197.7500 | NFM | Nationwide | Railtrack Channel 421 |
| 205.7625 | 197.7625 | NFM | East Yorkshire | Buses |
| | | NFM | Isle of Wight | Buses |
| | | NFM | Manchester | Buses |
| | | NFM | Nationwide | PMR Band III Channel |
| 205.7750 | 197.7750 | NFM | Nationwide | Trunked PMR |
| 205.7875 | 197.7875 | NFM | Nationwide | Trunked PMR |
| 205.8000 | 197.8000 | NFM | Nationwide | Railtrack Channel 425 |

| Base | Mobile | Mode | Location | User and Notes |
|---|---|---|---|---|
| 205.8125 | 197.8125 | NFM | Birmingham | West Midlands Bus Travel |
| | | NFM | Nationwide | National Express |
| | | NFM | Nationwide | PMR Band III Channel 14 |
| 205.8250 | 197.8250 | NFM | London | TNT Couriers |
| | | NFM | London | Thamesway Buses |
| 205.8375 | 197.8375 | NFM | Nationwide | Railtrack Channel 428 |
| | | NFM | Tayside | Data Link |
| 205.8500 | 197.8500 | NFM | Nationwide | Railtrack |
| 205.8625 | 197.8625 | NFM | Nationwide | National Express |
| 205.8750 | 197.8750 | NFM | Nationwide | Trunked PMR |
| 205.8875 | 197.8875 | NFM | Nationwide | Trunked PMR |
| | | NFM | Taunton | Data |
| 205.9000 | 197.9000 | NFM | London | Thamesway Buses |
| | | NFM | Nationwide | Railtrack Channel 433 |
| 205.9125 | 197.9125 | NFM | Gt. Yarmouth | Buses |
| | | NFM | London | Thamesway Buses |
| | | NFM | Merseyside | Buses |
| | | NFM | Southampton | Buses |
| 205.9250 | 197.9250 | NFM | Nationwide | Trunked PMR |
| 205.9375 | 197.9375 | NFM | Tayside | Data Link |
| 205.9500 | 197.9500 | NFM | Nationwide | Railtrack Channel 437 |
| 205.9625 | 197.9625 | NFM | Manchester | GM Buses |
| 205.9750 | 197.9750 | NFM | Nationwide | Trunked PMR |
| 205.9875 | 197.9875 | NFM | Nationwide | Trunked PMR |
| 206.0000 | 198.0000 | NFM | Nationwide | Railtrack Channel 441 |
| 206.0125 | 198.0125 | NFM | Birmingham | West Midlands Bus Travel |
| | | NFM | Edinburgh | SMT Buses |
| | | NFM | Kent, east | Buses |
| | | NFM | Merseyside | Buses |
| | | NFM | South Wales | Buses |
| 206.0250 | 198.0250 | NFM | Nationwide | Trunked PMR |
| 206.0375 | 198.0375 | NFM | Nationwide | Trunked PMR |
| 206.0625 | 198.0625 | NFM | Birmingham | West Midlands Bus Travel |
| | | NFM | Blackpool | Buses |
| | | NFM | Glasgow | Bus Company |
| | | NFM | Southdown | Buses |
| | | NFM | Strathclyde | Buses |
| | | NFM | Wales | Buses |
| 206.0750 | 198.0750 | NFM | Nationwide | Trunked PMR |
| 206.0875 | 198.0875 | NFM | Nationwide | Trunked PMR |
| 206.1000 | 198.1000 | NFM | Brecon | Data |
| | | NFM | London | Data |
| | | NFM | Manchester | Data |
| | | NFM | Nationwide | Railtrack Channel 449 |
| 206.1125 | 198.1125 | NFM | Merseyside | Buses |
| | | NFM | Southdown | Buses |
| | | NFM | Strathclyde | Buses |
| 206.1250 | 198.1250 | NFM | Nationwide | Trunked PMR |
| 206.1375 | 198.1375 | NFM | Nationwide | Trunked PMR |
| 206.1500 | 198.1500 | NFM | Nationwide | Railtrack Channel 453 |
| | | NFM | Tayside | Data Link |
| 206.1625 | 198.1625 | NFM | Birmingham | West Midlands Bus Travel |
| | | NFM | Bristol | City Line Buses (Minibuses) |
| | | NFM | London | London Transport Talking Clock |
| | | NFM | Manchester | GM Bus Inspectors |
| | | NFM | Manchester | Northern General. |

| Base | Mobile | Mode | Location | User and Notes |
|---|---|---|---|---|
| 206.1750 | 198.1750 | NFM | Nationwide | Trunked PMR Channel 455 |
| 206.1875 | 198.1875 | NFM | Nationwide | Trunked PMR Channel 456 |
| 206.2000 | 198.2000 | NFM | Nationwide | Railtrack Channel 28 |
| 206.2125 | 198.2125 | NFM | Birmingham | West Midlands Bus Travel |
| | | NFM | London | London Transport Stanford Hill |
| | | NFM | Manchester | GM Buses |
| 206.2500 | 198.2500 | NFM | Nationwide | Railtrack Channel 461 |
| 206.2625 | 198.2625 | NFM | Birmingham | West Midlands Bus Travel |
| | | NFM | London | London Transport Stockwell |
| 206.2875 | 198.2875 | NFM | Ayr | South Ayrshire Council Bin Lorries |
| 206.3000 | 198.3000 | NFM | Nationwide | Railtrack Channel 465 |
| 206.5125 | 198.5125 | NFM | Manchester | Lorries |
| 206.5250 | 198.5250 | NFM | Stockport | Engineers |
| 206.5750 | 198.5750 | FM | Cambridge | Skip Hire Company |
| 206.6375 | 198.6375 | NFM | Eastbourne | Hobbs Recovery |
| 206.9125 | 198.9125 | NFM | Macclesfield | Delivery |
| 207.4375 | 199.4375 | NFM | London | Christian Salveson Haulage |

### 207.5000 - 208.5000 MHz    BROADCASTING LINKS

| | | | | |
|---|---|---|---|---|
| 208.3000 | | NFM | Jersey | BBC Radio Jersey |

### 208.5000 - 217.2000 MHz    VHF B3 PMR BASE REPEATERS 12.5 KHZ
### (SPLIT +8.0 MHZ) & OUTSIDE  BROADCASTS

| | | | | |
|---|---|---|---|---|
| 208.6000 | | WFM | Nationwide | BBC Antiques Roadshow Mics |
| | | NFM | Nationwide | BBC Radio 1 Roadshow Mics |
| 208.8000 | | NFM | Nationwide | ITV Radio Microphone |
| 209.0000 | | NFM | Nationwide | BBC Radio Microphone |
| 209.1500 | | NFM | Jersey | PC Gartmore Speech |
| 212.2000 | | NFM | Wolverhampton | Beacon Radio O/B |
| 213.3000 | | WFM | London | Towndown Radio Feeder |
| 213.8750 | | NFM | Silverstone | BBV Outside Broadcasts |
| 213.9500 | | WFM | London | BBC Radio Car O/B |
| 214.0250 | | NFM | Castle Donington | Grand Prix Radio O/B Link |
| 214.1000 | | WFM | London | BBC Radio Car O/B |
| 216.8000 | | WFM | Nationwide | BBC Antiques Roadshow Mics |

### 217.5000 - 230.0000 MHz    FUTURE DIGITAL BROADCASTING BAND DAB

### 216.0000 - 225.0000 MHz    VHF M3 PMR MOBILES 12.5 KHZ
### (SPLIT +8.0 MHZ) RADIO MICROPHONES

| | | | | |
|---|---|---|---|---|
| 224.10000 | | NFM | Sheffield | BBC Radio Sheffield Outside B'casts |
| 224.21810 | | USB | Scotland | BBC Studio Feed |
| 224.23125 | | NFM | Bristol | BBC O/B Talkback |
| 224.23200 | | NFM | Scotland | BBC Clean Feed from Glasgow |

### 225.0000 - 399.9750 MHz    MILITARY AERONAUTICAL COMMUNICATIONS
### 25 KHZ

| | | | | |
|---|---|---|---|---|
| 225.20000 | | AM | Nationwide | RAF Discreet |

### 225.5000 -227.0000 MHz    BBC DAB TEXT TRANSMISSIONS
### (SOUTH EAST ENGLAND ONLY)

| | | | | |
|---|---|---|---|---|
| 225.64800 | | DAB | London | BBC Radio Ch12B |
| 225.75000 | | NFM | Nationwide | Turkish Star 5 Air Display Team |

**232.0000 - 236.0000 MHz   RADIO ASTRONOMY**
Darnhall, Defford, Jodrell Bank, Knockin, Pickmere and Wardle

**227.0000 - 241.0000 MHz   TACTICAL MILITARY EXERCISE**
**COMMUNICATIONS 25 kHz**

| Base | Mode | Location | User and Notes |
|------|------|----------|----------------|
| 226.600 | AM | RNAS Portland | Royal Navy |
| 230.050 | AM | RAF Buchan | Air Defence Region Ops |
|  | AM | RAF West Drayton | London Military (Dover/Lydd) |
| 230.150 | AM | RAF Boulmer | Air Defence Region Ops |
| 230.600 | AM | Nationwide | Air Defence Region |
|  | AM | Nationwide | Air-Air |
| 230.650 | AM | Nationwide | RAF AWACS Ops |
| 231.075 | AM | Nationwide | Air Defence Region |
| 231.250 | AM | Nationwide | Air Defence Region |
| 231.350 | AM | Nationwide | USAF Ops |
| 231.375 | AM | RAF Valley | 4FTS Air-Air |
| 231.550 | AM | RAF Buchan | Air Defence Region Ops |
| 231.600 | AM | Nationwide | NATO Air-Air |
| 231.625 | AM | RAF West Drayton | London Military (Pole Hill/Irish Sea) |
| 231.975 | AM | RAF West Drayton | London Military (Seaford/Hurn) |
| 232.075 | AM | Donna Nook | Range Secondary |
| 232.300 | AM | Nationwide | AWACS Ops |
| 232.350 | AM | RAF Neatishead | Air Defence Region Ops |
| 232.550 | AM | RAF Neatishead | Air Defence Region Ops |
| 232.700 | AM | RAF Neatishead | Air Defence Region Ops |
| 233.000 | AM | Royal Navy | Ship-Air |
| 233.150 | AM | RAF Portreath | Air Defence Region Ops |
| 233.200 | AM | Royal Navy | Ship-Air |
| 233.700 | AM | USAF Mildenhall | USAF Air-Air |
| 233.800 | AM | RAF West Drayton | London Military (London Upper) |
| 233.925 | AM | RNAS Portland | Royal Navy |
| 234.650 | AM | Cumbria | RAF Low Flying Air-Air |
|  | AM | Nationwide | RAF AWACS Ops |
| 234.900 | AM | Nationwide | RAF Volmet |
| 235.050 | AM | RAF West Drayton | London Military (London Upper) |
| 235.250 | AM | Nationwide | USAF Displays |
| 237.500 | NFM | Nationwide | Dynamic Sciences Surv. |
| 237.850 | AM | HMS Invincible | Air-Deck |
| 240.300 | AM | Nationwide | Air-Air Refuelling |
|  | AM | RAF Neatishead | Radar |
| 240.375 | NFM | West Sussex | London Mil |
| 240.400 | AM | AARA 1 (NW Scotland) | Refuelling Primary |
|  | AM | AARA 10 (NW Scotland) | Refuelling Primary |
|  | AM | AARA 7 (SW England) | Refuelling Primary |
| 241.000 | AM | Nationwide | Forward Air Controllers |
|  | AM | RAF Coningsby | Air-Air |
| 241.175 | AM | Cowden | Range Primary |
| 241.450 | AM | RAF Manston | Dispatcher |
| 241.600 | AM | Castle Martin | Range Air-Ground |
| 241.625 | AM | RAF Benson | Talkdown |
| 241.650 | AM | RAF Linton-On-Ouse | ATIS |
| 241.775 | AM | RAF Cowden | Range |
| 241.825 | AM | RAF Aldergrove | RAF Ops |
|  | AM | RAF St Mawgan | Tower |

| Base | Mobile | Mode | Location | User and Notes |
|---|---|---|---|---|
| 241.850 | | AM | RAF Neatishead | Radar Ops |
| | | AM | RAF Topcliffe | Ground |
| 241.950 | | AM | RNAS Culdrose | Approach/Radar |
| | | AM | RNAS Predannack | Culdrose Approach |
| 241.975 | | AM | RAF Honington | Ground/Ops |
| 242.000 | | AM | Nationwide | Red Arrows air display team |
| 242.050 | | AM | Nationwide | Red Arrows Display |
| 242.057 | | AM | RAF Wittering | Air-Air |
| 242.075 | | AM | USAF Lakenheath | Dep Con |
| 242.150 | | AM | USAF Lakenheath | Defence Exercises |
| 242.200 | | AM | Nationwide | Red Arrows Display |
| 242.275 | | AM | Nationwide | Air Defence Region |
| 242.325 | | AM | RAF Cottesmore | DATIS |
| 242.400 | | AM | RAF Leuchars | 111 Sqn Air-Air |
| 242.450 | | AM | RAF Wittering | 1 Sqn Ops (Willard Ops) |
| 242.550 | | AM | RAF Coningsby | 5 Sqn Ops |
| 242.600 | | AM | Nationwide | Patroulle De France Display Team |
| | | AM | Warton | Test Flights |
| 242.650 | | AM | Nationwide | Patroulle de Francais air display team |
| 242.850 | | AM | Nationwide | Patroulle de Francais air display team |
| 243.000 | | AM | International | Air Distress |
| | | NFM | Nationwide | Turkish Star 5 Air Display Team |
| 243.325 | | AM | RAF Leeming | 11 Sqn Air-Air |
| 243.450 | | AM | Nationwide | Red Arrows Display |
| 243.475 | | AM | Nationwide | USAF Ops |
| 243.600 | | AM | USAF Lakenheath | Radar |
| 243.800 | | AM | RAF Aerodrome | Radio Failure Frequency |

**243.9450 - 244.2500 MHz    US AFSATCOM DOWN LINKS**

| Base | Mobile | Mode | Location | User and Notes |
|---|---|---|---|---|
| 243.945 | | NFM | AFSATCOM F2 | NB Channel 11 |
| 243.955 | | NFM | AFSATCOM F2 | NB Channel 12 |
| 243.960 | | NFM | AFSATCOM F2 | NB Channel 13 |
| 243.965 | | NFM | AFSATCOM F2 | NB Channel 14 |
| 243.970 | | NFM | AFSATCOM F2 | NB Channel 15 |
| 243.975 | | NFM | AFSATCOM F2 | NB Channel 16 |
| 243.980 | | NFM | AFSATCOM F2 | NB Channel 17 |
| 243.985 | | NFM | AFSATCOM F2 | NB Channel 18 |
| 243.990 | | NFM | AFSATCOM F2 | NB Channel 19 |
| 243.995 | | NFM | AFSATCOM F2 | NB Channel 20 |
| 244.000 | | NFM | AFSATCOM F2 | NB Channel 21 |
| 244.010 | | NFM | AFSATCOM F2 | NB Channel 22 |
| 244.045 | | NFM | AFSATCOM F3 | NB Channel 11 |
| 244.055 | | NFM | AFSATCOM F3 | NB Channel 12 |
| 244.060 | | NFM | AFSATCOM F3 | NB Channel 13 |
| 244.065 | | NFM | AFSATCOM F3 | NB Channel 14 |
| 244.070 | | NFM | AFSATCOM F3 | NB Channel 15 |
| 244.075 | | NFM | AFSATCOM F3 | NB Channel 16 |
| 244.080 | | NFM | AFSATCOM F3 | NB Channel 17 |
| 244.085 | | NFM | AFSATCOM F3 | NB Channel 18 |
| 244.090 | | NFM | AFSATCOM F3 | NB Channel 19 |
| 244.095 | | NFM | AFSATCOM F3 | NB Channel 20 |
| 244.100 | | NFM | AFSATCOM F3 | NB Channel 21 |
| 244.110 | | NFM | AFSATCOM F3 | NB Channel 22 |
| 244.145 | | NFM | AFSATCOM F1 | NB Channel 11 |
| 244.155 | | NFM | AFSATCOM F1 | NB Channel 12 |
| 244.160 | | NFM | AFSATCOM F1 | NB Channel 13 |

| Base | Mobile | Mode | Location | User and Notes |
|------|--------|------|----------|----------------|
| 244.165 | | NFM | AFSATCOM F1 | NB Channel 14 |
| 244.170 | | NFM | AFSATCOM F1 | NB Channel 15 |
| 244.175 | | NFM | AFSATCOM F1 | NB Channel 16 |
| 244.180 | | NFM | AFSATCOM F1 | NB Channel 17 |
| 244.185 | | NFM | AFSATCOM F1 | NB Channel 18 |
| 244.190 | | NFM | AFSATCOM F1 | NB Channel 19 |
| 244.195 | | NFM | AFSATCOM F1 | NB Channel 20 |
| 244.200 | | NFM | AFSATCOM F1 | NB Channel 21 |
| 244.210 | | NFM | AFSATCOM F1 | NB Channel 22 |
| 244.275 | | AM | RAF Waddington | AWACS Wing Ops |
| 244.300 | | AM | RAF Valley | 4FTS Air-to-Air |
| 244.375 | | AM | Nationwide | Air Defence Region |
| 244.425 | | AM | RAF Northolt | Ops |
| 244.600 | | AM | Nationwide | UK Distress |
| | | AM | Plymouth | Plymouth Rescue |

## 244.6500 - 248.8000 MHz   TACTICAL MILITARY EXERCISE COMMUNICATIONS  25 kHz

| Base | Mobile | Mode | Location | User and Notes |
|------|--------|------|----------|----------------|
| 244.650 | | AM | AARA 6 (S North Sea) | Air-Air Refuelling |
| | | AM | RAF Buchan | Air Defence Region Ops |
| | | AM | RAF Neatishead | Air Defence Region Ops |
| 244.675 | | AM | Nationwide | 4 Sqn Air-Air |
| 244.700 | | AM | RAF Neatishead | Air Defence Region Ops |
| 244.875 | | AM | RAF Leconfield | Leconfield Rescue |
| 244.900 | | AM | RAF Leeming | 11 Sqn Air-Air |
| 245.050 | | AM | RAF Boulmer | Air Defence Region Ops |
| 245.100 | | AM | Cranwell | RAF Air-Air |
| | | AM | Nationwide | RAF Personal Locator Beacons |
| 246.050 | | AM | Nationwide | Air-Air Refuelling |
| 246.450 | | AM | Nationwide | Displays |
| 246.700 | | AM | Nationwide | Forward Air Controllers |
| 247.000 | | AM | RAF Boulmer | Air Defence Region |
| 247.175 | | AM | RAF Cranwell | DATIS |
| 247.275 | | AM | Nationwide | Air Defence Region |
| 247.700 | | AM | Nationwide | Forward Air Controllers |
| 248.100 | | AM | RAF Neatishead | Air Defence Region Ops |
| 248.150 | | AM | USAF Lakenheath | 493FS Discreet |
| 248.275 | | AM | USAF Lakenheath | 48FW Air-to-Air |
| 248.300 | | AM | Nationwide | Airborne Intercept Cmd |
| | | AM | Nationwide | RAF AWACS Ops |
| 248.400 | | AM | RAF Buchan | Air Defence Region Ops |
| 248.800 | | AM | Nationwide | Sharks Helicopter Display |

## 248.8500 049.3500 MHz   US AFSATCOM DOWN LINKS

| Base | Mobile | Mode | Location | User and Notes |
|------|--------|------|----------|----------------|
| 248.850 | 302.450 | NFM | MARISAT | Channel 1 |
| 248.875 | 302.475 | NFM | MARISAT | Channel 2 |
| 248.900 | 302.500 | NFM | MARISAT | Channel 3 |
| 248.925 | 302.525 | NFM | MARISAT | Channel 4 |
| 248.950 | 302.550 | NFM | MARISAT | Channel 5 |
| 248.975 | 302.575 | NFM | MARISAT | Channel 6 |
| 249.000 | 302.700 | NFM | MARISAT | Channel 7 |
| | | NFM | Nationwide | Dynamic Sciences Surv. |
| 249.025 | 302.725 | NFM | MARISAT | Channel 8 |
| 249.050 | 302.750 | NFM | MARISAT | Channel 9 |
| 249.075 | 302.775 | NFM | MARISAT | Channel 10 |

| Base | Mobile | Mode | Location | User and Notes |
|------|--------|------|----------|----------------|
| 249.100 | 302.800 | NFM | MARISAT | Channel 11 |
| 249.125 | 302.825 | NFM | MARISAT | Channel 12 |
| 249.150 | 302.850 | NFM | MARISAT | Channel 13 |
| 249.175 | 302.875 | NFM | MARISAT | Channel 14 |
| 249.200 | 302.900 | NFM | MARISAT | Channel 15 |
| 249.225 | 302.925 | NFM | MARISAT | Channel 16 |
| 249.250 | 302.950 | NFM | MARISAT | Channel 17 |
| 249.275 | 302.975 | NFM | MARISAT | Channel 18 |
| 249.300 | 303.000 | NFM | MARISAT | Channel 19 |
| 249.325 | 303.025 | NFM | MARISAT | Channel 20 |
| 249.350 | 303.050 | NFM | MARISAT | Channel 21 |
| 249.475 | | AM | Prestwick | Scottish Military |
| 249.525 | | AM | RAF Leeming | ATIS |
| 249.575 | | AM | RAF Leuchars | DATIS |
| 249.600 | | AM | RAF Marham | 617 Sqn Ops (Nigger Ops) |
| 249.625 | | AM | RAF West Drayton | London Military |
| 249.675 | | AM | RAF West Drayton | London Military |
| 249.700 | | NFM | Nationwide | Dynamic Sciences Surv. |
| 249.725 | | AM | RNAS Yeovilton | D School |
| 249.750 | | AM | RAF Mildenhall | Command Post Backup |
| 249.800 | | NFM | Nationwide | Dynamic Sciences Surv. |
| | | AM | RAF Chivenor | 7FTS Air-Air |
| 249.850 | | AM | RAF Waddington | Departures |
| 250.050 | | AM | RAF Cranwell | Zone |
| | | AM | RAF Lossiemouth | Talkdown |
| 250.150 | | AM | Nationwide | Forward Air Controllers (Fortune) |
| 250.275 | | AM | RAF West Drayton | London Military |

| Base | Mobile | Mode | Location | User and Notes |
|------|--------|------|----------|----------------|
| **250.350050.6500 MHz** | | | **US FLTSATCOM FLEET BROADCAST DOWN LINKS** | |
| 250.350 | 291.350 | NFM | FLTSATCOM | Channel W1 |
| 250.450 | 291.450 | NFM | FLTSATCOM F1 | Channel X1 |
| 250.475 | 250.475 | AM | Nationwide | Sharks Helicopter Display Team |
| 250.550 | 291.550 | NFM | FLTSATCOM F3 | Channel Y1 |
| 250.650 | 291.650 | NFM | FLTSATCOM F2 | Channel Z1 |
| 250.675 | 250.675 | AM | USAF Lakenheath | 48FW Air-to-Air |
| 250.700 | 250.700 | AM | Nationwide | Air Defence Region |
| 250.900 | | NFM | Nationwide | Dynamic Sciences Surv |
| 251.200 | 251.200 | AM | RNAS Culdrose | Kilderkin Ops |
| 251.375 | 251.375 | AM | RAF Wittering | 20 Sqn Ops (Bronze Ops) |
| 251.500 | 251.500 | AM | Nationwide | USAF Displays |
| 251.600 | | NFM | Nationwide | Dynamic Sciences Surv |
| 251.625 | 251.625 | AM | RAF West Drayton | London Military |
| 251.650 | 251.650 | AM | Nationwide | Air Defence Region |
| 251.725 | 251.725 | AM | RAF Newton | Approach |
| 251.750 | 251.750 | AM | Nationwide | Air Defence Region |
| 251.800 | | NFM | Nationwide | Dynamic Sciences Surv |
| 251.850 | 292.850 | NFM | FLTSATCOM | Channel W 2 |
| 251.900 | | NFM | Nationwide | Dynamic Sciences Surv |
| 251.950 | 292.950 | NFM | FLTSATCOM F1 | Channel X 2 |
| 252.050 | 293.050 | NFM | FLTSATCOM F3 | Channel Y 2 |
| 252.100 | 252.100 | AM | North Sea | ACMI Range Show Ground 1 |
| 252.150 | 293.150 | NFM | FLTSATCOM F2 | Channel Z 2 |
| 252.400 | 252.400 | AM | Nationwide | Air Defence Region |
| 252.450 | 225.450 | AM | RAF Valley | 4FTS Air-Air |
| 252.462 | 252.462 | AM | Prestwick | Scottish Military |
| 252.525 | | AM | RAF St Mawgan | DATIS |

| Base | Mobile | Mode | Location | User and Notes |
|---|---|---|---|---|
| 252.800 | 252.800 | AM | Nationwide | Search and Rescue Training |
| | | AM | RAF Chivenor | Chivenor Rescue |
| 252.900 | 252.900 | AM | Arran | Police Helicopter |
| | | AM | Colchester Garrison | Tower |
| | | AM | Nationwide | British Army |
| | | AM | Nationwide | Silver Eagles Helicopter Team |
| | | AM | RAF Dishforth | AAC Ops |
| 253.000 | | NFM | Nationwide | Dynamic Sciences Surv |
| 253.100 | 253.100 | AM | USAF Lakenheath | Rapcon |
| 253.300 | 253.300 | AM | Nationwide | Forward Air Controllers |
| 253.500 | 253.500 | AM | Netheravon (Army) | Salisbury Plain |
| 253.550 | 294.550 | NFM | FLTSATCOM | Channel W 3 |
| 253.650 | 294.650 | NFM | FLTSATCOM F1 | Channel X 3 |
| 253.750 | 294.750 | NFM | FLTSATCOM F3 | Channel Y 3 |
| 253.800 | 253.800 | AM | Nationwide | NATO SAR Training |
| 253.850 | 294.850 | NFM | FLTSATCOM F2 | Channel Z 3 |
| 253.900 | | NFM | Nationwide | Dynamic Sciences Surv |
| 254.075 | 254.075 | AM | RAF Marham | 2 Sqn Air-to-Air |
| 254.200 | 254.200 | AM | RAF Lossiemouth | Splash |
| | | AM | RAF Shawbury | Radar |
| 254.225 | 254.225 | AM | RAF West Drayton | London Military |
| 254.250 | 254.250 | AM | RAF Coltishall | Talkdown |
| 254.350 | 254.350 | AM | Nationwide | NATO Air-Air |
| 254.400 | 254.000 | AM | RAF Lossiemouth | 15 Sqn Ops |
| | | AM | RAF Marham | 27 Sqn Ops (Nellie Ops) |
| 254.425 | 254.425 | AM | Nationwide | Air Defence Region |
| 254.475 | 254.475 | AM | RAF Brize Norton | ATIS |
| 254.500 | 254.500 | AM | Aberporth | Range Tertiary |
| 254.525 | 254.525 | AM | RAF Church Fenton | Approach |
| 254.650 | 254.650 | AM | RAF Lyneham | Ops |
| 254.675 | 254.675 | AM | RAF Coningsby | 5 Sqn Ops (Maple Ops) |
| 254.825 | 254.825 | AM | RAF West Drayton | London Military |
| 254.875 | 254.875 | AM | RAF Honington | Approach |
| | | AM | USAF Mildenhall | Approach |
| 254.900 | 254.900 | AM | RAF West Drayton | London Military |
| 255.100 | 255.100 | AM | Nationwide | Forward Air Controllers |
| | | AM | Nationwide | RAF Falcons Parachutists |
| | | AM | Weston on the Green | Weston Radio |
| 255.250 | 296.250 | NFM | FLTSATCOM | Channel W 4 |
| 255.275 | 255.275 | AM | USAF Lakenheath | 48FW Aux |
| 255.350 | 296.350 | AM | FLTSATCOM F1 | Channel X 4 |
| 255.400 | 255.400 | AM | RAF Leuchars | Approach |
| | | AM | RAF West Drayton | London Military |
| 255.450 | 296.450 | AM | FLTSATCOM F3 | Channel Y 4 |
| 255.550 | 296.550 | AM | FLTSATCOM F2 | Channel Z 4 |
| 255.600 | 255.600 | AM | RAF Topcliffe | Director |
| 255.700 | 255.700 | AM | RAF West Drayton | London Military |
| 255.850 | 255.850 | AM | RAF Cottesmore | Air-to-Air |
| 256.000 | | AM | Farnborough | PAR |
| 256.000 | 256.000 | AM | Royal Navy | Ship-Air |
| 256.100 | 256.100 | AM | Royal Navy | Ship-Air |
| 256.125 | 256.125 | AM | Filton (BAe), Bristol | Approach/Radar |
| 256.600 | | NFM | Nationwide | Dynamic Sciences Surv |
| 256.850 | 297.850 | NFM | FLTSATCOM | Channel W 5 |
| 256.900 | 256.900 | AM | Nationwide | Forward Air Controllers |
| 256.950 | 297.950 | AM | FLTSATCOM F1 | Channel X 5 |

| Base | Mobile | Mode | Location | User and Notes |
|------|--------|------|----------|----------------|
| 257.050 | 298.050 | AM | FLTSATCOM F3 | Channel Y 5 |
| 257.100 | 257.100 | AM | RAF Brize Norton | Brize Radar |
| 257.150 | 298.150 | AM | FLTSATCOM F2 | Channel Z 5 |
| 257.200 | 257.200 | AM | Nationwide | Forward Air Controllers |
| | | AM | Otterburn | Range Primary |
| 257.225 | 257.225 | AM | RAF West Drayton | London Military |
| 257.750 | 257.750 | AM | USAF Mildenhall | Mildenhall Metro |
| 257.800 | 257.800 | AM | Edinburgh Airport | Tower/Ground |
| | | AM | Nationwide | Forward Air Controllers |
| | | AM | RAF Brize Norton | Tower |
| | | AM | RAF Church Fenton | Tower |
| | | AM | RAF Cottesmore | Tower |
| | | AM | RAF Cranwell | Tower |
| | | AM | RAF Kinloss | Tower |
| | | AM | RAF Leeming | Tower |
| | | AM | RAF Linton-on-Ouse | Tower |
| | | AM | RAF Manston | Tower |
| | | AM | RAF Marham | Tower |
| | | AM | RAF Newton | Tower |
| | | AM | RAF Northolt | Tower |
| | | AM | RAF Odiham | Tower |
| | | AM | RAF Shawbury | Tower |
| | | AM | RAF St Athan | Tower |
| | | AM | RAF Topcliffe | Tower |
| | | AM | RAF Valley | Tower |
| | | AM | RAF Waddington | Tower |
| | | AM | RAF Wittering | Tower |
| | | AM | USAF Fairford | Tower |
| | | AM | USAF Lakenheath | Tower |
| 258.050 | | AM | Nationwide | Air-Air Tanker Ops |
| 258.300 | | AM | Nationwide | Forward Air Controllers |
| 258.350 | 299.350 | NFM | FLTSATCOM | Channel W 6 |
| 258.400 | | AM | AARA 10 (NW Scotland) | Air-Air Refuelling |
| 258.450 | 299.450 | NFM | FLTSATCOM F1 | Channel X 6 |
| 258.500 | | AM | Nationwide | AWACS |
| 258.550 | 299.550 | NFM | FLTSATCOM F3 | Channel Y 6 |
| 258.650 | 299.650 | NFM | FLTSATCOM F2 | Channel Z 6 |
| 258.775 | | AM | RAF Chivenor | 7FTS Air-Air |
| 258.800 | | AM | Nationwide | British Army Air-Air |
| | | AM | RAF Benson | 60 Sqn Air-Air |
| 258.825 | | AM | RAF Valley | Radar |
| 258.825 | | AM | USAF Mildenhall | Tower |
| 258.850 | | AM | RAF Lossiemouth | Lossie Departures |
| 258.925 | | AM | RAF Leuchars | Tower |
| 258.975 | | AM | RAF Colerne | Tower |
| | | AM | RAF Newton | Ground |
| 259.000 | | AM | Farnborough (RAE Airfirld) | Talkdown |
| | | AM | MoD West Freugh | Radar |
| | | AM | RNAS Aberporth | Aberporth Information |
| 259.025 | | AM | Teesside | Radar |
| 259.075 | | AM | RAF Marham | 2 Sqn Ops (Melbourne Ops) |
| 259.100 | | AM | RAF Neatishead | Air Defence Region Ops |
| 259.175 | | AM | Prestwick | Scottish Military |
| 259.525 | | AM | Nationwide | RAF Discreet |
| 259.600 | | AM | RAF Neatishead | Air Defence Region Ops |
| 259.700 | | NFM | International | Space Shuttle Down Link |

| Base | Mobile | Mode | Location | User and Notes |
|------|--------|------|----------|----------------|
| 259.725 | | AM | Prestwick | Scottish Military |
| 259.750 | | AM | RNAS Culdrose | Talkdown |
| 259.775 | | AM | Prestwick | Scottish Military |
| 259.800 | | AM | RNAS Yeovilton | D School |
| 259.825 | | AM | RAF Dishforth | Tower |
| 259.850 | | AM | RAF Leuchars | Ground |
| | | AM | RAF Benson | Talkdown |
| 259.875 | | AM | RAF Linton-on-Ouse | Talkdown |
| 259.950 | | AM | RAF Woodvale | Tower |
| | | AM | RAF Kinloss | Director |
| | | AM | RAF Lossiemouth | Director |
| 259.975 | | AM | USAF Fairford | Ground |
| 260.000 | | AM | Cowden | Range |
| | | AM | RAF St Mawgan | Ops |
| 260.025 | | AM | RAF West Drayton | London Military |
| 260.150 | | AM | Nationwide | Air Defence Region |
| 260.350 | 293.950 | NFM | FLTSATCOM F1 | WB Channel A/X 1 |
| 260.375 | 293.975 | NFM | FLTSATCOM F1 | WB Channel A/X 2 |
| 260.400 | 294.000 | NFM | FLTSATCOM F1 | WB Channel A/X 3 |
| 260.425 | 294.025 | NFM | FLTSATCOM F1 | WB Channel A/X 4 |
| 260.450 | 294.050 | NFM | FLTSATCOM F1 | WB Channel A/X 5 |
| 260.475 | 294.075 | NFM | FLTSATCOM F1 | WB Channel A/X 6 |
| 260.500 | 294.100 | NFM | FLTSATCOM F1 | WB Channel A/X 7 |
| 260.525 | 294.125 | NFM | FLTSATCOM F1 | WB Channel A/X 8 |
| 260.550 | 294.150 | NFM | FLTSATCOM F1 | WB Channel A/X 9 |
| 260.575 | 294.175 | NFM | FLTSATCOM F1 | WB Channel A/X 10 |
| 260.600 | 294.200 | NFM | FLTSATCOM F1 | WB Channel A/X 11 |
| 260.625 | 294.225 | NFM | FLTSATCOM F1 | WB Channel A/X 12 |
| 260.650 | 294.250 | NFM | FLTSATCOM F1 | WB Channel A/X 13 |
| 260.675 | 294.275 | NFM | FLTSATCOM F1 | WB Channel A/X 14 |
| 260.700 | 294.300 | NFM | FLTSATCOM F1 | WB Channel A/X 15 |
| 260.725 | 294.325 | NFM | FLTSATCOM F1 | WB Channel A/X 16 |
| 260.750 | 294.350 | NFM | FLTSATCOM F1 | WB Channel A/X 17 |
| 260.775 | 294.375 | NFM | FLTSATCOM F1 | WB Channel A/X 18 |
| 260.800 | 294.400 | NFM | FLTSATCOM F1 | WB Channel A/X 19 |
| 260.825 | 294.425 | NFM | FLTSATCOM F1 | WB Channel A/X 20 |
| 260.850 | 294.450 | NFM | FLTSATCOM F1 | WB Channel A/X 21 |
| 260.950 | | AM | RAF Coningsby | Air-to-Air |
| 261.000 | | AM | RAF West Drayton | London Military |
| 261.025 | | AM | RAF West Drayton | London Military |
| 261.050 | | AM | RAF Barkston Heath | Director |
| | | AM | RAF Barkston Heath | Director |
| 261.075 | | AM | RAF Leeming | 23 Sqn Ops (Red Ops) |
| 261.200 | | AM | RAF Marham | ATIS |
| 261.450 | 295.050 | NFM | FLTSATCOM F3 | WB Channel B/Y 1 |
| 261.475 | 295.075 | NFM | FLTSATCOM F3 | WB Channel B/Y 2 |
| 261.500 | 295.100 | NFM | FLTSATCOM F3 | WB Channel B/Y 3 |
| 261.525 | 295.125 | NFM | FLTSATCOM F3 | WB Channel B/Y 4 |
| 261.550 | 295.150 | NFM | FLTSATCOM F3 | WB Channel B/Y 5 |
| 261.575 | 295.175 | NFM | FLTSATCOM F3 | WB Channel B/Y 6 |
| 261.600 | 295.200 | NFM | FLTSATCOM F3 | WB Channel B/Y 7 |
| 261.625 | 295.225 | NFM | FLTSATCOM F3 | WB Channel B/Y 8 |
| 261.650 | 295.250 | NFM | FLTSATCOM F3 | WB Channel B/Y 9 |
| 261.675 | 295.275 | NFM | FLTSATCOM F3 | WB Channel B/Y 10 |
| 261.700 | 295.300 | NFM | FLTSATCOM F3 | WB Channel B/Y 11 |
| 261.725 | 295.325 | NFM | FLTSATCOM F3 | WB Channel B/Y 12 |

| Base | Mobile | Mode | Location | User and Notes |
|---|---|---|---|---|
| 261.750 | 295.350 | NFM | FLTSATCOM F3 | WB Channel B/Y 13 |
| 261.775 | 295.375 | NFM | FLTSATCOM F3 | WB Channel B/Y 14 |
| 261.800 | 295.400 | NFM | FLTSATCOM F3 | WB Channel B/Y 15 |
| 261.825 | 295.425 | NFM | FLTSATCOM F3 | WB Channel B/Y 16 |
| 261.850 | 295.450 | NFM | FLTSATCOM F3 | WB Channel B/Y 17 |
| 261.875 | 295.475 | NFM | FLTSATCOM F3 | WB Channel B/Y 18 |
| 261.900 | 295.500 | NFM | FLTSATCOM F3 | WB Channel B/Y 19 |
| 261.925 | 295.525 | NFM | FLTSATCOM F3 | WB Channel B/Y 20 |
| 261.950 | 295.550 | NFM | FLTSATCOM F3 | WB Channel B/Y 21 |
| 262.050 | 295.650 | NFM | FLTSATCOM F2 | WB Channel C/Z 1 |
| 262.075 | 295.675 | NFM | FLTSATCOM F2 | WB Channel C/Z 2 |
| 262.100 | 295.700 | NFM | FLTSATCOM F2 | WB Channel C/Z 3 |
| 262.125 | 295.725 | NFM | FLTSATCOM F2 | WB Channel C/Z 4 |
| 262.150 | 295.750 | NFM | FLTSATCOM F2 | WB Channel C/Z 5 |
| 262.175 | 295.775 | NFM | FLTSATCOM F2 | WB Channel C/Z 6 |
| 262.200 | 295.800 | NFM | FLTSATCOM F2 | WB Channel C/Z 7 |
| 262.225 | 295.825 | NFM | FLTSATCOM F2 | WB Channel C/Z 8 |
| 262.250 | 295.850 | NFM | FLTSATCOM F2 | WB Channel C/Z 9 |
| 262.275 | 295.875 | NFM | FLTSATCOM F2 | WB Channel C/Z 10 |
| 262.300 | 295.900 | NFM | FLTSATCOM F2 | WB Channel C/Z 11 |
| 262.325 | 295.925 | NFM | FLTSATCOM F2 | WB Channel C/Z 12 |
| 262.350 | 295.950 | NFM | FLTSATCOM F2 | WB Channel C/Z 13 |
| 262.375 | 295.975 | NFM | FLTSATCOM F2 | WB Channel C/Z 14 |
| 262.400 | 296.000 | NFM | FLTSATCOM F2 | WB Channel C/Z 15 |
| 262.425 | 296.025 | NFM | FLTSATCOM F2 | WB Channel C/Z 16 |
| 262.450 | 296.050 | NFM | FLTSATCOM F2 | WB Channel C/Z 17 |
| 262.475 | 296.075 | NFM | FLTSATCOM F2 | WB Channel C/Z 18 |
| 262.500 | 296.100 | NFM | FLTSATCOM F2 | WB Channel C/Z 19 |
| 262.525 | 296.125 | NFM | FLTSATCOM F2 | WB Channel C/Z 20 |
| 262.550 | 296.150 | NFM | FLTSATCOM F2 | WB Channel C/Z 21 |
| 262.650 | | AM | RAF Valley | 4FTS Air-Air |
| 262.700 | | AM | RAF Church Fenton | Tower |
| 262.725 | | AM | RAF Lossiemouth | TWCU Air-to-Air |
| 262.900 | | AM | RAF Cottesmore | Talkdown |
| 262.925 | | AM | RNAS Yeovilton | Royal Navy Ops |
| 262.950 | | AM | RAF Coningsby | Director |
| 262.975 | | AM | RAF West Drayton | London Mil |
| 263.075 | | AM | RAF West Drayton | London Mil |
| 263.150 | | AM | Nationwide | Air Defence Region |
| 263.500 | | AM | Boscombe Down (MoD) | DATIS |
| 263.550 | 297.150 | NFM | FLTSATCOM | WB Channel W 1 |
| 263.575 | 297.175 | NFM | FLTSATCOM | WB Channel W 2 |
| 263.600 | 297.200 | NFM | FLTSATCOM | WB Channel W 3 |
| 263.625 | 297.225 | NFM | FLTSATCOM | WB Channel W 4 |
| 263.650 | 297.250 | NFM | FLTSATCOM | WB Channel W 5 |
| 263.675 | 297.275 | NFM | FLTSATCOM | WB Channel W 6 |
| 263.700 | 297.300 | NFM | FLTSATCOM | WB Channel W 7 |
| 263.725 | 297.325 | NFM | FLTSATCOM | WB Channel W 8 |
| 263.750 | 297.350 | NFM | FLTSATCOM | WB Channel W 9 |
| 263.775 | 297.375 | NFM | FLTSATCOM | WB Channel W 10 |
| 263.800 | 297.400 | NFM | FLTSATCOM | WB Channel W 11 |
| 263.825 | 297.425 | NFM | FLTSATCOM | WB Channel W 12 |
| 263.850 | 297.450 | NFM | FLTSATCOM | WB Channel W 13 |
| 263.875 | 297.475 | NFM | FLTSATCOM | WB Channel W 14 |
| 263.900 | 297.500 | NFM | FLTSATCOM | WB Channel W 15 |
| 263.925 | 297.525 | NFM | FLTSATCOM | WB Channel W 16 |

| Base | Mobile | Mode | Location | User and Notes |
|------|--------|------|----------|----------------|
| 263.950 | 297.550 | NFM | FLTSATCOM | WB Channel W 17 |
| 263.975 | 297.575 | NFM | FLTSATCOM | WB Channel W 18 |
| 264.000 | 297.600 | NFM | FLTSATCOM | WB Channel W 19 |
| 264.025 | 297.625 | NFM | FLTSATCOM | WB Channel W 20 |
| 264.050 | 297.650 | NFM | FLTSATCOM | WB Channel W 21 |
| 264.100 | | AM | USAF Lakenheath | Radar |
| 264.200 | | AM | Nationwide | Forward Air Controllers |
| 264.400 | | AM | Nationwide | RAF AWACS Ops |
| 264.475 | | AM | RAF West Drayton | London Military (Clacton) |
| 264.675 | | AM | USAF Lakenheath | MATZ Crossing |
| 265.250 | 306.250 | NFM | FLTSATCOM | Channel W 7 |
| 265.350 | 306.350 | NFM | FLTSATCOM F1 | Channel X 7 |
| 265.450 | 306.450 | NFM | FLTSATCOM F3 | Channel Y 7 |
| 265.550 | 306.550 | NFM | FLTSATCOM F2 | Channel Z 7 |
| 265.850 | | AM | Nationwide | Air-Air Refuelling |
| 265.900 | | AM | Nationwide | Air Defence Region |
| 266.275 | | AM | USAF Lakenheath | 494FS Discreet |
| 266.450 | | AM | RAF Neatishead | Air Defence Region Ops |
| 266.500 | | AM | Nationwide | USAF Air-Air Refuelling |
| 266.550 | | AM | RAF Neatishead | Air Defence Region Ops |
| 266.750 | 307.750 | NFM | FLTSATCOM | Channel W 8 |
| 266.800 | | NFM | Nationwide | Dynamic Sciences Surv |
| 266.850 | 307.850 | NFM | FLTSATCOM F1 | Channel X 8 |
| 266.950 | 307.950 | NFM | FLTSATCOM F3 | Channel Y 8 |
| 267.050 | 308.050 | NFM | FLTSATCOM F2 | Channel Z 8 |
| 267.400 | | NFM | Nationwide | Dynamic Sciences Surv |
| | | AM | USAF Mildenhall | Tower Discreet |
| 267.550 | | AM | RAF Boulmer | Air Defence Region Ops |
| | | AM | RAF Neatishead | Air Defence Region Ops |
| 267.900 | | AM | Nationwide | NATO Air-to-Air |
| 268.150 | 309.150 | NFM | FLTSATCOM | Channel W 9 |
| 268.250 | 309.250 | NFM | FLTSATCOM F1 | Channel X 9 |
| 268.350 | 309.350 | NFM | FLTSATCOM F3 | Channel Y 9 |
| 268.400 | | NFM | Nationwide | Dynamic Sciences Surv |
| 268.450 | 309.450 | NFM | FLTSATCOM F2 | Channel Z 9 |
| 268.575 | | AM | Prestwick | Scottish Military |
| 268.600 | | AM | RAF Coltishall | 6 Sqn Ops |
| 268.650 | | AM | RAF Valley | 4FTS Air-to-Air |
| 268.675 | | AM | RAF Chivenor | 7FTS Air-Air |
| 268.700 | | AM | RAF Coningsby | Wing Ops |
| 268.775 | | AM | RAF Leuchars | Finals |
| | | AM | RAF Mona | Valley Radar |
| | | AM | RAF Valley | Valley Radar |
| 268.800 | | NFM | Nationwide | Dynamic Sciences Surv |
| 268.825 | | AM | RAF Benson | Approach |
| 268.925 | | AM | RAF Chinevor | Ops |
| 269.000 | | NFM | Nationwide | Dynamic Sciences Surv |
| | | AM | Nationwide | Rakie Radar |
| 269.025 | | AM | RAF Lossiemouth | DATIS |
| 269.075 | | AM | USAF Lakenheath | Command Post |
| 269.100 | | AM | RAF Shawbury | Tower |
| 269.125 | | AM | Woodford | Radar |
| 269.650 | 310.650 | NFM | FLTSATCOM | Channel W 10 |
| 269.750 | 310.750 | NFM | FLTSATCOM F1 | Channel X 10 |
| | | AM | Nationwide | RAF Discreet |
| 269.850 | 310.850 | NFM | FLTSATCOM F3 | Channel Y 10 |

| Base | Mobile | Mode | Location | User and Notes |
|---|---|---|---|---|
| 269.900 | | NFM | Nationwide | Dynamic Sciences Surv |
| 269.950 | 310.950 | NFM | FLTSATCOM F2 | Channel Z 10 |
| 270.000 | | AM | RAF West Drayton | London Military |
| | | NFM | Space | NASA Space Shuttle |
| 270.025 | | AM | RAF Odiham | 7 Sqn Air-Air |
| 270.900 | | NFM | Nationwide | Dynamic Sciences Surv |
| 271.500 | | AM | Nationwide | ATC Channel U4 |
| 271.800 | | NFM | Nationwide | Dynamic Sciences Surv |
| 272.075 | | AM | RNAS Portland | Royal Navy Exercises |
| 272.225 | | AM | Nationwide | Air Defence Region |
| 273.000 | | AM | Nationwide | ATC Channel U3 |
| 273.525 | | AM | RNAS Portland | Royal Navy |
| 273.900 | | NFM | Nationwide | Dynamic Sciences Surv |
| | | AM | Nationwide | NATO Low-Level Flying |
| 274.400 | | NFM | Nationwide | Dynamic Sciences Surv |
| 274.850 | | AM | Nationwide | Forward Air Controller |
| 275.350 | | AM | Nationwide | USAF Displays |
| | | AM | RAF West Drayton | London Military (Central) |
| 275.450 | | AM | RAF Cottesmore | Air-to-Air |
| 275.475 | | AM | RAF West Drayton | London Military |
| 275.550 | | AM | RAF Cranwell | 3FTS Air-to-Air |
| 275.625 | | AM | Prestwick | Scottish Mil |
| 275.750 | | AM | Nationwide | Air Defence Region |
| 275.800 | | NFM | Nationwide | Dynamic Sciences Surv |
| | | AM | Upavon (Army) | Tower |
| 275.875 | | AM | RAF Coningsby | Tower |
| 275.900 | | AM | RAF Leuchars | 111 Sqn Ops (Sabre Ops) |
| 275.975 | | AM | RAF Coltishall | Talkdown |
| 276.075 | | AM | RAF Chetwynd | Shawbury Approach |
| | | AM | RAF Shawbury | Approach |
| 276.125 | | AM | RAF Cosford | Approach |
| 276.175 | | AM | RAF Odiham | ATIS |
| 276.200 | | AM | RAF Ty Croes | ADR Air-Ground |
| | | AM | RAF Valley | 4FTS Air-to-Air |
| 276.225 | | AM | USAF Lakenheath | 48FW Ops |
| 276.250 | | AM | RNAS Yeovilton | 801 Sqn Air-Air |
| 276.600 | | NFM | Nationwide | Dynamic Sciences Surv |
| 276.650 | | AM | RAF Neatishead | Air Defence Region Ops |
| 276.825 | | AM | RAF Ternhill | Approach |
| 276.850 | | AM | Boscombe Down (MoD) | Approach/PAR |
| 277.000 | | AM | Nationwide | NATO Magic Surveillance |
| | | AM | Royal Navy | Ship-Air |
| 277.075 | | AM | USAF Mildenhall | ATIS |
| 277.125 | | AM | RAF West Drayton | London Military |
| 277.225 | | AM | Cardiff | Approach/Radar |
| | | AM | RAF St Athan | Approach |
| 277.275 | | AM | RAF Colerne | Approach |
| 277.300 | | AM | RAF Leuchars | 43 Sqn Ops (Golf Ops) |
| 277.400 | | AM | Nationwide | Air Defence Region |
| 277.450 | | AM | RAF Cottesmore | Air-to-Air |
| 277.475 | | AM | RAF Waddington | Director |
| | | AM | Wattisham (Army Airfield) | Director |
| 277.500 | | AM | Aberporth | Range Tertiary |
| 277.625 | | AM | RAF Linton-On-Ouse | Departure |
| 277.750 | | AM | Nationwide | Air Defence Region |
| 277.775 | | AM | RAF West Drayton | London Military |

**The UK Scanning Directory**

| Base | Mobile | Mode | Location | User and Notes |
|------|--------|------|----------|----------------|
| 277.900 | | AM | RAF Chivenor | 7FTS Air-Air |
| 277.925 | | AM | RAF Lynham | ATIS |
| 277.950 | | AM | RAF West Drayton | London Military (Dover/Lydd) |
| 278.025 | | AM | RAF West Drayton | London Military |
| 278.150 | | AM | RAF West Drayton | London Military |
| | | AM | USAF Mildenhall | Ground |
| 278.850 | | AM | Nationwide | RAF AWACS Ops |
| 278.900 | | NFM | Nationwide | Dynamic Sciences Surv |
| 279.000 | | NFM | Space | Space Shuttle Down Link |
| 279.175 | | AM | RAF West Drayton | London Mil |
| 279.225 | | AM | RAF West Drayton | London Mil |
| 279.250 | | AM | USAF Lakenheath | Radar |
| 279.300 | | AM | RAF West Drayton | London Military |
| 279.325 | | AM | MoD Boscombe Down | ATIS |
| 279.350 | | AM | RAF Benson | Tower |
| 279.475 | | AM | RAF West Drayton | London Military |
| 279.525 | | AM | Nationwide | Air Defence Region |
| 279.600 | | NFM | Nationwide | Turkish Star 5 Air Display Team |
| 279.700 | | AM | USAF Lakenheath | ATIS |
| 279.725 | | AM | Nationwide | Air Defence Region |
| 279.800 | | AM | Nationwide | USAF Air-Air |
| 280.075 | | AM | Nationwide | Tactical |
| 280.400 | | AM | Nationwide | Forward Air Controllers |
| | | AM | Otterburn | Range Secondary |
| 280.600 | | NFM | Nationwide | Dynamic Sciences Surv |
| 280.725 | | AM | USAF Lakenheath | Aux-08 "Bite" |
| 281.100 | | AM | Nationwide | Air Defence Region |
| 281.150 | | AM | Lyme Bay | Range Primary |
| 281.200 | | AM | Royal Navy | Ship-Air |
| 281.550 | | AM | Nationwide | Air-Air |
| 281.725 | | AM | RNAS Portland | Naval Exercises |
| 281.800 | | AM | Nationwide | Displays |
| 282.000 | | AM | RAF Cranwell | Director |
| 282.100 | | AM | RNAS Culdrose | ATIS |
| 282.125 | | AM | RAF West Drayton | London Mil |
| 282.200 | | AM | West Drayton | RAF London Military |
| 282.250 | | AM | Netheravon (Army) | Salisbury Plain |
| | | AM | Salisbury Plain (Army) | Ops |
| 282.275 | | AM | RAF Honington | Tower |
| 282.800 | | AM | Nationwide | NATO SAR |
| | | AM | RAF Boulmer | Boulmer Rescue |
| | | AM | RAF Leconfield | Leconfield Rescue |
| | | AM | RAF Valley | SAR Approach |
| | | AM | RNAS Portland | Portland Radio |
| 283.450 | | AM | Nationwide | 9 Sqn Air-Air |
| 283.475 | | AM | Anglia | Anglian Radar |
| 283.525 | | AM | RAF West Drayton | London Mil |
| 283.575 | | AM | RAF Waddington | Zone |
| | | AM | Wattisham (Army Airfield) | Director |
| 283.600 | | AM | Nationwide | 17 Sqn Air-Air |
| 283.650 | | AM | Nationwide | Air Defence Region |
| 283.675 | | AM | RAF West Drayton | London Mil |
| 283.900 | | AM | RAF Lossiemouth | Safety |
| 284.300 | | AM | RAF West Drayton | London Mil |
| 284.600 | | AM | Newcastle | Approach/Radar |
| 284.875 | | AM | RAF West Drayton | London Mil |

| Base | Mobile | Mode | Location | User and Notes |
|---|---|---|---|---|
| 284.900 | | AM | USAF Lakenheath | Maintenance |
| 284.950 | | AM | RAF Lyneham | LTW Air-Air |
| 284.975 | | AM | Nationwide | Air Defence Region |
| 285.025 | | AM | RAF Leuchars | Ops |
| 285.050 | | AM | RAF Waddington | Tower |
| 285.075 | | AM | Prestwick | Scottish Military |
| 285.100 | | AM | Nationwide | FRADU Discreet |
| 285.150 | | AM | RAF Cranwell | Talkdown |
| 285.175 | | AM | RAF West Drayton | London Military |

**285.500 - 290.500 MHz**     TACTICAL MILITARY EXERCISE COMMUNICATIONS 25 kHz

| Base | Mobile | Mode | Location | User and Notes |
|---|---|---|---|---|
| 285.650 | | AM | RAF Neatishead | Air Defence Region Ops |
| 285.750 | | AM | RAF Buchan | Air Defence Region Ops |
| 285.850 | | AM | RAF Boulmer | Boulmer Rescue |
| 286.650 | | AM | RAF Lossiemouth | 12 Sqn Air-Air |
| 286.900 | | AM | RAF Buchan | Air Defence Region Ops |
| 287.250 | | AM | Nationwide | RAF Air-Air Tanker Ops |
| 287.650 | | AM | RAF Neatishead | Air Defence Region Ops |
| | | AM | Royal Navy | Ship-Air |
| 287.700 | | AM | Nationwide | Air Defence Region |
| | | AM | RAF Boulmer | Air Defence Region Ops |
| | | AM | RAF Neatishead | Air Defence Region Ops |
| | | AM | Scotland (South East) | Combat Air Patrol Area B |
| 288.600 | | AM | Nationwide | USAF AWACS Ops |
| | | AM | Nationwide | USAF Air-Air |
| 289.050 | | AM | RAF Boulmer | Air Defence Region Ops |
| 289.250 | | AM | RAF Lossiemouth | 16 Sqn Air-Air |
| 289.350 | | AM | RAF Neatishead | Air Defence Region Ops |
| 290.050 | | AM | RAF Neatishead | Air Defence Region Ops |
| 290.375 | | AM | Nationwide | Air Defence Region |
| 290.575 | | AM | RAF West Drayton | London Military |
| 290.600 | | AM | RAF Coltishall | Radar |
| 290.700 | | AM | RAF West Drayton | London Military |
| 290.800 | | AM | RAF Coningsby | Air-Air |
| 290.825 | | AM | USAF Lakenheath | Radar |
| 290.850 | | AM | RAF Coningsby | 29 Sqn Ops (Triplex Ops) |
| 290.925 | | AM | RAF West Drayton | London Military |
| 290.950 | | AM | Netheravon (Army) | Tower |
| | | AM | North Sea | ACMI Range Show Ground 4 |
| 291.000 | | AM | Prestwick Airport | Navy Prestwick |
| 291.075 | | AM | Nationwide | Air Defence Region |
| 291.125 | | AM | Wattisham (Army Airfield) | Approach |
| 291.225 | | AM | RAF Lossiemouth | 15 Sqn Air-to-Air |
| 291.650 | | AM | MoD Boscombe Down | Approach |
| 291.675 | | AM | RAF Waddington | DATIS |
| 291.700 | | AM | RAF Barkston Heath | Departures |
| 291.800 | | AM | West Drayton | London Military (LJAO) |
| 291.950 | | AM | RAF Marham | Approach |
| 292.450 | | AM | RAF Boulmer | Air Defence Region Ops |
| 292.475 | | AM | RAF Leuchars | Director |
| 292.500 | | AM | Salisbury Plain | Air/Ground |
| 292.525 | | AM | West Drayton | London Military |
| 292.600 | | AM | West Drayton | London Military |
| 292.675 | | AM | Prestwick | Scottish Military |
| 292.700 | | AM | RAF Leeming | Zone Radar |

| Base | Mobile | Mode | Location | User and Notes |
|---|---|---|---|---|
| 292.800 | | AM | RAF Linton-on-Ouse | Departures/Radar |
| 293.425 | | AM | RAF Coltishall | Zone |
| 293.475 | | AM | West Drayton | RAF London Military |
| 293.525 | | AM | RAF West Drayton | London Military |
| 293.575 | | AM | RAF West Drayton | London Military |
| 293.725 | | AM | USAF Lakenheath | Aux-07 493FS |
| 293.775 | | AM | RAF Marham | Director |
| 293.975 | | AM | RAF West Drayton | London Military |
| 294.800 | | AM | Nationwide | Air to Air Refuelling |
| 294.900 | | AM | RAF West Drayton | London Military |
| 295.850 | | AM | Prestwick | Scottish Military |
| 296.400 | | AM | Nationwide | Air Defence Region |
| 296.550 | | AM | Nationwide | Air Defence Region |
| 296.575 | | AM | Nationwide | RAF/USAF Discreet |
| 296.725 | | AM | RAF Coltishall | Ground |
| | | AM | RAF Kinloss | Information |
| | | AM | RNAS Culdrose | 705 Sqn Air-Air |
| | | AM | Teesside Airport | Approach/Radar |
| 296.750 | | AM | RAF Waddington | Radar |
| 296.800 | | AM | International | Space Shuttle Down Link |
| 296.900 | | AM | RAF Cranwell | Ground |
| | | AM | RAF Neatishead | Air Defence Region Ops |
| 297.800 | | AM | Nationwide | Rescue |
| 297.900 | | AM | RAF Cranwell | Ground |
| 298.650 | | AM | Nationwide | Air Defence Region |
| 299.100 | | AM | RAF Boulmer | Boulmer Rescue |
| 299.400 | | AM | Boscombe Down (MoD) | Ground |
| | | AM | RAF Lossiemouth | Ground |
| | | AM | RNAS Culdrose | Ground |
| 299.500 | | AM | Northern North Sea, AARA 3 | Air-Air Refuelling |
| 299.700 | | AM | Nationwide | Air Defence Region |
| 299.975 | | AM | RAF West Drayton | London Military |
| | | AM | West Drayton | RAF London Military |
| 300.000 | | AM | USAF Lakenheath | Air-Air |
| 300.050 | | AM | Portland Exercise Area | Ops |
| 300.075 | | AM | USAF Lakenheath | 492FS Bowler Ops |
| 300.100 | | AM | RAF Lyneham | LTW Air-Air |
| 300.150 | | AM | RAF Benbecula | Air Defence Region Ops |
| 300.175 | | AM | RNAS Portland | Approach/Radar |
| 300.200 | | AM | USAF Lakenheath | 492FS Air-to-Air |
| 300.250 | | AM | DRA Boscombe Down | ETPS Tester Ops |
| 300.350 | | AM | RAF Northolt | ATIS |
| 300.425 | | AM | RAF Linton-on-Ouse | Tower |
| 300.450 | | AM | RAF Odiham | Talkdown |
| 300.475 | | AM | RAF Lyneham | Director |
| 300.575 | | AM | RAF Waddington | Director |
| 300.600 | | AM | Warton | Ops |
| 300.625 | | AM | RAF Cranwell | 3FTS Air-to-Air |
| 300.650 | | AM | RAF Neatishead | Air Defence Region Ops |
| 300.675 | | AM | Yeovil (Westland) | Radar (Judwin) |
| 300.775 | | AM | RAF Church Fenton | Approach |
| 300.800 | | AM | Nationwide | NATO Low Level |
| 300.825 | | AM | Lilstock Range (D119) | Range Control |
| | | AM | USAF Lakenheath | Dispatcher |
| 300.875 | | AM | RAF Leeming | 11 Sqn Ops (Black Ops) |
| 300.925 | | AM | RAF Coningsby | Talkdown |

| Base | Mobile | Mode | Location | User and Notes |
|------|--------|------|----------|----------------|

**300.950 - 308.950 MHz**     TACTICAL MILITARY EXERCISE COMMUNICATIONS 25 KHZ

| Base | Mobile | Mode | Location | User and Notes |
|------|--------|------|----------|----------------|
| 300.950 | | AM | Nationwide | Air Defence Region |
| 301.325 | | AM | USAF Lakenheath | Air-Air |
| 303.000 | | AM | Nationwide | Air to Air Refuelling |
| 304.000 | | NFM | Worldwide | USAF Satcom Downlink |
| 304.800 | | AM | Nationwide | Air to Air Refuelling |
| 305.900 | | AM | RNAS Culdrose | 750 Sqn Ops |
| 306.400 | | AM | USAF Lakenheath | Operations |
| 306.500 | | AM | Southern North Sea, AARA 6 Air-Air Refuelling |
| 306.650 | | AM | SW Scotland | Combat Air Patrol Area C |
| 307.000 | | AM | RAF Neatishead | Air Defence Region Ops |
| 307.400 | | AM | RAF Cottesmore | TTTE Ops |
| 307.600 | | AM | RAF Neatishead | Air Defence Region Ops |
| 307.800 | | AM | Stanford | Stanford Ops |
| | | AM | USAF Fairford | Command Post |
| 308.000 | | AM | Northern North Sea, AARA 3 Air-Air Refuelling |
| 308.750 | | AM | RAF Chinevor | Ops |
| 309.075 | | AM | USAF Lakenheath | Radar |
| 309.550 | | AM | RAF Chetwynd | Ternhill Tower |
| 309.625 | | AM | RAF Odiham | Tower |
| 309.650 | | AM | Nationwide | AWACS |
| | | AM | RAF Valley | 4FTS Air-to-Air |
| 309.675 | | AM | RAF Waddington | Talkdown |
| 309.725 | | AM | RAF Topcliffe | Tower |
| 309.875 | | AM | RAF Leeming | Talkdown |
| 309.950 | | AM | RAF Honington | Approach |
| 310.000 | | AM | Northern North Sea, AARA 2 Air-Air Refuelling |
| | | AM | RAF Aldergrove | Approach/Tower/Radar |
| 310.900 | | AM | Nationwide | 17 Sqn Air-Air |
| 311.200 | | AM | RAF Valley | 4FTS Air-Air |
| 311.300 | | AM | RAF Lossiemouth | 12 Sqn Air-Air |
| | | AM | Warton | Approach/Tower |
| 311.325 | | AM | RAF Kinloss | Director |
| | | AM | RAF Lossiemouth | Lossie Director |
| | | AM | RNAS Yeovilton | Yeovil Ground |
| 311.475 | | AM | Nationwide | USAF Air-Air |
| 311.825 | | AM | RAF Cranwell | ATIS |
| | | AM | RAF Lossiemouth | 15 Sqn Air-to-Air |
| 311.950 | | AM | RAF Wittering | Ground |
| 311.975 | | AM | Nationwide | USAF General Air-Air |
| 312.000 | | AM | Middle Wallop (Army) | Wallop Approach |
| 312.075 | | AM | RAF Cottesmore | Approach/Director |
| 312.225 | | AM | RAF Coningsby | Approach |
| | | AM | RAF Coningsby | Stud 13 |
| 312.325 | | AM | RAF Manston | Talkdown |
| 312.350 | | AM | RAF Northolt | Tower |
| 312.400 | | AM | RAF Lossiemouth | Talkdown |
| | | AM | RNAS Portland | Talkdown |
| 312.425 | | AM | USAF Mildenhall | Command Post |
| 312.450 | | AM | USAF Mildenhall | Command Post |
| 312.500 | | AM | RAF Waddington | Approach |
| 312.550 | | AM | RAF Marham | Ops |
| 312.625 | | AM | Dunsfold | Approach |
| 312.675 | | AM | Middle Wallop (Army) | Director |
| 312.700 | | AM | RNAS Merryfield | Tower |

| Base | Mobile | Mode | Location | User and Notes |
|---|---|---|---|---|
| 312.800 | | AM | RAF Woodvale | Approach |
| 313.000 | | AM | Nationwide | USAF Air-Air |
| 313.100 | | AM | RAF Valley | 4FTS Air-Air |

**314.000 - 315.000 MHz    TACTICAL MILITARY EXERCISE COMMUNICATIONS  25 kHz**

| Base | Mobile | Mode | Location | User and Notes |
|---|---|---|---|---|
| 314.475 | | AM | Nationwide | Air Defence Region |
| 315.000 | | AM | RAF Neatishead | NATO AWACS Coord |
| 315.325 | | AM | RAF Coltishall | Approach |
| 315.525 | | AM | Farnborough (RAE Airfield) | Radar |
| 315.550 | | AM | Edinburgh | UAS Air-Air |
| 315.575 | | AM | RAF Honington | Departure |
| 315.575 | | AM | USAF Lakenheath | Dep Con |
| 315.650 | | AM | RNAS Lee-on-Solent | Tower |
| 315.750 | | AM | RAF Benson | SRE |
| 315.850 | | AM | RAF Neatishead | Air Defence Region Ops |
| 315.975 | | AM | RAF Odiham | Odiham Information |

**316.100 - 327.100 MHz    TACTICAL MILITARY EXERCISE COMMUNICATIONS  25 kHz**

| Base | Mobile | Mode | Location | User and Notes |
|---|---|---|---|---|
| 316.350 | | AM | Northern North Sea, AARA 8 | Air-Air Refuelling |
| 316.600 | | AM | Northern North Sea, AARA 4 | Air-Air Refuelling |
| 316.700 | | AM | USAF Lakenheath | 493FS Air-to-Air |
| 316.750 | | AM | Nationwide | USAF Air-Air |
| 316.800 | | AM | RAF Lossiemouth | Orange Alert |
| 316.875 | | AM | RAF St Mawgan | DATIS |
| 317.200 | | AM | Northern North Sea, AARA 4 | Air-Air Refuelling |
| 317.375 | | AM | USAF Lakenheath | 48FW Air-to-Air |
| 317.500 | | AM | Nationwide | Air Defence Region |
| 317.850 | | AM | Nationwide | Air Defence Region |
| | | AM | Nationwide | RAF AWACS Ops |
| 318.100 | | AM | Nationwide | Air Defence Region |
| 318.550 | | AM | Nationwide | Air-Air Refuelling |
| | | AM | RAF Boulmer | Air Defence Region Ops |
| 318.750 | | AM | RAF Neatishead | Air Defence Region Ops |
| 319.400 | | AM | RAF Neatishead | Air Defence Region Ops |
| 319.600 | | AM | Royal Navy | Ship-Air |
| 322.200 | | AM | Nationwide | USAF Air-Air |
| 322.400 | | NFM | Nationwide | TADIL-A Data Link |
| 322.950 | | AM | Cranfield | Runway 22 |
| | | AM | East Anglia | USAF Talk-through |
| | | AM | Edinburgh | Runway 07/25 |
| | | AM | Kerry | Runway 07/25 |
| | | AM | Nationwide | AWACS |
| | | AM | Nationwide | USAF Displays |
| 323.200 | | AM | Nationwide | USAF Air-Air |
| 325.200 | | AM | Nationwide | RAF Discreet |
| 326.900 | | AM | North Sea, AARA 5 | Air-Air Refuelling |

**326.5000 - 328.5000 MHz    RADIO ASTRONOMY, JODRELL BANK**

| Base | Mobile | Mode | Location | User and Notes |
|------|--------|------|----------|----------------|
| **328.600 - 335.400 MHz** | | | AERONAUTICAL ILS (GLIDESLOPE COMPONENT) | |
| 329.150 | | AM | Nationwide | Glideslope (Localiser 108.95 MHz) |
| | | AM | Woodford | Runway 25 |
| 329.300 | | AM | Nationwide | Glideslope (Localiser 108.90 MHz) |
| 329.450 | | AM | Filton | Runway 10/28 |
| 329.450 | | AM | Nationwide | Glideslope (Localiser 110.55 MHz) |
| 329.600 | | AM | Bournemouth | Runway 08/26 |
| | | AM | London/Stansted | Runway 05/23 |
| | | AM | Nationwide | Glideslope (Localiser 110.50 MHz) |
| 329.750 | | AM | Nationwide | Glideslope (Localiser 108.55 MHz) |
| 329.900 | | AM | Nationwide | Glideslope (Localiser 108.50 MHz) |
| | | AM | RAF Benson | Runway 19 |
| 330.050 | | AM | Nationwide | Glideslope (Localiser 110.75 MHz) |
| 330.200 | | AM | Cardiff | Runway 12/30 |
| | | AM | Connaught | Runway 27 |
| | | AM | London/Heathrow | Runway 23 |
| | | AM | Nationwide | Glideslope (Localiser 110.70 MHz) |
| | | AM | RAF Coningsby | Runway 26 |
| 330.350 | | AM | Humberside | Runway 21 |
| | | AM | Nationwide | Glideslope (Localiser 108.75 MHz) |
| 330.500 | | AM | Nationwide | Glideslope (Localiser 108.70 MHz) |
| | | AM | RAF Leuchars | Runway 27 |
| | | AM | RAF Shawbury | Runway 19 |
| | | AM | RAF St Mawgan | Runway 31 |
| 330.650 | | AM | Nationwide | Glideslope (Localiser 110.95 MHz) |
| 330.800 | | AM | Belfast (Aldergrove) | Runway 17 |
| | | AM | Jersey | Runway 09 |
| | | AM | Leeds & Bradford | Runway 32/14 |
| | | AM | London/Gatwick | Runway 08R/26L |
| | | AM | Nationwide | Glideslope (Localiser 110.90 MHz) |
| | | AM | Norwich | Runway 27 |
| | | AM | Ronaldsway, Isle of Man | Runway 27 |
| 330.950 | | AM | Nationwide | Glideslope (Localiser 111.95 MHz) |
| 331.250 | | AM | Luton | Runway 08/28 |
| | | AM | Nationwide | Glideslope (Localiser 109.15 MHz) |
| 331.300 | | AM | Nationwide | Glideslope (Localiser 111.90 MHz) |
| | | AM | RAF Brize Norton | Runway 08/26 |
| 331.400 | | AM | Nationwide | Glideslope (Localiser 109.10 MHz) |
| 331.550 | | AM | Nationwide | Glideslope (Localiser 111.15 MHz) |
| 331.700 | | AM | Nationwide | Glideslope (Localiser 111.10 MHz) |
| | | AM | RAF Lossiemouth | Runway 23 |
| | | AM | RAF Waddington | Runway 21 |
| | | AM | USAF Fairford | Runway 09/27 |
| | | AM | Wattisham (Army) | Runway 23 |
| 331.850 | | AM | Nationwide | Glideslope (Localiser 109.35 MHz) |
| 332.000 | | AM | Glasgow | Runway 23 |
| | | AM | Nationwide | Glideslope (Localiser 109.30 MHz) |
| | | AM | RAF Church Fenton | Runway 24 |
| 332.150 | | AM | Nationwide | Glideslope (Localiser 111.35 MHz) |
| 332.300 | | AM | Hatfield | Runway 24 |
| | | AM | Nationwide | Glideslope (Localiser 111.30 MHz) |
| | | AM | Teesside | Runway 23 |
| 332.450 | | AM | Nationwide | Glideslope (Localiser 109.55 MHz) |
| 332.600 | | AM | London/Heathrow | Runway 09R/27L |
| | | AM | Manchester | Runway 06/24 |
| | | AM | Nationwide | Glideslope (Localiser 109.50 MHz) |

| Base | Mobile | Mode | Location | User and Notes |
|---|---|---|---|---|
| 332.600 | | AM | Plymouth | Runway 31 |
| | | AM | Shannon | Runway 24 |
| 332.750 | | AM | Nationwide | Glideslope (Localiser 111.55 MHz) |
| | | AM | Newcastle | Runway 07/25 |
| 332.900 | | AM | Nationwide | Glideslope (Localiser 111.50 MHz) |
| | | AM | RAF Coltishall | Runway 22 |
| 333.050 | | AM | Coventry | Runway 23 |
| | | AM | Nationwide | Glideslope (Localiser 109.75 MHz) |
| 333.200 | | AM | Beauvais | Runway 31 |
| | | AM | Belfast (Aldergrove) | Runway 25 |
| | | AM | Dinard | Runway 36 |
| | | AM | Nationwide | Glideslope (Localiser 109.70 MHz) |
| | | AM | RAF Cranwell | Runway 27 |
| | | AM | RAF Kinloss | Runway 26 |
| | | AM | RAF Lyneham | Runway 25 |
| | | AM | RAF Valley | Runway 14 |
| 333.350 | | AM | Liverpool | Runway 09/27 |
| | | AM | Nationwide | Glideslope (Localiser 111.75 MHz) |
| 333.500 | | AM | Nationwide | Glideslope (Localiser 111.70 MHz) |
| | | AM | RAE Boscombe Down | Runway 24 |
| 333.650 | | AM | Nationwide | Glideslope (Localiser 109.95 MHz) |
| 333.800 | | AM | Aberdeen/Dyce | Runway 16/34 |
| | | AM | Cherbourg | Runway 29 |
| | | AM | Cork | Runway 17/35 |
| | | AM | East Midlands | Runway 09/27 |
| | | AM | Exeter | Runway 26 |
| | | AM | Nationwide | Glideslope (Localiser 109.90 MHz) |
| | | AM | Stornoway | Runway 18 |
| | | AM | Warton | Runway 26 |
| 333.950 | | AM | Nationwide | Glideslope (Localiser 108.35 MHz) |
| 334.100 | | AM | Bedford | Runway 27 |
| | | AM | Nationwide | Glideslope (Localiser 108.30 MHz) |
| | | AM | USAF Lakenheath | Runway 24 |
| 334.250 | | AM | Bristol | Runway 09/27 |
| | | AM | Nationwide | Glideslope (Localiser 110.15 MHz) |
| 334.400 | | AM | Birmingham | Runway 15/33 |
| | | AM | Glasgow | Runway 05 |
| | | AM | Nationwide | Glideslope (Localiser 110.10 MHz) |
| | | AM | RAF Marham | ILS Runway 24 |
| 334.550 | | AM | Blackpool | Runway 28 |
| | | AM | Lydd | Runway 22 |
| | | AM | Nationwide | Glideslope (Localiser 108.15 MHz) |
| 334.700 | | AM | Guernsey | Runway 09/27 |
| | | AM | Nationwide | Glideslope (Localiser 108.10 MHz) |
| | | AM | RAF Chivenor | Runway 28 |
| | | AM | USAF Mildenhall | Runway 11/29 |
| 334.750 | | AM | RAF Neatishead | MRSA |
| 334.850 | | AM | Nationwide | Glideslope (Localiser 110.35 MHz) |
| 335.000 | | AM | Jersey | Runway 27 |
| | | AM | London/Heathrow | Runway 09L/27R |
| | | AM | Nationwide | Glideslope (Localiser 110.30 MHz) |
| | | AM | Prestwick | Runway 13/31 |
| | | AM | RAF Cottesmore | Runway 23 |
| | | AM | RAF Leeming | Runway 16 |

| Base | Mobile | Mode | Location | User and Notes |
| --- | --- | --- | --- | --- |
| 335.4000 -99.9000 MHz | | | UHF MILITARY AVIATION 25 kHz | |
| 336.150 | | AM | Boscombe Down (MoD) | Radar |
| 336.225 | | AM | Manobier | Range |
| 336.275 | | AM | MoD Farnborough | Approach |
| 336.325 | | AM | Hawarden | Tower |
| 336.350 | | AM | RAF Kinloss | Tower |
| | | AM | RAF Leeming | Talkdown |
| | | AM | RAF Marham | Ground |
| 336.375 | | AM | RAF Cottesmore | Ground |
| 336.475 | | AM | Filton (BAe), Bristol | Director |
| | | AM | Warton | Radar |
| 336.525 | | AM | RAF St Athan | Tower |
| 336.550 | | AM | RAF St Mawgan | Talkdown |
| 337.575 | | AM | USAF Fairford | Tower |
| 337.600 | | AM | Jurby | Range Primary |
| | | AM | Lakenheath | Approach |
| 337.725 | | AM | RAF Valley | Director |
| 337.750 | | AM | RAF Cranwell | Ground |
| | | AM | RAF Lossiemouth | Tower |
| | | AM | RNAS Portland | Tower |
| | | AM | RNAS Prestwick | Navy Prestwick Ops |
| 337.825 | | AM | RAF Leeming | Approach |
| 337.850 | | AM | East Scotland | Combat Air Patrol Area A |
| 337.875 | | AM | RAF Cottesmore | Talkdown |
| 337.900 | | AM | RAF Marham | Tower |
| | | AM | RAF Shawbury | Ground |
| 337.925 | | AM | MoD West Freugh | Tower |
| 337.950 | | AM | RAF Wittering | Talkdown |
| 337.975 | | AM | RAF Coningsby | Talkdown |
| | | | | |
| 338.000 -397.950 MHz | | | TACTICAL MILITARY COMMUNICATIONS 25 kHz | |
| | | | | |
| 338.00 - 338.500 MHz | | | TACTICAL MILITARY EXERCISE COMMUNICATIONS 25 kHz | |
| 338.200 | | NFM | Nationwide | TADIL-A Data Link |
| 338.625 | | AM | RAF Manston | Manston Director |
| 338.650 | | AM | RAF Brize Norton | Brize Talkdown |
| 338.675 | | AM | USAF Lakenheath | Radar |
| 338.825 | | AM | RAF Ternhill | Tower |
| 338.850 | | AM | Leeming | RAF 11 Sqn Ops |
| | | AM | RAF Leeming | Ground |
| 338.875 | | AM | RNAS Yeovilton | Yeovil Director |
| 338.975 | | AM | RNAS Predannack | Tower |
| 339.950 | | AM | RAF Coltishall | Tower |
| | | AM | RNAS Culdrose | Radar |
| 339.975 | | AM | RNAS Yeovilton | Talkdown |
| 340.025 | | AM | RAF Linton-on-Ouse | Ground |
| | | AM | RAF Lyneham | Zone |
| 340.100 | | AM | RAF St Athan | Talkdown |
| 340.175 | | AM | RAF Lyneham | Ground |
| | | AM | RAF Valley | Tower |
| 340.200 | | AM | RAF Church Fenton | Ground |
| 340.250 | | AM | Warton | Special Tasks-Test Flying |
| 340.300 | | AM | Central Wales | Combat Air Patrol Area F |
| 340.325 | | AM | RAF Benson | Ground |

| Base | Mobile | Mode | Location | User and Notes |
|---|---|---|---|---|
| 340.425 | | AM | USAF Lakenheath | 493FS Aux-08 (Iceman) |
| 340.450 | | AM | RAF Neatishead | MRSA |
| 340.475 | | AM | RAF Barkston Heath | Approach (Cranwell) |
| | | AM | RAF Cranwell | Approach |
| 340.525 | | AM | RAF Barkston Heath | Barkston Approach |
| | | AM | RAF Barkston Heath | Ground |
| 340.550 | | AM | North Sea | ACMI Range Show Ground 3 |
| 340.575 | | AM | RAF Cottesmore | Approach |
| 341.675 | | AM | Nationwide | Air Defence Region |
| 342.025 | | AM | MoD Filton | Tower |
| 342.075 | | AM | RAF Barkston Heath | Barkston Tower |
| | | AM | RAF Barkston Heath | Tower |
| 342.100 | | AM | RAF Valley | 4FTS Air-Air |
| 342.125 | | AM | RAF Waddington | Ground |
| 342.150 | | AM | RAF Chinevor | 7FTS Ops |
| 342.175 | | AM | Donna Nook | Range Primary |
| 342.200 | | AM | Warton | Radar |
| 342.250 | | AM | RAF Coltishall | Director |
| 342.450 | | AM | RAF Brize Norton | Brize Approach |
| | | AM | USAF Fairford | Brize Radar |
| 342.650 | | AM | Nationwide | RAF AWACS Ops |
| | | AM | RAF Neatishead | Air Defence Region Ops |
| 343.200 | | AM | RAF Ty Croes | ADR Air-Ground |
| | | AM | RAF Neatishead | Air Defence Region Ops |
| 343.300 | | AM | USAF Lakenheath | 493FS Aux-08 (Crusty) |
| 343.425 | | AM | USAF Lakenheath | Air-Air |
| | | AM | Wattisham (Army) | Tower |
| 343.475 | | AM | RNAS Portland | ATIS |
| | | AM | USAF Lakenheath | 48FW Aux |
| 343.600 | | AM | USAF Croughton | Croughton Radio |
| | | AM | USAF Lakenheath | 493FS |
| 343.675 | | AM | RAF Leeming | 11 Sqn Air-Air |
| | | AM | USAF Lakenheath | 494FS Panther Ops |
| 343.700 | | AM | Warton | Radar |
| 344.000 | | AM | RAF Benson | Director |
| | | AM | RAF Brize Norton | Brize Director |
| | | AM | RAF Church Fenton | Director |
| | | AM | RAF Coningsby | Director |
| | | AM | RAF Cranwell | Director |
| | | AM | RAF Honington | NATO Director |
| | | AM | RAF Leeming | Director |
| | | AM | RAF Linton-On-Ouse | Director |
| | | AM | RAF Lyneham | Director |
| | | AM | RAF Manston | Director |
| | | AM | RAF Marham | Director |
| | | AM | RAF Shawbury | Radar |
| | | AM | RAF St Athan | Director |
| | | AM | RAF St Mawgan | Director |
| | | AM | RAF Topcliffe | Director |
| | | AM | RAF Valley | Director |
| | | AM | RAF Waddington | Director |
| | | AM | RAF Wittering | Dep Control |
| 344.100 | | AM | Nationwide | Air to Air Refuelling |
| 344.200 | | AM | RAF Lossiemouth | 16 Sqn Air-Air |
| | | AM | Warton | Radar |

| Base | Mobile | Mode | Location | User and Notes |
|------|--------|------|----------|----------------|
| 344.350 | | AM | RAF Manston | Tower |
| | | AM | RAF Topcliffe | Talkdown |
| | | AM | RNAS Yeovilton | Talkdown |
| 344.425 | | AM | RAF Chivenor | 7th Flying Traing School Air-Air |
| 344.450 | | AM | RAF Lossiemouth | DATIS |
| 344.475 | | AM | RAF Linton-on-Ouse | Director |
| 344.500 | | AM | Warton | Operations (Boffin Ops) |
| 344.575 | | AM | RAF Leeming | Tower |
| 344.625 | | AM | RAF Coningsby | Approach |
| 344.700 | | AM | RAF Marham | 13 Sqn Air-to-Air |
| 344.750 | | AM | RAF Cottesmore | Air-to-Air |
| 344.800 | | AM | USAF Mildenhall | Command Post |
| 344.975 | | AM | RAF Northolt | Approach |

**345.000 - 356.000 MHz   TACTICAL MILITARY EXERCISE COMMUNICATIONS 25 KHZ**

| Base | Mobile | Mode | Location | User and Notes |
|------|--------|------|----------|----------------|
| 345.000 | | AM | RAF Neatishead | Air Defence Region Ops |
| 345.025 | | AM | Filton (BAe), Bristol | Tower |
| | | AM | RAF Lyneham | Zone |
| 345.100 | | AM | RAF Wittering | 20 Sqn Ops |
| 345.200 | | AM | Larkhill | Range Primary |
| 349.175 | | AM | Prestwick | Scottish Mil |
| 352.475 | | AM | Nationwide | AWACS |
| 353.000 | | AM | RAF Boulmer | Air Defence Region Ops |
| 353.050 | | AM | RAF Buchan | Air Defence Region Ops |
| 353.200 | | AM | RAF Ternhill | Approach |
| 353.550 | | AM | Aberdeen | Approach/Radar |
| | | AM | DRA Boscombe Down | Gauntlet Ops |
| 354.450 | | AM | RNAS Portland | Naval Exercises |
| 355.025 | | AM | Nationwide | Forward Air Controllers |
| 355.975 | | AM | Nationwide | 31 Sqn Air-Air |
| 356.175 | | AM | Wattisham (Army Airfield) | Talkdown |
| 356.200 | | AM | Aberporth | Range Primary |
| 356.275 | | AM | RAF Halton | Halton Aero Club |
| 356.400 | | AM | RAF Valley | 4th Flying Traing School Air-Air |
| 356.725 | | AM | RAF Leeming | Seagull Ops |
| 356.750 | | AM | RAFValley | Ground |
| 356.850 | | AM | Nationwide | RAF AWACS Ops |
| 356.875 | | AM | RAF Brize Norton | Brize Director |
| 356.925 | | AM | RAF Cranwell | Talkdown |
| 356.975 | | AM | RAF Shawbury | Talkdown |
| 357.125 | | AM | RAF Cosford | Tower |
| 357.150 | | AM | RAF Wittering | Tower |
| 357.175 | | AM | RAF St Athan | Approach |
| 357.200 | | AM | RAF St Mawgan | Approach |
| 357.375 | | AM | RAF Topcliffe | Approach |
| 357.400 | | AM | MoD Farnborough | Tower |
| 357.475 | | AM | RAF Brize Norton | Brize Ops |
| 357.600 | | AM | Nationwide | AWACS |
| 358.400 | | AM | RAF Honington | Radar/NATO T/D |
| 358.475 | | AM | Northern England | Combat Air Patrol Area D West |
| 358.475 | | AM | RAF Kinloss | Ops |
| 358.525 | | AM | RAF Linton-on-Ouse | Talkdown |
| 358.550 | | AM | RAF Coningsby | Ground |
| 358.552 | | AM | Castle Martin | Range Air-Ground |

| Base | Mobile | Mode | Location | User and Notes |
|---|---|---|---|---|
| 358.575 | | AM | Woodford | Tower/Radar |
| 358.600 | | AM | USAF Fairford | Fairford Metro |
| | | AM | Wattisham (Army) | Tower |
| 358.650 | | AM | RAF Leeming | Director |
| 358.675 | | AM | RAF Valley | Talkdown |
| | | AM | USAF Lakenheath | Tower |
| 358.700 | | AM | RNAS Culdrose | Talkdown |
| 358.725 | | AM | RAF Cottesmore | Director |
| 358.750 | | AM | RAF Honington | Radar |
| | | AM | RAF Mona | Tower |
| 358.800 | | AM | RAF Benson | Zone |
| 358.850 | | AM | RAF Church Fenton | Director |
| 358.925 | | AM | Prestwick | Scottish Mil |
| 359.400 | | AM | North Sea | ACMI Range Show Ground 2 |
| 359.425 | | AM | RNAS Portland | Naval Exercises |
| 359.500 | | AM | RAF Lyneham | Approach |
| 359.775 | | AM | Boscombe Down (MoD) | Approach |
| 359.825 | | AM | Wattisham (Army) | Talkdown |
| 359.875 | | AM | RAF Wittering | Approach |
| 360.550 | | AM | RAF St Mawgan | Director |
| 360.720 | | AM | RAF Barkston Heath | Talkdown |
| 360.750 | | AM | RAF Colerne | Ground |
| 360.775 | | AM | Manobier | Range |
| 361.100 | | AM | RAF Leeming | 11 Sqn Air-Air |
| 361.975 | | AM | North Sea | ACMI Range Show Ground 5 |
| 362.050 | | AM | Salisbury Plain | Salisbury Ops |
| 362.125 | | AM | USAF Lakenheath | Ram Rod |
| 362.175 | | AM | RAF Lossiemouth | 15 Sqn Air-to-Air |
| 362.225 | | AM | Netheravon (Army) | Approach |
| 362.300 | | AM | Edinburgh Airport | Radar |
| | | AM | Glasgow Airport | Approach/Radar |
| | | AM | Inverness Airport | Approach |
| | | AM | RAF Benson | Approach/Zone |
| | | AM | RAF Brize Norton | Brize Approach |
| | | AM | RAF Church Fenton | Fenton Approach/Radar |
| | | AM | RAF Colerne | Approach |
| | | AM | RAF Coningsby | Approach |
| | | AM | RAF Cosford | Approach |
| | | AM | RAF Cranwell | Approach |
| | | AM | RAF Dishforth | Approach |
| | | AM | RAF Kinloss | Approach |
| | | AM | RAF Leeming | Approach |
| | | AM | RAF Leuchars | Approach |
| | | AM | RAF Linton-on-Ouse | Approach |
| | | AM | RAF Lossiemouth | Approach |
| | | AM | RAF Lyneham | Approach |
| | | AM | RAF Manston | Approach |
| | | AM | RAF Marham | Approach |
| | | AM | RAF Newton | Approach |
| | | AM | RAF Northolt | Approach |
| | | AM | RAF Shawbury | Approach |
| | | AM | RAF St Athan | Approach |
| | | AM | RAF St Mawgan | Approach |
| | | AM | RAF Ternhill | Approach |
| | | AM | RAF Topcliffe | Approach |
| | | AM | RAF Valley | Approach |

| Base | Mobile | Mode | Location | User and Notes |
|---|---|---|---|---|
| 362.300 | | AM | RAF Waddington | Approach |
| | | AM | RAF Wittering | Approach/Radar |
| | | AM | RNAS Portland | Approach/Radar/Tower |
| | | AM | RNAS Yeovilton | Approach/Director |
| | | AM | USAF Fairford | Brize Radar |
| | | AM | USAF Mildenhall | Approach |
| 362.475 | | AM | RAF Shawbury | Approach |
| 362.525 | | AM | RAF Valley | 4FTS Air-Air |
| 362.650 | | AM | Boscombe Down (MoD) | Approach |
| 362.675 | | AM | RAF Linton-on-Ouse | Approach |
| 362.825 | | AM | Nationwide | Air Defence Region |
| 362.900 | | AM | RAF Wittering | 1/20 Sqn Air-to-Air |
| 362.975 | | AM | RAF Coningsby | Ransack Ops |
| 364.200 | | AM | Faroe Islands | Pole Star |
| | | AM | Nationwide | NATO Magic Surveillance |
| | | AM | Nationwide | RAF AWACS Ops |
| | | AM | RAF Neatishead | Air Defence Region Ops |
| 364.650 | | AM | RAF Leeming | 25 Sqn Ops (Silver Ops) |
| 364.650 | | AM | RNAS Yeovilton | D School |
| 364.800 | | AM | RAF Coltishall | Ops |
| 364.825 | | AM | Middle Wallop (Army) | Talkdown |
| 364.850 | | AM | RAF Valley | 4FTS Air-Air |
| 364.975 | | AM | North Sea | Combat Air Patrol Area E |
| | | AM | RAF Coningsby | 56 Sqn Ops (Ransack Ops) |
| 365.025 | | AM | RAF Valley | 4FTS Air-to-Air |
| 365.050 | | AM | RAF Coningsby | Air-to-Air |
| 365.075 | | AM | RAF Chetwynd | Ternhill Approach |
| 365.100 | | AM | USAF Mildenhall | Dispatcher |

### 365.5000 -69.5000 MHz — TACTICAL MILITARY EXERCISE COMMUNICATIONS 25 kHz

| Base | Mobile | Mode | Location | User and Notes |
|---|---|---|---|---|
| 365.675 | | AM | RAF West Drayton | London Military |
| 366.225 | | AM | Manorbick | Range Primary |
| 366.600 | | AM | RNAS Culdrose | 750 Sqn Ops |
| 366.725 | | AM | RAF Church Fenton | PAR |
| 367.125 | | AM | Nationwide | Air Defence Region |
| 367.200 | | AM | Nationwide | Air Defence Region |
| | | AM | Nationwide | USAF Air-Air |
| 367.375 | | AM | Dunsfold | Approach |
| | | AM | Dunsfold | Radar |
| 368.300 | | AM | RAF Wittering | 1 Sqn Air-Air |
| 369.000 | | AM | RAF Marham | 13 Sqn Ops (Dagger Ops) |
| 369.050 | | AM | Northern England | Combat Air Patrol Area D East |
| 369.125 | | AM | Nationwide | Air Defence Region |
| 369.150 | | AM | RAF Spadeadam | Ops |
| 369.175 | | AM | Nationwide | Air Defence Region |
| 369.375 | | AM | USAF Lakenheath | 493FS Discreet |
| 369.650 | | AM | East Anglia | USAF Talk-through |
| 369.875 | | AM | RNAS Yeovilton | Radar |
| 369.900 | | AM | RAF Coningsby | 56 Sqn Ops (Lion Ops) |
| 369.975 | | AM | Yeovil (Westland) | Approach (Judwin) |
| 370.000 | | AM | RNAS Predannack | Tower |
| 370.025 | | AM | RAF Leuchars | Finals |
| 370.050 | | AM | RAF Cottesmore | Tower |
| | | AM | RAF Kinloss | Talkdown |

| Base | Mobile | Mode | Location | User and Notes |
|---|---|---|---|---|
| 370.075 | | AM | RAF Leuchars | Talkdown |
| 370.100 | | AM | MoD Boscombe Down | Tower |
| | | AM | Nationwide | Patrolle Swisse air display team (tower) |
| | | AM | Nationwide | Swedick Tower air display team |
| 370.250 | | AM | USAF Mildenhall | Tower |
| 370.300 | | AM | MoD Llanbedr | PAR |
| | | AM | RAF Brize Norton | Ground |
| 370.950 | | AM | USAF Mildenhall | AMC Ops |
| 371.200 | | AM | Nationwide | Air Defence Region |
| | | AM | USAF Fairford | Command Post |
| 372.050 | | AM | RAF Neatishead | Air Defence Region Ops |
| 372.250 | | AM | RAF Chivenor | 7FTS Air-Air |
| 372.300 | | AM | RNAS Culdrose | ATIS |
| 372.325 | | AM | RAF Mona | Valley Approach |
| | | AM | RAF Valley | Approach |
| 372.350 | | AM | RAF Coltishall | 54 Sqn Ops (Lion Ops) |
| 372.375 | | AM | RAF St Athan | Talkdown |
| 372.425 | | AM | Cambridge | Tower/Radar |
| | | AM | HMS Cambridge | Royal Navy |
| | | AM | Yeovil (Westland) | Tower (Judwin) |
| 372.625 | | AM | Middle Wallop (Army) | Wallop Tower |
| 372.650 | | AM | RAF Lossiemouth | 617 Sqn Air-Air |

### 373.000 - 375.000 MHz — TACTICAL MILITARY EXERCISE COMMUNICATIONS 25 kHz

| Base | Mobile | Mode | Location | User and Notes |
|---|---|---|---|---|
| 372.650 | | AM | RNAS Yeovilton | Tower |
| 373.100 | | AM | Nationwide | Air Defence Region |
| 374.300 | | AM | RAF West Drayton | London Mil |
| 374.425 | | AM | USAF Lakenheath | 493FS Discreet |
| 375.200 | | AM | RAF Lyneham | Talkdown |
| 375.325 | | AM | RAF Church Fenton | Director |
| 375.400 | | AM | Dunsfold | Tower |
| 375.425 | | AM | RAF Newton | Tower |
| 375.500 | | AM | RAF Northolt | Talkdown |
| 375.525 | | AM | RAF Kinloss | Talkdown |
| 376.525 | | AM | RAF Kinloss | Talkdown |
| 376.575 | | AM | RAF Cottesmore | Departure Control |
| | | AM | RAF Wittering | Dep Control |
| 376.600 | | AM | Jurby | Range Secondary |
| 376.625 | | AM | RAF Brize Norton | Director |
| | | AM | RAF St Mawgan | Grounds |
| | | AM | USAF Fairford | Director |
| 376.650 | | AM | RAF Kinloss | Approach |
| | | AM | RAF Lossiemouth | Approach |
| 377.600 | | AM | Nationwide | Red Arrows Display |
| 378.100 | | AM | Nationwide | RAF AWACS Ops |
| 378.150 | | AM | RAF Wittering | 1 Sqn Air-Air |
| 378.200 | | AM | RAF Neatishead | MRSA |
| 379.025 | | AM | RAF Manston | Approach |
| 379.125 | | AM | Nationwide | RAF AWACS Ops |
| 379.200 | | AM | Aberporth | Range Secondary |
| 379.275 | | AM | RAF Coltishall | Approach |
| 379.375 | | AM | RAF Coningsby | Air-to-Air |
| 379.400 | | AM | Aberporth | Range Secondary |
| 379.425 | | AM | RAF Northolt | Director |
| 379.475 | | AM | USAF Fairford | Dispatcher |

| Base | Mobile | Mode | Location | User and Notes |
|------|--------|------|----------|----------------|
| 379.500 | | AM | RNAS Culdrose | Radar |
| 379.525 | | AM | RAF Cranwell | Tower |
| 379.650 | | AM | RAF Marham | Talkdown |
| 379.675 | | AM | RAF Dishforth | Ground |
| 379.700 | | AM | RAF Mona | Approach |
| 379.750 | | AM | Nationwide | RAF AWACS Ops |
| | | AM | RNAS Yeovilton | ATIS |
| 379.800 | | AM | Teesside | Tower |
| 379.875 | | AM | Pembury | Range Primary |
| 379.900 | | AM | Nationwide | RAF AWACS Ops |
| 379.975 | | AM | MoD Farnborough | Ops |
| 380.025 | | AM | MoD Boscombe Down | Approach |
| 380.125 | | AM | RAF St Athan | Director |
| 380.150 | | AM | USAF Mildenhall | Ground |
| 380.175 | | AM | MoD Llanbedr | Tower |
| 380.200 | | AM | Nationwide | AAC Eagles Air to Air |
| 380.225 | | AM | RNAS Culdrose | Tower |
| 380.800 | | AM | Nationwide | Air-Air Refuelling |
| 380.875 | | AM | Nationwide | Air Defence Region |
| 380.950 | | AM | RAF Wittering | Approach |
| 381.000 | | AM | RAF Lyneham | ATIS |
| 381.075 | | AM | RAF Linton-on-Ouse | Departures |
| 381.100 | | AM | RAF Waddington | Raven |
| 381.125 | | AM | MoD Boscombe Down | PAR |
| 381.150 | | AM | RAF Coltishall | 41 Sqn Ops |
| 381.200 | | AM | RAF Brize Norton | Tower |
| 381.300 | | AM | Nationwide | USAF AWACS Ops |
| 381.575 | | AM | Nationwide | USAF AWACS Ops |
| 382.675 | | AM | Prestwick | Scottish Mil |
| 382.900 | | AM | HMS Drake (Plymouth) | Royal Navy |
| 383.150 | | NFM | Nationwide | TADIL-A Data Link |
| 383.225 | | AM | RAF Wittering | Talkdown |
| 383.375 | | AM | Nationwide | RAF Discreet |
| 383.475 | | AM | RAF Cranwell | Talkdown |
| | | AM | RAF West Drayton | London Mil |
| 383.525 | | AM | MoD West Freugh | Approach |
| 383.600 | | AM | RAF Valley | Air-to-Air |
| 385.400 | | AM | RAF Brize Norton | Talkdown |
| | | AM | RAF Church Fenton | Talkdown |
| | | AM | RAF Leeming | Talkdown |
| | | AM | RAF Lyneham | Talkdown |
| | | AM | RAF Manston | Talkdown |
| | | AM | RAF Marham | Talkdown |
| | | AM | RAF Northolt | Talkdown |
| | | AM | RAF Odiham | Talkdown |
| | | AM | RAF Shawbury | Talkdown |
| | | AM | RAF St Athan | Talkdown |
| | | AM | RAF St Mawgan | Talkdown |
| | | AM | RAF Topcliffe | Talkdown |
| | | AM | RAF Valley | Talkdown |
| | | AM | RAF Waddington | Talkdown |
| 386.500 | | AM | RAF St Athan | Ground |
| 386.525 | | AM | RAF Leeming | Ground |
| 386.650 | | AM | RAF Leuchars | 43 Sqn Air-Air |
| 386.675 | | AM | MoD Llanbedr | Approach |

| Base | Mobile | Mode | Location | User and Notes |
|---|---|---|---|---|
| 386.725 | | AM | Dartmouth | Military Helipad |
| | | AM | RAF Church Fenton | Talkdown |
| 386.775 | | AM | RAE Farnborough | Odiham Radar |
| | | AM | RAF Odiham | Approach |
| 386.825 | | AM | RAF Lyneham | Tower |
| 386.875 | | AM | RAF Shawbury | Radar |
| | | AM | RAF Shawbury | Zone |
| 386.900 | | AM | RAF Valley | Ground |
| 387.450 | | AM | RAF St Mawgan | Talkdown |
| | | AM | RAF Topcliffe | Ground |
| 387.550 | | AM | RAF Lossiemouth | 16 Sqn Air-Air |
| 388.000 | | AM | Nationwide | Sharks Helicopter Displays |
| | | AM | RNAS Culdrose | Talkdown |
| 388.525 | | AM | RAF Wittering | Approach/Radar |
| 393.200 | | AM | RAF West Drayton | London Military |
| 393.475 | | AM | RAF Coningsby | Air-to-Air |
| 394.050 | | AM | MoD Boscombe Down | Gauntlet Ops |
| 396.700 | | AM | RAF Brize Norton | Tower |
| 396.850 | | AM | RAF Wittering | Talkdown |
| | | AM | Nationwide | RAF AWACS Ops |
| 397.975 | | AM | USAF Lakenheath | Ground |
| 398.100 | | AM | RAF Lossiemouth | Approach |
| 398.200 | | AM | USAF Lakenheath | Command Post |
| 398.250 | | AM | Nationwide | NATO Air-Air |
| 398.350 | | AM | USAF Lakenheath | Approach (LARS) |
| 398.605 | | NFM | Nationwide | Illegal Bugging Devices |
| 398.875 | | AM | Nationwide | Air Defence Region |
| 399.455 | | NFM | Nationwide | Illegal Bugging Devices |

**399.9000 - 400.0500 MHz   RADIO NAVIGATION SATELLITE DOWN LINKS**

| Base | Mobile | Mode | Location | User and Notes |
|---|---|---|---|---|
| **400.0500 - 400.1500 MHz** | | | **SATELLITE DOWN LINKS & TELEMETRY** | |
| 400.1000 | | NFM | Nationwide | Satellite Standard Frequency |
| 401.0000 | | NFM | Nationwide | RAF Target Telemetry |

**400.1500 - 401.000 MHz   SATELLITE DOWN LINKS AND
                            METEOROLOGICAL AIDS**

| Base | Mobile | Mode | Location | User and Notes |
|---|---|---|---|---|
| **401.0000 - 406.0000 MHz** | | | **SATELLITE UP AND DOWN LINKS** | |
| 402.1135 | | NFM | Forties B | BP Weather Station |

**406.0000 - 406.1000 MHz   LOW POWERED SATELLITE EMERGENCY
                            POSITION RADIOBEACONS UP LINKS**

| Base | Mobile | Mode | Location | User and Notes |
|---|---|---|---|---|
| 406.0000 | | AM | International | Distress Frequency |
| | | NFM | Nationwide | Ship's EPIRB |
| 406.0250 | | AM | Nationwide | RAF Locator Beacons |
| 406.1000 | | AM | International | Distress Frequency Monitored by UK USA & Japan |

**406.1000 -410.0000 MHz** — RADIO ASTRONOMY, NORTH SEA RADIO POSITIONS BEACONS AND US EMBASSY CLOSE PROTECTION TEAM

| Base | Mobile | Mode | Location | User and Notes |
|------|--------|------|----------|----------------|
| 406.1500 | | NFM | Nationwide | US Navy On-Board Comms |
| 406.4250 | | NFM | USAF Lakenheath | Ops |
| 406.4250 | | NFM | USAF Mildenhall | Medics |
| 406.5500 | | NFM | Nationwide | US Navy On-Board Comms |
| 406.6250 | | NFM | USAF Fairford | Tower-Ground |
| | | NFM | USAF Lakenheath | Ops |
| | | NFM | USAF Mildenhall | Ops |
| 406.8750 | | NFM | USAF Mildenhall | Fire Channel |
| 406.9500 | | NFM | Nationwide | US Navy On-Board Comms |
| 407.2500 | | NFM | Nationwide | Police Channel 3 |
| 407.2750 | | NFM | USAF Fairford | Ops |
| | | NFM | USAF Mildenhall | Ops |
| 407.3500 | | NFM | Nationwide | US Navy On-Board Comms |
| 407.4250 | | NFM | London | US Embassy |
| 407.4750 | | NFM | RAF Chicksands | Security Channel 1 |
| 407.7250 | | NFM | London | US Embassy |
| 407.7500 | | NFM | USAF Mildenhall | Channel 1 |
| 408.0000 | | NFM | North Sea | Statfjord A & B |
| 408.1250 | | NFM | Nationwide | US Presidential Advance Team |
| 408.2750 | | NFM | London | US Embassy |
| 408.3000 | | NFM | Jersey | Data Link |
| 408.5500 | | NFM | Nationwide | US Presidential Guard |
| 408.6250 | | NFM | London | US Embassy Marines |
| 408.6750 | | NFM | London | US Embassy Marines |
| 408.7250 | | NFM | USAF Lakenheath | Ops |
| 408.8250 | | NFM | USAF Mildenhall | Ops |
| 409.0250 | 416.5500 | NFM | London | US Embassy (N Control) |
| | | NFM | USAF Lakenheath | Trunked Voice |
| 409.1250 | 408.1250 | NFM | Nationwide | Police Channel 2 |
| 409.7500 | 407.4500 | NFM | Nationwide | US Military Channel 1 |

**410.0000 - 425.0000 MHz** — MOD, USAF & MOULD USE 25 kHz FORMULA ONE RACING TEAM LINKS

**417.9000 - 418.1000 MHz** — LOWER POWERED TELEMETRY, TELECOMMAND AND ALARMS

| Base | Mobile | Mode | Location | User and Notes |
|------|--------|------|----------|----------------|
| 410.0000 | | NFM | Nationwide | USAF Base Common |
| 410.2500 | | FM | Lakenheath | RAF Ground Maintenance |
| 410.2700 | | NFM | USAF Fairford | Ground Maintenance |
| | | NFM | USAF Mildenhall | Base Ops |
| 410.2750 | 416.9000 | NFM | USAF Lakenheath | Trunked Voice |
| 410.2750 | 416.9000 | NFM | USAF Mildenhall | Trunked Voice |
| 410.2875 | 410.2875 | NFM | USAF Lakenheath | Ground Maintenance |
| 410.3250 | | NFM | USAF Mildenhall | Ops |
| 410.4750 | 410.4750 | NFM | USAF Fairford | Ground Support |
| | | NFM | USAF Fairford | Ops |
| 410.5000 | | NFM | USAF Lakenheath | Ops/Goldnet command |
| | | NFM | USAF Mildenhall | Phone Patches |
| 410.5250 | 410.5250 | NFM | Portsmouth | Navy Provosts |
| 410.6000 | 410.6000 | NFM | USAF Fairford | Base Security |
| | | NFM | USAF Mildenhall | Ops |

| Base | Mobile | Mode | Location | User and Notes |
|---|---|---|---|---|
| 410.6750 | 410.6750 | NFM | RAF Chicksands | Fire Channel 4 |
| | | NFM | USAF Fairford | Base Security |
| 410.7500 | | NFM | USAF Fairford | Ground Support |
| 410.7700 | 410.7700 | NFM | USAF Mildenhall | Ops |
| 410.7750 | 417.5500 | NFM | USAF Lakenheath | Trunked Voice |
| | | NFM | USAF Mildenhall | Trunked Voice |
| 410.7800 | 410.7800 | NFM | USAF Mildenhall | Ops |
| 410.7875 | 410.7875 | NFM | USAF Lakenheath | Ops |
| 410.8000 | 410.8000 | NFM | RAF Chicksands | Base Ops |
| | | NFM | USAF Fairford | Base Security |
| | | NFM | USAF Lakenheath | Ops |
| | | NFM | USAF Mildenhall | Fuel Tankers Channel 5 |
| 410.8500 | | NFM | Manchester | Piccadilly Radio Studio Link |
| 410.8500 | | NFM | USAF Mildenhall | Ops |
| 410.9000 | | NFM | Nationwide | MoD Transport |
| | | NFM | USAF Lakenheath | Ops |
| | | NFM | USAF Mildenhall | Command Network |
| 411.0000 | | NFM | USAF Fairford | Tanker Ops Channel 5 |
| 411.1250 | | NFM | USAF Lakenheath | Red Net |
| 411.1500 | | NFM | USAF Mildenhall | USAF Police |
| 411.1875 | | NFM | USAF Lakenheath | Ops |
| 411.2500 | | NFM | Northwood | NATO Command Centre |
| 411.2500 | | NFM | USAF Lakenheath | MTD |
| | | NFM | USAF Mildenhall | Security |
| 411.2750 | | NFM | USAF Lakenheath | Yellow Net |
| 411.3000 | | NFM | USAF Lakenheath | Base Ops |
| 411.4000 | | NFM | USAF Mildenhall | Ops |
| 411.4250 | 417.7500 | NFM | USAF Lakenheath | Trunked Voice (night) |
| 411.4250 | 417.7500 | NFM | USAF Mildenhall | Trunked Voice (night) |
| 411.4750 | | NFM | USAF Mildenhall | Ops |
| 411.5000 | 426.0000 | NFM | Statfjord A & C | Mobil To Hotel |
| 411.5000 | 411.5000 | NFM | USAF Mildenhall | Strategic Command |
| 411.5750 | 411.5750 | NFM | USAF Lakenheath | Ground Maintenance |
| | | NFM | USAF Mildenhall | Maintenance |
| 411.5875 | | NFM | Northwood | NATO Command Centre |
| 411.6000 | | NFM | USAF Lakenheath | Base Ops |
| 411.6250 | | NFM | USAF Mildenhall | Fire Paging |
| 411.6750 | 418.3500 | NFM | RAF Chicksands | Security Channel 2 |
| | | NFM | USAF Lakenheath | Trunked Voice (night) |
| | | NFM | USAF Mildenhall | Trunked Voice (night) |
| 411.7000 | 411.7000 | NFM | USAF Lakenheath | Base Ops |
| 411.7250 | 418.4000 | NFM | USAF Lakenheath | Trunked Voice |
| | | NFM | USAF Mildenhall | Trunked Voice (Bandit) |
| 411.7750 | 411.7750 | NFM | USAF Lakenheath | Ops |
| | | NFM | USAF Mildenhall | Security |
| 411.8000 | 411.8000 | NFM | USAF Lakenheath | Ops |
| | | NFM | USAF Mildenhall | Security |
| 411.9000 | 411.9000 | NFM | USAF Mildenhall | Security |
| 412.1750 | 412.1750 | NFM | USAF Lakenheath | Ops |
| | | NFM | USAF Mildenhall | Maintenance |
| 412.2750 | 412.2750 | NFM | USAF Fairford | USAF Ground |
| 412.2750 | 418.5000 | NFM | USAF Lakenheath | Trunked Voice (Dispatch) |
| | | NFM | USAF Mildenhall | Trunked voice and data (night) |
| 412.3750 | 418.5000 | NFM | USAF Mildenhall | Services Squadron |
| 412.4750 | 418.5000 | NFM | USAF Fairford | Ops |
| 412.5250 | 418.5000 | NFM | Brecon | MoD Mould Repeater |

| Base | Mobile | Mode | Location | User and Notes |
|------|--------|------|----------|----------------|
| 412.5500 | 412.5500 | NFM | USAF Lakenheath | Command Network |
| | | NFM | USAF Mildenhall | Base Ops |
| 412.5875 | | NFM | USAF Lakenheath | Ops |
| 412.7750 | 412.7750 | NFM | USAF Mildenhall | Ops |
| 412.8000 | 412.8000 | NFM | USAF Mildenhall | Ops |
| 412.8375 | | NFM | Brecon | MoD Mould Repeater |
| 412.9000 | 412.9000 | NFM | USAF Mildenhall | Ops |
| 412.9250 | 412.9250 | FM | Mildenhall | RAF Maintenance |
| 413.0000 | 413.0000 | NFM | USAF Mildenhall | Ops |
| | | NFM | USAF Mildenhall | USAF Police |
| 413.0750 | 413.0750 | NFM | USAF Lakenheath | Scrambled |
| | | NFM | USAF Mildenhall | Transit Alert |
| 413.0800 | 413.0800 | NFM | USAF Lakenheath | Base Ops |
| 413.1000 | 413.1000 | NFM | Nationwide | USAF Displays |
| 413.1200 | 413.1200 | NFM | USAF Lakenheath | Base Ops |
| 413.1250 | 413.1250 | NFM | USAF Mildenhall | Ops |
| 413.1500 | 413.1500 | NFM | Nationwide | USAF Base Common |
| 413.1750 | 413.1750 | NFM | USAF Lakenheath | Ops |
| | | NFM | USAF Mildenhall | Dispatch |
| 413.2000 | | NFM | RAF Chicksands | Command & Control Channel 8 |
| 413.2750 | | NFM | USAF Fairford | Ground Support F1 control |
| 413.3000 | | NFM | USAF Mildenhall | Ground |
| 413.3700 | 413.3700 | NFM | USAF Mildenhall | Base Ops |
| 413.3750 | 418.6500 | NFM | USAF Lakenheath | Trunked Data Signalling |
| | | NFM | USAF Mildenhall | Trunked Data Signalling |
| 413.4250 | 413.4250 | NFM | Malvern (MoD) | Security |
| 413.4500 | 413.4500 | NFM | Nationwide | MoD Transport |
| 413.5000 | 428.0500 | NFM | North Sea | Mobil to Statfjord B & C |
| 413.7000 | | NFM | USAF Mildenhall | Ground |
| 413.7500 | 413.7500 | NFM | USAF Mildenhall | Maintenance |
| 413.7750 | 413.7750 | NFM | USAF Lakenheath | Base Ops |
| 413.8000 | 413.8000 | NFM | Nationwide | Nuclear Security |
| | | NFM | USAF Mildenhall | Ops |
| 413.8500 | | NFM | USAF Mildenhall | Ground |
| 413.9000 | 413.9000 | NFM | USAF Mildenhall | Maintenance |
| 414.1500 | 414.1500 | NFM | USAF Lakenheath | Base Ops |
| 414.1500 | | NFM | USAF Mildenhall | Command Network |
| 414.2500 | | NFM | USAF Mildenhall | Ground |
| 414.3000 | 414.9000 | NFM | London | US Embassy |
| | | NFM | USAF Fairford | Ops |
| 414.3000 | 414.3000 | NFM | USAF Fairford | USAF Base Security |
| | | NFM | USAF Lakenheath | Base Ops |
| | | NFM | USAF Mildenhall | Aircraft maintenance Ops |
| 414.3000 | 414.9000 | NFM | USAF Mildenhall | Base Ops |
| 414.4000 | | NFM | USAF Mildenhall | Ground |
| 414.4875 | | NFM | Grand Prix Circuits | McLaren Team Voice Link |
| 414.7000 | 414.7000 | NFM | USAF Lakenheath | Security |
| 414.9800 | 414.9800 | NFM | USAF Lakenheath | Ops |
| 415.3500 | | NFM | USAF Fairford | Ops |
| 415.4000 | | NFM | USAF Mildenhall | Ground |
| 415.5625 | | NFM | Belfast | British Miltary Data Link |
| 415.7000 | 407.8500 | NFM | Nationwide | Air Force One Air-Ground |
| 415.7500 | | NFM | USAF Mildenhall | Ground |
| 415.9875 | | NFM | Grand Prix Circuits | McLaren Team Voice Link |
| 416.0000 | 416.0000 | NFM | Newport | Moss Car Alarms Remote |
| 416.1750 | | NFM | Northwood | NATO Command Centre |

| Base | Mobile | Mode | Location | User and Notes |
|---|---|---|---|---|
| 416.2175 | | NFM | Newmarket | RAF Security |
| 416.4750 | 416.4750 | FM | Mildenhall | RAF SP Control/ Main gate police |
| 416.4750 | 413.0000 | NFM | RAF Chicksands | Enlisted Spouses Assoc. |
| | | NFM | USAF Lakenheath | Ops |
| | | NFM | USAF Mildenhall | Ops |
| 416.5500 | | NFM | Ashford | Royal Marines Intelligence Unit |
| 416.5500 | 416.5500 | NFM | USAF Lakenheath | Base Ops |
| | | NFM | USAF Mildenhall | Ops |
| 416.5875 | | NFM | USAF Mildenhall | Crash Ops |
| 416.7000 | | NFM | USAF Mildenhall | Ground |
| 416.9000 | | NFM | USAF Lakenheath | Security (Dispatch) |
| 417.2000 | 417.2000 | NFM | USAF Mildenhall | Base Ops |
| 417.3000 | 417.3000 | NFM | USAF Lakenheath | Security |
| 417.5250 | | NFM | USAF Lakenheath | Ops |
| | | NFM | USAF Mildenhall | Aircrew Reception |
| 417.5300 | 417.5300 | NFM | USAF Lakenheath | Base Ops |
| 417.5750 | 417.5750 | NFM | USAF Fairford | Military Police |
| 417.9375 | | NFM | Manchester | Mould |
| 418.0000 | 418.0000 | NFM | Newport | Moss House Alarms |
| 418.0500 | 418.0500 | FM | Mildenhall | RAF Ground Crew Ops |
| 418.2000 | | NFM | Normandy | French Marine Channel 16 Link |
| 418.2250 | | NFM | USAF Mildenhall | Ops |
| 418.2300 | 418.2300 | NFM | USAF Lakenheath | Base Ops |
| 418.3000 | | NFM | Jersey | Data Link |
| 418.3250 | | NFM | Nationwide | US Presidential Guard |
| 418.3500 | | NFM | USAF Lakenheath | Operations |
| 418.5000 | | NFM | USAF Lakenheath | Engineering (Spectre 1) |
| 419.2000 | 419.2000 | FM | Lakenheath | RAF Channel 4 Ops |
| 419.2750 | | NFM | USAF Lakenheath | Scrambled |
| | | NFM | USAF Mildenhall | Scrambled |
| 419.6250 | | NFM | Newmarket | RAF Security |
| 419.9875 | | NFM | Grand Prix Circuits | McLaren Team Voice Link |
| 420.0125 | | NFM | Manchester | Mould |
| 420.4000 | | NFM | London | Wellington Barracks |
| 420.4750 | | NFM | Nationwide | Grand Prix Minarde Team |
| 421.5625 | | NFM | Manchester | Mould |
| 421.7875 | | NFM | Manchester | Mould |
| 421.9125 | | NFM | Strathclyde | Mould |
| 421.9817 | | NFM | Hertfordshire | Mould |
| 421.9875 | | NFM | Strathclyde | Mould |
| 422.1375 | 422.1375 | NFM | London Horseguards Parade | Trooping the Colour |
| 422.1375 | | NFM | Nationwide | MoD Police |
| 422.1500 | 427.6500 | NFM | London | Ircheck |
| 422.2125 | | NFM | Hertfordshire | Mould |
| 422.2375 | | NFM | Henlow | Mould |
| 422.3625 | | NFM | Strathclyde | Mould |
| 422.3750 | | NFM | London Horseguards Parade | Trooping the Colour |
| 422.4125 | | NFM | Hertfordshire | Mould |
| 422.9500 | 428.4500 | NFM | Glasgow | Taxis |
| 422.9500 | 411.9500 | FM | Lakenheath | RAF Motor Pool Ops |
| 423.0000 | 408.5000 | NFM | Flotel | Mobil To Statfjord A & B |
| 424.2500 | 424.2500 | NFM | Belfast | Police Mobile Data Link |
| 424.7500 | 424.7500 | NFM | Northern Ireland | Special Branch |

| Base | Mobile | Mode | Location | User and Notes |
|------|--------|------|----------|----------------|

**425.0000 - 425.5000 MHz   PMR MOBILE 12.5 KHZ NFM**
**(SPLIT +20.5 MHz)**

| Base | Mobile | Mode | Location | User and Notes |
|------|--------|------|----------|----------------|
| 425.00000 | 445.00000 | NFM | Halifax | Beacon Gas |
| 425.26250 | | NFM | London | Medicall |
| 425.28750 | | NFM | London | Medicall NW London |
| 425.30000 | | NFM | London | Medicall |
| 425.48750 | | NFM | Dorset | 2CR UHF Radio Microphones |

**425.5000 - 429.0000 MHz   PMR MOBILE 12.5 KHZ NFM**
**(SPLIT + 14.5 MHz)**

| Base | Mobile | Mode | Location | User and Notes |
|------|--------|------|----------|----------------|
| 425.70250 | | NFM | London | Burglar Alarms |
| 426.00000 | 411.50000 | NFM | North Sea | Mobil to Statfjord A & C |
| 426.07500 | | NFM | Glasgow | MoD HQ Security |
| 426.95000 | | NFM | Glasgow | Medicall |
| 427.22500 | | NFM | London | Surveillance ops used from time to time |
| 427.81250 | | NFM | Manchester | ITN O/B Studio Link |
| 428.00000 | 413.50000 | NFM | North Sea | Mobil To Statfjord B & C |
| 428.26250 | | NFM | London | Medicall |
| 428.32500 | | NFM | RAF Chicksands | Disaster Repeater Channel 7 |
| 428.67500 | | NFM | London | British Gas Engineers |
| 428.70000 | | NFM | London, West Drayton | British Gas Engineers |
| 428.71250 | | NFM | London | British Gas Engineers |
| 428.76250 | | NFM | Gerrards Cross | British Gas Engineers |

**429.0000 - 430.0000 MHz   MoD RADIOLOCATION BEACONS**

| Base | Mobile | Mode | Location | User and Notes |
|------|--------|------|----------|----------------|
| 429.08750 | | NFM | Strathclyde | Mould |
| 429.11250 | | NFM | Strathclyde | Mould |

**430.0000 - 431.0000 MHz   MoD ALLOCATION**

| Base | Mobile | Mode | Location | User and Notes |
|------|--------|------|----------|----------------|
| 430.90000 | 430.90000 | NFM | RAF Newton | Base Security |

**431.0000 - 432.0000 MHz   PMR**

**433.0000 - 434.0000 MHz   MoD MOULD REPEATERS 12.5 KHZ**

| Base | Mobile | Mode | Location | User and Notes |
|------|--------|------|----------|----------------|
| 433.0125 | | NFM | Birmingham | Mould |
| | | NFM | Strathclyde | Mould |
| 433.1375 | | NFM | Birmingham | Mould |
| | | NFM | Strathclyde | Mould |
| 433.1625 | | NFM | Hertfordshire | Mould |
| | | NFM | Strathclyde | Mould |
| 433.1875 | | NFM | Strathclyde | Mould |
| 433.2625 | | NFM | Strathclyde | Mould |
| 433.2875 | | NFM | Birmingham | Mould |
| 433.3875 | | NFM | Strathclyde | Mould |
| 433.4375 | | NFM | Strathclyde | Mould |

**430.000 - 440.000 MHz   70CM AMATEUR RADIO BAND**

| Base | Mobile | Mode | Location | User and Notes |
|------|--------|------|----------|----------------|
| 432.890 | | CW | Sutton Coldfield | Repeater (GB3SUT) |
| 432.910 | | CW | Emley Moor | Repeater (GB3MLY) |
| 432.934 | | CW | Bristol | Repeater (GB3BSL) |
| 432.965 | | CW | Lerwick | Repeater (GB3LER) |
| 432.970 | | CW | St Austall | Repeater (GB3MCB) |
| 432.980 | | CW | Dundee | Repeater (GB3ANG) |

| Base | Mobile | Mode | Location | User and Notes |
|---|---|---|---|---|
| 433.000 | 434.600 | NFM | Ashford | Repeater (GB3CK) |
| | | NFM | Bishop Stortford | Repeater (GB3SV) |
| | | NFM | Blackburn | Repeater (GB3PF) |
| | | NFM | Blandford Forum | Repeater (GB3DT) |
| | | NFM | Boston | Repeater (GB3SO) |
| | | NFM | Bracknell | Repeater (GB3BN) |
| | | NFM | Exeter | Repeater (GB3EX) |
| | | NFM | Llandudno | Repeater (GB3LL) |
| | | NFM | London Central | Repeater (GB3EL) |
| | | NFM | Milton Keynes | Repeater (GB3MK) |
| | | NFM | Newcastle | Repeater (GB3NT) |
| | | NFM | Norwich | Repeater (GB3NR) |
| | | NFM | Perth | Repeater (GB3PU) |
| | | NFM | Scarborough | Repeater (GB3NY) |
| | | NFM | Sheffield | Repeater (GB3US) |
| | | NFM | Wolverhampton | Repeater (GB3WN) |
| 433.025 | 434.625 | NFM | Bury | Repeater (GB3MA) |
| | | NFM | Doncaster | Repeater (GB3DV) |
| | | NFM | Harrogate | Repeater (GB3HJ) |
| | | NFM | Hemel Hempstead | Repeater (GB3BV) |
| | | NFM | Horsham | Repeater (GB3HO) |
| | | NFM | Melton Mowbray | Repeater (GB3EM) |
| | | NFM | Stonehaven | Repeater (GB3BA) |
| 433.050 | 434.650 | NFM | Aylesbury | Repeater (GB3AV) |
| | | NFM | Belfast | Repeater (GB3UL) |
| | | NFM | Blackpool | Repeater (GB3FC) |
| | | NFM | Corby | Repeater (GB3CI) |
| | | NFM | Enfield Town Ctre | Repeater (GB3LV) |
| | | NFM | Lincoln | Repeater (GB3LS) |
| | | NFM | Liskeard | Repeater (GB3CH) |
| | | NFM | Margate | Repeater (GB3EK) |
| | | NFM | Portsmouth | Repeater (GB3PH) |
| | | NFM | Selkirk | Repeater (GB3HK) |
| | | NFM | Stoke on Trent | Repeater (GB3ST) |
| | | NFM | Stourbridge | Repeater (GB3OS) |
| | | NFM | Wells | Repeater (GB3NN) |
| | | NFM | Yeovil | Repeater (GB3YS) |
| 433.075 | 434.675 | NFM | Chelmsford | Repeater (GB3ER) |
| | | NFM | Chichester | Repeater (GB3CC) |
| | | NFM | Hull | Repeater (GB3HU) |
| | | NFM | Mansfield | Repeater (GB3MD) |
| | | NFM | Northampton | Repeater (GB3NH) |
| | | NFM | Swindon | Repeater (GB3TD) |
| | | NFM | Taunton | Repeater (GB3VS) |
| | | NFM | Uxbridge | Repeater (GB3HL) |
| 433.100 | 434.700 | NFM | Anglesey | Repeater (GB3AN) |
| | | NFM | Bath | Repeater (GB3UB) |
| | | NFM | Bo'ness | Repeater (GB3OH) |
| | | NFM | Goole | Repeater (GB3GC) |
| | | NFM | Ipswich | Repeater (GB3IH) |
| | | NFM | Kings Lynn | Repeater (GB3KL) |
| | | NFM | Leicester | Repeater (GB3LE) |
| | | NFM | Pembroke | Repeater (GB3SP) |
| | | NFM | Wrotham | Repeater (GB3NK) |

| Base | Mobile | Mode | Location | User and Notes |
|---|---|---|---|---|
| 433.125 | 434.725 | NFM | Brentwood | Repeater (GB3EB) |
| | | NFM | Cheltenham | Repeater (GB3GH) |
| | | NFM | Douglas | Repeater (GB3IM) |
| | | NFM | Haywards Heath | Repeater (GB3HY) |
| | | NFM | Huntingdon | Repeater (GB3OV) |
| | | NFM | Scunthorpe | Repeater (GB3WJ) |
| | | NFM | Weston Super Mare | Repeater (GB3WB) |
| 433.150 | 434.725 | NFM | Ampthill | Repeater (GB3BD) |
| | | NFM | Barnsley | Repeater (GB3SY) |
| | | NFM | Brighton | Repeater (GB3BR) |
| | | NFM | Canterbury | Repeater (GB3SK) |
| | | NFM | Didcot | Repeater (GB3DI) |
| | | NFM | Hereford | Repeater (GB3HC) |
| | | NFM | Hull | Repeater (GB3HA) |
| | | NFM | London, central | Repeater (GB3LW) |
| | | NFM | Mold, Clwyd | Repeater (GB3CR) |
| | | NFM | Newtown, Powys | Repeater (GB3CW) |
| | | NFM | Rugby | Repeater (GB3ME) |
| | | NFM | Swansea | Repeater (GB3WG) |
| | | NFM | Wolverhampton | Repeater (GB3MM) |
| 433.175 | 434.775 | NFM | Bedford | Repeater (GB3BL) |
| | | NFM | Bridgend | Repeater (GB3MG) |
| | | NFM | Halifax | Repeater (GB3WY) |
| | | NFM | Nottingham | Repeater (GB3NM) |
| 433.200 | 434.800 | NFM | Banbury | Repeater (GB3EH) |
| | | NFM | Cambridge | Repeater (GB3PY) |
| | | NFM | Carmarthen | Repeater (GB3CM) |
| | | NFM | Leeds | Repeater (GB3LA) |
| | | NFM | Southampton | Repeater (GB3EA) |
| | | NFM | Telford | Repeater (GB3TF) |
| 433.225 | 434.825 | NFM | Bury St Edmunds | Repeater (GB3BE) |
| | | NFM | Clacton | Repeater (GB3CL) |
| | | NFM | Coventry | Repeater (GB3CV) |
| | | NFM | Huddersfield | Repeater (GB3HD) |
| | | NFM | Salisbury | Repeater (GB3SW) |
| | | NFM | Airdrie | Repeater (GB3ML) |
| | | NFM | Bristol | Repeater (GB3BS) |
| | | NFM | Dundee | Repeater (GB3DD) |
| | | NFM | Leamington Spa | Repeater (GB3MW) |
| | | NFM | Liverpool | Repeater (GB3LI) |
| | | NFM | Luton | Repeater (GB3LT) |
| | | NFM | Luton | Repeater (GB3LT) |
| | | NFM | Newbury | Repeater (GB3AW) |
| | | NFM | Peterborough | Repeater (GB3PB) |
| | | NFM | Reigate | Repeater (GB3NS) |
| | | NFM | Wirksworth | Repeater (GB3DY) |
| 433.275 | 434.875 | NFM | Grantham | Repeater (GB3GR) |
| | | NFM | Grimsby | Repeater (GB3GY) |
| | | NFM | Hinckley | Repeater (GB3HT) |
| | | NFM | Hitchin | Repeater (GB3HN) |
| | | NFM | Honiton | Repeater (GB3SH) |
| | | NFM | Hyde | Repeater (GB3WP) |
| | | NFM | Newhaven | Repeater (GB3LR) |
| | | NFM | Sunderland | Repeater (GB3DC) |

| Base | Mobile | Mode | Location | User and Notes |
|------|--------|------|----------|----------------|
| 433.300 | 434.900 | NFM | Bolton | Repeater (GB3MT) |
| | | NFM | Boroughbridge | Repeater (GB3HM) |
| | | NFM | Chesterfield | Repeater (GB3EE) |
| | | NFM | Guildford | Repeater (GB3GF) |
| | | RTTY | Nationwide | Channel SU17 |
| | | NFM | Oxford | Repeater (GB3OX) |
| | | NFM | Royston | Repeater (GB3PT) |
| 433.325 | 434.925 | NFM | Carlisle | Repeater (GB3CA) |
| | | NFM | Daventry | Repeater (GB3XX) |
| | | NFM | Leek | Repeater (GB3SM) |
| | | NFM | Louth | Repeater (GB3LC) |
| | | NFM | Romford | Repeater (GB3HW) |
| | | NFM | St Peter Port | Repeater (GB3GU) |
| | | NFM | Welwyn Garden City | Repeater (GB3VH) |
| | | NFM | Worksop | Repeater (GB3DS) |
| | | NFM | York | Repeater (GB3CY) |
| 433.350 | 434.950 | NFM | Aberdeen | Repeater (GB3AB) |
| | | NFM | Bideford | Repeater (GB3ND) |
| | | NFM | Birmingham | Repeater (GB3CB) |
| | | NFM | Colchester | Repeater (GB3CE) |
| | | NFM | Edinburgh | Repeater (GB3ED) |
| | | NFM | Glasgow | Repeater (GB3GL) |
| | | NFM | Glasgow | Repeater (GB3GL) |
| | | NFM | Harrow | Repeater (GB3HR) |
| | | NFM | Hastings | Repeater (GB3HE) |
| | | NFM | Lancaster | Repeater (GB3LF) |
| | | NFM | Leeds | Repeater (GB3WF) |
| | | NFM | Lowestoft | Repeater (GB3YL) |
| | | NFM | Spalding | Repeater (GB3TL) |
| | | NFM | Stockport | Repeater (GB3MR) |
| | | NFM | Weymouth | Repeater (GB3SD) |
| 433.375 | 434.975 | NFM | Bournemouth | Repeater (GB3SZ) |
| | | NFM | Cardiff | Repeater (GB3SG) |
| | | NFM | Farnham | Repeater (GB3FN) |
| | | NFM | Omagh | Repeater (GB3OM) |
| | | NFM | Preston | Repeater (GB3PP) |
| | | NFM | Shrewsbury | Repeater (GB3LH) |
| | | NFM | St Austell | Repeater (GB3HB) |
| | | NFM | St Austell | Repeater (GB3HB) |
| | | NFM | Sudbury | Repeater (GB3SU) |
| | | NFM | Tamworth | Repeater (GB3TH) |
| | | NFM | Wakefield | Repeater (GB3WU) |
| | | NFM | Wisbech | Repeater (GB3WI) |
| 433.500 | 433.500 | NFM | Nationwide | Channel SU20 Calling |
| 433.700 | | NFM | Leicester | Raynet |
| 433.725 | | NFM | Leicester | Raynet |
| 435.075 | | NFM | Space | Oscar 14 |
| 435.150 | | NFM | Space | Oscar 19 Data |
| 435.250 | | NFM | Space | Oscar 14 |
| 435.910 | | NFM | Space | Oscar 20 Beacon |

433.7200 - 434.5120 MHz    Vehicle Radio Keys

| Base | Mobile | Mode | Location | User and Notes |
|------|--------|------|----------|----------------|

**433.76250 - 439.4500 MHz  MoD, North Sea Rigs and Space**

| Base | Mobile | Mode | Location | User and Notes |
|------|--------|------|----------|----------------|
| 433.7625 | | AM | Mildenhall | Air Display Co-ordination |
| 433.7750 | 433.7750 | NFM | Mildenhall | Raynet |
| 433.8750 | | NFM | USAF Mildenhall | Ops |
| 435.0625 | | NFM | Taunton | Town security system link-up |
| 435.6250 | 435.6250 | NFM | Nationwide | RAF Cadets Channel U2 |
| 435.7250 | 435.7250 | NFM | Nationwide | RAF Cadets Channel U5 Data |
| 435.7500 | 435.7500 | NFM | Nationwide | RAF Cadets NATO Channel U1 |
| 435.9750 | | NFM | Space | Polar Bear 8688A |
| 437.8875 | 437.8875 | NFM | London | Capital Radio Relay |
| 438.0750 | | NFM | USAF Mildenhall | Ops |
| 438.3500 | 445.3500 | NFM | North Sea | Ekofisk Senter Phillips |
| 438.4000 | 445.4000 | NFM | North Sea | Ekofisk Senter Phillips |
| 438.4500 | 445.4500 | NFM | North Sea | Ekofisk Senter Phillips |
| 438.5000 | 445.5000 | NFM | North Sea | Ekofisk Senter Phillips |
| 438.5500 | | NFM | Edinburgh | Sky TV Sound Relay |
| 438.6000 | 445.6000 | NFM | North Sea | Ekofisk Senter Phillips |
| 439.0000 | 446.0000 | NFM | North Sea | Ekofisk Senter Phillips |
| 439.2000 | 446.2000 | NFM | North Sea | Amoco Valhall Field |
| 439.2250 | 446.2250 | NFM | North Sea | Ekofisk Senter Phillips |
| 439.2750 | 446.2750 | NFM | North Sea | Amoco Valhall Field |
| 439.4500 | 446.4500 | NFM | North Sea | Amoco Valhall Field |

**440.00625 - 442.25625 MHz     PMR Base Repeaters 12.5 kHz**
**(Split -14.5 MHz)**

| Base | Mobile | Mode | Location | User and Notes |
|------|--------|------|----------|----------------|
| 440.0250 | | NFM | London | Port of London (S) |
| 440.0250 | | NFM | London (Heathrow) | Ground Staff |
| 440.0375 | 425.5375 | NFM | London | RAM Mobile Data Network |
| 440.0500 | 425.5500 | NFM | Coventry | Council Roads Dept |
| | | NFM | Lanarkshire | Monklands Direct Works |
| 440.0500 | 425.6500 | NFM | Leicester | City Council Depots |
| 440.0750 | 425.5750 | NFM | Harlow | Council in Chief Emergency |
| | | NFM | Liverpool | Liverpool Ranger Service |
| | | NFM | London | Wandsworth Council Parks |
| | | NFM | Newcastle | Highways |
| | | NFM | Solihull | Binmen |
| 440.1000 | 425.6000 | NFM | Barrow | VSEL Submarine Guards |
| | | NFM | Glasgow | Parcel Firm |
| | | NFM | Leicester | City Council 24hr Repairs |
| | | NFM | Liverpool | Police Mersey Tunnel Channel 1 |
| | | NFM | London | Wimbledon Borough Council |
| 440.1125 | 425.6125 | NFM | Blackpool | Doctors on Call |
| | | NFM | London | Mobile Data Network |
| 440.1250 | 425.6250 | NFM | Glasgow | Waste Collection |
| | | NFM | Nationwide | TNT Offices |
| | | NFM | Watford | Watford Borough Council |
| | | NFM | Wigan | Emergency Repairs |
| 440.1750 | 425.6750 | NFM | Liverpool | Police Mersey Tunnel Channel 1 |
| | | NFM | London | London Transport Buses |
| 440.1875 | 425.6875 | NFM | London | RAM Mobile Data Network |
| 440.2000 | 425.7000 | NFM | Greenford | Glaxo Fire and Security |
| | | NFM | London (Gatwick) | Delta Airlines |
| | | NFM | Wilton | ICI |

| Base | Mobile | Mode | Location | User and Notes |
|------|--------|------|----------|----------------|
| 440.2250 | 425.7250 | NFM | Bexley | L.B. Bexley |
| | | NFM | Birmingham | NEC Security & Maintenance |
| | | NFM | Glasgow | Regional Council |
| 440.2250 | 425.7250 | NFM | Hull | Hull Telephone Repairs |
| | | NFM | London | London Transport Buses |
| | | NFM | Manchester | Data Relay |
| | | NFM | Newcastle | Highways |
| 440.2625 | 425.7625 | NFM | London | RAM Mobile Data Network |
| 440.2750 | 425.7750 | NFM | Liverpool | Mersey Port Police |
| | | NFM | London (Heathrow) | Trunked Network |
| 440.2875 | 425.7875 | NFM | London | RAM Mobile Data Network |
| 440.3000 | 425.8000 | NFM | Glasgow | Data Link |
| | | NFM | London | Kenwood Car Service |
| | | NFM | London (Heathrow) | Trunked Network |
| | | NFM | Wilton | ICI |
| 440.3125 | 425.8125 | NFM | London | RAM Mobile Data Network |
| 440.3250 | 425.8250 | NFM | London | London Transport Buses |
| 440.3375 | 425.8375 | NFM | Glasgow | Data Link |
| | | NFM | London | RAM Mobile Data Network |
| | | NFM | Newcastle | The Metro Centre Data Link |
| 440.3500 | 425.8500 | NFM | London (Heathrow) | Trunked Network |
| 440.3750 | 425.8750 | NFM | London | Securiplan Security |
| 440.4000 | 425.9000 | NFM | Co. Durham | Taxis |
| | | NFM | London | RAM Mobile Data Network |
| | | NFM | Surrey | Ambulance Incident Control |
| 440.4250 | 425.9250 | NFM | London (Heathrow) | Ground Staff |
| 440.4625 | 425.9625 | NFM | London | RAM Mobile Data Network |
| 440.4750 | 425.9750 | NFM | London | London Transport Buses |
| | | NFM | M6 | Motorway Maintenance |
| | | NFM | Wilton | ICI |
| 440.4875 | 425.9875 | NFM | London | RAM Mobile Data Network |
| | | NFM | West Perthshire | Data Link |
| 440.5000 | 426.0000 | NFM | London | London Transport Buses |
| 440.5250 | 426.0250 | NFM | London | London Transport Buses |
| 440.5375 | | NFM | London | Outback Inn |
| 440.5375 | 426.0375 | NFM | London | PMR Parking/Demo |
| 440.5500 | 426.0500 | NFM | London | London Transport Buses |
| 440.5750 | 426.0750 | NFM | Gateshead | Metro Centre Security |
| | | NFM | Glasgow | TOA Taxis Channel 1 (Data) |
| | | NFM | London | London Taxis North/Central |
| | | NFM | Manchester | Construction Company |
| | | NFM | Wigan | Park Wardens |
| 440.5875 | 426.0875 | NFM | London | London Taxis N1/N7 |
| 440.6000 | 426.1000 | NFM | Glasgow | TOA Taxis Channel 2 (Data) |
| | | NFM | Knowsley | Council Security |
| | | NFM | London | London Taxis WC/SW1 |
| 440.6250 | 426.1250 | NFM | Birmingham | NEC Catering |
| | | NFM | Glasgow | TOA Taxis Channel 3 (Voice) |
| | | NFM | London | London Taxis Gt London |
| 440.6500 | 426.1500 | NFM | Birmingham | NEC Catering |
| | | NFM | Edinburgh | Radio Cabs |
| | | NFM | London | London Taxis Gt London |
| 440.6625 | 426.1625 | NFM | Edinburgh | Taxis |
| 440.6750 | 426.1750 | NFM | Birmingham | NEC Traffic |
| | | NFM | Edinburgh | Radio Cabs |
| | | NFM | London | Taxis |

| Base | Mobile | Mode | Location | User and Notes |
|------|--------|------|----------|----------------|
| 440.7000 | 426.2000 | NFM | London | Centracom Ltd |
| | | NFM | Stoke on Trent | Plant Hire (Star Base) |
| | | NFM | Sutton | Taxis |
| 440.7250 | 426.2250 | NFM | Birmingham | NEC Maintenance |
| | | NFM | Edinburgh | Acolade Cars |
| | | NFM | London | Central London Messanger |
| 440.7500 | 426.2500 | NFM | London | Taxis |
| | | NFM | London (Gatwick) | HM Customs & Excise |
| | | NFM | Manchester Airport | HM Customs & Immigration |
| 440.7625 | 426.2625 | NFM | London (Heathrow) | NMRL CBS Tristar House |
| 440.7750 | 426.2750 | NFM | London (Heathrow) | Main Customs Net |
| | | NFM | Luton Airport | HM Customs & Immigration |
| | | NFM | Manchester Airport | HM Customs & Immigration |
| | | NFM | Nationwide | HM Customs & Excise Channel. 1 |
| | | NFM | Nationwide | HM Customs & Excise Channel. 4 |
| 440.8000 | 426.3000 | NFM | Central London | Taxis |
| | | NFM | London | Security Company |
| | | NFM | Swansea | HM Customs & Excise |
| 440.8250 | 426.3250 | NFM | London (Heathrow) | HM Customs Surveillance |
| 440.8250 | | NFM | London (Heathrow) | HM Customs Surveillance |
| 440.8250 | 440.8250 | NFM | Nationwide | HM Customs & Excise Channel 2 |
| | | NFM | Nationwide | HM Customs & Excise Channel 5 |
| | | NFM | North-West | Covert Customs Surveillance |
| | | NFM | Shoreham | HM Customs & Excise |
| 440.8500 | 426.3500 | NFM | London (Heathrow) | HM Customs & Excise |
| | | NFM | Nationwide | HM Customs & Excise Channel 3 |
| | | NFM | Nationwide | HM Customs & Excise Channel 6 |
| | | NFM | Newhaven | HM Customs & Excise |
| | | NFM | Southampton Docks | HM Customs & Excise (Aztec) |
| 440.8750 | 426.3750 | NFM | London, North | Taxis |
| | | NFM | Nationwide | HM Customs & Excise Channel 7 |
| 440.9000 | 426.4000 | NFM | Birmingham | Rackhams Security |
| | | NFM | London (Heathrow) | Trunked Network |
| | | NFM | London, Gower St | University College London security |
| | | NFM | Manchester | Construction/Repairs |
| | | NFM | Wilton | ICI |
| 440.9250 | 426.4250 | NFM | Harlow | Council in Chief Emergency |
| | | NFM | Liverpool | Council Security |
| | | NFM | London | Barts Hospital |
| | | NFM | London | Road repairs |
| | | NFM | London | Taxis |
| | | NFM | Manchester | North West Water |
| | | NFM | Stockport | Local Authority |
| 440.9375 | 426.4375 | NFM | London | Taxis |
| 440.9500 | 426.4500 | NFM | London (Heathrow) | Trunked Network |
| | | NFM | Wilton | ICI |
| 440.9750 | 426.4750 | NFM | Viewpark | Denton Security |
| 440.9875 | 426.4875 | NFM | Hendon | Couriers |
| | | NFM | London, north | Taxis |
| 441.0000 | 426.5000 | NFM | Birmingham | NEC Maintenance |
| | | NFM | City of Westminster | Traffic Wardens |
| | | NFM | Co. Durham | Radio Engineers |
| | | NFM | Nationwide | Xerox Copiers |
| | | NFM | Plumstead | Taxis |
| 441.0250 | 426.5250 | NFM | Leicester | Leicester Buses |
| 441.0375 | 426.5375 | NFM | London (Heathrow) | Trunked Network |

| Base | Mobile | Mode | Location | User and Notes |
|------|--------|------|----------|----------------|
| 441.0500 | 426.5500 | NFM | London | Builders |
|          |          | NFM | London (Heathrow) | Trunked Network |
| 441.0625 | 426.5625 | NFM | Coventry | Builders Suppliers |
| 441.0750 | 426.5750 | NFM | Birmingham Hockley | Blocked Drains |
|          |          | NFM | Birmingham International | Ground Staff |
|          |          | NFM | Glasgow | Council |
|          |          | NFM | London (Gatwick) | Trunked Network |
|          |          | NFM | London (Heathrow) | Ground Staff |
|          |          | NFM | London, south east | Couriers |
| 441.1000 | 426.6000 | NFM | London | Medicall |
|          |          | NFM | Nationwide | MediCall |
| 441.1125 | 426.6125 | NFM | London (Heathrow) | Trunked Network |
| 441.1250 | 426.1250 | NFM | Birmingham International | Police armed |
|          |          | NFM | London (Gatwick) | Trunked Network |
|          |          | NFM | Walsall | Myseal |
|          |          | NFM | West Midlands | Security Firm |
| 441.1500 | 426.6500 | NFM | Birmingham International | AirCall |
|          |          | NFM | London | Alex Brand Couriers |
|          |          | NFM | London | Courier Company |
|          |          | NFM | Saddleworth | Haulage Firm |
| 441.1750 | 426.6750 | NFM | Birmingham | Eagle Car Clampers |
|          |          | NFM | Co. Durham | TV Engineers |
|          |          | NFM | Coatbridge | Shanks McEwen Skip Hire |
|          |          | NFM | Coventry | Satellite Installation |
|          |          | NFM | Denton | FMR Investigations |
|          |          | NFM | Glasgow | Vehicle Removal Unit |
|          |          | NFM | Luton | Communications Repeater |
|          |          | NFM | Manchester | Pub Machine Suppliers |
| 441.1750 | 441.1750 | NFM | Manchester | Security |
|          |          | NFM | Middlesborough | Prichard Security |
|          |          | NFM | Perthshire | Builders |
| 441.2000 | 426.7000 | NFM | Birmingham | Police CID Scrambled |
|          |          | NFM | Cambridge | Community Repeater |
|          |          | NFM | Dorking | Apollo Cars |
|          |          | NFM | Dorking | Keynet CBS |
|          |          | NFM | Dorking | Silver Cars |
|          |          | NFM | Manchester | Couriers |
|          |          | NFM | Manchester | TV Repairs |
|          |          | NFM | Coventry | Parcel Delivery |
| 441.2250 | 426.7250 | NFM | Dorking | Apollo Taxis |
|          |          | NFM | London | CBS Car Telephones |
|          |          | NFM | London (Heathrow) | Trunked Network |
|          |          | NFM | London, Plumstead | Parking wardens (P) |
| 441.2500 | 426.7500 | NFM | Aberdeen | Nat Radiofone CBS |
|          |          | NFM | Bradford | Nat Radiofone CBS |
|          |          | NFM | Glasgow Warlaw Hill | Nat Radiofone CBS |
|          |          | NFM | Leicester | Nat Radiofone CBS |
|          |          | NFM | London | Onyx UK Ltd cleaners |
|          |          | NFM | London (Gatwick) | Trunked Network |
|          |          | NFM | London (Heathrow) | Ground Staff |
|          |          | NFM | Manchester | Nat Radiofone CBS |
|          |          | NFM | Newcastle | Highways |
|          |          | NFM | Pontop Pike | Nat Radiofone CBS |
|          |          | NFM | Preston | B.D. Electronics |
|          |          | NFM | Tyneside | Couriers |
|          |          | NFM | Waltham-on-Wolds | Nat Radiofone CBS |

| Base | Mobile | Mode | Location | User and Notes |
|---|---|---|---|---|
| 441.2750 | 441.2750 | NFM | London (Gatwick) | Trunked Network |
| | | NFM | Stoke on Trent | Medics |
| | | NFM | Stoke-On-Trent | Skip Hire |
| 441.3000 | 426.8000 | NFM | London | Security Company |
| | | NFM | London Hilton | Nat Radiofone CBS |
| | | NFM | Newcastle | Security Firm |
| 441.3250 | 426.8250 | NFM | Co. Durham | Private Security |
| | | NFM | London (Gatwick) | Trunked Network |
| 441.3500 | 426.8500 | NFM | Crewe | Taxis |
| | | NFM | Glasgow | Security |
| | | NFM | Home Moss Pennine | Nat Radiofone CBS |
| | | NFM | London (Gatwick) | Trunked Network |
| | | NFM | London (Heathrow) | Trunked Network |
| | | NFM | Newcastle | Security Firm |
| | | NFM | Wakefield | RJB Mining |
| 441.3750 | 426.8750 | NFM | London | Couriers |
| | | NFM | Manchester | Plant Company |
| | | NFM | Newcastle | Security Firm |
| | | NFM | Tyne & Wear | Security Firm |
| 441.4000 | 426.9000 | NFM | London | Couriers |
| | | NFM | Manchester | Springfield Hospital Porters |
| | | NFM | Sheffield | A1 Security |
| | | NFM | St Annes | Taxis |
| 441.4250 | 426.9250 | NFM | London | Motorola engineers |
| 441.4375 | 426.9375 | NFM | London | Courier Company |
| | | NFM | Nottinghamshire | Steetley Haulage Ltd |
| 441.4500 | 426.9500 | NFM | Glasgow | Paramedics |
| | | NFM | Manchester Airport | TNT Carriers |
| 441.4740 | 427.0750 | NFM | Tamworth | Delivery Firm |
| 441.4750 | 426.9750 | NFM | Blackburn | Garage Recovery |
| | | NFM | Burnley | Breakdown Recovery |
| | | NFM | Coventry | City engineers |
| 441.5000 | 427.0000 | NFM | London | Taxis |
| | | NFM | Turners Hill | Nat Radiofone CBS |
| 441.5250 | 427.0250 | NFM | Glasgow | Games Machines Firm |
| | | NFM | Glasgow | Security |
| | | NFM | Highgate | Nat Radiofone CBS |
| | | NFM | Lanark | Security Firm |
| | | NFM | Manchester | Motoring Organisation |
| | | NFM | Newcastle | Security Firm |
| | | NFM | Preston | Drinks Machine Suppliers |
| | | NFM | Tyneside | Safe-Guard Security |
| 441.5500 | 427.0500 | NFM | Frodsham | Nat Radiofone CBS |
| | | NFM | London (Heathrow) | Trunked Network |
| | | NFM | Sheffield | Nat Radiofone CBS |
| 441.5750 | 427.0750 | NFM | Cannock | Taxi |
| | | NFM | London | Hospital patient transport |
| | | NFM | London | Vehicle recovery |
| | | NFM | Manchester | Harcross Building Supplies |
| | | NFM | Manchester | NSPCC Investigation Branch |
| 441.6000 | 427.1000 | NFM | London | Chase Couriers (CHASE) |
| 441.6250 | 427.1250 | NFM | Doncaster | Constant Security |
| | | NFM | London | Council |
| | | NFM | London | Courier |

| Base | Mobile | Mode | Location | User and Notes |
|------|--------|------|----------|----------------|
| 441.6500 | 427.1500 | NFM | Alba | FSU Chevron Shuttle DGP Data |
| | | NFM | Central London | Taxis |
| | | NFM | Chalfont St Peter | OAP transport service |
| | | NFM | London | OAP transport service |
| 441.6620 | 427.1620 | NFM | Preston | Medicall |
| 441.6625 | 427.1625 | NFM | Blackpool | Delivery Firm |
| | | NFM | Skelmersdale | Couriers |
| 441.6750 | 427.1750 | NFM | London | Taxis |
| | | NFM | Manchester | Security |
| | | NFM | Walsall | Mygoal |
| 441.7000 | 427.2000 | NFM | London (Heathrow) | Trunked Network |
| | | NFM | Manchester | Breakdown Recovery |
| | | NFM | Stoke | Nat Radiofone CBS |
| | | NFM | Waltham-on-Wolds | Nat Radiofone CBS |
| 441.7250 | 427.2250 | NFM | Doncaster | Browns Farm |
| | | NFM | Doncaster | Roy Bolland Skips |
| | | NFM | Glasgow | Medicall |
| | | NFM | South London | NMRL CBS |
| 441.7375 | 427.2375 | NFM | London | Courier firm |
| 441.7500 | 427.2500 | NFM | London | Medicall |
| | | NFM | London | VIP outside caterers |
| 441.8000 | 427.3000 | NFM | London (Heathrow) | Trunked Network |
| | | NFM | Manchester | Security |
| 441.8125 | 427.3125 | NFM | Basildon | Amtrak |
| | | NFM | London | Haulage |
| | | NFM | London, south east | Builders |
| 441.8250 | 427.3250 | NFM | London (Victoria) | Minicabs |
| | | NFM | West Midlands | Delivery Service |
| 441.8500 | 427.3500 | NFM | Cannock | Taxi |
| | | NFM | Liverpool | Expo Boarding-Up Service |
| | | NFM | London | Delivery Service |
| 441.8750 | 441.8750 | NFM | London | Police SAV Repeater |
| 441.8750 | 427.3750 | NFM | London, south east | Taxis |
| | | NFM | Pontop | Nat Radiofone CBS |
| 441.8875 | 427.3875 | NFM | London | Vehicle Recovery services |
| 441.9000 | 427.4000 | NFM | London, Hilton | NMRL CBS 2 |
| 441.9250 | 441.9250 | NFM | Cheshire | Security |
| 441.9250 | 427.4250 | NFM | Turners Hill | Nat Radiofone CBS |
| 441.9500 | 427.4500 | NFM | London (Heathrow) | Trunked Network |
| | | NFM | London, south east | Taxis |
| | | NFM | Sandiways, Cheshire | Four Ways Granite Quarry |
| 441.9750 | 427.4750 | NFM | London | Bus Tour Company |
| | | NFM | London | Crime Prevention Guards |
| | | NFM | West Midlands | Delivery Service |
| 442.0000 | 427.7000 | NFM | Gatley | Breakdown Service |
| | | NFM | London (Heathrow) | Trunked Network |
| | | NFM | London Hilton | NMRL CBS 2 |
| 442.0250 | 427.5250 | NFM | Coventry | Building Merchant |
| | | NFM | Hounslow | Rapid Document Hadling Services |
| 442.0500 | 427.7500 | NFM | London, west | Couriers |
| 442.0750 | 427.7750 | NFM | Turners Hill | Nat Radiofone CBS |
| 442.1000 | 427.6000 | NFM | Birmingham | Security |
| | | NFM | London | Circle Security |
| | | NFM | London, Highgate | Grovefair Security Services |
| | | NFM | Walsall | Mercia Lifting Gear |

| Base | Mobile | Mode | Location | User and Notes |
|------|--------|------|----------|----------------|
| 442.1250 | 427.8250 | NFM | London | Incheck Security Services |
| 442.1250 | 427.6250 | NFM | London | Lynx Express Deliveries |
| 442.1250 | 427.8250 | NFM | Waltham-on-Wolds | Nat Radiofone CBS |
| 442.1500 | 427.6500 | NFM | Chelmsford | Boreham Tyre Services |
| | | NFM | London | Security Company |
| 442.1750 | 427.6750 | NFM | London | London Wheel Clamping |
| | | NFM | London | Pronto Bikes |
| | | NFM | Stoke | Doctors on Call |
| 442.2000 | 427.7000 | NFM | London | Blackheath Cleansing Dept |
| | | NFM | London, Greenwich | Council |
| | | NFM | Manchester | Construction Company |

**442.2750 - 442.4875 MHz    BROADCASTING LINKS**

| Base | Mobile | Mode | Location | User and Notes |
|------|--------|------|----------|----------------|
| 442.2750 | 427.7750 | NFM | London | BBC TV Talkback |
| 442.2875 | 427.7875 | NFM | London | BBC Radio 5 Talkback |
| 442.3250 | 427.8250 | NFM | London | BBC TV Talkback |
| 442.3375 | 427.8375 | NFM | London | BBC TV Talkback |
| 442.3625 | 427.8625 | NFM | London | BBC TV Talkback |
| 442.3865 | 427.8865 | NFM | London | BBC TV Talkback |
| 442.3875 | 427.8875 | NFM | London | ITN Talkback |
| 442.4250 | 427.8250 | NFM | London | ITN Reverse Prog Circuit |
| 442.4312 | | NFM | Birmingham | ITN Talkback |
| 442.4375 | 427.9375 | NFM | London | ITV Talkback |
| 442.4500 | 427.9500 | NFM | London | ITV Talkback |
| 442.4625 | 427.9625 | NFM | London | ITN Reverse Prog Circuit |
| 442.4750 | 427.9750 | NFM | Grays | ITN MCR |
| 442.4875 | 427.9875 | NFM | London | ITN Talkback |

**442.5187 - 443.49375 MHz  PMR BASE REPEATERS 12.5 KHZ**
**(SPLIT -14.5 MHZ)**

| Base | Mobile | Mode | Location | User and Notes |
|------|--------|------|----------|----------------|
| 442.5250 | 428.0250 | NFM | London | Hackney Council |
| | | NFM | Wilton | ICI |
| 442.5500 | 428.0500 | NFM | London | Canary Wharf security (CW) |
| 442.5875 | 428.0875 | NFM | Basildon | Integrated Security Group |
| | | NFM | London | Pilkenton Security |
| 442.5875 | 428.0875 | NFM | Manchester | Skip Co |
| 442.6125 | 428.1125 | NFM | Hounslow | Hounslow Car Spares |
| | | NFM | Wembley | Actonian School of Motoring |
| 442.6250 | 428.1250 | NFM | Greenwich | National Maritime Museum |
| | | NFM | London | British Museum |
| | | NFM | London | Royal London Hospital |
| | | NFM | London (Heathrow) | Ground Staff |
| | | NFM | Maidstone | Chequers Shopping Centre |
| 442.6500 | 428.1750 | NFM | Liverpool | Merseyside Maritime Museum |
| 442.6750 | 428.1750 | NFM | Clydebank | Clyde Shopping Centre Security |
| | | NFM | Glenrothes | Kingdom Shopping Centre Security |
| | | NFM | Liverpool | Inshore Lifeboats |
| | | NFM | London | Jubilee Line Extension engineers |
| | | NFM | London (Heathrow) | Ground Repeater |
| | | NFM | Wilton | ICI |
| 442.7250 | 428.2250 | NFM | London (Gatwick) | American Airlines |
| | | NFM | Wilton | ICI |
| 442.7500 | 428.2500 | NFM | London (Heathrow) | Quantas |

| Base | Mobile | Mode | Location | User and Notes |
|---|---|---|---|---|
| 442.7750 | 428.2750 | NFM | Croydon | Whitgift Security |
| | | NFM | Glasgow | Collins Books |
| | | NFM | London (Heathrow) | Trunked Network |
| 442.8000 | 428.3000 | NFM | Glasgow | Council Environmental Dept. |
| | | NFM | Glasgow | Electricians |
| | | NFM | London (Heathrow) | Trunked Network |
| 442.8500 | 428.3500 | NFM | Glasgow | Trojan Security |
| | | NFM | London (Gatwick) | Virgin Ops |
| 442.8750 | 428.3750 | NFM | London (Heathrow) | Trunked Network |
| 442.9000 | 428.4000 | NFM | Glasgow | Glasgow Transport |
| | | NFM | London Hilton | NMRL CBS 2 |
| | | NFM | SE London | Taxis |
| 442.9125 | 428.4125 | NFM | Glasgow | Glasgow Transport |
| 442.9250 | 428.4250 | NFM | Central London | Taxis |
| | | NFM | Glasgow | TOA Taxis |
| | | NFM | Nottinghamshire | Target Express Parcels |
| 442.9500 | 428.4500 | NFM | Glasgow | Taxis |
| 442.9625 | 428.4625 | NFM | London | West One Couriers |
| 443.0000 | 428.5000 | NFM | London | National Portrait Gallery security |
| | | NFM | London | Tate Gallery Security |
| | | NFM | Wilton | ICI |
| 443.0500 | 428.5500 | NFM | London | Videotron Cable TV |
| | | NFM | London (Gatwick) | Continental Ops |
| | | NFM | Sunbury | RCA Records |
| 443.0875 | 428.5875 | NFM | London | Coach Company |
| 443.1000 | 428.6000 | NFM | Merseyside | Guardrite Security |
| 443.1500 | 428.6500 | NFM | London | Builders |
| | | NFM | Surrey | Radiofone |
| 443.1750 | 428.6750 | NFM | London | Haulage |
| 443.1875 | 428.6875 | NFM | London | Minicabs |
| 443.2625 | 428.6625 | NFM | Manchester | Washing Machine Repairs |
| | | NFM | Manchester Shaw | Radio Cars |
| | | NFM | Surrey | Radiofone |
| 443.2750 | 428.7750 | NFM | Warrington | Security Company |
| 443.3750 | 428.8750 | NFM | SE London | Plumbers |
| 443.3870 | 428.8870 | NFM | Coventry | Motor Factors |
| 443.4125 | 428.9125 | NFM | London | Minicabs |
| 443.4370 | 428.9375 | NFM | Birmingham | Cleaning Company |
| | | NFM | London | Pizza Delivery Company |
| 443.4500 | 428.9500 | NFM | London (Heathrow) | Ground Repeater |
| 443.4625 | 428.9625 | NFM | London | Pizza Delivery Company |
| 443.4750 | 428.9750 | NFM | Watford | Watford Borough Council |
| 443.4875 | 428.9875 | NFM | London | International Couriers |
| 443.5000 -45.3000 MHz | | | MoD Radiolocation & Base Comms 25 kHz | |
| 443.5750 | | NFM | Whitehall | Military Police |
| 443.6750 | | NFM | Whitehall | Military Police |
| 443.7450 | | NFM | London, Hampstead | Kenwood House |
| 443.7500 | | NFM | Colchester | 36 DWS REME |
| 443.8875 | | NFM | Boscombe Down | Military Police (BD) |
| 443.9000 | | NFM | London | Foreign & Commonwealth Office |
| 443.9375 | | NFM | Boscombe Down | Army transport and escorts |
| 444.0250 | | NFM | Colchester | 36 DWS REME |
| 444.0500 | | NFM | USAF Fairford | International Air Tattoo Tanker Ops |
| 444.0750 | | NFM | Nationwide | Radiocommunications Agency |
| 444.2750 | 449.5750 | NFM | USAF Fairford | International Air Tattoo Campsite |

| Base | Mobile | Mode | Location | User and Notes |
|---|---|---|---|---|
| 444.3000 | 449.6000 | NFM | USAF Fairford | International Air Tattoo Chalets |
| 444.3250 | | NFM | Colchester | 36 DWS REME |
| 444.3750 | 449.6750 | NFM | USAF Fairford | International Air Tattoo Comms |
| 444.5000 | 449.8000 | NFM | USAF Fairford | International Air Tattoo Exhibition Cntrl |
| 444.5500 | 449.8500 | NFM | USAF Fairford | International Air Tattoo Admissions |
| 444.6500 | | NFM | Colchester | 36 DWS REME |

**445.0000 -447.9875 MHz    SHOP & POST OFFICE SECURITY**
**25 KHZ SIMPLEX**

| Base | Mobile | Mode | Location | User and Notes |
|---|---|---|---|---|
| 445.0000 | | NFM | Manchester | GMS Bases |
| 445.0250 | 454.0250 | NFM | Manchester | Medical Voice Pager |
| 445.0375 | 445.0375 | NFM | Nationwide | Security Express |
| 445.1500 | 445.1500 | NFM | Birmingham | British Rail Post Office |
| 445.1875 | | NFM | Portsmouth | Marine Re-fuelling |
| 445.2500 | | NFM | Aberdeen | BBC Film Crews |
| 445.3500 | 438.3500 | NFM | North Sea | Ekofisk Senter Phillips |
| 445.4000 | 438.4000 | NFM | North Sea | Ekofisk Senter Phillips |

**445.5000 -446.0000 MHz    PMR BASE 12.5 KHZ NFM**
**(SPLIT -20.5 MHZ)**

| Base | Mobile | Mode | Location | User and Notes |
|---|---|---|---|---|
| 445.4500 | 438.4500 | NFM | North Sea | Ekofisk Senter Phillips |
| 445.5000 | 438.5000 | NFM | North Sea | Ekofisk Senter Phillips |
| 445.5125 | 445.5125 | NFM | London | Post Office |
| 445.5250 | 425.0250 | NFM | London | Taxis |
| 445.5500 | 445.5500 | NFM | Glasgow | Taxis |
| | | NFM | Plymouth | Post Office Security |
| 445.5750 | 425.0750 | NFM | Glasgow | Courier Service |
| 445.5875 | 425.0875 | NFM | Bootle | Security Firm |
| 445.6000 | 425.1000 | NFM | London, Kensington | Council Traffic Wardens |
| 445.6000 | 445.6000 | NFM | London, south east | Borough Traffic Wardens |
| 445.6000 | 438.6000 | NFM | North Sea | Ekofisk Senter Phillips |
| 445.6500 | 425.1500 | NFM | London (Heathrow) | British Airways Engineering |
| 445.6750 | 425.1750 | NFM | London | High Court Security |
| 445.7000 | 425.2000 | NFM | Nationwide | MediCall |
| 445.7000 | | NFM | Newcastle | Trunked Network |
| 445.7250 | 425.2250 | NFM | London | DER Repeater (Crystal Palace) |
| | | NFM | London | Underground Aldgate East |
| | | NFM | London | Underground Bayswater |
| | | NFM | London | Underground Cannon Street |
| | | NFM | London | Underground Chancery Lane |
| | | NFM | London | Underground Earls' Court |
| | | NFM | London | Underground Embankment |
| | | NFM | London | Underground Euston |
| | | NFM | London | Underground Gloucester Road |
| | | NFM | London | Underground Hamersmith |
| | | NFM | London | Underground Holburn |
| | | NFM | London | Underground Kings Cross |
| | | NFM | London | Underground Leicester Square |
| | | NFM | London | Underground Liverpool Street |
| | | NFM | London | Underground Mile End |
| | | NFM | London | Underground Moorgate |
| | | NFM | London | Underground Sloane Square |
| | | NFM | London | Underground South Kensington |
| | | NFM | London | Underground St James's Park |
| | | NFM | London | Underground Stations Channel 1 |

| Base | Mobile | Mode | Location | User and Notes |
|------|--------|------|----------|----------------|
| 445.7250 | 425.2250 | NFM | London | Underground Temple |
| | | NFM | London | Underground Tottenham Crt Rd |
| | | NFM | London | Underground Tower Hill |
| | | NFM | London | Underground Victoria |
| | | NFM | London | Underground Whitechapel |
| | | NFM | London (Heathrow) | Underground (Heathrow Control) |
| 445.7500 | 425.2500 | NFM | London | Medicall |
| | | NFM | London | Underground Liverpool Street |
| 445.7625 | 425.2625 | NFM | London | Medicall |
| 445.7750 | 425.2750 | NFM | London | Underground Blackfriars |
| | | NFM | London | Underground Edgeware Road |
| | | NFM | London | Underground Embankment |
| | | NFM | London | Underground Gloucester Road |
| | | NFM | London | Underground Goldhawk Road |
| | | NFM | London | Underground Hamersmith |
| | | NFM | London | Underground Ladbrooke Grove |
| | | NFM | London | Underground Latimar Grove |
| | | NFM | London | Underground Paddington |
| | | NFM | London | Underground Royal Oak |
| | | NFM | London | Underground Shepards Bush |
| | | NFM | London | Underground Stations Channel 2 |
| | | NFM | London | Underground Wembley Park |
| | | NFM | London | Underground Westbourne Park |
| | | NFM | London | Underground Westminster |
| | | NFM | Nationwide | HM Customs & Excise |
| 445.7875 | 425.2875 | NFM | London | Medicall |
| | | NFM | Manchester | Haulage Company |
| 445.8000 | 425.3000 | NFM | Liverpool | North West Water |
| | | NFM | London | Underground Bow Road |
| | | NFM | London | Underground Farringdon |
| | | NFM | London | Underground High St Kensington |
| | | NFM | London | Underground Ladbrooke Grove |
| | | NFM | London | Underground Mansion House |
| | | NFM | London | Underground Stations Channel 3 |
| | | NFM | London (Heathrow) | Ground Repeater |
| 445.8250 | 425.3250 | NFM | Central London | Couriers |
| | | NFM | Glasgow | Skypack |
| | | AM | Nationwide | DoT Motorway Spot Checks |
| | | NFM | Nationwide | HM Customs & Excise |
| 445.8375 | 445.8375 | NFM | Nationwide | BBC |
| 445.8500 | 445.8500 | NFM | Nationwide | HM Customs & Excise |
| 445.9000 | 445.9000 | NFM | Nationwide | BBC |
| | | NFM | Nationwide | BBC O/B Link (OL-94) |
| 445.9125 | 425.4125 | NFM | Manchester | Debt Collectors |
| 445.9625 | 425.4625 | NFM | Bootle | Site Deliveries |
| | | NFM | Preston | Haulage |
| 445.9750 | 425.4750 | NFM | Newcastle | Trunked Network |
| | | NFM | Tyneside | Fencing Contractors |
| 446.0000 | 439.0000 | NFM | Ekofisk | Senter Phillips |
| 446.0000 | 425.5000 | NFM | London, Covent Gdns | Roadhouse Restaurant |
| | | WFM | Sheffield | BBC Radio Sheffield O/B |
| | | NFM | Solihull | Business Park Security |
| 446.0125 | 425.5125 | NFM | Manchester | Hospital (ALFA) |
| 446.0250 | 425.5250 | NFM | Harlow | Security SmithKline Beecham |
| | | NFM | London | Royal Albert Hall |
| | | NFM | London, Docklands | Underground Channel 1-3 |

| Base | Mobile | Mode | Location | User and Notes |
|------|--------|------|----------|----------------|
| 446.0375 | 425.5375 | NFM | London | Royal Albert Hall |
| 446.0500 | 425.5500 | NFM | Edinburgh | Stevenson College Janitors |
| | | NFM | London | American Airlines |
| 446.0600 | 425.5600 | NFM | London, Trocadero | Emaginator |
| 446.1000 | 425.6000 | NFM | London | Go Kart Racing |
| | | NFM | London, Picadilly | "Planet Hollywood" staff |
| 446.1125 | 425.6125 | NFM | London | Tate Gallery |
| 446.1250 | 425.6250 | NFM | Guildford | Debenhams Security |
| | | NFM | Nottingham | Debenhams Security |
| | | NFM | Romford | Shopping Centre security |
| | | NFM | Stapeley | Stapeley Water Gardens |
| | | NFM | Stirling | Debenhams |
| 446.1375 | 425.6375 | NFM | London | Securiplan Security |
| 446.1875 | 425.6875 | NFM | London | Barnet College security |
| | | NFM | London | Securiplan Security |
| 446.2000 | | NFM | Edinburgh | Virgin Record Shop Security |
| 446.2000 | 439.2000 | NFM | Valhall Field | Amoco |
| 446.2125 | | NFM | London, Wimbledon | Centre Court Shopping Centre |
| 446.2250 | 439.2250 | NFM | Lewisham | Lewisham Shopping Centre |
| | | NFM | London | National Science Museum |
| | | NFM | North Sea | Ekofisk Senter Phillips |
| | | NFM | Reading | Thames Water |
| 446.2375 | 425.7375 | NFM | London | Apollo Theatre |
| | | NFM | London | Burlington Arcade security |
| | | NFM | London | Marble Arch Hotel |
| | | NFM | London | Royal Academy of Dramatic Art security |
| 446.2500 | | NFM | London | Royal Albert Hall Catering |
| 446.2500 | | NFM | London (Gatwick) | Thomas Cook |
| 446.2500 | 439.2250 | NFM | London Oxford St | Virgin Megastore |
| | | NFM | Edinburgh | The Gyle Centre Security |
| | | NFM | London | Royal Albert Hall |
| 446.2750 | 446.2750 | NFM | Luton Airport | TNT Carriers |
| 446.2750 | 439.2750 | NFM | Valhall Field | Amoco |
| 446.2875 | | NFM | London | Tower Pageant Exhibition |
| 446.3000 | | NFM | Edinburgh | Lorry Loaders |
| | | NFM | London | Capital Radio Flying Eye |
| 446.3375 | | NFM | London | Buckingham Palace Tours |
| 446.3500 | | NFM | Chelmsley Wood | Security |
| 446.3625 | | NFM | London, Leicester Square | Equinox Discotheque |
| | | NFM | Nationwide | Public Health Lab Service (DEFDER) |
| 446.3875 | | NFM | Derbyshire, NE | Council Ranger Service (RANGER) |
| | | NFM | London | Old Bailey |
| 446.4000 | | NFM | Nationwide | Radio Investigations Service |
| 446.4500 | | NFM | Nationwide | British Pipeline Agency |
| 446.4500 | | NFM | Nationwide | Radio Investigations Service |
| | | NFM | Thetford | British Pipeline Agency |
| 446.4500 | 439.4500 | NFM | North Sea | Amoco Valhall Field |

**446.5000 - 447.5000 MHz    ITC, BBC AND MoD ALLOCATIONS**

| Base | Mobile | Mode | Location | User and Notes |
|------|--------|------|----------|----------------|
| 446.5625 | | NFM | Essex | BBC Radio Essex Links |
| 446.5625 | | WFM | London | BBC-TV London Marathon |
| 446.6375 | | NFM | Nationwide | BBC Local Radio Talkback |
| | | NFM | Nottinghamshire | Radio Nottingham O/B |
| | | NFM | Stoke on Trent | Radio Stoke O/B |
| 446.6875 | 446.6275 | NFM | Nationwide | BBC Talkback |
| 446.7000 | | NFM | London | Medicall |

| Base | Mobile | Mode | Location | User and Notes |
|------|--------|------|----------|----------------|
| 446.7375 | | NFM | Manchester | BBC GMR O/B |
| 446.7375 | 446.7375 | NFM | Nationwide | BBC Local Radio Talkback |
| 446.7875 | | NFM | Belfry (Ryder Cup) | BBC Radio 5 |
| | | NFM | Kent | BBC Radio O/B |
| | | NFM | London | BBC Radio 5 Talkback |
| 446.8375 | | NFM | Derbyshire | Radio Derby Outside Broadcast |
| | | NFM | Nationwide | BBC Local Radio Talkback |
| | | NFM | Preston | Ladies Lancashire Talk back |
| 446.8500 | | NFM | Kent | BBC Raio O/B |
| 446.9000 | | NFM | London | Post Office (Euston) |
| 446.9375 | 141.3000 | NFM | Leicester | BBC Radio Leicester O/B |
| 446.9375 | 446.9375 | NFM | Nationwide | BBC |
| 446.9375 | | NFM | Nationwide | BBC Local Radio Talkback |
| 447.0000 | | NFM | Silverstone | Japanese TV Talkback |
| 447.0875 | | NFM | Birmingham | 96.4 FM BRMB/Xtra O/B |
| 447.0875 | 447.0875 | NFM | Birmingham | ILR X-tra AM |
| 447.0875 | | NFM | Hull | Viking Radio O/B |
| | | NFM | Stoke on Trent | Signal Radio O/B |
| 447.0892 | | NFM | London | Independent Radio Talkback |
| 447.1312 | | NFM | Manchester | Piccadilly Gold |
| 447.1875 | 447.1875 | NFM | Blackpool | Radio Wave O/B |
| 447.1875 | | NFM | Hull | Viking Radio O/B |
| | | NFM | London | Independent Radio Talkback |
| | | NFM | Manchester | Picadilly Radio Talk back |
| | | NFM | Stockport | Signal Cheshire |
| 447.2375 | | NFM | Manchester | Piccadilly Radio Studio Link |
| | | NFM | Salisbury | Spire FM |
| 447.2875 | | NFM | London | Independent Radio Talkback |
| | | NFM | Preston | Red Rose Ladies Talkback |
| 447.3375 | | NFM | Birmingham | Buzz FM Outside Broadcasts |
| | | NFM | Liverpool | Radio City Talkback |
| 447.4000 | | NFM | Silverstone | US TV Talkback |
| 447.4250 | | NFM | Ferrybridge | Engineering Talkback |
| | | NFM | Liverpool | Brookside Studio |
| | | NFM | Yorkshire | Yorkshire Television |
| 447.4300 | | WFM | Sheffield | Yorkshire TV O/B |
| 447.4375 | | NFM | Leeds | Yorkshire TV O/B |
| 447.4750 | | NFM | London | Independent Radio Talkback |
| 447.4875 | 447.4875 | NFM | Liverpool | Brookside TV Director |
| 447.5000 | | NFM | London | Independent Radio Talkback |
| | | NFM | Silverstone | US TV Talkback |
| 447.5500 | | NFM | Aberystwyth | Radio 1 Roadshow OB Talkback |

**447.78750 - 449.49375 MHz     PMR   (MOBILES - 17 MHz)**

| Base | Mobile | Mode | Location | User and Notes |
|------|--------|------|----------|----------------|
| 447.78750 | | NFM | London | London Underground Engineering |
| | | NFM | Sheffield | Dry ski slope |
| 447.87500 | | NFM | London | Namco Amusements |
| 448.02500 | | NFM | London | Taxis |
| 448.07500 | | NFM | London, east | Taxis |
| 448.12500 | | NFM | London | Motorbike Couriers |
| 448.19375 | | NFM | London | Courier (PD) |
| 448.22500 | 451.22500 | NFM | Birmingham | French Diplomatic Service |
| 448.25625 | | NFM | London | London Hilton Trunking System |
| 448.50000 | | NFM | Central London | Contract Wheel Clampers (Whisky) |
| 448.51250 | | NFM | London | Cab data |

| Base | Mobile | Mode | Location | User and Notes |
|---|---|---|---|---|
| 448.57500 | | NFM | London | Rotherhithe Couriers |
| 448.60000 | | NFM | Birmingham | RSPCA |
| | | NFM | City of Westminster | Traffic Wardens (Papa Sierra) |
| 448.71250 | | NFM | London, Ealing | Oxo Station Taxis |
| 448.87500 | 431.87500 | NFM | Tunbridge Wells | The Wells |
| 448.88750 | | NFM | Dartford | Vehicle recovery garage |
| 448.93750 | | NFM | Aldermaston | AWE surport services Ch1 (ESF) |
| 449.65000 | | NFM | Aldermaston | AWE site bus |
| 449.72500 | | NFM | Rhyl | Police (WA) |
| 449.75000 | | NFM | Aldermaston | AWE surport services |
| 449.77500 | | NFM | Aldermaston | AWE security Channel 4 |

## 450.0000 - 453.0000 MHz    POLICE MOBILE PMR SYSTEM
### (ENGLAND & WALES)

| Base | Mobile | Mode | Location | User and Notes |
|---|---|---|---|---|
| 450.0250 | 464.0250 | NFM | Mansfield | Police Channel 1 |
| | | NFM | Wilmslow | Police |
| | | NFM | London | Notting Hill Carnival 1 |
| 450.0500 | 450.0500 | NFM | England & Wales | Police Channel 77 |
| | | NFM | Bournemouth | Police Bournemouth Football Club |
| | | NFM | London | Police Arsenal Football Club |
| | | NFM | Sheffield | Police Sheffield Wednesday Security |
| 450.0500 | 464.0500 | NFM | England & Wales | Police Channel 61 |
| | | NFM | Ashford | Police (Tour de France) Race Control |
| | | NFM | Birmingham | Police |
| | | NFM | Blackpool | Police Special Events |
| | | NFM | Chichester | Police |
| | | NFM | Coventry | Police Coventry City Football Club |
| | | NFM | London | City of London Divisional Support Units |
| | | NFM | London | Police Chelsea Football Club |
| | | NFM | London | Police Wembley Football Club |
| | | NFM | Luton | Police Luton Town Football Club |
| | | NFM | Oldham | Police Oldham Football Club |
| | | NFM | Wirral | Police (Tranmere Rov) Ch 1 |
| | | NFM | Wolverhampton | Police Wolverhampton Football Club |
| 450.0500 | 450.0500 | NFM | Blackpool | Police Football Control |
| | | NFM | Carlisle | Police (Football Security) |
| | | NFM | Leicester | Police (Coventry Football Club ) |
| | | NFM | Milton Keynes | Police MK Bowl Security |
| | | NFM | Tranmere | Police Tranmere Rovers Football Club |
| | | NFM | West Midlands | Police Dog Handlers |
| 450.0750 | 464.0750 | NFM | Blackpool | Police Blackpool Football Club |
| | | NFM | Luton Airport | Police |
| 450.0750 | 450.0750 | NFM | England & Wales | Police Channel 62 |
| | | NFM | Birmingham | Police (Aston Villa Football Club ) |
| | | NFM | Birmingham | Police (Birmingham City Football Club ) |
| | | NFM | Blackpool | Police Special Events |
| | | NFM | Bolton | Police Bolton Wanderers Football Club |
| | | NFM | Brighton | Police Brighton & Hove Albion Football Club |
| | | NFM | Folkestone | Police |
| | | NFM | Goodwood | Police Race Course Security (M2KB) |
| | | NFM | Halifax | Police Football Club |
| | | NFM | Hove | Police |
| | | NFM | London | Police Charlton Football Club |
| | | NFM | London | Police Millwall Football Club |
| | | NFM | London | Police Tottenhan Football Club |

| Base | Mobile | Mode | Location | User and Notes |
|------|--------|------|----------|----------------|
| 450.0750 | 450.0750 | NFM | Milford Haven | Police |
| | | NFM | Northampton | Police |
| | | NFM | Port Vale | Police Port Vale Football Club |
| | | NFM | Scarborough | Police Scarborough Football Club |
| | | NFM | Sheffield | Police Sheffield United Security |
| | | NFM | Shoreham | Police |
| | | NFM | Stoke on Trent | Police Stoke City Football Club |
| | | NFM | Tamworth | Police (Encrypted) |
| | | NFM | West Midlands | Police Motorway Accidents |
| 450.1250 | 464.1250 | NFM | England & Wales | Police Channel 63 |
| | | NFM | England & Wales | Police Special Events Only |
| | | NFM | Ashford | Police (Tour de France) Race Control |
| | | NFM | London | Police Notting Hill Carnival Ch 3 |
| | | NFM | London, Kensington | Police hotel raids |
| | | NFM | Maidstone | Crown Court |
| | | NFM | Northampton | Police (SILVER CONTROL) |
| | | NFM | Plymouth | Police Operational Support |
| 450.1250 | 450.1250 | NFM | England & Wales | Police Channel 79 |
| | | NFM | Blackpool | Police Special Events |
| | | NFM | Charlton | Police Charlton Football Club |
| | | NFM | Leicester | Police Leicester City Football Club |
| | | NFM | London | Police Queens Park Rangers FC |
| | | NFM | London | Police West Ham Football Club |
| | | NFM | Plymouth | Police Special Ops |
| | | NFM | Portsmouth | Police (Fratton Park) |
| | | NFM | Southend on Sea | Police Southend Utd Football Club |
| | | NFM | Thames Valley | Police Scrambled |
| | | NFM | West Bromwich | Police (W Bromwich Football Club ) |
| 450.1500 | 464.1500 | NFM | England & Wales | Police Channel 64 |
| | | NFM | Beeston | Police Encrypted |
| | | NFM | Brentford | Police Brentford Football Club |
| | | NFM | Burnley | Police Football Security |
| | | NFM | Halifax | Police Rugby Club |
| | | NFM | Liverpool | Police (Everton Football Club ) Ch 1 |
| | | NFM | London | Police Crystal Palace Football Club |
| | | NFM | Northampton | Police (NG) |
| | | NFM | Plymouth | Police Ward |
| | | NFM | Stockport | Police Stockport Football Club |
| | | NFM | Suffolk | Police Events |
| | | NFM | Tunbridge Wells | Police (Tour de France) Race Control |
| 450.1500 | 450.1500 | NFM | England & Wales | Police Channel 80 |
| | | NFM | Blackpool | Police CID |
| | | NFM | Bradford | Police Bradford City Football Club |
| | | NFM | Charlton | Police Charlton Football Club |
| | | NFM | London | Met Police Testing (MP2MT) |
| | | NFM | Manchester | Police (Part Time Use) |
| | | NFM | Plymouth | Police Special Ops |
| | | NFM | Sunderland | Police Sunderland Football Club |
| | | NFM | Thames Valley | Police |
| | | NFM | Walsall | Police Walsall Football Club |
| 450.1750 | 464.1750 | NFM | England & Wales | Police Channel 65 |
| | | NFM | Folkestone | Police (Tour de France) Race Control |
| | | NFM | Leicester | Police football matches |
| | | NFM | London | Notting Hill Carnival Ch 2 |
| | | NFM | Merseyside | Police St Helens Rugby League Club |
| | | NFM | South Wales | BR Transport Police |

| Base | Mobile | Mode | Location | User and Notes |
|---|---|---|---|---|
| 450.1750 | 464.1750 | NFM | Southend | Police Southend United Football Club |
| | | NFM | Stoke on Trent | Police Stoke City Football Club |
| | | NFM | Wirral | Police (Tranmere Rov) Ch 1 |
| | | NFM | Worthing | Police Special Events (WO) |
| 450.1750 | 450.1750 | NFM | England & Wales | Channel 81 |
| | | NFM | London | Police Arsenal Football Club |
| | | NFM | London | Police Chelsea Football Club |
| | | NFM | London | Police Fulham Football Club |
| | | NFM | Port Vale | Police Port Vale Football Club |
| 450.1875 | 450.1875 | NFM | London, Ealing | Police (LD, LS) |
| 450.2000 | 464.2000 | NFM | England & Wales | Police Channel 66 |
| | | NFM | Blackpool | Police Special Events |
| | | NFM | Dover | Police (used for animal rights protests) |
| | | NFM | Gillingham | Police Gillingham Football Club |
| | | NFM | Ipswich | Police Ipswich Football Club |
| | | NFM | Leeds | Police |
| | | NFM | Liverpool | Police (Everton Football Club ) Ch 2 |
| | | NFM | London | Police Millwall Football Club |
| | | NFM | London | Police Tottenham Hotspur Football Club |
| | | NFM | MoD Boscombe Down | Police airfield control |
| | | NFM | Manchester | Police Man. United Football Club |
| | | NFM | Portsmouth | Police (Portsmouth Football Club ) |
| | | NFM | Tunbridge Wells | Police (Tour de France) Race Control |
| | | NFM | Widsor | Police castle daily parades |
| 450.2000 | 450.2000 | NFM | England & Wales | Police Channel 82 |
| | | NFM | Gloucester | Police |
| | | NFM | Maidstone | Police |
| 450.2250 | 450.2250 | NFM | England & Wales | Police Channel 83 |
| 450.2250 | 464.2250 | NFM | England & Wales | Police Channel 67 |
| | | NFM | Blackpool | Police Special Events |
| | | NFM | Brands Hatch | Police Security |
| | | NFM | London | Police West Ham Football Club |
| 450.2250 | 464.1250 | NFM | Bolton | Police Bolton Wanderers Football Club |
| | | NFM | Brighton | Police Area Incident Channel |
| | | NFM | London | Police Crystal Palace Football Club |
| | | NFM | Manchester (Moss Side) | Police Drugs Squad |
| 450.2250 | 450.2250 | NFM | Brighton | Police CID Special Ops |
| | | NFM | Hull | Police Hull Kingston Rovers |
| | | NFM | Milton Keynes | Police MK Bowl Security |
| | | NFM | Nottingham | Police (Nott's Forest Football Club ) |
| | | NFM | Southampton | Police (Southampton Football Club ) |
| | | NFM | Worthing | Police Pro-active Unit (encrypted) |
| 450.2500 | 450.2500 | NFM | England & Wales | Police Channel 84 |
| | | NFM | Blackpool Conference | Army Bomb Squad |
| | | NFM | London | Police Crystal Palace Football Club |
| 450.2500 | 464.1500 | NFM | Brighton | Police Area Incident Channel |
| 450.2500 | 464.2500 | NFM | England & Wales | Police Channel 68 |
| | | NFM | Bognor Regis | Police |
| | | NFM | Brockenhurst | Police |
| | | NFM | Colchester | Police (Foxtrot) |
| | | NFM | Doncaster | Police Doncaster Rovers Football Club |
| | | NFM | Gainsborough | Police (E) |
| | | NFM | Plymouth | Police Football Control |
| | | NFM | Tunbridge Wells | Police (Tour de France) Race Control |
| | | NFM | USAF Fairford | International Air Tattoo Fire Control |

| Base | Mobile | Mode | Location | User and Notes |
|------|--------|------|----------|----------------|
| 450.2750 | 464.2750 | NFM | England & Wales | Police Channel 69 |
| | | NFM | Gwynedd | Fire Brigade |
| 450.3000 | 450.3000 | NFM | England & Wales | Fire Command Channel 70 |
| 450.3125 | | NFM | Rhyl | Police (WA) |
| 450.3250 | 450.3250 | NFM | London | Police |
| 450.3750 | 450.3750 | NFM | London | Police |
| 450.4000 | 450.4000 | NFM | London | Police |
| 450.4500 | 450.4500 | NFM | London | Police |
| 450.5250 | | NFM | Irlam | Police |
| 450.5500 | 450.5500 | NFM | Birmingham | Police |
| | | NFM | Crewe | Police |
| | | NFM | Solihull | Police (LX, CI) Ch 2 |
| 450.5750 | | NFM | Birmingham | Police |
| | | NFM | Colwyn Bay | Police (WA) |
| | | NFM | Coventry | Police (MX, M2) Ch 2 |
| | | NFM | Llandudno | Police (WA) |
| | | NFM | St Helens | Police |
| | | NFM | Warrington | Police |
| 450.6000 | | NFM | Portsmouth | Police |
| 450.6250 | 450.6250 | NFM | England & Wales | Police Channel 88 Air-to-Ground |
| | | NFM | Birmingham | Police |
| | | NFM | Hampshire | Police Optica (Boxer 10) |
| | | NFM | Herefordshire | Police Helicopter |
| | | NFM | Luton Airport | Police Air Support Unit (XA99) |
| | | NFM | Merseyside | Police Helicopter (M1) |
| | | NFM | Shropshire | Police Helicopter |
| | | NFM | Skelmersdale | Police Helicopter |
| | | NFM | South Wales | Police Helicopter (WO99) |
| | | NFM | West Midlands | Police Helicopter (AO1) |
| | | NFM | West Sussex | Police Helicopter (Hotel 900) |
| | | NFM | Worcester | Air Ambulance (DELTA 03) |
| | | NFM | Worcester | Police Helicopter (AIR 1) |
| 450.6750 | 450.6750 | NFM | England & Wales | Police Channel 89 Air-to-Ground |
| | | NFM | Birmingham | Police |
| | | NFM | Lancashire | Police Helicopter |
| | | NFM | Leicester | Police Helicopter |
| | | NFM | Northampton, Sywel | Police Helicopter |
| | | NFM | Warickshire | Police Helicopter |
| 450.7750 | | NFM | Birmingham | Police |
| 450.8000 | | NFM | Birmingham | Police |
| | | NFM | Gatley | Police |
| | | NFM | Gt Manchester | Police (Encrypted) |
| | | NFM | Liverpool Toxteth | Police |
| | | NFM | Merseyside | Police Drug Squad (Encrypted) |
| | | NFM | West Midlands | Police Motorway Incident Unit |
| 450.8250 | | NFM | North Wales | Police (D) |
| | | NFM | Rhyl | Police (WA) |
| | | NFM | Salwick | AEA Police |
| | | NFM | Warwickshire | Police Ch 72 |
| 450.8500 | 450.8500 | NFM | Birmingham | Police |
| | | NFM | Chemsley Wood | Police (LX, L1) |
| | | NFM | Barton Airfield | Police Helicopter |
| | | NFM | Manchester Airport | Police |
| | | NFM | Manchester Ringway | Police |
| 451.0000 | 464.9000 | NFM | Various Areas | Police |

| Base | Mobile | Mode | Location | User and Notes |
|------|--------|------|----------|----------------|
| 451.0250 | 464.9250 | NFM | England & Wales | Police Channel T1 |
| 451.0375 | 465.7500 | NFM | West Midlands | Police (YM) |
| 451.0500 | 464.9500 | NFM | England & Wales | Police Channel T2 |
| 451.0500 | 451.0500 | NFM | Sunderland | Police Football Club Security |
| 451.0750 | 451.0750 | NFM | Hendon | Police Training College |
| 451.0750 | 464.9750 | NFM | England & Wales | Police Channel T3 |
| | | NFM | Hendon | Police Radio Training |
| 451.1000 | 465.0000 | NFM | England & Wales | Police Channel T4 |
| 451.1000 | 465.0000 | NFM | England & Wales | Antenna Rigging & Testing |
| | | NFM | Preston | Police |
| 451.1250 | 465.0125 | NFM | England & Wales | Police Channel T5 |
| | | NFM | England & Wales | Bomb Disposal Unit (Bravo) |
| 451.1250 | 465.1250 | NFM | London | Notting Hill Carnival 4 |
| 451.1500 | 451.1500 | NFM | England & Wales | Police Channel 00 |
| | | NFM | England & Wales | Police Covert Surveillance |
| | | NFM | Wigan | Police motor bike training |
| 451.1750 | 465.0750 | NFM | Birmingham | Police |
| | | NFM | England & Wales | Police Channel 87 |
| | | NFM | Colwyn Bay | Police (WA) |
| | | NFM | Cosham | Police |
| | | NFM | Llandudno | Police |
| | | NFM | North Wales | Police (A) |
| | | NFM | Portsmouth | Police |
| 451.2000 | 465.1000 | NFM | England & Wales | Police Channel 86 |
| | | NFM | Ashford | Police (JZ) |
| | | NFM | Liverpool | Police |
| | | NFM | Manchester, Gorton | Police |
| | | NFM | Manchester, Greenheys | Police |
| | | NFM | Manchester, Levenshulme | Police |
| | | NFM | Manchester, Longsight | Police |
| | | NFM | Manchester, Moss Side | Police |
| | | NFM | Manchester, Whalley Range | Police |
| | | NFM | New Brighton | Police |
| | | NFM | Pow-t-Ffordd | Police |
| | | NFM | Wallasey | Police (A1) |
| | | NFM | Walsall | Traffic Wardens |
| | | NFM | Warrington | Police |
| | | NFM | Wirral | Police |
| 451.2250 | 465.1250 | NFM | England & Wales | Police Channel 85 |
| | | NFM | Ashford | Police (DA) |
| | | NFM | Cleveland | Police |
| | | NFM | Manchester | Police (Gorton) |
| | | NFM | Warrington | Police |
| | | NFM | Windsor | Police castle security Ch 3 |
| 451.2500 | 465.1500 | NFM | England & Wales | Police Channel 84 |
| | | NFM | London | Police Diplomatic Protection |
| 451.2700 | | NFM | England & Wales | Police Reserve Channel B |
| 451.2750 | 464.8750 | NFM | Humberside | Police Channel 02 |
| | | NFM | England & Wales | Police Reserve Channel B |
| 451.2750 | 465.1750 | NFM | England & Wales | Police Channel 05 |
| | | NFM | Birmingham Airport | Police (M2YMEA) |
| | | NFM | Manchester, Bredbury | Police |
| | | NFM | Manchester, Brinnington | Police |
| | | NFM | Manchester, Cheadle | Police |
| | | NFM | Manchester, Hazel Grove | Police |
| | | NFM | Manchester, Marple | Police |

| Base | Mobile | Mode | Location | User and Notes |
|---|---|---|---|---|
| 451.2750 | 465.1750 | NFM | Manchester, Reddish | Police |
| | | NFM | Stockport | Police |
| 451.2750 | 465.8750 | NFM | England & Wales | Police Reserve Channel B |
| | | NFM | Broadstairs | Police (E/E) Ch 5 |
| | | NFM | Cambridge | Police VB Ch 1 Repeater |
| | | NFM | Cheadle | Police |
| | | NFM | Margate | Police (E/D) Ch 5 |
| | | NFM | Stockport | Police |
| | | NFM | Thames Valley | Police |
| 451.3000 | 451.3000 | NFM | England & Wales | Optica Surveillance Air-Ground |
| | | NFM | England & Wales | Police Motorcycle Training |
| | | NFM | Thames Valley | Police |
| 451.3000 | 465.2000 | NFM | England & Wales | Police Airborne |
| | | NFM | Leicester | Police Traffic Helicopter |
| | | NFM | London Gatwick | Police Immigration |
| | | NFM | West Yorksshire | Ambulance Hand Held |
| 451.3000 | 465.2000 | NFM | Cwnbran | Police Training College |
| | | NFM | Trowbridge | Police Speed Traps |
| 451.3125 | 465.2652 | NFM | Birmingham | Police |
| | | NFM | Newport | Police Newport Rangers Football Club |
| | | NFM | Hastings | Police (H) |
| 451.3250 | 465.2250 | NFM | England & Wales | Police Channel 07 |
| | | NFM | Burnley | Police |
| | | NFM | Dover | Police football security |
| | | NFM | England & Wales | CID Covert/CID SOCO/Speed Traps |
| | | NFM | Essex | Police Helicopter (H900) |
| | | NFM | Heysham (Port) | Special Branch |
| | | NFM | Kent | Police (Tour de France) |
| | | NFM | London | HM Customs/Police Link |
| | | NFM | Wellingbrough | Police CID |
| | | NFM | Worthing | Police (WO) |
| 451.3250 | 465.3250 | NFM | Ingoldmells | Police |
| | | NFM | London Gatwick | Armed Police Tactical Liaison |
| | | NFM | London Heathrow | Armed Police Tactical Liaison |
| | | NFM | N Wales | Police Helicopter (W1) |
| | | NFM | Neath | Police |
| | | NFM | Plymouth Airport | Fire Appliance |
| | | NFM | Scarborough | Special Constabules/CID Overt |
| | | NFM | Thames Valley | Police Traffic |
| 451.3500 | 465.2500 | NFM | England & Wales | Police Channel 08 |
| | | NFM | Birmingham Airport | HM Immigration |
| | | NFM | London | Police Port Authority of London |
| | | NFM | London Gatwick | HM Immigration |
| | | NFM | London Heathrow | HM Immigration |
| | | NFM | Newhaven | HM Immigration |
| | | NFM | Stansted Airport | HM Immigration |
| 451.3750 | 465.2750 | NFM | England & Wales | Police Channel 09 |
| | | NFM | Abergele | Police |
| | | NFM | Acklington | HM Prison Acklington (M2MU) |
| | | NFM | Andover | Police |
| | | NFM | Bangor | Police |
| | | NFM | Basildon | Police |
| | | NFM | Birmingham | HM Prison Winson Green |
| | | NFM | Burnley | Police Traffic |
| | | NFM | Buckley | Police |
| | | NFM | Canvey Island | Police |

| Base | Mobile | Mode | Location | User and Notes |
|---|---|---|---|---|
| 451.3750 | 465.2750 | NFM | Cardiff | Police |
| | | NFM | Cleveland | HM Prison Homehouse |
| | | NFM | Droitwich | Police |
| | | NFM | Farnborough | Police |
| | | NFM | Feltham | HM Prison |
| | | NFM | Frankley | Police (RA) |
| | | NFM | Full Sutton | HM Prison Full Sutton |
| | | NFM | Gloucester | Police |
| | | NFM | High Wycombe | Police (AE) |
| | | NFM | Holbeck | Police |
| | | NFM | Horley | Police |
| | | NFM | Kirby Lonsdale | Police |
| | | NFM | Leeds | Police (Holbeck) |
| | | NFM | Leeds Holbeck | Police |
| | | NFM | Littlehey | HM Prison |
| | | NFM | Liverpool | Police |
| | | NFM | London | HM Prison Pentonville |
| | | NFM | Manchester, Arndale Centre | Police |
| | | NFM | Manchester, Bootle Street | Police |
| | | NFM | Manchester, City Centre | Police |
| | | NFM | Manchester, Newton Street | Police |
| | | NFM | Marlow | Police |
| | | NFM | Milford Haven | Police |
| | | NFM | MoD Boscombe Down | Police Control Link |
| | | NFM | Norfolk | HM Prison Wayland |
| | | NFM | North Wales | Police Mobile Repeater |
| | | NFM | Northampton | Police |
| | | NFM | Nottingham | Police City Centre |
| | | NFM | Pembroke | Police |
| | | NFM | Preston | HM Prison Garth |
| | | NFM | Preston | HM Prison Kirkham |
| | | NFM | Renishaw | Police |
| | | NFM | Rye | Police (M2KBEO+ER) |
| | | NFM | Spalling | Police |
| | | NFM | St Asaph | Police |
| | | NFM | Stockton-on-Tees | HM Prison Stockton |
| | | NFM | Wayland, Norfolk | HM Prison Wayland |
| | | NFM | Wisbech | Police |
| 451.4000 | 451.4000 | NFM | England & Wales | Police/Fire Link Channel 97 |
| | | NFM | England & Wales | Fire Services Channel 01 |
| 451.4000 | 465.3000 | NFM | England & Wales | Police Channel 10 |
| | | NFM | Guernsey | Fire Brigade |
| 451.4000 | 465.4000 | NFM | London | Fire Brigade |
| | | NFM | London | Special Air Services discrete Ch |
| | | NFM | Edinburgh | Fire Brigade |
| | | NFM | Falmouth | Police |
| | | NFM | Newquay | Police |
| | | NFM | Northampton | Police Ch 64 |
| 451.4000 | 451.0000 | NFM | Newport | Radio Auth. Surveillance |
| 451.4250 | 465.3250 | NFM | England & Wales | Police Channel 11 |
| | | NFM | Aylesbury | Police (AA) |
| | | NFM | Birmingham, Acocks Green | Police |
| | | NFM | Birmingham, Dunstall Rd | Police |
| | | NFM | Bristol | Police |
| | | NFM | Catherton | Police |
| | | NFM | Connah's Quay | Police |

| Base | Mobile | Mode | Location | User and Notes |
|------|--------|------|----------|----------------|
| 451.4250 | 465.3250 | NFM | Ecclesfied, South Yorkshire | Police (F2) |
| | | NFM | Essex | Police |
| | | NFM | Faringdon | Police |
| | | NFM | Garston | Police (D2) |
| | | NFM | Gloucestershire | Police |
| | | NFM | Grays | Police |
| | | NFM | Haverigg | HM Prison Millom |
| | | NFM | Leeds Pudsey | Police |
| | | NFM | Liverpool, St Helens | Police |
| | | NFM | Long Eaton | Police |
| | | NFM | Malton | Police |
| | | NFM | Manchester, Ancoats | Police |
| | | NFM | Manchester, Blackley | Police |
| | | NFM | Manchester, Bradford | Police |
| | | NFM | Manchester, Cheetham Hill | Police |
| | | NFM | Manchester, Collyhurst | Police |
| | | NFM | Manchester, Harpurhey | Police |
| | | NFM | Manchester, Newton Heath | Police |
| | | NFM | Millom, Cumbria | HM Prison Haverigg |
| | | NFM | New Furry | Police |
| | | NFM | Newbury | Police (M2FA) |
| | | NFM | Nottingham | Police Eastwood |
| | | NFM | Portsmouth, Ferry Point | Immigration |
| | | NFM | Pudsey | Police |
| | | NFM | Reading East | Police (EX) |
| | | NFM | Reading West | Police (EA) |
| | | NFM | Rossington | Police |
| | | NFM | Shaftsbury | HM Young Offenders Institution Guys Marsh (2BV) |
| | | NFM | Speke | Police (D1) |
| | | NFM | Stansted Airport | Police (GF/GM) |
| | | NFM | Thames Valley | Police (AB) |
| | | NFM | Wantage | Police |
| | | NFM | Wendover | Police |
| | | NFM | Whitley Bay | Police (M2LBC2)/(H1) |
| | | NFM | Wickford | Police |
| | | NFM | Windsor | Police Special Branch Ch 11 |
| | | NFM | Witney | Police |
| | | NFM | Woodbridge | HM Prison Hollesley Gay Colony |
| | | NFM | Wolverhampton | Police North (M2YMG) |
| 451.4500 | 451.4500 | NFM | England & Wales | Police/Fire Link Channel 99 |
| | | NFM | England & Wales | Fire Services Channel 3 |
| 451.4500 | 465.3500 | NFM | England & Wales | Channel 12 |
| | | NFM | England & Wales | Police Channel 12 |
| | | NFM | Bedworth | Police |
| | | NFM | Dudley | Police |
| | | NFM | Merseyside | Police (Encrypted) |
| | | NFM | Pudsey | Police (CB) |
| 451.4500 | 465.4500 | NFM | England | Fire Service Channel 02 |
| 451.4750 | 451.4750 | NFM | England | General Fire Incidents Channel 4 |
| | | NFM | Northampton | Police |

| Base | Mobile | Mode | Location | User and Notes |
|------|--------|------|----------|----------------|
| 451.4750 | 465.3750 | NFM | England & Wales | Police Channel 13 |
| | | NFM | Aldridge | Police (M2YMHX) |
| | | NFM | Alton | Police |
| | | NFM | Basingstoke | Police |
| | | NFM | Billericay | Police |
| | | NFM | Birmingham | Police |
| | | NFM | Bridgewater | Police (G Control) |
| | | NFM | Brighton | Crown Court |
| | | NFM | Burnham | Police (CC) |
| | | NFM | Campsfield | Campsfield House Detention Cnt |
| | | NFM | Cleveland, Eston | Police |
| | | NFM | Cleveland | Police |
| | | NFM | Erlestoke | HM Prison Erlestoke |
| | | NFM | Greyshott | Police |
| | | NFM | Harrogate | Police |
| | | NFM | Hull | Police |
| | | NFM | Ilkley | Police |
| | | NFM | Isle of Wight | Police Relay |
| | | NFM | Keithley | Police |
| | | NFM | London | HM Prison Wandsworth |
| | | NFM | Maidenhead | Police (M2CG) |
| | | NFM | Manchester, Chadderton | Police |
| | | NFM | Manchester, Failsworth | Police |
| | | NFM | Manchester, Royton | Police |
| | | NFM | Manchester, Uppermill | Police |
| | | NFM | Newcastle | Police |
| | | NFM | Oldham | Police |
| | | NFM | Petersfield | Police |
| | | NFM | Ripley | Police |
| | | NFM | South Godstone | Police |
| | | NFM | Statford upon Avon | Police |
| | | NFM | Thames Valley | Police |
| | | NFM | Throne, S. Yorkshire | Police (A2) |
| | | NFM | Tonbridge | Police (CC) |
| | | NFM | Torquay | Police (EC) |
| | | NFM | Uttoxeter | Police |
| | | NFM | Wakefield | HM Prison Wakefield |
| | | NFM | Wallsend | Police (M2LBC3)/(I1) |
| | | NFM | Walsall | Police (M2YMHX) |
| | | NFM | Wickford | Police |
| 451.5000 | 465.4000 | NFM | England & Wales | Police Channel 14 |
| | | NFM | London | Police Special Branch (RANGER) |
| 451.5250 | 465.4250 | NFM | Birkenhead | Police |
| | | NFM | Birmingham Solihull | Police (M2YML) |
| | | NFM | Bradford Laisterdyke | Police |
| | | NFM | Cardiff Central | Police (WY) |
| | | NFM | Carterton | Police (FJ) |
| | | NFM | Collyhurst | Police |
| | | NFM | Essex | Police |
| | | NFM | Godalming | Police (WO) |
| | | NFM | Grays | Police |
| | | NFM | Hazelmere | Police (WO) |
| | | NFM | Huntingdon | Police |
| | | NFM | Long Eaton | Police |
| | | NFM | Manchester, Collyhurst | Police |
| | | NFM | Mexborough | Police (A3) |

| Base | Mobile | Mode | Location | User and Notes |
|------|--------|------|----------|----------------|
| 451.5250 | 465.4250 | NFM | Miles Platting | Police |
| | | NFM | Plymouth | Police |
| | | NFM | Shirley | Police |
| | | NFM | Stafford | Police |
| | | NFM | Thames Valley | Police |
| | | NFM | West Bridgford | Police |
| | | NFM | Weymouth | Police |
| | | NFM | Wirley | Police (FI) |
| | | NFM | Wirral | Police |
| | | NFM | Wolverhampton | Police (M2YMG) |
| 451.5250 | 451.5250 | NFM | England & Wales | Fire Breathing Apparatus Ch 6 |
| 451.5250 | 465.4250 | NFM | England & Wales | Police Channel 15 |
| | | NFM | Adwick | Police |
| | | NFM | Basildon | Police |
| | | NFM | Birkenhead | Police (A2) |
| | | NFM | Birtley | Police (K2) |
| | | NFM | Blaydon | Police (K3) |
| | | NFM | Bristol | Traffic Wardens |
| | | NFM | Eastchurch | HM Prison Elmley |
| | | NFM | Exeter | Police (EV) |
| | | NFM | Faringdon | Police |
| | | NFM | Farncombe | Police |
| | | NFM | Malvern | Police |
| | | NFM | Manchester, Ancoats | Police |
| | | NFM | Manchester, Blackley | Police |
| | | NFM | Manchester, Bradford | Police |
| | | NFM | Manchester, Cheetham Hill | Police |
| | | NFM | Manchester, Collyhurst | Police |
| | | NFM | Manchester, Harpurhey | Police |
| | | NFM | Manchester, Newton Heath | Police |
| | | NFM | Newcastle | Police |
| | | NFM | Nottingham | Police |
| | | NFM | Oldhill | Police |
| | | NFM | Oxford | Police |
| | | NFM | Plymouth | Police VHF-UHF Repeater |
| | | NFM | Poole | Police |
| | | NFM | Solihull | Police (L1) |
| | | NFM | Southampton City | Police |
| | | NFM | Whickham | Police (K1) |
| | | NFM | Wirral | Police |
| | | NFM | Witney | Police |
| | | NFM | Wolverhampton | Police (G3) |
| 451.5375 | 465.4375 | NFM | Merseyside | Police (Encrypted) |
| 451.5500 | 451.5500 | NFM | England & Wales | Police Channel 02 |
| 451.5500 | 465.4500 | NFM | England & Wales | Police Channel 16 |
| | | NFM | London | Police Buckingham Palace (RB) |
| | | NFM | London | Police Diplomatic Protection |
| 451.5750 | 465.6750 | NFM | England & Wales | Police Channel 17 |
| | | NFM | Accrington | Police |
| | | NFM | Bradford Central | Police |
| | | NFM | Breiley Hill | Police |
| | | NFM | Bristol | Police (M2QP) |
| | | NFM | Castelford | Police |
| | | NFM | Cleveland | HM Prison Kirklevington |
| | | NFM | Doncaster | HM Prison Lindholme |
| | | NFM | Dover | Dover Detention Centre |

| Base | Mobile | Mode | Location | User and Notes |
|---|---|---|---|---|
| 451.5750 | 465.6750 | NFM | Dudley | Police (M2YMJ) |
| | | NFM | Eastleigh | Police |
| | | NFM | Evesham | HM Prison Long Lartin |
| | | NFM | Faringdon | Police (M2FE) |
| | | NFM | Farnham | Police (WF) |
| | | NFM | Garstang | Police |
| | | NFM | Gosforth | Police (M2LBB5) |
| | | NFM | Haslingden | Police |
| | | NFM | Jesmond | Police |
| | | NFM | Kenton | Police (G3) |
| | | NFM | Lancaster | Police |
| | | NFM | Liverpool | HMP |
| | | NFM | London | HM Prison Pentonville |
| | | NFM | Milton Keynes | HM Prison Woodhill |
| | | NFM | Northampton | Police (EQ/NQ) |
| | | NFM | Ranby | HM Prison |
| | | NFM | Richmond | HM Prison Latchmere House |
| | | NFM | Rochester | Borstal |
| | | NFM | Romsey | Police |
| | | NFM | Saltash | Police |
| | | NFM | Sedgley | Police |
| | | NFM | Somerset | Police |
| | | NFM | Southampton West | Police |
| | | NFM | Swindon | Police |
| | | NFM | Taunton | Police |
| | | NFM | Telford | Police |
| | | NFM | Thames Valley | Police |
| | | NFM | Torpoint | Police B Division |
| | | NFM | Walton | HM Prison |
| | | NFM | Wantage | Police (FF) |
| | | NFM | Warrington | Police (D2) |
| | | NFM | Wellingborough | HM Prison |
| | | NFM | Whitehaven | Police |
| | | NFM | Worcestershire | HM Prison Long Lartin |
| | | NFM | Yorkshire (M62) | Police |
| 451.6000 | 465.5000 | NFM | England & Wales | Police Channel 18 |
| | | NFM | Addlestone | Police (NA) |
| | | NFM | Birmingham | Police Central (M2YMF) |
| | | NFM | Boston | HM Prison North Sea Camp |
| | | NFM | Cradley Heath | Police |
| | | NFM | Doncaster | HM Prison |
| | | NFM | Gipton | Police (BB) |
| | | NFM | Lancaster | Police |
| | | NFM | Maidstone | Police |
| | | NFM | Manchester, Altrincham | Police |
| | | NFM | Manchester, Sale | Police |
| | | NFM | Manchester, Stretford | Police |
| | | NFM | Manchester, Trafford | Police |
| | | NFM | Manchester, Urmston | Police |
| | | NFM | Middlesbrough | Police |
| | | NFM | Nottinghamshire | HM Prison Whatton |
| | | NFM | Oldham | Police |
| | | NFM | Preston | Police |
| | | NFM | Ramsgate | Police |
| | | NFM | Sale | Police |
| | | NFM | Southwick | Police (M1) Encrypted |

| Base | Mobile | Mode | Location | User and Notes |
|------|--------|------|----------|----------------|
| 451.6000 | 465.5000 | NFM | Southwood | Police (F3) |
| | | NFM | Sunderland | Police (M2LBF3) |
| | | NFM | Wellingborough | Police |
| 451.6125 | 451.6125 | NFM | England & Wales | Fire Breathing Apparatus Ch 2 |
| | | NFM | Plymouth Airport | Fire Appliance |
| 451.6250 | 465.5250 | NFM | England & Wales | Police Channel 19 |
| | | NFM | Birmingham | Police (NEC Motor Show) |
| | | NFM | Blackpool | Police Football Control |
| | | NFM | Brighton | Police Special Ops |
| | | NFM | Cambridge | Police Football Control |
| | | NFM | Derby | Police Derby City Football Club / Vice Squad |
| | | NFM | Dover | Police Operations Centre |
| | | NFM | Dyfed | Police Helicopter (X99) |
| | | NFM | Essex | Police |
| | | NFM | Gt Manchester | Police Surveillance (Part Time) |
| | | NFM | Guernsey | Police Channel 2 |
| | | NFM | Ipswich | Police Mobile Repeater (Spare) |
| | | NFM | Kendal | Police |
| | | NFM | Leicester | Police |
| | | NFM | London | Police Special Branch |
| | | NFM | London Gatwick | Police M2KB (GatPol) Special Ops |
| | | NFM | Nationwide | CID Use/National Emergencies |
| | | NFM | Northampton | Police |
| | | NFM | Nottingham | Police covering The Goose Fair |
| | | NFM | Peterborough | Police Ops |
| | | NFM | Slough | Police |
| | | NFM | Stoke on Trent | Police |
| | | NFM | Tenterden | Police |
| | | NFM | Thames Valley | Police Special Events |
| | | NFM | West Sussex | Police Emergency Use |
| | | NFM | Yorkshire | Police Football Control |
| 451.6375 | 465.5375 | NFM | Oxford | Police |
| 451.6500 | 465.5500 | NFM | England & Wales | Police Channel 20 |
| | | NFM | Bagshot | Police |
| | | NFM | Birmingham | Police |
| | | NFM | Cambridge | Police Mobile Repeater |
| | | NFM | Caterham | Police |
| | | NFM | Chiddingford | Police |
| | | NFM | Cornwall | Police Mobile Repeater |
| | | NFM | Devon | Police Mobile Repeater |
| | | NFM | Flint | Police |
| | | NFM | Hertfordshire | Police Mobile Repeater |
| | | NFM | Humberside | Police Mobile Repeater |
| | | NFM | Leeds | Police Force Control |
| | | NFM | Lincolnshire | Police Mobile Repeater |
| | | NFM | Lowestoft | Police |
| | | NFM | Merseyside | Police Mobile Repeater |
| | | NFM | Milton Keynes | Police (TS/NG) |
| | | NFM | Northumberland | Police Repeaters |
| | | NFM | Nottinghamshire | Police Mobile Repeater |
| | | NFM | Poole | Police RCS Encrypted (Cougar) |
| | | NFM | Shirehall | Police Link |
| | | NFM | South Cumbria | Police Repeater |
| | | NFM | South Wales | Police Mobile Repeater |
| | | NFM | South Yorkshire | Police Mobile Repeater |

| Base | Mobile | Mode | Location | User and Notes |
|---|---|---|---|---|
| 451.6500 | 465.5500 | NFM | St Ives | Police |
| | | NFM | Staffordshire | Police Mobile Repeater |
| | | NFM | Thames Valley | Police Mobile Repeater |
| | | NFM | Tyne and Wear | Police Repeaters |
| | | NFM | Ulverstone | Police |
| | | NFM | West Mercia | Police |
| | | NFM | West Midlands | Police Mobile Repeater |
| | | NFM | West Sussex | Police Mobile Repeater |
| | | NFM | West Yorkshire | Police Mobile Repeater |
| | | NFM | Weybridge | Police |
| | | NFM | Wrexham | Police |
| 451.6500 | 465.7500 | NFM | Leeds | HM Prison Armley |
| 451.6250 | 465.5250 | NFM | Conwy Valley | Police Mobile Repeater |
| | | NFM | London Gatwick | Police Ch.19 |
| | | NFM | Co Durham | Police (LA) |
| 451.6750 | 465.5750 | NFM | England & Wales | Police Channel 21 |
| | | NFM | Angelsey | Police |
| | | NFM | Barnsley | Police |
| | | NFM | Benfleet | Police |
| | | NFM | Birmingham | Police |
| | | NFM | Bishop Stortford | Police |
| | | NFM | Bradford | Police |
| | | NFM | Buxton | Police |
| | | NFM | Canvey Island | Police |
| | | NFM | Cardiff Central | Police |
| | | NFM | Chipping Norton | Police |
| | | NFM | City Of London | Police Channel 2 (AJ) |
| | | NFM | Cornwall | Police (Mobile Repeater) |
| | | NFM | Cosham | Police |
| | | NFM | Devon | Police Mobile Repeater |
| | | NFM | Gateshead South | Police |
| | | NFM | Glossop | Police |
| | | NFM | Havant | Police |
| | | NFM | Henley | Police (M2EE) |
| | | NFM | Hertfordshire | Police Mobile Repeater (VH) |
| | | NFM | Kirky in Ashfield | Police |
| | | NFM | Leicester | Police |
| | | NFM | Liverpool | Police |
| | | NFM | Mansfield | Police |
| | | NFM | Matlock | Police |
| | | NFM | Merseyside | Police HQ Div A (Encrypted) |
| | | NFM | Newcastle | Police (M2LBB3)/(F1) |
| | | NFM | Northampton | Police |
| | | NFM | Northwich | Police (E1) |
| | | NFM | Pangbourne | Police |
| | | NFM | Portsmouth | Police |
| | | NFM | Reading | Police (EG) |
| | | NFM | Redditch | Police |
| | | NFM | Shinfield | Police |
| | | NFM | Stoke on Trent | Police |
| | | NFM | Sutton | Police |
| | | NFM | Sutton in Ashfield | Police |
| | | NFM | Tamworth | Police (Encrypted) |
| | | NFM | Theale | Police |
| | | NFM | Twyford | Police |
| | | NFM | Welwyn Garden City | Police |

| Base | Mobile | Mode | Location | User and Notes |
|------|--------|------|----------|----------------|
| 451.6750 | 465.5750 | NFM | Wokingham | Police |
| | | NFM | Woodley | Police (EB) |
| 451.7000 | 465.6000 | NFM | England & Wales | Police Channel 22 |
| | | NFM | Arnold | Police |
| | | NFM | Ashford | Police |
| | | NFM | Birmingham, Bourneville | Police (M2YMB) |
| | | NFM | Bitterne | Police |
| | | NFM | Burscough | Police |
| | | NFM | Chorley | Police |
| | | NFM | Coppull | Police |
| | | NFM | Dorking | Police (ED) |
| | | NFM | Durham | Police (BD) |
| | | NFM | Folkestone | Police |
| | | NFM | Gillingham | Police (BB) |
| | | NFM | Leatherhead | Police (EL) |
| | | NFM | Manchester, Eccles | Police |
| | | NFM | Manchester, Hr. Broughton | Police |
| | | NFM | Manchester, Little Hulton | Police |
| | | NFM | Manchester, Pendleton | Police |
| | | NFM | Manchester, Salford | Police |
| | | NFM | Manchester, Swinton | Police |
| | | NFM | Manchester, Walkden | Police |
| | | NFM | Rainham | Police (BB) |
| | | NFM | Sheffield | Police (E1) |
| | | NFM | Southampton | Police |
| | | NFM | Thames Valley | Police |
| 451.7250 | 465.6250 | NFM | England & Wales | Police Channel 23 |
| | | NFM | Ammanford | Police |
| | | NFM | Birmingham | Police NEC Security |
| | | NFM | Blackpool | Police |
| | | NFM | Brighton | Police Conference Security |
| | | NFM | Cardiff | Police Special Events |
| | | NFM | Cheadle Hume | Police |
| | | NFM | Humberside | Police Football Control |
| | | NFM | Leicester | Police |
| | | NFM | Manchester | Police |
| | | NFM | Northumberland | Police Mobile Control (M2LBX+Y) |
| | | NFM | Suffolk | Police Special Events |
| | | NFM | Thames Valley | Police |
| | | NFM | Wakefield | Police HQ |
| 451.7250 | 465.7250 | NFM | London | Notting Hill Carnival 3 |
| 451.7500 | 465.6500 | NFM | England & Wales | Police Channel 24 |
| | | NFM | Birmingham Ward End | Police (M2YME) |
| | | NFM | Blackpool | Police |
| | | NFM | Boscombe | Police |
| | | NFM | Bournemouth | Police |
| | | NFM | Bramford | Police |
| | | NFM | Burnley | Police |
| | | NFM | Bury | Police |
| | | NFM | Cardiff | Police L Division (WY) |
| | | NFM | Croxteth | Police (C1) |
| | | NFM | Ely | Police |
| | | NFM | Flint | Police |
| | | NFM | Hinckley | Police |
| | | NFM | Kirkham | Police |
| | | NFM | Liverpool Huyton | Police |

| Base | Mobile | Mode | Location | User and Notes |
|---|---|---|---|---|
| 451.7500 | 465.6500 | NFM | London | Police Special Branch surveillance |
| | | NFM | Lytham | Police |
| | | NFM | Manchester, Birch | Police |
| | | NFM | Manchester, Motorway Post | Police |
| | | NFM | Manchester, Prestwich | Police |
| | | NFM | Manchester, Radcliffe | Police |
| | | NFM | Manchester, Ramsbottom | Police |
| | | NFM | Manchester, Whitefield | Police |
| | | NFM | Market Harborough | Police |
| | | NFM | Melksham | Police |
| | | NFM | Merseyside | Police HQ Div D (Encrypted) |
| | | NFM | Middleton | Police |
| | | NFM | Notty Ash | Police |
| | | NFM | Peterlee | Police (BE) |
| | | NFM | Retford | Police |
| | | NFM | Rochford | Police |
| | | NFM | Salisbury | HM Prison Salisbury |
| | | NFM | Skegness | Police |
| | | NFM | St Annes | Police |
| | | NFM | Thames Valley | Police |
| | | NFM | Warton | Police |
| | | NFM | Weeton | Police |
| | | NFM | Workington | Police |
| | | NFM | Worksop | Police |
| 451.7750 | 465.6750 | NFM | England & Wales | Fire Breathing Apparatus Ch 3 |
| | | NFM | England & Wales | Police Channel 25 |
| | | NFM | Blackpool | Police Conference Security |
| | | NFM | Brighton | Brighton Crown Court (CROWN CONTROL) |
| | | NFM | Cambridge | Police Special Branch |
| | | NFM | Cardiff | Police CID |
| | | NFM | Farnborough | Police Air Show Security |
| | | NFM | Hull | Police Football Control |
| | | NFM | Lancashire | Police Emergency Channel |
| | | NFM | Leicester | Police |
| | | NFM | Lincoln | Police |
| | | NFM | Maidstone | Police |
| | | NFM | Manchester | Police Surveillance (Part Time) |
| | | NFM | Merseyside | Police HQ Div F (Encrypted) |
| | | NFM | Northumberland | Police Mobile Control (M2LBX+Y) |
| | | NFM | Rotherham | Police Football Control |
| | | NFM | Suffolk | Police FHQ Repeater |
| | | NFM | Sunninghill | Police |
| | | NFM | Thames Valley | Police Special Events |
| | | NFM | USAF Lakenheath | Police Base Security |
| 451.7750 | 465.7250 | NFM | London | Notting Hill Carnival 5 |
| 451.8000 | 465.7000 | NFM | England & Wales | Police Channel 26 |
| | | NFM | Ainsdale | Police |
| | | NFM | Birmingham Acock's Green | Police (M2YME) |
| | | NFM | Bolton | Police |
| | | NFM | Bootle | Police (B1) |
| | | NFM | Burton-on-Trent | Police (encrypted) |
| | | NFM | Crosby | Police |
| | | NFM | Eastbourne | Police (EE) |
| | | NFM | Felling | Police (M2LBD2)/(J2) |
| | | NFM | Formby | Police |

| Base | Mobile | Mode | Location | User and Notes |
|------|--------|------|----------|----------------|
| 451.8000 | 465.7000 | NFM | Gateshead | Police Stadium Area |
| | | NFM | Gloucester | Police |
| | | NFM | Lancashire | Police radio and vehicle maintenance |
| | | NFM | Leeds Gipton | Police |
| | | NFM | Leeds Killingbeck | Police |
| | | NFM | Liverpool Marsh Lane | Police |
| | | NFM | London | Police Special Branch |
| | | NFM | Manchester, Astley Bridge | Police |
| | | NFM | Manchester, Breightmet | Police |
| | | NFM | Manchester, Farnworth | Police |
| | | NFM | Manchester, Horwich | Police |
| | | NFM | Manchester, Middle Hulton | Police |
| | | NFM | Manchester, Westhoughton | Police |
| | | NFM | Manchester Airport | Police |
| | | NFM | Merseyside | Police HQ Div B (Encrypted) |
| | | NFM | New Forest | Police |
| | | NFM | Oldbury | Police |
| | | NFM | Ringwood | Police |
| | | NFM | Seacroft | Police |
| | | NFM | Southampton Totton | Police |
| | | NFM | Southport | Police (B2) |
| | | NFM | Thames Valley | Police |
| | | NFM | Wallington | Police |
| | | NFM | Windsor | Police Castle (RL) |
| | | NFM | Wisbeach | Police |
| 451.8250 | 465.7250 | NFM | England & Wales | Police Channel 27 |
| | | NFM | Abingdon | Police |
| | | NFM | Ashford | Sandgate Police Centre |
| | | NFM | Barry | Police |
| | | NFM | Bispham | Police |
| | | NFM | Blyth | Police (M2LBC5) |
| | | NFM | Bristol | Police |
| | | NFM | Canning | Police |
| | | NFM | Canterbury | HM Prison Canterbury |
| | | NFM | Cleveleys | Police |
| | | NFM | Clitheroe | Police |
| | | NFM | Cowley | Police (BC) |
| | | NFM | Eastchurch | HM Prison Swaleside |
| | | NFM | Eastleigh | Police |
| | | NFM | Eccleshall | Police |
| | | NFM | Egham | Police |
| | | NFM | Fleetwood | Police |
| | | NFM | Frampton Cotterill | Police |
| | | NFM | Gloucester | Police |
| | | NFM | Harlow | Police |
| | | NFM | Langley | Police (CE) |
| | | NFM | Malvern | Police (CA) |
| | | NFM | Manchester, Heywood | Police |
| | | NFM | Manchester, Kirkholt | Police |
| | | NFM | Manchester, Littleborough | Police |
| | | NFM | Manchester, Middleton | Police |
| | | NFM | Manchester, Milnrow | Police |
| | | NFM | Neath | Police |
| | | NFM | Nelson Colne | Police |
| | | NFM | Newcastle | Police |

| Base | Mobile | Mode | Location | User and Notes |
|---|---|---|---|---|
| 451.8250 | 465.7250 | NFM | Oxford | Police (BA) |
| | | NFM | Pendle | Police |
| | | NFM | Port Talbot | Police |
| | | NFM | Poulton le Fyde | Police |
| | | NFM | Rochdale | Police |
| | | NFM | Slough | Police HQ (CA) |
| | | NFM | Spennymoor | Police (AL) |
| | | NFM | Stratford-Upon-Avon | Police |
| | | NFM | Tadcaster | Police |
| | | NFM | Thames Valley | Police |
| | | NFM | Wigan | Police |
| | | NFM | Woking | HM Prison Coldingley |
| | | NFM | Woodsetts | Police (E2) |
| | | NFM | Yate | Police |
| 451.8250 | 445.7250 | NFM | Corringham | Police |
| | | NFM | South Ockendon | Police |
| 451.8250 | 465.7250 | NFM | Bristol | Police CID |
| | | NFM | Wombourne | Police |
| 451.8500 | 465.7500 | NFM | England & Wales | Police Channel 28 |
| | | NFM | Amersham | Police |
| | | NFM | Aylesbury | Police |
| | | NFM | Beaconsfield | Police (AC) |
| | | NFM | Biringham | Police |
| | | NFM | Bletchley | Police (DG) |
| | | NFM | Bristol | Police |
| | | NFM | Buckingham | Police (DB) |
| | | NFM | Congleton | Police |
| | | NFM | Corby | Police (XD/DS) |
| | | NFM | Doncaster | Thorne Young Offenders Centre |
| | | NFM | Gerrards Cross | Police (AC) |
| | | NFM | Grays | Police |
| | | NFM | Havant | Police |
| | | NFM | Horndean | Police |
| | | NFM | Leeds | HM Prison Armley |
| | | NFM | Lincoln | HM Prison Morton Hall |
| | | NFM | Lincoln | Police |
| | | NFM | Macclesfield | Police (C1) |
| | | NFM | Manchester | Police |
| | | NFM | Milton Keynes | Police |
| | | NFM | Nottingham | HM Prison Nottingham |
| | | NFM | Oldbury | Police |
| | | NFM | Ormskirk | Police |
| | | NFM | Smethwick | Police |
| | | NFM | Stanley | Police (CH) |
| | | NFM | Thames Valley | Police |
| | | NFM | Waterlooville | Police |
| | | NFM | Wednesbury | Police (M2YMK) |
| 451.8500 | 465.8500 | NFM | London | Notting Hill Carnival 6 |
| 451.8750 | 465.7750 | NFM | England & Wales | Police Channel 29 |
| | | NFM | Birmingham | Police |
| | | NFM | Boroughbridge | Police |
| | | NFM | Bournemouth | Police Football Security |
| | | NFM | Cambridge | Police |
| | | NFM | City of London | Police |
| | | NFM | Cosham | Police |
| | | NFM | Farnborough | Police Air Show Security |

| Base | Mobile | Mode | Location | User and Notes |
|------|--------|------|----------|----------------|
| 451.8750 | 465.7750 | NFM | Gloucester | Police |
| | | NFM | Kent | Police Depot Emergencies |
| | | NFM | Lakenheath | Police |
| | | NFM | Lancashire | Police Emergency Channel |
| | | NFM | Leeds | Police observation |
| | | NFM | Northumberland | Police Mobile Control (M2LBX+Y) |
| | | NFM | Portsmouth | Police |
| | | NFM | Southend | Police |
| | | NFM | Southsea | Police |
| | | NFM | Suffolk | Police Special Events |
| | | NFM | Thames Valley | Police |
| | | NFM | Warickshire | Police (YJ) |
| | | NFM | Wigston | Police (CA/W) |
| | | NFM | Wolverhampton | Police |
| 451.8750 | 451.8750 | NFM | Peterborough | Police Crowd Control |
| | | NFM | Liverpool | Police Hooligan Van |
| 451.9000 | 465.8000 | NFM | England & Wales | Police Channel 30 |
| | | NFM | Bury | Police |
| | | NFM | Camberley | Police (NC) |
| | | NFM | Colchester | Military Prision |
| | | NFM | Coventry South | Police (M2YMM) |
| | | NFM | Cwymbran, Gwent | Police - Bravo 3 Section |
| | | NFM | Darlington | Police |
| | | NFM | Dover | Police Special Branch |
| | | NFM | Egham | Police (NE) |
| | | NFM | Fletchamstead | Police |
| | | NFM | Folkestone | Police Special Branch |
| | | NFM | Holywell | Police |
| | | NFM | Leeds, Horsforth | Police (AB) |
| | | NFM | Liverpool Kirby | Police |
| | | NFM | London | HM Prison Holloway |
| | | NFM | Manchester, Birch | Police |
| | | NFM | Manchester, Motorway Post | Police |
| | | NFM | Manchester, Prestwich | Police |
| | | NFM | Manchester, Radcliffe | Police |
| | | NFM | Manchester, Ramsbottom | Police |
| | | NFM | Manchester, Whitefield | Police |
| | | NFM | Mostyn | Police |
| | | NFM | Newcastle | Police |
| | | NFM | Ormskirk | Police |
| | | NFM | Portsmouth | Police Scrambled |
| | | NFM | Thames Valley | Police |
| | | NFM | Wednesfield | Police (M2YMG) |
| | | NFM | Wolverhampton | Police (GX) |
| 451.9250 | 465.8250 | NFM | England & Wales | Police Channel 31 |
| | | NFM | Bedford | Police (C/G) |
| | | NFM | Birmingham | Police |
| | | NFM | Blackpool Divisional HQ | Police |
| | | NFM | Bracknell | Police (M2CH) |
| | | NFM | Buckingham | Police (DB) |
| | | NFM | Buckley | Police |
| | | NFM | Caergwle | Police |
| | | NFM | Coalville | Police |
| | | NFM | Crowthorne | Police (M2CF) |
| | | NFM | Dorchester | Police |
| | | NFM | Dorking | Police |

| Base | Mobile | Mode | Location | User and Notes |
|------|--------|------|----------|----------------|
| 451.9250 | 465.8250 | NFM | Ely | Police |
| | | NFM | Hackenthorpe | Police (E1) |
| | | NFM | Hatfield | Police |
| | | NFM | Hungerford | Police (FB) |
| | | NFM | Kirby | Police |
| | | NFM | Lancaster | HM Prison |
| | | NFM | Langley | Police |
| | | NFM | Manchester, Eccles | Police |
| | | NFM | Manchester, Hr. Broughton | Police |
| | | NFM | Manchester, Little Hulton | Police |
| | | NFM | Manchester, Pendleton | Police |
| | | NFM | Manchester, Salford | Police |
| | | NFM | Manchester, Swinton | Police |
| | | NFM | Manchester, Walkden | Police |
| | | NFM | Milton Keynes | Police |
| | | NFM | Morley | Police |
| | | NFM | Newbury (FA) | Police |
| | | NFM | Newcastle | Police (M2LBB1) |
| | | NFM | Newport Pagnell | Police (DD) |
| | | NFM | Northallerton | Police |
| | | NFM | Redhill | Police (ER) |
| | | NFM | Reigate | Police (ER) |
| | | NFM | Saxmundham | Police (VL) |
| | | NFM | Southend | Police |
| | | NFM | Stafford | Police |
| | | NFM | Thatcham | Police |
| | | NFM | Welwyn Garden City | Police |
| | | NFM | Wolverton | Police |
| 451.9500 | 465.8500 | NFM | England & Wales | Police Channel 32 |
| | | NFM | Aldershot | Police |
| | | NFM | Ash | Police |
| | | NFM | Bewdley | Police |
| | | NFM | Birmingham Kings Heath | Police |
| | | NFM | Blackpool | Police |
| | | NFM | Bournemouth | Police |
| | | NFM | Brownhills | Police |
| | | NFM | Exeter | Police CID |
| | | NFM | Farnborough | Police Air Show Security |
| | | NFM | Forest Hill | Police (M2LBC4)/(I2) |
| | | NFM | Garthforth | Police |
| | | NFM | Hitchin | Police |
| | | NFM | Kings Heath | Police (M2YMB) |
| | | NFM | Lancashire | Police Spare Channel |
| | | NFM | Leeds Garforth | Police |
| | | NFM | Lichfield | Police |
| | | NFM | Long Benton | Police |
| | | NFM | Mytchett | Police |
| | | NFM | Newark | Police |
| | | NFM | Plymouth | Police Response Team |
| | | NFM | Redditch | Police |
| | | NFM | Stourport | Police |
| | | NFM | Thames Valley | Police |
| | | NFM | Widnes | Police (D1) |
| 451.9750 | 465.8750 | NFM | Burnley | Police |
| 452.0000 | 465.9000 | NFM | Leyland | Police |

| Base | Mobile | Mode | Location | User and Notes |
|------|--------|------|----------|----------------|
| 452.0500 | 465.9500 | NFM | Birmingham | Police |
| | | NFM | Skelmersdale | Police |
| 452.1250 | 465.1250 | NFM | Nationwide | Engineering Test Channel |
| 452.1500 | 466.0500 | NFM | Birmingham | Police |
| | | NFM | Brentwood | Police |
| | | NFM | Morecambe Bay | Police |
| | | NFM | Sywell, Northants | Police (X55) Ch 93 |
| | | NFM | Thames Valley | Police Special Use |
| 452.1750 | 466.0750 | NFM | Preston | Police |
| 452.2000 | | NFM | Nationwide | National Power Leaky Feeders |
| 452.2250 | 466.1250 | NFM | Blackburn | Police |
| | | NFM | Hendon | Police Training Centre (S) |
| 452.2500 | 446.4750 | NFM | England & Wales | Fire Service Channel 02 |
| | | NFM | England & Wales | Police Use |
| 452.2500 | 452.2500 | NFM | Powys | Fire Brigade |
| | | NFM | England & Wales | Police Channel 73 |
| 452.2750 | 465.9250 | NFM | England & Wales | Police Channel 57 |
| | | NFM | Belper | Police |
| | | NFM | Droitwich | Police (CA) |
| | | NFM | England & Wales | Police Reserve Channel A |
| | | NFM | Manchester, Chadderton | Police |
| | | NFM | Manchester, Failsworth | Police |
| | | NFM | Manchester, Royton | Police |
| | | NFM | Manchester, Uppermill | Police |
| | | NFM | Oldham | Police |
| | | NFM | Thames Valley | Police |
| | | NFM | Merseyside | Armed Police (TH) |
| 452.3000 | 465.9000 | NFM | England & Wales | Police Channel 60 |
| | | NFM | England & Wales | Police Reserve Channel C |
| | | NFM | Bridgnorth | Police |
| | | NFM | Manchester | Police |
| | | NFM | Northwich | Police |
| | | NFM | Nuneaton | Police |
| | | NFM | Portsmouth | Diplomatic Protection |
| | | NFM | Thames Valley | Police |
| | | NFM | Winsford | Police |
| 452.3125 | 457.3125 | NFM | Nationwide | Grand Prix Team Martin Brundle |
| 452.3250 | 466.2250 | NFM | Darwin | Police |
| | | NFM | Manchester | Police |
| 452.3250 | 452.3250 | NFM | England & Wales | Police Channel 06 |
| | | NFM | England & Wales | Police Channel 74 |
| | | NFM | Thames Valley | Police Support Units |
| | | NFM | Nationwide | Police Radio Engineers |
| | | NFM | Nationwide | Police Covert |
| 452.3500 | 466.2500 | NFM | England & Wales | Police Channel 59 |
| | | NFM | England & Wales | Police Reserve Channel B |
| | | NFM | Cannock | Police |
| | | NFM | Houghton | Police (O2) Encrypted |
| | | NFM | Manchester, Ashton-U-Lyne | Police |
| | | NFM | Manchester, Denton | Police |
| | | NFM | Manchester, Droylsden | Police |
| | | NFM | Manchester, Hyde | Police |
| | | NFM | Manchester, Mottram | Police |
| | | NFM | Manchester, Stalybridge | Police |
| | | NFM | Thames Valley | Police |
| | | NFM | Thameside | Police |

| Base | Mobile | Mode | Location | User and Notes |
|------|--------|------|----------|----------------|
| 452.3625 | 452.3625 | NFM | England & Wales | Fire Services Channel 2 |
| 452.3750 | 452.3750 | NFM | England & Wales | Channel 75 |
| | | NFM | England & Wales | Police Channel 75 |
| | | NFM | England & Wales | Tactical Firearms Unit |
| | | NFM | London | Tactical Firearms Unit |
| | | NFM | Jersey | Tactical Firearms Unit Ch 1 |
| 452.3750 | 466.2750 | NFM | England & Wales | Channel 76 |
| | | NFM | England & Wales | Police Channel 76 |
| | | NFM | England & Wales | Tactical Firearms Unit |
| | | NFM | Jersey | Tactical Firearms Unit Ch 2 |
| | | NFM | County Durham | HM Prison Frankland |
| 452.3750 | 452.3750 | NFM | Scarborough | Police CID |
| | | NFM | Jersey | Tactical Firearms Unit Ch 3 |
| 452.4000 | 466.3000 | NFM | England & Wales | Police Channel 33 |
| | | NFM | Arundel | HM Prison Ford (open prison) |
| | | NFM | Attercliffe | Police (D2) |
| | | NFM | Birmingham | HM Prison Digbeth |
| | | NFM | Birmingham Aiport | Police |
| | | NFM | Birmingham Central | Police (M2YMF) |
| | | NFM | Bolton | Police |
| | | NFM | Burnley | Police |
| | | NFM | Cambridge | Police |
| | | NFM | Canterbury | HM Prison Canterbury |
| | | NFM | Crosby | Police (B3) |
| | | NFM | Derby | Police (O1) |
| | | NFM | Digbeth | Police |
| | | NFM | East Dereham | Police |
| | | NFM | Epping | Police |
| | | NFM | Exeter | Police (Delta Control) |
| | | NFM | Great Yarmouth | Police |
| | | NFM | Harpenden | Police |
| | | NFM | Hebburn | Police (L4) |
| | | NFM | Huddersfield | Police |
| | | NFM | Hull | Police |
| | | NFM | Humberside | Police |
| | | NFM | Hunstanton | Police |
| | | NFM | Huntingdon | Police |
| | | NFM | Jarrow | Police (M2LBE2) |
| | | NFM | Lancaster | HM Prison |
| | | NFM | Leicester | HM Prison |
| | | NFM | Lewes | HM Prison |
| | | NFM | Liverpool Marsh Lane | Police |
| | | NFM | London | HM Prison Wandsworth |
| | | NFM | London | HM Prison Wormwood Scrubs |
| | | NFM | Manchester, Arndale Centre | Police |
| | | NFM | Manchester, Bootle Street | Police |
| | | NFM | Manchester, City Centre | Police |
| | | NFM | Manchester, Newton Street | Police |
| | | NFM | Merseyside | Police HQ Div B (Encrypted) |
| | | NFM | Neots | Police |
| | | NFM | Newcastle | Police |
| | | NFM | Norwich | Police |
| | | NFM | Padiham | Police |
| | | NFM | Pickering | Police |
| | | NFM | Plymouth | Police |
| | | NFM | Portland Bill | HM Borstal |

| Base | Mobile | Mode | Location | User and Notes |
|---|---|---|---|---|
| 452.4000 | 466.3000 | NFM | Portsmouth | Police (Encrypted) |
| | | NFM | Sheffield Attercliffe | Police (F3) |
| | | NFM | Shipley | Police |
| | | NFM | St Albans | Police |
| | | NFM | St Austell | Police |
| | | NFM | Stafford | HM Prison Stafford |
| | | NFM | Swansea | HM Prison Swansea |
| | | NFM | Swindon | Police |
| | | NFM | Thames Valley | Police |
| | | NFM | Thetford | Police |
| | | NFM | West Midlands, Bradford St | Police |
| | | NFM | York | Traffic Wardens |
| 452.4000 | 466.5000 | NFM | St Austell | Police |
| 452.4000 | 466.4500 | NFM | Windermere | Police |
| | | NFM | Woodbridge | Police |
| | | NFM | Maghull | Police |
| 452.4000 | 452.4000 | NFM | Lancashire | Drug Squad |
| 452.4250 | 466.3250 | NFM | England & Wales | Police Channel 34 |
| | | NFM | Bedworth | Police |
| | | NFM | Bradford Queenshouse | Police |
| | | NFM | Bridgend | Police |
| | | NFM | Channel Tunnel | French Police |
| | | NFM | Derby South West | Police (O2) |
| | | NFM | Gosport | Police |
| | | NFM | Hadleigh | Police |
| | | NFM | Ipswich | Police Ispwich Football Club |
| | | NFM | Leyland | Police |
| | | NFM | London | HM Prison Wormwood Scrubbs |
| | | NFM | Malton | Police |
| | | NFM | Manchester Altrincham | Police |
| | | NFM | Manchester Sale | Police |
| | | NFM | Manchester Stretford | Police |
| | | NFM | Manchester Trafford | Police |
| | | NFM | Manchester Urmston | Police |
| | | NFM | Manningham | Police |
| | | NFM | Preston HQ | Police (BD) |
| | | NFM | Scarborough | Police |
| | | NFM | Stockton on Tees | Police |
| | | NFM | Thames Valley | Police |
| | | NFM | Wombwell | Police (B2) |
| 452.4250 | 466.4500 | NFM | London | Notting Hill Carnival 7 |
| | | NFM | Bradford | Police |
| | | NFM | Fareham | Police |
| | | NFM | Gosport | Police |
| | | NFM | Portsmouth | Police |
| | | NFM | Preston | Police |
| 452.4375 | 466.3375 | NFM | Orpington | Police |
| 452.4500 | 466.3500 | NFM | England & Wales | Police Channel 35 |
| | | NFM | Amersham | Police (AD) |
| | | NFM | Birmingham | Police |
| | | NFM | Boroughbridge | Police |
| | | NFM | Bradford Odsal | Police |
| | | NFM | Bridgend | Police |
| | | NFM | Briglington | Police |
| | | NFM | Cheltenham | Police |
| | | NFM | Chequers, Bucks | Police (AZ) |

| Base | Mobile | Mode | Location | User and Notes |
|------|--------|------|----------|----------------|
| 452.4500 | 466.3500 | NFM | Chesham | Police (AH) |
| | | NFM | Colwyn Bay | Police |
| | | NFM | Deal | Police |
| | | NFM | Derby Central | Police |
| | | NFM | Digbeth | Police |
| | | NFM | Dorking | Police (ED) |
| | | NFM | Dover | Police |
| | | NFM | Eastbourne | Police (M2KBEO+EE) |
| | | NFM | Egbaston | Police (M2YMB) |
| | | NFM | Ely | Police |
| | | NFM | Exmouth | Police |
| | | NFM | Farnborough | Police |
| | | NFM | Farringdon | Police (N1) Encrypted |
| | | NFM | Fleet | Police |
| | | NFM | Folkestone | Police |
| | | NFM | Frome | Police |
| | | NFM | Gorleston-on-Sea | Police |
| | | NFM | Yarmouth | Police |
| | | NFM | Halewood | Police |
| | | NFM | Hillsborough | Police |
| | | NFM | Hull | Police |
| | | NFM | Huntingdon | Police |
| | | NFM | Knutsford | Police |
| | | NFM | Leatherhead | Police (EL) |
| | | NFM | Liverpool | Police |
| | | NFM | Manchester, Heywood | Police |
| | | NFM | Manchester, Kirkholt | Police |
| | | NFM | Manchester, Littleborough | Police |
| | | NFM | Manchester, Middleton | Police |
| | | NFM | Manchester, Milnrow | Police |
| | | NFM | Medway | Police |
| | | NFM | Medway Towns | Police |
| | | NFM | North Wales | Police |
| | | NFM | Norwich Rural | Police |
| | | NFM | Nottingham Radford Rd | Police |
| | | NFM | Rochdale | Police |
| | | NFM | Ruabun | Police |
| | | NFM | Ryhope | Police (N2) Encrypted |
| | | NFM | Salisbury City | Police |
| | | NFM | Sheffield Hammerton Rd | Police (F1) |
| | | NFM | Speke | Police |
| | | NFM | Stroud | Police |
| | | NFM | Sunderland | Police (M2LBF2) |
| | | NFM | Thirsk | Police |
| | | NFM | West Midlands, Belgrave Rd | Police |
| | | NFM | West Worcester | Police |
| | | NFM | Westbury | Police |
| | | NFM | Wilmslow | Police (C2) |
| | | NFM | Workington | Police |
| 452.4625 | 466.3625 | NFM | Northumbria | Police Car-Car (M2LB) |
| 452.4750 | 466.3750 | NFM | England & Wales | Police Channel 36 |
| | | NFM | Beumont Leys | Police |
| | | NFM | Birmingham Brierley Hill | Police (M2YMJ) |
| | | NFM | Bootle | Police |
| | | NFM | Brierley Hill | Police |
| | | NFM | Brighton | Police (M2KBCO+CB) |

| Base | Mobile | Mode | Location | User and Notes |
|------|--------|------|----------|----------------|
| 452.4750 | 466.3750 | NFM | Broadmoor | Secure Hospital |
| | | NFM | Caterham | Police |
| | | NFM | Chelmsley Wood | Police |
| | | NFM | Durham | HM Prison Frankland (M2NE) |
| | | NFM | Farnborough | Police Air Show Security |
| | | NFM | Kingswinford | Police |
| | | NFM | Leicester | Police |
| | | NFM | Lloyd House Central | Police |
| | | NFM | New Forest | Police |
| | | NFM | North Watford | Police |
| | | NFM | Ormskirk | Police |
| | | NFM | Oxley | Police |
| | | NFM | Oxted | Police |
| | | NFM | Rawmarsh | Police (C2) |
| | | NFM | Shrewsbury | Police |
| | | NFM | Skelmersdale | Police |
| | | NFM | Thames Valley | Police |
| 452.5000 | 466.4000 | NFM | England & Wales | Police Channel 37 |
| | | NFM | Aldershot | Police |
| | | NFM | Ashford | HM Prison |
| | | NFM | Barton on Humber | Police |
| | | NFM | Bicester | HM Prison Bullingdon |
| | | NFM | Birmingham | Police |
| | | NFM | Bishop Auckland | Police (AA) |
| | | NFM | Braintree | Police |
| | | NFM | Brighton | Police |
| | | NFM | Bristol | Police |
| | | NFM | Byker | Police (E1) |
| | | NFM | Carmarthen | Police |
| | | NFM | Chelmsford | HM Prison Chelmsford (PG) |
| | | NFM | Clacton-on-Sea | Police |
| | | NFM | Colchester | Prison |
| | | NFM | East Grinstead | Police |
| | | NFM | Exeter | Police CID |
| | | NFM | Farnborough | Police |
| | | NFM | Fleet | Police |
| | | NFM | Great Yarmouth | Police |
| | | NFM | Hailsham | Police (M2KBEO+EA) |
| | | NFM | Harbourne | Police (M2YMC) |
| | | NFM | Harpenden | Police |
| | | NFM | Haverfordwest | Police |
| | | NFM | Headingley | Police |
| | | NFM | Heaton | Police (E3) |
| | | NFM | Hove | Police (M2KBCO+CH) |
| | | NFM | Kirkdale | Police |
| | | NFM | Lancashire | Police Spare Channel |
| | | NFM | Landywood | Police |
| | | NFM | Leeds Weetwood | Police |
| | | NFM | Letchwood | Police |
| | | NFM | Liverpool City Centre | Police |
| | | NFM | London | HM Prison Brixton |
| | | NFM | Longsight | Police |
| | | NFM | Loughborough | Police (B/L) |
| | | NFM | Manchester Airport | Police |
| | | NFM | Manchester, Baguley | Police |
| | | NFM | Manchester, Benchill | Police |

| Base | Mobile | Mode | Location | User and Notes |
|------|--------|------|----------|----------------|
| 452.5000 | 466.4000 | NFM | Manchester, Chorlton | Police |
| | | NFM | Manchester, Didsbury | Police |
| | | NFM | Manchester, Northenden | Police |
| | | NFM | Manchester, Northern Moor | Police |
| | | NFM | Manchester, Rusholme | Police |
| | | NFM | Manchester, Withington | Police |
| | | NFM | March | Police |
| | | NFM | Market Drayton | Police (JH) |
| | | NFM | Merseyside | Police HQ Div A (Encrypted) |
| | | NFM | Nationwide | Police Airborne |
| | | NFM | Nationwide | Police special use |
| | | NFM | Newcastle | Police (M2LBB2) |
| | | NFM | Newport | Police Ch 2 |
| | | NFM | Newtown | Police |
| | | NFM | Northampton | Police |
| | | NFM | Preston | HM Prison Preston |
| | | NFM | Redcar | Police |
| | | NFM | South Killingholme | Police |
| | | NFM | St Albans | Police |
| | | NFM | Stockport | Police |
| | | NFM | Swanley | Police |
| | | NFM | Swanscombe | Police |
| | | NFM | Thames Valley | Police |
| | | NFM | Walker | Police (E2) |
| | | NFM | Walton | Police (C4) |
| | | NFM | Weetwood | Police (AA) |
| | | NFM | Wellington | Police (JA) |
| | | NFM | Wem | Police (JF) |
| | | NFM | West Kingsdown | Police |
| | | NFM | Weymouth | Police |
| | | NFM | Whitchurch | Police (JG) |
| | | NFM | Winterton | Police |
| | | NFM | Worcester | Police (CA) |
| 452.5250 | 450.1750 | NFM | Leeds | Police CID |
| 452.5250 | 466.4250 | NFM | England & Wales | Police Channel 38 |
| | | NFM | Birmingham | Police |
| | | NFM | England & Wales | Special use Channel 88 |
| | | NFM | Nationwide | Police Special use |
| | | NFM | Nationwide | Police Airborne |
| | | NFM | Newport | Police Ch 2 |
| | | NFM | Redcar | Police |
| | | NFM | Gt Manchester | Police |
| | | NFM | Stockport | Police |
| 452.5375 | 452.5375 | NFM | England & Wales | Fire/Police Link Repeaters Ch 8 |
| 452.5500 | 466.4500 | NFM | England & Wales | Police Channel 39 |
| | | NFM | Banbury | Police (BD) |
| | | NFM | Barnstable | Police |
| | | NFM | Bicester | Police (BE) |
| | | NFM | Birmingham | Police |
| | | NFM | Canvey Island | Police |
| | | NFM | Carlisle | Police Encrypted |
| | | NFM | Carlton | Police |
| | | NFM | Dalton | Police |
| | | NFM | Dishforth | Police |
| | | NFM | Hanley | Police |
| | | NFM | Hessle | Police |

| Base | Mobile | Mode | Location | User and Notes |
|------|--------|------|----------|----------------|
| 452.5500 | 466.4500 | NFM | Hull | Police |
| | | NFM | Keswick | Police |
| | | NFM | Kings Lynn | Police |
| | | NFM | Leeds | Police |
| | | NFM | Liverpool | Police |
| | | NFM | Luton | Police |
| | | NFM | Luton Airport | Police |
| | | NFM | Manchester, Ashton-U-Lyne | Police |
| | | NFM | Manchester, Denton | Police |
| | | NFM | Manchester, Droylsden | Police |
| | | NFM | Manchester, Hyde | Police |
| | | NFM | Manchester, Mottram | Police |
| | | NFM | Manchester, Stalybridge | Police |
| | | NFM | March | Police |
| | | NFM | Merseyside | Police HQ Div D (Encrypted) |
| | | NFM | Milford Haven | Police |
| | | NFM | Millgarth | Police |
| | | NFM | Newport | Police Ch 1 |
| | | NFM | Newton Abbot | Police |
| | | NFM | Newton Aycliffe | Police (AK) |
| | | NFM | Norwich | British Transport Police |
| | | NFM | Nottingham | Police |
| | | NFM | Rhos | Police |
| | | NFM | Rotherham | Police (C1) |
| | | NFM | Smethwick | Police (M2YMK) |
| | | NFM | Soho Road | Police |
| | | NFM | Southampton City | Police CID |
| | | NFM | Swindon | Police |
| | | NFM | Thames Valley | Police |
| | | NFM | Thameside | Police |
| | | NFM | Trowbridge | Police |
| | | NFM | Tubrook | Police |
| | | NFM | Uckfield | Police (M2KBCU+EU) |
| | | NFM | Whitby | Police |
| | | NFM | Whitehaven | Police |
| | | NFM | Wilmslow | Police |
| | | NFM | Windermere | Police |
| | | NFM | Witby | Police |
| | | NFM | Woking | Police (NW) |
| 452.5750 | 466.4750 | NFM | England & Wales | Police Channel 40 |
| | | NFM | Bacup | Police |
| | | NFM | Basingstoke | Police |
| | | NFM | Billericay | Police |
| | | NFM | Bradford Toller Lane | Police |
| | | NFM | Canterbury | Police |
| | | NFM | Gosport | Police |
| | | NFM | Hexham | Police (B1) |
| | | NFM | Lancaster | Police |
| | | NFM | Leeds, Queens Road | Police (HB) |
| | | NFM | Manchester, Ashton-in-M'field | Police |
| | | NFM | Manchester, Hindley | Police |
| | | NFM | Manchester, Leigh | Police |
| | | NFM | Manchester, Lower Ince | Police |
| | | NFM | Manchester, Pemberton | Police |
| | | NFM | Manchester, Standish | Police |
| | | NFM | Manchester, Tyldesley | Police |

| Base | Mobile | Mode | Location | User and Notes |
|---|---|---|---|---|
| 452.5750 | 466.4750 | NFM | Morecambe | Police |
| | | NFM | Morpeth | Police (M2LBA1) |
| | | NFM | Nationwide | British Transport Police |
| | | NFM | Newhaven Docks | Police Special Branch |
| | | NFM | Portsmouth Docks | Police |
| | | NFM | Rawtenstall | Police |
| | | NFM | Rossendale | Police |
| | | NFM | Sevenoaks | Police |
| | | NFM | Stockton-on-Tees | Police |
| | | NFM | Thames Valley | Police |
| | | NFM | Waterfoot | Police |
| | | NFM | Welwyn Garden City | Police |
| | | NFM | Wickford | Police |
| | | NFM | Wigan | Police |
| 452.5875 | 452.4875 | NFM | London Chislehurst | Police |
| 452.6000 | 466.5000 | NFM | England & Wales | Police Channel 41 |
| | | NFM | Alnwick | Police (M2LBA3) |
| | | NFM | Ascot | Police (M2CB) |
| | | NFM | Berkhamstead | Police |
| | | NFM | Birmingham W. Bromwich | Police (M2YMK) |
| | | NFM | Bognor Regis | Police (WO) |
| | | NFM | Bristol | Police |
| | | NFM | Bromsgrove | Police |
| | | NFM | Buckinghamshire | HM Prison Grendon |
| | | NFM | Bury St Edmunds | Police |
| | | NFM | Canterbury | Police |
| | | NFM | Cardiff | Police |
| | | NFM | Chichester | Police |
| | | NFM | Crewe | Police (B1) |
| | | NFM | Darlington | Police (DJ) Encrypted |
| | | NFM | Derby | Police |
| | | NFM | Droitwich | Police |
| | | NFM | Exeter | Police |
| | | NFM | Fallowfields | Police |
| | | NFM | Felixstowe | Police |
| | | NFM | Fulwood | Police |
| | | NFM | Glenfield | Police |
| | | NFM | Gravesend | Police |
| | | NFM | Grimsby | Police |
| | | NFM | Hastings | Police (M2KBEO+EH) |
| | | NFM | Haverhill | Police |
| | | NFM | Hemel Hempstead | Police |
| | | NFM | Hertford | Police |
| | | NFM | Holmfirth | Police |
| | | NFM | Hook | Police |
| | | NFM | Leamington Spa | Police |
| | | NFM | Leicester | Police |
| | | NFM | Leiston | Police |
| | | NFM | London | Police Clarance House |
| | | NFM | London | Police St James Palace |
| | | NFM | Manchester, Gorton | Police |
| | | NFM | Manchester, Greenheys | Police |
| | | NFM | Manchester, Levenshulme | Police |
| | | NFM | Manchester, Longsight | Police |
| | | NFM | Manchester, Moss Side | Police |
| | | NFM | Manchester, Whalley Range | Police |

| Base | Mobile | Mode | Location | User and Notes |
|------|--------|------|----------|----------------|
| 452.6000 | 466.5000 | NFM | Midhurst | Police (M2KBWO,C,M) |
| | | NFM | Mildenhall | Police |
| | | NFM | Nantwich | Police |
| | | NFM | Northfleet | Police |
| | | NFM | Northampton | Police |
| | | NFM | Petworth | Police (M2KBWO, C, M, P) |
| | | NFM | Preston | Police |
| | | NFM | Rubery | Police |
| | | NFM | Scunthorpe | Police |
| | | NFM | Seaham | Police (BF) |
| | | NFM | Selsey | Police (M2KBWO, C) |
| | | NFM | Stavely | Police |
| | | NFM | Stow | Police |
| | | NFM | Swansea | Police |
| | | NFM | Syston | Police (B/S) |
| | | NFM | Thames Valley | Police |
| | | NFM | Tring | Police |
| | | NFM | Wallasey | Police |
| | | NFM | Ware | Police |
| | | NFM | West Bromwich | Police |
| | | NFM | Windsor | Police (CD) |
| | | NFM | Worksop | Police |
| 452.6250 | 466.5250 | NFM | England & Wales | Police Channel 42 |
| | | NFM | Barrow-in-Furness | Police (BB) |
| | | NFM | Benwell | Police (F1) |
| | | NFM | Birmingham | Police |
| | | NFM | Carlisle | Police |
| | | NFM | Chichester | Police (M2KBWO, C) |
| | | NFM | Cumbria South Lakes | Police (BB) |
| | | NFM | Erdington | Police (M2YMD) |
| | | NFM | Habrough | Police |
| | | NFM | Hove | Police |
| | | NFM | Immingham | Police |
| | | NFM | Kendal | Police |
| | | NFM | Lancashire | Police |
| | | NFM | Leicester City Centre | Police |
| | | NFM | Malvern | Police |
| | | NFM | Manchester, Eccles | Police |
| | | NFM | Manchester, Hr. Broughton | Police |
| | | NFM | Manchester, Little Hulton | Police |
| | | NFM | Manchester, Pendleton | Police |
| | | NFM | Manchester, Salford | Police |
| | | NFM | Manchester, Swinton | Police |
| | | NFM | Manchester, Walkden | Police |
| | | NFM | Mansfield | Police Encrypted |
| | | NFM | Newburn | Police (M2LBB4) |
| | | NFM | Newcastle | Police |
| | | NFM | Penrith | Police |
| | | NFM | Scotswood | Police (F1) |
| | | NFM | Shoreham-by-Sea | Police (CO) Ch 5 |
| | | NFM | Stoke on Trent | Police |
| | | NFM | Swinton | Police (K2) |
| | | NFM | Tamworth | Police |
| | | NFM | Thames Valley | Police |
| | | NFM | Wigston | Police (CA) |
| | | NFM | Wolverhampton | Police |

| Base | Mobile | Mode | Location | User and Notes |
|------|--------|------|----------|----------------|
| 452.6250 | 466.5250 | NFM | Yorkshire | Police Technical Support Units |
| 452.6375 | 452.6375 | NFM | England | General Fire Incidents |
| 452.6375 | 466.5375 | NFM | Oprington | Police |
| | | NFM | St Mary Cray | Police |
| | | NFM | Chislehurst | Police |
| | | NFM | Biggin Hill | Police |
| | | NFM | Farnborough | Police |
| 452.6500 | 466.5500 | NFM | England & Wales | Police Channel 43 |
| | | NFM | Ambleside | Police |
| | | NFM | Arundel | Police |
| | | NFM | Baskingstoke | Police |
| | | NFM | Bedford | Police |
| | | NFM | Bexhill | Police |
| | | NFM | Birmingham Aldridge & Bnhills | Police (M2YMH) |
| | | NFM | Blackburn | Police |
| | | NFM | Bodmin | Police |
| | | NFM | Bootle | HM Prison Bootle |
| | | NFM | Brentwood | Police |
| | | NFM | Bridgend | Police |
| | | NFM | Bridgnorth | Police |
| | | NFM | Brighton | Police HQ |
| | | NFM | Bristol | Police |
| | | NFM | Cambourne | Police |
| | | NFM | Chapletown | Police (AC) |
| | | NFM | Chelmsford | Police |
| | | NFM | Chester | Police (A1) |
| | | NFM | Christchurch | Police |
| | | NFM | Colchester | Police |
| | | NFM | Coventry | Police |
| | | NFM | Crowborough | Police (M2KBNR) |
| | | NFM | Derby City Centre | Police(O3) |
| | | NFM | Durham | HM Prison Durham (M2MW) |
| | | NFM | Ely | Police |
| | | NFM | Gateshead Metro Centre | Police (M2LBD1)/(J1) |
| | | NFM | Gosport | Police |
| | | NFM | Hagley | Police |
| | | NFM | Hartlepool | Police |
| | | NFM | Helston | Police |
| | | NFM | Hemel Hempstead | Police |
| | | NFM | Hoddesdon | Police |
| | | NFM | Kidderminster | Police |
| | | NFM | Leicester | Police (452.8750 Alternate) |
| | | NFM | Lewes HQ | Police |
| | | NFM | Lincoln | HM Prison Lincoln |
| | | NFM | Liskeard | Police Town Net |
| | | NFM | Littlehampton | Police (M2KBWO, L) |
| | | NFM | Liverpool | HM Prison Liverpool |
| | | NFM | Longbridge | Police |
| | | NFM | London | HM Prison Holloway |
| | | NFM | Longton | Police |
| | | NFM | Luton | Police (BL) |
| | | NFM | Maryport | Police |
| | | NFM | Millom | Police |
| | | NFM | Morpeth | Police |
| | | NFM | New Town | Police |
| | | NFM | Newcastle | Police |

| Base | Mobile | Mode | Location | User and Notes |
|------|--------|------|----------|----------------|
| 452.6500 | 466.5500 | NFM | Nuneaton | Police (M2YJN) |
| | | NFM | Portsmouth | Police |
| | | NFM | Preston | Police |
| | | NFM | Rhymney Valley | Police |
| | | NFM | Sheffield | Police |
| | | NFM | Shrewsbury | HM Prison Shrewsbury (M2JY) |
| | | NFM | Stratford-upon-Avon | Police |
| | | NFM | Swansea | Police |
| | | NFM | Telford | Police |
| | | NFM | Thames Valley | Police |
| | | NFM | Truro | Police |
| | | NFM | Walsall | Police |
| | | NFM | Ware | Police |
| | | NFM | West Bar | Police (E3) |
| | | NFM | West Sussex HQ | Police |
| | | NFM | West Yorkshire | Police Mobile Repeater |
| | | NFM | Weston Super Mere | Police (M Control) |
| | | NFM | Wigton | Police |
| | | NFM | Woodbridge | Police |
| 452.6750 | 466.5750 | NFM | England & Wales | Police Channel 44 |
| | | NFM | Ashington | Police (M2LBA6) |
| | | NFM | Aston | Police (M2YMD1) |
| | | NFM | Baskingstoke | Police |
| | | NFM | Birmingham Stoney Stanton | Police |
| | | NFM | Coventry North | Police (M2YMM) |
| | | NFM | Debenham | Police (VL) |
| | | NFM | Dover | Police Special Branch |
| | | NFM | Grantham | Police |
| | | NFM | Hollbeach | Police |
| | | NFM | Maltby | Police (C3) |
| | | NFM | Manchester Airport | Police |
| | | NFM | Manchester, Baguley | Police |
| | | NFM | Manchester, Benchill | Police |
| | | NFM | Manchester, Chorlton | Police |
| | | NFM | Manchester, Didsbury | Police |
| | | NFM | Manchester, Northenden | Police |
| | | NFM | Manchester, Northern Moor | Police |
| | | NFM | Manchester, Rusholme | Police |
| | | NFM | Manchester, Withington | Police |
| | | NFM | Merseyside | Police (Encrypted) |
| | | NFM | Middlesborough | Police (M2) |
| | | NFM | Newbury | Police (G2) |
| | | NFM | Rotherham | Police |
| | | NFM | Telford | Police |
| | | NFM | Thames Valley | Police |
| 452.7000 | 466.6000 | NFM | England & Wales | Police Channel 45 |
| | | NFM | Barrow In Furness | Police |
| | | NFM | Battle | Police |
| | | NFM | Bilston | Police |
| | | NFM | Birmingham | Police |
| | | NFM | Bognor Regis | Police (M2KBNO) |
| | | NFM | Boston | Police |
| | | NFM | Bristol | Police |
| | | NFM | Burgess Hill | Police |
| | | NFM | Cambridge City Centre | Police |
| | | NFM | Cheshire | Police |

| Base | Mobile | Mode | Location | User and Notes |
|------|--------|------|----------|----------------|
| 452.7000 | 466.6000 | NFM | Chippenham | Police |
| | | NFM | Chipping Norton | Police (BF) |
| | | NFM | Congleton | Police (B2) |
| | | NFM | Doncaster | Police |
| | | NFM | Dover | HM Immigration |
| | | NFM | Easingwood | Police |
| | | NFM | Essex | Police |
| | | NFM | Flint | Police |
| | | NFM | Grays | Police |
| | | NFM | Guildford | Police (WG) |
| | | NFM | Halesowen & Stourbridge | Police (M2YMJ) |
| | | NFM | Halifax | Police |
| | | NFM | Harrogate | Police |
| | | NFM | Hayworth Heath | Police (M2KBNO, NA) |
| | | NFM | Hucknall | Police |
| | | NFM | Irby | Police (A3) |
| | | NFM | Kettering | Police |
| | | NFM | Knaresborough | Police |
| | | NFM | Lancing | Police |
| | | NFM | Leighton Buzzard | Police |
| | | NFM | Longtown, Cumbria | Police |
| | | NFM | Merseyside | Police HQ Div E (Encrypted) |
| | | NFM | Morpeth | Police |
| | | NFM | Newark | Police |
| | | NFM | Peterborough | Police |
| | | NFM | Rugby | Police |
| | | NFM | Salisbury | Police |
| | | NFM | Scarborough | Police |
| | | NFM | Shoreham | Police |
| | | NFM | South Shields | Police (M2LBE1)/(L1) |
| | | NFM | Stockton | Police |
| | | NFM | Sutton Coldfield | Police (M2YMD) |
| | | NFM | Thames Valley | Police |
| | | NFM | Ulverston | Police |
| | | NFM | West Midlands | Police (M2KBNO, B) |
| | | NFM | Whitehaven | Police |
| | | NFM | Woodstock | Police |
| | | NFM | Worthing | Police |
| 452.7250 | 466.6250 | NFM | England & Wales | Police Channel 46 |
| | | NFM | Birmingham | Police |
| | | NFM | Bloxwich | Police (M2YMH) |
| | | NFM | Bloxwich | Police (M2YMHX) |
| | | NFM | Broadmoor | HM Prison Broadmoor |
| | | NFM | Brownhills | Police (M2YMHX) |
| | | NFM | Cheshire | HM Prison Risley |
| | | NFM | Cleckheaton | Police |
| | | NFM | Cleethorpes | Police |
| | | NFM | Coventry Central | Police (M2YMM) |
| | | NFM | Cowes | Police |
| | | NFM | Darlaston | Police (M2YMHX) |
| | | NFM | Grimsby | Police |
| | | NFM | Guernsey | HM Prison Les Nicholles |
| | | NFM | Horsham | Police (M2KBNO, H) |
| | | NFM | Houghton le Spring | Police |
| | | NFM | Isle of Wight | Police |
| | | NFM | Keswick | Police |

| Base | Mobile | Mode | Location | User and Notes |
|---|---|---|---|---|
| 452.7250 | 466.6250 | NFM | Liverpool Toxteth | Police |
| | | NFM | Manchester | HM Prison Strangeways |
| | | NFM | Mold | Police |
| | | NFM | Ryde | Police |
| | | NFM | Sittingbourne | Police |
| | | NFM | Stechford | Police |
| | | NFM | Stockport | Police |
| | | NFM | Thames Valley | Police |
| | | NFM | Tunstall | Police |
| | | NFM | Washington | Police (M2LBF4) Encrypted |
| | | NFM | Wednesbury | Police |
| | | NFM | Willenhall | Police (M2YMHX) |
| | | NFM | Wrexham | Police |
| 452.7375 | 465.6375 | NFM | Westerham | Police |
| 452.7500 | 466.6500 | NFM | England & Wales | Police Channel 47 |
| | | NFM | Arundel | Police |
| | | NFM | Baldock | Police |
| | | NFM | Basildon | Police |
| | | NFM | Bath | Police |
| | | NFM | Beeston | Police |
| | | NFM | Beverley | Police |
| | | NFM | Birkenhead | Police |
| | | NFM | Birmingham Yardley | Police (M2YME) |
| | | NFM | Blackwater | Police |
| | | NFM | Boston | Police |
| | | NFM | Bridgeford | Police |
| | | NFM | Brighton | Police CID |
| | | NFM | Bristol | Police |
| | | NFM | Burslem | Police |
| | | NFM | Bury St Edmonds | Police |
| | | NFM | Camberley | Police (NC) |
| | | NFM | Cardiff | Police |
| | | NFM | Chelmsford | Police |
| | | NFM | Dartford | Police |
| | | NFM | Dewsbury | Police |
| | | NFM | Dover | Police |
| | | NFM | Egham | Police (NE) |
| | | NFM | Ellesmere Port | Police |
| | | NFM | Goole | Police |
| | | NFM | Guernsey | Police (M2GY) |
| | | NFM | Hadleigh | Police |
| | | NFM | Halifax | Police |
| | | NFM | Handsworth | Police (M2YMC) |
| | | NFM | Hitchin | Police |
| | | NFM | Ilkley | Police |
| | | NFM | Ipswich | Police Div HQ |
| | | NFM | Johnstown | Police |
| | | NFM | Keithley | Police |
| | | NFM | Lancing | Police |
| | | NFM | Leicester Wigston | Police |
| | | NFM | Lewes | Police (M2KBEO, L) |
| | | NFM | Littlehampton | Police |
| | | NFM | London Gatwick | Police (GatPol) |
| | | NFM | Lowestoft | Police |
| | | NFM | Manchester, Bredbury | Police |
| | | NFM | Manchester, Brinnington | Police |

| Base | Mobile | Mode | Location | User and Notes |
|------|--------|------|----------|----------------|
| 452.7500 | 466.6500 | NFM | Manchester, Cheadle | Police |
| | | NFM | Manchester, Hazel Grove | Police |
| | | NFM | Manchester, Marple | Police |
| | | NFM | Manchester, Reddish | Police |
| | | NFM | Manchester, Ringway | Police |
| | | NFM | Merseyside | Police (Encrypted) |
| | | NFM | Mexborough | Police |
| | | NFM | Needham Market | Police |
| | | NFM | Newmarket | Police |
| | | NFM | Nottingham | Police |
| | | NFM | Oxhey | Police |
| | | NFM | Pitsea | Police |
| | | NFM | Pontypool | Police - Bravo 1 Section |
| | | NFM | Redcar | Police |
| | | NFM | Rickmansworth | Police |
| | | NFM | Ripon | Police |
| | | NFM | Royston | Police |
| | | NFM | Sheerness | Police |
| | | NFM | Stockport | Police |
| | | NFM | Sudbury | Police |
| | | NFM | Sullbridge | Police (F1) |
| | | NFM | Sunderland | Police (M2LBF1) Encrypted |
| | | NFM | Swansea | Police |
| | | NFM | Thames Valley | Police |
| | | NFM | Tipton | Police |
| | | NFM | Tonbridge | Police |
| | | NFM | Tunbridge Wells | Police |
| | | NFM | Wakefield | Police |
| | | NFM | Wallsey | Police |
| | | NFM | Wellingborough | Police (WV) |
| | | NFM | Worthing | Police (M2KBWO, WW) |
| 452.7750 | 466.6750 | NFM | England & Wales | Police Channel 48 |
| | | NFM | Basildon | Police |
| | | NFM | Beeston | Police |
| | | NFM | Birkenhead | Police |
| | | NFM | Birmingham | Police |
| | | NFM | Burslem | Police |
| | | NFM | Dewsbury | Police |
| | | NFM | Ellesmere Port | Police (A2) |
| | | NFM | Gt Manchester Ringway | Police |
| | | NFM | Handsworth | Police (M2YMC) |
| | | NFM | Jonnstown | Police |
| | | NFM | Pitsea | Police |
| | | NFM | Redcar | Police |
| | | NFM | Ripon | Police |
| | | NFM | Thames Valley | Police |
| | | NFM | Tipton | Police |
| | | NFM | Wallsey | Police |
| | | NFM | West Midlands, Thornhill Rd | Police |
| 452.8000 | 466.7000 | NFM | England & Wales | Police Channel 49 |
| | | NFM | Abingdon | Police (FH) |
| | | NFM | Beeston | Police |
| | | NFM | Berwick | Police |
| | | NFM | Berwick-upon-Tweed | Police (M2LBA2) |
| | | NFM | Brighouse | Police |
| | | NFM | Bristol | HM Prison Horfield |

| Base | Mobile | Mode | Location | User and Notes |
|------|--------|------|----------|----------------|
| 452.8000 | 466.7000 | NFM | Camborne | Police |
| | | NFM | Chester le Street | Police (CG) |
| | | NFM | Cornwall | Police |
| | | NFM | Crawley | Police (M2KBNO, NC) |
| | | NFM | Daventry | Police |
| | | NFM | Didcot | Police (M2Football Club ) |
| | | NFM | Dyfed | Police |
| | | NFM | Eastbourne | Police |
| | | NFM | Evesham | Police |
| | | NFM | Falmouth | Police |
| | | NFM | Grantham | Police |
| | | NFM | Hailsham | Police (EA) |
| | | NFM | Harwich | Police |
| | | NFM | Hastings | Police (EH) |
| | | NFM | Haverfordwest | Police |
| | | NFM | Hayle | Police |
| | | NFM | Hemsworth | Police |
| | | NFM | Horsham | Police |
| | | NFM | Hull | HM Prison Hull |
| | | NFM | Ipswich | Police |
| | | NFM | Landywood | Police (M2YMC) |
| | | NFM | Leicester Beumont Leys | Police (A/B) |
| | | NFM | Lewes | Police (EL) |
| | | NFM | Llanelly | Police |
| | | NFM | London | Police City of London |
| | | NFM | Louth | Police |
| | | NFM | Lowestoff | HM Prison Blundiston |
| | | NFM | Maidstone | HM Prison Maidstone |
| | | NFM | Manchester, Salford West | Police Encrypted |
| | | NFM | Merseyside | Police HQ Div C (Encrypted) |
| | | NFM | New Quay | Police |
| | | NFM | Newbury | Police |
| | | NFM | Newcastle | Police |
| | | NFM | Newhaven | Police (M2KBEO, EN) |
| | | NFM | North Shields | Police (M2LBC1) |
| | | NFM | Norwich | HM Prison Norwich |
| | | NFM | Penry | Police |
| | | NFM | Penzance | Police |
| | | NFM | Polgate | Police Traffic (TP) |
| | | NFM | Pontefract | Police |
| | | NFM | Powys | Police |
| | | NFM | Preston | HM Prison |
| | | NFM | Rhyl | Police |
| | | NFM | Risca Area, Gwent | Police - Charkie 2 Section |
| | | NFM | Seaford | Police |
| | | NFM | Skipton | Police |
| | | NFM | St Ives | Police |
| | | NFM | Stevenage | Police |
| | | NFM | Stoke on Trent | Police |
| | | NFM | Stradishall | HM Prison Highpoint |
| | | NFM | Telford | Police |
| | | NFM | Todmorden | Police (XW) Ch 5 |
| | | NFM | Thames Valley | Police |
| | | NFM | Truro | Police |
| | | NFM | Turbrook | Police (C2) |
| | | NFM | Wallingford | Police |

| Base | Mobile | Mode | Location | User and Notes |
|------|--------|------|----------|----------------|
| 452.8000 | 466.7000 | NFM | Warton | Police |
| | | NFM | Watford | Police |
| | | NFM | Wellington | Police |
| | | NFM | Willenhall | Police |
| | | NFM | Witham | Police |
| 452.8250 | 466.7250 | NFM | England & Wales | Police Channel 50 |
| | | NFM | England & Wales | Police Special use Channel 50 |
| | | NFM | Jersey | HM Prison La Moye Ch 1 |
| | | NFM | Nationwide | Police Vehicle Trackers |
| 452.8250 | 466.6750 | NFM | Jersey | HM Prison La Moye |
| 452.8500 | 466.7500 | NFM | England & Wales | Police Channel 51 |
| | | NFM | Altrincham | Police |
| | | NFM | Birmingham | Police |
| | | NFM | Bromborough | Police |
| | | NFM | Jersey | Police Special Events |
| | | NFM | England & Wales | Police Vehicle Trackers |
| | | NFM | Witham | Police |
| 452.8500 | 466.7000 | NFM | Jersey | Diplomatic Protection |
| 452.8750 | 455.7750 | NFM | England & Wales | Police Channel 52 |
| | | NFM | Birmingham | Police |
| | | NFM | Bolton | Police |
| | | NFM | Chelmsley Wood | Police (M2YML) |
| | | NFM | Christchurch | Police |
| | | NFM | Coventry | Police |
| | | NFM | Farnworth | Police |
| | | NFM | Leicester, Central | Police (C/A) |
| | | NFM | Manchester, Astley Bridge | Police |
| | | NFM | Manchester, Breightmet | Police |
| | | NFM | Manchester, Farnworth | Police |
| | | NFM | Manchester, Horwich | Police |
| | | NFM | Manchester, Middle Hulton | Police |
| | | NFM | Manchester, Westhoughton | Police |
| | | NFM | North Yorkshire | Police Link to Ravenscar Ch. 4 |
| | | NFM | Poole | Police Encrypted |
| | | NFM | Rayleigh | Police |
| | | NFM | Southend on Sea | Police |
| | | NFM | Thames Valley | Police |
| | | NFM | Winchester | Police |
| 452.9000 | 466.8000 | NFM | England & Wales | Police Channel 53 |
| | | NFM | Barrow In Furness | Police |
| | | NFM | Birmingham | HM Prison Winston Green |
| | | NFM | Burton Down | Police |
| | | NFM | Chester le Street | Police (CG) |
| | | NFM | Leigh | Police |
| | | NFM | Lewport, Gwent | Police Traffic (WO) |
| | | NFM | Manchester, Ashton-in-M'field | Police |
| | | NFM | Manchester, Hindley | Police |
| | | NFM | Manchester, Leigh | Police |
| | | NFM | Manchester, Lower Ince | Police |
| | | NFM | Manchester, Pemberton | Police |
| | | NFM | Manchester, Standish | Police |
| | | NFM | Manchester, Tyldesley | Police |
| | | NFM | Mid Glamorgan | Police |
| | | NFM | North Cumbria | Police Mobile Repeater |
| | | NFM | Thames Valley | Police |
| | | NFM | Wigan | Police |

| Base | Mobile | Mode | Location | User and Notes |
|------|--------|------|----------|----------------|
| 452.9250 | 452.9250 | NFM | England & Wales | Police Channel 05 |
| | | NFM | Lyme | Police |
| | | NFM | Warrington | Police |
| 452.9250 | 466.7750 | NFM | Jersey | Traffic Wardens |
| 452.9250 | 466.8250 | NFM | England & Wales | Police Channel 54 |
| | | NFM | Christchurch | Police |
| | | NFM | Derby | Police |
| | | NFM | Ely | Police |
| | | NFM | Essex | Police |
| | | NFM | Ipswich | Police |
| | | NFM | Leicester | Police |
| | | NFM | Linconshire | Police Mobile Repeater |
| | | NFM | South Hams | Police VHF-UHF Repeater |
| | | NFM | South Yorkshire | Police Mobile Repeater |
| | | NFM | Thames Valley | Police |
| | | NFM | Warwickshire | Police Mobile Repeater |
| | | NFM | West Mercia | Police |
| 452.9500 | 466.8500 | NFM | England & Wales | Police Channel 55 |
| | | NFM | Badsworth | Police |
| | | NFM | Kidsgrove | Police |
| | | NFM | Minsthorpe | Police |
| | | NFM | North Yorkshire | Police Link to Ravenscar Ch. 2 |
| | | NFM | Newport | Traffic Police |
| | | NFM | Pontefract | Police |
| | | NFM | Runcorn | Police (E2) |
| | | NFM | South Yorkshire | Police Mobile Repeater |
| | | NFM | Thames Valley | Police |
| | | NFM | Widnes | Police |
| 452.9750 | 452.9750 | NFM | England & Wales | Police Channel 01 |
| 452.9750 | 466.8250 | NFM | Jersey | Tactical Firearms Unit Ch 3 |
| | | NFM | Jersey | HM Prison La Moye Ch 2 |
| 452.9750 | 466.8750 | NFM | England & Wales | Police Channel 56 |
| | | NFM | Blyth | Police (M2LBC5) |
| | | NFM | Bolton | Police Ch 2 |
| | | NFM | Crook Weardale | Police (AB) |
| | | NFM | Manchester, Astley Bridge | Police |
| | | NFM | Manchester, Breightmet | Police |
| | | NFM | Manchester, Farnworth | Police |
| | | NFM | Manchester, Horwich | Police |
| | | NFM | Manchester, Middle Hulton | Police |
| | | NFM | Manchester, Westhoughton | Police |
| | | NFM | Scarborough | Police |
| | | NFM | Thames Valley | Police |

## 453.0000 - 454.0000 MHz   PMR Mobile Band 12.5 kHz
## (Split +6.5 MHz)

| Base | Mobile | Mode | Location | User and Notes |
|------|--------|------|----------|----------------|
| 453.0250 | 459.5250 | NFM | Bath | National Car Parks maintenance |
| 453.0250 | 459.5250 | NFM | Bolton | Shopping Centre Security |
| | | NFM | Bristol | City CCTV System |
| | | NFM | Dover | Hoverspeed |
| | | NFM | Edinburgh | Waverley Market Security |
| | | NFM | Felixstowe | Harbour Channel |
| | | NFM | Gloucestershire Airport | Ground Control |
| | | NFM | Guernsey | Harbour Channel |
| | | NFM | Harwich | Harbour Channel |
| | | NFM | Jersey | Shell Aviation Fuel Supplies |

| Base | Mobile | Mode | Location | User and Notes |
|------|--------|------|----------|----------------|
| 453.0250 | 459.5250 | NFM | Leicester | Shopping Centre Security |
| 453.0250 | 453.0250 | NFM | Lomond | Amoco CTCSS 131.8 Hz |
| | | NFM | London (Heathrow) | Ground Repeater |
| | | NFM | London, Wood Green | Shop Watch Scheme Channel 2 |
| | | NFM | Middlesborough | BSC Ros Railways |
| | | NFM | Moray Firth | Beatrice Alpha Platform |
| | | NFM | Nigg Bay | BP Oil Terminal Control |
| | | NFM | North Sea | Amoco NW Hutton |
| | | NFM | North Sea | Amoco North Everest |
| | | NFM | North Sea | Beatrice A BP |
| | | NFM | North Sea | Beryl B Mobil Temp. Const. Facility |
| | | NFM | North Sea | Shell Fulmar FSU |
| | | NFM | Stansted | Ground Repeater |
| | | NFM | Staverton | Staverton Airport Ground |
| | | NFM | Warwick | Castle staff Channel 2 |
| 453.0375 | 459.5375 | NFM | London (Heathrow) | Airline & BAA Ops |
| | | NFM | Blackpool | Premier Cabs |
| | | NFM | Bournemouth | Winfaith Security |
| | | NFM | Brighton | American Express |
| | | NFM | Brighton | Shop Security |
| | | NFM | Burnley | Burnley & Pendle Buses |
| | | NFM | Coventry | Car Park Attendants |
| | | NFM | Edinburgh | Royal Infirmary Porters |
| | | NFM | Guernsey | Princess Elizabeth Hospital |
| | | NFM | Hull | Royal Infirmary Security |
| | | NFM | Immingham | Coal Products Docking |
| | | NFM | Leicester | Bradgate & Brecon Rangers |
| | | NFM | London (Heathrow) | Airline & BAA Ops |
| | | NFM | Luton Airport | Fuel & Catering |
| 453.0500 | 467.5500 | NFM | Magor | Whitbread Beer Secuirty |
| | | NFM | Nationwide | Air Rangers |
| | | NFM | Nationwide | R.R. Security |
| | | NFM | Nationwide | Shopping Centre Security |
| 453.0500 | 459.5500 | NFM | North Sea | Chevron Alba ANP PABX Interface - Mobiles |
| 453.0500 | 467.5500 | NFM | Peterborough | Peter Brotherhood |
| | | NFM | Rhyl | Security |
| | | NFM | Sheffield | Council emergency glaziers |
| | | NFM | Stoke On Trent | Roebuck Centre |
| 453.0625 | 459.5625 | NFM | Charham | Shopwatch scheme |
| | | NFM | Kent | Medway Shop Security |
| | | NFM | Manchester | Hospital Porters |
| | | NFM | Manchester | Springfield Hospital Porters |
| 453.0750 | 460.1750 | NFM | Billingham | ICI |
| 453.0750 | 459.5625 | NFM | Bristol | Portland Dock Control |
| | | NFM | Carnforth | Wimpey Quarry |
| | | NFM | Coryton | Shell Haven Oil Refinery |
| | | NFM | Dover | Docks security |
| | | NFM | Felixstowe | Quay Shipping |
| | | NFM | Harwich | Quay Shipping |
| | | NFM | Jersey | Harbour/Marina Channel 2 |
| | | NFM | London (Heathrow) | Airline & BAA Ops |
| | | NFM | Manchester | Aircraft Fitters |
| | | NFM | Manchester | Airport Motor Pool Maintenance |
| | | NFM | March | March Ground Services |
| | | NFM | Middlesborough | ICI Ammonia Base |

| Base | Mobile | Mode | Location | User and Notes |
|------|--------|------|----------|----------------|
| 453.0750 | 459.5750 | NFM | North Sea | Amoco Bacton |
| 453.0750 | 453.0750 | NFM | North Sea | Amoco Montrose A |
| 453.0750 | 459.5625 | NFM | North Sea | Amoco NW Hutton |
| 453.0750 |  | NFM | Oxford | University Science Area |
| 453.0875 | 459.5875 | NFM | Coventry | Coal Authority |
|  |  | NFM | London | Selfridges |
|  |  | NFM | London, Kensington | British Home Stores |
|  |  | NFM | London, Kensington | River Island |
|  |  | NFM | London, Oxford Street | D H Evans security |
| 453.1000 | 459.6000 | NFM | Beeston | Boots |
|  |  | NFM | Belfast | Queen's University Security |
|  |  | NFM | Blackpool | Local Health Authority |
|  |  | NFM | Blackpool | Tramcar Inspectors |
|  |  | NFM | Cowley | Rover Plant Channel 1 |
|  |  | NFM | Edinburgh | Rocksteady Security |
|  |  | NFM | Fleetwood | Tram Inspectors |
|  |  | NFM | Glasgow | Ibrox Match Control |
|  |  | NFM | Keynsham | Fry's Chocolate |
|  |  | NFM | London | Docklands Security |
|  |  | NFM | London (Heathrow) | Indian Language Channel |
|  |  | NFM | Maltby | Buttlers Roadstone |
|  |  | NFM | Moray Firth | Beatrice Bravo Platform |
|  |  | NFM | Newcastle | Tyne & Wear Metro |
|  |  | NFM | North Sea | BP Beatrice B |
|  |  | NFM | North Sea | Unocal Heather A |
|  |  | NFM | Oldham | Building Site Security |
|  |  | NFM | Peterborough | Queensgate Shopping Cent. |
|  |  | NFM | South Walden | Schering Agrochemicals |
|  |  | NFM | Southampton | Hospital Transport Channel 1 |
|  |  | NFM | Telford | Shopping Centre Security |
| 453.1000 | 456.6000 | NFM | Tyneside | Metro Repairs |
| 453.1125 | 459.6125 | NFM | London | Brent Cross Shopping Centre control |
|  |  | NFM | Manchester | Council |
| 453.1250 | 459.6250 | NFM | Coventry | Jaguar Cars Ltd. Security |
|  |  | NFM | Coventry | Orchards Security |
|  |  | NFM | Cowley | Rover Plant Channel 4 |
| 453.1250 | 453.1250 | NFM | Dover | Western Docks Jetfoil |
| 453.1250 | 459.6250 | NFM | East Midlands Airport | British Midland |
|  |  | NFM | Glasgow | British Midland |
|  |  | NFM | Guernsey | St. Sampson's Harbour |
|  |  | NFM | Harwich | Carless Solvents |
|  |  | NFM | Immingham | Conoco Oil Refinery |
|  |  | NFM | Jersey Airport | British Midland Handling |
|  |  | NFM | London (Heathrow) | Airline & BAA Ops |
|  |  | NFM | Nigg Bay | BP Oil Terminal Fire Channel |
|  |  | NFM | North Sea | Conoco Murchison |
|  |  | NFM | North Sea | Conoco Viking Field |
|  |  | NFM | Norwich | Colmans Foods |
|  |  | NFM | Oldham | Garforth Glass |
|  |  | NFM | Speke | Halewood Ford Plant Sec. |
| 453.1375 | 459.6375 | NFM | London | Police Dartford Tunnel |
|  |  | NFM | Manchester | Data Link |
|  |  | NFM | Morecambe | Data Link |

| Base | Mobile | Mode | Location | User and Notes |
|---|---|---|---|---|
| 453.1500 | 459.6500 | NFM | Ahston under Lyme | Shopping Security |
| | | NFM | Birmingham International | Ops |
| | | NFM | Coventry | Housing Dept |
| | | NFM | Edinburgh | City Centre Couriers |
| | | NFM | Fleetwood | P & O Security |
| | | NFM | London | City Security |
| | | NFM | London | Metro Bus Orpington |
| | | NFM | London (Heathrow) | Airline & BAA Ops |
| | | NFM | Sheffield | Council Cleansing Dept. |
| | | NFM | Stanstead Airport | El-Al Security |
| | | NFM | Swansea | Storenet Security |
| | | NFM | Swindon | Council Maintenance |
| | | NFM | Whittlesey | McCain Intenational |
| | | NFM | Wigan | Central Park Rugby Grnd OB |
| | | NFM | Wiltshire | Reading Cable TV |
| 453.1625 | 459.6625 | NFM | Aberdyfi | Lifeboat |
| | | NFM | Oldham | Two Counties |
| 453.1750 | 459.6750 | NFM | Bedford | 3M UK |
| | | NFM | Billingham | ICI |
| | | NFM | Bristol | Bus Inspectors |
| | | NFM | Cardiff | Docks Security |
| | | NFM | Coventry | Courtaulds Security |
| | | NFM | Edinburgh | Royal Infirmary Security |
| | | NFM | Essex | County Council |
| | | NFM | Grimsby | Tioxide UK Chemical Plant |
| | | NFM | Ipswich | Docks Security |
| | | NFM | Manchester North | Security Firm |
| 453.1750 | 453.1750 | NFM | Moray Firth | Beatrice Alpha Platform |
| 453.1750 | 459.6750 | NFM | Nationwide | Railtrack |
| | | NFM | Newcastle | Tyne & Wear Metro |
| | | NFM | North Sea | Amoco Lomond |
| | | NFM | North Sea | Amoco NW Hutton |
| | | NFM | North Sea | Amoco North Everest |
| 453.1750 | 453.1750 | NFM | North Sea | BP Beatrice A |
| 453.1750 | 459.6750 | NFM | North Sea | Shell Bacton |
| | | NFM | North Sea | Shell Inde J |
| | | NFM | North Sea | Shell Inde K |
| | | NFM | North Sea | Shell Leman B |
| | | NFM | North Sea | Shell St. Fergus |
| | | NFM | Sheffield | City Parks Security |
| | | NFM | Suffolk | County Council |
| 453.2000 | 459.7000 | NFM | Birmingham | Taxi Co |
| | | NFM | Boston | Acorn Cabs |
| | | NFM | Enfield | Police chase cars |
| | | NFM | Fleetwood | Plumbers |
| | | NFM | Glasgow | City Centre Council Patrol |
| | | NFM | Hull | Hospital Porters |
| | | NFM | Ipswich | Transport Police |
| | | NFM | Jersey Harbour | Shell Fuel Supplies |
| | | NFM | London | Glaxo Security Ch1 |
| | | NFM | Milton Keynes | MK Security |
| 453.2000 | 453.2000 | NFM | North Sea | Conoco Murchison |
| 453.2000 | 459.7000 | NFM | Plymouth | City Bus Inspectors |
| | | NFM | Portsmouth | Taxis |
| | | NFM | Ramsbottom | Civic Private Hire |
| | | NFM | Rotherham | Bus Inspectors |

| Base | Mobile | Mode | Location | User and Notes |
|---|---|---|---|---|
| 453.2000 | 459.7000 | NFM | Sheffield | Main line trains maintenance |
| 453.2125 | 459.7125 | NFM | Dundee | Data Link |
| | | NFM | Morecambe | Data Link |
| 453.2250 | 453.2250 | NFM | Alba Chevron | FSU Shuttle Operations |
| 453.2250 | 459.7250 | NFM | Jersey | Harbour Channel 1 |
| | | NFM | London (Heathrow) | Airline & BAA Ops |
| | | NFM | North Sea | Chevron Ninian South |
| | | NFM | North Sea | Shell Eider |
| | | NFM | Peterborough | Aggregate Company |
| | | NFM | Tilbury | Rover Security |
| | | NFM | Belfast | Ulster Folk & Transport Museum |
| | | NFM | Forest Hill | Taxi |
| | | NFM | Leeds | Traffic Wardens |
| | | NFM | London (Central) | Traffic Wardens |
| | | NFM | London (Gatwick) | Ground Repeater |
| | | NFM | London, Gatwick | Airline & BAA Ops |
| | | NFM | London, Heathrow | Airline & BAA Ops |
| 453.2500 | 459.7750 | NFM | Manchester | Taxi |
| | | NFM | North Sea | BP Clyde A |
| | | NFM | North Sea | Conoco Murchison |
| 453.2500 | 453.2500 | NFM | North Sea | Marathon Brae N |
| 453.2500 | 459.7750 | NFM | Whiston | Whiston Hospital Security |
| 453.2625 | 459.7625 | NFM | Newcastle | Data Link |
| | | NFM | Oldham | Courier |
| 453.2750 | 459.7750 | NFM | London, Heathrow | Airline & BAA Ops |
| 453.2750 | | NFM | London, Heathrow | Ground Repeater |
| 453.2750 | | NFM | Middlesborough | British Steel Medics |
| 453.2750 | | NFM | North Sea | Shell Base Leman BH |
| 453.2750 | 453.2750 | NFM | North Sea | Shell Brent B |
| 453.3000 | 459.8000 | NFM | Humberside | Lindsey Oil Refinery |
| | | NFM | Liverpool | Buses |
| | | NFM | Liverpool | Merseybus Inspectors |
| | | NFM | North Sea | Amoco Lomond |
| | | NFM | North Sea | Amoco Montrose A |
| | | NFM | North Sea | Amoco NW Hutton |
| | | NFM | North Sea | Amoco North Everest |
| | | NFM | North Sea | BP Magnus |
| 453.3000 | 453.3000 | NFM | North Sea | Marathon Brae N |
| 453.3000 | 459.8000 | NFM | Stevenage | Pulse Disco & Vogue Nightclub |
| 453.3125 | 459.8125 | NFM | Perth | Data Link |
| 453.3250 | 459.8250 | NFM | Cheltenham | Hospital Porters |
| | | NFM | East Sussex | Ambulance Incident Vehicle |
| | | NFM | Gloucester | Royal General Hospital Porters |
| | | NFM | London, Heathrow | Ground Repeater |
| | | NFM | Manchester | Doctors on Call |
| | | NFM | March | St Mary's Hospital Security |
| | | NFM | Stansted | Ground Repeater |
| 453.3500 | 459.8500 | NFM | Humberside Airport | Bond Helicopters |
| | | NFM | London | Security Co. |
| 453.3500 | 453.3500 | NFM | North Sea | Conoco Murchison |
| 453.3500 | 459.8500 | NFM | North Sea | Marathon Brea N |
| | | NFM | Nottingham | City Engineers |
| | | NFM | Walsall | Council Works Yard |
| 453.3625 | 459.8625 | NFM | Nationwide | DSS |

| Base | Mobile | Mode | Location | User and Notes |
|------|--------|------|----------|----------------|
| 453.3750 | 459.8750 | NFM | Cambridge | Addenbrooks Porters |
| | | NFM | Cowley | Rover Plant Channel 2 |
| | | NFM | Immingham | Conoco Oil Refinery Fire & Sec. |
| | | NFM | Immingham | Lindsey Oil Fire Service |
| 453.3750 | 453.3750 | NFM | Liverpool | All Docks Handhelds |
| 453.3750 | 459.8750 | NFM | Luton Airport | Buses & Luggage Handlers Channel 5 |
| | | NFM | Nationwide | DSS |
| | | NFM | Port Talbot | BP Works |
| 453.3875 | 459.8875 | NFM | Nationwide | DSS |
| 453.4000 | 459.9000 | NFM | Glasgow | Prince's Sq. Shopping Mall Sec. |
| | | NFM | Hull | City Council |
| | | NFM | Ipswich | Port Authority |
| | | NFM | Jersey Airport | Esso Refuelling |
| | | NFM | London (Gatwick) | Ground Repeater |
| | | NFM | London, Heathrow | Airline & BAA Ops |
| | | NFM | Nigg Bay | Oil Terminal Maintenance |
| 453.4000 | 453.4000 | NFM | Nigg Terminal | BP |
| 453.4000 | 459.9000 | NFM | North Sea | Chevron Ninian North |
| | | NFM | North Sea | Marathon Brae N, S |
| | | NFM | North Sea | Shell St. Fergus |
| | | NFM | Nottingham | Formans |
| | | NFM | Oxford | University Science Area |
| | | NFM | West Midlands | Bus Route 52 |
| 453.4250 | 459.9250 | NFM | Alba Chevron | FSU Maintenance |
| 453.4250 | 453.4250 | NFM | Eastbourne | Debenhams |
| 453.4250 | 459.9250 | NFM | Immingham | Conoco Oil Refinery |
| | | NFM | London, Gatwick | Ground Repeater |
| | | NFM | London, Heathrow | Ground Repeater |
| | | NFM | Middlesborough | British Steel Security |
| | | NFM | North Sea | BP Buchan |
| 453.4250 | 453.4250 | NFM | North Sea | BP Clyde A |
| 453.4250 | 459.9250 | NFM | North Sea | BP Magnus |
| | | NFM | Swansea | DVLA Security |
| 453.4500 | 459.9500 | NFM | Cardiff | Inland Revenue Security |
| | | NFM | Cowley | Rover Plant Channel 3 |
| | | NFM | Guernsey | HM Customs & Excise |
| | | NFM | Leicester | Haymarket Centre Security |
| | | NFM | Leicester | Universities of Christian Fellowship |
| | | NFM | Llantrisant | Royal Mint Security |
| | | NFM | London, Gatwick | Ground Repeater |
| | | NFM | London, Heathrow | Ground Repeater |
| | | NFM | Nationwide | BAA Police |
| | | NFM | North Sea | Shell Dunlin |
| | | NFM | Stoke-on-Trent | Police |
| 453.4625 | 459.9625 | NFM | Brighton | Inland Revenue Security |
| | | NFM | Nationwide | Inland Revenue Security |
| 453.4750 | 459.9750 | NFM | Bishopton | Compaq Security |
| | | NFM | Coventry | Community Radio Link |
| | | NFM | Dover | Harbour Board Police |
| | | NFM | Flint | CBM Security |
| | | NFM | Grimsby | Council |
| | | NFM | Guernsey | HM Customs Surveillance |
| | | NFM | London, Gatwick | Airline & BAA Ops |
| | | NFM | Luton Airport | Arrivals/Departures Channel 3 |
| | | NFM | Manchester | Arndale Shopping Centre Sec. |
| | | NFM | Manchester | Manchester University Security |

| Base | Mobile | Mode | Location | User and Notes |
|------|--------|------|----------|----------------|
| 453.4750 | 459.9750 | NFM | Nationwide | CAA Ground Movements |
| | | NFM | Newcastle | Metro Centre |
| | | NFM | North Sea | BP Buchan |
| | | NFM | North Sea | Conoco Murchison |
| | | NFM | Peterborough | Football Ground Control |
| | | NFM | Rotherham | Council |
| | | NFM | Sheffield | Council emergency plumbers |
| | | NFM | Stansted | Security |
| | | NFM | Swindon | Austin Rover Security |
| 453.4875 | 459.9875 | NFM | East Midlands Airport | Airport Fire |
| 453.5000 | 460.0000 | NFM | Belfast | Castlecourt Shopping Centre |
| | | NFM | Folkestone | Stena Sealink |
| | | NFM | London, Gatwick | Airline & BAA Ops |
| | | NFM | London, Heathrow | British Midland |
| | | NFM | Nationwide | Railtrack Security |
| | | NFM | Newport | Raitrack Security |
| | | NFM | North Sea | Shell Eider |
| | | NFM | Sheffield | Council Markets Security (Ester) |
| | | NFM | Southampton | Sealink |
| | | NFM | Stansted | Airline & BAA Ops |
| | | NFM | Tyne & Wear | Metro |
| | | NFM | Wigan | Factory Repeater |
| 453.5250 | 460.0250 | NFM | Brighton | British Rail Transport Police |
| | | NFM | East Midlands Airport | Fire Channel 1 |
| | | NFM | Ellesmere Port | Shell Security |
| | | NFM | Hull | City Council Housing |
| | | NFM | Ipswich | Railtrack |
| | | NFM | Jersey | Harbour Channel 2 |
| | | NFM | Leicester | Leicester Polytechnic Security |
| | | NFM | Nationwide | Transport Police |
| 453.5250 | 453.5250 | NFM | Nigg Bay | Oil Terminal Security |
| 453.5250 | 460.0250 | NFM | North Sea | Alba Chevron ANP East Crane |
| | | NFM | North Sea | Chevron Ninian North |
| | | NFM | Sheffield | Council emergency gas fitters |
| 453.5500 | 460.0500 | NFM | Aberdeen | Railtrack |
| | | NFM | Barrow in Furness | Railtrack |
| | | NFM | Bedford | Railtrack |
| | | NFM | Birmingham | Railtrack Birmingham New St. |
| | | NFM | Blackpool | Railtrack |
| | | NFM | Bletchley | Railtrack Bletchley Yard |
| | | NFM | Brentwood | Railtrack Shenfield |
| | | NFM | Brighton | Railtrack (Brighton Depot) |
| | | NFM | Cardiff | Great Western Railway |
| | | NFM | Carlisle | Railtrack |
| | | NFM | Chester | Railtrack |
| | | NFM | Coventry | Railtrack |
| | | NFM | Crewe | Railtrack |
| | | NFM | Doncaster | Railtrack |
| | | NFM | East Croydon | Railtrack |
| | | NFM | Eastbourne | Railtrack Eastbourne Station |
| | | NFM | Edinburgh | Railtrack, (Waverley) |
| | | NFM | Ely | Railtrack |
| | | NFM | Glasgow | Railtrack, (Queen Street) |
| | | NFM | Harwich | Railtrack, Parkeston Yard |
| | | NFM | Hull | Railtrack, Hull Paragon |
| | | NFM | Ipswich | Railtrack |

| Base | Mobile | Mode | Location | User and Notes |
|---|---|---|---|---|
| 453.5500 | 460.0500 | NFM | Leeds | Railtrack |
| | | NFM | Leicester | Railtrack |
| | | NFM | London | Railtrack (Cannon Street) |
| | | NFM | London | Railtrack (Clapham Junction Yard) |
| | | NFM | London | Railtrack (East Croydon) |
| | | NFM | London | Railtrack (Fenchurch Street) |
| | | NFM | London | Railtrack (Ilford Car Sheds) |
| | | NFM | London | Railtrack (Liverpool Street) |
| | | NFM | London | Railtrack (Paddington) |
| | | NFM | London | Railtrack (Slade Green Depot) |
| | | NFM | London | Railtrack (Waterloo) |
| | | NFM | London | Railtrack (Wimbledon Park) |
| | | NFM | Manchester | Railtrack (Picadilly) |
| | | NFM | Nationwide | Railtrack Stations Channel 1 |
| | | NFM | Newcastle | Railway Station |
| | | NFM | North Sea | Chevron Alba ANP Construction |
| | | NFM | North Sea | Chevron Ninian South |
| 453.5500 | 453.5500 | NFM | North-West | BR Track Workers to Trains Channel 1 |
| 453.5500 | 460.0500 | NFM | Norwich | Railtrack (Crown Point) |
| | | NFM | Nottingham | City Council |
| | | NFM | Penzance | Railtrack |
| | | NFM | Preston | Railtrack |
| | | NFM | Reading | Railtrack |
| | | NFM | Salford | Railtrack |
| | | NFM | Selhurst Junction | Railtrack |
| | | NFM | Sheffield | Railtrack |
| | | NFM | Shrewsbury | Railtrack |
| | | NFM | Slade Green Depot | Railtrack |
| | | NFM | Stansted | Railtrack |
| | | NFM | Stratford-Upon-Avon | Railtrack |
| | | NFM | Wigan | Railtrack |
| | | NFM | Woking | Railtrack |
| | | NFM | Wolverhampton | Railtrack |
| | | NFM | York | Railtrack |
| 453.5625 | 460.0625 | NFM | Nationwide | Railtrack |
| 453.5750 | 460.0750 | NFM | Felixstowe | Freightliners |
| | | NFM | Immingham | Conoco Oil Refinery |
| | | NFM | London | Covent Garden security |
| | | NFM | Nationwide | British Airways |
| | | NFM | North Sea | BP Buchan |
| | | NFM | North Sea | BP Magnus |
| | | NFM | Whitsnade | Whitsnade Zoo |
| | | NFM | Worksop | Tesco |
| 453.5875 | 460.0875 | NFM | Newcastle | Data Link |
| 453.6000 | 460.1000 | NFM | Bristol | Debenhams Security |
| | | NFM | Coventry | Shops Radio Link to Police |
| | | NFM | Cowley | Rover Assembly |
| | | NFM | Humberside | County Council |
| | | NFM | London | Australian High Commission |
| | | NFM | London (Gatwick) | Ground Repeater |
| | | NFM | London (Heathrow) | Airline & BAA Ops |
| | | NFM | London, Picadilly | Regent Palace Hotel |
| | | NFM | Newport | Godings Steel Holdings |
| | | NFM | North Sea | Amoco N W Hutton |
| 453.6000 | 453.6000 | NFM | North Sea | Texaco Tartan |

| Base | Mobile | Mode | Location | User and Notes |
|------|--------|------|----------|----------------|
| 453.6000 | 460.1000 | NFM | Prestatyn | Ship Technicians |
|  |  | NFM | Stansted | Ground Repeater |
| 453.6250 | 460.1250 | NFM | Doncaster | Doncaster Cable |
|  |  | NFM | Immingham | Tioxide Chemicals |
|  |  | NFM | Jersey | British Airways Handling |
|  |  | NFM | London, Trocadero | Funland |
|  |  | NFM | Milford Haven | Refinery |
|  |  | NFM | North Sea | Chevron Alba FSU General Ops. |
|  |  | NFM | Swansea Docks | Cargo Handlers |
| 453.6500 | 460.1500 | NFM | Edinburgh | Lothian Regional Transport |
|  |  | NFM | Leicester | Fosse Park Car Park Security |
|  |  | NFM | London (Heathrow) | Airline & BAA Ops |
|  |  | NFM | London, Southbank | LWT security |
|  |  | NFM | Newmarket | Race course security |
|  |  | NFM | Newport | Godings Workers Handhelds |
| 453.6500 | 453.6500 | NFM | North Sea | Shell Leman AK |
| 453.6500 | 453.6500 | NFM | North Sea | Texaco Tartan |
| 453.6500 | 460.1500 | NFM | York | Refuse collection |
|  |  | NFM | York | York Council Car Parks |
| 453.6750 | 460.1750 | NFM | Bletchley | Leisure Centre |
|  |  | NFM | Edinburgh | Lothian Regional Transport |
|  |  | NFM | Liverpool | Stanlow Oil Refinery |
|  |  | NFM | London | Docklands Light Railway |
|  |  | NFM | Stallingbough | SCM |
| 453.7000 | 460.2000 | NFM | Bristol | Bristol Intercity (Security) |
|  |  | NFM | Coventry | Dunlop Security |
|  |  | NFM | Dover | Eastern Docks Port Ops |
|  |  | NFM | Hull | Kingston Upon Hull Corp. Trans. |
|  |  | NFM | London (Gatwick) | Airline & BAA Ops |
|  |  | NFM | Manchester Shaw | Aerial Company |
|  |  | NFM | Middlesborough | Cleveland Centre Security |
|  |  | NFM | Milton Keynes | John Lewis store |
|  |  | NFM | Newcastle | The Metro Centre Paging |
| 453.7000 | 453.7000 | NFM | North Sea | Alba Chevron FSU Crane Operations |
| 453.7000 | 460.2000 | NFM | North Sea | Chevron Ninian North |
|  |  | NFM | North Sea | Shell North Cormorant |
|  |  | NFM | Oldham | Austin Timber Security |
|  |  | NFM | Sheffield | Sheffield Wednesday FC stewards |
|  |  | NFM | Stockport | Merseybus Inspectors |
| 453.7125 | 453.7125 | NFM | Immingham | Conoco Oil Maintainance |
| 453.7250 | 460.7250 | NFM | Leicester | Shires Centre Surveillance |
| 453.7250 | 460.2250 | NFM | Manchester | Hospital porters |
|  |  | NFM | Morecambc Bay | BGE & P |
|  |  | NFM | North Sea | Alba Chevron ANP Production -Mobiles |
|  |  | NFM | North Sea | Chevron Ninian Central |
|  |  | NFM | Oldham | Royal Oldham Hospital |
|  |  | NFM | West Midlands | Engineering Town Planning |
| 453.7500 | 460.2500 | NFM | Aberdeen (Dyce Airport) | Staff |
|  |  | NFM | Bournemouth | Repeater |
|  |  | NFM | Brighton | American Express |
| 453.7500 | 453.7500 | NFM | Brighton | Conference Centre |
| 453.7500 | 460.2500 | NFM | Gloucestershire | Great Western Security |
|  |  | NFM | London (Gatwick) | Airline & BAA Ops |
|  |  | NFM | Manchester | Shopping Centre Security |
|  |  | NFM | Newport | Godings Security |
| 453.7500 | 459.5750 | NFM | North Sea | Amoco Bacton |

| Base | Mobile | Mode | Location | User and Notes |
|------|--------|------|----------|----------------|
| 453.7500 | 460.2500 | NFM | North Sea | Amoco Lomond |
| | | NFM | North Sea | Amoco NW Hutton |
| | | NFM | North Sea | Amoco North Everest |
| | | NFM | Oldham | The Spindlers Security |
| | | NFM | Wiltshire | Great Western Security |
| 453.7750 | 460.2750 | NFM | Birkenhead | Pyramid Shopping Centre Sec. |
| | | NFM | Cambridge | City Centre Security |
| | | NFM | Culham | UKAEA |
| | | NFM | Hatfield | Galleria Shopping Centre Sec. |
| | | NFM | Leicester | Fosse Park Shop Security |
| | | NFM | Liverpool | St Johns Shopping Centre Sec. |
| | | NFM | London, Gatwick | Ground Repeater |
| | | NFM | London, Heathrow | Ground Repeater |
| | | NFM | Newcastle Airport | Airline Ops |
| | | NFM | North Sea | Phillips Maureen telemetry |
| | | NFM | Northampton | C & A Security |
| | | NFM | Northampton | Debenhams Security |
| | | NFM | Northampton | Grosvenor Centre Security |
| | | NFM | Runcorn | Shopping Centre Security |
| | | NFM | Southampton | Hospital Transport Channel 2 |
| | | NFM | Stansted | Ground Repeater |
| 453.7750 | 453.7750 | NFM | Stansted | Light Railway |
| 453.8000 | 460.3000 | NFM | Brighton | Brighton & Hove Bus & Coach |
| | | NFM | Cheltenham | Regent Arcade Security |
| | | NFM | Coventry | Warwick University |
| | | NFM | Hull | City centre bases |
| | | NFM | London, Gatwick | Ground Repeater |
| | | NFM | London, Heathrow | Airline & BAA Ops |
| | | NFM | Maltby | Tarmac |
| | | NFM | Milford Haven | Refinery |
| | | NFM | Newmarket | The Jockey Club |
| 453.8000 | 453.8000 | NFM | North Sea | Amoco Lomond |
| 453.8000 | 460.3000 | NFM | North Sea | Amoco North Everest |
| | | NFM | North Sea | Chevron Ninian  South |
| | | NFM | North Sea | Shell Tem |
| 453.8250 | 460.3250 | NFM | Bury | Premier Cars |
| | | NFM | Doncaster | Frenchgate Centre |
| | | NFM | Ipswich | Cranfield Bros. |
| | | NFM | London | National Gallery |
| | | NFM | London (Heathrow) | Ground Repeater |
| | | NFM | New Holland | Howarth Timber |
| 453.8250 | 453.8250 | NFM | North Sea | Amoco Lomond |
| | | NFM | North Sea | Amoco North Everest |
| 453.8500 | 460.3500 | NFM | Aberdeen | Hospital |
| | | NFM | Bealieu | Motor Museum Security |
| | | NFM | Belfast | Ulsterbus |
| | | NFM | Bellingham | ICI |
| | | NFM | Brighton | Buses |
| | | FM | Cambridge | Collage Security |
| | | NFM | Hampshire | Buses |
| | | NFM | London, Gatwick | Ground Repeater |
| | | NFM | London, Heathrow | Ground Repeater |
| | | NFM | Luton Airport | Car Parks Channel 6 |
| | | NFM | Merseyside | Merseyside Electric |
| | | NFM | Newmarket | Security |
| | | NFM | Newport | Docks |

| Base | Mobile | Mode | Location | User and Notes |
|---|---|---|---|---|
| 453.8500 | 460.3500 | NFM | Norfolk | Norwich & Norfolk Hospital |
| | | NFM | North Sea | BP Forties E |
| | | NFM | Rochdale | Queensway Private Hire |
| | | NFM | Sheffield | Forge Alert Security |
| | | NFM | Stansted | Catering |
| | | NFM | Wirral | Merseybus Inspectors |
| 453.8750 | 460.3750 | NFM | Aberdeen | Dyce Airport, Staff |
| | | NFM | Edinburgh | Lothian Regional Transport |
| | | NFM | London, Gatwick | Airline & BAA Ops |
| | | NFM | London, Heathrow | Airline & BAA Ops |
| | | NFM | Luton Airport | Monarch Airlines |
| | | NFM | Manchester | Freightliners Supervisors |
| | | NFM | North Sea | Chevron Alba Field Safety |
| | | NFM | North sea | Chevron Ninian Central |
| 453.9000 | 460.4000 | NFM | Ashford | Railtrack |
| | | NFM | Barry | Docks Security |
| | | NFM | Birmingham | Railtrack B'ham International |
| | | NFM | Derby | Railtrack |
| | | NFM | Doncaster | Railtrack |
| | | NFM | Edinburgh | ScotRail Haymarket Depot |
| | | NFM | Glasgow | ScotRail Glasgow Central |
| | | NFM | Guildford | Railtrack |
| | | NFM | Hoo Junction Deport | Railtrack |
| | | NFM | Hull | Railtrack Paragon Signal Box |
| | | NFM | Killingholme | Railtrack/Oil Refineries |
| | | NFM | Liverpool | Railtrack Liverpool Lime Street |
| | | NFM | London | Railtrack (Barking) |
| | | NFM | London | Railtrack (Charing Cross) |
| | | NFM | London | Railtrack (Euston) |
| | | NFM | London | Railtrack (Gatwick Airport) |
| | | NFM | London | Railtrack (Kings Cross) |
| | | NFM | London | Railtrack (Victoria) |
| | | NFM | London | Railtrack (Waterloo City) |
| | | NFM | London | Railtrack (Willesden Yard) |
| | | NFM | Manchester | Railtrack (Heaton Depot) |
| | | NFM | Nationwide | Railtrack Stations |
| | | NFM | Newport | Railtrack Porters |
| 453.9000 | 453.9000 | NFM | North Sea | Shell Cormorant A |
| 453.9000 | 460.4000 | NFM | Norwich | Railtrack (Norwich Crown Point) |
| | | NFM | Nottingham | Railtrack |
| | | NFM | Perth | ScotRail |
| | | NFM | Peterborough | Railtrack |
| | | NFM | Ramsgate | Railtrack Station & Depot |
| | | NFM | Reading | Railtrack |
| | | NFM | Sheffield | Railtrack Tensley Hill marshalling yard |
| | | NFM | Thames | RailtrackTurbo Workshop |
| | | NFM | Watford | Railtrack (Watford Junction) |
| 453.9175 | 460.4175 | NFM | Machynlleth | Railtrack |
| 453.9250 | 460.4250 | NFM | County Durham | Security Firm |
| | | NFM | Edinburgh | Ambulance Service |
| | | NFM | Leicester | Shires Centre Security Channel 1 |
| | | NFM | London | Docklands Light Railway |
| | | NFM | London, Gatwick | Airline & BAA Ops |
| | | NFM | London, Heathrow | Airline & BAA Ops |
| | | NFM | Milford Haven | Refinery |
| | | NFM | Newport | Patent Office Security |

| Base | Mobile | Mode | Location | User and Notes |
|------|--------|------|----------|----------------|
| 453.9250 | 460.4250 | NFM | North Sea | BP Forties E |
| | | NFM | Stansted | Loading |
| | | NFM | Swindon | Austin Rover Security |
| 453.9375 | 460.4375 | NFM | Edinburgh | ScotRail Data Links |
| | | NFM | Glasgow | ScotRail Data Links |
| | | NFM | Perth | ScotRail Data Links |
| 453.9500 | 460.4500 | NFM | Immingham | Conoco Oil Refinery |
| | | NFM | Newport | Spencer & Llanwern Docks |
| | | NFM | North Sea | Chevron Alba ANP Maintenance |
| | | NFM | North Sea | Chevron Ninian Central |
| | | NFM | North Sea | Marathon Brae North |
| 453.9625 | 460.5625 | NFM | London | London Taxis |
| 453.9750 | 460.4750 | NFM | Barrow in Furness | Taxi |
| | | NFM | Bath | University Security |
| | | NFM | Cowley | Rover Security Channel 7 |
| | | NFM | Kingston Upon Thames | Parking Wardens control |
| | | NFM | Leicester | Road Contractors |
| | | NFM | Liverpool | John Moore University Security |
| | | NFM | London | Kodak |
| | | NFM | London (Heathrow) | Airline & BAA Ops |
| | | NFM | Luton | Vauxhall Motors |
| | | NFM | North Sea | BP Forties E |

## 454.0125 - 454.8375 MHz   PRIVATE RADIO PAGING SYSTEMS 25 kHz

| Base | Mobile | Mode | Location | User and Notes |
|------|--------|------|----------|----------------|
| 454.0250 | | NFM | Birmingham | Heartlands Nursing |
| | | NFM | Birmingham | Police |
| | | NFM | Birmingham | QE Hospital Pagers |
| | | NFM | London | US Embassy |
| | | NFM | Nationwide | Hospital Voice Paging |
| | | NFM | Newcastle | Hospital Emerg. Voice Paging |
| | | NFM | Ninian North | Chevron |
| | | NFM | North Sea | Elf Enterprise Claymore A |
| | | NFM | North Sea | Elf Enterprise Piper |
| 454.0500 | | NFM | North Sea | Chevron Ninian North |
| | | NFM | North Sea | Elf Enterprise Claymore A |
| | | NFM | North Sea | Elf Enterprise Piper |
| 454.0750 | | NFM | London | Kings College Hospital voice pagers |
| 454.0750 | 447.5750 | NFM | Nationwide | Aircall Voice Paging |
| 454.0750 | | NFM | North Sea | Amoco Bacton Paging System |
| 454.1000 | | NFM | Birmingham | Hospital Paging |
| | | NFM | Manchester | Hospital Pager |
| | | NFM | North Sea | Shell Brent B |
| | | NFM | Whiston | Hospital Voice Paging |
| 454.1250 | | NFM | North Sea | Chevron Ninian North |
| | | NFM | North Sea | Elf Enterprise Claymore A |
| | | NFM | North Sea | Elf Enterprise Piper |
| 454.1625 | | NFM | North Sea | Chevron Ninian Central |
| 454.1750 | | NFM | Cambridge | Addenbrookes Hospital Paging |
| | | NFM | Leeds | General Infirmary voice pager |
| | | NFM | Leeds, Killinbeck | Pager Calls |
| | | NFM | Nationwide | Hospital Voice Paging |
| | | NFM | Newcastle | Hospital Emerg. Voice Paging |
| | | NFM | Ninian South | Chevron |
| | | NFM | Sheffield | Royal Hallamshire Hospital Pager |
| | | NFM | Stevenage | Lister Hospital Pagers |

| Base | Mobile | Mode | Location | User and Notes |
|------|--------|------|----------|----------------|
| 454.2000 | | NFM | Derbyshire | Centracom Doctors Paging |
| | | NFM | Manchester | Hospital Pager |
| | | NFM | Nationwide | Medical Pagers |
| 454.2500 | | NFM | Milton Keynes | Hospital Pagers |
| 454.2750 | | NFM | North Sea | Alba Chevron ANP West Crane |
| | | NFM | North Sea | Chevron Ninian South |
| | | NFM | North Sea | Elf Enterprise Claymore A |
| | | NFM | North Sea | Elf Enterprise Piper |
| 454.3000 | | NFM | Edinburgh Airport | Radiopagers Channel 9 |
| | | NFM | Leicester | Mosque |
| | | NFM | Merseyside | Hospital Voice Pagers |
| 454.3120 | | NFM | Manchester Shaw | Doctors |
| 454.3125 | 459.3125 | NFM | Castle Donington | Grand Prix Team |
| | | NFM | Nationwide | Ligier Formula One Team |
| 454.3250 | | NFM | Basildon | Hospital Data/Paging |
| 454.3250 | | NFM | County Durham | Hospital Emerg. Voice Paging |
| | | NFM | North Sea | Elf Enterprise Claymore A |
| | | NFM | North Sea | Elf Enterprise Piper |
| | | NFM | Oxford | Medical Paging |
| 454.3500 | | NFM | North Sea | Chevron Ninian Central |
| 454.3750 | | NFM | Jersey | King Street Department Store |
| 454.4000 | | NFM | London (Gatwick) | Airline & BAA Ops |
| 454.4000 | 468.4000 | NFM | North Sea | BP Forties A |
| 454.4000 | 454.4000 | NFM | North Sea | Chevron Alba ANP Drilling |
| | | NFM | North Sea | Chevron Ninian South |
| 454.4250 | | NFM | North Sea | Chevron Ninian Central |
| 454.4500 | | NFM | Coventry | Council |
| | | NFM | North Sea | Elf Enterprise Claymore A |
| | | NFM | North Sea | Elf Enterprise Piper |
| 454.4750 | 468.4250 | NFM | Anglia | Anglia TV O/B |
| 454.4750 | | NFM | Southampton | AirCall Pagers |
| 454.5000 | | NFM | Nationwide | UK Atomic Energy Authority |
| 454.5250 | 468.5250 | NFM | Anglia | Anglia TV O/B |
| 454.5500 | | NFM | London | Taxis |
| 454.5750 | | NFM | Guernsey | HM Customs & Excise |
| 454.5750 | 460.0750 | NFM | North Sea | BP Magnus |
| 454.6250 | | NFM | Newport | Royal Gwent Hospital Pagers |
| 454.6750 | | NFM | Nationwide | Hutchison Paging |
| | | NFM | Nationwide | Millicomm Paging |
| 454.6875 | | NFM | London, Heathrow | Airline & BAA Ops |
| 454.7000 | | NFM | Bromley | Bromley Health Pagers |
| 454.7500 | | NFM | Birmingham | Police |
| | | NFM | Jersey Airport | British Airways |
| 454.7750 | | NFM | Hull | Air Call Paging |
| | | NFM | Nationwide | AirCall Paging |
| 454.8000 | | NFM | Southampton | Meridian Pagers |
| 454.8250 | | NFM | Machynlleth | Hospital Paging |
| | | NFM | Nationwide | Page Boy Paging |
| 454.8500 | | NFM | Glasgow | Paging |

| Base | Mobile | Mode | Location | User and Notes |
|------|--------|------|----------|----------------|

454.8375 - 454.9875 MHZ    LIMITED MOD & PMR ALLOACTIONS

| Base | Mobile | Mode | Location | User and Notes |
|------|--------|------|----------|----------------|
| 454.8500 | | NFM | London | Railtrack Operations (Wimbledon) |
| | | NFM | Stevenage | Railtrack Operations |
| 454.8750 | | NFM | Baldock | Railtrack Operations |
| 454.8875 | | NFM | Bishopton | Railtrack Operations |
| | | NFM | Gidea Park | Railtrack Operations |
| | | NFM | Liverpool | Railtrack Operations |
| | | NFM | London | Railtrack Operations (Waterloo) |
| | | NFM | Reedham | Railtrack Operations |
| 454.9000 | | NFM | London | Railtrack Operations (Alexandra Palace) |
| | | NFM | London | Railtrack Operations (Stratford) |
| | | NFM | Selhurst | Railtrack Operations |
| 454.9250 | | NFM | Hitchin | Railtrack Operations |
| | | NFM | Threebridges | Railtrack Operations |
| 454.9375 | | NFM | Motherwell | Railtrack Operations |
| | | NFM | Threebridges | Railtrack Operations |
| 454.9500 | | NFM | Burgess Hill | Railtrack Operations |
| 454.9625 | | NFM | London | Railtrack Operations (Victoria) |
| | | NFM | Motherwell | Railtrack Operations |
| 454.9750 | | NFM | Jordanhill | Railtrack Operations |
| 454.9750 | | NFM | Letchworth | Railtrack Operations |
| | | NFM | London | Railtrack Operations (Victoria) |
| | | NFM | Redhill | Railtrack Operations |
| 454.9875 | | NFM | Motherwell | Railtrack Operations |
| | | NFM | Stoke On Trent | Stoke City Video Surveillance |
| 454.9925 | | NFM | Edinburgh | Grampian TV O/B Talkback |
| | | NFM | Glasgow | Grampian TV O/B Talkback |
| | | NFM | Perth | Grampian TV O/B Talkback |
| 454.9935 | | NFM | East Anglia | Anglia TV Talkback |
| | | NFM | Nationwide | ITV O/B |
| 454.9950 | | NFM | Liverpool | Granada TV Talkback |

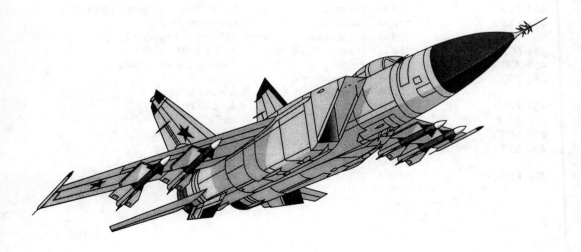

| Base | Mobile | Mode | Location | User and Notes |
|------|--------|------|----------|----------------|

| Base | Mobile | Mode | Location | User and Notes |

**455.0000 - 467.7500 MHz   IRISH POLICE BASE 25kHz**

| Base | Mobile | Mode | Location | User and Notes |
|------|--------|------|----------|----------------|
| 455.0000 | 469.0000 | NFM | Dublin | Police O |
| 455.0250 | 469.0250 | NFM | Dublin | Police O |
| 455.0500 | 469.0500 | NFM | Dublin | Police O |
| 455.0750 | 469.0750 | NFM | Dublin | Police O |
| 455.1000 | 469.1000 | NFM | Dublin | Police O |
| 455.1250 | 469.1250 | NFM | Dublin | Police T (Traffic) |
| 455.1500 | 469.1500 | NFM | Dublin | Police T (Traffic) |
| 455.1750 | 469.1750 | NFM | Dublin | Police W |
| 455.2000 | 469.2000 | NFM | Dublin | Police N |
| 455.2250 | 469.2250 | NFM | Dublin | Police F |
| 455.2500 | 469.2500 | NFM | Dublin | Police F |
| 455.2750 | 469.2750 | NFM | Dublin | Police P |
| 455.3000 | 469.3000 | NFM | Dublin | Police M |
| 455.3250 | | NFM | Dublin | Police L/B/A |
| 455.3500 | | NFM | Dublin | Police G |
| 455.3750 | | NFM | Dublin | Police G |
| 455.4000 | 469.4000 | NFM | Dublin | Police E |
| 455.4250 | | NFM | Dublin | Police A |
| 455.4500 | | NFM | Dublin | Police B |
| 455.4750 | 469.4750 | NFM | Dublin | Police B |
| 455.5000 | 469.5000 | NFM | Dublin | Police J |
| 455.5250 | 469.5250 | NFM | Dublin | Police R |
| 455.5500 | 469.5500 | NFM | Dublin | Police K |
| 455.5750 | 469.5750 | NFM | Dublin | Police H |
| 455.6000 | 469.6000 | NFM | Dublin | Police H |
| 455.6250 | 469.6250 | NFM | Dublin | Police C |
| 455.6500 | 469.6500 | NFM | Dublin | Police U |
| 455.6750 | 469.6750 | NFM | Dublin | Police D |
| 455.7250 | 469.7250 | NFM | Dublin | Police W/N/T |
| 455.7500 | 469.7500 | NFM | Dublin | Police D/U/C |
| 455.7750 | 469.7750 | NFM | Dublin | Police R/H/J/K |
| 455.8000 | 469.8000 | NFM | Dublin | Police E/B/A |
| 455.8250 | 469.8250 | NFM | Dublin | Police L/M/G/P |

**455.0000 - 455.4500 MHz   BBC TV O/B TALKBACK AND FORMULA ONE RACING**

| Base | Mobile | Mode | Location | User and Notes |
|------|--------|------|----------|----------------|
| 455.00000 | | WFM | Nationwide | Central TV O/B |
| | | NFM | Southampton | Meridian TV O/B |
| 455.01250 | 468.05000 | NFM | Jersey | Channel TV O/B |
| 455.01250 | | NFM | Nationwide | Ozi TV O/B |
| | | NFM | Wales | S4C O/B Unit |
| 455.02500 | | WFM | Nationwide | Central TV O/B |
| 455.03125 | | NFM | London | Independent TV Talkback |
| 455.06250 | | NFM | Dorset | 2CR Eye-In-The-Sky |
| | | NFM | London | BBC South East |
| | | NFM | Southampton | Ocean Sound Helicopter |
| | | NFM | Stoke on Trent | Signal Radio O/B Link |
| 455.07500 | | NFM | London | Capital Radio Flying Eye |
| 455.09400 | | WFM | Nationwide | CTV Outside Broadcast |
| 455.10000 | | NFM | Nottingham | BBC Radio Nottingham |
| 455.10625 | | WFM | London | BBC-TV London Marathon |

| Base | Mobile | Mode | Location | User and Notes |
|------|--------|------|----------|----------------|
| 455.12500 | 468.39000 | NFM | Jersey | Channel TV O/B |
| 455.12500 | | NFM | Liverpool | Granada TV Talkback |
| 455.13200 | | NFM | Edinburgh | Grampian TV O/B Talkback |
| | | NFM | Glasgow | Grampian TV O/B Talkback |
| | | WFM | Perth | Grampian TV O/B Talkback |
| 455.13260 | | NFM | Nationwide | BBC TV Sports Commentary |
| 455.13750 | | WFM | Nationwide | Central TV Outside Broadcast |
| | | NFM | Newcastle Airport | Stores |
| 455.15000 | | NFM | Anglia | Anglia TV Studio Producer |
| | | NFM | Manchester | Piccadilly Eye in the Sky |
| 455.16250 | | NFM | Birmingham | 96.4 FM BRMB Radio Talkback |
| | | NFM | Birmingham | 96.4 FM BRMB/Extra AM Flying Eye |
| | | NFM | Dorset | 2CR Outside Broadcast Feeder |
| | | NFM | London | BBC South East |
| | | NFM | Manchester | Radio Piccadilly Eye In Sky |
| | | NFM | Milton Keynes | Chilton Radio OB |
| | | NFM | Oxfordshire | Chilton Radio Heli Traffic Reports |
| | | NFM | Stoke on Trent | Signal Radio O/B Link |
| 455.18750 | | NFM | Stoke on Trent | Stock City O/B Microphones |
| 455.20000 | | WFM | Nationwide | Central TV O/B |
| | | NFM | Nationwide | Radio Investigations Service |
| | | NFM | Newmarket | Channel 4 Racing O/B |
| 455.22500 | | NFM | Burnley | Granada TV OB |
| | | NFM | Manchester | ITN O/B Studio Link |
| | | WFM | Nationwide | Central TV O/B |
| | | NFM | Nationwide | Radio Investigations Service |
| | | NFM | Newmarket | Channel 4 Racing O/B |
| 455.23500 | | NFM | Grand Prix Circuits | Ferrari Team Voice Link |
| 455.23750 | | NFM | Nuneaton | George Elliot Hosp. Crash Pager |
| 455.24000 | | WFM | Leicester | BBC East Midlands O/B |
| 455.24370 | 468.16870 | NFM | Belfry (Ryder Cup) | BBC TV OB |
| 455.24500 | | NFM | Birmingham | ITV camera crew |
| 455.25000 | | NFM | Nationwide | Radio Investigations Service |
| 455.25620 | 468.19370 | NFM | Nationwide | BBC TV O/B Talkback |
| 455.26870 | | WFM | London | BBC TV London Marathon |
| 455.28000 | | WFM | Leicester | BBC East Midlands O/B |
| | | WFM | Portsmouth | BBC1 OB |
| 455.28120 | 468.29370 | NFM | Belfry (Ryder Cup) | BBC TV |
| 455.28500 | | NFM | Edinburgh | BBC Scotland O/B |
| | | NFM | Glasgow | BBC Scotland O/B |
| | | WFM | Perth | BBC Scotland O/B |
| 455.28750 | | NFM | Goodwood | BBC Glorious Goodwood OB |
| 455.31000 | | NFM | Blyth | O/B Football (Saturdays) |
| 455.31200 | | WFM | Salisbury | BBC Wiltshire Sound |
| 455.31250 | | NFM | Belfry (Ryder Cup) | BBC Radio 5 |
| | | WFM | Jersey | BBC Jersey O/B |
| 455.31250 | 455.31250 | NFM | Nationwide | BBC Radio 1 O/B |
| 455.31250 | 469.11250 | WFM | Salisbury | BBC Wiltshire Sound |
| 455.36250 | | NFM | Belfry (Ryder Cup) | BBC Radio 5 |
| | | NFM | Bristol | Radio Bristol (O) |
| | | NFM | Carlisle | BBC Radio Cumbria OB |
| | | WFM | Jersey | BBC Jersey O/B |
| 455.36250 | 455.36250 | NFM | Nationwide | BBC Radio 1 O/B |

| Base | Mobile | Mode | Location | User and Notes |
|---|---|---|---|---|
| 455.36500 | | WFM | Hampshire | BBC Radio Solent Radio Car |
| 455.37500 | | NFM | USAF Fairford | IAT Emergency Control |
| 455.39370 | | NFM | Belfry (Ryder Cup) | BBC TV |
| | | NFM | Nationwide | BBC TV O/B Talkback |
| 455.40000 | | NFM | Farnborough | BBC Talkback (RAE Airfield) |
| 455.41870 | | NFM | Belfry (Ryder Cup) | BBC TV |
| 455.42500 | | NFM | Cumbria, south | Data Link |
| 455.43120 | | NFM | Belfry (Ryder Cup) | BBC TV |
| 455.43750 | 455.43750 | NFM | Preston | Radio Lancashire O/B |
| 455.44500 | | NFM | Leicester | Radio Leicester O/B Channel 2 |
| 455.45000 | | NFM | Irvine | Police U A Div Pocket Phone |
| 455.46250 | 469.90000 | NFM | London | BBC Eastenders Production |

### 455.46875 - 455.85625 MHz     PMR AIRPORT SECURITY AND GROUND REPEATERS

| Base | Mobile | Mode | Location | User and Notes |
|---|---|---|---|---|
| 455.4750 | 460.7750 | NFM | Birmingham International | Ground Staff |
| | | NFM | London, Gatwick | Tower Rebroadcast |
| | | NFM | Woodford Airfield | Crash Ops |
| 455.4875 | 461.7875 | NFM | Bournemouth (Hurn) | Tower Repeater |
| | | NFM | East Midlands Airport | Ground |
| | | NFM | Liverpool Airport | Apron Supervisor |
| | | NFM | London (Heathrow) | Police Armed (Hunter Delta) |
| 455.5000 | | NFM | Guernsey | Tower Rebroadcast |
| 455.5000 | 460.8000 | NFM | USAF Fairford | IAT Medical Control |
| 455.5125 | | NFM | Cranfield Airport | Fire Services |
| | | NFM | Duxford | Data Link |
| | | NFM | Glasgow | BT Police (BX) |
| 455.5125 | 455.5125 | NFM | Nationwide | Transport Police (Bravo Xray) |
| 455.5250 | 460.8250 | NFM | Bristol Airport | HM Customs & Excise |
| 455.5250 | 461.1750 | NFM | Cranfield Airfield | Fire & Security |
| | | NFM | East Midlands Airport | Fire Service |
| | | NFM | London (Heathrow) | Tower Rebroadcast (118.50MHz AM rebroadcast) |
| | | NFM | Manchester Airport | Ops 3 |
| | | NFM | Nationwide | Airport Customs |
| 455.5250 | 455.5250 | NFM | Nationwide | HM Customs & Excise |
| 455.5375 | 460.5375 | NFM | Birmingham International | Ground Control |
| | | NFM | London Bridge | BR Driver Only Operation |
| | | NFM | Luton Airport | Maintenance |
| | | NFM | USAF Fairford | IAT |
| 455.5500 | 461.8500 | NFM | Doncaster | Parking Meter Attendants |
| | | NFM | Leeds Airport | Security/Fire |
| | | NFM | London, Heathrow | Ground Repeater (121.9 MHz AM rebroadcast) |
| | | NFM | Manchester Airport | Tower Repeater |
| 455.5500 | 461.2000 | NFM | Stansted | Ground Rebroadcast/Tower Repeater |
| 455.5625 | 455.5625 | NFM | Stansted | Crash Vehicles |
| 455.5750 | 461.2250 | NFM | BAe Woodford | Tower Link |
| 455.5750 | | NFM | Birmingham International | Fire |
| | | NFM | London (Heathrow) | Passport Control |
| | | NFM | USAF Fairford | IAT Barriers |
| | | NFM | Various Airports | Fire Services |
| | | NFM | Woodford Airfield | Tower-Ground |

| Base | Mobile | Mode | Location | User and Notes |
|------|--------|------|----------|----------------|
| 455.5875 | | NFM | Liverpool | Railtrack Operations |
| | | NFM | Wimbeldon | Railtrack Operations |
| 455.6000 | 455.6000 | NFM | Blackpool | Ground |
| 455.6000 | 460.9000 | NFM | East Midlands Airport | Terminal Security |
| 455.6000 | | NFM | Filton (BAe), Bristol | Security |
| | | NFM | Jersey Aiport | Securicor |
| | | NFM | London, Gatwick | Airline & BAA Ops |
| 455.6000 | 469.0000 | NFM | North Sea | BP Forties C |
| 455.6125 | | NFM | Leeds Bradford Airport | Ground Staff/Fire |
| 455.6125 | 461.9125 | NFM | London (Heathrow) | Ground |
| 455.6125 | | NFM | USAF Fairford | IAT |
| 455.6250 | | NFM | Glasgow | Cargo Handlers |
| | | NFM | Jersey | Airport Ground |
| 455.6250 | 460.9250 | NFM | Nationwide | Red Devil Parachute Team |
| 455.6250 | | NFM | Prestwick Airport | Ground Ops Link |
| 455.6375 | 460.9375 | NFM | Liverpool Airport | Ground Movement Control |
| 455.6375 | | NFM | London (Gatwick) | Crash Ops |
| | | NFM | London (Heathrow) | Airline & BAA Ops |
| | | NFM | Luton Airport | Crash Ops Channel 2 |
| | | NFM | Stansted | Maintenance |
| | | NFM | USAF Fairford | IAT Transport Control |
| 455.6500 | 460.8500 | NFM | Birmingham International | Airway Crossing/Security |
| 455.6500 | | NFM | London (Heathrow) | Fire Service |
| | | NFM | Manchester Airport | Ground Repeater |
| | | NFM | MoD Airfields | Fire Control |
| | | NFM | Newcastle Airport | Grass Cutting |
| | | NFM | Stansted | Crash Ops |
| | | NFM | USAF Fairford | IAT Fire Control |
| 455.6750 | 455.6750 | NFM | Norwich | HM Customs & Excise |
| 455.6875 | 460.9875 | NFM | Ronaldsway Airport | Tower-Ground |
| 455.7000 | 461.0000 | NFM | Birmingham International | Apron Channel 4 |
| 455.7000 | | NFM | Bournemouth (Hurn) | Ground Services |
| | | NFM | Cardiff | Airport Security |
| | | NFM | Edinburgh Airport | Channel 5/25 |
| | | NFM | Hawarden Airfield | Ground |
| | | NFM | London, Heathrow | Tower Rebroadcast |
| | | NFM | London,Gatwick | BAA Ops |
| | | NFM | USAF Fairford | IAT Engineering |
| 455.7125 | | NFM | East Midlands Airport | Fire Service |
| | | NFM | London, Docklands | Ground Control |
| | | NFM | London, Heathrow | Weather Information Relay |
| | | NFM | Manchester Airport | Ground Handling |
| 455.7250 | | NFM | Edinburgh Airport | Channel 23 |
| 455.7250 | 461.0250 | NFM | Edinburgh Airport | Channel 3 |
| 455.7250 | 461.0250 | NFM | London, Heathrow | Police Armed (Hunter Whiskey) |
| | | NFM | Nationwide | Airport Tower Rebroadcasts |
| | | NFM | Woodford Airfield | Fuel & Maintenance |
| 455.7375 | 461.0375 | NFM | Coventry Airport | Ground Ops |
| | | NFM | London (Gatwick) | BAA Ops |
| | | NFM | Manchester Airport | Coach Ops |
| | | NFM | Newcastle Airport | Tower Repeater |
| | | NFM | RAE Farnborough | Maintenance/Fuel |
| | | NFM | USAF Fairford | IAT Speedbird |
| 455.7500 | 461.0500 | NFM | Newcastle Airport | Tower Repeater |

| Base | Mobile | Mode | Location | User and Notes |
|------|--------|------|----------|----------------|
| 455.7625 | 461.0625 | NFM | Birmingham International | Ground Staff |
| | | NFM | Liverpool Airport | Security |
| | | NFM | USAF Fairford | IAT (Zodiac Base) |
| 455.7750 | 461.0750 | NFM | Edinburgh Airport | Channel 2/22 |
| | | NFM | London, Gatwick | Ground Control Link |
| | | NFM | London, Heathrow | Police Armed (Hunter Whiskey) |
| 455.7750 | 455.7750 | NFM | Nationwide | HM Customs (Airports) |
| 455.7875 | | NFM | Manchester Airport | Car Park Security |
| 455.8000 | 461.1000 | NFM | Birmingham International | Baggage Handlers |
| | | NFM | USAF Fairford | IAT Emergency Control |
| | | NFM | Weston-super-Mare | Airport Security |
| 455.8125 | 461.1125 | NFM | Aberdeen (Dyce Airport) | Ground |
| | | NFM | Edinburgh Airport | PMR Channel 4 |
| | | NFM | London, Heathrow | Seagull & Checker |
| | | NFM | Manchester Airport | Ground Handling |
| | | NFM | Newcastle Airport | Baggage Handling |
| | | NFM | Stansted | Security Ops |
| 455.8250 | 461.1250 | NFM | Birmingham International | Maglev |
| | | NFM | Birmingham International | Maintenance |
| | | NFM | East Midlands Airport | Maintenance |
| | | NFM | London, Gatwick | Data |
| | | NFM | Luton Airport | Ground Movements Ch1 |
| | | NFM | Luton Airport | MacAlpine Aviation |
| | | NFM | Luton Airport | Magec Ops |
| | | NFM | Nationwide | HM Customs (Airport) |
| | | NFM | Stansted | Tower |
| | | NFM | USAF Fairford | IAT Message Centre |
| 455.8375 | 461.1375 | NFM | Edinburgh Airport | PMR Channel 1 |
| | | NFM | Glasgow | Baggage Handlers |
| | | NFM | Liverpool Airport | Fire Control |
| | | NFM | Lydd Airfield | Ground Repeater |
| 455.8500 | 455.8500 | NFM | Nationwide | HM Customs (Airport) |
| 455.8500 | 461.1500 | NFM | London (Gatwick) | Baggage Handlers |
| | | NFM | USAF Fairford | IAT Security Control |
| | | NFM | Woodford Airfield | VIP & Crew Bus |

**455.8750 - 456.0000 MHz    EMERGENCY SERVICES 12.5 kHz NFM**

| Base | Mobile | Mode | Location | User and Notes |
|------|--------|------|----------|----------------|
| 455.8750 | 461.1750 | NFM | London (Heathrow) | Approach |
| 455.9250 | | NFM | London (Heathrow) | Airline & BAA Ops |
| 455.9875 | 455.9875 | NFM | Edinburgh | Fire Brigade |
| | | NFM | Fife | Fire Brigade Channel 7 |
| | | NFM | Glasgow | Fire Brigade |
| | | NFM | Leeds | Fire/Police Inter Agency |
| | | NFM | London, Heathrow | Airline & BAA Ops |
| | | NFM | Nationwide | Airfield Fire Channel 7 |
| 455.9875 | 455.9875 | NFM | Nationwide | Airfield Fire Channel 8 |

**456.0000 - 457.0000 MHz    PMR 12.5 kHz (SPLIT + 5.5 MHz)**
**FORMULA ONE RACING TEAM LINKS**

| Base | Mobile | Mode | Location | User and Notes |
|------|--------|------|----------|----------------|
| 455.9875 | 456.0000 | NFM | Jersey | Securicor Handhelds |
| 455.9875 | 462.5375 | NFM | Nationwide | Interagency Liaison |
| 455.9875 | 461.4875 | NFM | Southampton | Securicor |
| | | NFM | St. Fergus | Shell |
| | | NFM | West Yorkshire | Fire/Police Inter Agency |

| Base | Mobile | Mode | Location | User and Notes |
|---|---|---|---|---|
| 456.0250 | 461.5250 | NFM | Birmingham, Solihull | Land Rover Security |
| | | NFM | Blackpool | Spectrum Security |
| | | NFM | Dover | Docks security |
| | | NFM | Immingham | DFDS Transport |
| | | NFM | London | Hamley's Toy Shop Security |
| | | NFM | London, Gatwick | Security |
| | | NFM | London, Heathrow | Ground Repeater |
| | | NFM | London, Queensway | Whiteley Shopping Centre security |
| | | NFM | Luton | Vauxhall Motors |
| | | NFM | Manchester | Airport Ground Services |
| | | NFM | Middlesborough | ICI Leaks |
| | | NFM | Nottingham | Streamline Taxis |
| | | NFM | Stansted | Aviation Traders |
| | | NFM | Swansea City | Quadrant Shopping Centre Security |
| | | NFM | West Midlands | Fire Alarms |
| 456.0375 | 461.0375 | NFM | Oldham | Delivery Company |
| 456.0375 | 461.0375 | NFM | Stansted | Air UK Flight Despatch |
| 456.0500 | 456.0500 | NFM | Birmingham | Flightlink Coaches |
| | | NFM | Blackpool | Trams |
| | | NFM | Bristol | UKAEA Power Station Security |
| | | NFM | Grays Thurrock | Council Refuse Collection |
| | | NFM | London, Heathrow | Airline & BAA Ops |
| | | NFM | Maidstone | Shop Watch Scheme |
| | | NFM | North Sea | BGE&P Rough A |
| | | NFM | North Sea | Marathon Brae South |
| | | NFM | North Sea | Shell Brent D |
| | | NFM | North Sea | Shell N. Cormorant |
| | | NFM | Sheffield | Meadowhall Centre |
| | | NFM | York | Council car parks |
| 456.0625 | 461.0625 | NFM | London, Heathrow | Airline & BAA Ops |
| 456.0750 | 461.5750 | NFM | Belfast | City Hospital Security |
| | | NFM | London, Heathrow | Airline & BAA Ops |
| 456.0875 | 461.5875 | NFM | Jersey | Airport Ground Services |
| 456.0875 | 461.5875 | NFM | Leiston | Sizewell A Security |
| | | NFM | Nationwide | National Power |
| 456.1000 | 461.6000 | NFM | London, Heathrow | Airline & BAA Ops |
| 456.1000 | | NFM | Manchester Airport | Tugs |
| 456.1000 | | NFM | North Sea | BGE&P Rough A |
| 456.1000 | | NFM | North Sea | Marathon Brae S |
| 456.1000 | | NFM | Southampton | National Power |
| 456.1125 | 461.6125 | NFM | Barrow in Furness | Gas Terminal Maintenance |
| 456.1250 | 461.6250 | NFM | Birmingham | City Council |
| | | NFM | Cemaes Bay | Wylfa Power Station |
| | | NFM | Edinburgh | Scottish Hydro Electric |
| | | NFM | Edinburgh | United Artist Cable Layers |
| | | NFM | Leiston | Sizewell Power Station |
| | | NFM | London | Trunked Network |
| | | NFM | North Sea | BP Sulair Magnus |
| | | NFM | Salford | Hospital Trust Managers. |
| | | NFM | The Port of Heysham | Isle of Man Steam Packet |
| 456.1375 | 461.6375 | NFM | London | Vediotron Ltd |
| | | NFM | Newcastle Airport | Stores Department |
| 456.1500 | 461.6500 | NFM | London | London Electric |
| | | NFM | Manchester | Sub Station Audio Alarm |
| 456.1525 | 456.1525 | NFM | Dover | Harbour security |
| 456.1625 | 461.6625 | NFM | London | Victoria Coach Station |

| Base | Mobile | Mode | Location | User and Notes |
|------|--------|------|----------|----------------|
| 456.1750 | 461.6750 | NFM | Alwyn | Total |
| | | NFM | Calverton | National Coal Board |
| | | NFM | Dungeness | Power Station |
| | | NFM | Heysham | Power Station |
| | | NFM | Nationwide | National Power Operations |
| | | NFM | Oldham | Pizza Delivery |
| 456.1875 | 461.6875 | NFM | Lichfield | Intruder Alert |
| | | NFM | London | Electricity Engineers |
| | | NFM | Morecambe | Voice Alarm |
| 456.2000 | 461.7000 | NFM | Belfast | City Bus Channel 1 |
| | | NFM | Berkeley | BNFL Command & Control |
| | | NFM | Leicester | British Gas Security |
| | | NFM | North Sea | Shell Auk |
| | | NFM | North Sea | Shell Brent A |
| | | NFM | North Sea | Shell Dunlin |
| 456.2125 | 461.7125 | NFM | London | Electricity Engineers |
| | | NFM | Surrey | Electricity Engineers |
| 456.2250 | 461.7250 | NFM | Leiston | Sizewell Power Station |
| | | NFM | Morecambe | Data Link |
| | | NFM | Nationwide | National Power Maintenance |
| | | NFM | North Sea | BGE&P Rough A |
| | | NFM | North Sea | Shell Dunfin |
| 456.2375 | 461.7375 | NFM | Coventry | Coal Authority |
| | | NFM | London | London Electric |
| 456.2500 | 461.7500 | NFM | Berkeley | BNFL Command & Control |
| | | NFM | Manchester | British Transport Police |
| 456.2625 | 461.7625 | NFM | Barrow in Furness | VSEL Test Engineers |
| | | NFM | Canvey Island | British Gas |
| | | NFM | London (Heathrow) | Airline & BAA Ops |
| 456.2750 | 461.7750 | NFM | Doncaster | Power Station |
| | | NFM | Dungeness | Power Station |
| | | NFM | London | London Electric |
| | | NFM | Nationwide | National Power Operations tones |
| | | NFM | North Sea | Shell Brent D |
| | | NFM | North Sea | Shell N Cormorant |
| 456.3000 | 461.8000 | NFM | Barrow in Furness | VSEL Security |
| | | NFM | Easington | British Gas Terminal |
| | | NFM | London (Heathrow) | Airline & BAA Ops |
| | | NFM | North Sea | Marathon Brae N |
| 456.3125 | 461.8125 | NFM | London | Eastern Electricity |
| 456.3250 | 461.8250 | NFM | Dungeness | Power Station |
| | | NFM | London (Heathrow) | General Purpose Channel |
| | | NFM | North Sea | Shell Brent B |
| | | NFM | North Sea | Shell Cormorant A |
| 456.3375 | 461.8375 | NFM | Nationwide | British Rail Transport Police |
| 456.3500 | 461.8500 | NFM | Aberdeen | City Buses |
| 456.3500 | 462.8500 | NFM | Billingham | ICI |
| | | NFM | Brighton | Royal Pavillion |
| | | NFM | Cheltenham | Water Company Engineering Dept |
| | | NFM | Eastbourne | City Buses |
| | | NFM | London | Brent Cross Shopping Centre storewatch scheme |
| | | NFM | London (Gatwick) | Cleaners & Cargo Loaders |
| | | NFM | London (Heathrow) | Airline & BAA Ops |
| | | NFM | Moray Firth | Beatrice Bravo Platform |
| | | NFM | North Sea | BP Beatrice B |

| Base | Mobile | Mode | Location | User and Notes |
|------|--------|------|----------|----------------|
| 456.3500 | 462.8500 | NFM | Nottingham | City Engineers |
| | | NFM | Reading | University campus security |
| | | NFM | Saltend | BP Oil Refinery |
| 456.3625 | 461.8625 | NFM | London | British Transport Police relay |
| 456.3750 | 461.8375 | NFM | Birmingham | Transport Police Ch 2 |
| | | NFM | Cleveland | DSS Dole Frauds Channel 8 |
| | | NFM | Doncaster | DSS |
| | | NFM | Doncaster | Transport Police Channel 2 |
| | | NFM | Exeter | Transport Police Channel 2 |
| | | NFM | London | Docks Light Railway Channel 10 |
| | | NFM | London | Tower of London |
| | | NFM | London | Westminster Abbey |
| | | NFM | Nationwide | Transport Police Channel 2 |
| | | NFM | Sheffield | Transport Police Channel 2 |
| 456.3875 | 461.8875 | NFM | London | Old Bailey Crown Court |
| 456.4000 | 461.9000 | NFM | Blackpool | CAA Repeater |
| | | NFM | Cleveland | DSS Dole Frauds Channel 9 |
| | | NFM | Luton Airport | HM Customs & Excise |
| | | NFM | M1 | Bullion Movements |
| | | NFM | Manchester Airport | HM Customs & Excise |
| | | NFM | Martlesham Heath | British Telecom |
| | | NFM | Nationwide | HM Customs (Airport) |
| | | NFM | Nationwide | Royal Mail Police |
| | | NFM | Nationwide Rail Stations | Post Offices |
| | | NFM | Sheffield | City Buses |
| | | NFM | Thornton | ICI Emergency |
| 456.4250 | 461.9250 | NFM | Birmingham | Transport Police |
| | | NFM | Doncaster | Transport Police |
| | | NFM | Edinburgh | Transport Police |
| | | NFM | Glasgow | Transport Police |
| | | NFM | Hull | Docks Police |
| | | NFM | Leeds | Police Transport |
| | | NFM | Liverpool | Transport Police |
| | | NFM | London | "Her Majesty's Theatre" backstage |
| | | NFM | London | Transport Police (LT) |
| | | NFM | London, Gatwick | Ground Control Link |
| | | NFM | London, Heathrow | Airline & BAA Ops |
| | | NFM | Nationwide | Transport Police Ops Channel. 3 |
| | | NFM | Preston | British Transport Police |
| | | NFM | Sheffield | Council Works Department |
| 456.4500 | 461.9500 | NFM | Aberdeen | City Buses |
| | | NFM | Brighton | Buses |
| | | NFM | Bury | Council |
| | | NFM | Cambridge | National Car Parks |
| | | NFM | Coventry | Skip Hire |
| | | NFM | Dartford | Imperial War Museum Ch1 |
| | | NFM | Duxford | Security |
| | | NFM | Leicester | City Council Cleansing |
| | | NFM | Newcastle Airport | Airport Security |
| | | NFM | North Sea | Phillips Bacton |
| | | NFM | North Sea | Shell Brent B |
| | | NFM | North Sea | Shell Cormorant A |
| | | NFM | North Sea | Shell Dunlin |
| | | NFM | Norwich | Car parks |
| | | NFM | Nottingham | Traffic Light Repairs |
| | | NFM | Rotherham | Council |

| Base | Mobile | Mode | Location | User and Notes |
|------|--------|------|----------|----------------|
| 456.4500 | 461.9500 | NFM | Sheffield | Council 24 hour repairs |
| | | NFM | Sullom Voe | Shell |
| | | NFM | Thamesmead | Caretakers & Lift Ops |
| 456.4625 | 461.9625 | NFM | Cleethorpes | Ross Young Fish Factory |
| 456.4750 | 461.9750 | NFM | Birmingham | Safari Park Control |
| | | NFM | Clayton | Maynes Buses |
| | | NFM | Duxford | Management/Maintenance |
| | | NFM | Edinburgh | St James Centre Security |
| | | NFM | Glasgow | Baggage Handlers |
| | | NFM | Grimsby | Appleby's Coaches |
| | | NFM | Immingham | Exxtor Shipping |
| | | NFM | Immingham | Tor Line Docks |
| | | NFM | Leicester | Security |
| | | NFM | Leicester | Woods Coaches Ch2 |
| | | NFM | Liverpool | Dockside Crane Control |
| | | NFM | London, Gatwick | Aircraft Tugs |
| | | NFM | London, Gatwick | Airline & BAA Ops |
| | | NFM | London, Heathrow | Airline & BAA Ops |
| | | NFM | London, Heathrow | Airline & BAA Ops |
| | | NFM | London, Oxford Street | Marks & Spencer |
| | | NFM | Luton | Vauxhall Motors |
| | | NFM | Middleton | Diamond Cars |
| | | NFM | Nationwide | Federal Express |
| | | NFM | Nationwide | HM Customs & Excise |
| | | NFM | Nationwide | Independent Coach Ops |
| | | NFM | North Welsh Coast | ESSO Rig |
| | | NFM | Norwich Airport | Ground Movements |
| | | NFM | Preston | Skips & Bottle Banks |
| | | NFM | Sheffield | Crystal Peaks security |
| | | NFM | Stockport | TNT Carriers |
| | | NFM | Thistle A | BP |
| | | NFM | Wilton | ICI Fire & Security |
| 456.5000 | 456.5000 | NFM | Bristol | Police Link |
| 456.5000 | 462.0000 | NFM | Dartford | Do. - Air to Ground Ch3 |
| | | NFM | Dungeness | Power Station |
| | | NFM | London | London Docklands Corp |
| | | NFM | Sheffield | City centre store detectives (TRACK) |
| | | NFM | York | OAP warden services |
| 456.5220 | 462.0250 | NFM | London Waterloo | Euro Star Staff and Security |
| | | NFM | Ashford | Eurostar staff |
| | | NFM | Billingham | ICI |
| | | NFM | Birmingham International | Ops |
| | | NFM | Birmingham International | HM Customs & Excise |
| | | NFM | Bristol | Galleries Shopping Centre Control |
| | | NFM | Bristol Airport | Ground Repeater |
| | | NFM | Coventry | West Orchards Shopping Centre |
| | | NFM | Gateshead | Metro Centre Security |
| | | NFM | Halifax | Mackintoshes Security |
| | | NFM | Immingham | Docks/Repairs |
| | | NFM | Ipswich | Port Authority |
| | | NFM | Leicester | LCFC Stewards |
| | | NFM | London (Gatwick) | Aircraft Tugs |
| | | NFM | Nationwide | HM Customs & Excise |
| | | NFM | North Sea | Shell Brent C |
| | | NFM | Salisbury | Hospital Emergency/Security |
| | | NFM | Saltend | BP Oil Refinery |

| Base | Mobile | Mode | Location | User and Notes |
|------|--------|------|----------|----------------|
| 456.5220 | 462.0250 | NFM | Sheffield | Sheffield University Ch A (CAMPUS) |
|          |          | NFM | Stansted | Ground Repeater |
|          |          | NFM | Stoke-on-Trent | Police |
|          |          | NFM | York | Hospital patient transport |
| 456.5500 | 461.0500 | NFM | Brighton | Royal Sussex County Hospital |
|          |          | NFM | Bristol | Federal Express |
|          |          | NFM | Coventry | Rolls Royce Ltd. Security |
|          |          | NFM | Filton | BAe Security |
|          |          | NFM | Hull | University Security |
|          |          | NFM | Lancashire | 24Hr Vehicle Recovery |
|          |          | NFM | London, Gatwick | Ground Control Link |
|          |          | NFM | London, Gatwick | Ground Repeater |
|          |          | NFM | London, Heathrow | Aircraft Maintanence |
|          |          | NFM | London, Heathrow | Airline & BAA Ops |
|          |          | NFM | London, Heathrow | Ground Repeater |
|          |          | NFM | Morecambe | Parcel Service |
|          |          | NFM | Newcastle | Eldon Shopping Centre Security |
|          |          | NFM | Nottingham | Cap Count Victoria Centre |
|          |          | NFM | Nottinghamshire | Lex Wilkinson |
|          |          | NFM | Perth | TeleWest Cable Company |
|          |          | NFM | Poole | Borough Council |
|          |          | NFM | Stirling | Scottish Hydro Electric Engineers |
|          |          | NFM | Stoke-on-Trent | Potteries Shopping Centre |
| 456.5750 | 462.0750 | NFM | Ashford | Learner Motor Cycles |
|          |          | NFM | Beeston | Boots |
|          |          | NFM | Brighton | British Home Stores Security |
|          |          | NFM | Bristol | Poly-Tech Security |
|          |          | NFM | Hull | Hull University |
|          |          | NFM | Immingham | Associated Petroleum Terminals |
|          |          | NFM | Jersey | Servisair Handling |
|          |          | NFM | London | St. James Park wardens Channel 1 |
|          |          | NFM | London, Heathrow | Ground Repeater |
|          |          | NFM | Nationwide | D.O.T Motorcycle Tests |
|          |          | NFM | Newtown | MotorcycleTests |
|          |          | NFM | North Sea | BP Miller |
|          |          | NFM | North Sea | Shell Auk |
|          |          | NFM | North Sea | Shell Brent A |
|          |          | NFM | North Sea | Shell Dunlin |
|          |          | NFM | Southampton | ESSO Fawley (CCR3) |
|          |          | NFM | Swansea | Motorcycle Training |
|          |          | NFM | Weston Super Mare | Motor Cycle Instructors |
| 456.6000 | 462.1000 | NFM | Aberdeen | Dyce Airport Loading |
|          |          | NFM | Alwvn | Total |
|          |          | NFM | Belfast Airport | Tower |
|          |          | NFM | Bristol | Broadmead Store Detectives |
|          |          | NFM | Bristol Filton | Ground Repeater |
|          |          | NFM | Cardiff | RadioNet Shop Security |
|          |          | NFM | Coventry | Massey Ferguson Security |
|          |          | NFM | Dover | Shopping Security |
|          |          | NFM | Halifax | Buses |
|          |          | NFM | Leicester | Shires Sopping Centre Security |
|          |          | NFM | Manchester Airport | Aircraft Cleaners |
|          |          | NFM | North Sea | Phillips Maureen |
|          |          | NFM | Saltend | BP Oil Refinery Ch2 |
|          |          | NFM | Thornton | ICI |

| Base | Mobile | Mode | Location | User and Notes |
|---|---|---|---|---|
| 456.6125 | 462.1125 | NFM | Newcastle Airport | Tower |
| 456.6150 | 462.1250 | NFM | Grand Prix Circuits | Ferrari Team Voice Link |
| 456.6250 | 462.1250 | NFM | Barrow in Furness | VSEL Traffic Department |
| | | NFM | Birmingham | Birmingham University Security |
| | | NFM | Cleethorpes | Ross Young Fish Factory |
| | | NFM | Coventry | Warwick University Security |
| | | NFM | Croydon | Drummond Shopping Centre |
| | | NFM | Duxford | Fire Control |
| | | NFM | Jersey Airport | Ground |
| | | NFM | London | Victoria Coach Station |
| | | NFM | London (Gatwick) | Ground Control Link |
| | | NFM | London, White City | BBC Worldwide Sales Channel 2 |
| | | NFM | Manchester | Airline Ops |
| | | NFM | North Sea | Shell Brent C |
| | | NFM | North Sea | Shell Fulmar A |
| | | NFM | Oxford | Clarendon Centre |
| | | NFM | Peterborough | Security Company |
| | | NFM | Southampton | ESSO Fawley |
| 456.6300 | 456.6300 | NFM | North Cormorant | Shell |
| 456.6500 | 462.1500 | NFM | Coventry | Warwick University Conference Room |
| | | NFM | Edinburgh Airport | PMR Channel 6 |
| | | NFM | Glasgow | Ground |
| | | NFM | Hull | North Sea Ferries Channel 1 |
| | | NFM | London, Gatwick | Aviation Fuel |
| | | NFM | London, Heathrow | Ground Staff Terminal 1 |
| | | NFM | Manchester Airport | Ground Control |
| | | NFM | North Sea | BP Miller |
| | | NFM | Nuneaton | Retail Security Link |
| | | NFM | Sandwich | Pfizers |
| | | NFM | Sheffield | Meadowhall Shopping Centre |
| | | NFM | Southampton | ESSO Fawley (PET-M) |
| | | NFM | Stansted | Long Term Car Park |
| 456.6625 | 462.1625 | NFM | Newcastle Airport | Stand Services |
| 456.6750 | 462.1750 | NFM | Aberdeen | Dyce Airport Staff |
| | | NFM | Ashford | Shop Watch Scheme |
| | | NFM | Billingham | ICI |
| | | NFM | Liverpool | Medic Control |
| | | NFM | London | British Library |
| | | NFM | London | North Thames Electricity |
| | | NFM | London | Securicor [DMTF] |
| | | NFM | London (Heathrow) | Air France Passenger Services |
| | | NFM | Manchester | City Centre Vehicle Clamping |
| | | NFM | Manchester | Paramedic Teams |
| | | NFM | North Sea | BP Miller |
| | | NFM | North Sea | Shell Brent D |
| | | NFM | North Sea | Shell North Cormorant |
| | | NFM | Nottingham | J. Player & Son |
| | | NFM | Oldbury | BNFL Backup Channel |
| | | NFM | Oldham | Minicabs |
| | | NFM | Southampton | ESSO Fawley (Lubes) |
| | | NFM | Stoke-on-Trent | Police |
| | | NFM | Warton | Fence Security |
| | | NFM | Windsor | Windsor Castle Wardens |
| | | NFM | Woburn | Woburn Abbey Wildlife Park |
| 456.6875 | 456.6875 | NFM | Morecambe | Parcel Service |

| Base | Mobile | Mode | Location | User and Notes |
|---|---|---|---|---|
| 456.7000 | 462.2000 | NFM | Basildon | Eastgate Centre security |
| | | NFM | Grays | Lakeside Centre Car Park |
| | | NFM | Great Coates | Courtaulds |
| | | NFM | Killingholme | Lindsey Oil Refinery |
| | | NFM | Lancaster | Lancaster University Security |
| | | NFM | London | BR Signal Engineers |
| | | NFM | London (Heathrow) | Ground Repeater |
| 456.7000 | 456.2000 | NFM | Nationwide | Marconi Communications |
| | | NFM | Nationwide | Motorola |
| 456.7000 | 462.2000 | NFM | North Sea | Shell Brent C |
| | | NFM | North Sea | Shell Fulmar A |
| | | NFM | Perth | Car Park Security |
| | | NFM | Saltend | BP Oil Refinery, Channel 1 fire |
| | | NFM | Sheffield | University security (CAMPUS) |
| | | NFM | Southampton | ESSO Fawley (RED) Fire |
| | | NFM | Welwyn Garden City | Cereal Partners |
| | | NFM | York | University |
| 456.7250 | 462.2250 | NFM | Canvey Island | Texaco Oil Refinery |
| | | NFM | Cowley | Rover Plant Channel 5 |
| | | NFM | Edinburgh | Herriot Watt Univ. Security |
| | | NFM | Hull | North Sea Ferries Channel 2 |
| | | NFM | Jersey | Dock Crane Operators |
| | | NFM | Leicester | Council Roads Dept |
| | | NFM | London (Gatwick) | Avionics Maintenance |
| | | NFM | London (Heathrow) | Airline & BAA Ops |
| | | NFM | Luton Airport | Maintenance Engineers |
| | | NFM | Nationwide | UHF Demonstration Channel 99 |
| | | NFM | North Sea | BP SMV |
| | | NFM | Peterborough | City Council |
| | | NFM | Southampton | ESSO Fawley (OMES) |
| | | NFM | Southend-on-Sea | Store Security |
| | | NFM | Stevenston | ICI Security and Fire Service |
| | | NFM | Swansea Docks | Shipping Pilots |
| | | NFM | Ulverston | Glaxo UK |
| 456.7500 | 462.2500 | NFM | Aberdeen | Dyce Airport Loading |
| | | NFM | Barrow | VSEL Fire & Nuclear Incidents |
| | | NFM | Coventry | Warwick University |
| | | NFM | Glasgow | Cargo Handlers |
| | | NFM | London | Bexley Heath Shopping Cen Sec |
| | | NFM | Skelmersdale | Town Centre Security |
| 456.7750 | 462.2750 | NFM | Aberdeen | Dyce Airport BP |
| | | NFM | Blackpool | Blackpool Pleasure Beach |
| | | NFM | Eastham | Manchester Ship Canal |
| | | NFM | Glasgow | Police |
| | | NFM | Harwich | Trinity House |
| | | NFM | Hull | Docks Cranes/Loading |
| | | NFM | Leicester | Area Traffic Control |
| | | NFM | Liverpool | Manchester Ship Canan (Eastham) |
| | | NFM | London, Gatwick | Ground Repeater |
| | | NFM | London, Heathrow | Kuwaiti Airlines |
| | | NFM | Manchester Shaw | Security |
| | | NFM | Millbrook | Test Track |
| | | NFM | Nuneaton | George Elliot Hosp. Security |
| | | NFM | Redditch | King Fisher Shopping Centre |
| | | NFM | Southampton | ESSO Fawley (Chemicals) |

| Base | Mobile | Mode | Location | User and Notes |
|------|--------|------|----------|----------------|
| 456.7875 | 462.4875 | NFM | London | Museum of Moving Images |
| 456.8000 | 462.3000 | NFM | Beeston | Boots |
| | | NFM | Guildford | Army & Navy Stores |
| 456.8000 | 462.1000 | NFM | London (Gatwick) | Aviation Fuel |
| 456.8000 | 462.3000 | NFM | North Sea | Chevron Drilling Ninian Central |
| | | NFM | North Sea | Chevron Drilling Ninian South |
| 456.8250 | 462.3250 | NFM | Bath | University Security |
| | | NFM | Billingham | ICI |
| | | NFM | Bournemouth | Chase Manhatten Bank |
| | | NFM | Brighton | Sussex University Security |
| | | NFM | Cheltenham | Shop Security Network |
| | | NFM | Coventry | Warwick University Maintenance |
| | | NFM | Dover | Coastguard Cliff Rescue |
| | | NFM | Immingham | BSC |
| | | NFM | London (Heathrow) | Airline & BAA Ops |
| | | NFM | Manchester Airport | Airline Ops |
| | | NFM | Nationwide | NCB & Docks |
| | | NFM | Nottingham | Patent Brick |
| | | NFM | Sandwich | Pfizers |
| | | NFM | Southampton | ESSO Fawley CCR1 |
| | | NFM | St Helens | Pilkingtons Security |
| | | NFM | Stansted | Telephone Ops |
| | | NFM | Tamworth | Borough Council |
| | | NFM | Woburn | Woburn Abbey Wildlife Park |
| 456.8500 | 462.3500 | NFM | Coventry | Community Nurses |
| | | NFM | Coventry | Social Services |
| | | NFM | Cowley | Rover Plant |
| | | NFM | Leicester | Council Road Dept |
| | | NFM | London | Greenwich Maritime |
| | | NFM | London (Heathrow) | Airline & BAA Ops |
| | | NFM | Manchester | Taxis |
| | | NFM | Nationwide | J Sisk & Son (Construction) Ch1 |
| | | NFM | Nottingham | Mapperly Hospital |
| | | NFM | Skelmersdale | Taxis |
| | | NFM | Stansted | Long Term Car Park |
| | | NFM | Tilbury | Docks Security |
| | | NFM | Wansford | Nene Valley Railway |
| | | NFM | Wigan | Taxis |
| | | NFM | Worthing | Taxi |
| 456.8625 | 462.3625 | NFM | Coventry | Call Security |
| | | NFM | Coventry | Delphi Packard security |
| | | NFM | Eastbourne | Pier |
| | | NFM | Edinburgh | Teviot House Security |
| | | NFM | London | Alexandra Palace exhibitions |
| | | NFM | London | Bayleys Nightclub doorman |
| | | NFM | London | Cable & Wireless security |
| | | NFM | London | Wembley Stadium VIP Catering |
| | | NFM | London, Picadilly | Sega Mega World |
| | | NFM | Maidstone | Borough Council |
| | | NFM | Nationwide | Short Term Hire |
| | | NFM | RAE Farnborough | British Aerospace highway security |
| | | NFM | River Thames | Ship On-Board Comms |
| | | NFM | Sheffield | Schools security |
| | | NFM | Warwick | Aviation Executive Bodyguards |
| | | NFM | Woodford Airfield | BAe Security |

| Base | Mobile | Mode | Location | User and Notes |
|------|--------|------|----------|----------------|
| 456.8750 | 462.3750 | NFM | Birmingham International | Ops |
| | | NFM | Birmingham | Midland Airport Service |
| | | NFM | Cowdenbeath | Mossmorran Complex |
| | | NFM | Grays | Lakeside Centre Security |
| | | NFM | Guernsey | Esso |
| | | NFM | Hestmonceux | College |
| | | NFM | Lancashire | Vanguard Couriers |
| | | NFM | London, Gatwick | Handling |
| | | NFM | North Sea | Shell Auk |
| | | NFM | North Sea | Shell Brent A |
| | | NFM | North Sea | Shell Dunlin |
| | | NFM | Nottingham | Esso Colwick |
| | | NFM | Southampton | ESSO Fawley Jetty |
| | | NFM | Stevenston | ICI Acid Plant Maintenance |
| | | NFM | Swansea | Docks Security |
| | | NFM | Warwick | Castle staff Channel 1 |
| | | NFM | Welsh North Coast | ESSO Rig |
| 456.9000 | 462.4000 | NFM | Barrow | VSEL Works Security Control |
| | | NFM | Bournemouth | Bournemouth Zoo |
| | | NFM | East Midlands Airport | Servisair |
| | | NFM | Edinburgh Airport | Baggage Handlers |
| | | NFM | Glasgow | Ops |
| | | NFM | Ipswich | Port |
| | | NFM | Liverpool Airport | Servisair |
| | | NFM | London, Gatwick | Airline & BAA Ops |
| | | NFM | London, Heathrow | Tower Rebroadcast |
| | | NFM | Manchester Airport | Aircraft Tugs |
| | | NFM | Newcastle Airport | Refuelling |
| 456.9250 | 462.4250 | NFM | Ayr | Shop to Shop Security |
| | | NFM | Basildon | Alders of Basildon |
| | | NFM | Blackpool | Store Detectives |
| | | NFM | Burnley | Asda |
| | | NFM | Cowley | Rover Plant Channel 6 |
| | | NFM | Ealing | Shopping Centre |
| | | NFM | London | Wembley Stadium VIP Catering |
| | | NFM | London | Wood Green Shopping Centre |
| | | NFM | London, Heathrow | Ground Repeater |
| | | NFM | London, Picadilly | Cafe de Paris |
| | | NFM | London, Piccadilly | Waxy O'Connon's Irish Pubs |
| | | NFM | Nationwide | BAA Airport Security |
| | | NFM | Nationwide | Power Station Security |
| | | NFM | Nationwide | Short Term Hire |
| | | NFM | Nationwide | UHF Demonstration Channel |
| | | NFM | Sellafield | Security |
| | | NFM | West Midlands | Short term hire mobiles |
| | | NFM | Wigan | Galleries Shopping Centre Sec. |
| 456.9375 | 462.4375 | NFM | London | Sega World Channel 1 |
| 456.9500 | 462.4500 | NFM | Birmingham International | Ops |
| | | NFM | Bournemouth | Repeater |
| | | NFM | Halewood | Ford Plant Shop Stewards |
| | | NFM | Leamington | Shopmet |
| | | NFM | Liverpool | Cherry Tree Shopping Cent Sec. |
| | | NFM | London (Gatwick) | Airline & BAA Ops |
| | | NFM | London (Heathrow) | Virgin Airlines |
| | | NFM | RAE Farnborough | British Aerospace transport |
| | | NFM | Southampton | ESSO Fawley Chemicals |

| Base | Mobile | Mode | Location | User and Notes |
|------|--------|------|----------|----------------|
| 456.9500 | 462.4500 | NFM | Wilmslow | Taxi |
| 456.9750 | 462.4750 | NFM | Birmingham, Longbridge | Rover Group Ltd. Security & Fire |
| | | NFM | Doncaster | Winifreda Coach Co. |
| | | NFM | Flitwick | Buffalo Bus Co. |
| | | NFM | Humberside | Appleby's Coaches |
| | | NFM | Leamington Spa | British Leyland |
| | | NFM | Leicester | Woods Coaches Ch1 |
| | | NFM | Nationwide | Bus & Coach Operators |
| | | NFM | Nationwide | Formula One Racing Team Links |
| | | NFM | Newcastle Airport | Brittania Airways |
| | | NFM | Newport | New Borough Transport |
| | | NFM | Rochdale | Buses |
| | | NFM | Stansted | Stansted Cars |
| 456.9875 | 462.4875 | NFM | Barking | Vicarage Fields Shopping Centre |
| | | NFM | Brighton | Royal Sussex County Hospital |
| | | NFM | Bristol | Pinkerton Security Services |
| | | NFM | IWM Duxford | Car Parks |
| | | NFM | London (Heathrow) | Airline & BAA Ops |
| | | NFM | Nationwide | Short Term Hire |
| | | NFM | SE Sussex | Security Patrol |
| | | NFM | Tunbrigde Wells | Tour de France Barrier Erectors |

**457.0000 - 457.5000 MHz**  EMERGENCY SERVICES, FIRE MOBILE LINKS
12.5 KHZ  SIMPLEX AND DUPLEX BASE
(SPLIT +5.5 MHZ)
SCOTTISH HYDRO ELECTRIC AND
FORMULA ONE RACING TEAM LINKS

| Base | Mobile | Mode | Location | User and Notes |
|------|--------|------|----------|----------------|
| 457.00000 | | NFM | Doncaster | Fire Brigade handhelds |
| 457.00000 | 457.00000 | NFM | England & Wales | Police Channel 93 |
| 457.01250 | 457.01250 | NFM | Edinburgh | Fire Brigade |
| 457.01250 | | NFM | Glasgow | Fire Brigade |
| 457.01250 | 462.51250 | NFM | London | Fire Brigade |
| 457.02500 | 462.52500 | NFM | Gairloch | Scottish Hydro Electric |
| 457.02500 | | NFM | Nationwide | Minardi Formula One Voice |
| 457.03750 | 457.03750 | NFM | Cumbria | Fire Brigade Portables |
| | | NFM | Doncaster | Fire Brigade handhelds |
| | | NFM | Dyfed | Fire Motorola Ascom Channel 1 |
| | | NFM | Edinburgh | Fire Brigade |
| | | NFM | Fife | Fire Brigade Channel 1 |
| | | NFM | Glasgow | Fire Brigade |
| 457.03750 | 462.53750 | NFM | Halifax | Fire Brigade Channel 1 |
| 457.03750 | 462.53750 | NFM | London | Fire Brigade |
| | | NFM | Merseyside | Fire Brigade Channel 1 |
| | | NFM | Nationwide | Airfield Fire Channel 1 |
| | | NFM | Perth | Fire Brigade Portable to Tender |
| 457.03750 | 457.03750 | NFM | West Midlands | Fire on Site handhelds Channel 1 |
| 457.05000 | 457.05000 | NFM | England & Wales | Police Channel 91 |
| 457.05000 | | NFM | Nationwide | Minardi Formula One Voice |
| 457.07500 | 462.57500 | NFM | Achanshellach | Scottish Hydro Electric |
| 457.07500 | | NFM | London, Heathrow | Airline & BAA Ops |
| 457.07500 | 462.57500 | NFM | Ninian South | Chevron Back-up to Ninian N |

| Base | Mobile | Mode | Location | User and Notes |
|------|--------|------|----------|----------------|
| 457.08750 | 462.58750 | NFM | Dyfed | Fire Motorola Ascom Channel 2 |
| | | NFM | Edinburgh | Fire Brigade |
| | | NFM | Glasgow | Fire Brigade |
| | | NFM | London | Fire Brigade |
| 457.10000 | 462.60000 | NFM | England & Wales | Police Channel 92 |
| | | NFM | Gairloch | Scottish Hydro Electric |
| | | NFM | Loch A'Burra | Scottish Hydro Electric |
| 457.12500 | | NFM | London (Heathrow) | Airline & BAA Ops |
| 457.13750 | 457.13750 | FM | Cambridgeshire | Fire Bridge (VC) Hand helds |
| | | NFM | Edinburgh | Fire Brigade |
| | | NFM | Glasgow | Fire Brigade |
| 457.13750 | 462.63750 | NFM | London | Fire Brigade |
| | | NFM | London, Gatwick | Fire Brigade |
| 457.15000 | 462.65000 | NFM | England & Wales | Police Channel 95 |
| 457.18750 | 457.18750 | NFM | Edinburgh | Fire Brigade |
| | | NFM | Fife | Fire Brigade Channel 4 |
| | | NFM | Glasgow | Fire Brigade |
| | | NFM | Perth | Fire Brigade CFO/Handhelds |
| 457.18750 | 462.68750 | NFM | London | Fire Brigade |
| 457.20000 | 457.25000 | NFM | England & Wales | Police Channel 94 |
| 457.20000 | 462.70000 | NFM | Nationwide | NCB Mine Rescue |
| 457.21250 | | NFM | London (Heathrow) | Airline & BAA Ops |
| 457.22500 | | NFM | Ipswich | Data Traffic |
| 457.23750 | 457.23750 | NFM | Cumbria | Fire Brigade Portables |
| | | NFM | Edinburgh | Fire Brigade |
| | | NFM | Fife | Fire Brigade Channel 6 |
| | | NFM | Glasgow | Fire Brigade |
| | | NFM | London | Fire Brigade |
| 457.25000 | 457.25000 | NFM | England & Wales | Police Channel 96 |
| 457.25620 | | NFM | London, Southbank | National Theatre |
| 457.25750 | 457.25750 | NFM | West Midlands | Fire on Site handhelds Channel 37 |
| 457.28125 | | NFM | London | Palace Theatre - "Les Miserables" |
| 457.31250 | | NFM | Grand Prix Circuits | Ligier Team Voice Link |
| 457.32500 | | NFM | Glasgow | SkyTV Ibrox Park |
| 457.35000 | 462.85000 | NFM | Gairloch | Scottish Hydro Electric |
| | | NFM | Nationwide | AA UHF Mobiles |
| 457.37500 | 462.87500 | NFM | Gairloch | Scottish Hydro Electric |
| | | NFM | Inverness | Automobile Association |
| 457.38750 | 462.88750 | NFM | Dyfed | Fire Motorola Ascom Channel 3 |
| | | NFM | London, Heathrow | Airline & BAA Ops |
| 457.45000 | | NFM | Gairloch | Scottish Hydro Electric |
| 457.47500 | | NFM | Garve | Scottish Roads |
| 457.48750 | | NFM | Fife | Fire Brigade Channel 3 |
| | | NFM | West Midlands | Fire Brigade Handhelds |

**457.50625 - 458.49375 MHz    FIXED SCAN TELEMETRY LINKS**

| Base | Mobile | Mode | Location | User and Notes |
|------|--------|------|----------|----------------|
| 457.55000 | | NFM | Morecambe | Data Link |
| | | NFM | Newmarket | Scan Data Link |
| 457.56250 | | NFM | Newmarket | Data Link |
| 457.66250 | | NFM | Newcastle | Data Link |
| 457.67500 | | NFM | Newmarket | Data Link |
| 457.76250 | | NFM | Stirling | Data Link |
| 457.77500 | | NFM | North Sea | Shell Fulmar Telemetary |
| 457.80000 | | NFM | Birmingham | West Midlands GA Data Link |
| 457.85000 | 463.35000 | NFM | Viking Field | Conoco Telcmctry |
| 457.87500 | 463.37500 | NFM | North Sea | BP Buchan |

| Base | Mobile | Mode | Location | User and Notes |
|------|--------|------|----------|----------------|
| 457.87500 | 463.37500 | NFM | North Sea | BP Forties D |
| 457.93750 | | NFM | Stirling | Data Link |
| 457.95000 | | NFM | Newcastle | Data Link |
| 458.00000 | | NFM | Lincoln | Data Link |
| 458.02500 | | NFM | Newcastle | Data Link |
| | | NFM | Law | Railway Telemetry |
| 458.05000 | 463.55000 | NFM | Beryl A | Mobil Telemetry |
| 458.17500 | | NFM | Lea Valley | Southern Water |
| 458.22500 | | NFM | North Sea | Shell Dunlin A |
| 458.24375 | | NFM | West Cumbria | Water Telemetry |
| 458.27000 | | NFM | Carlisle | Railway Telemetry |
| 458.27500 | 462.77500 | NFM | North Sea | Conoco Murchison |
| 458.32500 | | NFM | North Sea | Conoco Murchison |
| 458.36250 | | NFM | Dundee | Data Link |
| | | NFM | Morecambe | Data Link |
| 458.41875 | 463.90625 | NFM | North Sea | Chevron Alba FSU Shuttle Green Line Data |
| 458.41875 | 463.91875 | NFM | North Sea | Shell Cormorant A |
| 458.41875 | | NFM | North Sea | Shell Kittiwake Loading Buoy |
| 458.43125 | 463.93125 | NFM | North Sea | Shell Tanker (Kittiwake) Loading Buoy |
| 458.45000 | 463.95000 | NFM | Dunlin A | Shell |
| 458.45625 | 463.90625 | NFM | North Sea | Chevron Alba ANP Data |

**457.525 - 457.575 MHz**     INTERNATIONAL MARINE ON-BOARD HANDHELD TRANSCEIVERS 12.5 KHZ

| Base | Mobile | Mode | Location | User and Notes |
|------|--------|------|----------|----------------|
| 457.5250 | 457.5250 | NFM | Maritime | Ship Portable Channel 1 |
| | | NFM | Balmoral Oil Field | Sun Oil Portables |
| | | NFM | Maritime | BT Marine Cable Laying |
| | | NFM | North Sea | Elf Frigg Field |
| 457.5375 | 457.5375 | NFM | Maritime | Ship Portable Channel 2 |
| 457.5500 | 457.5500 | NFM | Maritime | Ship Portable Channel 3 |
| | | NFM | Balmoral | Sun Oil Portables |
| | | NFM | Maritime | BT Marine Cable Laying |
| | | NFM | North Sea | Elf Frigg Field |
| | | NFM | Southampton | P&O Marine |
| 457.5625 | 457.5625 | NFM | Maritime | Ships Portable Channel 4 |
| 457.5750 | 467.5750 | NFM | Maritime | Ship Portable Channel 5 |
| | | NFM | North Sea | BP Lolair |
| | | NFM | North Sea | Elf Ffigg Field |
| | | NFM | North Sea | Sun Oil Balmoral |
| | | NFM | Southampton | P&O Marine |

**457.475 -457.500 MHz**     EMERGENCY SERVICES

**458.5000 458.8000 MHz**     LOW POWER DEVICES USED FOR INDUSTRIAL AND COMMERCIAL TELEMENTRY PLUS TELECOMMAND 25 KHZ

| Base | Mobile | Mode | Location | User and Notes |
|------|--------|------|----------|----------------|
| 458.5000 | | NFM | Flimby | Factory Telemetry |
| | | NFM | Nationwide | Telemetry |
| | | NFM | Nationwide | UHF Demonstration Channel |
| 458.5125 | | NFM | Nationwide | Telemetry |
| 458.5250 | | NFM | Morecambe | Data Link |
| 458.5375 | | NFM | Chichester | J Sainsbury Inventory Data |

| Base | Mobile | Mode | Location | User and Notes |
|------|--------|------|----------|----------------|
| 458.5500 | | NFM | Edinburgh Airport | Telemetry Channel 8 |
| | | NFM | Jersey | Telemetry Marina |
| 458.5750 | | NFM | Jersey | Telemetry Beaumont |
| 458.5950 | | NFM | Glasgow | Alarm Systems |
| 458.6000 | | NFM | Jersey | Telemetry Rozel Area |
| 458.6500 | | NFM | Nationwide | Telemetry |
| 458.6750 | | NFM | Jersey | BGS Seismic Telemetry |
| | | NFM | Nationwide | Shell Geophysical |
| 458.7000 | | NFM | Nationwide | Telemetry |
| 458.7250 | | NFM | Jersey | BGS Seismic Telemetry |
| 458.7500 | | NFM | Jersey | Telemetry Queens Valley |
| 458.8000 | | NFM | Jersey | BGS Seismic Telemetry |
| | | NFM | Jersey | Telemetry Val de la Mare |

### 458.5000 459.5000 MHz   UHF REMOTE CONTROLLED MODEL BAND

### 458.8250 459.4875 MHz   LOW POWER PAGING TELEMETRY, FIXED ALARMS, MEDICAL AND BIOLOGICAL EQUIPMENT

| Base | Mobile | Mode | Location | User and Notes |
|------|--------|------|----------|----------------|
| 458.8250 | | NFM | Nationwide | Fixed Alarm Paging |
| 458.8375 | | NFM | Nationwide | Transportable & Mobile Alarm |
| 458.8500 | | NFM | Jersey | Telemetry Queens Valley Area |
| 458.8500 | | NFM | Magnus | BP Paging-Base |
| 458.9000 | | NFM | Flimby | Factory Telemetry |
| | | NFM | Nationwide | Car Theft Alarm Paging & Radio Keys |
| 458.9500 | | NFM | Bassenthwaite | Lake Telemetry |
| 458.9750 | 458.9750 | NFM | North Sea | Mobil Statfjord A |
| 459.0000 | | NFM | Nationwide | Medical & Biological Telemetry |
| | | NFM | North Sea | Mobil Statfjord A |
| 459.0250 | | NFM | Jersey | BGS Seismic Telemetry |
| 459.0250 | 459.0250 | NFM | North Sea | Mobil Statfjord A |
| 459.0500 | | NFM | North Sea | Conoco Murchison |
| 459.0750 | 453.4750 | NFM | North Sea | BP Buchan |
| | | NFM | North Sea | Conoco Murchison |
| 459.0750 | 459.0750 | NFM | North Sea | Mobil Statfjord B |
| 459.1000 | 459.1000 | NFM | North Sea | Mobil Statfjord B |
| 459.1050 | | NFM | Nationwide | Betacom Cordless Telephones |
| 459.1050 | 161.0000 | NFM | Nationwide | Paging |
| 459.1250 | 459.1250 | NFM | North Sea | Mobil Statfjord B |
| 459.1500 | 161.0250 | NFM | Nationwide | Marina Paging |
| 459.1500 | 459.1500 | NFM | North Sea | Mobil Stattjord C |
| 459.1750 | | NFM | Perth | Paging |
| 459.2000 | | NFM | Leicester | Mackro Centre paging |
| 459.2000 | 459.2000 | NFM | North Sea | Mobil Statfjord C |
| 459.2500 | | NFM | Earls Court | Voice Pagers |
| 459.2500 | 161.0500 | NFM | Nationwide | Paging |
| 459.2500 | 459.2500 | NFM | North Sea | Mobil Statfjord C |
| 459.2500 | 459.2500 | NFM | North Sea | Phillips Edda |
| 459.2750 | 459.2750 | NFM | North Sea | Mobil Statijord A tankers |
| 459.2750 | 459.2750 | NFM | West Midlands | Paging Systems |
| 459.3000 | | NFM | London | Two Way Tone Paging |
| 459.3250 | | NFM | Heysham Power Station | Paging |
| | | NFM | Leicester | Holiday Inn voice paging |
| | | NFM | London, Brent Cross | Fenwicks |

| Base | Mobile | Mode | Location | User and Notes |
|------|--------|------|----------|----------------|
| 459.3250 | 161.0125 | NFM | Nationwide | Paging |
| | | NFM | North Sea | Chevron Alba ANP Paging |
| | | NFM | Romford | Tesco Staff Paging |
| 459.3250 | 459.3250 | NFM | Scarborough | Voice Paging |
| 459.3500 | 161.0250 | NFM | London | Old Bailey Voice Paging |
| 459.3500 | 161.0250 | NFM | Nationwide | Paging |
| | | NFM | North Sea | Marathon Brae South Paging |
| | | NFM | North Sea | Mobil Brett 2,1 A Paging |
| 459.3750 | 161.0375 | NFM | Basildon | Hospital Porters Paging |
| 459.3750 | 161.0375 | NFM | Dumfries | Gates Rubber Company |
| | | NFM | London | Selfridges voice pager |
| | | NFM | London, Marble Arch | Littlewoods voice pager |
| 459.3750 | 161.0375 | NFM | Nationwide | Paging |
| 459.3750 | 469.3750 | NFM | North Sea | Mobil ALP Statfjord C |
| 459.3750 | | NFM | Romford | BAC Staff Paging |
| | | NFM | Thornton | Multitone ICI |
| | | NFM | Wirral | Mobil Oil Security |
| 459.4000 | | NFM | London | Earls Court Voice Pagers |
| 459.4000 | 161.0500 | NFM | Nationwide | Paging |
| 459.4000 | 459.4000 | NFM | North Sea | Phillips Ekofisk Senter |
| 459.4250 | | NFM | Coventry | Pagers |
| | | NFM | Heysham Power Station | Paging |
| 459.4250 | 161.0625 | NFM | London | BBC Bush House Pagers |
| 459.4250 | 459.4250 | NFM | North Sea | BP Clyde A Paging |
| 459.4250 | 469.4250 | NFM | North Sea | Mobil Statfjord B |
| 459.4500 | | NFM | Heysham Power Station | Paging |
| 459.4500 | 459.4500 | NFM | Manchester | Paging |
| 459.4500 | 161.1000 | NFM | Nationwide | Paging |
| 459.4500 | 459.4500 | NFM | North Sea | Mobil Statfjord C |
| 459.4750 | 161.1125 | NFM | Eastbourne | Store Paging |
| 459.4750 | | NFM | Luton | Arndale Shopping Centre |
| 459.4750 | 161.1125 | NFM | Nationwide | Paging |
| 459.4750 | | NFM | Romford | BHS Staff Paging |
| | | NFM | Sleaford | Padley's Poultry (PAPA BASE) |
| | | NFM | Wirral | Sainsbury's |

**459.5000 - 460.5000 MHz** AMBULANCE HANDSETS AND VARIOUS PMR MOBILE 12.5 KHZ (SPLIT-5.5 MHZ) FORMULA ONE RACING TEAMLINKS

| Base | Mobile | Mode | Location | User and Notes |
|------|--------|------|----------|----------------|
| 459.5000 | 459.5000 | NFM | Blackpool | Tower Ascent |
| 459.5000 | 469.5000 | NFM | North Sea | Mobil A.L.P.Statfjord A |
| | | NFM | North Sea | Phillips Albuskjell A |
| 459.5250 | 453.0250 | NFM | Felixstowe | Docks police |
| 459.5250 | 453.0250 | NFM | North Sea | BP Beatrice A |
| 459.5250 | 469.5250 | NFM | North Sea | Mobil A. L. P. Statfjord B |
| | | NFM | North Sea | Mobil Beryl B Temp. Const. Facility |
| 459.5250 | 459.5250 | NFM | North Sea | Phillips Albuskjell F |
| 459.5250 | | NFM | Stansted | Telephone Ops |
| 459.5500 | | NFM | Doncaster | Peglers Security |
| 459.5500 | 453.0500 | NFM | North Sea | Chevron Alba ANP PABX Interface |
| 459.5750 | 459.5750 | NFM | Montrose Basin | Rangers |
| 459.5750 | 453.0750 | NFM | North Sea | Amoco Bacton |
| 459.5750 | | NFM | North Sea | Total Frigg Field |
| 459.6000 | | NFM | Blackpool | Tram and Bus Inspectors |

| Base | Mobile | Mode | Location | User and Notes |
|------|--------|------|----------|----------------|
| 459.6000 | 453.1000 | NFM | North Sea | BP Beatrice B |
| 459.6000 | | NFM | North Sea | BP Clyde A |
| | | NFM | North Sea | Total Frigg Field |
| | | NFM | North Sea | Unocol Heather A |
| 459.6250 | 453.1250 | NFM | North Sea | Conoco Viking Field |
| 459.6250 | | NFM | North Sea | Total Frigg Field |
| 459.6500 | | NFM | North Sea | Total Frigg Field |
| 459.6500 | 453.1500 | NFM | Nottingham | Boots, Broadmarch Shopping Centre |
| 459.6750 | 453.1750 | NFM | North Sea | Shell Bacton |
| | | NFM | North Sea | Shell Indc J |
| | | NFM | North Sea | Shell Inde K |
| | | NFM | North Sea | Shell Leman B |
| | | NFM | North Sea | Shell St. Fergus |
| | | NFM | North Sea | Total Frigg Field |
| 459.7000 | 459.7000 | NFM | Bristol | HTV Television |
| | | NFM | London (Gatwick) | Ground Repeater |
| | | NFM | North Sea | BP Magnus |
| | | NFM | North Sea | Total Frigg Field |
| 459.7250 | 453.2250 | NFM | England & Wales | Police and Fire Channel |
| 459.7250 | 455.2250 | NFM | Felixstowe | Docks fire brigade |
| 459.7250 | 459.7250 | NFM | Guernsey | Fuel Supplies |
| | | NFM | North Sea | Chevron Ninian South |
| | | NFM | North Sea | Phillips Tor |
| | | NFM | North Sea | Shell Eider |
| | | NFM | North Sea | Total Frigg Field |
| 459.7500 | 459.7500 | NFM | North Sea | Conoco Murchison |
| | | NFM | North Sea | Marathon Brae South |
| | | NFM | North Sea | Phillips Ekofisk Center to Ekofisk B |
| 459.7750 | 453.2750 | NFM | Nationwide | Ambulance UHF to VHF |
| 459.7750 | 459.7750 | NFM | Nationwide | Philips Security |
| | | NFM | North Sea | Phillips Eldfisk B to Ekofisk Center |
| | | NFM | North Sea | Shell Cormorant A |
| | | NFM | North Sea | Shell Leman BH Portables |
| | | NFM | North Sea | Total Frigg Field |
| 459.8000 | 459.8000 | NFM | Milford Haven | Texaco Refinery Control |
| | | NFM | North Sea | BP Magnus |
| 459.8000 | 459.8000 | NFM | North Sea | Marathon Brae South |
| | | NFM | North Sea | Phillips Ekofisk Senter |
| | | NFM | North Sea | Total Frigg Field |
| | | NFM | Waddington | BAE ACMI |
| 459.8250 | | NFM | Hampshire | Ambulance Pagers |
| | | NFM | West Yorkshire | Ambulance Service |
| 459.8375 | | NFM | Swindon | Brunel Security |
| 459.8500 | | NFM | Harrow on the Hill | St Anne's Shopping Centre |
| | | NFM | Jersey | Alpha Airport Catering Service |
| | | NFM | Morecambe Bay | BGE&P |
| 459.8500 | 453.3500 | NFM | Nationwide | Ambulance UHF to VHF |
| 459.8500 | | NFM | North Sea | Conoco Murchison |
| 459.8500 | 459.8500 | NFM | North Sea | Marathon Brae South |
| 459.8500 | | NFM | Swindon | Brunel Security |
| 459.8750 | | NFM | Salisbury | Hospital Security |
| 459.9000 | | NFM | North Sea | Chevron Ninian North |
| 459.9000 | 453.4000 | NFM | North Sea | Marathon Brae N, S |
| | | NFM | North Sea | Shell St. Fergus |

| Base | Mobile | Mode | Location | User and Notes |
|---|---|---|---|---|
| 459.9250 | 453.4250 | NFM | North Sea | BP Buchan |
| | | NFM | North Sea | BP Magnus |
| | | NFM | North Sea | Chevron Alba FSU Maintenance |
| 459.9500 | 453.4500 | NFM | Bournmouth Airport | Ground Services |
| | | NFM | London (Gatwick) | Messages for Captains |
| 459.9500 | 459.9500 | NFM | Morecambe Bay | BGE&P |
| | | NFM | Dorset | BP Wytch Farm |
| | | NFM | Mutchison | Conoco |
| 459.9750 | 453.4750 | NFM | North Sea | BP Buchan |
| 459.9750 | 459.9750 | NFM | North Sea | Shell St. Fergus |
| 460.0000 | 453.5000 | NFM | North Sea | Shell Eider |
| 460.0150 | 453.5250 | NFM | North Sea | Chevron Ninian North |
| 460.0250 | | NFM | London, Picaddilly | The Body Shop |
| 460.0250 | 453.6250 | NFM | Morecambe Bay | BGE&P |
| 460.0250 | 453.7500 | NFM | Northumberland | Geological Surveys |
| 460.0500 | 453.5500 | NFM | North Sea | Chevron Alba ANP Construction |
| 460.0500 | | NFM | North Sea | Chevron Ninian South |
| 460.0750 | 460.0750 | NFM | Morecambe Bay | BGE&P |
| 460.0750 | 453.5450 | NFM | Nationwide | Safeways Supermarkets |
| 460.0750 | 453.5750 | NFM | North Sea | BP Buchan |
| 460.0750 | | NFM | North Sea | BP Magnus |
| 460.1000 | 453.6000 | NFM | Bedford | Debenhams Security |
| | | NFM | Birmingham | Debenhams Security |
| | | NFM | Cambridge | Debenhams Security |
| | | NFM | Derby | Debenhams Security |
| | | NFM | Folkestone | Debenhams Security |
| 460.1000 | 453.6000 | NFM | North Sea | Amoco N W Hutton |
| | | NFM | North Sea | Texaco Tartan |
| 460.1000 | 460.1000 | NFM | Plymouth | Debenhams Store Detectives |
| 460.1125 | | NFM | Doncaster | Railtrack |
| | | NFM | London | British Rail (Richmond) |
| | | NFM | Newcastle Airport | Passenger Information |
| 460.1250 | | NFM | Coventry | Central Library |
| | | NFM | Lincoln | Hospital maintenance |
| | | NFM | London, Oxford Circus | Top Shop |
| 460.1250 | 453.6250 | NFM | North Sea | Chevron Alba FSU General Ops |
| 460.1250 | | NFM | Swansea | University Security |
| 460.1500 | | NFM | Lincoln | Council |
| | | NFM | North Sea | Shell Brent C |
| 460.1500 | 460.1500 | NFM | North Sea | Shell TCM |
| 460.2000 | 453.7000 | NFM | North Sea | Chevron Ninian North |
| 460.2000 | 460.1000 | NFM | North Sea | Shell Eider |
| 460.2000 | | NFM | North Sea | Shell Leman A portables |
| 460.2250 | | NFM | Isle of Grain | Oil |
| | | NFM | Morecambe Bay | BGE&P |
| 460.2250 | 453.7250 | NFM | North Sea | Chevron Alba ANP Production |
| 460.2250 | 453.7000 | NFM | North Sea | Chevron Ninian North |
| 460.2500 | | NFM | Bradford | Allied Colloids Chemicals |
| 460.2500 | 453.7500 | NFM | Nottingham | Formans |
| 460.2750 | | NFM | Culham | UKAEA Laboratory Fire Team |
| 460.2750 | 453.7750 | NFM | North Sea | Phillips Maureen telemetry |
| 460.3000 | | NFM | Newmarket | Community Repeater |
| 460.3000 | 453.8000 | NFM | North Sea | Amoco Lomond |
| 460.3000 | | NFM | North Sea | Amoco North Everest |
| | | NFM | North Sea | Chevron Ninian South |
| | | NFM | North Sea | Shell TCM |

| Base | Mobile | Mode | Location | User and Notes |
|---|---|---|---|---|
| 460.3250 | 460.3250 | NFM | Plymouth | Dedenhams Maintenance |
| 460.3500 | | NFM | Bradford | Allied Colloids Chemicals |
| | | NFM | County Durham | Taxis |
| 460.3500 | 453.8500 | NFM | North Sea | BP Forties E |
| | | NFM | North Sea | BP Magnus |
| 460.3500 | 460.8500 | NFM | North Sea | Shell TCM |
| 460.3625 | 462.3625 | NFM | Bristol | Pinkerton Security Services |
| 460.3750 | 453.8750 | NFM | North Sea | Chevron Alba Field Safety |
| | | NFM | North Sea | Chevron Ninian Central |
| 460.4000 | 453.9000 | NFM | Bristol | Railtrack Bristol Temple Meads |
| | | NFM | Doncaster | Railtrack Doncater Yard |
| | | NFM | London | Railtrack (Euston) |
| | | NFM | London | Railtrack (Gatwick Airport) |
| | | NFM | London | Railtrack (Hornsey Depot) |
| | | NFM | London | Railtrack (Marylebone) |
| | | NFM | London | Railtrack (Victoria) |
| 460.4000 | | NFM | North Sea | Shell Brent C |
| 460.4250 | 453.9250 | NFM | North Sea | BP Forties E |
| | | NFM | North Sea | BP Magnus |
| 460.4500 | | NFM | Croughton | USAF securiity police |
| 460.4500 | 453.9500 | NFM | Glasgow | Virgin Records Security |
| | | NFM | North Sea | Chevron Alba ANP Maintenance |
| | | NFM | North Sea | Chevron Ninian Central |
| | | NFM | North Sea | Marathon Brae North |
| 460.4750 | 453.9750 | NFM | London | HMV Shop Security |
| 460.4750 | 453.9750 | NFM | North Sea | BP Forties E |
| | | NFM | North Sea | BP Magnus |
| 460.4750 | | NFM | USAF Croughton | Police |

**460.5000 - 461.5000 MHz**   EMERGENCY SERVICES, UHF POINT TO POINT LINKS 25 KHZ (SPLIT+6.5MHZ)

| Base | Mobile | Mode | Location | User and Notes |
|---|---|---|---|---|
| 460.50620 | | NFM | Belfry (Ryder Cup) | US TV Talkback |
| 460.50620 | 467.00620 | NFM | Nationwide | Sky TV O/B Talkback |
| 460.52500 | 467.02500 | NFM | Bristol | HM Prison (MY) |
| 460.52500 | 467.02500 | NFM | Carstairs | HM Prison Hospital (YX) |
| | | NFM | Lincoln | HM Prison (O) |
| 460.52500 | 467.02500 | NFM | London | HM Prison Pentonville (JP) |
| 460.52500 | 467.02500 | NFM | March, Cambs | HM Prison Whitemoor |
| 460.52500 | 467.02500 | NFM | Rochester | HM Borstal (PR) |
| 460.53120 | | NFM | Castle Donington | US TV Talkback |
| 460.53750 | 467.03750 | NFM | Brixton | HM Prison (JX) |
| 460.55000 | 467.05000 | NFM | Jersey Airport | Air Traffic Control Link |
| | | NFM | Kent | Southern Gas |
| | | NFM | Nationwide | Sky TV Talkback |
| 460.55000 | 467.55000 | NFM | London | HM Prision Holloway (MJ) |
| 460.55000 | 467.05000 | NFM | Swaleside, Kent | HM Prison (KS) |
| 460.56250 | | NFM | Falkirk | Police (G) |

| Base | Mobile | Mode | Location | User and Notes |
|------|--------|------|----------|----------------|
| 460.56870 | 467.06870 | NFM | Castle Donington | Japanese TV Talkback |
| 460.57500 | | NFM | Bristol | Ambulance Service |
| | | NFM | Cornwall | Ambulance Service |
| | | NFM | Devon | Ambulance Service |
| | | NFM | East Hertfordshire | Ambulance Service |
| | | NFM | Gloucester | Ambulance Service |
| | | NFM | Nationwide | Sky TV OB |
| | | NFM | North Bedfordshire | Ambulance Service |
| | | NFM | Scilly Isles | Ambulance Service |
| | | NFM | Somerset | Ambulance Service |
| | | NFM | Wales | BBC Wales Talkback |
| 460.58125 | | NFM | Belfry (Ryder Cup) | German TV Talkback |
| | | NFM | Castle Donington | Japanese TV Talkback |
| 460.58375 | | NFM | Nationwide | Sky TV OB Talkback |
| 460.58750 | | NFM | Wales | BBC Wales Talkback |
| 460.59375 | | NFM | Belfry (Ryder Cup) | US TV Talkback |
| 460.60000 | | NFM | Buckinghamshire | Ambulance Service |
| | | NFM | Northamptonshire | Ambulance Service |
| | | NFM | Oxford | Ambulance Service |
| | | NFM | West Berkshire | Ambulance Service |
| 460.61870 | 467.11870 | NFM | Belfry (Ryder Cup) | German TV Talkback |
| 460.62500 | | NFM | Buckinghamshire | Ambulance Service |
| | | NFM | Cleveland | Ambulance Service |
| | | NFM | Cumbria | Ambulance Service |
| | | NFM | Durham | Ambulance Service |
| | | NFM | Northamptonshire | Ambulance Service |
| | | NFM | Northumbria | Ambulance Service |
| | | NFM | Oxford | Ambulance Service |
| | | NFM | Wales | BBC Wales Announcer |
| | | NFM | West Berkshire | Ambulance Service |
| 460.62500 | 460.62500 | NFM | North Sea | Mobil Statfjord A,B,C |
| 460.64370 | | NFM | Belfry (Ryder Cup) | US TV Talkback |
| 460.65000 | | NFM | Wales | Ambulance Service |
| 460.66250 | 467.16250 | NFM | London | HM Prison Belmarsh (MB) |
| 460.66250 | | NFM | Woodbridge, Suffolk | HM Prison & Borstal Hollesley Bay Colony |
| 460.67500 | 467.17500 | NFM | Cleveland | Ambulance Service |
| | | NFM | Cumbria | Ambulance Service |
| | | NFM | Durham | Ambulance Service |
| | | NFM | Humbershire | Ambulance Service |
| | | NFM | Northumbria | Ambulance Service |
| | | NFM | Silverstone | French TV Talkback |
| | | NFM | Yorkshire | Ambulance Service |
| | | NFM | Wales | BBC Wales Studio Controller |
| 460.70000 | | NFM | Dublin | Fire Service |
| 460.70620 | | NFM | Nationwide | Sky TV Talkback |
| 460.72500 | | NFM | Bristol | Ambulance Service |
| | | NFM | Cornwall | Ambulance Service |
| | | NFM | Devon | Ambulance Service |
| 460.72500 | 467.22500 | NFM | Doncaster | HM Prison (XD) |
| 460.72500 | | NFM | Gloucester | Ambulance Service |
| | | NFM | Nationwide | Sky TV OB |
| | | NFM | Scilly Isles | Ambulance Service |
| | | NFM | Somerset | Ambulance Service |
| 460.72500 | 467.22500 | NFM | Warrington | HM Young Offenders Institution Thorn Cross (BO) |

| Base | Mobile | Mode | Location | User and Notes |
|---|---|---|---|---|
| 460.74370 | | NFM | Nationwide | BBC TV OB Production |
| 460.75000 | | NFM | Cleveland | Ambulance Service |
| | | NFM | Cumbria | Ambulance Service |
| | | NFM | Durham | Ambulance Service |
| | | NFM | Northumbria | Ambulance Service |

### 460.76875- 462.49375 MHz PMR Simplex (Airports & North Sea Rigs)

| Base | Mobile | Mode | Location | User and Notes |
|---|---|---|---|---|
| 460.7700 | | NFM | Birmingham | Airport Marshals. |
| | | NFM | Manchester | Air Frame Ground Staff |
| 460.7875 | 467.2875 | NFM | Nationwide | National Air Traffic Service |
| 460.7875 | | NFM | Poole | Point-to-Point Link |
| 460.8500 | 460.3500 | NFM | North Sea | Shell TCM |
| 460.9250 | 460.9250 | NFM | Newcastle Airport | Airport Mobiles |
| 460.9500 | 460.9500 | NFM | Edinburgh Airport | PMR Channel 7 |
| 461.0000 | 455.7000 | NFM | Edinburgh Airport | PMR Channel 15 |
| 461.0000 | 467.5000 | NFM | Filton (BAe), Bristol | Ground Crews |
| 461.0000 | | NFM | Nationwide | RAF Falcons Display Team |
| 461.0250 | | NFM | Easington | BP To West Sole A |
| 461.0250 | 461.0250 | NFM | Edinburgh Airport | Channel 33 |
| 461.0250 | 455.7250 | NFM | Edinburgh Airport | PMR Channel 13 |
| 461.0250 | 467.5250 | NFM | Nationwide | National Air Traffic Service |
| 461.0250 | | NFM | North Sea | Shell Brent B |
| | | NFM | North Sea | Shell Brent D |
| | | NFM | North Sea | Shell Brent Spar |
| 461.0500 | 467.5500 | NFM | North Sea | Shell Fulmar A |
| 461.0750 | 467.5750 | NFM | Easington | BP to West Sole A |
| 461.0750 | 461.0750 | NFM | Edinburgh Airport | Channel 32 |
| 461.0750 | 455.7750 | NFM | Edinburgh Airport | PMR Channel 12 |
| 461.1000 | | NFM | Newcastle Airport | Tower & Following |
| 461.1000 | 467.6000 | NFM | North Sea | Shell Fulmar A |
| 461.1125 | | NFM | Newcastle Airport | Luggage Control |
| 461.1625 | | NFM | Newcastle Airport | Baggage Handing |
| 461.1750 | 467.6750 | NFM | Gt. Yarmouth | Phillips To Hewett |
| 461.2000 | | NFM | London (Heathrow) | Ground Staff |
| 461.2150 | | NFM | London, Brent Cross | C & A staff |

### 461.25625 - 461.45000 MHz    PMR   Simplex

| Base | Mobile | Mode | Location | User and Notes |
|---|---|---|---|---|
| 461.2625 | 461.2625 | NFM | Basildon | Eastgate Shopping Centre maintce. |
| | | NFM | London | Capital Radio Restaurant doorman |
| | | NFM | London, Oxford St | Sabrewatch shop security |
| | | NFM | London, Stratford | JD Sports |
| | | NFM | Nationwide | Motorola Business Radios Channel 1 |
| 461.2750 | 461.2750 | NFM | North Sea | Shell Brent A |
| 461.2785 | 461.2875 | NFM | London White City | BBC Worldwide Ch1 |
| | | NFM | Cheltenham | Race Course Car Park |
| | | NFM | Guernsey | Brock Fireworks |
| | | NFM | Guernsey | Performing Arts Handhelds |
| | | NFM | London, Stratford | Motor cycle training |
| | | NFM | Sheffield | Sheffield Arena security |
| 461.3000 | 461.3000 | NFM | Doncaster | Tickhill Garden Centre |
| | | NFM | Nationwide | Motorola Business Radios Channel 2 |
| 461.3125 | 461.3215 | NFM | Ashford | County Square Security |
| | | NFM | Eastbourne | Theatre |
| | | NFM | Felixstowe | Spa Pavillion Theatre |
| | | NFM | London | Brent Cross Shopping Centre security |

| Base | Mobile | Mode | Location | User and Notes |
|------|--------|------|----------|----------------|
| 461.3125 | 461.3125 | NFM | Nationwide | TNT Loaders Channel 1 |
| | | NFM | Sheffield | Sheffield Arena security |
| 461.3250 | 461.3250 | NFM | Ashington | Wansbeck General Hospital Car Park |
| | | NFM | Cheltenham | Shopping Arcade Security |
| | | NFM | Doncaster | DMBC Security |
| | | NFM | Ipswich | Docks |
| | | NFM | Jersey | General Hospital |
| | | NFM | London, Oxford Street | CLH staff |
| | | NFM | Nationwide | British Aerospace security police |
| | | NFM | Sheffield | Sheffield Arena security |
| | | NFM | Southampton | Sealink Car Ferries |
| | | NFM | Burton upon Trent | Shopping Centre Security |
| | | NFM | Doncaster | Warner Bros. Cinema |
| | | NFM | London, Oxford Street | Top Shop |
| | | NFM | Nationwide | TNT Loaders Channel 2 |
| | | NFM | Sheffield | Sheffield Arena security |
| | | NFM | Widnes | Widnes Leisure Centre |
| 461.3500 | 461.3500 | NFM | Coventry | Cathedral Lanes Shopping Centre |
| | | NFM | Eastbourne | Arndale Security |
| | | NFM | Jersey | Builders (On-Site Radios) |
| | | NFM | Sheffield | William Brothers |
| 461.3505 | 461.3505 | NFM | Coventry | Cathedral Lane Shopping Centre |
| 461.3625 | 461.3625 | NFM | Ashford | Shop Security |
| | | NFM | Harrow on the Hill | St Georges's Shopping Centre |
| | | NFM | Worcester | Crowngate Shopping Centre |
| 461.3750 | 461.3750 | NFM | Basildon | Hospital car park security |
| | | NFM | Cheltenham | Race Court Tic Tac Men |
| | | NFM | Coventry | Virgin Megastore Security |
| | | NFM | Liverpool | Virgin Megastore |
| | | NFM | London | Scorpion Security |
| | | NFM | London, Haymarket | Sports Cafe |
| | | NFM | Nationwide | Sky TV Engineers |
| | | NFM | North Sea | Shell Brent B |
| | | NFM | Sheffield | Sheffield Arena security (LINK) |
| | | NFM | Dover | P & O Ferries |
| | | NFM | Eastbourne | Sovereign Leisure & Swimming Pool |
| 461.4000 | 461.4000 | NFM | Eastbourne | Hospital Porters |
| | | NFM | Harrow on the Hill | The Edge Cafe |
| | | NFM | Hitchin | Wilkinson Home & Garden Store |
| | | NFM | Jersey | PMR |
| | | NFM | London | Her Majestys Theatre |
| | | NFM | Southend on Sea | Victoria Plaza |

**461.425 0 - 461.4875 MHz   PMR (Split +6.5 MHz)**

| Base | Mobile | Mode | Location | User and Notes |
|------|--------|------|----------|----------------|
| 461.4250 | 467.9250 | NFM | London (Gatwick) | Cellular Link |
| | | NFM | North Sea | Shell Auk A to ELSBM |
| | | NFM | North Sea | Shell Brent D |
| 461.4500 | 461.4500 | NFM | Ashford | Shop Security |
| | | NFM | Basildon | Hospital car park security |
| | | NFM | Jersey | C.A. Mauger Builders |
| | | NFM | London | Lord Mayors firework display |
| | | NFM | London, Oxford Street | CLH staff |

| Base | Mobile | Mode | Location | User and Notes |
|------|--------|------|----------|----------------|
| 461.4625 | 467.9625 | NFM | Dagenham | Ford Motor Co. |
| | | NFM | Dartford | Do. - Security and Works Dept Ch4 |
| | | NFM | Doncaster | Traffic Wardens |
| | | NFM | Duxford | Security (OSCAR BASE) |
| | | NFM | East Ham | London Borough of Newham |
| | | NFM | Hull | Princes Quay Shopping Security |
| | | NFM | Lewisham | Lewisham College |
| | | NFM | London | Odeon Cinemas Ltd. |
| | | NFM | London Fleet St | Law Courts |
| | | NFM | Nationwide | DSS |
| | | NFM | Nationwide | Dept. of Employment |
| | | NFM | Nationwide | National Audit Office |
| | | NFM | Walthamstow | Hawker Siddeley Transfomer |
| | | NFM | West Drayton | Heathrow Sterling Hotel |
| | | NFM | Worcester | Lychgate Shopping Centre |
| 461.4750 | 467.9750 | NFM | Essex | Cable TV engineers |
| | | NFM | Nationwide | Marks & Spencer Security |
| | | NFM | Nationwide | Motorola Business Radios Channel 3 |
| | | NFM | North Sea | Shell Auk A to ELSBM |
| | | NFM | Preston | Sharoe Green Hospital |
| | | NFM | Worthing | Motor Cycle Driving Test Instructor |
| 461.4875 | 467.9875 | NFM | Ashford | Marks & Spencer Sabrewatch security |
| | | NFM | Canvey Island | Cornelius Vermugden School |
| | | NFM | London, Oxford St | JD Sports |
| | | NFM | Nationwide | Motorola Business Radios Channel 4 |
| | | NFM | Southend | C & A staff |
| | | NFM | Worthing | Motor Cycle Driving Test Instructor |

## 461.5000 - 462.5000 MHz    PMR UHF Band Base 12.5 kHz
## (Split -5.5 MHz)

| Base | Mobile | Mode | Location | User and Notes |
|------|--------|------|----------|----------------|
| 461.5000 | 456.0000 | NFM | Leicester | City Council Repairs |
| | | NFM | Penzance | BR Repairs |
| | | NFM | Southampton | Group 4 Security |
| 461.5250 | 456.0250 | NFM | North Sea | Total Alwyn |
| 461.5400 | | NFM | London, Brent Cross | C & A security |
| 461.5500 | 456.0500 | NFM | Brae South | Marathon |
| 461.5500 | | NFM | Jersey | La Collette Power Station |
| 461.5500 | 461.5500 | NFM | North Sea | BGE&P Rough A |
| | | NFM | North Sea | BGE&P Rough B |
| | | NFM | North Sea | Total Alwyn |
| 461.5750 | 456.0750 | NFM | Bath | SW Electricity Disconnections |
| | | NFM | Nationwide | Coal Mine Security |
| 461.6000 | 461.6000 | NFM | North Sea | BGE&P Rough B |
| 461.6000 | 456.1000 | NFM | North Sea | Marathon Brae S |
| 461.6250 | 461.6250 | NFM | Nationwide | Simply Red Crew |
| 461.6250 | 456.1150 | NFM | North Sea | BP Sulair Magnus |
| 461.6750 | 456.1750 | NFM | North Sea | Total Alwyn |
| 461.7000 | 461.7000 | NFM | North Sea | Shell Dunlin A |
| | | NFM | North Sea | Total MCP-01 |
| 461.7250 | 401.7215 | NFM | North Sea | BGE&P Rough B |
| 461.7750 | 456.2750 | NFM | North Sea | Shell Brent D |
| 461.7750 | | NFM | North Sea | Shell Cormorant N |
| 461.7750 | 456.2500 | NFM | Nottingham | Esso Colwick |
| 461.8000 | 456.3000 | NFM | North Sea | Marathon Brae North |
| 461.8500 | 456.3500 | NFM | Nottingham | Technical Services |
| 461.9000 | 456.4000 | NFM | Nationwide | HM Customs Covert Repeater |

| Base | Mobile | Mode | Location | User and Notes |
|---|---|---|---|---|
| 461.9000 | 461.9000 | NFM | Nationwide | HM Customs Surveillance |
| | | NFM | North Sea | Total Alwyn |
| | | NFM | Southend | Victoria Plaza Car Park security |
| 461.9125 | | NFM | East Midlands | Government surveillance using MASC encryption |
| 461.9250 | 461.9250 | NFM | Manchester | British Rail Security |
| | | NFM | Nationwide | British Telecom Police Security |
| | | NFM | North Sea | BP Thistle A |
| 461.9500 | 456.4500 | NFM | Birmingham | RSPCA |
| | | NFM | Duxford Aerodrome | Imperial War Museum Security |
| | | NFM | North Sea | BP SMV |
| | | NFM | North Sea | Shell Brent B |
| | | NFM | North Sea | Shell Cormorant A |
| | | NFM | Sullom Voe | Shell |
| 461.9750 | 456.4750 | NFM | North Sea | BP Thistle A |
| 461.9750 | 461.9750 | NFM | North Sea | BP Thistle A |
| 462.0000 | 456.5000 | NFM | Doncaster | Tesco |
| | | NFM | Duxford Aerodrome | Imperial War Museum Gnd Mmnt |
| | | NFM | Nationwide | Securicor Datatrak System |
| 462.0125 | | NFM | London | Taxis |
| 462.2500 | | NFM | Doncaster | Marks & Spencer (M) |
| 462.0250 | 456.5250 | NFM | London | Taxis |
| | | NFM | North Sea | Shell Brent C |
| 462.0500 | 462.0500 | NFM | Eastbourne | Tesco Supermarket |
| | | NFM | London | Cable & Wireless |
| | | NFM | London, Brent Cross | Marks & Spencer security |
| | | NFM | London, Brent Cross | W H Smith |
| | | NFM | London, Oxford St | John Lewis |
| | | NFM | Milton Keynes | W H Smith Ltd. |
| | | NFM | Nationwide | Tesco Supermarkets |
| | | NFM | North Sea | BP Thistle A |
| | | NFM | Peterborough | Tesco's |
| | | NFM | Stirling | Castle security |
| 462.0750 | 453.5750 | NFM | London, Heathrow | BP Oil |
| 462.0750 | 456.5750 | NFM | North Sea | BP Buchan |
| | | NFM | North Sea | BP Darlington |
| | | NFM | North Sea | BP Easington |
| | | NFM | North Sea | BP Miller |
| | | NFM | North Sea | Shell Auk |
| | | NFM | North Sea | Shell Brent A |
| | | NFM | North Sea | Shell Dunlin |
| 462.0950 | | NFM | Girton | Tarmac Quarries |
| 462.1000 | 456.6000 | NFM | Nationwide | Visual Comm. Systems Engineers |
| | | NFM | North Sea | Total Alwyn |
| 462.1000 | 462.1000 | NFM | Welton | BP |
| 462.1250 | 456.6250 | NFM | Duxford Aerodrome | Imperial War Museum Fire |
| 462.1250 | 456.6215 | NFM | North Sea | Shell Fulmar A |
| 462.1250 | 462.1250 | NFM | North Sea | Total St. Fergus |
| 462.1500 | 456.6500 | NFM | North Sea | BP Miller |
| 462.1625 | 462.1625 | NFM | Cheshire | Haulage |
| 462.1750 | 456.6750 | NFM | London, Heathrow | Ground Staff |
| | | NFM | North Sea | BP Miller |
| | | NFM | North Sea | Shell Brent D |
| | | NFM | North Sea | Shell North Cormorant |
| 462.2000 | 462.2000 | FM | Nationwide | John Sisk & Son Construction Ch 2 |
| | | NFM | North Sea | Shell Auk |

| Base | Mobile | Mode | Location | User and Notes |
|------|--------|------|----------|----------------|
| 462.2250 | | NFM | Hull | Docks |
| 462.2250 | 456.7250 | NFM | London Chelsea | National Army Museum |
| 462.2250 | 456.2250 | NFM | North Sea | BP Miller |
| 462.2250 | 456.7250 | NFM | North Sea | BP SMV |
| 462.2500 | 462.2500 | NFM | Barrow in Furness | VSEL Nuclear Incident Channel |
| | | NFM | Blackpool | Security |
| | | NFM | Bournemouth | Marks & Spencer Security |
| | | NFM | Coventry | Marks & Spencer Security |
| | | NFM | Ipswich | Littlewoods |
| | | NFM | Kirkcaldy | Marks & Spencers Security |
| | | NFM | London (Heathrow) | Ground Staff |
| | | NFM | Peterborough | Marks & Spencer Security |
| 462.2500 | 446.2500 | NFM | Stevenage | Marks & Spencer Security |
| 462.2740 | 345.8750 | FM | Nationwide | John Sisk & Son Construction Ch 1 |
| 462.2750 | 456.7750 | NFM | Aberdeen, Dyce Airport | BP |
| 462.2750 | 462.2750 | NFM | Blackpool | Pleasure Beach Patrol |
| 462.3000 | 462.3000 | NFM | Blackpool | Security Town Centre Stores |
| 462.3000 | 456.8000 | NFM | Brent B | Shell PMR |
| | | NFM | Cormorant A | Shell PMR |
| | | NFM | Fulmar | Shell PMR |
| 462.3000 | 462.3000 | NFM | North Sea | Total MCP-01 |
| 462.3000 | 456.8000 | NFM | North Sea | Total St. Fergus |
| | | NFM | Slough | Coopers-Payen Ltd Security |
| 462.3250 | 456.8250 | NFM | Harrow on the Hill | St Georges's Shopping Centre |
| | | NFM | Ipswich | Port Authority Channel 4 |
| | | NFM | London | Earls Court & Olympia Security |
| 462.3625 | 462.3625 | NFM | Jersey | PMR |
| | | NFM | Nationwide | Short Term Hire |
| 462.3750 | 456.8750 | NFM | Doncaster | Car Park Security |
| | | NFM | North Sea | Shell Auk |
| | | NFM | North Sea | Shell Brent A |
| | | NFM | North Sea | Shell Dunlin |
| | | NFM | Peterborough | Boots Security |
| | | NFM | London, central | Black Taxi control |
| 462.4000 | 456.9000 | NFM | Chelmsford | Town Centre Security |
| | | NFM | London | Corporation of London |
| | | NFM | North Sea | BP SMV |
| | | NFM | North Sea | Total Alwyn |
| | | NFM | North Sea | Total St. Fergus |
| | | NFM | Stevenage | ICL security |
| 462.4250 | 462.4250 | NFM | Bristol | Zoo |
| | | NFM | Jersey | Short Term Hire Radios |
| | | NFM | London | TV Programme 'The Bill' |
| | | NFM | Nationwide | Short Term Hire |
| | | NFM | North Sea | BP Welton |
| | | NFM | Sheffield | Sheffield Arena |
| | | NFM | Southend-on-Sea | Victoria Circus Precinct Security |
| 462.4750 | 456.9750 | NFM | Ashford | Shop Security |
| | | NFM | Doncaster | RJB Mining |
| | | NFM | Jersey | Short Term Hire Radios |
| | | NFM | London | Horse Guards Parade security |
| | | NFM | London | TV Programme 'The Bill' |
| | | NFM | London, Oxford Street | British Home Stores security |
| | | NFM | Nationwide | Short Term Hire Equipment |
| | | NFM | North Sea | Shell St. Fergus |
| | | NFM | Shire Oaks | Shire Oaks Colliery NCB Security |

| Base | Mobile | Mode | Location | User and Notes |
|------|--------|------|----------|----------------|
| 462.4875 | 462.4875 | NFM | Brighton | Marina Asda Supermarket |
| | | NFM | Doncaster | Clarks Shoes |
| | | NFM | Jersey | Short Term Hire Radios |
| | | NFM | Nationwide | Short Term Hire |

**462.5000 - 462.7500 MHz    EMERGENCY SERVICES 12.5 kHz NFM**

| Base | Mobile | Mode | Location | User and Notes |
|------|--------|------|----------|----------------|
| 462.5750 | 457.0750 | NFM | Aberdeen | Scottish Hydro Electric |
| 462.5875 | | NFM | Fife | Fire Brigade Channel 2 |
| 462.6000 | 462.6000 | NFM | Cheshire | Parcel Delivery |
| 462.6250 | 462.6250 | NFM | Nationwide | Red Devils Parachute Team |
| 462.6275 | | NFM | Fife | Fire Brigade Channel 5 |
| 462.6500 | 466.5500 | NFM | Poole | Police |
| 462.7750 | | NFM | Ipswich | Data Traffic |
| 462.7750 | 458.2750 | NFM | North Sea | Conoco Murchison DKN |
| 462.8500 | | NFM | Merseyside | Haulage |
| 462.9250 | | NFM | Cambridgeshire | Ambulance Service |
| | | NFM | Norfolk | Ambulance Service |
| | | NFM | Suffolk | Ambulance Service |
| 462.9500 | | NFM | Cleveland | Ambulance Service |
| | | NFM | Cumbria | Ambulance Service |
| | | NFM | Durham | Ambulance Service |
| | | NFM | East Dorset | Ambulance Service |
| | | NFM | Hampshire | Ambulance Service |
| | | NFM | Isle of Wight | Ambulance Service |
| | | NFM | Northumbria | Ambulance Service |
| 462.9750 | | NFM | Cambridgeshire | Ambulance Service |
| | | NFM | Norfolk | Ambulance Service |
| | | NFM | Suffolk | Ambulance Service |

**463.0000 - 464.0000 MHz    SCANNING TELEMETRY LINKS**

| Base | Mobile | Mode | Location | User and Notes |
|------|--------|------|----------|----------------|
| 463.05500 | | NFM | Tamworth | BT data |
| 463.27500 | 457.77500 | NFM | Fulmar | FSU Shell Telemetry |
| 463.35000 | 457.85000 | NFM | North Sea | Conoco Viking Field |
| 463.37500 | 463.37500 | NFM | North Sea | BP Buchan |
| 463.37500 | 457.87500 | NFM | North Sea | BP ESV III |
| | | NFM | North Sea | BP Forties D to Forties Kiwi |
| 463.72500 | 458.22500 | NFM | North Sea | Conoco Murchison |
| | | NFM | North Sea | Shell Brent A PLIS backup to Dunlin A |
| | | NFM | North Sea | Shell Brent B PLIS backup to Dunlin A |
| | | NFM | North Sea | Shell Brent C PLIS backup to Dunlin A |
| | | NFM | North Sea | Shell Brent D |
| | | NFM | North Sea | Shell Brent Spar |
| | | NFM | North Sea | Shell Cormorant A |
| | | NFM | North Sea | Shell N. Cormorant |
| 463.82500 | | NFM | North Sea | Conoco Murchison |
| 463.90620 | 458.45620 | NFM | North Sea | FSU Chevron Alba to ANP, FSD data |
| 463.91870 | 458.41870 | NFM | North Sea | Shell Kittiwake Loading Buoy |
| | | NFM | North Sea | Shell Stadfill Cormorant A |
| 463.93120 | 458.43120 | NFM | North Sea | Shell Kittiwake Tanker Loading Buoy |
| 463.95000 | 458.45000 | NFM | Murchison | Conoco |
| | | NFM | North Sea | Shell Brent A |
| | | NFM | North Sea | Shell Brent B PEL Backup to Dunlin A |
| | | NFM | North Sea | Shell Brent C PEL Backup to Dunlin A |
| | | NFM | North Sea | Shell Brent D PEL Backup to Dunlin A |
| | | NFM | North Sea | Shell Brent Spar |
| | | NFM | North Sea | Shell Cormorant N |

| Base | Mobile | Mode | Location | User and Notes |
|------|--------|------|----------|----------------|

464.0000 - 467.2500 MHz   POLICE AND AMBULANCE PR BASE &
REPEATER SYSTEM SCOTLAND .
LIMITED USE IN ENGLAND.

| Base | Mobile | Mode | Location | User and Notes |
|------|--------|------|----------|----------------|
| 464.0750 | 450.0750 | NFM | Edinburgh | Police Tynecastle Match Control |
| 464.1250 | 464.1250 | NFM | Bishop Auckland | Police Footbal Security |
| 464.2000 | 460.2000 | NFM | Cumbernauld | Police Channel 15 (N) |
| 464.3500 | 450.3500 | NFM | Edinburgh | Police Special Events |
| 464.4000 | 450.4000 | NFM | Edinburgh | Police Special Events |
| 464.4500 | 450.4500 | NFM | Edinburgh | Police Special Events |
| 464.5000 | 450.5000 | NFM | Edinburgh | Police Special Events |
| 464.6750 | 450.6750 | NFM | Edinburgh | Police Special Events |
| 464.7500 | 450.7500 | NFM | Edinburgh | Police Special Events |
| 464.7750 | 450.7750 | NFM | Edinburgh | Police Special Events |
| 465.0000 | 451.0000 | NFM | Edinburgh | Police |
| 465.0000 | | NFM | Musselburgh | Police |
| 465.0250 | 451.0250 | NFM | Lothian and Borders | Police (N) East Lothian |
| 465.0500 | 451.0500 | NFM | Bristol | Private Traffic Wardens |
| | | NFM | Dalkeith | Police |
| | | NFM | Lothian and Borders | Police |
| 465.1000 | 451.1000 | NFM | Broxburn | Police (F) |
| 465.1250 | 451.1250 | NFM | Edinburgh | Police |
| 465.1500 | 451.1500 | NFM | South Queensferry | Police (F) |
| 465.2500 | 451.2500 | NFM | Bristol | Transport Police (Temple Meads) |
| | | NFM | Edinburgh | Police (CV) Corstorphine |
| 465.2750 | 451.2750 | NFM | Edinburgh | Police (CH) Westerhailes |
| 465.3000 | 451.3000 | NFM | Denny | Police Channel 7 (F) |
| | | NFM | Fife | Police |
| | | NFM | Kilmarnock | Police U Div Pocket Phone |
| | | NFM | Troon | Police |
| 465.3250 | 451.3250 | NFM | Hawick | Police |
| | | NFM | Perth | Police (W) |
| 465.4250 | 465.4250 | NFM | Dubly Hill | Police (GB) |
| 465.4250 | 451.4250 | NFM | Fife | Police |
| 465.4750 | 451.4750 | NFM | Brechin | Police |
| | | NFM | Montrose | Police |
| 465.6000 | 451.6000 | NFM | Bonnyrigg | Police |
| | | NFM | Glasgow | Police |
| | | NFM | Larkhall | Police |
| | | NFM | Pennicook | Police |
| 465.6250 | 451.6250 | NFM | Bristol | City Line Buses |
| | | NFM | Edinburgh | Police Special Events |
| | | NFM | Falkirk | Falkirk Football Square |
| | | NFM | Glasgow | Police Special Events |
| | | NFM | Perth | Police Special Events |
| 465.6250 | 466.5250 | NFM | Hove | Police |
| 465.6500 | 465.6500 | NFM | Glasgow | Police |
| 465.6500 | 451.6500 | NFM | Hamilton | Police |
| 465.6750 | 451.6750 | NFM | Edinburgh | Police Special Events |
| | | NFM | Glasgow | Police Special Events |
| | | NFM | Perth | Party Conference (L Control) |
| 465.6750 | 451.7000 | NFM | Motherwell | Police |
| 465.7250 | 451.7250 | NFM | Edinburgh | Police Hibernian FC (ZH) |
| | | NFM | Edinburgh | Shoplifting Squad |
| | | NFM | Glasgow | Police Special Events |
| | | NFM | Perth | Party Conference (S Control) |

| Base | Mobile | Mode | Location | User and Notes |
|------|--------|------|----------|----------------|
| 465.7500 | 451.7500 | NFM | Wishaw | Police |
| 465.7750 | 451.7750 | NFM | Edinburgh | Police Special Events |
| | | NFM | Glasgow | Police Special Events |
| | | NFM | Perth | Party Conference (C Control) |
| | | NFM | Yorkshire | Police Command Vehicle |
| 465.8000 | 451.8000 | NFM | Dunbar | Police |
| | | NFM | Edinburgh | Police |
| 465.8750 | 465.8750 | NFM | Midlands | Police Helicopter (Air 1) |
| 465.9000 | 465.9000 | NFM | West Midlands | Police Helicopter Channel 2 |
| 465.9250 | 451.8250 | NFM | Glasgow | Police |
| 466.0250 | 452.0250 | NFM | Stirling | Police |
| 466.1750 | | NFM | Lancashire | Police Ch9 |
| 466.2500 | 452.2500 | NFM | Aberdeen | Police |
| | | NFM | Ayr | Police |
| | | NFM | Dalkeith | Police |
| | | NFM | Dumfries &Galloway | Police |
| | | NFM | Edinburgh | Police Firearms Support Group |
| | | NFM | Edinburgh | St Leonards Div HQ (B) Channel 2 |
| | | NFM | Glasgow | Police Firearms Support Group |
| 466.2750 | 452.2750 | NFM | Aberdeen | Police |
| | | NFM | Ayr | Traffic Wardens (TW) |
| | | NFM | Dumfries & Galloway | Police |
| | | NFM | Edinburgh | Police (C) Edinburgh Tattoo |
| | | NFM | Edinburgh | Traffic Wardens (TW and TM) |
| | | NFM | Glasgow | Traffic Wardens (TW) |
| | | NFM | Lanark | Traffic Wardens (TW) |
| | | NFM | Perth | Police (Racecourse Control) |
| | | NFM | Perth | Traffic Wardens (TW) |
| 466.3000 | 452.3000 | NFM | Fife | Traffic Wardens |
| 466.3250 | 452.3250 | NFM | Dumbarton | Police (L) |
| | | NFM | Edinburgh | Police Oxgangs (CO) |
| | | NFM | Edinburgh | Police Westerhailes (CH) |
| 466.3500 | 451.3500 | NFM | Glasgow | Police (E ) |
| 466.3750 | 452.3750 | NFM | Edinburgh | Police |
| | | NFM | Glasgow | Police Barrhead (K) |
| 466.4000 | 451.4000 | NFM | Aberdeen | HM Prison  Aberdeen |
| | | NFM | Dumfries | HM Young Offenders Instution |
| | | NFM | Edinburgh | HM Prison  Saughton |
| | | NFM | Forfar | HM Prison  Noranside |
| | | NFM | Glasgow | HM Prison  Barlinnie |
| | | NFM | Lothian and Borders | Police (E) |
| | | NFM | Perth | HM Prison  Friarton |
| | | NFM | St Andrews | Traffic Wardens |
| | | NFM | Stirling | HM Prison  Corinton Vale (Control) |
| 466.4250 | 452.4250 | NFM | Edinburgh | Police |
| | | NFM | Peebles | Police |
| 466.4500 | 452.4500 | NFM | Dundee | Police (ZS) |
| | | NFM | Glasgow | Police North (C) |
| 466.4750 | 452.4750 | NFM | Dumfries & Galloway | Police |
| 466.5000 | 452.5000 | NFM | Alloa | Police Channel 6 (A) |
| | | NFM | Arbroath | Police |
| | | NFM | Argyll | Police (A) |
| | | NFM | Dalbeattie | Police |
| | | NFM | Dumfries & Galloway | Police |
| | | NFM | Edinburgh | Police |
| | | NFM | Forfar | Police |

| Base | Mobile | Mode | Location | User and Notes |
|------|--------|------|----------|----------------|
| 466.5000 | 452.5000 | NFM | Glasgow | Police Central (A) |
| | | NFM | Kirkcudbright | Police |
| | | NFM | Moffat | Police |
| | | NFM | Perth | Police (W) |
| | | NFM | Stirling | Police |
| 466.5250 | 452.5250 | NFM | Edinburgh | Police City Centre |
| | | NFM | Perth | Police St. Johnstone FC |
| | | NFM | Selkirk | Police |
| 466.5500 | 452.5500 | NFM | Argyll | Police (B) |
| | | NFM | Glasgow | Police West (B) |
| | | NFM | Inverness | Police |
| | | NFM | Irvine | Police (U) |
| | | NFM | Kilbirnie | Police (G) |
| | | NFM | Killwinning | Police (U) |
| | | NFM | Kilmarnock | Police (U) |
| | | NFM | Stirling | Police Channel 5 (S) |
| 466.5750 | 452.5750 | NFM | Edinburgh | Police West End Div HQ (C) |
| 466.6000 | 452.6000 | NFM | Aberdeen | Police |
| | | NFM | Angus | Police |
| | | NFM | Cupar | Police |
| | | NFM | Glasgow | Police Easterhill (D) |
| | | NFM | Kilmarnock | Police |
| 466.6250 | 452.6250 | NFM | Aberdeen | Police |
| | | NFM | Edinburgh | Police Gayfield (BG) |
| | | NFM | Fort William | Police |
| | | NFM | Thurso | Police (M2URCE) |
| 466.6500 | 452.6500 | NFM | Aberdeen | Police |
| | | NFM | Ayr | Police (R) |
| | | NFM | Ballater | Police (UBK5) |
| | | NFM | Edinburgh | Police Drylaw (DR ) |
| | | NFM | Edinburgh | Police Royston (Encrypted) |
| | | NFM | Glasgow | Police Kilpatrick (M) |
| | | NFM | Glasgow | Police South/East (F) |
| 466.6750 | 452.6750 | NFM | Edinburgh | Police Portobello |
| | | NFM | Portobello | Police (DJ & DN) |
| 466.7000 | 452.7000 | NFM | Ayr | Police (X) |
| | | NFM | Musselburgh | Police |
| | | NFM | Strathclyde | Police Helicopter |
| 466.7250 | 452.7250 | NFM | Livingstone | Police (F) |
| 466.7400 | | NFM | Falkirk | Police Channel 3 (F) |
| 466.7500 | 452.7750 | NFM | Falkirk | Police |
| | | NFM | Glasgow | Police Ibrox (G) |
| | | NFM | Stirling | Police |
| | | NFM | Glasgow | Police Hamilton (Q) |
| | | NFM | Grangemouth | Police Channel 4 (G) |
| | | NFM | Hamilton | Police (Q) |
| 466.8000 | 452.8000 | NFM | Edinburgh | Police Firearms Support Group |
| | | NFM | Glasgow | Police Firearms Support Group |
| 466.8000 | 452.9000 | NFM | Truleigh Hill | Fire Brigade |
| 466.8250 | | NFM | Airdrie | Police |
| 466.8250 | 452.8250 | NFM | Edinburgh | Police Leith |
| | | NFM | Lanark | Police (N) |
| | | NFM | Leith | Police (D) Division HQ |
| | | NFM | Nationwide | Army Air Corps Parachute Team Loader |

| Base | Mobile | Mode | Location | User and Notes |
|------|--------|------|----------|----------------|
| 466.8750 | 452.8750 | NFM | Galashiels | Police |
| 466.8750 | 452.9000 | NFM | Truleigh Hill | Fire Brigade |
| 466.9000 | 452.9000 | NFM | Edinburgh | Police Firearms Support Group |
|  |  | NFM | Glasgow | Police Firearms Support Group |
| 466.9250 |  | NFM | Abington | Police Repeater |
| 466.9750 |  | NFM | Enniskillen | Military Data Link |
| 467.0250 |  | NFM | Hereford | Ambulance Service |
|  |  | NFM | Mid Staffordshire | Ambulance Service |
|  |  | NFM | Salop | Ambulance Service |
|  |  | NFM | South Warwickshire | Ambulance Service |
|  |  | NFM | Worcestershire | Ambulance Service |
| 467.0375 | 457.0375 | NFM | Dartford | Fire Service handhelds and Combs fire handhelds (VC) |
| 467.0500 | 460.5500 | NFM | Guernsey | ATC Link |
|  |  | NFM | Jersey | ATC Link |
| 467.0500 |  | NFM | Wales | Ambulance Service |
| 467.1250 |  | NFM | Cleveland | Ambulance Service |
|  |  | NFM | Cumbria | Ambulance Service |
|  |  | NFM | Durham | Ambulance Service |
|  |  | NFM | Northumbria | Ambulance Service |
| 467.1500 |  | NFM | Cleveland | Ambulance Service |
|  |  | NFM | Cumbria | Ambulance Service |
|  |  | NFM | Durham | Ambulance Service |
|  |  | NFM | Northumbria | Ambulance Service |
| 467.2000 |  | NFM | Dublin | Fire Service |
| 467.2250 |  | NFM | Bristol | Ambulance Service |
|  |  | NFM | Cornwall | Ambulance Service |
|  |  | NFM | Devon | Ambulance Service |
|  |  | NFM | Gloucester | Ambulance Service |
|  |  | NFM | Scilly Isles | Ambulance Service |
|  |  | NFM | Somerset | Ambulance Service |
| 467.2500 |  | NFM | Cleveland | Ambulance Service |
|  |  | NFM | Cumbria | Ambulance Service |
|  |  | NFM | Durham | Ambulance Service |
|  |  | NFM | Northumbria | Ambulance Service |
|  |  | NFM | Wales | Ambulance Service |
| 467.3000 |  | NFM | Nationwide | BBC Radio 5 O/B |
| 467.3500 |  | NFM | Wirral | Emergency Doctors |
| 467.4237 |  | NFM | London | BBC Radio 5 Talkback |
| 467.4250 |  | NFM | London | BBC Radio Engineers |
| 467.4750 |  | NFM | Burnley | Granada TV OB |
|  |  | NFM | Wales | Ambulance Service |
| 467.4937 |  | NFM | London | Carlton TV Talkback |
|  |  | NFM | London | ITV Weather |

**467.5250 - 467.5750 MHz    INTERNATIONAL MARINE ON-BOARD HANDHELD TRANSCEIVERS 6.25 kHz (SPLIT + 5.5 MHz)**

| Base | Mobile | Mode | Location | User and Notes |
|------|--------|------|----------|----------------|
| 467.5250 | 457.5250 | NFM | Maritime | Ship Portable Channel 6 |
| 467.5250 | 467.5250 | NFM | Maritime | Ship Communications |
| 467.5250 | 461.0250 | NFM | North Sea | BP West Sole A to Easington |
| 467.5375 |  | NFM | Maritime | Ships Portable Channel 7 |
| 467.5500 | 467.5500 | NFM | Maritime | Ship Portable Channel 8 |
|  |  | NFM | North Sea | BP Thistle A |

| Base | Mobile | Mode | Location | User and Notes |
|------|--------|------|----------|----------------|
| 467.5500 | 461.0500 | NFM | North Sea | Stiell Brent A |
| 467.5500 | 467.5500 | NFM | North Sea | Unocol Heather A |
| 467.5625 | | NFM | Maritime | Ships Portable Channel 9 |
| 467.5750 | 467.5750 | NFM | Maritime | Ship Portable Channel 10 |
| 467.5750 | 457.5750 | NFM | Montrose Docks | Big Orange XVIII |
| | | NFM | North Sea | BP Thistle A |
| | | NFM | North Sea | BP West Sole A to Easington |
| | | NFM | North Sea | Sun Oil Balmoral portables |

## 467.57500 - 470.000 MHz  BROADCASTING AND UHF POINT TO POINT LINKS (SPLIT 6.0 MHz)

| Base | Mobile | Mode | Location | User and Notes |
|------|--------|------|----------|----------------|
| 467.57500 | | NFM | Belfast | Downtown Radio O/B |
| 467.61250 | | WFM | Salisbury | Spire FM O/B |
| 467.62500 | 461.12500 | NFM | North Sea | FSU Shell Fulmar |
| 467.66250 | | NFM | Coventry | Mercia Sound Outside Broadcast |
| 467.66250 | 467.61250 | NFM | London | Capital Radio Flying Eye |
| 467.67500 | 467.67500 | NFM | Maritime | Ship Communications |
| 467.67500 | 461.17500 | NFM | North Sea | Phillips Hewett Field to Gt Yarmouth |
| 467.71250 | | WFM | Berkshire | Radio 210 Outside Broadcasts |
| | | WFM | Hampshire | Radio 210 Outside Broadcasts |
| | | NFM | Swansea | Swansea Sound O/B |
| 467.72500 | 462.25000 | NFM | Castle Donington | Grand Prix Team |
| 467.72500 | | NFM | Nationwide | Grand Prix Benneton Team |
| 467.75000 | | NFM | Dublin | Police L/M/G/P |
| 467.77500 | | NFM | North Sea | Shell Brent A |
| 467.87500 | 461.87500 | NFM | Nationwide | Philips Telecom Mobiles |
| | | NFM | North Sea | Shell Brent A |
| 467.87500 | 461.37500 | NFM | North Sea | Shell Brent Spar |
| 467.87500 | 461.37500 | NFM | North Sea | Shell Fulmar A to Auk-A |
| 467.91500 | | NFM | North Sea | Shell N. Cormorant |
| 467.92500 | 461.92500 | NFM | Nationwide | Philips Telecom Mobiles |
| 467.92500 | 461.42500 | NFM | North Sea | Shell to Auk-A |
| 467.97500 | 461.47500 | NFM | North Sea | Shell To Auk-A |

## 468.0000 - 468.3500 MHz  O/B TALKBACK AND UHF POINT TO POINT LINKS 25 kHz

| Base | Mobile | Mode | Location | User and Notes |
|------|--------|------|----------|----------------|
| 468.00000 | 141.00000 | NFM | London | LWT |
| 468.02500 | 468.02500 | NFM | North Sea | Chevron Ninian South |
| 468.05000 | | NFM | Jersey | Channel TV Talkback |
| 468.05000 | 468.05000 | NFM | North Sea | Chevron Ninian South |
| 468.07500 | | NFM | Kent | Invicta Radio |
| 468.08750 | 141.18000 | NFM | Kent | Heli-Teli Radio Uplink |
| | | NFM | Leicester | Sunrise Radio O/B |
| | | NFM | Tayside | Radio Tay Talkback |
| | | NFM | York | Great Yorkshire Gold c/b |
| 468.12500 | 468.12500 | NFM | North Sea | Chevron Ninian South |
| 468.13670 | | NFM | London | Spectrum Radio Flying Eye |
| 468.13750 | 141.08750 | NFM | Manchester | Key 103 Eye in the Sky |
| 468.13750 | 468.13750 | NFM | Sussex | Local Radio Flying Eye |
| 468.15000 | | NFM | Castle Donington | Italian TV Talkback |
| | | NFM | Nationwide | BBC Radio 1 Roadshow O/B |
| 468.16250 | 468.16250 | NFM | North Sea | Chevron Ninian South |
| 468.25000 | | NFM | Nationwide | BBC Radio 1 O/B |
| 468.27500 | | NFM | Nationwide | BBC Radio 1 O/B |

| Base | Mobile | Mode | Location | User and Notes |
|------|--------|------|----------|----------------|

**468.3500 - 469.4750 MHz** OUTSIDE BROADCAST TALKBACK AND
UHF POINT TO POINT LINKS

| Base | Mobile | Mode | Location | User and Notes |
|------|--------|------|----------|----------------|
| 468.35000 | 468.35000 | NFM | Ninian South | Chevron |
| 468.37500 | 468.37500 | NFM | Nationwide | ITV Cameras |
| 468.39000 | | NFM | Jersey | Channel TV Talkback |
| 468.40000 | 454.40000 | NFM | North Sea | BP Forties A |
| 468.42500 | 468.42500 | NFM | England | Central TV Base Link Input |
| | | NFM | North Sea | Chevron Ninian South |
| 468.46250 | 468.46250 | NFM | Inverness | Moray Firth Radio O/B |
| 468.47500 | 468.47500 | NFM | Nationwide | IBA Riggers |
| 468.50000 | 468.50000 | NFM | Nationwide | ITV O/B |
| 469.00000 | 455.60000 | NFM | North Sea | BP Forties C |
| | | NFM | Preston | Radio Lancashire O/B |
| 469.01250 | 469.01250 | NFM | Berkshire | BBC Radio Berkshire Radio Car |
| | | NFM | Humberside | BBC Radio Humberside O/B |
| | | NFM | Shropshire | BBC Radio Shropshire O/B |
| 469.06250 | 469.06250 | NFM | Nationwide | BBC Radio 5 O/B |
| 469.11250 | | NFM | Lincoln | BBC Radio Lincolnshire O/B |
| | | NFM | London | BBC Radio 5 Talkback |
| | | NFM | London | Choice FM Flying Eye |
| | | NFM | London | Jazz FM Flying Eye |
| | | NFM | London | Star FM Flying Eye |
| | | NFM | York | BBC Radio York |
| 469.21250 | 469.21250 | NFM | Nationwide | BBC Radio 5 O/B |
| 469.24000 | 469.24000 | NFM | London | Executive Buses |
| 469.26250 | | NFM | Liverpool | Radio City Talkback |
| | | NFM | London | LBC FM Flying Eye |
| 469.31250 | 469.31250 | NFM | East Sussex | Radio Mercury |
| 469.36250 | 469.36250 | NFM | Berkshire | Radio 210 Outside Broadcasts |
| | | NFM | Glasgow | Radio Clyde Traffic Helicopter |
| | | NFM | Hampshire | Radio 210 Outside Broadcasts |
| | | NFM | Swansea | Swansea Sound O/B |
| | | NFM | Wrexham | Marcher Gold Talkback |
| 469.36975 | | NFM | Essex | BBC Radio Essex Flying Eye |
| 469.37500 | | NFM | Manchester | BBC Radio O/B |
| 469.41250 | 469.41250 | NFM | Essex | Saxon Radio |
| | | NFM | London | LBC Aircraft Downlink |
| 469.46250 | 141.18750 | NFM | Cowley | Fox FM Flying Eye Downlink |
| 469.46250 | | NFM | Kent | Invicta Heli-Radio Uplink |
| | | NFM | London | Kiss FM Flying Eye |
| 469.57500 | | NFM | Doncaster | Continental Landscapes Ltd |
| 469.66250 | | NFM | Manchester | Picadilly Radio Programme link |
| 469.75000 | 469.75000 | NFM | Castle Donington | French TV Talkback |
| | | NFM | North Sea | Phillips EkoFisk-B |

**469.8750 - 470.0000 MHz** EMERGENCY SERVICES NFM

470.0000 - 590.0000 MHz    UK AND IRISH TV CHANNELS (SOUND/VIDEO)
LOCAL RADIO TALKBACK AND
THEATRE RADIOMICROPHONES (10mW MAX)

## UK Television
Band IV

| Sound | Vision | | | |
|---|---|---|---|---|
| 477.250 | 471.250 | WFM | Nationwide | Channel 21 |
| 485.250 | 479.250 | WFM | Nationwide | Channel 22 |
| 493.250 | 487.250 | WFM | Nationwide | Channel 23 |
| 501.250 | 495.250 | WFM | Nationwide | Channel 24 |
| 509.250 | 503.250 | WFM | Nationwide | Channel 25 |
| 511.250 | 517.250 | WFM | Nationwide | Channel 26 |
| 525.250 | 519.250 | WFM | Nationwide | Channel 27 |
| 533.250 | 527.250 | WFM | Nationwide | Channel 28 |
| 541.250 | 535.250 | WFM | Nationwide | Channel 29 |
| 549.250 | 543.250 | WFM | Nationwide | Channel 30 |
| 557.250 | 551.250 | WFM | Nationwide | Channel 31 |
| 565.250 | 559.250 | WFM | Nationwide | Channel 32 |
| 573.250 | 567.250 | WFM | Nationwide | Channel 33 |
| 581.250 | 575.250 | WFM | Nationwide | Channel 34 |
| 583.250 | 589.250 | WFM | Nationwide | Channel 35 Channel 5 TV |
| 599.250 | 605.250 | WFM | Nationwide | Channel 37 Channel 5 TV |

## Local Radio Talkback and Theatre Radiomicrophones

| | | | |
|---|---|---|---|
| 470.50650 | NFM | Nationwide | British Telecom |
| 474.05000 | NFM | Norwich | Anglia TV Channel 1 |
| 474.10000 | NFM | Norwich | Anglia TV Channel 2 |
| 474.20000 | NFM | Norwich | Anglia TV Channel 3 |
| 474.40000 | NFM | Norwich | Anglia TV Channel 4 |
| 476.47500 | NFM | London | Capital Radio Flying Eye |
| 478.00000 | NFM | London | Radio London |
| 478.70000 | NFM | Nationwide | Theatre Radiomicrophone |
| 479.65000 | NFM | London | "Her Majesty's Theatre" |
| | NFM | Nationwide | Theatre Radiomicrophone |
| 479.95000 | NFM | London | "Her Majesty's Theatre" |
| 480.20000 | NFM | London | "Her Majesty's Theatre" |
| | NFM | Nationwide | Theatre Radiomicrophone |
| 480.40000 | NFM | Nationwide | Theatre Radiomicrophone |
| 488.82500 | NFM | London | Talking Clock |
| 488.98750 | NFM | Aldermaston | AWE surport services Ch2 (ESF) |
| 497.50000 | NFM | Nationwide | Theatre Radiomicrophone |
| 497.70000 | NFM | Nationwide | Theatre Radiomicrophone |
| 498.48000 | NFM | Nationwide | Theatre Radiomicrophone |
| 498.78000 | NFM | Nationwide | Theatre Radiomicrophone |
| 499.61000 | NFM | Nationwide | Theatre Radiomicrophone |
| 500.00000 | AM | Nationwide | NATO Mayday Discreet |
| 500.28000 | NFM | Nationwide | Theatre Radiomicrophone |
| 502.44000 | NFM | Nationwide | Theatre Radiomicrophone |
| 502.69000 | NFM | Nationwide | Theatre Radiomicrophone |
| 583.69000 | NFM | Nationwide | Theatre Radiomicrophone |
| 584.15000 | NFM | Nationwide | Theatre Radiomicrophone |

| Base | Mobile | Mode | Location | User and Notes |
|------|--------|------|----------|----------------|

**Irish Television**

| Base | Mobile | Mode | Location | User and Notes |
|------|--------|------|----------|----------------|
| 477.250 | 471.250 | WFM | Ballybofey | RTE 1 |
| | | WFM | Cahir | RTE 1 |
| | | WFM | Stranolar | RTE 1 |
| 485.250 | 479.250 | WFM | Kerry | RTE 1 |
| | | WFM | Malin | RTE 1 |
| 493.250 | | WFM | Dingle | RTE 1 |
| 493.250 | | WFM | Donegal | RTE 1 |
| 501.250 | | WFM | Cahir | Network 2 |
| 509.250 | | WFM | Kerry | Network 2 |
| | | WFM | Malin | Network 2 |
| 511.250 | | WFM | Dingle | Network 2 |
| | | WFM | Donegal | Network 2 |
| 519.250 | | WFM | Clonmel | RTE 1 |
| 541.250 | | WFM | Co. Cork | RTE 1 |
| | | WFM | Dublin | RTE 1 |
| 549.250 | | WFM | Youghal | RTE 1 |
| 549.259 | | WFM | Bandon | RTE 1 |
| | | WFM | Knockmoyle | RTE 1 |
| 557.250 | | WFM | Ballybofey | Network 2 |
| | | WFM | Clonmel | Network 2 |
| | | WFM | Stranolar | Network 2 |
| 573.250 | | WFM | Co. Cork | Network 2 |
| | | WFM | Dublin | Network 2 |
| 581.250 | | WFM | Bandon | Network 2 |
| | | WFM | Knockmoyle | Network 2 |
| | | WFM | Youghal | Network 2 |

590.0000 - 598.0000 MHz   CIVIL & DEFENCE RADAR

606.0000 - 614.0000 MHz   RADIO ASTRONOMY

614.0000 - 854.0000 MHz   UK AND IRISH TELEVISION CHANNELS
(SOUND/VIDEO)

UK Television
Band V

| Sound | Vision | | | |
|-------|--------|------|----------|----------------|
| 621.250 | 615.250 | WFM | Nationwide | Channel 39 |
| 629.250 | 623.250 | WFM | Nationwide | Channel 40 |
| 637.250 | 631.250 | WFM | Nationwide | Channel 41 |
| 645.250 | 639.250 | WFM | Nationwide | Channel 42 |
| 653.250 | 647.250 | WFM | Nationwide | Channel 43 |
| 661.250 | 655.250 | WFM | Nationwide | Channel 44 |
| 669.250 | 663.250 | WFM | Nationwide | Channel 45 |
| 677.250 | 671.250 | WFM | Nationwide | Channel 46 |
| 685.250 | 679.250 | WFM | Nationwide | Channel 47 |
| 693.250 | 687.250 | WFM | Nationwide | Channel 48 |
| 701.250 | 695.250 | WFM | Nationwide | Channel 49 |
| 709.250 | 703.250 | WFM | Nationwide | Channel 50 |
| 717.250 | 711.250 | WFM | Nationwide | Channel 51 |
| 725.250 | 719.250 | WFM | Nationwide | Channel 52 |
| 733.250 | 727.250 | WFM | Nationwide | Channel 53 |
| 741.250 | 735.250 | WFM | Nationwide | Channel 54 |

| Base | Mobile | Mode | Location | User and Notes |
|---|---|---|---|---|
| Sound | Vision | | | |
| 749.250 | 743.250 | WFM | Nationwide | Channel 55 |
| 757.250 | 751.250 | WFM | Nationwide | Channel 56 |
| 765.250 | 759.250 | WFM | Nationwide | Channel 57 |
| 773.250 | 767.250 | WFM | Nationwide | Channel 58 |
| 781.250 | 775.250 | WFM | Nationwide | Channel 59 |
| 789.250 | 783.250 | WFM | Nationwide | Channel 60 |
| 797.250 | 791.250 | WFM | Nationwide | Channel 61 |
| 805.250 | 799.250 | WFM | Nationwide | Channel 62 |
| 813.250 | 807.250 | WFM | Nationwide | Channel 63 |
| 821.250 | 815.250 | WFM | Nationwide | Channel 64 |
| 829.250 | 823.250 | WFM | Nationwide | Channel 65 |
| 837.250 | 831.250 | WFM | Nationwide | Channel 66 |
| 845.250 | 839.250 | WFM | Nationwide | Channel 67 |
| 853.250 | 847.250 | WFM | Nationwide | Channel 68 |

Irish Television

| Base | | Mode | Location | User and Notes |
|---|---|---|---|---|
| 621.250 | | WFM | Bantry | RTE 1 |
| | | WFM | Cork City | RTE 1 |
| | | WFM | Glenbeigh | RTE 1 |
| 629.250 | | WFM | Dunquin | RTE 1 |
| | | WFM | Longford | RTE 1 |
| 645.250 | | WFM | Glenbeigh | Network 2 |
| | | WFM | Dunquin | Network 2 |
| | | WFM | Longford | Network 2 |
| 693.250 | | WFM | Limerick City | RTE 1 |
| 701.250 | | WFM | Bantry | Network 2 |
| | | WFM | Cork City | Network 2 |
| 725.250 | | WFM | Limerick City | Network 2 |
| | | WFM | Louth | RTE 1 |
| 733.250 | | WFM | Inistioge | RTE 1 |
| 749.250 | | WFM | Crosshaven | RTE 1 |
| 757.250 | | WFM | Louth | Network 2 |
| 765.250 | | WFM | Inistioge | Network 2 |
| 781.250 | | WFM | Crosshaven | Network 2 |
| 797.250 | | WFM | Carlingford | RTE 1 |
| 845.250 | | WFM | Carlingford | Network 2 |

**854.7500 - 855.2500 MHz   RADIO MICROPHONES**

| Base | Mode | Location | User and Notes |
|---|---|---|---|
| 854.75000 | WFM | Nationwide | Channel 1 |
| 854.77500 | WFM | Nationwide | Channel 2 |
| 854.80000 | WFM | Nationwide | Channel 3 |
| 854.82500 | WFM | Nationwide | Channel 4 |
| 854.85000 | WFM | Nationwide | Channel 5 |
| 854.87500 | WFM | Nationwide | Channel 6 |
| 854.90000 | WFM | Nationwide | Channel 7 |
| 854.92500 | WFM | Nationwide | Channel 8 |
| 854.95000 | WFM | Nationwide | Channel 9 |
| 854.97500 | WFM | Nationwide | Channel 10 |
| 855.00000 | WFM | Nationwide | Channel 11 |
| 855.02500 | WFM | Nationwide | Channel 12 |
| 855.05000 | WFM | Nationwide | Channel 13 |
| 855.07500 | WFM | Nationwide | Channel 14 |
| 855.10000 | WFM | Nationwide | Channel 15 |
| 855.12500 | WFM | Nationwide | Channel 16 |

| Base | Mobile | Mode | Location | User and Notes |
|------|--------|------|----------|----------------|
| 855.15000 | | WFM | Nationwide | Channel 17 |
| 855.17500 | | WFM | Nationwide | Channel 18 |
| 855.20000 | | WFM | Nationwide | Channel 19 |
| 855.22500 | | WFM | Nationwide | Channel 20 |

**860.2500 - 860.7500 MHz     RADIO MICROPHONES**

| Base | Mobile | Mode | Location | User and Notes |
|------|--------|------|----------|----------------|
| 860.25000 | | WFM | Nationwide | Channel 1 |
| 860.27500 | | WFM | Nationwide | Channel 2 |
| 860.30000 | | WFM | Nationwide | Channel 3 |
| 860.32500 | | WFM | Nationwide | Channel 4 |
| 860.35000 | | WFM | Nationwide | Channel 5 |
| 860.37500 | | WFM | Nationwide | Channel 6 |
| 860.40000 | | WFM | Nationwide | Channel 7 |
| 860.42500 | | WFM | Nationwide | Channel 8 |
| 860.45000 | | WFM | Nationwide | Channel 9 |
| 860.47500 | | WFM | Nationwide | Channel 10 |
| 860.50000 | | WFM | Nationwide | Channel 11 |
| 860.52500 | | WFM | Nationwide | Channel 12 |
| 860.55000 | | WFM | Nationwide | Channel 13 |
| 860.57500 | | WFM | Nationwide | Channel 14 |
| 860.60000 | | WFM | Nationwide | Channel 15 |
| 860.62500 | | WFM | Nationwide | Channel 16 |
| 860.65000 | | WFM | Nationwide | Channel 17 |
| 860.67500 | | WFM | Nationwide | Channel 18 |
| 860.70000 | | WFM | Nationwide | Channel 19 |
| 860.72500 | | WFM | Nationwide | Channel 20 |

**862.0000 - 864.0000 MHz     MOBILE EMERGENCY SERVICES & FUTURE CT2 DIGITAL PHONES**

**863.0000 - 864.0000 MHz     LAND MOBILE EXPERIMENTAL USE**

**864.0000 - 868.0000 MHz     CT2 DIGITAL PHONES ( 30 x 100 kHz CHANNELS)**

**868.0000 - 869.9750 MHz     DEREGULATED BAND FOR LOW POWER DEVICES & FUTURE CT2 DIGITAL PHONES**

| Base | Mobile | Mode | Location | User and Notes |
|------|--------|------|----------|----------------|
| 870.02500 | | NFM | Bournemouth | BBC O/B Link |

**870.0000 - 872.0000 MHz     MINISTRY OF DEFENCE (SPLIT + 45 MHz)**

**872.0000 - 904.9875 MHz     UHF ETACS CELLULAR TELEPHONE MOBILES**

| Base | Mobile | Mode | Location | User and Notes |
|------|--------|------|----------|----------------|
| 875.00000 | | WFM | Nationwide | WFM BBC Music Link |
| 880.00000 | | WFM | Nationwide | WFM BBC Music Link |

**888.0000 - 889.0000 MHz     LOW POWER DEVICES**

**888.0000 - 890.0000 MHz     FUTURE DSRR ( 76 x 25 kHz CHANNELS)**

**890.0000 - 915.0000 MHz     TACS , GSM MOBILES AND INDUSTRIAL, SCIENTIFIC AND MEDICAL EQUIPMENT**

**914.0125 - 914.9875 MHz** NEW CYBERNET/UNIDEN CORDLESS
TELEPHONES HANDSET

**915.0000 - 917.0000 MHz** MINISTRY OF DEFENCE (SPLIT - 45 MHz)

**917.0125 - 949.9875 MHz** UHF CELLULAR ETACS
(EXTENDED TOTAL ACCESS COMMUNICATIONS
SYSTEM) TELEPHONE NODES

| Base | Mobile | Mode | Location | User and Notes |
|------|--------|------|----------|----------------|
| 917.01250 | 872.01250 | NFM | Nationwide | Vodafone Channel 1329 |
| 917.03750 | 872.03750 | NFM | Nationwide | Vodafone Channel 1330 |
| 917.06250 | 872.06250 | NFM | Nationwide | Vodafone Channel 1331 |
| 917.08750 | 872.08750 | NFM | Nationwide | Vodafone Channel 1332 |
| 917.16250 | 872.16250 | NFM | Nationwide | Vodafone Channel 1335 |
| 917.21250 | 872.21250 | NFM | Nationwide | Vodafone Channel 1337 |
| 917.26250 | 872.26250 | NFM | Nationwide | Vodafone Channel 1339 |
| 917.31250 | 872.31250 | NFM | Nationwide | Vodafone Channel 1341 |
| 917.33750 | 872.33750 | NFM | Nationwide | Vodafone Channel 1342 |
| 917.36250 | 872.36250 | NFM | Nationwide | Vodafone Channel 1343 |
| 917.38750 | 872.38750 | NFM | Nationwide | Vodafone Channel 1344 |
| 917.41250 | 872.41250 | NFM | Nationwide | Vodafone Channel 1345 |
| 917.43750 | 872.43750 | NFM | Nationwide | Vodafone Channel 1346 |
| 917.46250 | 872.46250 | NFM | Nationwide | Vodafone Channel 1347 |
| 917.48750 | 872.48750 | NFM | Nationwide | Vodafone Channel 1348 |
| 917.51250 | 872.51250 | NFM | Nationwide | Vodafone Channel 1349 |
| 917.53750 | 872.53750 | NFM | Nationwide | Vodafone Channel 1350 |
| 917.56250 | 872.56250 | NFM | Nationwide | Vodafone Channel 1351 |
| 917.58750 | 872.58750 | NFM | Nationwide | Vodafone Channel 1352 |
| 917.61250 | 872.61250 | NFM | Nationwide | Vodafone Channel 1353 |
| 917.68750 | 872.68750 | NFM | Nationwide | Vodafone Channel 1356 |
| 917.73750 | 872.73750 | NFM | Nationwide | Vodafone Channel 1358 |
| 917.78750 | 872.78750 | NFM | Nationwide | Vodafone Channel 1360 |
| 917.83750 | 872.83750 | NFM | Nationwide | Vodafone Channel 1362 |
| 917.86250 | 872.86250 | NFM | Nationwide | Vodafone Channel 1363 |
| 917.88750 | 872.88750 | NFM | Nationwide | Vodafone Channel 1364 |
| 917.91250 | 872.91250 | NFM | Nationwide | Vodafone Channel 1365 |
| 917.93750 | 872.93750 | NFM | Nationwide | Vodafone Channel 1366 |
| 917.96250 | 872.96250 | NFM | Nationwide | Vodafone Channel 1367 |
| 918.01250 | 873.01250 | NFM | Nationwide | Vodafone Channel 1369 |
| 918.03750 | 873.03750 | NFM | Nationwide | Vodafone Channel 1370 |
| 918.06250 | 873.06250 | NFM | Nationwide | Vodafone Channel 1371 |
| 918.08750 | 873.08750 | NFM | Nationwide | Vodafone Channel 1372 |
| 918.11250 | 873.11250 | NFM | Nationwide | Vodafone Channel 1373 |
| 918.13750 | 873.13750 | NFM | Nationwide | Vodafone Channel 1374 |
| 918.21250 | 873.21250 | NFM | Nationwide | Vodafone Channel 1377 |
| 918.26250 | 873.26250 | NFM | Nationwide | Vodafone Channel 1379 |
| 918.31250 | 873.31250 | NFM | Nationwide | Vodafone Channel 1381 |
| 918.36250 | 873.36250 | NFM | Nationwide | Vodafone Channel 1383 |
| 918.38750 | 873.38750 | NFM | Nationwide | Vodafone Channel 1384 |
| 918.41250 | 873.41250 | NFM | Nationwide | Vodafone Channel 1385 |
| 918.43750 | 873.43750 | NFM | Nationwide | Vodafone Channel 1386 |
| 918.48750 | 873.48750 | NFM | Nationwide | Vodafone Channel 1388 |
| 918.51250 | 873.51250 | NFM | Nationwide | Vodafone Channel 1389 |
| 918.53750 | 873.53750 | NFM | Nationwide | Vodafone Channel 1390 |
| 918.56250 | 873.56250 | NFM | Nationwide | Vodafone Channel 1391 |

| Base | Mobile | Mode | Location | User and Notes |
|------|--------|------|----------|----------------|
| 918.58750 | 873.58750 | NFM | Nationwide | Vodafone Channel 1392 |
| 918.61250 | 873.61250 | NFM | Nationwide | Vodafone Channel 1393 |
| 918.63750 | 873.63750 | NFM | Nationwide | Vodafone Channel 1394 |
| 918.66250 | 873.66250 | NFM | Nationwide | Vodafone Channel 1395 |
| 918.73750 | 873.73750 | NFM | Nationwide | Vodafone Channel 1398 |
| 918.78750 | 873.78750 | NFM | Nationwide | Vodafone Channel 1400 |
| 918.83750 | 873.83750 | NFM | Nationwide | Vodafone Channel 1402 |
| 918.88750 | 873.88750 | NFM | Nationwide | Vodafone Channel 1404 |
| 918.91250 | 873.91250 | NFM | Nationwide | Vodafone Channel 1405 |
| 918.93750 | 873.93750 | NFM | Nationwide | Vodafone Channel 1406 |
| 918.96250 | 873.96250 | NFM | Nationwide | Vodafone Channel 1407 |
| 919.01250 | 874.01250 | NFM | Nationwide | Vodafone Channel 1409 |
| 919.06250 | 874.06250 | NFM | Nationwide | Vodafone Channel 1411 |
| 919.08750 | 874.08750 | NFM | Nationwide | Vodafone Channel 1412 |
| 919.11250 | 874.11250 | NFM | Nationwide | Vodafone Channel 1413 |
| 919.13750 | 874.13750 | NFM | Nationwide | Vodafone Channel 1414 |
| 919.16250 | 874.16250 | NFM | Nationwide | Vodafone Channel 1415 |
| 919.18750 | 874.18750 | NFM | Nationwide | Vodafone Channel 1416 |
| 919.23750 | 874.23750 | NFM | Nationwide | Vodafone Channel 1418 |
| 919.26250 | 874.26250 | NFM | Nationwide | Vodafone Channel 1419 |
| 919.31250 | 874.31250 | NFM | Nationwide | Vodafone Channel 1421 |
| 919.36250 | 874.36250 | NFM | Nationwide | Vodafone Channel 1423 |
| 919.41250 | 874.41250 | NFM | Nationwide | Vodafone Channel 1425 |
| 919.43750 | 874.43750 | NFM | Nationwide | Vodafone Channel 1426 |
| 919.46250 | 874.46250 | NFM | Nationwide | Vodafone Channel 1427 |
| 919.48750 | 874.48750 | NFM | Nationwide | Vodafone Channel 1428 |
| 919.53750 | 874.53750 | NFM | Nationwide | Vodafone Channel 1430 |
| 919.56250 | 874.56250 | NFM | Nationwide | Vodafone Channel 1431 |
| 919.58750 | 874.58750 | NFM | Nationwide | Vodafone Channel 1432 |
| 919.61250 | 874.61250 | NFM | Nationwide | Vodafone Channel 1433 |
| 919.63750 | 874.63750 | NFM | Nationwide | Vodafone Channel 1434 |
| 919.66250 | 874.66250 | NFM | Nationwide | Vodafone Channel 1435 |
| 919.68750 | 874.68750 | NFM | Nationwide | Vodafone Channel 1436 |
| 919.71250 | 874.71250 | NFM | Nationwide | Vodafone Channel 1437 |
| 919.76250 | 874.76250 | NFM | Nationwide | Vodafone Channel 1439 |
| 919.78750 | 874.78750 | NFM | Nationwide | Vodafone Channel 1440 |
| 919.83750 | 874.83750 | NFM | Nationwide | Vodafone Channel 1442 |
| 919.88750 | 874.88750 | NFM | Nationwide | Vodafone Channel 1444 |
| 919.91250 | 874.91250 | NFM | Nationwide | Vodafone Channel 1445 |
| 919.93750 | 874.93750 | NFM | Nationwide | Vodafone Channel 1446 |
| 919.96250 | 874.96250 | NFM | Nationwide | Vodafone Channel 1447 |
| 919.98750 | 874.98750 | NFM | Nationwide | Vodafone Channel 1448 |
| 920.01250 | 875.01250 | NFM | Nationwide | Vodafone Channel 1449 |
| 920.06250 | 875.06250 | NFM | Nationwide | Vodafone Channel 1451 |
| 920.08750 | 875.08750 | NFM | Nationwide | Vodafone Channel 1452 |
| 920.11250 | 875.11250 | NFM | Nationwide | Vodafone Channel 1453 |
| 920.13750 | 875.13750 | NFM | Nationwide | Vodafone Channel 1454 |
| 920.16250 | 875.16250 | NFM | Nationwide | Vodafone Channel 1455 |
| 920.18750 | 875.18750 | NFM | Nationwide | Vodafone Channel 1456 |
| 920.21250 | 875.21250 | NFM | Nationwide | Vodafone Channel 1457 |
| 920.23750 | 875.23750 | NFM | Nationwide | Vodafone Channel 1458 |
| 920.31250 | 875.31250 | NFM | Nationwide | Vodafone Channel 1461 |
| 920.36250 | 875.36250 | NFM | Nationwide | Vodafone Channel 1463 |
| 920.41250 | 875.41250 | NFM | Nationwide | Vodafone Channel 1465 |
| 920.46250 | 875.46250 | NFM | Nationwide | Vodafone Channel 1467 |
| 920.48750 | 875.48750 | NFM | Nationwide | Vodafone Channel 1468 |

| Base | Mobile | Mode | Location | User and Notes |
|------|--------|------|----------|----------------|
| 920.53750 | 875.53750 | NFM | Nationwide | Vodafone Channel 1470 |
| 920.58750 | 875.58750 | NFM | Nationwide | Vodafone Channel 1472 |
| 920.61250 | 875.61250 | NFM | Nationwide | Vodafone Channel 1473 |
| 920.63750 | 875.63750 | NFM | Nationwide | Vodafone Channel 1474 |
| 920.66250 | 875.66250 | NFM | Nationwide | Vodafone Channel 1475 |
| 920.68750 | 875.68750 | NFM | Nationwide | Vodafone Channel 1476 |
| 920.71250 | 875.71250 | NFM | Nationwide | Vodafone Channel 1477 |
| 920.73750 | 875.73750 | NFM | Nationwide | Vodafone Channel 1478 |
| 920.76250 | 875.76250 | NFM | Nationwide | Vodafone Channel 1479 |
| 920.83750 | 875.83750 | NFM | Nationwide | Vodafone Channel 1482 |
| 920.88750 | 875.88750 | NFM | Nationwide | Vodafone Channel 1484 |
| 920.93750 | 875.93750 | NFM | Nationwide | Vodafone Channel 1486 |
| 920.98750 | 875.98750 | NFM | Nationwide | Vodafone Channel 1488 |
| 921.01250 | 876.01250 | NFM | Nationwide | Vodafone Channel 1489 |
| 921.06250 | 876.06250 | NFM | Nationwide | Vodafone Channel 1491 |
| 921.11250 | 876.11250 | NFM | Nationwide | Vodafone Channel 1493 |
| 921.13750 | 876.13750 | NFM | Nationwide | Vodafone Channel 1494 |
| 921.16250 | 876.16250 | NFM | Nationwide | Vodafone Channel 1495 |
| 921.18750 | 876.18750 | NFM | Nationwide | Vodafone Channel 1496 |
| 921.21250 | 876.21250 | NFM | Nationwide | Vodafone Channel 1497 |
| 921.23750 | 876.23750 | NFM | Nationwide | Vodafone Channel 1498 |
| 921.26250 | 876.26250 | NFM | Nationwide | Vodafone Channel 1499 |
| 921.28750 | 876.28750 | NFM | Nationwide | Vodafone Channel 1500 |
| 921.36250 | 876.36250 | NFM | Nationwide | Vodafone Channel 1503 |
| 921.41250 | 876.41250 | NFM | Nationwide | Vodafone Channel 1505 |
| 921.46250 | 876.46250 | NFM | Nationwide | Vodafone Channel 1507 |
| 921.51250 | 876.51250 | NFM | Nationwide | Vodafone Channel 1509 |
| 921.53750 | 876.53750 | NFM | Nationwide | Vodafone Channel 1510 |
| 921.58750 | 876.58750 | NFM | Nationwide | Vodafone Channel 1512 |
| 921.63750 | 876.63750 | NFM | Nationwide | Vodafone Channel 1514 |
| 921.66250 | 876.66250 | NFM | Nationwide | Vodafone Channel 1515 |
| 921.68750 | 876.68750 | NFM | Nationwide | Vodafone Channel 1516 |
| 921.71250 | 876.71250 | NFM | Nationwide | Vodafone Channel 1517 |
| 921.73750 | 876.73750 | NFM | Nationwide | Vodafone Channel 1518 |
| 921.76250 | 876.76250 | NFM | Nationwide | Vodafone Channel 1519 |
| 921.78750 | 876.78750 | NFM | Nationwide | Vodafone Channel 1520 |
| 921.81250 | 876.81250 | NFM | Nationwide | Vodafone Channel 1521 |
| 921.88750 | 876.88750 | NFM | Nationwide | Vodafone Channel 1524 |
| 921.93750 | 876.93750 | NFM | Nationwide | Vodafone Channel 1526 |
| 921.98750 | 876.98750 | NFM | Nationwide | Vodafone Channel 1528 |
| 922.03750 | 877.03750 | NFM | Nationwide | Vodafone Channel 1530 |
| 922.06250 | 877.06250 | NFM | Nationwide | Vodafone Channel 1531 |
| 922.08750 | 877.08750 | NFM | Nationwide | Vodafone Channel 1532 |
| 922.11250 | 877.11250 | NFM | Nationwide | Vodafone Channel 1533 |
| 922.16250 | 877.16250 | NFM | Nationwide | Vodafone Channel 1535 |
| 922.21250 | 877.21250 | NFM | Nationwide | Vodafone Channel 1537 |
| 922.23750 | 877.23750 | NFM | Nationwide | Vodafone Channel 1538 |
| 922.26250 | 877.26250 | NFM | Nationwide | Vodafone Channel 1539 |
| 922.28750 | 877.28750 | NFM | Nationwide | Vodafone Channel 1540 |
| 922.31250 | 877.31250 | NFM | Nationwide | Vodafone Channel 1541 |
| 922.33750 | 877.33750 | NFM | Nationwide | Vodafone Channel 1542 |
| 922.41250 | 877.41250 | NFM | Nationwide | Vodafone Channel 1545 |
| 922.46250 | 877.46250 | NFM | Nationwide | Vodafone Channel 1547 |
| 922.51250 | 877.51250 | NFM | Nationwide | Vodafone Channel 1549 |
| 922.56250 | 877.56250 | NFM | Nationwide | Vodafone Channel 1551 |
| 922.58750 | 877.58750 | NFM | Nationwide | Vodafone Channel 1552 |

| Base | Mobile | Mode | Location | User and Notes |
|------|--------|------|----------|----------------|
| 922.63750 | 877.63750 | NFM | Nationwide | Vodafone Channel 1554 |
| 922.68750 | 877.68750 | NFM | Nationwide | Vodafone Channel 1556 |
| 922.73750 | 877.73750 | NFM | Nationwide | Vodafone Channel 1558 |
| 922.76250 | 877.76250 | NFM | Nationwide | Vodafone Channel 1559 |
| 922.78750 | 877.78750 | NFM | Nationwide | Vodafone Channel 1560 |
| 922.81250 | 877.81250 | NFM | Nationwide | Vodafone Channel 1561 |
| 922.83750 | 877.83750 | NFM | Nationwide | Vodafone Channel 1562 |
| 922.86250 | 877.86250 | NFM | Nationwide | Vodafone Channel 1563 |
| 922.93750 | 877.93750 | NFM | Nationwide | Vodafone Channel 1566 |
| 922.98750 | 877.98750 | NFM | Nationwide | Vodafone Channel 1568 |
| 923.03750 | 878.03750 | NFM | Nationwide | Vodafone Channel 1570 |
| 923.08750 | 878.08750 | NFM | Nationwide | Vodafone Channel 1572 |
| 923.11250 | 878.11250 | NFM | Nationwide | Vodafone Channel 1573 |
| 923.16250 | 878.16250 | NFM | Nationwide | Vodafone Channel 1575 |
| 923.21250 | 878.21250 | NFM | Nationwide | Vodafone Channel 1577 |
| 923.26250 | 878.26250 | NFM | Nationwide | Vodafone Channel 1579 |
| 923.28750 | 878.28750 | NFM | Nationwide | Vodafone Channel 1580 |
| 923.31250 | 878.31250 | NFM | Nationwide | Vodafone Channel 1581 |
| 923.36250 | 878.36250 | NFM | Nationwide | Vodafone Channel 1583 |
| 923.38750 | 878.38750 | NFM | Nationwide | Vodafone Channel 1584 |
| 923.46250 | 878.46250 | NFM | Nationwide | Vodafone Channel 1587 |
| 923.51250 | 878.51250 | NFM | Nationwide | Vodafone Channel 1589 |
| 923.56250 | 878.56250 | NFM | Nationwide | Vodafone Channel 1591 |
| 923.61250 | 878.61250 | NFM | Nationwide | Vodafone Channel 1593 |
| 923.63750 | 878.63750 | NFM | Nationwide | Vodafone Channel 1594 |
| 923.68750 | 878.68750 | NFM | Nationwide | Vodafone Channel 1596 |
| 923.71250 | 878.71250 | NFM | Nationwide | Vodafone Channel 1597 |
| 923.73750 | 878.73750 | NFM | Nationwide | Vodafone Channel 1598 |
| 923.78750 | 878.78750 | NFM | Nationwide | Vodafone Channel 1600 |
| 923.83750 | 878.83750 | NFM | Nationwide | Vodafone Channel 1602 |
| 923.86250 | 878.86250 | NFM | Nationwide | Vodafone Channel 1603 |
| 923.88750 | 878.88750 | NFM | Nationwide | Vodafone Channel 1604 |
| 923.91250 | 878.91250 | NFM | Nationwide | Vodafone Channel 1605 |
| 923.98750 | 878.98750 | NFM | Nationwide | Vodafone Channel 1608 |
| 924.03750 | 879.03750 | NFM | Nationwide | Vodafone Channel 1610 |
| 924.08750 | 879.08750 | NFM | Nationwide | Vodafone Channel 1612 |
| 924.13750 | 879.13750 | NFM | Nationwide | Vodafone Channel 1614 |
| 924.16250 | 879.16250 | NFM | Nationwide | Vodafone Channel 1615 |
| 924.21250 | 879.21250 | NFM | Nationwide | Vodafone Channel 1617 |
| 924.26250 | 879.26250 | NFM | Nationwide | Vodafone Channel 1619 |
| 924.31250 | 879.31250 | NFM | Nationwide | Vodafone Channel 1621 |
| 924.33750 | 879.33750 | NFM | Nationwide | Vodafone Channel 1622 |
| 924.36250 | 879.36250 | NFM | Nationwide | Vodafone Channel 1623 |
| 924.38750 | 879.38750 | NFM | Nationwide | Vodafone Channel 1624 |
| 924.41250 | 879.41250 | NFM | Nationwide | Vodafone Channel 1625 |
| 924.43750 | 879.43750 | NFM | Nationwide | Vodafone Channel 1626 |
| 924.51250 | 879.51250 | NFM | Nationwide | Vodafone Channel 1629 |
| 924.56250 | 879.56250 | NFM | Nationwide | Vodafone Channel 1631 |
| 924.61250 | 879.61250 | NFM | Nationwide | Vodafone Channel 1633 |
| 924.66250 | 879.66250 | NFM | Nationwide | Vodafone Channel 1635 |
| 924.68750 | 879.68750 | NFM | Nationwide | Vodafone Channel 1636 |
| 924.73750 | 879.73750 | NFM | Nationwide | Vodafone Channel 1638 |
| 924.78750 | 879.78750 | NFM | Nationwide | Vodafone Channel 1640 |
| 924.83750 | 879.83750 | NFM | Nationwide | Vodafone Channel 1642 |
| 924.86250 | 879.86250 | NFM | Nationwide | Vodafone Channel 1643 |
| 924.88750 | 879.88750 | NFM | Nationwide | Vodafone Channel 1644 |

| Base | Mobile | Mode | Location | User and Notes |
|------|--------|------|----------|----------------|
| 924.91250 | 879.91250 | NFM | Nationwide | Vodafone Channel 1645 |
| 924.93750 | 879.93750 | NFM | Nationwide | Vodafone Channel 1646 |
| 924.96250 | 879.96250 | NFM | Nationwide | Vodafone Channel 1647 |
| 928.38750 | 883.38750 | NFM | Nationwide | Cellnet Channel 1784 |

**933.0000 MHz**      RADIO LOCATION DEVICES

**934.0125 - 934.9875 MHz**      UHF CB BAND

| Base | Mobile | Mode | Location | User and Notes |
|------|--------|------|----------|----------------|
| 934.01250 | 934.01250 | NFM | Nationwide | Channel 1 |
| 934.06250 | 934.06250 | NFM | Nationwide | Channel 2 |
| 934.11250 | 934.11250 | NFM | Nationwide | Channel 3 |
| 934.16250 | 934.16250 | NFM | Nationwide | Channel 4 |
| 934.21250 | 934.21250 | NFM | Nationwide | Channel 5 |
| 934.26250 | 934.26250 | NFM | Nationwide | Channel 6 |
| 934.31250 | 934.31250 | NFM | Nationwide | Channel 7 |
| 934.36250 | 934.36250 | NFM | Nationwide | Channel 8 |
| 934.41250 | 934.41250 | NFM | Nationwide | Channel 9 |
| 934.46250 | 934.46250 | NFM | Nationwide | Channel 10 |
| 934.51250 | 934.51250 | NFM | Nationwide | Channel 11 |
| 934.56250 | 934.56250 | NFM | Nationwide | Channel 12 |
| 934.61250 | 934.61250 | NFM | Nationwide | Channel 13 |
| 934.66250 | 934.66250 | NFM | Nationwide | Channel 14 |
| 934.71250 | 934.71250 | NFM | Nationwide | Channel 15 |
| 934.76250 | 934.76250 | NFM | Nationwide | Channel 16 |
| 934.81250 | 934.81250 | NFM | Nationwide | Channel 17 |
| 934.86250 | 934.86250 | NFM | Nationwide | Channel 18 |
| 934.91250 | 934.91250 | NFM | Nationwide | Channel 19 |
| 934.96250 | 934.96250 | NFM | Nationwide | Channel 20 |

**926.0000 - 934.0000 MHz**      RADIO ASTRONOMY USED FOR PULARS

**935.0000 - 950.0000 MHz**      UHF CELLULAR RADIO TELEPHONES
(CELLNET & VODAFONE) REPEATER SITES

### Eirean Telecom

| Base | Mobile | Mode | Location | User and Notes |
|------|--------|------|----------|----------------|
| 935.13750 | | NFM | Galway | Eirean Telecom |
| 935.18750 | | NFM | Galway | Eirean Telecom |
| 935.23750 | | NFM | Ballinrobe | Eirean Telecom |
| 935.26250 | | NFM | Galway | Eirean Telecom |
| 935.31250 | | NFM | Galway | Eirean Telecom |
| 935.43750 | | NFM | Castlebar | Eirean Telecom |
| 935.66250 | | NFM | Galway | Eirean Telecom |
| 935.81250 | | NFM | Galway | Eirean Telecom |
| 935.96250 | | NFM | Castlebar | Eirean Telecom |
| 936.01250 | | NFM | Galway | Eirean Telecom |
| 936.18750 | 891.18750 | NFM | Galway | Eirean Telecom |
| 936.23750 | 891.23750 | NFM | Galway | Eirean Telecom |
| 936.28750 | 891.28750 | NFM | Ballinrobe | Eirean Telecom |
| 936.31250 | 891.31250 | NFM | Galway | Eirean Telecom |
| 936.36250 | 891.36250 | NFM | Galway | Eirean Telecom |
| 936.83750 | 891.83750 | NFM | Galway | Eirean Telecom |
| 936.88750 | 891.88750 | NFM | Galway | Eirean Telecom |
| 937.06250 | 892.06250 | NFM | Galway | Eirean Telecom |
| 937.41250 | 892.41250 | NFM | Galway | Eirean Telecom |

| Base | Mobile | Mode | Location | User and Notes |
|---|---|---|---|---|
| 937.86250 | 892.86250 | NFM | Ballinrobe | Eirean Telecom |
| 937.88750 | 892.88750 | NFM | Galway | Eirean Telecom |
| 937.93750 | 892.93750 | NFM | Galway | Eirean Telecom |
| 938.11250 | 893.11250 | NFM | Galway | Eirean Telecom |
| 938.38750 | 893.38750 | NFM | Ballinrobe | Eirean Telecom |
| 938.41250 | 893.41250 | NFM | Galway | Eirean Telecom |
| 938.58750 | 893.58750 | NFM | Castlebar | Eirean Telecom |
| 938.63750 | 893.63750 | NFM | Galway | Eirean Telecom |
| 938.66250 | 893.66250 | NFM | Castlebar | Eirean Telecom |
| 938.91250 | 893.91250 | NFM | Ballinrobe | Eirean Telecom |
| 938.93750 | 893.93750 | NFM | Galway | Eirean Telecom |
| 938.98750 | 893.98750 | NFM | Galway | Eirean Telecom |
| 939.16250 | 894.16250 | NFM | Galway | Eirean Telecom |
| 939.33750 | 894.33750 | NFM | Galway | Eirean Telecom |
| 939.38750 | 894.38750 | NFM | Galway | Eirean Telecom |
| 939.43750 | 894.43750 | NFM | Ballinrobe | Eirean Telecom |
| 939.46250 | 894.46250 | NFM | Galway | Eirean Telecom |
| 939.68750 | 894.68750 | NFM | Galway | Eirean Telecom |
| 939.91250 | 894.91250 | NFM | Galway | Eirean Telecom |
| 939.96250 | 894.96250 | NFM | Ballinrobe | Eirean Telecom |
| 939.98750 | 894.98750 | NFM | Galway | Eirean Telecom |
| 940.03750 | 895.03750 | NFM | Galway | Eirean Telecom |
| 940.21250 | 895.21250 | NFM | Galway | Eirean Telecom |
| 940.38750 | 895.38750 | NFM | Galway | Eirean Telecom |
| 940.43750 | 895.43750 | NFM | Galway | Eirean Telecom |
| 940.48750 | 895.48750 | NFM | Ballinrobe | Eirean Telecom |
| 940.56250 | 895.56250 | NFM | Galway | Eirean Telecom |
| 940.68750 | 895.68750 | NFM | Castlebar | Eirean Telecom |
| 940.73750 | 895.73750 | NFM | Galway | Eirean Telecom |
| 941.01250 | 896.01250 | NFM | Galway | Eirean Telecom |
| 941.03750 | 896.03750 | NFM | Galway | Eirean Telecom |
| 941.08750 | 896.08750 | NFM | Galway | Eirean Telecom |
| 941.21250 | 896.21250 | NFM | Ballinrobe | Eirean Telecom |
| 941.26250 | 896.26250 | NFM | Galway | Eirean Telecom |
| 941.31250 | 896.31250 | NFM | Galway | Eirean Telecom |
| 941.56250 | 896.56250 | NFM | Galway | Eirean Telecom |
| 941.78750 | 896.78750 | NFM | Galway | Eirean Telecom |
| 941.96250 | 896.96250 | NFM | Galway | Eirean Telecom |
| 942.08750 | 897.08750 | NFM | Galway | Eirean Telecom |
| 942.48750 | 897.48750 | NFM | Galway | Eirean Telecom |
| 942.53750 | 897.53750 | NFM | Galway | Eirean Telecom |
| 942.61250 | 897.61250 | NFM | Galway | Eirean Telecom |
| 942.83750 | 897.83750 | NFM | Galway | Eirean Telecom |
| 943.13750 | 898.13750 | NFM | Galway | Eirean Telecom |
| 943.18750 | 898.18750 | NFM | Galway | Eirean Telecom |
| 943.68750 | 898.68750 | NFM | Galway | Eirean Telecom |
| 944.38750 | 899.38750 | NFM | Galway | Eirean Telecom |
| | | | | |
| 935.06250 | 890.06250 | NFM | Nationwide | Vodafone Channel 3 |
| 935.13750 | 890.13750 | NFM | Nationwide | Vodafone Channel 6 |
| 935.18750 | 890.18750 | NFM | Nationwide | Vodafone Channel 8 |
| 935.21250 | 890.21250 | NFM | Nationwide | Vodafone Channel 9 |
| 935.23750 | 890.23750 | NFM | Nationwide | Vodafone Channel 10 |
| 935.26250 | 890.26250 | NFM | Nationwide | Vodafone Channel 11 |
| 935.28750 | 890.28750 | NFM | Nationwide | Vodafone Channel 12 |

| Base | Mobile | Mode | Location | User and Notes |
|---|---|---|---|---|
| 935.31250 | 890.31250 | NFM | Nationwide | Vodafone Channel 13 |
| 935.33750 | 890.33750 | NFM | Nationwide | Vodafone Channel 14 |
| 935.36250 | 890.36250 | NFM | Nationwide | Vodafone Channel 15 |
| 935.38750 | 890.38750 | NFM | Nationwide | Vodafone Channel 16 |
| 935.41250 | 890.41250 | NFM | Nationwide | Vodafone Channel 17 |
| 935.43750 | 890.43750 | NFM | Nationwide | Vodafone Channel 18 |
| 935.46250 | 890.46250 | NFM | Nationwide | Vodafone Channel 19 |
| 935.56250 | | NFM | Nationwide | Vodafone Data Control |
| 935.56250 | 890.56250 | NFM | Nationwide | Vodafone Channel 23 |
| 935.58750 | | NFM | Nationwide | Vodafone Data Control |
| 935.58750 | 890.58750 | NFM | Nationwide | Vodafone Channel 24 |
| 935.61250 | | NFM | Nationwide | Vodafone Data Control |
| 935.61250 | 890.61250 | NFM | Nationwide | Vodafone Channel 25 |
| 935.63750 | | NFM | Nationwide | Vodafone Data Control |
| 935.63750 | 890.63750 | NFM | Nationwide | Vodafone Channel 26 |
| 935.66250 | | NFM | Nationwide | Vodafone Data Control |
| 935.66250 | 890.66250 | NFM | Nationwide | Vodafone Channel 27 |
| 935.68750 | | NFM | Nationwide | Vodafone Data Control |
| 935.68750 | 890.68750 | NFM | Nationwide | Vodafone Channel 28 |
| 935.71250 | 890.71250 | NFM | Nationwide | Vodafone Channel 29 |
| 935.71250 | | NFM | Nationwide | Vodafone Data Control |
| 935.73750 | | NFM | Nationwide | Vodafone Data Control |
| 935.73750 | 890.73750 | NFM | Nationwide | Vodafone Channel 30 |
| 935.76250 | 890.76250 | NFM | Nationwide | Vodafone Channel 31 |
| 935.78750 | 890.78750 | NFM | Nationwide | Vodafone Channel 32 |
| 935.78750 | | NFM | Nationwide | Vodafone Data Control |
| 935.81250 | | NFM | Nationwide | Vodafone Data Control |
| 935.81250 | 890.81250 | NFM | Nationwide | Vodafone Channel 33 |
| 935.83750 | | NFM | Nationwide | Vodafone Data Control |
| 935.83750 | 890.83750 | NFM | Nationwide | Vodafone Channel 34 |
| 935.86250 | | NFM | Nationwide | Vodafone Data Control |
| 935.86250 | 890.86250 | NFM | Nationwide | Vodafone Channel 35 |
| 935.88750 | | NFM | Nationwide | Vodafone Data Control |
| 935.88750 | 890.88750 | NFM | Nationwide | Vodafone Channel 36 |
| 935.91250 | 890.91250 | NFM | Nationwide | Vodafone Channel 37 |
| 935.91250 | | NFM | Nationwide | Vodafone Data Control |
| 935.93750 | 890.93750 | NFM | Nationwide | Vodafone Channel 38 |
| 935.93750 | | NFM | Nationwide | Vodafone Data Control |
| 935.96250 | 890.96250 | NFM | Nationwide | Vodafone Channel 39 |
| 935.96250 | | NFM | Nationwide | Vodafone Data Control |
| 935.98750 | | NFM | Nationwide | Vodafone Data Control |
| 935.98750 | 890.98750 | NFM | Nationwide | Vodafone Channel 40 |
| 936.01250 | | NFM | Nationwide | Vodafone Data Control |
| 936.01250 | 891.01250 | NFM | Nationwide | Vodafone Channel 41 |
| 936.03750 | | NFM | Nationwide | Vodafone Data Control |
| 936.03750 | 891.03750 | NFM | Nationwide | Vodafone Channel 42 |
| 936.06250 | 891.06250 | NFM | Nationwide | Vodafone Channel 43 |
| 936.11250 | 891.11250 | NFM | Nationwide | Vodafone Channel 45 |
| 936.18750 | 891.18750 | NFM | Nationwide | Vodafone Channel 48 |
| 936.21250 | 891.21250 | NFM | Nationwide | Vodafone Channel 49 |
| 936.23750 | 891.23750 | NFM | Nationwide | Vodafone Channel 50 |
| 936.26250 | 891.26250 | NFM | Nationwide | Vodafone Channel 51 |
| 936.28750 | 891.28750 | NFM | Nationwide | Vodafone Channel 52 |
| 936.31250 | 891.31250 | NFM | Nationwide | Vodafone Channel 53 |
| 936.33750 | 891.33750 | NFM | Nationwide | Vodafone Channel 54 |
| 936.36250 | 891.36250 | NFM | Nationwide | Vodafone Channel 55 |

| Base | Mobile | Mode | Location | User and Notes |
|------|--------|------|----------|----------------|
| 936.38750 | 891.38750 | NFM | Nationwide | Vodafone Channel 56 |
| 936.41250 | 891.41250 | NFM | Nationwide | Vodafone Channel 57 |
| 936.51250 | 891.51250 | NFM | Nationwide | Vodafone Channel 61 |
| 936.63750 | 891.63750 | NFM | Nationwide | Vodafone Channel 66 |
| 936.68750 | 891.68750 | NFM | Nationwide | Vodafone Channel 68 |
| 936.73750 | 891.73750 | NFM | Nationwide | Vodafone Channel 70 |
| 936.76250 | 891.76250 | NFM | Nationwide | Vodafone Channel 71 |
| 936.81250 | 891.81250 | NFM | Nationwide | Vodafone Channel 73 |
| 936.83750 | 891.83750 | NFM | Nationwide | Vodafone Channel 74 |
| 936.88750 | 891.88750 | NFM | Nationwide | Vodafone Channel 76 |
| 936.93750 | 891.93750 | NFM | Nationwide | Vodafone Channel 78 |
| 937.03750 | 892.03750 | NFM | Nationwide | Vodafone Channel 82 |
| 937.06250 | 892.06250 | NFM | Nationwide | Vodafone Channel 83 |
| 937.16250 | 892.16250 | NFM | Nationwide | Vodafone Channel 87 |
| 937.26250 | 892.26250 | NFM | Nationwide | Vodafone Channel 91 |
| 937.28750 | 892.28750 | NFM | Nationwide | Vodafone Channel 92 |
| 937.31250 | 892.31250 | NFM | Nationwide | Vodafone Channel 93 |
| 937.33750 | 892.33750 | NFM | Nationwide | Vodafone Channel 94 |
| 937.41250 | 892.41250 | NFM | Nationwide | Vodafone Channel 97 |
| 937.43750 | 892.43750 | NFM | Nationwide | Vodafone Channel 98 |
| 937.46250 | 892.46250 | NFM | Nationwide | Vodafone Channel 99 |
| 937.51250 | 892.51250 | NFM | Nationwide | Vodafone Channel 101 |
| 937.56250 | 892.56250 | NFM | Nationwide | Vodafone Channel 103 |
| 937.58750 | 892.58750 | NFM | Nationwide | Vodafone Channel 104 |
| 937.66250 | 892.66250 | NFM | Nationwide | Vodafone Channel 107 |
| 937.78750 | 892.78750 | NFM | Nationwide | Vodafone Channel 112 |
| 937.86250 | 892.86250 | NFM | Nationwide | Vodafone Channel 115 |
| 937.88750 | 892.88750 | NFM | Nationwide | Vodafone Channel 116 |
| 937.93750 | 892.93750 | NFM | Nationwide | Vodafone Channel 118 |
| 937.98750 | 892.98750 | NFM | Nationwide | Vodafone Channel 120 |
| 938.01250 | 893.01250 | NFM | Nationwide | Vodafone Channel 121 |
| 938.03750 | 893.03750 | NFM | Nationwide | Vodafone Channel 122 |
| 938.08750 | 893.08750 | NFM | Nationwide | Vodafone Channel 124 |
| 938.11250 | 893.11250 | NFM | Nationwide | Vodafone Channel 125 |
| 938.13750 | 893.13750 | NFM | Nationwide | Vodafone Channel 126 |
| 938.16250 | 893.16250 | NFM | Nationwide | Vodafone Channel 127 |
| 938.18750 | 893.18750 | NFM | Nationwide | Vodafone Channel 128 |
| 938.21250 | 893.21250 | NFM | Nationwide | Vodafone Channel 129 |
| 938.31250 | 893.31250 | NFM | Nationwide | Vodafone Channel 133 |
| 938.38750 | 893.38750 | NFM | Nationwide | Vodafone Channel 136 |
| 938.41250 | 893.41250 | NFM | Nationwide | Vodafone Channel 137 |
| 938.46250 | 893.46250 | NFM | Nationwide | Vodafone Channel 139 |
| 938.51250 | 893.51250 | NFM | Nationwide | Vodafone Channel 141 |
| 938.53750 | 893.53750 | NFM | Nationwide | Vodafone Channel 142 |
| 938.56250 | 893.56250 | NFM | Nationwide | Vodafone Channel 143 |
| 938.58750 | 893.58750 | NFM | Nationwide | Vodafone Channel 144 |
| 938.61250 | 893.61250 | NFM | Nationwide | Vodafone Channel 145 |
| 938.63750 | 893.63750 | NFM | Nationwide | Vodafone Channel 146 |
| 938.66250 | 893.66250 | NFM | Nationwide | Vodafone Channel 147 |
| 938.73750 | 893.73750 | NFM | Nationwide | Vodafone Channel 150 |
| 938.78750 | 893.78750 | NFM | Nationwide | Vodafone Channel 152 |
| 938.83750 | 893.83750 | NFM | Nationwide | Vodafone Channel 154 |
| 938.86250 | 893.86250 | NFM | Nationwide | Vodafone Channel 155 |
| 938.88750 | 893.88750 | NFM | Nationwide | Vodafone Channel 156 |
| 938.91250 | 893.91250 | NFM | Nationwide | Vodafone Channel 157 |
| 938.93750 | 893.93750 | NFM | Nationwide | Vodafone Channel 158 |

| Base | Mobile | Mode | Location | User and Notes |
|---|---|---|---|---|
| 938.98750 | 893.98750 | NFM | Nationwide | Vodafone Channel 160 |
| 939.03750 | 894.03750 | NFM | Nationwide | Vodafone Channel 162 |
| 939.13750 | 894.13750 | NFM | Nationwide | Vodafone Channel 166 |
| 939.16250 | 894.16250 | NFM | Nationwide | Vodafone Channel 167 |
| 939.26250 | 894.26250 | NFM | Nationwide | Vodafone Channel 171 |
| 939.31250 | 894.31250 | NFM | Nationwide | Vodafone Channel 173 |
| 939.33750 | 894.33750 | NFM | Nationwide | Vodafone Channel 174 |
| 939.36250 | 894.36250 | NFM | Nationwide | Vodafone Channel 175 |
| 939.38750 | 894.38750 | NFM | Nationwide | Vodafone Channel 176 |
| 939.43750 | 894.43750 | NFM | Nationwide | Vodafone Channel 178 |
| 939.46250 | 894.46250 | NFM | Nationwide | Vodafone Channel 179 |
| 939.48750 | 894.48750 | NFM | Nationwide | Vodafone Channel 180 |
| | | | | |
| 939.68750 | 894.68750 | NFM | Nationwide | Cellnet Channel 188 |
| 939.76250 | 894.76250 | NFM | Nationwide | Cellnet Channel 191 |
| 939.81250 | 894.81250 | NFM | Nationwide | Cellnet Channel 193 |
| 939.86250 | 894.86250 | NFM | Nationwide | Cellnet Channel 195 |
| 939.88750 | 894.88750 | NFM | Nationwide | Cellnet Channel 196 |
| 939.91250 | 894.91250 | NFM | Nationwide | Cellnet Channel 197 |
| 939.96250 | 894.96250 | NFM | Nationwide | Cellnet Channel 199 |
| 939.98750 | 894.98750 | NFM | Nationwide | Cellnet Channel 200 |
| 940.01250 | 895.01250 | NFM | Nationwide | Cellnet Channel 201 |
| 940.03750 | 895.03750 | NFM | Nationwide | Cellnet Channel 202 |
| 940.21250 | 895.21250 | NFM | Nationwide | Cellnet Channel 209 |
| 940.23750 | 895.23750 | NFM | Nationwide | Cellnet Channel 210 |
| 940.36250 | 895.36250 | NFM | Nationwide | Cellnet Channel 215 |
| 940.38750 | 895.38750 | NFM | Nationwide | Cellnet Channel 216 |
| 940.41250 | 895.41250 | NFM | Nationwide | Cellnet Channel 217 |
| 940.43750 | 895.43750 | NFM | Nationwide | Cellnet Channel 218 |
| 940.46250 | 895.46250 | NFM | Nationwide | Cellnet Channel 219 |
| | | | | |
| 940.48750 | 895.48750 | NFM | Nationwide | (Not Used) Channel 220 |
| 940.53750 | 895.53750 | NFM | Nationwide | Vodafone Channel 222 |
| 940.56250 | 895.56250 | NFM | Nationwide | Vodafone Channel 223 |
| 940.61250 | 895.61250 | NFM | Nationwide | Vodafone Channel 225 |
| 940.63750 | 895.63750 | NFM | Nationwide | Vodafone Channel 226 |
| 940.68750 | 895.68750 | NFM | Nationwide | Vodafone Channel 228 |
| 940.71250 | 895.71250 | NFM | Nationwide | Vodafone Channel 229 |
| 940.73750 | 895.73750 | NFM | Nationwide | Vodafone Channel 230 |
| 940.83750 | 895.83750 | NFM | Nationwide | Vodafone Channel 234 |
| 940.93750 | 895.93750 | NFM | Nationwide | Vodafone Channel 238 |
| 941.01250 | 896.01250 | NFM | Nationwide | Vodafone Channel 241 |
| 941.03750 | 896.03750 | NFM | Nationwide | Vodafone Channel 242 |
| 941.06250 | 896.06250 | NFM | Nationwide | Vodafone Channel 243 |
| 941.08750 | 896.08750 | NFM | Nationwide | Vodafone Channel 244 |
| 941.13750 | 896.13750 | NFM | Nationwide | Vodafone Channel 246 |
| 941.21250 | 896.21250 | NFM | Nationwide | Vodafone Channel 249 |
| 941.23750 | 896.23750 | NFM | Nationwide | Vodafone Channel 250 |
| 941.26250 | 896.26250 | NFM | Nationwide | Vodafone Channel 251 |
| 941.31250 | 896.31250 | NFM | Nationwide | Vodafone Channel 253 |
| 941.51250 | 896.51250 | NFM | Nationwide | Vodafone Channel 261 |
| 941.53750 | 896.53750 | NFM | Nationwide | Vodafone Channel 262 |
| 941.56250 | 896.56250 | NFM | Nationwide | Vodafone Channel 263 |
| 941.61250 | 896.61250 | NFM | Nationwide | Vodafone Channel 265 |
| 941.66250 | 896.66250 | NFM | Nationwide | Vodafone Channel 267 |
| 941.78750 | 896.78750 | NFM | Nationwide | Vodafone Channel 272 |

| Base | Mobile | Mode | Location | User and Notes |
|------|--------|------|----------|----------------|
| 941.83750 | 896.83750 | NFM | Nationwide | Vodafone Channel 274 |
| 941.88750 | 896.88750 | NFM | Nationwide | Vodafone Channel 276 |
| 941.96250 | 896.96250 | NFM | Nationwide | Vodafone Channel 279 |
| 942.03750 | 897.03750 | NFM | Nationwide | Vodafone Channel 282 |
| 942.08750 | 897.08750 | NFM | Nationwide | Vodafone Channel 284 |
| 942.16250 | 897.16250 | NFM | Nationwide | Vodafone Channel 287 |
| 942.21250 | 897.21250 | NFM | Nationwide | Vodafone Channe! 289 |
| 942.26250 | 897.26250 | NFM | Nationwide | Vodafone Channel 291 |
| 942.36250 | 897.36250 | NFM | Nationwide | Vodafone Channel 295 |
| 942.43750 | 897.43750 | NFM | Nationwide | Vodafone Channel 298 |
| 942.48750 | 897.48750 | NFM | Nationwide | Vodafone Channel 300 |
| | | | | |
| 942.53750 | 897.53750 | NFM | Nationwide | Cellnet Channel 302 |
| 942.56250 | 897.56250 | NFM | Nationwide | Cellnet Channel 303 |
| 942.61250 | 897.61250 | NFM | Nationwide | Cellnet Channel 305 |
| 942.76250 | 897.76250 | NFM | Nationwide | Cellnet Channel 311 |
| 942.81250 | 897.81250 | NFM | Nationwide | Cellnet Channel 313 |
| 942.83750 | 897.83750 | NFM | Nationwide | Cellnet Channel 314 |
| 942.86250 | 897.86250 | NFM | Nationwide | Cellnet Channel 315 |
| 942.96250 | 897.96250 | NFM | Nationwide | Cellnet Channel 319 |
| 943.06250 | 898.06250 | NFM | Nationwide | Cellnet Channel 323 |
| 943.08750 | 898.08750 | NFM | Nationwide | Cellnet Channel 324 |
| 943.11250 | 898.11250 | NFM | Nationwide | Cellnet Channel 325 |
| 943.13750 | 898.13750 | NFM | Nationwide | Cellnet Channel 326 |
| 943.16250 | 898.16250 | NFM | Nationwide | Cellnet Channel 327 |
| 943.18750 | 898.18750 | NFM | Nationwide | Cellnet Channel 328 |
| 943.21250 | 898.21250 | NFM | Nationwide | Cellnet Channel 329 |
| 943.23750 | 898.23750 | NFM | Nationwide | Cellnet Channel 330 |
| 943.26250 | 898.26250 | NFM | Nationwide | Cellnet Channel 331 |
| 943.28750 | 898.28750 | NFM | Nationwide | Cellnet Channel 332 |
| 943.31250 | 898.31250 | NFM | Nationwide | Cellnet Channel 333 |
| 943.33750 | 898.33750 | NFM | Nationwide | Cellnet Channel 334 |
| 943.36250 | 898.36250 | NFM | Nationwide | Cellnet Channel 335 |
| 943.38750 | 898.38750 | NFM | Nationwide | Cellnet Channel 336 |
| 943.41250 | 898.41250 | NFM | Nationwide | Cellnet Channel 337 |
| 943.43750 | 898.43750 | NFM | Nationwide | Cellnet Channel 338 |
| 943.46250 | 898.46250 | NFM | Nationwide | Cellnet Channel 339 |
| 943.48750 | 898.48750 | NFM | Nationwide | Cellnet Channel 340 |
| 943.51250 | 898.51250 | NFM | Nationwide | Cellnet Channel 341 |
| 943.53750 | 898.53750 | NFM | Nationwide | Cellnet Channel 342 |
| 943.56250 | 898.56250 | NFM | Nationwide | Cellnet Channel 343 |
| 943.63750 | 898.63750 | NFM | Nationwide | Cellnet Channel 346 |
| 943.68750 | 898.68750 | NFM | Nationwide | Cellnet Channel 348 |
| 943.78750 | 898.78750 | NFM | Nationwide | Cellnet Channel 352 |
| 943.81250 | 898.81250 | NFM | Nationwide | Cellnet Channel 353 |
| 943.96250 | 898.96250 | NFM | Nationwide | Channel 359 Data Control |
| 944.01250 | 899.01250 | NFM | Nationwide | Cellnet Channel 361 |
| 944.06250 | 899.06250 | NFM | Nationwide | Cellnet Channel 363 |
| 944.11250 | 899.11250 | NFM | Nationwide | Cellnet Channel 365 |
| 944.13750 | 899.13750 | NFM | Nationwide | Cellnet Channel 366 |
| 944.18750 | 899.18750 | NFM | Nationwide | Cellnet Channel 368 |
| 944.23750 | 899.23750 | NFM | Nationwide | Cellnet Channel 370 |
| 944.38750 | 899.38750 | NFM | Nationwide | Cellnet Channel 376 |
| 944.43750 | 899.43750 | NFM | Nationwide | Cellnet Channel 378 |
| 944.46250 | 899.46250 | NFM | Nationwide | Cellnet Channel 379 |
| 944.48750 | 899.48750 | NFM | Nationwide | Cellnet Channel 380 |

| Base | Mobile | Mode | Location | User and Notes |
|------|--------|------|----------|----------------|
| 944.51250 | 899.51250 | NFM | Nationwide | Cellnet Channel 381 |
| 944.56250 | 899.56250 | NFM | Nationwide | Cellnet Channel 383 |
| 944.61250 | 899.61250 | NFM | Nationwide | Cellnet Channel 385 |
| 944.66250 | 899.66250 | NFM | Nationwide | Cellnet Channel 387 |
| 944.83750 | 899.83750 | NFM | Nationwide | Cellnet Channel 394 |
| 944.98750 | 899.98750 | NFM | Nationwide | Cellnet Channel 400 |
| 945.03750 | 900.03750 | NFM | Nationwide | Cellnet Channel 402 |
| 945.11250 | 900.11250 | NFM | Nationwide | Cellnet Channel 405 |
| 945.16250 | 900.16250 | NFM | Nationwide | Cellnet Channel 407 |
| 945.26250 | 900.26250 | NFM | Nationwide | Cellnet Channel 411 |
| 945.63750 | 900.63750 | NFM | Nationwide | Cellnet Channel 426 |
| 945.68750 | 900.68750 | NFM | Nationwide | Cellnet Channel 428 |
| 945.76250 | 900.76250 | NFM | Nationwide | Cellnet Channel 431 |
| 945.81250 | 900.81250 | NFM | Nationwide | Cellnet Channel 433 |
| 945.86250 | 900.86250 | NFM | Nationwide | Cellnet Channel 435 |
| 946.01250 | 901.01250 | NFM | Nationwide | Cellnet Channel 441 |
| 946.11250 | 901.11250 | NFM | Nationwide | Cellnet Channel 445 |
| 946.18750 | 901.18750 | NFM | Nationwide | Cellnet Channel 448 |
| 946.23750 | 901.23750 | NFM | Nationwide | Cellnet Channel 450 |
| 946.26250 | 901.26250 | NFM | Nationwide | Cellnet Channel 451 |
| 946.28750 | 901.28750 | NFM | Nationwide | Cellnet Channel 452 |
| 946.36250 | 901.36250 | NFM | Nationwide | Cellnet Channel 455 |
| 946.46250 | 901.46250 | NFM | Nationwide | Cellnet Channel 459 |
| | | | | |
| 946.51250 | 901.51250 | NFM | Nationwide | Vodafone Channel 461 |
| 946.61250 | 901.61250 | NFM | Nationwide | Vodafone Channel 465 |
| 946.73750 | 901.73750 | NFM | Nationwide | Vodafone Channel 470 |
| 946.83750 | 901.83750 | NFM | Nationwide | Vodafone Channel 474 |
| 946.88750 | 901.88750 | NFM | Nationwide | Vodafone Channel 476 |
| 946.91250 | 901.91250 | NFM | Nationwide | Vodafone Channel 477 |
| 947.03750 | 902.03750 | NFM | Nationwide | Vodafone Channel 482 |
| 947.16250 | 902.16250 | NFM | Nationwide | Vodafone Channel 487 |
| 947.26250 | 902.26250 | NFM | Nationwide | Vodafone Channel 491 |
| 947.36250 | 902.36250 | NFM | Nationwide | Vodafone Channel 495 |
| 947.41250 | 902.41250 | NFM | Nationwide | Vodafone Channel 497 |
| 947.58750 | 902.58750 | NFM | Nationwide | Vodafone Channel 504 |
| 947.66250 | 902.66250 | NFM | Nationwide | Vodafone Channel 507 |
| 947.88750 | 902.88750 | NFM | Nationwide | Vodafone Channel 516 |
| 947.93750 | 902.93750 | NFM | Nationwide | Vodafone Channel 518 |
| 947.96250 | 902.96250 | NFM | Nationwide | Vodafone Channel 519 |
| 948.18750 | 903.18750 | NFM | Nationwide | Vodafone Channel 528 |
| 948.41250 | 903.41250 | NFM | Nationwide | Vodafone Channel 537 |
| 948.46250 | 903.46250 | NFM | Nationwide | Vodafone Channel 539 |
| 948.48750 | 903.48750 | NFM | Nationwide | Vodafone Channel 540 |
| 948.93750 | 903.93750 | NFM | Nationwide | Vodafone Channel 558 |
| 948.96250 | 903.96250 | NFM | Nationwide | Vodafone Channel 559 |
| | | | | |
| 949.03750 | 904.03750 | NFM | Nationwide | Cellnet Channel 562 |
| 949.23750 | 904.23750 | NFM | Nationwide | Cellnet Channel 570 |
| 949.41250 | 904.41250 | NFM | Nationwide | Cellnet Channel 577 |
| 949.48750 | 904.48750 | NFM | Nationwide | Cellnet Channel 580 |
| 949.71250 | 904.71250 | NFM | Nationwide | Cellnet Channel 589 |
| 949.91250 | 904.91250 | NFM | Nationwide | Cellnet Channel 597 |

| Base | Mobile | Mode | Location | User and Notes |
|------|--------|------|----------|----------------|

**JERSEY GMS**

| Base | Mobile | Mode | Location | User and Notes |
|------|--------|------|----------|----------------|
| 935.2000 | 890.2000 | WFM | Five Oaks | GMS |
| 936.4000 | 891.4000 | WFM | Fort Regent | GMS |
| 938.6000 | 893.6000 | WFM | Springfield | GSM |
| 939.0000 | 894.0000 | WFM | La Chasse, St Ouens | GSM |
| 942.0000 | 897.0000 | WFM | Rozel Mill | GSM |
| 943.6000 | 898.6000 | WFM | Five Oaks | GSM |
| 944.0000 | 899.0000 | WFM | Near East Exchange | GSM |
| 944.4000 | 899.4000 | WFM | St John's Parish Hall | GSM |
| 946.6000 | 901.6000 | WFM | Gorsey | GSM |
| 946.80000 | 901.80000 | WFM | St Helier, Jersey | GSM |
| 947.4000 | 902.4000 | WFM | Five Oaks | GSM |
| 949.0000 | 904.0000 | WFM | Steam Museum, Sion | GSM |
| 950.4000 | 905.4000 | WFM | St Peter's | GSM |
| 950.6000 | 905.6000 | WFM | Fort Regent | GSM |
| 951.4000 | 906.4000 | WFM | La Chasse, St Ouens | GSM |
| 952.2000 | 907.2000 | WFM | Gorey | GSM |
| 953.0000 | 908.0000 | WFM | Le Hocq | GSM |
| 945.0000 | 909.0000 | WFM | St Ouen's Bay | GSM |
| 954.2000 | 909.2000 | WFM | First Tower | GSM |
| 955.4000 | 910.4000 | WFM | Fort Regent | GSM |
| 956.2000 | 911.2000 | WFM | La Chasse, St Ouens | GSM |
| 956.6000 | 911.6000 | WFM | Fort Regent | GSM |
| 957.0000 | 912.0000 | WFM | St Brelade | GSM |
| 958.4000 | 913.4000 | WFM | St Lawrence | GSM |
| 958.8000 | 913.8000 | WFM | St Brelade, Red Houses | GSM |

**950.0000 - 960.0000 MHz   PAN EUROPEAN DIGITAL CELLULAR SERVICE**

| Base | Mobile | Mode | Location | User and Notes |
|------|--------|------|----------|----------------|
| 950.00000 | 905.00000 | WFM | Steam Museum, Jersey | GSM |
| 950.80000 | 905.80000 | WFM | Gorey, Jersey | GSM |
| 950.80000 | 905.80000 | WFM | St Helier, Jersey | GSM |
| 951.20000 | 906.20000 | WFM | Five Oaks, Jersey | GSM |
| 951.20000 | 906.20000 | WFM | Rozel Hill, Jersey | GSM |
| 951.60000 | 906.60000 | WFM | Five Oaks, Jersey | GSM |
| 952.00000 | 907.00000 | WFM | Queen's Valley, Jersey | GSM |
| 952.60000 | 907.60000 | WFM | St Helier, Jersey | GSM |
| 952.80000 | 907.80000 | WFM | St Peter, Jersey | GSM |
| 953.00000 | 908.00000 | WFM | Les Platons, Jersey | GSM |
| 953.40000 | 908.40000 | WFM | First Tower, Jersey | GSM |
| 953.40000 | 908.40000 | WFM | St Ouen's Bay, Jersey | GSM |
| 953.80000 | 908.80000 | WFM | Ouaisne, Jersey | GSM |
| 954.80000 | 909.80000 | WFM | St Helier, Jersey | GSM |

**959.0125 - 959.9875 MHz   NEW CYBERNET/UNIDEN CORDLESS TELEPHONE BASE**

| Base | Mobile | Mode | Location | User and Notes |
|------|--------|------|----------|----------------|
| 959.01250 | 914.01250 | NFM | Nationwide | Channel 1 |
| 959.02500 | 914.02500 | NFM | Nationwide | Channel 2 |
| 959.03750 | 914.03750 | NFM | Nationwide | Channel 3 |
| 959.05000 | 914.05000 | NFM | Nationwide | Channel 4 |
| 959.06250 | 914.06250 | NFM | Nationwide | Channel 5 |
| 959.07500 | 914.07500 | NFM | Nationwide | Channel 6 |

| Base | Mobile | Mode | Location | User and Notes |
|------|--------|------|----------|----------------|
| 959.08750 | 914.08750 | NFM | Nationwide | Channel 7 |
| 959.10000 | 914.10000 | NFM | Nationwide | Channel 8 |
| 959.11250 | 914.11250 | NFM | Nationwide | Channel 9 |
| 959.12500 | 914.12500 | NFM | Nationwide | Channel 10 |
| 959.13750 | 914.13750 | NFM | Nationwide | Channel 11 |
| 959.15000 | 914.15000 | NFM | Nationwide | Channel 12 |
| 959.16250 | 914.16250 | NFM | Nationwide | Channel 13 |
| 959.17500 | 914.17500 | NFM | Nationwide | Channel 14 |
| 959.18750 | 914.18750 | NFM | Nationwide | Channel 15 |
| 959.20000 | 914.20000 | NFM | Nationwide | Channel 16 |
| 959.21250 | 914.21250 | NFM | Nationwide | Channel 17 |
| 959.22500 | 914.22500 | NFM | Nationwide | Channel 18 |
| 959.23750 | 914.23750 | NFM | Nationwide | Channel 19 |
| 959.25000 | 914.25000 | NFM | Nationwide | Channel 20 |
| 959.26250 | 914.26250 | NFM | Nationwide | Channel 21 |
| 959.27500 | 914.27500 | NFM | Nationwide | Channel 22 |
| 959.28750 | 914.28750 | NFM | Nationwide | Channel 23 |
| 959.30000 | 914.30000 | NFM | Nationwide | Channel 24 |
| 959.31250 | 914.31250 | NFM | Nationwide | Channel 25 |
| 959.32500 | 914.32500 | NFM | Nationwide | Channel 26 |
| 959.33750 | 914.33750 | NFM | Nationwide | Channel 27 |
| 959.35000 | 914.35000 | NFM | Nationwide | Channel 28 |
| 959.36250 | 914.36250 | NFM | Nationwide | Channel 29 |
| 959.37500 | 914.37500 | NFM | Nationwide | Channel 30 |
| 959.38750 | 914.38750 | NFM | Nationwide | Channel 31 |
| 959.40000 | 914.40000 | NFM | Nationwide | Channel 32 |
| 959.41250 | 914.41250 | NFM | Nationwide | Channel 33 |
| 959.42500 | 914.42500 | NFM | Nationwide | Channel 34 |
| 959.43750 | 914.43750 | NFM | Nationwide | Channel 35 |
| 959.45000 | 914.45000 | NFM | Nationwide | Channel 36 |
| 959.46250 | 914.46250 | NFM | Nationwide | Channel 37 |
| 959.47500 | 914.47500 | NFM | Nationwide | Channel 38 |
| 959.48750 | 914.48750 | NFM | Nationwide | Channel 39 |
| 959.50000 | 914.50000 | NFM | Nationwide | Channel 40 |
| 959.51250 | 914.51250 | NFM | Nationwide | Channel 41 |
| 959.52500 | 914.52500 | NFM | Nationwide | Channel 42 |
| 959.53750 | 914.53750 | NFM | Nationwide | Channel 43 |
| 959.55000 | 914.55000 | NFM | Nationwide | Channel 44 |
| 959.56250 | 914.56250 | NFM | Nationwide | Channel 45 |
| 959.57500 | 914.57500 | NFM | Nationwide | Channel 46 |
| 959.58750 | 914.58750 | NFM | Nationwide | Channel 47 |
| 959.60000 | 914.60000 | NFM | Nationwide | Channel 48 |
| 959.61250 | 914.61250 | NFM | Nationwide | Channel 49 |
| 959.62500 | 914.62500 | NFM | Nationwide | Channel 50 |
| 959.63750 | 914.63750 | NFM | Nationwide | Channel 51 |
| 959.65000 | 914.65000 | NFM | Nationwide | Channel 52 |
| 959.66250 | 914.66250 | NFM | Nationwide | Channel 53 |
| 959.67500 | 914.67500 | NFM | Nationwide | Channel 54 |
| 959.68750 | 914.68750 | NFM | Nationwide | Channel 55 |
| 959.70000 | 914.70000 | NFM | Nationwide | Channel 56 |
| 959.71250 | 914.71250 | NFM | Nationwide | Channel 57 |
| 959.72500 | 914.72500 | NFM | Nationwide | Channel 58 |
| 959.73750 | 914.73750 | NFM | Nationwide | Channel 59 |
| 959.75000 | 914.75000 | NFM | Nationwide | Channel 60 |
| 959.76250 | 914.76250 | NFM | Nationwide | Channel 61 |
| 959.77500 | 914.77500 | NFM | Nationwide | Channel 62 |

| Base | Mobile | Mode | Location | User and Notes |
|---|---|---|---|---|
| 959.78750 | 914.78750 | NFM | Nationwide | Channel 63 |
| 959.80000 | 914.80000 | NFM | Nationwide | Channel 64 |
| 959.81250 | 914.81250 | NFM | Nationwide | Channel 65 |
| 959.82500 | 914.82500 | NFM | Nationwide | Channel 66 |
| 959.83750 | 914.83750 | NFM | Nationwide | Channel 67 |
| 959.85000 | 914.85000 | NFM | Nationwide | Channel 68 |
| 959.86250 | 914.86250 | NFM | Nationwide | Channel 69 |
| 959.87500 | 914.87500 | NFM | Nationwide | Channel 70 |
| 959.88750 | 914.88750 | NFM | Nationwide | Channel 71 |
| 959.90000 | 914.90000 | NFM | Nationwide | Channel 72 |
| 959.91250 | 914.91250 | NFM | Nationwide | Channel 73 |
| 959.92500 | 914.92500 | NFM | Nationwide | Channel 74 |
| 959.93750 | 914.93750 | NFM | Nationwide | Channel 75 |
| 959.95000 | 914.95000 | NFM | Nationwide | Channel 76 |
| 959.96250 | 914.96250 | NFM | Nationwide | Channel 77 |
| 959.97500 | 914.97500 | NFM | Nationwide | Channel 78 |
| 959.98750 | 914.98750 | NFM | Nationwide | Channel 79 |

## 960.0000 - 1215.0000 MHz DME Aeronautical Radio Navigation and Transponder Equipment

| Base | Mobile | Mode | Location | User and Notes |
|---|---|---|---|---|
| 962.00000 | 1025.00000 | AM | Nationwide | DME Channel 1X Not Used |
| 963.00000 | 1026.00000 | AM | Nationwide | DME Channel 2X Not Used |
| 964.00000 | 1027.00000 | AM | Nationwide | DME Channel 3X Not Used |
| 965.00000 | 1028.00000 | AM | Nationwide | DME Channel 4X Not Used |
| 966.00000 | 1029.00000 | AM | Nationwide | DME Channel 5X Not Used |
| 967.00000 | 1030.00000 | AM | Nationwide | DME Channel 6X Not Used |
| 968.00000 | 1031.00000 | AM | Nationwide | DME Channel 7X Not Used |
| 969.00000 | 1032.00000 | AM | Nationwide | DME Channel 8X Not Used |
| 970.00000 | 1033.00000 | AM | Nationwide | DME Channel 9X Not Used |
| 971.00000 | 1034.00000 | AM | Nationwide | DME Channel 10X Not Used |
| 972.00000 | 1035.00000 | AM | Nationwide | DME Channel 11X Not Used |
| 973.00000 | 1036.00000 | AM | Nationwide | DME Channel 12X Not Used |
| 974.00000 | 1037.00000 | AM | Nationwide | DME Channel 13X Not Used |
| 975.00000 | 1038.00000 | AM | Nationwide | DME Channel 14X Not Used |
| 976.00000 | 1039.00000 | AM | Nationwide | DME Channel 15X Not Used |
| 977.00000 | 1040.00000 | AM | Nationwide | DME Channel 16X Not Used |
| 978.00000 | 1041.00000 | AM | Nationwide | DME Channel 17X (108.00 Mhz) |
| 979.00000 | 1042.00000 | AM | Dundee Airport | DME |
| 979.00000 | 1042.00000 | AM | Nationwide | DME Channel 18X (108.10 MHz) |
| 979.00000 | 1042.00000 | AM | RAF Cottesmore | TACAN |
| 980.00000 | 1043.00000 | AM | Boscombe Down (MoD) | TACAN |
| 980.00000 | 1043.00000 | AM | Nationwide | DME Channel 19X (108.20 MHz) |
| 981.00000 | 1044.00000 | AM | Nationwide | DME Channel 20X (108.30 MHz) |
| 982.00000 | 1045.00000 | AM | Nationwide | DME Channel 21X (108.40 MHz) |
| 982.00000 | 1045.00000 | AM | RAF Valley | TACAN |
| 983.00000 | 1046.00000 | AM | Nationwide | DME Channel 22X (108.50 MHz) |
| 983.00000 | 1046.00000 | AM | Sumburgh Airport | DME |
| 983.00000 | 1046.00000 | AM | Teesside Airport | DME |
| 984.00000 | 1047.00000 | AM | Kirkwall Airport | DME |
| 984.00000 | 1047.00000 | AM | Nationwide | DME Channel 23X (108.60 MHz) |
| 985.00000 | 1048.00000 | AM | Nationwide | DME Channel 24X (108.70 MHz) |
| 985.00000 | 1048.00000 | AM | Newton Point | TACAN |
| 986.00000 | 1049.00000 | AM | Nationwide | DME Channel 25X (108.80 MHz) |
| 986.00000 | 1049.00000 | AM | Weathersfield | TACAN |
| 987.00000 | 1050.00000 | AM | Edinburgh Airport | DME |
| 987.00000 | 1050.00000 | AM | Nationwide | DME Channel 26X (108.90 MHz) |

| Base | Mobile | Mode | Location | User and Notes |
|------|--------|------|----------|----------------|
| 987.00000 | 1050.00000 | AM | Ventnor | TACAN |
| 988.00000 | 1051.00000 | AM | Nationwide | DME Channel 27X (109.00 MHz) |
| 989.00000 | 1052.00000 | AM | Nationwide | DME Channel 28X (109.10 MHz) |
| 990.00000 | 1053.00000 | AM | Inverness Airport | DME |
| 990.00000 | 1053.00000 | AM | Nationwide | DME Channel 29X (109.20 MHz) |
| 990.00000 | 1053.00000 | AM | Swansea Aerodrome | DME |
| 991.00000 | 1054.00000 | AM | Nationwide | DME Channel 30X (109.30 MHz) |
| 992.00000 | 1055.00000 | AM | Barrow Airport | DME |
| 992.00000 | 1055.00000 | AM | Nationwide | DME Channel 31X (109.40 MHz) |
| 993.00000 | 1056.00000 | AM | London (Heathrow) | DME |
| 993.00000 | 1056.00000 | AM | Manchester Airport | DME |
| 993.00000 | 1056.00000 | AM | Nationwide | DME Channel 32X (109.50 MHz) |
| 993.00000 | 1056.00000 | AM | Plymouth Airport | DME |
| 994.00000 | 1057.00000 | AM | Nationwide | DME Channel 33X (109.60 MHz) |
| 994.00000 | 1057.00000 | AM | RAF Linton-on-Ouse | TACAN |
| 994.00000 | 1057.00000 | AM | RAF Odiham | TACAN |
| 995.00000 | 1058.00000 | AM | Nationwide | DME Channel 34X (109.70 MHz) |
| 996.00000 | 1059.00000 | AM | Nationwide | DME Channel 35X (109.80 MHz) |
| 996.00000 | 1059.00000 | AM | RAF Kinloss | TACAN |
| 997.00000 | 1060.00000 | AM | Nationwide | DME Channel 36X (109.90 MHz) |
| 997.00000 | 1060.00000 | AM | Warton (MoD) | DME |
| 998.00000 | 1061.00000 | AM | Nationwide | DME Channel 37X (110.00 MHz) |
| 999.00000 | 1062.00000 | AM | Birmingham International | DME |
| 999.00000 | 1062.00000 | AM | Nationwide | DME Channel 38X (110.10 MHz) |
| 1000.00000 | 1063.00000 | AM | Nationwide | DME Channel 39X (110.20 MHz) |
| 1000.00000 | 1063.00000 | AM | USAF Lakenheath | TACAN |
| 1001.00000 | 1064.00000 | AM | Nationwide | DME Channel 40X (110.30 MHz) |
| 1002.00000 | 1065.00000 | AM | Bournemouth (Hurn) | DME |
| 1002.00000 | 1065.00000 | AM | Nationwide | DME Channel 41X (110.40 MHz) |
| 1003.00000 | 1066.00000 | AM | Nationwide | DME Channel 42X (110.50 MHz) |
| 1003.00000 | 1066.00000 | AM | RAF Leuchars | TACAN |
| 1003.00000 | 1066.00000 | AM | Stansted | DME |
| 1004.00000 | 1067.00000 | AM | Cardiff Airport | DME |
| 1004.00000 | 1067.00000 | AM | Carlisle Airport | DME |
| 1004.00000 | 1067.00000 | AM | London (Heathrow) | DME |
| 1004.00000 | 1067.00000 | AM | Nationwide | DME Channel 43X (110.60 MHz) |
| 1005.00000 | 1068.00000 | AM | Nationwide | DME Channel 44X (110.70 MHz) |
| 1006.00000 | 1069.00000 | AM | Nationwide | DME Channel 45X (110.80 MHz) |
| 1007.00000 | 1070.00000 | AM | Jersey Airport | DME |
| 1007.00000 | 1070.00000 | AM | London (Gatwick) | DME |
| 1007.00000 | 1070.00000 | AM | Nationwide | DME Channel 46X (110.90 MHz) |
| 1007.00000 | 1070.00000 | AM | Ronaldsway, Isle of Man | DME |
| 1008.00000 | 1071.00000 | AM | Nationwide | DME Channel 47X (111.00 MHz) |
| 1008.00000 | 1071.00000 | AM | RNAS Yeovilton | TACAN |
| 1009.00000 | 1072.00000 | AM | Nationwide | DME Channel 48X (111.10 MHz) |
| 1010.00000 | 1073.00000 | AM | Nationwide | DME Channel 49X (111.20 MHz) |
| 1011.00000 | 1074.00000 | AM | London (Heathrow) | DME |
| 1011.00000 | 1074.00000 | AM | Nationwide | DME Channel 50X (111.30 MHz) |
| 1012.00000 | 1075.00000 | AM | Nationwide | DME Channel 51X (111.40 MHz) |
| 1012.00000 | 1075.00000 | AM | RAF Coningsby | TACAN |
| 1013.00000 | 1076.00000 | AM | London (City Airport) | DME |
| 1013.00000 | 1076.00000 | AM | Nationwide | DME Channel 52X (111.50 MHz) |
| 1013.00000 | 1076.00000 | AM | Newcastle Airport | DME |
| 1013.00000 | 1076.00000 | AM | USAF Fairford | TACAN |
| 1014.00000 | 1077.00000 | AM | Nationwide | DME Channel 53X (111.60 MHz) |
| 1014.00000 | 1077.00000 | AM | RAF Chivenor | TACAN |

| Base | Mobile | Mode | Location | User and Notes |
|---|---|---|---|---|
| 1015.00000 | 1078.00000 | AM | Nationwide | DME Channel 54X (111.70 MHz) |
| 1016.00000 | 1079.00000 | AM | Nationwide | DME Channel 55X (111.80 MHz) |
| 1017.00000 | 1080.00000 | AM | Nationwide | DME Channel 56X (111.90 MHz) |
| 1017.00000 | 1080.00000 | AM | RAF Brize Norton | TACAN |
| 1018.00000 | 1081.00000 | AM | Nationwide | DME Channel 57X (112.00 MHz) |
| 1019.00000 | 1082.00000 | AM | Nationwide | DME Channel 58X (112.10 MHz) |
| 1019.00000 | 1082.00000 | AM | Pole Hill | DME |
| 1020.00000 | 1083.00000 | AM | Nationwide | DME Channel 59X (112.20 MHz) |
| 1020.00000 | 1083.00000 | AM | Ronaldsway, Isle of Man | DME |
| 1021.00000 | 1084.00000 | AM | Nationwide | DME Channel 60X (112.30 MHz) |
| 1022.00000 | 1085.00000 | AM | Nationwide | DME Channel 61X Not Used |
| 1023.00000 | 1086.00000 | AM | Nationwide | DME Channel 62X Not Used |
| 1024.00000 | 1087.00000 | AM | Nationwide | DME Channel 63X Not Used |
| 1025.00000 | 1088.00000 | AM | Nationwide | DME Channel 64X Not Used |
| 1026.00000 | 1089.00000 | AM | Nationwide | DME Channel 65X Not Used |
| 1027.00000 | 1090.00000 | AM | Nationwide | DME Channel 66X Not Used |
| 1028.00000 | 1091.00000 | AM | Nationwide | DME Channel 67X Not Used |
| 1029.00000 | 1092.00000 | AM | Nationwide | DME Channel 68X Not Used |
| 1030.00000 | 1093.00000 | AM | Nationwide | DME Channel 69X Not Used |
| 1030.00000 | 1090.00000 | AM | Nationwide | Transponder Interrog./Reply |
| 1031.00000 | 1094.00000 | AM | Nationwide | DME Channel 70X (112.30 MHz) |
| 1032.00000 | 1095.00000 | AM | Nationwide | DME Channel 71X (112.40 MHz) |
| 1033.00000 | 1096.00000 | AM | Nationwide | DME Channel 72X (112.50 MHz) |
| 1033.00000 | 1096.00000 | AM | St Abbs | DME |
| 1034.00000 | 1097.00000 | AM | Nationwide | DME Channel 73X (112.60 MHz) |
| 1034.00000 | 1097.00000 | AM | RAF St Mawgan | TACAN |
| 1035.00000 | 1098.00000 | AM | Berry Head | DME |
| 1035.00000 | 1098.00000 | AM | Donegal Aerodrome | DME |
| 1035.00000 | 1098.00000 | AM | Nationwide | DME Channel 74X (112.70 MHz) |
| 1036.00000 | 1099.00000 | AM | Gamston Aerodrome | DME |
| 1036.00000 | 1099.00000 | AM | Nationwide | DME Channel 75X (112.80 MHz) |
| 1037.00000 | 1100.00000 | AM | Nationwide | DME Channel 76X (112.90 MHz) |
| 1038.00000 | 1101.00000 | AM | Nationwide | DME Channel 77X (113.00 MHz) |
| 1039.00000 | 1102.00000 | AM | Nationwide | DME Channel 78X (113.10 MHz) |
| 1039.00000 | 1102.00000 | AM | Strumble | DME |
| 1040.00000 | 1103.00000 | AM | Nationwide | DME Channel 79X (113.20 MHz) |
| 1040.00000 | 1103.00000 | AM | Warton (MoD) | TACAN |
| 1041.00000 | 1104.00000 | AM | Nationwide | DME Channel 80X (113.30 MHz) |
| 1042.00000 | 1105.00000 | AM | Nationwide | DME Channel 81X (113.40 MHz) |
| 1043.00000 | 1106.00000 | AM | Nationwide | DME Channel 82X (113.50 MHz) |
| 1044.00000 | 1107.00000 | AM | London (Heathrow) | DME |
| 1044.00000 | 1107.00000 | AM | Nationwide | DME Channel 83X (113.60 MHz) |
| 1044.00000 | 1107.00000 | AM | Wick Aerodrome | TACAN |
| 1045.00000 | 1108.00000 | AM | Nationwide | DME Channel 84X (113.70 MHz) |
| 1046.00000 | 1109.00000 | AM | Nationwide | DME Channel 85X (113.80 MHz) |
| 1046.00000 | 1109.00000 | AM | Talla | DME |
| 1047.00000 | 1110.00000 | AM | Nationwide | DME Channel 86X (113.90 MHz) |
| 1047.00000 | 1110.00000 | AM | Ottringham | DME |
| 1048.00000 | 1111.00000 | AM | Midhurst | DME |
| 1048.00000 | 1111.00000 | AM | Nationwide | DME Channel 87X (114.00 MHz) |
| 1049.00000 | 1112.00000 | AM | Nationwide | DME Channel 88X (114.10 MHz) |
| 1049.00000 | 1112.00000 | AM | Wallasey | DME |
| 1050.00000 | 1113.00000 | AM | Land's End Airport | DME |
| 1050.00000 | 1113.00000 | AM | Nationwide | DME Channel 89X (114.20 MHz) |
| 1051.00000 | 1114.00000 | AM | Aberdeen (Dyce Airport) | DME |
| 1051.00000 | 1114.00000 | AM | Nationwide | DME Channel 90X (114.30 MHz) |

| Base | Mobile | Mode | Location | User and Notes |
|------|--------|------|----------|----------------|
| 1052.00000 | 1115.00000 | AM | Benbecula Airport | TACAN |
| 1052.00000 | 1115.00000 | AM | Nationwide | DME Channel 91X (114.40 MHz) |
| 1053.00000 | 1116.00000 | AM | Koksijde | DME |
| 1053.00000 | 1116.00000 | AM | Nationwide | DME Channel 92X (114.50 MHz) |
| 1054.00000 | 1117.00000 | AM | Nationwide | DME Channel 93X (114.60 MHz) |
| 1055.00000 | 1118.00000 | AM | Nationwide | DME Channel 94X (114.70 MHz) |
| 1056.00000 | 1119.00000 | AM | Nationwide | DME Channel 95X (114.80 Mhz) |
| 1057.00000 | 1120.00000 | AM | Nationwide | DME Channel 96X (114.90 MHz) |
| 1057.00000 | 1120.00000 | AM | Vallafield | TACAN |
| 1058.00000 | 1121.00000 | AM | Nationwide | DME Channel 97X (115.00 MHz) |
| 1058.00000 | 1121.00000 | AM | Stornoway Airport | TACAN |
| 1059.00000 | 1122.00000 | AM | Biggin Hill | DME |
| 1059.00000 | 1122.00000 | AM | Nationwide | DME Channel 98X (115.10 MHz) |
| 1060.00000 | 1123.00000 | AM | Dean Cross | DME |
| 1060.00000 | 1123.00000 | AM | Nationwide | DME Channel 99X (115.20 MHz) |
| 1061.00000 | 1124.00000 | AM | Nationwide | DME Channel 100X (115.30 MHz) |
| 1061.00000 | 1124.00000 | AM | Ockham | DME |
| 1062.00000 | 1125.00000 | AM | Glasgow | DME |
| 1062.00000 | 1125.00000 | AM | Nationwide | DME Channel 101X (115.40 MHz) |
| 1063.00000 | 1126.00000 | AM | Nationwide | DME Channel 102X (115.50 MHz) |
| 1064.00000 | 1127.00000 | AM | Lambourne | DME |
| 1064.00000 | 1127.00000 | AM | Nationwide | DME Channel 103X (115.60 MHz) |
| 1065.00000 | 1128.00000 | AM | Nationwide | DME Channel 104X (115.70 MHz) |
| 1065.00000 | 1128.00000 | AM | Stoke on Trent | DME |
| 1066.00000 | 1129.00000 | AM | Nationwide | DME Channel 105X (115.80 MHz) |
| 1067.00000 | 1130.00000 | AM | Nationwide | DME Channel 106X (115.90 MHz) |
| 1067.00000 | 1130.00000 | AM | USAF Mildenhall | TACAN |
| 1068.00000 | 1131.00000 | AM | Nationwide | DME Channel 107X (116.00 MHz) |
| 1069.00000 | 1132.00000 | AM | Nationwide | DME Channel 108X (116.10 MHz) |
| 1070.00000 | 1133.00000 | AM | Blackbushe | DME |
| 1070.00000 | 1133.00000 | AM | Nationwide | DME Channel 109X (116.20 MHz) |
| 1071.00000 | 1134.00000 | AM | Nationwide | DME Channel 110X (116.30 MHz) |
| 1072.00000 | 1135.00000 | AM | Daventry | DME |
| 1072.00000 | 1135.00000 | AM | Nationwide | DME Channel 111X (116.40 MHz) |
| 1073.00000 | 1136.00000 | AM | Nationwide | DME Channel 112X (116.50 MHz) |
| 1073.00000 | 1136.00000 | AM | RAF Coltishall | TACAN |
| 1074.00000 | 1137.00000 | AM | Nationwide | DME Channel 113X (116.60 MHz) |
| 1075.00000 | 1138.00000 | AM | Nationwide | DME Channel 114X (116.70 MHz) |
| 1076.00000 | 1139.00000 | AM | Nationwide | DME Channel 115X (116.80 MHz) |
| 1077.00000 | 1140.00000 | AM | Nationwide | DME Channel 116X (116.90 MHz) |
| 1078.00000 | 1141.00000 | AM | Nationwide | DME Channel 117X (117.00 MHz) |
| 1078.00000 | 1141.00000 | AM | Seaford | DME |
| 1079.00000 | 1142.00000 | AM | Nationwide | DME Channel 118X (117.10 MHz) |
| 1080.00000 | 1143.00000 | AM | Nationwide | DME Channel 119X (117.20 MHz) |
| 1081.00000 | 1144.00000 | AM | Detling | DME |
| 1081.00000 | 1144.00000 | AM | Nationwide | DME Channel 120X (117.30 MHz) |
| 1082.00000 | 1145.00000 | AM | Connaught Airport | DME |
| 1082.00000 | 1145.00000 | AM | Nationwide | DME Channel 121X (117.40 MHz) |
| 1082.00000 | 1145.00000 | AM | RAF Cranwell | TACAN |
| 1083.00000 | 1146.00000 | AM | Brookmans Park | DME |
| 1083.00000 | 1146.00000 | AM | Nationwide | DME Channel 122X (117.50 MHz) |
| 1083.00000 | 1146.00000 | AM | Turnberry | DME |
| 1084.00000 | 1147.00000 | AM | Nationwide | DME Channel 123X (117.60 MHz) |
| 1084.00000 | 1147.00000 | AM | RAF Wittering | TACAN |
| 1085.00000 | 1148.00000 | AM | Nationwide | DME Channel 124X (117.70 MHz) |
| 1085.00000 | 1148.00000 | AM | Oxford/Kidlington | DME |

| Base | Mobile | Mode | Location | User and Notes |
|------|--------|------|----------|----------------|
| 1085.00000 | 1148.00000 | AM | Tiree | DME |
| 1086.00000 | 1149.00000 | AM | Nationwide | DME Channel 125X  (117.80 MHz) |
| 1087.00000 | 1150.00000 | AM | Mayfield | DME |
| 1087.00000 | 1150.00000 | AM | Nationwide | DME Channel 126X  (117.90 MHz) |
| 1088.00000 | 1025.00000 | AM | Nationwide | DME Channel 1Y  Not Used |
| 1089.00000 | 1026.00000 | AM | Nationwide | DME Channel 2Y  Not Used |
| 1090.00000 | 1027.00000 | AM | Nationwide | DME Channel 3Y  Not Used |
| 1091.00000 | 1028.00000 | AM | Nationwide | DME Channel 4Y  Not Used |
| 1092.00000 | 1029.00000 | AM | Nationwide | DME Channel 5Y  Not Used |
| 1093.00000 | 1030.00000 | AM | Nationwide | DME Channel 6Y  Not Used |
| 1094.00000 | 1031.00000 | AM | Nationwide | DME Channel 7Y  Not Used |
| 1095.00000 | 1032.00000 | AM | Nationwide | DME Channel 8Y  Not Used |
| 1096.00000 | 1033.00000 | AM | Nationwide | DME Channel 9Y  Not Used |
| 1097.00000 | 1034.00000 | AM | Nationwide | DME Channel 10Y  Not Used |
| 1098.00000 | 1035.00000 | AM | Nationwide | DME Channel 11Y  Not Used |
| 1099.00000 | 1036.00000 | AM | Nationwide | DME Channel 12Y  Not Used |
| 1100.00000 | 1037.00000 | AM | Nationwide | DME Channel 13Y  Not Used |
| 1101.00000 | 1038.00000 | AM | Nationwide | DME Channel 14Y  Not Used |
| 1102.00000 | 1039.00000 | AM | Nationwide | DME Channel 15Y  Not Used |
| 1103.00000 | 1040.00000 | AM | Nationwide | DME Channel 16Y  Not Used |
| 1104.00000 | 1041.00000 | AM | Lydd Airport | DME |
| 1104.00000 | 1041.00000 | AM | Nationwide | DME Channel 17Y  (108.05 MHz) |
| 1105.00000 | 1042.00000 | AM | Blackpool | DME |
| 1105.00000 | 1042.00000 | AM | Nationwide | DME Channel 18Y  (108.15 MHz) |
| 1106.00000 | 1043.00000 | AM | Nationwide | DME Channel 19Y  (108.25 MHz) |
| 1107.00000 | 1044.00000 | AM | Nationwide | DME Channel 20Y  (108.35 MHz) |
| 1108.00000 | 1045.00000 | AM | Nationwide | DME Channel 21Y  (108.45 MHz) |
| 1109.00000 | 1046.00000 | AM | Nationwide | DME Channel 22Y  (108.55 MHz) |
| 1110.00000 | 1047.00000 | AM | Nationwide | DME Channel 23Y  (108.65 MHz) |
| 1111.00000 | 1048.00000 | AM | Humberside Airport | DME |
| 1111.00000 | 1048.00000 | AM | Nationwide | DME Channel 24Y  (108.75 MHz) |
| 1112.00000 | 1049.00000 | AM | Nationwide | DME Channel 25Y  (108.85 MHz) |
| 1113.00000 | 1050.00000 | AM | Nationwide | DME Ch26Y  (108.95 MHz) |
| 1113.00000 | 1050.00000 | AM | Woodford | DME |
| 1114.00000 | 1051.00000 | AM | Nationwide | DME Channel 27Y  (109.05 MHz) |
| 1114.00000 | 1051.00000 | AM | Yeovil Aerodrome | DME |
| 1115.00000 | 1052.00000 | AM | Luton Airport | DME |
| 1115.00000 | 1052.00000 | AM | Nationwide | DME Channel 28Y  (109.15 MHz) |
| 1116.00000 | 1053.00000 | AM | Nationwide | DME Channel 29Y  (109.25 MHz) |
| 1117.00000 | 1054.00000 | AM | Nationwide | DME Channel 30Y  (109.35 MHz) |
| 1118.00000 | 1055.00000 | AM | Nationwide | DME Channel 31Y  (109.45 MHz) |
| 1119.00000 | 1056.00000 | AM | Nationwide | DME Channel 32Y  (109.55 MHz) |
| 1120.00000 | 1057.00000 | AM | Nationwide | DME Channel 33Y  (109.65 MHz) |
| 1121.00000 | 1058.00000 | AM | Nationwide | DME Channel 34Y  (109.75 MHz) |
| 1122.00000 | 1059.00000 | AM | Fair Oaks Aerodrome | DME |
| 1122.00000 | 1059.00000 | AM | Nationwide | DME Channel 35Y  (109.85 MHz) |
| 1123.00000 | 1060.00000 | AM | Nationwide | DME Ch36Y  (109.95 MHz) |
| 1124.00000 | 1061.00000 | AM | Nationwide | DME Channel 37Y  (110.05 MHz) |
| 1125.00000 | 1062.00000 | AM | Nationwide | DME Channel 38Y  (110.15 MHz) |
| 1126.00000 | 1063.00000 | AM | Nationwide | DME Ch39Y  (110.25 MHz) |
| 1127.00000 | 1064.00000 | AM | Nationwide | DME Channel 40Y  (110.35 MHz) |
| 1128.00000 | 1065.00000 | AM | Nationwide | DME Channel 41Y  (110.45 MHz) |
| 1129.00000 | 1066.00000 | AM | Nationwide | DME Channel 42Y  (110.55 MHz) |
| 1130.00000 | 1067.00000 | AM | Nationwide | DME Channel 43Y  (110.65 MHz) |
| 1131.00000 | 1068.00000 | AM | Nationwide | DME Channel 44Y  (110.75 MHz) |
| 1132.00000 | 1069.00000 | AM | Nationwide | DME Channel 45Y  (110.85 MHz) |

| Base | Mobile | Mode | Location | User and Notes |
|---|---|---|---|---|
| 1133.00000 | 1070.00000 | AM | Nationwide | DME Channel 46Y (110.95 MHz) |
| 1134.00000 | 1071.00000 | AM | Nationwide | DME Channel 47Y (111.05 MHz) |
| 1135.00000 | 1072.00000 | AM | Nationwide | DME Channel 48Y (111.15 MHz) |
| 1136.00000 | 1073.00000 | AM | Nationwide | DME Channel 49Y (111.25 MHz) |
| 1137.00000 | 1074.00000 | AM | Nationwide | DME Channel 50Y (111.35 MHz) |
| 1137.00000 | 1074.00000 | AM | Southend Airport | DME |
| 1138.00000 | 1075.00000 | AM | Nationwide | DME Channel 51Y (111.45 MHz) |
| 1139.00000 | 1076.00000 | AM | Nationwide | DME Channel 52Y (111.55 MHz) |
| 1140.00000 | 1077.00000 | AM | Nationwide | DME Channel 53Y (111.65 MHz) |
| 1141.00000 | 1078.00000 | AM | Liverpool Airport | DME |
| 1141.00000 | 1078.00000 | AM | Nationwide | DME Channel 54Y (111.75 MHz) |
| 1142.00000 | 1079.00000 | AM | Nationwide | DME Channel 55Y (111.85 MHz) |
| 1143.00000 | 1080.00000 | AM | Nationwide | DME Channel 56Y (111.95 MHz) |
| 1144.00000 | 1081.00000 | AM | Nationwide | DME Channel 57Y (112.05 MHz) |
| 1145.00000 | 1082.00000 | AM | Nationwide | DME Channel 58Y (112.15 MHz) |
| 1146.00000 | 1083.00000 | AM | Nationwide | DME Channel 59Y (112.25 MHz) |
| 1147.00000 | 1084.00000 | AM | Nationwide | DME Channel 60Y Not Used |
| 1148.00000 | 1085.00000 | AM | Nationwide | DME Channel 61Y Not Used |
| 1149.00000 | 1086.00000 | AM | Nationwide | DME Channel 62Y Not Used |
| 1150.00000 | 1087.00000 | AM | Nationwide | DME Channel 63Y Not Used |
| 1151.00000 | 1088.00000 | AM | Nationwide | DME Channel 64Y Not Used |
| 1152.00000 | 1089.00000 | AM | Nationwide | DME Channel 65Y Not Used |
| 1153.00000 | 1090.00000 | AM | Nationwide | DME Channel 66Y Not Used |
| 1154.00000 | 1091.00000 | AM | Nationwide | DME Channel 67Y Not Used |
| 1155.00000 | 1092.00000 | AM | Nationwide | DME Channel 68Y Not Used |
| 1156.00000 | 1093.00000 | AM | Nationwide | DME Channel 69Y Not Used |
| 1157.00000 | 1094.00000 | AM | Nationwide | DME Channel 70Y (112.35 MHz) |
| 1158.00000 | 1095.00000 | AM | Nationwide | DME Channel 71Y (112.45 MHz) |
| 1159.00000 | 1096.00000 | AM | Nationwide | DME Channel 72Y (112.55 MHz) |
| 1160.00000 | 1097.00000 | AM | Nationwide | DME Channel 73Y (112.65 MHz) |
| 1161.00000 | 1098.00000 | AM | Nationwide | DME Channel 74Y (112.75 MHz) |
| 1162.00000 | 1099.00000 | AM | Nationwide | DME Channel 75Y (112.85 MHz) |
| 1163.00000 | 1100.00000 | AM | Nationwide | DME Channel 76Y (112.95 MHz) |
| 1164.00000 | 1101.00000 | AM | Nationwide | DME Channel 77Y (113.05 MHz) |
| 1165.00000 | 1102.00000 | AM | Nationwide | DME Channel 78Y (113.15 MHz) |
| 1166.00000 | 1103.00000 | AM | Nationwide | DME Channel 79Y (113.25 MHz) |
| 1167.00000 | 1104.00000 | AM | Nationwide | DME Channel 80Y (113.35 MHz) |
| 1168.00000 | 1105.00000 | AM | Nationwide | DME Channel 81Y (113.45 MHz) |
| 1169.00000 | 1106.00000 | AM | Manchester Airport | DME |
| 1169.00000 | 1106.00000 | AM | Nationwide | DME Channel 82Y (113.55 MHz) |
| 1170.00000 | 1107.00000 | AM | Honiley | DME |
| 1170.00000 | 1107.00000 | AM | Nationwide | DME Channel 83Y (113.65 MHz) |
| 1171.00000 | 1108.00000 | AM | Bovingdon | DME |
| 1171.00000 | 1108.00000 | AM | Nationwide | DME Channel 84Y (113.75 MHz) |
| 1172.00000 | 1109.00000 | AM | Nationwide | DME Channel 85Y (113.85 MHz) |
| 1173.00000 | 1110.00000 | AM | Nationwide | DME Channel 86Y (113.95 MHz) |
| 1174.00000 | 1111.00000 | AM | Nationwide | DME Channel 87Y (114.05 MHz) |
| 1175.00000 | 1112.00000 | AM | Nationwide | DME Channel 88Y (114.15 MHz) |
| 1176.00000 | 1113.00000 | AM | Nationwide | DME Channel 89Y (114.25 MHz) |
| 1177.00000 | 1114.00000 | AM | Compton | DME |
| 1177.00000 | 1114.00000 | AM | Nationwide | DME Ch90Y (114.35 MHz) |
| 1178.00000 | 1115.00000 | AM | Nationwide | DME Channel 91Y (114.45 MHz) |
| 1179.00000 | 1116.00000 | AM | Clacton Aerodrome | DME |
| 1179.00000 | 1116.00000 | AM | Nationwide | DME Channel 92Y (114.55 MHz) |
| 1180.00000 | 1117.00000 | AM | Nationwide | DME Channel 93Y (114.65 MHz) |
| 1181.00000 | 1118.00000 | AM | Nationwide | DME Channel 94Y (114.75 MHz) |

| Base | Mobile | Mode | Location | User and Notes |
|------|--------|------|----------|----------------|
| 1182.00000 | 1119.00000 | AM | Nationwide | DME Channel 95Y (114.85 MHz) |
| 1183.00000 | 1120.00000 | AM | Dover | DME |
| 1183.00000 | 1120.00000 | AM | Nationwide | DME Channel 96Y (114.95 MHz) |
| 1184.00000 | 1121.00000 | AM | Nationwide | DME Channel 97Y (115.05 MHz) |
| 1185.00000 | 1122.00000 | AM | Nationwide | DME Channel 98Y (115.15 MHz) |
| 1186.00000 | 1123.00000 | AM | Nationwide | DME Channel 99Y (115.25 MHz) |
| 1187.00000 | 1124.00000 | AM | Nationwide | DME Channel 100Y (115.35 MHz) |
| 1188.00000 | 1125.00000 | AM | Nationwide | DME Channel 101Y (115.45 MHz) |
| 1189.00000 | 1126.00000 | AM | Gloucestershire Airport | DME |
| 1189.00000 | 1126.00000 | AM | Nationwide | DME Channel 102Y (115.55 MHz) |
| 1190.00000 | 1127.00000 | AM | Nationwide | DME Channel 103Y (115.65 MHz) |
| 1191.00000 | 1128.00000 | AM | Nationwide | DME Channel 104Y (115.75 MHz) |
| 1192.00000 | 1129.00000 | AM | Nationwide | DME Channel 105Y (115.85 MHz) |
| 1193.00000 | 1130.00000 | AM | Nationwide | DME Channel 106Y (115.95 MHz) |
| 1194.00000 | 1131.00000 | AM | Nationwide | DME Channel 107Y (116.05 MHz) |
| 1195.00000 | 1132.00000 | AM | Nationwide | DME Channel 108Y (116.15 MHz) |
| 1196.00000 | 1133.00000 | AM | Barkway | DME |
| 1196.00000 | 1133.00000 | AM | Nationwide | DME Channel 109Y (116.25 MHz) |
| 1197.00000 | 1134.00000 | AM | Nationwide | DME Channel 110Y (116.35 MHz) |
| 1198.00000 | 1135.00000 | AM | Nationwide | DME Channel 111Y (116.45 MHz) |
| 1199.00000 | 1136.00000 | AM | Nationwide | DME Channel 112Y (116.55 MHz) |
| 1200.00000 | 1137.00000 | AM | Nationwide | DME Channel 113Y (116.65 MHz) |
| 1201.00000 | 1138.00000 | AM | Cambridge Airport | DME |
| 1201.00000 | 1138.00000 | AM | Nationwide | DME Channel 114Y (116.75 MHz) |
| 1202.00000 | 1139.00000 | AM | Nationwide | DME Channel 115Y (116.85 MHz) |
| 1203.00000 | 1140.00000 | AM | Nationwide | DME Channel 116Y (116.95 MHz) |
| 1204.00000 | 1141.00000 | AM | Nationwide | DME Channel 117Y (117.05 MHz) |
| 1205.00000 | 1142.00000 | AM | Nationwide | DME Channel 118Y (117.15 MHz) |
| 1206.00000 | 1143.00000 | AM | Nationwide | DME Channel 119Y (117.25 MHz) |
| 1207.00000 | 1144.00000 | AM | Nationwide | DME Channel 120Y (117.35 MHz) |
| 1207.00000 | 1144.00000 | AM | Sumburgh Airport | DME |
| 1208.00000 | 1145.00000 | AM | Brecon | DME |
| 1208.00000 | 1145.00000 | AM | Nationwide | DME Channel 121Y (117.45 MHz) |
| 1209.00000 | 1146.00000 | AM | Nationwide | DME Channel 122Y (117.55 MHz) |
| 1210.00000 | 1147.00000 | AM | Nationwide | DME Channel 123Y (117.65 MHz) |
| 1211.00000 | 1148.00000 | AM | Nationwide | DME Channel 124Y (117.75 MHz) |
| 1212.00000 | 1149.00000 | AM | Nationwide | DME Channel 125Y (117.85 MHz) |
| 1213.00000 | 1150.00000 | AM | Nationwide | DME Channel 126Y (117.95 MHz) |

### 1215.0000 - 1365.0000 MHz    DEFENCE AND CIVIL RADAR SYSTEMS

### 1215.0000 - 1240.0000 MHz    SATELLITE NAVIGATION SYSTEMS

| Base | Mobile | Mode | Location | User and Notes |
|------|--------|------|----------|----------------|
| 1227.60000 | | NFM | Nationwide | Military GPS Navstar |

### 1240.0000 - 1296.0000 MHz    RADIO LOCATION AND SATELLITE POSITIONING SYSTEMS

| Base | Mobile | Mode | Location | User and Notes |
|------|--------|------|----------|----------------|
| 1246.00000 | | NFM | Nationwide | Military Glonass Channel 0 |
| 1246.43750 | | NFM | Nationwide | Military Glonass Channel 1 |
| 1246.87500 | | NFM | Nationwide | Military Glonass Channel 2 |
| 1247.31250 | | NFM | Nationwide | Military Glonass Channel 3 |
| 1247.75000 | | NFM | Nationwide | Military Glonass Channel 4 |
| 1248.18750 | | NFM | Nationwide | Military Glonass Channel 5 |
| 1248.62500 | | NFM | Nationwide | Military Glonass Channel 6 |
| 1249.06250 | | NFM | Nationwide | Military Glonass Channel 7 |
| 1249.50000 | | NFM | Nationwide | Military Glonass Channel 8 |

| Base | Mobile | Mode | Location | User and Notes |
|------|--------|------|----------|----------------|
| 1249.93750 | | NFM | Nationwide | Military Glonass Channel 9 |
| 1250.37500 | | NFM | Nationwide | Military Glonass Channel 10 |
| 1250.81250 | | NFM | Nationwide | Military Glonass Channel 11 |
| 1251.25000 | | NFM | Nationwide | Military Glonass Channel 12 |
| 1251.68750 | | NFM | Nationwide | Military Glonass Channel 13 |
| 1252.12500 | | NFM | Nationwide | Military Glonass Channel 14 |
| 1252.56250 | | NFM | Nationwide | Military Glonass Channel 15 |
| 1253.00000 | | NFM | Nationwide | Military Glonass Channel 16 |
| 1253.43750 | | NFM | Nationwide | Military Glonass Channel 17 |
| 1253.87500 | | NFM | Nationwide | Military Glonass Channel 18 |
| 1254.31250 | | NFM | Nationwide | Military Glonass Channel 19 |
| 1254.75000 | | NFM | Nationwide | Military Glonass Channel 20 |
| 1255.18750 | | NFM | Nationwide | Military Glonass Channel 21 |
| 1255.62500 | | NFM | Nationwide | Military Glonass Channel 22 |
| 1256.06250 | | NFM | Nationwide | Military Glonass Channel 23 |
| 1256.50000 | | NFM | Nationwide | Military Glonass Channel 24 |
| 1260.00000 | | NFM | Nationwide | German Bugging Devices |
| | | | | |
| 1265.000 | 1265.000 | WFM | Nationwide | Amateur TV |
| 1255.000 | 1255.000 | WFM | Nationwide | Amateur TV |

**1296.0000 - 1325.0000 MHz    25 cm Amateur Radio Band**

| Base | Mobile | Mode | Location | User and Notes |
|------|--------|------|----------|----------------|
| 1296.810 | | CW | Orpington | Beacon (GB3NWK) |
| 1296.830 | | CW | Martlesham | Beacon (GB3MHL) |
| 1296.850 | | CW | Farnborough | Beacon (GB3FRS) |
| 1296.860 | | CW | St Austell | Beacon (GB3MCB) |
| 1296.875 | | CW | Bristol | Repeater (GB3USK) |
| 1296.890 | | CW | Dunstable | Beacon (GB3DUN) |
| 1296.900 | | CW | Newport | Beacon (GB3IOW) |
| 1296.910 | | CW | Clee Hill, Salop | Beacon (GB3CLE) |
| 1296.930 | | CW | Emley Moor | Beacon (GB3MLE) |
| 1296.990 | | CW | Edinburgh | Beacon (GB3EDN) |
| 1297.000 | 1291.000 | NFM | Bolton | Repeater (GB3MC) |
| | | NFM | Bolton | Repeater (GB3MC) |
| | | NFM | Norwich | Repeater (GB3NO) |
| | | NFM | Norwich | Repeater (GB3NR) |
| 1297.050 | 1291.050 | NFM | Farnham | Repeater (GB3FM) |
| | | NFM | Farnham | Repeater (GB3FM) |
| 1297.075 | 1291.075 | NFM | Royston | Repeater (GB3PS) |
| | | NFM | Stoke on Trent | Repeater (GB3SE) |
| 1297.125 | 1291.125 | NFM | Northampton | Repeater (GB3CN) |
| 1297.375 | 1291.375 | NFM | Wakefield | Repeater (GB3WC) |
| | | NFM | Wakefield | Repeater (GB3WC) |
| 1297.500 | | NFM | Nationwide | Amateur Channel SM 20 |
| 1297.525 | | NFM | Nationwide | Amateur Channel SM 21 |
| 1297.550 | | NFM | Nationwide | Amateur Channel SM 22 |
| 1297.575 | | NFM | Nationwide | Amateur Channel SM 23 |
| 1297.600 | | NFM | Nationwide | Amateur Channel SM 24 |
| 1297.625 | | NFM | Nationwide | Amateur Channel SM 25 |
| 1297.650 | | NFM | Nationwide | Amateur Channel SM 26 |
| 1297.675 | | NFM | Nationwide | Amateur Channel SM 27 |
| 1297.700 | | NFM | Nationwide | Amateur Channel SM 28 |
| 1297.725 | | NFM | Nationwide | Amateur Channel SM 29 |

| Base | Mobile | Mode | Location | User and Notes |
|---|---|---|---|---|
| 1297.750 | | NFM | Nationwide | Amateur Channel SM 30 |
| 1308.000 | 1249.000 | NFM | Hull | Repeater (GB3EY) |
| 1308.000 | 1248.000 | NFM | Sheerness | Repeater (GB3KT) |
| 1311.500 | 1276.500 | NFM | Bath | Repeater (GB3UT) |
| 1318.000 | 1249.000 | NFM | Almwich | Repeater (GB3TM) |
| | | NFM | Brighton | Repeater (GB3VR) |
| | | NFM | Bristol | Repeater (GB3ZZ) |
| | | NFM | Cambridge | Repeater (GB3PV) |
| | | NFM | Coventry | Repeater (GB3RT) |
| | | NFM | Dunstable | Repeater (GB3TV) |
| | | NFM | Fakenham | Repeater (GB3TN) |
| | | NFM | Huddersfield | Repeater (GB3ET) |
| | | NFM | Lowestoft | Repeater (GB3LO) |
| | | NFM | Markfield | Repeater (GB3GV) |
| | | NFM | Northampton | Repeater (GB3MV) |
| | | NFM | Plymouth | Repeater (GB3WV) |
| | | NFM | Southampton | Repeater (GB3AT) |

| | | | | |
|---|---|---|---|---|
| 1325.0000 - 1400.0000 MHz | | | POINT-TO-POINT DIGITAL MULTIPLEXED MICROWAVE LINKS | |
| 1328.02000 | | MUX | Poole | Bulbarrow Main Site |
| 1331.20000 | | MUX | Poole | Bulbarrow Main Site |
| 1334.00000 | | MUX | Poole | Bulbarrow Main Site |
| 1450.60000 | | MUX | Poole | Bulbarrow Main Site |

| | | | | |
|---|---|---|---|---|
| 1400.0000 - 1427.0000 MHz | | | RADIO ASTRONOMY | |

| | | | | |
|---|---|---|---|---|
| 1427.0000 - 1429.0000 MHz | | | SATELLITE UPLINKS | |

| | | | | |
|---|---|---|---|---|
| 1429.0000 - 1450.0000 MHz | | | MoD ALLOCATIONS | |

| | | | | |
|---|---|---|---|---|
| 1450.0000 - 1530.0000 MHz | | | POINT-TO-POINT DIGITAL MICROWAVE LINKS | |
| 1451.15625 | | NFM | West Midlands | 96.4 FM BRMB |
| 1455.35000 | | NFM | Merseyside | Police DCR Link |
| 1457.64000 | | MUX | Poole | 70.8625 MHz Fire Brigade |
| 1458.24750 | | NFM | Badminton | Palace Link |
| 1459.15000 | | MUX | Poole | Microwave Link |
| 1460.43000 | | MUX | Poole | Microwave Link |
| 1461.62500 | | NFM | Wiltshire | Fire Brigade |
| 1461.64000 | | MUX | Poole | Microwave Link |
| 1466.87500 | 1529.37500 | NFM | Nationwide | UK Test & Development |
| 1467.12500 | 1529.62500 | NFM | Nationwide | UK Test & Development |
| 1468.77000 | | MUX | Poole | Microwave Link |
| 1469.68000 | | MUX | Poole | 171.2875 MHz Feeder |
| 1470.33000 | | MUX | Poole | Bulbarrow Main Site |
| 1472.00000 | | MUX | Poole | Corfe Castle |
| 1472.65000 | | MUX | Poole | Microwave Link |
| 1472.98750 | 1492.85000 | NFM | Channel Islands | Aurigny Airlines Link |
| 1473.15000 | | MUX | Poole | Bulbarrow Main Site |
| 1492.30000 | | MUX | Poole | 454.1 MHz Paging Feeder |
| | | MUX | Poole | Microwave Link |

| Base | Mobile | Mode | Location | User and Notes |
|------|--------|------|----------|----------------|

## 1575.4200 -1616.5000 MHz Radio Location and Satellite Positioning Systems

| Base | Mobile | Mode | Location | User and Notes |
|------|--------|------|----------|----------------|
| 1575.42000 | | NFM | Nationwide | Civilian GPS Navstar |
| 1602.00000 | | NFM | Nationwide | Civil Glonass Channel 0 |
| 1602.56250 | | NFM | Nationwide | Civil Glonass Channel 1 |
| 1603.12500 | | NFM | Nationwide | Civil Glonass Channel 2 |
| 1603.67850 | | NFM | Nationwide | Civil Glonass Channel 3 |
| 1604.25000 | | NFM | Nationwide | Civil Glonass Channel 4 |
| 1604.81250 | | NFM | Nationwide | Civil Glonass Channel 5 |
| 1605.37500 | | NFM | Nationwide | Civil Glonass Channel 6 |
| 1605.93750 | | NFM | Nationwide | Civil Glonass Channel 7 |
| 1606.50000 | | NFM | Nationwide | Civil Glonass Channel 8 |
| 1607.06250 | | NFM | Nationwide | Civil Glonass Channel 9 |
| 1607.62500 | | NFM | Nationwide | Civil Glonass Channel 10 |
| 1608.18750 | | NFM | Nationwide | Civil Glonass Channel 11 |
| 1608.75000 | | NFM | Nationwide | Civil Glonass Channel 12 |
| 1609.31250 | | NFM | Nationwide | Civil Glonass Channel 13 |
| 1609.87500 | | NFM | Nationwide | Civil Glonass Channel 14 |
| 1610.43750 | | NFM | Nationwide | Civil Glonass Channel 15 |
| 1611.00000 | | NFM | Nationwide | Civil Glonass Channel 16 |
| 1611.56250 | | NFM | Nationwide | Civil Glonass Channel 17 |
| 1612.12500 | | NFM | Nationwide | Civil Glonass Channel 18 |
| 1612.67850 | | NFM | Nationwide | Civil Glonass Channel 19 |
| 1613.25000 | | NFM | Nationwide | Civil Glonass Channel 20 |
| 1613.81250 | | NFM | Nationwide | Civil Glonass Channel 21 |
| 1614.37500 | | NFM | Nationwide | Civil Glonass Channel 22 |
| 1614.93750 | | NFM | Nationwide | Civil Glonass Channel 23 |
| 1616.50000 | | NFM | Nationwide | Civil Glonass Channel 24 |

## 1670.000 - 1675.000 MHz    Terrestrial Flight Telephone Uplinks

| Base | Mobile | Mode | Location | User and Notes |
|------|--------|------|----------|----------------|
| 1691.000 | | NFM | Nationwide | Meteosat Channel A1/GOES |
| 1694.500 | | NFM | Nationwide | Meteosat Channel A2/FAX |
| 1698.000 | | NFM | Nationwide | NOAA-10 |
| 1707.000 | | NFM | Nationwide | NOAA-9, 11 |

## 1800.000 - 1805.000 MHz   Terrestrial Flight Telephone Downlinks

# Part 2

# Civil Aviation Band

---

| Base | Mobile | Mode | Location | User and Notes |
|------|--------|------|----------|----------------|
| | | | | |

117.9750 - 136.9750 MHz    INTERNATIONAL CIVIL AVIATION BAND
50 kHz

| Base | Mode | Location | User and Notes |
|------|------|----------|----------------|
| 122.60000 | AM | Abbeyshrule, Eire | Air/Ground |
| 118.10000 | AM | Aberdeen (Dyce Airport) | Tower |
| 120.40000 | AM | Aberdeen (Dyce Airport) | Approach/Radar |
| 121.25000 | AM | Aberdeen (Dyce Airport) | Radar |
| 121.60000 | AM | Aberdeen (Dyce Airport) | Fire Channel |
| 121.70000 | AM | Aberdeen (Dyce Airport) | Ground |
| 121.85000 | AM | Aberdeen (Dyce Airport) | ATIS |
| 122.05000 | AM | Aberdeen (Dyce Airport) | British Airways |
| 122.95000 | AM | Aberdeen (Dyce Airport) | Bristow Helicopters |
| 125.72500 | AM | Aberdeen (Dyce Airport) | Scottish VOLMET |
| 128.30000 | AM | Aberdeen (Dyce Airport) | Radar |
| 130.05000 | AM | Aberdeen (Dyce Airport) | Ground Staff |
| 130.60000 | AM | Aberdeen (Dyce Airport) | Air UK |
| 130.60000 | AM | Aberdeen (Dyce Airport) | Servisair |
| 130.62500 | AM | Aberdeen (Dyce Airport) | Granite Ops |
| 131.85000 | AM | Aberdeen (Dyce Airport) | British Airways Ops |
| 135.17500 | AM | Aberdeen (Dyce Airport) | Information |
| 134.10000 | AM | Aberdeen (Dyce) | Radar |
| 122.15000 | AM | Aberporth | AFIS |
| 122.12500 | AM | Aberporth (MoD) | AFIS |
| 122.30000 | AM | Alderney | Aurigny Airlines |
| 125.35000 | AM | Alderney | Tower |
| 128.65000 | AM | Alderney | Approach (Guernsey) |
| 129.70000 | AM | Alderney | Trinity Lightship Heliport |
| 120.62500 | AM | Andrewsfield | Radar (Stansted) |
| 130.55000 | AM | Andrewsfield | Air/Ground |
| 122.52500 | AM | Ashcroft Farm | Air/Ground |
| 122.35000 | AM | Audley End | Air/Ground |
| 123.17500 | AM | Badminton | Air/Ground |
| 123.25000 | AM | Bagby (Thirsk) | Air/Ground |
| 122.00000 | AM | Baldonnel, Eire | Approach |
| 122.30000 | AM | Baldonnel, Eire | IAC Military Radar |
| 122.80000 | AM | Baldonnel, Eire | Area Control |
| 123.10000 | AM | Baldonnel, Eire | Ground |
| 123.50000 | AM | Baldonnel, Eire | Tower |
| 129.70000 | AM | Baldonnel, Eire | IAC Military Radar |
| 129.70000 | AM | Baldonnel, Eire | Radar |
| 123.62500 | AM | Ballykelly | Approach (Eglinton)ATZ |
| 122.40000 | AM | Bantry, Eire | Air/Ground |
| 118.07500 | AM | Barra, Scotland | AFIS |
| 123.20000 | AM | Barrow (Walney Island) | Air/Ground |
| 122.70000 | AM | Barton Aerodrome | Air/Ground |
| 134.60000 | AM | Beccles Heliport | Air/Ground |
| 118.30000 | AM | Belfast (Aldergrove) | Tower |
| 120.00000 | AM | Belfast (Aldergrove) | Radar |
| 120.90000 | AM | Belfast (Aldergrove) | Approach/Radar |
| 121.75000 | AM | Belfast (Aldergrove) | Ground |
| 125.72500 | AM | Belfast (Aldergrove) | Scottish VOLMET |
| 127.00000 | AM | Belfast (Aldergrove) | Dublin VOLMET |
| 128.20000 | AM | Belfast (Aldergrove) | ATIS |
| 130.60000 | AM | Belfast (Aldergrove) | Servisair |
| 131.57500 | AM | Belfast (Aldergrove) | British Midland |
| 131.85000 | AM | Belfast (Aldergrove) | British Airways Ops |
| 130.75000 | AM | Belfast (City) | Tower |

| Base | Mobile | Mode | Location | User and Notes |
|---|---|---|---|---|
| 130.85000 | | AM | Belfast (City) | Approach/Radar |
| 134.80000 | | AM | Belfast (City) | Radar |
| 130.10000 | | AM | Bellarena | Air/Ground Gliders |
| 123.60000 | | AM | Belmullet, Eire | AFIS and Air/Ground |
| 123.25000 | | AM | Bembridge, Ise of Wight | AFIS and Air/Ground |
| 119.20000 | | AM | Benbecula | Approach/Tower and FIS |
| 131.85000 | | AM | Benbecula | British Airways Ops |
| 123.50000 | | AM | Berwick-on-Tweed (Winfield) | Winfield Radio |
| 123.05000 | | AM | Beverley (Linley Hill) | Tower |
| 120.52500 | | AM | Biggin Hill | Speedbird Ops |
| 121.87500 | | AM | Biggin Hill | ATIS |
| 129.40000 | | AM | Biggin Hill | Approach |
| 130.02500 | | AM | Biggin Hill | Srikair |
| 132.75000 | | AM | Biggin Hill | Radar (Thames) |
| 134.80000 | | AM | Biggin Hill | Tower |
| 118.05000 | | AM | Birmingham International | Radar/Approach |
| 118.30000 | | AM | Birmingham International | Tower |
| 121.60000 | | AM | Birmingham International | Fire Service |
| 121.80000 | | AM | Birmingham International | Ground |
| 126.27500 | | AM | Birmingham International | ATIS |
| 128.60000 | | AM | Birmingham International | London VOLMET (South) |
| 130.60000 | | AM | Birmingham International | Servisair |
| 131.42500 | | AM | Birmingham International | Allied |
| 131.42500 | | AM | Birmingham International | Ogden Aviation |
| 131.57500 | | AM | Birmingham International | Loganair |
| 131.57500 | | AM | Birmingham International | TEA Operations |
| 131.70000 | | AM | Birmingham International | Air 2000 Ops |
| 131.77500 | | AM | Birmingham International | Air Foyle |
| 131.85000 | | AM | Birmingham International | Birmingham Executive |
| 131.85000 | | AM | Birmingham International | British Airways Ops |
| 131.92500 | | AM | Birmingham International | Lufthansa |
| 122.95000 | | AM | Birr Aerodrome, Eire | Air/Ground (Birr Radio) |
| 122.50000 | | AM | Bitteswell Aerodrome | Air/Ground |
| 122.30000 | | AM | Blackbushe | AFIS and Air/Ground |
| 129.70000 | | AM | Blackbushe | A.T.S. |
| 130.17500 | | AM | Blackbushe | Air Lynton Ops |
| 130.37000 | | AM | Blackbushe | Air Hanson Ops |
| 118.40000 | | AM | Blackpool | Tower |
| 119.95000 | | AM | Blackpool | Approach |
| 121.75000 | | AM | Blackpool | ATIS |
| 126.60000 | | AM | Blackpool | London VOLMET (North) |
| 130.17500 | | AM | Blackpool | Janes Ops |
| 130.17500 | | AM | Blackpool | Lynton Ops |
| 130.60000 | | AM | Blackpool | Servisair |
| 135.95000 | | AM | Blackpool | Radar |
| 122.70000 | | AM | Bodmin | Tower |
| 126.70000 | | AM | Boscombe Down (MoD) | Radar |
| 130.00000 | | AM | Boscombe Down (MoD) | Radar |
| 130.75000 | | AM | Boscombe Down (MoD) | Tower/Ground |
| 129.80000 | | AM | Bourn Aerodrome | Air/Ground |
| 118.65000 | | AM | Bournemouth (Hurn) | Radar |
| 119.62500 | | AM | Bournemouth (Hurn) | Approach/Radar |
| 121.70000 | | AM | Bournemouth (Hurn) | Ground |
| 121.95000 | | AM | Bournemouth (Hurn) | ATIS |
| 125.60000 | | AM | Bournemouth (Hurn) | Tower |
| 128.60000 | | AM | Bournemouth (Hurn) | London VOLMET (South) |
| 130.60000 | | AM | Bournemouth (Hurn) | Channel Express |

| Base | Mobile | Mode | Location | User and Notes |
|---|---|---|---|---|
| 130.65000 | | AM | Bournemouth (Hurn) | Services |
| 130.77500 | | AM | Braintree Airfield | Air/Ground |
| 129.80000 | | AM | Breighton | Air/Ground |
| 124.35000 | | AM | Bristol Airport | Radar |
| 126.02500 | | AM | Bristol Airport | ATIS |
| 128.55000 | | AM | Bristol Airport | Approach |
| 128.60000 | | AM | Bristol Airport | London VOLMET (South) |
| 130.60000 | | AM | Bristol Airport | Servisair |
| 130.62500 | | AM | Bristol Airport | Clifton Ops |
| 133.85000 | | AM | Bristol Airport | Tower |
| 118.25000 | | AM | Brittas Bay, Eire | Air/Ground (Brittas Bay Radio) |
| 122.35000 | | AM | Brooklands | Air/Ground |
| 130.55000 | | AM | Brough Aerodrome | Tower and Air/Ground |
| 122.82500 | | AM | Bruntingthorpe | Air/Ground |
| 119.85000 | | AM | Burtonwood | US Army Helicopter Ops |
| 122.25000 | | AM | Caernarfon Aerodrome | Tower |
| 130.17500 | | AM | Cambridge | Suckling Ops |
| 122.20000 | | AM | Cambridge Airport | Tower |
| 123.60000 | | AM | Cambridge Airport | Approach |
| 130.17500 | | AM | Cambridge Airport | Magnet Air |
| 130.75000 | | AM | Cambridge Airport | Radar |
| 125.90000 | | AM | Campbeltown | Flight Information |
| 126.35000 | | AM | Canterbury | Traffic information (Manston) |
| 128.60000 | | AM | Cardiff | London VOLMET (South) |
| 129.90000 | | AM | Cardiff | Tremorfa Heliport |
| 119.47500 | | AM | Cardiff Airport | ATIS |
| 122.35000 | | AM | Cardiff Airport | Operations |
| 124.10000 | | AM | Cardiff Airport | Radar |
| 125.00000 | | AM | Cardiff Airport | Tower |
| 125.85000 | | AM | Cardiff Airport | Approach/Radar |
| 130.60000 | | AM | Cardiff Airport | Servisair |
| 123.45000 | | AM | Cark | Cark Radio |
| 123.60000 | | AM | Carlisle Airport | Approach/Tower and Air/Ground |
| 122.60000 | | AM | Castlebar, Eire | Air/Ground |
| 130.50000 | | AM | Castleforbes, Eire | Air/Ground |
| 121.07500 | | AM | Cheltenham Racecourse | Heliport |
| 124.95000 | | AM | Chester Garrison | Army Helicopter |
| 129.85000 | | AM | Chester Garrison | Army Helicopter Tower |
| 122.45000 | | AM | Chichester | Military Police Helicopter Ops |
| 122.45000 | | AM | Chichester (Goodwood) | AFIS |
| 135.40000 | | AM | Clacton Aerodrome | Air/Ground |
| 128.55000 | | AM | Clonbullogue, Eire | Air/Ground |
| 129.90000 | | NFM | Cockerham | Parachuting |
| 122.70000 | | AM | Compton Abbas Aerodrome | Air/Ground |
| 121.90000 | | AM | Connaught (Knock) Airport | Ground |
| 130.70000 | | AM | Connaught (Knock) Airport | Tower |
| 123.00000 | | AM | Connemara, Eire | Air/Ground |
| 129.90000 | | AM | Coonagh, Eire | Air/Ground |
| 118.80000 | | AM | Cork Airport | Radar |
| 119.30000 | | AM | Cork Airport | Tower |
| 119.90000 | | AM | Cork Airport | Approach |
| 120.92500 | | AM | Cork Airport | ATIS |
| 121.70000 | | AM | Cork Airport | Tower |
| 121.80000 | | AM | Cork Airport | Ground |
| 127.00000 | | AM | Cork Airport | Dublin VOLMET |
| 131.50000 | | AM | Cork Airport | Aer Lingus Ops |

| Base | Mobile | Mode | Location | User and Notes |
|---|---|---|---|---|
| 131.85000 | | AM | Cork Airport | Aer Lingus Company Chan. |
| 130.20000 | | AM | Cottesmore | Approach (LARS and MATZ) |
| 126.05000 | | AM | Coventry | ATIS |
| 119.25000 | | AM | Coventry Airport | Approach |
| 121.70000 | | AM | Coventry Airport | Ground |
| 122.00000 | | AM | Coventry Airport | Radar |
| 124.80000 | | AM | Coventry Airport | Tower |
| 122.75000 | | AM | Cowden Range | Range Control |
| 121.87500 | | AM | Cranfield | Approach/ATIS |
| 122.85000 | | AM | Cranfield | Approach |
| 134.92500 | | AM | Cranfield | Tower |
| 129.82500 | | AM | Cromer (Northrepps) | Air/Ground (Micro) |
| 122.77500 | | AM | Crowfield Aerodrome | Air/Ground |
| 120.60000 | | AM | Cumbernauld Airport | AFIS |
| 127.57500 | | AM | Deanethorpe | Approach |
| 130.72500 | | AM | Denham | Air/Ground and AFIS |
| 118.35000 | | AM | Derby | Air/Ground |
| 119.65000 | | AM | Derby | Approach (East Midlands) |
| 125.00000 | | AM | Dishforth | Approach |
| 130.10000 | | AM | Dishforth | Air/Ground Gliders |
| 129.80000 | | AM | Donegal (Carrickfinn),Eire | Tower/AFIS |
| 119.35000 | | AM | Dornoch Aerodrome | Approach (Lossiemouth) |
| 122.40000 | | AM | Dounreay Aerodrome | Tower |
| 124.52500 | | AM | Dublin | ATIS |
| 129.17500 | | AM | Dublin | Area Control Centre (North Sector) |
| 131.42500 | | AM | Dublin | British Midlands Ops |
| 131.47500 | | AM | Dublin | Translift Ops |
| 131.55000 | | AM | Dublin | Ryanair Ops |
| 131.82500 | | AM | Dublin | Park Aviation |
| 131.95000 | | AM | Dublin | Aer Turas Ops |
| 118.50000 | | AM | Dublin Airport | Director |
| 118.60000 | | AM | Dublin Airport | Tower |
| 119.55000 | | AM | Dublin Airport | Radar |
| 121.10000 | | AM | Dublin Airport | Approach |
| 121.80000 | | AM | Dublin Airport | Ground |
| 121.87500 | | AM | Dublin Airport | Delivery |
| 123.30000 | | AM | Dublin Airport | Dublin Military ATC |
| 124.65000 | | AM | Dublin Airport | Area Control Centre (South Sector) & Radar |
| 127.00000 | | AM | Dublin Airport | Dublin VOLMET |
| 131.50000 | | AM | Dublin Airport | Aer Lingus |
| 135.37500 | | AM | Dublin Airport | London VOLMET (Main) |
| 122.90000 | | AM | Dundee | Approach Tower |
| 123.47500 | | AM | Dunkeswell Aerodrome | Air/Ground |
| 135.17500 | | AM | Dunsfold | Approach/Radar |
| 122.55000 | | AM | Dunsfold Aerodrome | Radar |
| 124.32500 | | AM | Dunsfold Aerodrome | Tower |
| 121.07500 | | AM | Duxford | Air Display Channel |
| 122.07500 | | AM | Duxford | Information |
| 122.67500 | | AM | Duxford | Ops |
| 128.50000 | | AM | Duxford | Air Display Channel |
| 130.67500 | | AM | Duxford | Air Display Channel |
| 134.85000 | | AM | Duxford | Air Display Channel |
| 123.00000 | | AM | Eaglescott | Air/Ground |
| 122.42500 | | AM | Earls Colne | Air/Ground |
| 130.25000 | | AM | East Midlands | Donington Aviation |

| Base | Mobile | Mode | Location | User and Notes |
|---|---|---|---|---|
| 131.60000 | | AM | East Midlands | UPS Ops |
| 119.65000 | | AM | East Midlands Airport | Approach |
| 120.12500 | | AM | East Midlands Airport | Radar |
| 121.60000 | | AM | East Midlands Airport | Fire Service |
| 121.90000 | | AM | East Midlands Airport | Ground |
| 122.35000 | | AM | East Midlands Airport | Air Bridge Carriers Ops |
| 124.00000 | | AM | East Midlands Airport | Tower |
| 126.60000 | | AM | East Midlands Airport | London VOLMET (North) |
| 128.22500 | | AM | East Midlands Airport | ATIS |
| 130.62500 | | AM | East Midlands Airport | Donington Aviation Ops |
| 131.57500 | | AM | East Midlands Airport | British Midland |
| 131.57500 | | AM | East Midlands Airport | Excalibur Ops |
| 118.70000 | | AM | Edinburgh Airport | Tower |
| 121.20000 | | AM | Edinburgh Airport | Approach/Radar |
| 121.75000 | | AM | Edinburgh Airport | Ground |
| 122.35000 | | AM | Edinburgh Airport | Execair Operations |
| 125.72500 | | AM | Edinburgh Airport | Scottish VOLMET |
| 128.97500 | | AM | Edinburgh Airport | Radar |
| 130.40000 | | AM | Edinburgh Airport | Approach (gliders) |
| 130.60000 | | AM | Edinburgh Airport | Servisair |
| 131.57500 | | AM | Edinburgh Airport | British Midland |
| 131.80000 | | AM | Edinburgh Airport | British Airways |
| 132.07500 | | AM | Edinburgh Airport | ATIS |
| 123.50000 | | AM | Eggesford Aerodrome | Tower |
| 130.42500 | | AM | Elmsett | Air/Ground (Elmsett Radio) |
| 122.40000 | | AM | Elstree Aerodrome | Air/Ground/AFIS |
| 129.70000 | | AM | English Channel | Bishops Rock Trinity Lightship |
| 129.70000 | | AM | English Channel | Casquets Trinity Lightship |
| 129.70000 | | AM | English Channel | Flatholm Trinity Lightship |
| 129.70000 | | AM | English Channel | Hanois Trinity Lightship |
| 129.70000 | | AM | English Channel | Inner Dowsing Trinity L.ship |
| 129.70000 | | AM | English Channel | Longships Trinity Lightship |
| 129.70000 | | AM | English Channel | Lundy South Trinity Lightship |
| 129.70000 | | AM | English Channel | Round Island Trinity Lightship |
| 129.70000 | | AM | English Channel | Royal Sovereign Trinity Lightship |
| 129.70000 | | AM | English Channel | Skerries Trinity Lightship |
| 129.70000 | | AM | English Channel | Skokholm Trinity Lightship |
| 129.70000 | | AM | English Channel | Smalls Trinity Lightship |
| 129.70000 | | AM | English Channel | South Bishop Trinity Lightship |
| 129.70000 | | AM | English Channel | St Anns Head Trinity Lightship |
| 130.80000 | | AM | English Channel | Fisheries Protection |
| 123.20000 | | AM | Enniskillen (St. Angelo) | FIS |
| 129.87500 | | AM | Enstone Aerodrome | Air/Ground |
| 123.72500 | | AM | Epson Aerodrome | Tower |
| 123.45000 | | AM | Errol Aerodrome | Drop Zone Control |
| 129.82000 | | AM | Esholt | Air/Ground (Esholt Radio Weekends) |
| 119.80000 | | AM | Exeter | Tower |
| 130.17500 | | AM | Exeter | Markair Ops |
| 119.05000 | | AM | Exeter Airport | Radar |
| 128.15000 | | AM | Exeter Airport | Approach/Radar |
| 130.17500 | | AM | Exeter Airport | Handling |
| 123.22000 | | AM | Fadmoor Aerodrome | Air/Ground |
| 123.15000 | | AM | Fair Isle | Approach (Sumburgh) |
| 123.42500 | | AM | Fairoaks | Tower and AFIS |
| 118.10000 | | AM | Farnborough | Air Show Tower |

| Base | Mobile | Mode | Location | User and Notes |
|------|--------|------|----------|----------------|
| 130.37500 | | AM | Farnborough | Executive Ops |
| 135.75000 | | AM | Farnborough | Air Show Approach |
| 122.50000 | | AM | Farnborough (RAE Airfield) | Tower |
| 125.25000 | | AM | Farnborough (RAE Airfield) | Radar |
| 130.05000 | | AM | Farnborough (RAE Airfield) | Precision Approach Radar |
| 134.35000 | | AM | Farnborough (RAE Airfield) | Approach |
| 123.50000 | | AM | Felthorpe Aerodrome | Tower |
| 122.92500 | | AM | Fenland | Air/Ground and AFIS |
| 122.72500 | | AM | Filton (BAe), Bristol | Approach/Radar |
| 127.97500 | | AM | Filton (BAe), Bristol | Approach/Radar |
| 129.75000 | | AM | Filton (BAe), Bristol | Rolls Royce Ops |
| 132.35000 | | AM | Filton (BAe), Bristol | Tower |
| 134.50000 | | AM | Filton (BAe), Bristol | Filton Ops |
| 118.27500 | | AM | Fishburn | Air/Ground |
| 122.12500 | | AM | Flotta Airfield | Tower |
| 130.65000 | | AM | Foulsham Aerodrome | Tower |
| 120.92500 | | AM | Fowlemere | Air/Ground |
| 132.32500 | | AM | Full Sutton | Air/Ground |
| 122.50000 | | AM | Galway | Air/Ground and AFIS |
| 118.80000 | | AM | Glasgow | Tower |
| 119.10000 | | AM | Glasgow | Approach/Radar |
| 119.30000 | | AM | Glasgow | Radar |
| 121.30000 | | AM | Glasgow | Radar |
| 121.70000 | | AM | Glasgow | Ground |
| 122.35000 | | AM | Glasgow | Execair |
| 129.70000 | | AM | Glasgow | Northwest |
| 130.65000 | | AM | Glasgow | Loganair Ops |
| 130.65000 | | AM | Glasgow | Maersk Ops |
| 131.37500 | | AM | Glasgow | Air Canada |
| 131.70000 | | AM | Glasgow | Air 2000 Ops |
| 131.97500 | | AM | Glasgow | British Airways |
| 132.17500 | | AM | Glasgow | ATIS |
| 130.45000 | | AM | Glenrothes | Air/Ground |
| 120.97500 | | AM | Gloucestershire Airport | Radar |
| 122.90000 | | AM | Gloucestershire Airport | Tower |
| 125.65000 | | AM | Gloucestershire Airport | Approach |
| 127.47500 | | AM | Gloucestershire Airport | ATIS |
| 122.20000 | | AM | Gormanston, Eire | IAC Military Approach |
| 122.70000 | | AM | Gormanston, Eire | IAC Military Tower |
| 123.40000 | | AM | Great Yarmouth (N. Denes) | Approach, Tower and Air/Ground |
| 122.35000 | | AM | Grimsby (Cuxwold) | Air/Ground |
| 118.90000 | | AM | Guernsey | Radar |
| 119.95000 | | AM | Guernsey | Tower |
| 121.80000 | | AM | Guernsey | Ground |
| 122.35000 | | AM | Guernsey | Aurigny Air Services |
| 124.50000 | | AM | Guernsey | Radar |
| 130.60000 | | AM | Guernsey | Servisair |
| 131.57500 | | AM | Guernsey | British Midland Ops |
| 123.00000 | | AM | Halfpenny Green Aerodrome | FIS |
| 130.42500 | | AM | Halton Aerodrome | Air/Ground |
| 119.30000 | | AM | Hatfield Aerodrome | Radar |
| 123.35000 | | AM | Hatfield Aerodrome | Approach |
| 123.65000 | | AM | Hatfield Aerodrome | Hatair Ops |
| 130.80000 | | AM | Hatfield Aerodrome | Tower |
| 122.20000 | | AM | Haverfordwest Aerodrome | Air/Ground |
| 123.35000 | | AM | Hawarden Aerodrome | Approach |

| Base | Mobile | Mode | Location | User and Notes |
|---|---|---|---|---|
| 124.95000 | | AM | Hawarden Aerodrome | Tower |
| 130.25000 | | AM | Hawarden Aerodrome | Radar |
| 119.40000 | | AM | Haydock Park | Approach |
| 123.65000 | | AM | Hayes Heliport | Air/Ground (Macline Hayes) |
| 121.10000 | | AM | Henlow | Air/Ground |
| 130.25000 | | AM | Henstridge | Tower |
| 122.35000 | | AM | Hethel | Air/Ground |
| 129.87500 | | AM | Hethersett Aerodrome | Hethersett Radio |
| 120.62500 | | AM | High Easter Aerodrome | Approach (Stansted) |
| 119.45000 | | AM | Hinton in the Hedges | Air/Ground |
| 122.35000 | | AM | Hitchin (Rush Green) | Air/Ground |
| 130.80000 | | AM | Hucknall Aerodrome | Air/Ground |
| 122.20000 | | AM | Huddersfield(Crossland Moor) | Air/Ground |
| 124.67000 | | AM | Hull (Mount Airy) | Approach (Humberside) |
| 122.37500 | | AM | Humberside | Bond Helicopters |
| 118.55000 | | AM | Humberside Airport | Tower |
| 123.15000 | | AM | Humberside Airport | Radar |
| 124.12500 | | AM | Humberside Airport | ATIS |
| 124.67500 | | AM | Humberside Airport | Approach/Radar |
| 123.00000 | | AM | Inisheer, Eire | Air/Ground |
| 123.00000 | | AM | Inishman, Eire | Air/Ground |
| 123.00000 | | AM | Inishmore, Eire | Air/Ground |
| 129.82500 | | AM | Insch Airfield | Air/Ground |
| 122.60000 | | AM | Inverness Airport | Approach/Tower |
| 125.72500 | | AM | Inverness Airport | Scottish VOLMET |
| 131.85000 | | AM | Inverness Airport | British Airways Ops |
| 118.32500 | | AM | Ipswich Airport | AFIS |
| 123.15000 | | AM | Islay Airport | AFIS |
| 128.60000 | | AM | Jerset Airport | London VOLMET (South) |
| 118.55000 | | AM | Jersey | Approach |
| 129.70000 | | AM | Jersey | Aviation Beauport Ops |
| 130.60000 | | AM | Jersey | Servisair |
| 130.65000 | | AM | Jersey | Company Ops |
| 131.57500 | | AM | Jersey | British Midland Jersey Ops |
| 131.82500 | | AM | Jersey | Company Ops |
| 131.85000 | | AM | Jersey | British Airways Jersey Ops |
| 118.55000 | | AM | Jersey Airport | Radar |
| 119.45000 | | AM | Jersey Airport | Tower |
| 120.30000 | | AM | Jersey Airport | Approach/Radar |
| 120.45000 | | AM | Jersey Airport | Air Traffic Control (Zone)/Radar |
| 121.90000 | | AM | Jersey Airport | Ground |
| 125.20000 | | AM | Jersey Airport | Air Traffic Control (Zone)/Radar |
| 118.90000 | | AM | Kemble | Air/Ground |
| 134.30000 | | AM | Kemble | Radar (Brize) |
| 121.60000 | | AM | Kerry | Ground |
| 124.10000 | | AM | Kerry | Tower |
| 122.90000 | | AM | Kilkenny | Air/Ground |
| 130.40000 | | AM | Kilkenny | Air/Ground (Weekends) |
| 118.30000 | | AM | Kirkwall Airport | Tower/Approach |
| 130.65000 | | AM | Kyle of Lochalsh | Royal Navy Heliport |
| 130.70000 | | AM | Land's End (St Just) | Tower/Approach and Air/Ground |
| 129.90000 | | AM | Langar Airfield | Drop Zone |
| 130.20000 | | AM | Langar Airfield | Approach |
| 125.25000 | | AM | Lasham | Approach (Farnborough) |
| 129.90000 | | AM | Lasham Aerodrome | Glider Ops |
| 122.00000 | | AM | Lashenden (Headcorn) | Air/Ground |

| Base | Mobile | Mode | Location | User and Notes |
|---|---|---|---|---|
| 135.70000 | | AM | Lee-on-Solent | Tower (Fleatlands) |
| 118.02500 | | AM | Leeds/Bradford Airport | ATIS |
| 120.30000 | | AM | Leeds/Bradford Airport | Tower |
| 121.05000 | | AM | Leeds/Bradford Airport | Radar |
| 123.75000 | | AM | Leeds/Bradford Airport | Approach |
| 126.60000 | | AM | Leeds/Bradford Airport | London VOLMET (North) |
| 122.12500 | | AM | Leicester Aerodrome | Air/Ground |
| 122.60000 | | AM | Lerwick (Tingwall) | Air/Ground and Air Ambulance |
| 129.72500 | | AM | Lewes (Deanland) | Air/Ground |
| 129.90000 | | AM | Limerick (Coonagh) | Air/Ground |
| 129.90000 | | AM | Liskeard | Civil Heliport |
| 130.85000 | | AM | Little Gransden Aerodrome | Air/Ground |
| 124.15000 | | AM | Little Snoring Aerodrome | Air/Ground |
| 123.92500 | | AM | Little Staughton | Air/Ground |
| 122.05000 | | AM | Liverpool | Keenair Ops |
| 122.35000 | | AM | Liverpool | Cheshire Air Training Ops |
| 118.10000 | | AM | Liverpool Airport | Tower |
| 118.45000 | | AM | Liverpool Airport | Radar |
| 119.85000 | | AM | Liverpool Airport | Approach/Radar |
| 126.60000 | | AM | Liverpool Airport | London VOLMET (North) |
| 130.17500 | | AM | Liverpool Airport | Emerald Ops |
| 130.17500 | | AM | Liverpool Airport | Royal Mail Ops |
| 135.97500 | | AM | Liverpool Airport | Mail Flights (Air-Air) |
| 122.50000 | | AM | Llanbedr (MoD) | Tower/Radar |
| 121.30000 | | AM | Lochaber | Air Ambulance |
| 122.35000 | | NFM | Lochaber | PLM Helicopters |
| 122.05000 | | AM | London | Jersey Air Ops |
| 122.95000 | | AM | London | Air Ambulance Ops |
| 130.02500 | | AM | London | Capital Radio Flying Eye Ops |
| 118.07500 | | AM | London (City Airport) | Tower |
| 127.95000 | | AM | London (City Airport) | Tower/ATIS |
| 128.02500 | | AM | London (City Airport) | Radar/City Radar |
| 132.70000 | | AM | London (City Airport) | Approach/Thames Radar |
| 118.60000 | | AM | London (Gatwick) | Radar |
| 118.95000 | | AM | London (Gatwick) | Radar |
| 119.60000 | | AM | London (Gatwick) | Radar |
| 119.80000 | | AM | London (Gatwick) | Police Helicopter Ops |
| 121.02500 | | AM | London (Gatwick) | ATIS |
| 121.80000 | | AM | London (Gatwick) | Ground |
| 121.95000 | | AM | London (Gatwick) | Delivery |
| 124.22500 | | AM | London (Gatwick) | Tower |
| 125.87500 | | AM | London (Gatwick) | Radar |
| 126.60000 | | AM | London (Gatwick) | London VOLMET (North) |
| 126.82500 | | AM | London (Gatwick) | Approach (Director) |
| 127.00000 | | AM | London (Gatwick) | Dublin VOLMET |
| 129.02500 | | AM | London (Gatwick) | Radar Standby |
| 130.07500 | | AM | London (Gatwick) | Servisair Ops |
| 130.57500 | | AM | London (Gatwick) | Interflight Ops |
| 130.60000 | | AM | London (Gatwick) | British Caledonian |
| 130.65000 | | AM | London (Gatwick) | American Airlines |
| 130.65000 | | AM | London (Gatwick) | China Airlines |
| 130.65000 | | AM | London (Gatwick) | Handling |
| 130.65000 | | AM | London (Gatwick) | Korean Airlines |
| 130.65000 | | AM | London (Gatwick) | Northwest Orient |
| 131.07500 | | AM | London (Gatwick) | Servisair |
| 131.42500 | | AM | London (Gatwick) | Air New Zealand Ops |
| 131.42500 | | AM | London (Gatwick) | Ogden Aviation Ops |

| Base | Mobile | Mode | Location | User and Notes |
|---|---|---|---|---|
| 131.42500 | | AM | London (Gatwick) | Virgin Ops |
| 131.47500 | | AM | London (Gatwick) | British Airways Maintence. |
| 131.47500 | | AM | London (Gatwick) | Caledonian Ops |
| 131.60000 | | AM | London (Gatwick) | City Flyer Ops |
| 131.60000 | | AM | London (Gatwick) | TWA Ops |
| 131.62500 | | AM | London (Gatwick) | British Caledonian |
| 131.62500 | | AM | London (Gatwick) | Canadian Pacific Ops |
| 131.70000 | | AM | London (Gatwick) | Jetset Ops |
| 131.75000 | | AM | London (Gatwick) | Continental |
| 131.90000 | | AM | London (Gatwick) | Air 2000 |
| 131.92500 | | AM | London (Gatwick) | American Airlines |
| 134.22500 | | AM | London (Gatwick) | Aproach/Radar |
| 135.37500 | | AM | London (Gatwick) | London VOLMET (Main) |
| 135.57500 | | AM | London (Gatwick) | Radar Standby |
| 131.62500 | | AM | London (Gatwick) | British Airways (S. Terminal) |
| 118.50000 | | AM | London (Heathrow) | Tower |
| 118.70000 | | AM | London (Heathrow) | Tower |
| 119.72500 | | AM | London (Heathrow) | Approach (Director) |
| 119.90000 | | AM | London (Heathrow) | Radar |
| 120.40000 | | AM | London (Heathrow) | Approach |
| 121.90000 | | AM | London (Heathrow) | Ground |
| 121.97500 | | AM | London (Heathrow) | Delivery |
| 122.35000 | | AM | London (Heathrow) | Gulf Air Terminal 3 |
| 123.65000 | | AM | London (Heathrow) | British Airways |
| 123.90000 | | AM | London (Heathrow) | ATIS |
| 124.47500 | | AM | London (Heathrow) | Stand-by Ground |
| 125.62500 | | AM | London (Heathrow) | Radar |
| 125.72500 | | AM | London (Heathrow) | Scottish VOLMET |
| 127.00000 | | AM | London (Heathrow) | Dublin VOLMET |
| 127.52500 | | AM | London (Heathrow) | Approach |
| 127.55000 | | AM | London (Heathrow) | Approach |
| 127.62500 | | AM | London (Heathrow) | Approach |
| 129.70000 | | AM | London (Heathrow) | Mam Aviation |
| 130.07500 | | AM | London (Heathrow) | Air Malta Ops |
| 130.15000 | | AM | London (Heathrow) | Emirates Ops |
| 130.17500 | | AM | London (Heathrow) | Ambassador Ops |
| 130.17500 | | AM | London (Heathrow) | Corporate Jet Ops |
| 130.17500 | | AM | London (Heathrow) | Gama Ops |
| 130.57500 | | AM | London (Heathrow) | Shell Ops |
| 130.60000 | | AM | London (Heathrow) | Fields Aviation Ops |
| 130.60000 | | AM | London (Heathrow) | Huntair |
| 131.40000 | | AM | London (Heathrow) | Bangladesh Biman |
| 131.40000 | | AM | London (Heathrow) | CSA |
| 131.40000 | | AM | London (Heathrow) | Kenya Airways |
| 131.40000 | | AM | London (Heathrow) | Trans Mediterranean |
| 131.40000 | | AM | London (Heathrow) | Zambian Airlines |
| 131.42500 | | AM | London (Heathrow) | British Midlands Ops |
| 131.42500 | | AM | London (Heathrow) | Royal Jordanian Ops |
| 131.42500 | | AM | London (Heathrow) | Saudia Ops |
| 131.45000 | | AM | London (Heathrow) | Aer Lingus Ops |
| 131.45000 | | AM | London (Heathrow) | Air Canada Ops |
| 131.45000 | | AM | London (Heathrow) | Air Malta Ops |
| 131.45000 | | AM | London (Heathrow) | Alitalia Ops |
| 131.45000 | | AM | London (Heathrow) | BWIA Ops |
| 131.45000 | | AM | London (Heathrow) | Cathay Pacific Ops |
| 131.45000 | | AM | London (Heathrow) | KLM Ops |
| 131.45000 | | AM | London (Heathrow) | Pakistan International Ops |

| Base | Mobile | Mode | Location | User and Notes |
|---|---|---|---|---|
| 131.45000 | | AM | London (Heathrow) | Thai Airways Ops |
| 131.47500 | | AM | London (Heathrow) | All Nippon Ops |
| 131.47500 | | AM | London (Heathrow) | GB Airways Ops |
| 131.47500 | | AM | London (Heathrow) | Maersk Ops |
| 131.47500 | | AM | London (Heathrow) | Sabena |
| 131.47500 | | AM | London (Heathrow) | Speedbird Control North |
| 131.47500 | | AM | London (Heathrow) | TAT Ops |
| 131.50000 | | AM | London (Heathrow) | Air France Ops |
| 131.50000 | | AM | London (Heathrow) | British Airways Ops |
| 131.50000 | | AM | London (Heathrow) | Kuwait Airways Ops |
| 131.55000 | | AM | London (Heathrow) | British Airways Parking |
| 131.55000 | | AM | London (Heathrow) | Luxair Ops |
| 131.55000 | | AM | London (Heathrow) | Ryanair Ops |
| 131.55000 | | AM | London (Heathrow) | Springbok Ops |
| 131.57500 | | AM | London (Heathrow) | Channnel Express Ops |
| 131.57500 | | AM | London (Heathrow) | El Al |
| 131.57500 | | AM | London (Heathrow) | Iran Air Ops |
| 131.57500 | | AM | London (Heathrow) | Manx Ops |
| 131.60000 | | AM | London (Heathrow) | Air Lines Ops |
| 131.60000 | | AM | London (Heathrow) | Fields Ops |
| 131.60000 | | AM | London (Heathrow) | TWA Ops |
| 131.62500 | | AM | London (Heathrow) | Royal Jordanian Ops |
| 131.62500 | | AM | London (Heathrow) | Sabena |
| 131.65000 | | AM | London (Heathrow) | Air Malta Ops |
| 131.65000 | | AM | London (Heathrow) | Japan Airlines Ops |
| 131.65000 | | AM | London (Heathrow) | KLM Ops Terminal 4 |
| 131.70000 | | AM | London (Heathrow) | Air 2000 Ops |
| 131.70000 | | AM | London (Heathrow) | Crossair Ops |
| 131.70000 | | AM | London (Heathrow) | Delta Ops |
| 131.70000 | | AM | London (Heathrow) | KLM |
| 131.70000 | | AM | London (Heathrow) | SAS Ops |
| 131.70000 | | AM | London (Heathrow) | Sabena |
| 131.70000 | | AM | London (Heathrow) | Swissair Ops |
| 131.75000 | | AM | London (Heathrow) | Aer Lingus Ops |
| 131.75000 | | AM | London (Heathrow) | Air UK |
| 131.75000 | | AM | London (Heathrow) | Kenya Airways |
| 131.75000 | | AM | London (Heathrow) | Lufthansa Ops |
| 131.75000 | | AM | London (Heathrow) | TAP Air Portugal |
| 131.77500 | | AM | London (Heathrow) | Aeroflot |
| 131.77500 | | AM | London (Heathrow) | British Airways Ops |
| 131.77500 | | AM | London (Heathrow) | CSA |
| 131.77500 | | AM | London (Heathrow) | Icelandair |
| 131.77500 | | AM | London (Heathrow) | JAT |
| 131.77500 | | AM | London (Heathrow) | Korean Air Ops |
| 131.77500 | | AM | London (Heathrow) | LOT |
| 131.77500 | | AM | London (Heathrow) | Malev |
| 131.77500 | | AM | London (Heathrow) | Olympic |
| 131.77500 | | AM | London (Heathrow) | Sabena |
| 131.80000 | | AM | London (Heathrow) | British Airways |
| 131.82500 | | AM | London (Heathrow) | Cathay Pacific Ops |
| 131.82500 | | AM | London (Heathrow) | Federal Express Ops |
| 131.82500 | | AM | London (Heathrow) | Gibair Ops |
| 131.85000 | | AM | London (Heathrow) | Emirates Ops |
| 131.85000 | | AM | London (Heathrow) | Malaysian Airlines |
| 131.85000 | | AM | London (Heathrow) | United Ops |
| 131.85000 | | AM | London (Heathrow) | Zambian Airlines |
| 131.87500 | | AM | London (Heathrow) | Quantas Ops |

| Base | Mobile | Mode | Location | User and Notes |
|------|--------|------|----------|----------------|
| 131.90000 | | AM | London (Heathrow) | British Airways Speedbird Ops |
| 131.90000 | | AM | London (Heathrow) | Conair Ops |
| 131.90000 | | AM | London (Heathrow) | South African Airlines |
| 131.90000 | | AM | London (Heathrow) | TAT Ops |
| 131.92500 | | AM | London (Heathrow) | Air India Ops |
| 131.92500 | | AM | London (Heathrow) | American Airlines Maintence |
| 131.92500 | | AM | London (Heathrow) | American Ops |
| 131.92500 | | AM | London (Heathrow) | Lufthansa |
| 131.95000 | | AM | London (Heathrow) | El Al |
| 131.95000 | | AM | London (Heathrow) | Federal Express |
| 131.95000 | | AM | London (Heathrow) | Iberia Airlines Ops |
| 131.95000 | | AM | London (Heathrow) | MEA Ops |
| 131.95000 | | AM | London (Heathrow) | Nigerian Airlines Ops |
| 131.95000 | | AM | London (Heathrow) | Olympic Airways Ops |
| 131.95000 | | AM | London (Heathrow) | Singapore Airlines Ops |
| 131.95000 | | AM | London (Heathrow) | Viva Ops |
| 131.97500 | | AM | London (Heathrow) | El Al |
| 131.97500 | | AM | London (Heathrow) | Nigerian Airlines Ops |
| 131.97500 | | AM | London (Heathrow) | United Ops |
| 132.05000 | | AM | London (Heathrow) | Departure/TMA |
| 132.65000 | | AM | London (Heathrow) | Medivac |
| 132.70000 | | AM | London (Heathrow) | Thames Radar |
| 133.07500 | | AM | London (Heathrow) | ATIS |
| 134.45000 | | AM | London (Heathrow) | London Zone |
| 134.97500 | | AM | London (Heathrow) | Approach |
| 135.37500 | | AM | London (Heathrow) | London VOLMET (Main) |
| 122.90000 | | AM | London, Westland Heliport | Tower (Battersea) |
| 123.62500 | | AM | Londonderry | Approach |
| 134.15000 | | AM | Londonderry | Tower |
| 122.90000 | | AM | Long Marston Aerodrome | Tower |
| 130.10000 | | AM | Long Marston Aerodrome | Tower |
| 120.57500 | | AM | Luton Airport | ATIS |
| 121.75000 | | AM | Luton Airport | Ground |
| 122.35000 | | AM | Luton Airport | Reed Aviation |
| 126.72500 | | AM | Luton Airport | Approach/Radar |
| 128.60000 | | AM | Luton Airport | London VOLMET (South) |
| 128.75000 | | AM | Luton Airport | Approach/Radar |
| 129.55000 | | AM | Luton Airport | Approach/Radar |
| 130.17500 | | AM | Luton Airport | Magec Ops |
| 131.52500 | | AM | Luton Airport | London European Airways |
| 131.52500 | | AM | Luton Airport | Monarch Airlines |
| 131.52500 | | AM | Luton Airport | Ryan Air |
| 131.67500 | | AM | Luton Airport | Britannia Airways |
| 131.77500 | | AM | Luton Airport | Air Foyle |
| 131.77500 | | AM | Luton Airport | BA Maintence |
| 132.55000 | | AM | Luton Airport | Tower |
| 120.70000 | | AM | Lydd Airport | AFIS |
| 118.57500 | | AM | Manchester | ATC arrivals |
| 121.60000 | | AM | Manchester | Fire Service |
| 122.35000 | | AM | Manchester | Air Kilroe Ops |
| 123.30000 | | AM | Manchester | ATC |
| 128.17500 | | AM | Manchester | ATIS |
| 130.17500 | | AM | Manchester | Ryan Air Ops |
| 130.37500 | | AM | Manchester | FLS Engineering Ops |
| 130.60000 | | AM | Manchester | Servisair |
| 130.65000 | | AM | Manchester | Aer Lingus Ops |
| 130.65000 | | AM | Manchester | Handling |

| Base | Mobile | Mode | Location | User and Notes |
|---|---|---|---|---|
| 130.65000 | | AM | Manchester | LTU Ops |
| 130.65000 | | AM | Manchester | Northern Executive |
| 130.75000 | | AM | Manchester | Aer Lingus Ops |
| 131.42500 | | AM | Manchester | Cathay Pacific Ops |
| 131.52500 | | AM | Manchester | American Ops |
| 131.70000 | | AM | Manchester | Air 2000 Ops |
| 131.70000 | | AM | Manchester | SAS Ops |
| 131.70000 | | AM | Manchester | Swissair Ops |
| 131.75000 | | AM | Manchester | Aer Lingus Ops |
| 131.85000 | | AM | Manchester | British Airways Ops |
| 131.87500 | | AM | Manchester | Euro Manx Ops |
| 131.92500 | | AM | Manchester | Lufthansa |
| 131.95000 | | AM | Manchester | Federal Express |
| 132.90000 | | AM | Manchester | Pennine Radar |
| 118.57500 | | AM | Manchester Airport | Radar standby |
| 118.62500 | | AM | Manchester Airport | Tower |
| 119.40000 | | AM | Manchester Airport | Approach/Radar (Director) |
| 121.35000 | | AM | Manchester Airport | Radar |
| 121.70000 | | AM | Manchester Airport | Delivery/Ground |
| 121.85000 | | AM | Manchester Airport | Ground |
| 124.20000 | | AM | Manchester Airport | Manchester Air Traffic Control |
| 125.10000 | | AM | Manchester Airport | Manchester Air Traffic Control |
| 125.95000 | | AM | Manchester Airport | Manchester Air Traffic Control |
| 126.60000 | | AM | Manchester Airport | London VOLMET (North) |
| 126.65000 | | AM | Manchester Airport | Manchester Air Traffic Control |
| 127.00000 | | AM | Manchester Airport | Dublin VOLMET |
| 128.67500 | | AM | Manchester Airport | Pennine Radar |
| 133.05000 | | AM | Manchester Airport | Manchester Air Traffic Control |
| 133.40000 | | AM | Manchester Airport | Manchester Air Traffic Control |
| 135.37500 | | AM | Manchester Airport | London VOLMET (Main) |
| 122.97500 | | AM | Marston Moor Aerodrome | Tower |
| 122.10000 | | AM | Middle Wallop Army Airfield | Tower/Approach |
| 126.70000 | | AM | Middle Wallop Army Airfield | Army Air/Ground |
| 123.37500 | | AM | Morecambe Bay | British Gas Helicopters |
| 122.37500 | | AM | Morecambe Bay BP Field | Helicopters |
| 123.45000 | | AM | Mull | Mull Traffic |
| 122.10000 | | AM | N of 56N | Fisheries Protection |
| 118.00000 | | AM | Nationwide | Air-Air Display Coordination |
| 118.00000 | | AM | Nationwide | Marlboro Aerobatic Display |
| 119.00000 | | AM | Nationwide | RAF Common |
| 120.80000 | | AM | Nationwide | Battle Of Britain Flight |
| 121.50000 | | AM | Nationwide | Civil Aviation Distress Channel |
| 121.50000 | | AM | Nationwide | Distress & Emergency |
| 121.60000 | | AM | Nationwide | Airfield Fire & Rescue |
| 122.05000 | | AM | Nationwide | Brymon Airways |
| 122.10000 | | AM | Nationwide | Military Tower Common |
| 122.27500 | | AM | Nationwide | CAA Calibrator Aircraft |
| 122.30000 | | AM | Nationwide | Aircraft Exercise frequency |
| 122.47500 | | AM | Nationwide | Hot Air Ballooning |
| 122.95000 | | AM | Nationwide | Freemans Aviation |
| 123.10000 | | AM | Nationwide | Search and Rescue |
| 123.30000 | | AM | Nationwide | Military Airfield Radar |
| 123.45000 | | AM | Nationwide | Air-Air Common |
| 123.65000 | | AM | Nationwide | Brymon Airways |
| 124.15000 | | AM | Nationwide | Army Helicopter Common |
| 126.15000 | | AM | Nationwide | RAF Flight Checker |
| 127.05000 | | AM | Nationwide | CAA Test Flights |

| Base | Mobile | Mode | Location | User and Notes |
|---|---|---|---|---|
| 127.75000 | | AM | Nationwide | Air UK Company Channel |
| 128.85000 | | AM | Nationwide | Eastern Airlines Packet Ch |
| 129.00000 | | AM | Nationwide | Hang Gliders & Ballons |
| 129.02500 | | AM | Nationwide | Air France Company Channel |
| 129.20000 | | AM | Nationwide | American Airlines Packet |
| 129.25000 | | AM | Nationwide | CAA Special Events |
| 129.50000 | | AM | Nationwide | Delta Airlines Packet Channel |
| 129.60000 | | AM | Nationwide | Delta Airlines Packet Channel |
| 129.62500 | | AM | Nationwide | TWA Packet Frequency |
| 129.70000 | | AM | Nationwide | Britannia Ops |
| 129.70000 | | AM | Nationwide | Trinity House Helicopters |
| 129.75000 | | AM | Nationwide | Air Express Ops |
| 129.75000 | | AM | Nationwide | BMA Ops |
| 129.75000 | | AM | Nationwide | Brymon Airways |
| 129.75000 | | AM | Nationwide | Loganair Ops |
| 129.75000 | | AM | Nationwide | Manx Ops |
| 129.82500 | | AM | Nationwide | Microlight Common |
| 129.90000 | | AM | Nationwide | Air Ambulance |
| 129.90000 | | AM | Nationwide | Hang Gliding |
| 129.90000 | | AM | Nationwide | Hot Air Ballooning |
| 129.90000 | | NFM | Nationwide | RAC Network Q Medivac Helo |
| 129.90000 | | AM | Nationwide | RAF Formation Air to Air |
| 129.97500 | | AM | Nationwide | Gliding |
| 130.02500 | | AM | Nationwide | Dollar Air Metro |
| 130.10000 | | AM | Nationwide | Gliders |
| 130.12500 | | AM | Nationwide | Glider Training |
| 130.25000 | | AM | Nationwide | American Airlines Packet |
| 130.40000 | | AM | Nationwide | Gliders Channel |
| 130.42500 | | AM | Nationwide | SAR Incident |
| 130.50000 | | AM | Nationwide | Aquilla Spanish air display team Air-to-Air |
| 130.57500 | | FM | Nationwide | Philips Airship Air to Ground |
| 130.60000 | | AM | Nationwide | Brymon Airways Ops |
| 130.60000 | | AM | Nationwide | Delta Airlines Ops |
| 130.60000 | | AM | Nationwide | Servisair |
| 131.10000 | | AM | Nationwide | British Airways Packet |
| 131.47500 | | AM | Nationwide | Canadian Armed Forces |
| 131.72500 | | AM | Nationwide | ACARS Frequency |
| 131.80000 | | AM | Nationwide | Air to Air Common |
| 131.80000 | | AM | Nationwide | Fisheries Protection |
| 131.85000 | | AM | Nationwide | British Airways Ops |
| 131.95000 | | AM | Nationwide | AAC Eagles Air to Air Secondary |
| 131.95000 | | AM | Nationwide | Air France Company Channel |
| 132.65000 | | AM | Nationwide | Royal Flights |
| 134.65000 | | AM | Nationwide | RAF Flight Checker |
| 134.97500 | | AM | Nationwide | CAA Tests Flight |
| 135.00000 | | AM | Nationwide | CAA Tests Flight |
| 135.47500 | | AM | Nationwide | CAA Tests Flight |
| 135.75000 | | AM | Nationwide | CAA Tests Flight |
| 135.97500 | | AM | Nationwide | Army Air-Air |
| 135.97500 | | AM | Nationwide | Ryanair (Air-Air) |
| 118.00000 | | AM | Natiownde | Civilian Air-Air |
| 122.75000 | | AM | Netheravon (Army) | Air/Ground (Salisbury Plain) |
| 126.70000 | | AM | Netheravon (Army) | Approach (ATZ) |
| 128.30000 | | AM | Netheravon (Army) | Drop Zone Radio |
| 128.30000 | | AM | Netheravon (Army) | Tower |

| Base | Mobile | Mode | Location | User and Notes |
|------|--------|------|----------|----------------|
| 130.10000 | | AM | Netheravon (Army) | Tower |
| 130.15000 | | AM | Netheravon (Army) | Salisbury Plain Tower |
| 123.27500 | | AM | Netherthorpe | Air/Ground |
| 124.37500 | | AM | Newcastle | Approach/Radar |
| 130.60000 | | AM | Newcastle | Servisair |
| 130.65000 | | AM | Newcastle | Samson Ops |
| 118.50000 | | AM | Newcastle Airport | Radar |
| 119.70000 | | AM | Newcastle Airport | Tower |
| 126.60000 | | AM | Newcastle Airport | London VOLMET (North) |
| 128.35000 | | AM | Newcastle Airport | Army Tower |
| 119.12000 | | AM | Newton | Approach/Tower |
| 123.50000 | | AM | Newtownards | Air/Ground |
| 120.15000 | | AM | North Coates | Air/Ground |
| 122.75000 | | AM | North Coates | Air/Ground Donna Nook Range |
| 118.05000 | | AM | North Sea | Frigg Oil Field deck |
| 120.07500 | | AM | North Sea | Pickerill Oil Field deck |
| 120.07500 | | AM | North Sea | Trent Oil Field deck |
| 120.07500 | | AM | North Sea | Tyne Oil Field deck |
| 120.07500 | | AM | North Sea | Viking Oil Field log |
| 120.45000 | | AM | North Sea | Oil Rig Heliport Common |
| 122.00000 | | AM | North Sea | BP Buchan Field |
| 122.00000 | | AM | North Sea | BP Cyprus Field |
| 122.00000 | | AM | North Sea | BP Forties Field |
| 122.00000 | | AM | North Sea | BP Gyda Field |
| 122.00000 | | AM | North Sea | Caister Oil Field deck |
| 122.00000 | | AM | North Sea | Unity Oil Field deck |
| 122.02500 | | AM | North Sea | Murdoch Oil Field deck |
| 122.05000 | | AM | North Sea | Chevron Ninian Field log |
| 122.05000 | | AM | North Sea | Conoco Murchison Field deck |
| 122.05000 | | AM | North Sea | Ninian Field |
| 122.05000 | | AM | North Sea | Shell/Esso Auk Field |
| 122.05000 | | AM | North Sea | Shell/Esso Fulmar Field |
| 122.05000 | | AM | North Sea | Shell/Esso Kittiwake Field |
| 122.05000 | | AM | North Sea | Thistle Field deck |
| 122.12500 | | AM | North Sea | Hamilton Argyll Field |
| 122.17500 | | AM | North Sea | Mobil Beryl Field |
| 122.25000 | | AM | North Sea | Shell/Esso Brent Field |
| 122.32500 | | AM | North Sea | Hamilton Esmond Field |
| 122.32500 | | AM | North Sea | Hamilton Forbes Field |
| 122.32500 | | AM | North Sea | Hamilton Gordon Field |
| 122.35000 | | AM | North Sea | Total Alwyn Field |
| 122.37500 | | AM | North Sea | BP Magnus Field Deck |
| 122.39500 | | AM | North Sea | Magnus BP |
| 122.45000 | | AM | North Sea | Claymore & Tartan |
| 122.45000 | | AM | North Sea | Occidental Claymore Field |
| 122.45000 | | AM | North Sea | Piper Oil Field deck |
| 122.45000 | | AM | North Sea | Saltire Oil Field deck |
| 122.45000 | | AM | North Sea | Texaco Tartan Field |
| 122.52500 | | AM | North Sea | Hamilton Pipe Field |
| 122.52500 | | AM | North Sea | Judy Oil Field deck |
| 122.52500 | | AM | North Sea | Clyde Oil Field deck |
| 122.62500 | | AM | North Sea | Conoco Viking Field |
| 122.65000 | | AM | North Sea | Nelson Oil Field deck |
| 122.77500 | | AM | North Sea | Scott Oil Field deck |
| 122.80000 | | AM | North Sea | Unionoil Heather Field |
| 122.87500 | | AM | North Sea | Excalibur Oil Field deck |

| Base | Mobile | Mode | Location | User and Notes |
|------|--------|------|----------|----------------|
| 122.87500 | | AM | North Sea | Galahad Oil Field deck |
| 122.87500 | | AM | North Sea | Guinevere Oil Field deck |
| 122.87500 | | AM | North Sea | Lancelot Oil Field deck |
| 122.87500 | | AM | North Sea | Phillips Hewett Field |
| 122.92500 | | AM | North Sea | Phillip Ekofisk Field |
| 122.95000 | | AM | North Sea | Eko/Tees Pip Oil Field deck |
| 122.95000 | | AM | North Sea | Kotter Oil Field deck |
| 122.95000 | | AM | North Sea | Logger Oil Field deck |
| 122.95000 | | AM | North Sea | Nam Nam Field |
| 122.95000 | | AM | North Sea | Nam Noordwinning |
| 122.95000 | | AM | North Sea | Penzoil Noordwinning |
| 122.95000 | | AM | North Sea | Petroland Petroland Field |
| 122.95000 | | AM | North Sea | Placid Placid Field |
| 122.95000 | | AM | North Sea | Zanddijk |
| 123.00000 | | AM | North Sea | Ivanhoe Oil Field deck |
| 123.02500 | | AM | North Sea | Hamilton Ravenspurnn North |
| 123.05000 | | AM | North Sea | Brent Oil Field log |
| 123.05000 | | AM | North Sea | North Cormorant log |
| 123.05000 | | AM | North Sea | Shell/Esso Eider Field log |
| 123.05000 | | AM | North Sea | Shell/Esso Tern Field log |
| 123.05000 | | AM | North Sea | South Cormorant log |
| 123.22500 | | AM | North Sea | Arco Thames Field |
| 123.22500 | | AM | North Sea | Bruce Oil Field deck |
| 123.40000 | | AM | North Sea | Dab Duc Skjold Field |
| 123.45000 | | AM | North Sea | Amoco Indefatigable Field |
| 123.45000 | | AM | North Sea | Marathon East Kinsale |
| 123.45000 | | AM | North Sea | Marathon West Kinsale |
| 123.45000 | | AM | North Sea | Rolf Oil Field deck |
| 123.55000 | | AM | North Sea | Captian Oil Field deck |
| 123.55000 | | AM | North Sea | Sun Balmoral Field |
| 123.57500 | | AM | North Sea | Tiffany Oil Field deck |
| 123.62500 | | AM | North Sea | Amoco Indefatigable Field |
| 123.62500 | | AM | North Sea | Amoco Leman Field |
| 123.62500 | | AM | North Sea | Bessemer Oil Field deck |
| 123.62500 | | AM | North Sea | Camelott Oil Field deck |
| 123.62500 | | AM | North Sea | Davey Oil Field deck |
| 123.62500 | | AM | North Sea | Shell/Esso Indefatigable |
| 123.62500 | | AM | North Sea | Shell/Esso Leman Field |
| 123.62500 | | AM | North Sea | Shell/Esso Sean Field |
| 123.62500 | | AM | North Sea | Thames Oil Field deck |
| 123.65000 | | AM | North Sea | Beatrice Field deck |
| 123.65000 | | AM | North Sea | Brae Oil Field deck |
| 123.65000 | | AM | North Sea | East Brae Oil Field deck |
| 123.87500 | | AM | North Sea | Maureen Oil Field deck |
| 124.45000 | | AM | North Sea | Tyra Oil Field deck |
| 125.17500 | | AM | North Sea | Markham Oil Field deck |
| 125.17500 | | AM | North Sea | Noordwinning Oil Field deck |
| 125.17500 | | AM | North Sea | Nordwinning/Zanddijk Oil Field deck |
| 125.17500 | | AM | North Sea | Petroland Oil Field deck |
| 125.17500 | | AM | North Sea | Placid Oil Field deck |
| 129.65000 | | AM | North Sea | Statfjord Oil Field deck |
| 129.70000 | | AM | North Sea | Amoco Arbroath Field |
| 129.70000 | | AM | North Sea | Amoco Montrose Field |
| 129.70000 | | AM | North Sea | Everest Oil Field deck |
| 129.70000 | | AM | North Sea | Gannet Oil Field deck |
| 129.70000 | | AM | North Sea | Lomond Oil Field deck |

| Base | Mobile | Mode | Location | User and Notes |
|---|---|---|---|---|
| 129.75000 | | AM | North Sea | Elf Aquataine Norge Frigg |
| 129.75000 | | AM | North Sea | Kewanee Nordsee Field |
| 129.75000 | | AM | North Sea | Total/Elf Frigg Field |
| 129.77500 | | AM | North Sea | Lennox Oil Field deck |
| 129.77500 | | AM | North Sea | North Hamiton Oil Field deck |
| 129.87500 | | AM | North Sea | Amethyst Field deck |
| 129.87500 | | AM | North Sea | BP Cleeton Field deck |
| 129.87500 | | AM | North Sea | BP Ravenspurn North Field deck |
| 129.87500 | | AM | North Sea | BP West Sole Field deck |
| 129.87500 | | AM | North Sea | British Gas Rough Field deck |
| 129.87500 | | AM | North Sea | West Sole Oil Field deck |
| 129.90000 | | AM | North Sea | Eider Oil Field deck |
| 129.90000 | | AM | North Sea | Phillips Eko/EMB Pipe Oil Field deck |
| 129.95000 | | AM | North Sea | North Cormorant Deck |
| 129.95000 | | AM | North Sea | Shell/Esso Dunlin Field deck |
| 129.95000 | | AM | North Sea | Shell/Esso Tern Field deck |
| 129.95000 | | AM | North Sea | South Cormorant Oil Field deck |
| 129.97500 | | AM | North Sea | Helicopter Common |
| 130.20000 | | AM | North Sea | Alwyn North Oil Field log |
| 130.20000 | | AM | North Sea | Dunbar Oil Field deck |
| 130.55000 | | AM | North Sea | Amoco Vauxhall Field |
| 130.55000 | | AM | North Sea | Phillips Albuskjell Field |
| 130.55000 | | AM | North Sea | Phillips Cod Field |
| 130.55000 | | AM | North Sea | Phillips Edda Field |
| 130.55000 | | AM | North Sea | Phillips Ekofisk Field |
| 130.55000 | | AM | North Sea | Phillips Eldfisk Field |
| 130.55000 | | AM | North Sea | Phillips Tor Field |
| 130.55000 | | AM | North Sea | Valhall Oil Field deck |
| 130.72500 | | AM | North Sea | FRG/STFS Pipe |
| 130.80000 | | AM | North Sea | Amoco NW Hutton Deck |
| 130.80000 | | AM | North Sea | Conoco Hutton Deck |
| 130.87000 | | AM | North Sea | Kittiwake Oil Field deck |
| 130.87500 | | AM | North Sea | Alba Oil Field deck |
| 130.87500 | | AM | North Sea | Andrew Oil Field deck |
| 133.57500 | | AM | North Sea | Clipper Oil Field deck |
| 133.57500 | | AM | North Sea | Galleon Oil Field deck |
| 133.87500 | | AM | North Sea | Barque Oil Field deck |
| 123.02500 | | AM | North sea | Gryphon Oil Field deck |
| 121.07500 | | AM | North Weald | Fighter Grouping meet |
| 121.17500 | | AM | North Weald | Display frequency |
| 123.52500 | | AM | North Weald | Air/Ground |
| 129.97500 | | AM | North Weald | Gliders |
| 130.17500 | | AM | North Weald | Aceair Company Channel |
| 122.70000 | | AM | Northampton (Sywell) | AFIS |
| 119.35000 | | AM | Norwich Airport | Approach/Radar |
| 124.25000 | | AM | Norwich Airport | Tower |
| 128.32500 | | AM | Norwich Airport | Radar |
| 128.60000 | | AM | Norwich Airport | London VOLMET (South) |
| 129.75000 | | AM | Norwich Airport | Air UK Ops |
| 122.05000 | | AM | Nottingham Aerodrome | Hutchins Crop Sprayers |
| 122.80000 | | AM | Nottingham Aerodrome | Air/Ground |
| 123.05000 | | AM | Nuthampstead, Royston | Air/Ground |
| 122.77500 | | AM | Oaksey Park | Air/Ground |
| 130.10000 | | AM | Oban | Air/Ground |

| Base | Mobile | Mode | Location | User and Notes |
|---|---|---|---|---|
| 123.20000 | | AM | Old Sarum | Air/Ground |
| 123.05000 | | AM | Old Warden (Biggleswade) | Tower (Display days only) |
| 118.87500 | | AM | Oxford (Kidlington Airport) | Tower/AFIS |
| 121.75000 | | AM | Oxford (Kidlington Airport) | ATIS |
| 121.95000 | | AM | Oxford (Kidlington Airport) | Ground |
| 125.32500 | | AM | Oxford (Kidlington Airport) | Approach |
| 120.25000 | | AM | Panshanger | Air/Ground |
| 118.10000 | | AM | Penzance Heliport | Tower |
| 119.75000 | | AM | Perranporth | Air/Ground |
| 130.10000 | | AM | Perranporth | Glider Ops |
| 119.80000 | | AM | Perth (Scone) | Air/Ground and AFIS |
| 129.72500 | | AM | Peterborough (Conington) | Air/Ground |
| 122.30000 | | AM | Peterborough (Sibson) | Approach/Radar |
| 130.20000 | | AM | Peterborough (Sibson) | MATZ and LARS |
| 122.37500 | | AM | Peterhead/Longside | Air/Ground Bond Helicopters |
| 122.37500 | | AM | Plockton Airfield | Air/Ground |
| 122.60000 | | AM | Plymouth City Airport | Tower |
| 131.57500 | | AM | Plymouth City Airport | Brymon |
| 133.55000 | | AM | Plymouth City Airport | Approach |
| 129.90000 | | AM | Pocklington | Base |
| 130.10000 | | AM | Pocklington | Air/Ground glider ops |
| 129.80000 | | AM | Popham Aerodrome | Popham Radio |
| 131.62500 | | AM | Portishead | Aero Radio Telephones |
| 119.87500 | | AM | Prestwick | Scottish ACC (Information) |
| 123.37500 | | AM | Prestwick | Scottish Control TMA |
| 123.77500 | | AM | Prestwick | Scottish Control |
| 124.05000 | | AM | Prestwick | Scottish Control |
| 124.50000 | | AM | Prestwick | Scottish Control |
| 124.82500 | | AM | Prestwick | Scottish Control (0700-2145) |
| 125.67500 | | AM | Prestwick | Scottish Control |
| 126.10000 | | AM | Prestwick | Highland Radar |
| 126.25000 | | AM | Prestwick | Scottish Control (Information) |
| 126.30000 | | AM | Prestwick | Scottish Control (2145-0700) |
| 126.85000 | | AM | Prestwick | Scottish Control |
| 127.27500 | | AM | Prestwick | Scottish ACC (Information) |
| 128.50000 | | AM | Prestwick | Scottish Control (TMA) |
| 129.22500 | | AM | Prestwick | Scottish Control |
| 131.30000 | | AM | Prestwick | Scottish Control (Stornoway) |
| 132.20000 | | AM | Prestwick | Reykjavik Oceanic (Polar Track) |
| 132.72500 | | AM | Prestwick | Scottish Control |
| 133.20000 | | AM | Prestwick | Scottish Information |
| 133.67500 | | AM | Prestwick | Scottish ACC (Entire Route) |
| 134.10000 | | AM | Prestwick | Highland Radar |
| 134.77500 | | AM | Prestwick | Scottish Control |
| 135.52500 | | AM | Prestwick | Shanwick Oceanic (Clearances) |
| 135.85000 | | AM | Prestwick | Scottish Control UIR |
| 118.15000 | | AM | Prestwick Airport | Tower |
| 119.45000 | | AM | Prestwick Airport | Radar |
| 120.55000 | | AM | Prestwick Airport | Approach/Radar |
| 121.80000 | | AM | Prestwick Airport | Ground |
| 125.72500 | | AM | Prestwick Airport | Scottish VOLMET |
| 127.12500 | | AM | Prestwick Airport | ATIS (Information) |
| 129.70000 | | AM | Prestwick Airport | Ogden Aviation |
| 131.45000 | | AM | Prestwick Airport | Air Canada Ops |
| 131.90000 | | AM | Prestwick Airport | Eastern Airlines Ops |
| 134.30000 | | AM | Prestwick Airport | Scottish Military |

| Base | Mobile | Mode | Location | User and Notes |
|---|---|---|---|---|
| 134.47500 | | AM | Prestwick Airport | Scottish Military |
| 134.85000 | | AM | Prestwick Airport | Scottish Air Traffic Control |
| 135.67500 | | AM | Prestwick Airport | Scottish Air Traffic Control |
| 130.40000 | | AM | Punchestown | Air/Ground (Parachute & Glider OPs) |
| 120.42500 | | AM | RAF Barkston Heath | Tower |
| 120.90000 | | AM | RAF Benson | Zone |
| 122.10000 | | AM | RAF Benson | Approach |
| 123.30000 | | AM | RAF Benson | Radar |
| 127.15000 | | AM | RAF Benson | Approach |
| 130.25000 | | AM | RAF Benson | Tower/Zone |
| 134.30000 | | AM | RAF Benson | Centralised Approach Control |
| 123.10000 | | AM | RAF Boulmer | Boulmer Rescue |
| 119.00000 | | AM | RAF Brize Norton | Zone |
| 123.30000 | | AM | RAF Brize Norton | Brize Talkdown |
| 126.50000 | | AM | RAF Brize Norton | Tower/Ground |
| 130.07500 | | AM | RAF Brize Norton | Brize Ops |
| 133.75000 | | AM | RAF Brize Norton | Brize Director |
| 134.30000 | | AM | RAF Brize Norton | Brize Radar |
| 130.20000 | | AM | RAF Chivenor | Air/Ground |
| 122.10000 | | AM | RAF Church Fenton | Tower/Ground |
| 123.30000 | | AM | RAF Church Fenton | Talkdown |
| 126.50000 | | AM | RAF Church Fenton | Approach (MATZ) |
| 122.10000 | | AM | RAF Colerne | Approach/Tower |
| 122.10000 | | AM | RAF Coltishall | Approach/Tower |
| 123.30000 | | AM | RAF Coltishall | Radar |
| 125.90000 | | AM | RAF Coltishall | Director |
| 119.97500 | | AM | RAF Coningsby | Tower |
| 120.80000 | | AM | RAF Coningsby | Approach (LARS and MATZ) |
| 122.10000 | | AM | RAF Coningsby | Approach/Tower and Ground |
| 123.30000 | | AM | RAF Coningsby | Radar |
| 118.92500 | | AM | RAF Cosford | Approach/Tower |
| 121.95000 | | AM | RAF Cosford | Ground |
| 122.10000 | | AM | RAF Cottesmore | Tower/Ground |
| 123.30000 | | AM | RAF Cottesmore | Talkdown |
| 130.20000 | | AM | RAF Cottesmore | Approach/Director |
| 119.37500 | | AM | RAF Cranwell | Approach |
| 122.10000 | | AM | RAF Cranwell | Tower |
| 123.30000 | | AM | RAF Cranwell | Talkdown |
| 122.10000 | | AM | RAF Dishforth (also Army) | Approach/Tower and Ground |
| 125.50000 | | AM | RAF Faiford | International Air Tattoo Base |
| 123.30000 | | AM | RAF Honington | Approach |
| 119.35000 | | AM | RAF Kinloss | Approach |
| 122.10000 | | AM | RAF Kinloss | Tower |
| 123.30000 | | AM | RAF Kinloss | Radar |
| 123.05000 | | AM | RAF Leconfield | Leconfield Rescue |
| 120.50000 | | AM | RAF Leeming | Tower |
| 122.10000 | | AM | RAF Leeming | Tower |
| 127.75000 | | AM | RAF Leeming | Approach/Director |
| 122.10000 | | AM | RAF Leuchars | Tower/Ground |
| 123.30000 | | AM | RAF Leuchars | Tower/Radar |
| 126.50000 | | AM | RAF Leuchars | Approach (LARS and MATZ) |
| 129.15000 | | AM | RAF Linton-On-Ouse | Director/Radar and Departures |
| 122.10000 | | AM | RAF Linton-on-Ouse | Tower/Ground |
| 123.30000 | | AM | RAF Linton-on-Ouse | Radar |
| 129.12500 | | AM | RAF Linton-on-Ouse | Approach (LARS and MATZ) |
| 118.90000 | | AM | RAF Lossiemouth | Tower |

| Base | Mobile | Mode | Location | User and Notes |
|---|---|---|---|---|
| 119.35000 | | AM | RAF Lossiemouth | Approach (LARS/MATZ) |
| 122.10000 | | AM | RAF Lossiemouth | Tower |
| 118.42500 | | AM | RAF Lyneham | Approach/Radar (Director) |
| 119.22500 | | AM | RAF Lyneham | Tower |
| 122.10000 | | AM | RAF Lyneham | Tower/Ground |
| 123.30000 | | AM | RAF Lyneham | Talkdown |
| 123.40000 | | AM | RAF Lyneham | Radar (Zone) |
| 129.47500 | | AM | RAF Lyneham | Ground |
| 134.30000 | | AM | RAF Lyneham | Radar (Brize) |
| 119.27500 | | AM | RAF Manston | Tower |
| 119.92500 | | AM | RAF Manston | Radar |
| 122.10000 | | AM | RAF Manston | Tower |
| 123.30000 | | AM | RAF Manston | Talkdown |
| 126.35000 | | AM | RAF Manston | Approach/Radar (LARS/MATZ) |
| 128.77500 | | AM | RAF Manston | Tower |
| 130.60000 | | AM | RAF Manston | KIA Ops |
| 122.10000 | | AM | RAF Marham | Tower |
| 123.30000 | | AM | RAF Marham | Radar |
| 124.15000 | | AM | RAF Marham | Approach |
| 122.00000 | | AM | RAF Mona | Air/Ground (weekends only) |
| 134.35000 | | AM | RAF Mona | Radar |
| 119.12500 | | AM | RAF Newton | Tower |
| 122.10000 | | AM | RAF Newton | Tower |
| 120.32500 | | AM | RAF Northolt | Departure |
| 124.97500 | | AM | RAF Northolt | Radar/Tower |
| 125.87500 | | AM | RAF Northolt | Talkdown |
| 126.45000 | | AM | RAF Northolt | Approach |
| 130.35000 | | AM | RAF Northolt | Radar (Director) |
| 132.65000 | | AM | RAF Northolt | Queen's Flight Ops |
| 119.90000 | | AM | RAF Odiham | Helicopter Ops |
| 121.10000 | | AM | RAF Odiham | Odiham Information |
| 122.10000 | | AM | RAF Odiham | Tower |
| 123.30000 | | AM | RAF Odiham | Talkdown |
| 125.25000 | | AM | RAF Odiham | Approach |
| 120.77500 | | AM | RAF Shawbury | Approach/Tower (LARS and MATZ) |
| 122.10000 | | AM | RAF Shawbury | Tower |
| 123.30000 | | AM | RAF Shawbury | Talkdown |
| 122.10000 | | AM | RAF Spadeadam | SRE |
| 119.47500 | | AM | RAF St Athan | Cardiff Information |
| 122.10000 | | AM | RAF St Athan | Tower |
| 123.30000 | | AM | RAF St Athan | Talkdown |
| 125.85000 | | AM | RAF St Athan | Approach |
| 122.10000 | | AM | RAF St Mawgan | Approach/Tower |
| 123.30000 | | AM | RAF St Mawgan | Radar |
| 123.40000 | | AM | RAF St Mawgan | Tower |
| 125.55000 | | AM | RAF St Mawgan | Approach |
| 126.50000 | | AM | RAF St Mawgan | Approach (LARS and MATZ) |
| 120.77500 | | AM | RAF Ternhill | Approach |
| 122.10000 | | AM | RAF Ternhill | Approach |
| 124.15000 | | AM | RAF Ternhill | Army Approach |
| 122.10000 | | AM | RAF Topcliffe | Approach/Tower |
| 123.30000 | | AM | RAF Topcliffe | Talkdown |
| 125.00000 | | AM | RAF Topcliffe | Director |
| 122.10000 | | AM | RAF Valley | Tower |
| 123.30000 | | AM | RAF Valley | Director/Talkdown |
| 134.35000 | | AM | RAF Valley | Radar (LARS and MATZ) |

| Base | Mobile | Mode | Location | User and Notes |
|---|---|---|---|---|
| 123.30000 | | AM | RAF Waddington | Radar |
| 125.35000 | | AM | RAF Waddington | Zone |
| 127.35000 | | AM | RAF Waddington | Radar (LARS and MATZ) |
| 118.37500 | | AM | RAF West Drayton | Air Traffic Control |
| 126.60000 | | AM | RAF West Drayton | London VOLMET (North) |
| 128.58750 | | AM | RAF West Drayton | London VOLMET (South) |
| 135.15000 | | AM | RAF West Drayton | London Military Radar |
| 135.27500 | | AM | RAF West Drayton | London Military Radar |
| 122.10000 | | AM | RAF Wittering | Tower |
| 123.30000 | | AM | RAF Wittering | Radar |
| 130.20000 | | AM | RAF Wittering | Radar |
| 119.75000 | | AM | RAF Woodvale | Tower |
| 121.00000 | | AM | RAF Woodvale | Approach |
| 123.60000 | | AM | Rathkenny | Air/Ground (Rathkenny Radio) |
| 121.92500 | | AM | Redhill | Ground (Airshows only) |
| 120.27500 | | AM | Redhill | Tower/AFIS |
| 130.47500 | | AM | Retford | Air/Ground |
| 122.10000 | | AM | RNAS Culdrose | Tower |
| 123.30000 | | AM | RNAS Culdrose | Tower/Talkdown |
| 134.05000 | | AM | RNAS Culdrose | Approach/Radar |
| 122.10000 | | AM | RNAS Merryfield | Tower |
| 122.10000 | | AM | RNAS Portland | Tower |
| 123.30000 | | AM | RNAS Portland | Tower |
| 124.15000 | | AM | RNAS Portland | Approach (LARS and MATZ) |
| 122.10000 | | AM | RNAS Predannack | Tower |
| 134.05000 | | AM | RNAS Predannack | Culdrose Approach |
| 122.10000 | | AM | RNAS Yeovilton | Tower |
| 123.30000 | | AM | RNAS Yeovilton | Director/Talkdown |
| 127.35000 | | AM | RNAS Yeovilton | Approach/Radar |
| 132.90000 | | AM | RNAS Yeovilton | Display director |
| 122.25000 | | AM | Rochester Aerodrome | AFIS |
| 118.20000 | | AM | Ronaldsway, Isle of Man | Radar |
| 118.90000 | | AM | Ronaldsway, Isle of Man | Tower |
| 120.85000 | | AM | Ronaldsway, Isle of Man | Approach/Radar |
| 125.30000 | | AM | Ronaldsway, Isle of Man | Radar |
| 126.60000 | | AM | Ronaldsway, Isle of Man | London VOLMET (North) |
| 130.62500 | | AM | Ronaldsway, Isle of Man | Island Aviation |
| 129.97500 | | AM | Rufforth, York | Air/Ground |
| 123.65000 | | AM | S of 56N | Fisheries Protection |
| 122.75000 | | AM | Salisbury Plain (Army) | Ops |
| 123.50000 | | AM | Sandown, Isle of Wight | Air/Ground |
| 130.42500 | | AM | Sandtoft Aerodrome | Tower |
| 130.12500 | | AM | Scarborough | Air/Ground Glider Ops |
| 122.40000 | | AM | Scatsa Aerodrome | Radar |
| 123.60000 | | AM | Scatsa Aerodrome | Approach/Tower |
| 123.15000 | | AM | Scilly Isles (St. Marys) | Approach/Tower |
| 122.67500 | | AM | Scotland | Bonzai Sqn Air-Air |
| 123.10000 | | AM | Scotland | Air Mountain Rescue |
| 122.60000 | | AM | Seething Aerodrome | Air/Ground |
| 121.70000 | | AM | Shannon | Clearance Delivery |
| 123.95000 | | AM | Shannon | Shanwick Oceanic ACC |
| 124.70000 | | AM | Shannon | Shannon Control |
| 127.90000 | | AM | Shannon | Shanwick Oceanic ACC (Shanwick Radio) |
| 131.15000 | | AM | Shannon | Shannon Control ACC (Cork sector) |
| 131.45000 | | AM | Shannon | Servisair |

| Base | Mobile | Mode | Location | User and Notes |
|---|---|---|---|---|
| 131.62500 | | AM | Shannon | Aerofolt Ops |
| 132.15000 | | AM | Shannon | Shannon Control ACC |
| 134.27500 | | AM | Shannon | ACC |
| 135.22500 | | AM | Shannon | Shannon Control Southern Sector |
| 118.70000 | | AM | Shannon Airport | Tower |
| 120.20000 | | AM | Shannon Airport | Approach |
| 121.40000 | | AM | Shannon Airport | Approach |
| 121.80000 | | AM | Shannon Airport | Ground |
| 127.50000 | | AM | Shannon Airport | ACC |
| 127.65000 | | AM | Shannon Airport | Shanwick Oceanic ACC |
| 130.95000 | | AM | Shannon Airport | ATIS |
| 133.80000 | | AM | Shannon Airport | North Altantic Track Broadcasts |
| 135.52500 | | AM | Shannon Airport | Shanwick Oceanic ACC (Clearences) |
| 135.60000 | | AM | Shannon Airport | ACC |
| 128.52500 | | AM | Sheffield City | AFIS |
| 122.60000 | | AM | Sherburn-in-Elmet Aerodrome | Tower |
| 134.15000 | | AM | Shetland | Radar |
| 129.95000 | | AM | Shetland Basin | Viking Approach |
| 119.00000 | | AM | Shetlands | East Shetland Information |
| 119.55000 | | AM | Shipdam | Air/Ground and AFIS |
| 123.50000 | | AM | Shobdon Aerodrome | Air/Ground |
| 132.40000 | | AM | Shoreham | ATIS |
| 123.15000 | | AM | Shoreham Aerodrome | Approach/Tower |
| 125.40000 | | AM | Shoreham Aerodrome | Tower (when directed) |
| 121.07500 | | AM | Silverstone | Air/Ground |
| 122.70000 | | AM | Silverstone | Tower |
| 130.45000 | | AM | Skegness Aerodrome | Tower |
| 130.65000 | | AM | Skye | Tower |
| 122.45000 | | AM | Sleap Aerodrome | Air/Ground |
| 121.00000 | | AM | Sligo | Tower/AFIS |
| 120.25500 | | AM | Solent | Interial contact frequency |
| 118.20000 | | AM | Southampton Airport | Tower |
| 120.22500 | | AM | Southampton Airport | Approach Solent |
| 128.85000 | | AM | Southampton Airport | Approach (as directed)/Radar |
| 130.65000 | | AM | Southampton Airport | Ops |
| 131.00000 | | AM | Southampton Airport | Approach Southampton |
| 122.05000 | | AM | Southend | Heavilift Ops |
| 129.70000 | | AM | Southend | Express Flight |
| 130.02500 | | AM | Southend | British World ops |
| 121.80000 | | AM | Southend Airport | ATIS |
| 127.72500 | | AM | Southend Airport | Approach/Tower |
| 128.95000 | | AM | Southend Airport | Approach/Radar |
| 130.62500 | | AM | Southend Airport | British Air Ferries Ops |
| 121.75000 | | NFM | Space | Soyuz Space Station/Mir |
| 130.16250 | | NFM | Space | Mir |
| 130.10000 | | AM | Spalding (Crowland) | Tower |
| 130.40000 | | AM | Spalding (Crowland) | Tower (gliders) |
| 123.30000 | | AM | Spanish Point, Eire | Air/Ground |
| 123.20000 | | AM | St Angelo | Tower |
| 128.10000 | | AM | St Kilda | Tower |
| 120.62500 | | AM | Stansted | Approach/Radar |
| 121.72500 | | AM | Stansted | Ground |
| 123.80000 | | AM | Stansted | Tower |
| 125.55000 | | AM | Stansted | Tower |
| 126.95000 | | AM | Stansted | Radar |

| Base | Mobile | Mode | Location | User and Notes |
|---|---|---|---|---|
| 127.17500 | | AM | Stansted | ATIS |
| 129.75000 | | AM | Stansted | Servisair Ops |
| 130.57500 | | AM | Stansted | Universal Air Handling |
| 130.60000 | | AM | Stansted | Air UK Leisure Ops |
| 131.77500 | | AM | Stansted | Air Foyle |
| 135.37500 | | AM | Stansted | London VOLMET (Main) |
| 122.05000 | | AM | Stapleford | Aeromega Ops. (Helicopter ops) |
| 122.80000 | | AM | Stapleford | Air/Ground |
| 130.62000 | | AM | Stapleford | Stapleford Ops |
| 123.05000 | | AM | Stevenage Aerodrome | British Aerospace |
| 123.50000 | | AM | Stornoway Airport | Approach/Tower and AFIS |
| 125.72500 | | AM | Stornoway Airport | Scottish VOLMET |
| 129.90000 | | AM | Strathallan Aerodrome | Air/Ground |
| 130.10000 | | AM | Strubby Aerodrome | Air/Ground (Strubby Base) gliders |
| 122.37500 | | AM | Strubby Heliport | Air/Ground |
| 119.42500 | | AM | Stubton Park | Air/Ground |
| 130.30000 | | AM | Sturgate Aerodrome | Air/Ground |
| 125.72500 | | AM | Sumburgh | Scottish VOLMET |
| 130.05000 | | AM | Sumburgh | Radar |
| 118.25000 | | AM | Sumburgh Airport | Tower |
| 123.15000 | | AM | Sumburgh Airport | Approach/Radar |
| 125.85000 | | AM | Sumburgh Airport | ATIS |
| 129.95000 | | AM | Sumburgh Airport | Helicopter Information |
| 131.30000 | | AM | Sumburgh Airport | Radar (N. Sea Offshore Advisory) |
| 119.70000 | | AM | Swansea | Air/Ground |
| 132.65000 | | AM | Swansea | Air Sea Rescue |
| 129.97500 | | AM | Swansea Airport | ATC Glider Training |
| 123.50000 | | AM | Swanton Morley Aerodrome | Air/Ground |
| 129.82500 | | AM | Swindon (Draycott) | Air/Ground |
| 124.07500 | | AM | Tatenhill Aerodrome | Air/Ground |
| 126.60000 | | AM | Teeside Airport | London VOLMET (North) |
| 118.85000 | | AM | Teesside Airport | Approach/Radar |
| 119.80000 | | AM | Teesside Airport | Tower |
| 122.35000 | | AM | Teesside Airport | Air Cam |
| 128.85000 | | AM | Teesside Airport | Radar |
| 130.40000 | | AM | Thirsk (Sutton Bank) | Air/Ground (gliders) |
| 130.45000 | | AM | Thruxton Aerodrome | Air/Ground |
| 129.97000 | | AM | Tibenham | Air/Ground |
| 130.10000 | | AM | Tibenham | Air/Ground (Gliders) |
| 122.70000 | | AM | Tiree | AFIS |
| 130.25000 | | AM | Tresco | Civil Heliport |
| 123.30000 | | AM | Trim, Eire | Air/Ground |
| 129.80000 | | AM | Truro Aerodrome | Air/Ground |
| 122.17500 | | AM | Turweston Aerodrome | Air/Ground |
| 123.45000 | | AM | Unst (Saxavord) | Ops |
| 130.35000 | | AM | Unst (Saxavord) | Air/Ground |
| 119.00000 | | AM | USAF Fairford | Approach |
| 119.15000 | | AM | USAF Fairford | Tower |
| 122.10000 | | AM | USAF Fairford | Approach |
| 126.50000 | | AM | USAF Fairford | Tower (Airshows Only) |
| 129.25000 | | AM | USAF Fairford | Tower (Airshows Only) |
| 134.30000 | | AM | USAF Fairford | Centralised Approach Control |
| 135.97500 | | AM | USAF Fairford | Silver Eagles Display Team |
| 122.10000 | | AM | USAF Lakenheath | Tower |

| Base | Mobile | Mode | Location | User and Notes |
|------|--------|------|----------|----------------|
| 123.30000 | | AM | USAF Lakenheath | Radar |
| 128.90000 | | AM | USAF Lakenheath | MATZ |
| 122.55000 | | AM | USAF Mildenhall | Tower |
| 123.62500 | | AM | Walton Wood | Air/Ground |
| 124.45000 | | AM | Warton (BAe) | Radar |
| 127.97500 | | AM | Warton (BAe) | Ops |
| 129.72500 | | AM | Warton (BAe) | Radar |
| 130.80000 | | AM | Warton (BAe) | Tower |
| 129.85000 | | AM | Waterford | Tower and AFIS |
| 122.10000 | | AM | Wattisham (Army Airfield) | Tower |
| 125.80000 | | AM | Wattisham (Army Airfield) | Approach |
| 123.30000 | | AM | Wattishan (Army Airfield) | Approach |
| 124.02500 | | AM | Wellesbourne Mountford | Air/Ground |
| 123.25000 | | AM | Welshpool | Air/Ground |
| 118.47500 | | AM | West Drayton | London ATC |
| 118.82500 | | AM | West Drayton | London Control ACC |
| 119.77500 | | AM | West Drayton | London Control |
| 120.02500 | | AM | West Drayton | London Control |
| 120.17500 | | AM | West Drayton | London Control Inbound |
| 120.47500 | | AM | West Drayton | London Control SIDs |
| 120.52500 | | AM | West Drayton | London Control ACC |
| 121.22500 | | AM | West Drayton | London Control |
| 121.27500 | | AM | West Drayton | London Control |
| 121.32500 | | AM | West Drayton | London Control TMA |
| 124.27500 | | AM | West Drayton | London Control |
| 124.60000 | | AM | West Drayton | London Control FIR Information |
| 124.75000 | | AM | West Drayton | London Control Information |
| 125.47500 | | AM | West Drayton | London Control Information |
| 125.80000 | | AM | West Drayton | London Control Radar Departure |
| 126.07500 | | AM | West Drayton | London Control |
| 126.30000 | | AM | West Drayton | London Control Inbound |
| 126.87500 | | AM | West Drayton | London Control Inbound |
| 127.10000 | | AM | West Drayton | London Control |
| 127.42500 | | AM | West Drayton | London Control Upper Sector East |
| 127.45000 | | AM | West Drayton | London Military Northwest |
| 127.65000 | | AM | West Drayton | Oceanic Clearance (E of 30_W) |
| 127.70000 | | AM | West Drayton | London Control |
| 127.87500 | | AM | West Drayton | London Control |
| 128.12500 | | AM | West Drayton | London Control North Sea |
| 128.25000 | | AM | West Drayton | London Military |
| 128.42500 | | AM | West Drayton | London Control |
| 128.60000 | | AM | West Drayton | London VOLMET (South) |
| 128.70000 | | AM | West Drayton | London Military Radar |
| 129.07500 | | AM | West Drayton | London Control |
| 129.10000 | | AM | West Drayton | London Control |
| 129.20000 | | AM | West Drayton | London Control |
| 129.37500 | | AM | West Drayton | London Control |
| 129.42500 | | AM | West Drayton | London Control |
| 129.60000 | | AM | West Drayton | London Control |
| 130.92500 | | AM | West Drayton | London Control TMA |
| 131.05000 | | AM | West Drayton | London Control Nort East UIR |
| 131.12500 | | AM | West Drayton | London Control |
| 132.20000 | | AM | West Drayton | Reykjavik Oceanic (Polar Tracks) |

| Base | Mobile | Mode | Location | User and Notes |
|---|---|---|---|---|
| 132.45000 | | AM | West Drayton | London Control |
| 132.60000 | | AM | West Drayton | London Control SW Approach |
| 132.80000 | | AM | West Drayton | London Control (Bristol) |
| 132.95000 | | AM | West Drayton | London Control |
| 133.17500 | | AM | West Drayton | London Control |
| 133.30000 | | AM | West Drayton | London Military Radar |
| 133.45000 | | AM | West Drayton | London Control |
| 133.52500 | | AM | West Drayton | London Control North Sea |
| 133.60000 | | AM | West Drayton | London Control |
| 133.70000 | | AM | West Drayton | London Control |
| 133.80000 | | AM | West Drayton | Oceanic Track Broadcasts |
| 133.90000 | | AM | West Drayton | London Military Brize Radar |
| 134.12500 | | AM | West Drayton | London Control |
| 134.25000 | | AM | West Drayton | London Control North Sea |
| 134.42500 | | AM | West Drayton | London Control Irish Sea |
| 134.45000 | | AM | West Drayton | London Control (Hurn) |
| 134.75000 | | AM | West Drayton | London Control Upper Sector West |
| 134.90000 | | AM | West Drayton | London Control |
| 135.05000 | | AM | West Drayton | London Control |
| 135.25000 | | AM | West Drayton | London Control (Cardiff) |
| 135.32500 | | AM | West Drayton | London Control (Cardiff) |
| 135.37500 | | AM | West Drayton | London VOLMET (Main) |
| 135.42500 | | AM | West Drayton | London Control |
| 122.55000 | | AM | West Freugh (MoD) | Tower |
| 130.05000 | | AM | West Freugh (MoD) | Approach |
| 130.72500 | | AM | West Freugh (MoD) | Radar |
| 122.40000 | | AM | Weston (Dublin) | Air/Ground |
| 133.65000 | | AM | Weston on the Green | Weston Radio |
| 122.50000 | | AM | Weston-super-Mare | Tower |
| 122.07500 | | AM | Whitchurch (Tilstock) | Air/Ground |
| 122.60000 | | AM | White Waltham Aerodrome | Air/Ground |
| 119.70000 | | AM | Wick | Air/Ground |
| 130.37000 | | AM | Wick | Air/Ground (Far North) |
| 122.45000 | | AM | Wickenby Aerodrome | Air/Ground |
| 123.05000 | | AM | Wigtown | Tower |
| 126.92500 | | AM | Woodford | Approach/Tower |
| 130.02500 | | AM | Woodford | BAe Ops |
| 130.05000 | | AM | Woodford | Tower |
| 130.75000 | | AM | Woodford | Approach |
| 118.42500 | | AM | Wroughton | Approach |
| 121.85000 | | AM | Wroughton | PFA Delivery |
| 121.92500 | | AM | Wroughton | PFA Ground |
| 129.22500 | | AM | Wroughton | PFA Circuit |
| 130.70000 | | AM | Wroughton | Tower |
| 132.90000 | | AM | Wroughton | PFA Arrivals |
| 133.65000 | | AM | Wroughton | Tower |
| 121.77500 | | AM | Wycombe Air Park (Booker) | Ground |
| 126.55000 | | AM | Wycombe Air Park (Booker) | Tower/AFIS |
| 118.00000 | | AM | Yeovil | Westland Helicopter Tests |
| 127.35000 | | AM | Yeovil | Radar (LAKS) |
| 125.40000 | | AM | Yeovil (Westland) | Tower and Air/Ground (Judwin Radio) |
| 130.80000 | | AM | Yeovil (Westland) | Approach/Radar (Judwin) |

# Part 3

# European Frequencies

# European VHF/UHF Frequencies

The following European frequencies have been included because many of these stations can be heard from the south coast of England and Ireland as well as the Channel Islands. The list will also be useful to our growing number of European readers and travellers in Europe.

## Austria

| Base | Mobile | Mode | Location | User and Notes |
|---|---|---|---|---|
| 171.4000 | 166.8000 | NFM | | Police & Gendarmerie Ch 1 |
| 171.4250 | 166.8250 | NFM | | Police & Gendarmerie Ch 2 |
| 171.4500 | 166.8500 | NFM | | Police & Gendarmerie Ch 3 |
| 171.4750 | 166.8750 | NFM | | Police & Gendarmerie Ch 4 |
| 171.5000 | 166.9000 | NFM | | Police & Gendarmerie Ch 5 |
| 171.5250 | 166.9250 | NFM | | Police & Gendarmerie Ch 6 |
| 171.5500 | 166.9500 | NFM | | Police & Gendarmerie Ch 7 |
| 171.5750 | 166.9750 | NFM | | Police & Gendarmerie Ch 8 |
| 171.6000 | 167.0000 | NFM | | Police & Gendarmerie Ch 9 |
| 171.6250 | 167.0250 | NFM | | Police & Gendarmerie Ch 10 |
| 171.6500 | 167.0500 | NFM | | Police & Gendarmerie Ch 11 |
| 171.6750 | 167.0750 | NFM | | Police & Gendarmerie Ch 12 |
| 171.7000 | 167.1000 | NFM | | Police & Gendarmerie Ch 13 |
| 171.7250 | 167.1250 | NFM | | Police & Gendarmerie Ch 14 |
| 171.7500 | 167.1500 | NFM | | Police & Gendarmerie Ch 15 |
| 171.7750 | 167.1750 | NFM | | Police & Gendarmerie Ch 16 |
| 171.8000 | 167.2000 | NFM | | Police & Gendarmerie Ch 17 |
| 171.8250 | 167.2250 | NFM | | Police & Gendarmerie Ch 18 |
| 171.8500 | 167.2500 | NFM | | Police & Gendarmerie Ch 19 |
| 171.8750 | 167.2750 | NFM | | Police & Gendarmerie Ch 20 |
| 171.9000 | 167.3000 | NFM | | Police & Gendarmerie Ch 21 |
| 171.9250 | 167.3250 | NFM | | Police & Gendarmerie Ch 22 |
| 171.9500 | 167.3500 | NFM | | Police & Gendarmerie Ch 23 |
| 171.9750 | 167.3750 | NFM | | Police & Gendarmerie Ch 24 |
| 172.0000 | 167.4000 | NFM | | Police & Gendarmerie Ch 25 |
| 172.0250 | 167.4250 | NFM | | Police & Gendarmerie Ch 26 |
| 172.0500 | 167.4500 | NFM | | Police & Gendarmerie Ch 27 |
| 172.0750 | 167.4750 | NFM | | Police & Gendarmerie Ch 28 |
| 172.1000 | 167.5000 | NFM | | Police & Gendarmerie Ch 29 |
| 172.1250 | 167.5250 | NFM | | Police & Gendarmerie Ch 30 |
| 172.1500 | 167.5500 | NFM | | Police & Gendarmerie Ch 31 |
| 172.1750 | 167.5750 | NFM | | Police & Gendarmerie Ch 32 |
| 172.2000 | 167.6000 | NFM | | Police & Gendarmerie Ch 33 |
| 172.2250 | 167.6250 | NFM | | Police & Gendarmerie Ch 34 |
| 172.2500 | 167.6500 | NFM | | Police & Gendarmerie Ch 35 |
| 172.2750 | 167.6750 | NFM | | Police & Gendarmerie Ch 36 |
| 172.3000 | 167.7000 | NFM | | Police & Gendarmerie Ch 37 |
| 172.3250 | 167.7250 | NFM | | Police & Gendarmerie Ch 38 |
| 172.3500 | 167.7500 | NFM | | Police & Gendarmerie Ch 39 |
| 172.3750 | 167.7750 | NFM | | Police & Gendarmerie Ch 40 |
| 172.4000 | 167.8000 | NFM | | Customs Ch 41 |
| 172.4250 | 167.8250 | NFM | | Customs Ch 42 |
| 172.4500 | 167.8500 | NFM | | Customs Ch 43 |
| 172.4750 | 167.8750 | NFM | | Customs Ch 44 |
| 172.5000 | 167.9000 | NFM | | Customs Ch 45 |

| Base | Mobile | Mode | Location | User and Notes |
|---|---|---|---|---|
| 172.5250 | 167.9250 | NFM | | Customs Ch 46 |
| 172.5500 | 167.9500 | NFM | | Customs Ch 47 |
| 172.5750 | 167.9750 | NFM | | Customs Ch 48 |
| 172.6000 | 168.0000 | NFM | | Fire Brigade Ch 49 |
| 172.6250 | 168.0250 | NFM | | Fire Brigade Ch 50 |
| 172.6500 | 168.0500 | NFM | | Fire Brigade Ch 51 |
| 172.6750 | 168.0750 | NFM | | Fire Brigade Ch 52 |
| 172.7000 | 168.1000 | NFM | | Fire Brigade Ch 53 |
| 172.7250 | 168.1250 | NFM | | Fire Brigade Ch 54 |
| 172.7500 | 168.1500 | NFM | | Fire Brigade Ch 55 |
| 172.7750 | 168.1750 | NFM | | Fire Brigade Ch 56 |
| 172.8000 | 168.2000 | NFM | | Fire Brigade Ch 57 |
| 172.8250 | 168.2250 | NFM | | Fire Brigade Ch 58 |
| 172.8500 | 168.2500 | NFM | | Fire Brigade Ch 59 |
| 172.8750 | 168.2750 | NFM | | Fire Brigade Ch 60 |
| 172.9000 | 168.3000 | NFM | | Fire Brigade Ch 61 |
| 172.9250 | 168.3250 | NFM | | Fire Brigade Ch 62 |
| 172.9500 | 168.2500 | NFM | | Fire Brigade Ch 63 |
| 172.9750 | 168.3750 | NFM | | Fire Brigade Ch 64 |
| 173.0000 | 168.4000 | NFM | | Fire Brigade Ch 65 |
| 173.0250 | 168.4250 | NFM | | Fire Brigade Ch 66 |
| 173.0500 | 168.4500 | NFM | | Road and Motorway maintenance Ch 67 |
| 173.0750 | 168.4750 | NFM | | Road and Motorway maintenance Ch 68 |
| 173.1000 | 168.5000 | NFM | | Road and Motorway maintenance Ch 69 |
| 173.1250 | 168.5250 | NFM | | Road and Motorway maintenance Ch 70 |
| 173.1500 | 168.5500 | NFM | | Road and Motorway maintenance Ch 71 |
| 173.1750 | 168.5750 | NFM | | User unknown Ch 72 |
| 173.2000 | 168.6000 | NFM | | User unknown Ch 73 |
| 173.2250 | 168.6250 | NFM | | Red Cross (Ambulance Service) Ch 74 |
| 173.2500 | 168.6500 | NFM | | User unknown Ch 75 |
| 173.2750 | 168.6750 | NFM | | User unknown Ch 76 |
| 173.3000 | 168.7000 | NFM | | User unknown Ch 77 |
| 173.3250 | 168.7250 | NFM | | Red Cross (Ambulance Service) Ch 78 |
| 173.3500 | 168.7500 | NFM | | Red Cross (Ambulance Service) Ch 79 |
| 173.3750 | 168.7750 | NFM | | Red Cross (Ambulance Service) Ch 80 |
| 173.4000 | 168.8000 | NFM | | Red Cross (Ambulance Service) Ch 81 |
| 173.4250 | 168.8250 | NFM | | Red Cross (Ambulance Service) Ch 82 |
| 173.4500 | 168.8500 | NFM | | Red Cross (Ambulance Service) Ch 83 |
| 173.4750 | 168.8750 | NFM | | Red Cross (Ambulance Service) Ch 84 |
| 173.5000 | 168.9000 | NFM | | Red Cross (Ambulance Service) Ch 85 |
| 173.5250 | 168.9250 | NFM | | User unknown Ch 86 |
| 173.5500 | 168.9500 | NFM | | User unknown Ch 87 |
| 173.5750 | 168.9750 | NFM | | User unknown Ch 88 |
| 173.6000 | 169.0000 | NFM | | User unknown Ch 89 |
| 173.6250 | 169.0250 | NFM | | User unknown Ch 90 |
| 173.6500 | 169.0500 | NFM | | User unknown Ch 91 |
| 173.6750 | 169.0750 | NFM | | User unknown Ch 92 |
| 173.7000 | 169.1000 | NFM | | User unknown Ch 93 |
| 173.7250 | 169.1250 | NFM | | User unknown Ch 94 |
| 173.7500 | 169.1500 | NFM | | User unknown Ch 95 |
| 173.7750 | 169.1750 | NFM | | User unknown Ch 96 |
| 173.8000 | 169.2000 | NFM | | User unknown Ch 97 |
| 173.8250 | 169.2250 | NFM | | Red Cross Ch 98 |
| 173.8500 | 169.2500 | NFM | | User unknown Ch 99 |

| Base | Mobile | Mode | Location | User and Notes |
|------|--------|------|----------|----------------|
| | | | | **Belgium** |
| 118.7000 | 118.7000 | AM | Ostend Airport | Tower |
| 120.6000 | 120.6000 | AM | Ostend Airport | Approach |
| 121.9000 | 121.9000 | AM | Ostend Airport | Ground |
| 122.5000 | 122.5000 | AM | Brussels Airport | ACC |
| 125.0000 | 125.0000 | AM | Brussels Airport | ACC |
| 126.7500 | 126.7500 | AM | Brussels Airport | ACC |
| 126.9000 | 126.9000 | AM | Brussels Airport | ACC |
| 128.2000 | 128.2000 | AM | Brussels Airport | ACC |
| 128.4500 | 128.4500 | AM | Brussels Airport | ACC |
| 128.8000 | 128.8000 | AM | Brussels Airport | ACC |
| 129.6500 | 129.6500 | AM | Brussels Airport | ACC |
| 130.5500 | 130.5500 | AM | Brussels | Abelag Ops. |
| 131.4500 | 131.4500 | AM | Brussels | Speedbird Ops. |
| 131.4750 | 131.4750 | AM | Brussels | Servisair |
| 131.6000 | 131.6000 | AM | Brussels Airport | TWA Ops. |
| 165.8100 | 165.8100 | NFM | Belgium | Fire & Ambulance |
| 165.8300 | 165.8300 | NFM | Belgium | Fire & Ambulance |
| 165.8500 | 165.8500 | NFM | Belgium | Fire & Ambulance |
| 165.8700 | 165.8700 | NFM | Belgium | Fire & Ambulance |
| 165.8900 | 165.8900 | NFM | Belgium | Fire & Ambulance |
| 165.9100 | 165.9100 | NFM | Belgium | Fire & Ambulance |
| 165.9300 | 165.9300 | NFM | Belgium | Fire & Ambulance |
| 165.9500 | 170.7500 | NFM | Belgium | Fire & Ambulance |
| 165.9700 | 165.9700 | NFM | Belgium | Fire & Ambulance |
| 165.9900 | 165.9900 | NFM | Belgium | Fire & Ambulance |
| 166.0100 | 166.0100 | NFM | Belgium | Fire & Ambulance |
| 166.0300 | 166.0300 | NFM | Belgium | Fire & Ambulance |
| 166.0500 | 166.0500 | NFM | Belgium | Fire & Ambulance |
| 166.0700 | 166.0700 | NFM | Belgium | Fire & Ambulance |
| 166.0900 | 166.0900 | NFM | Belgium | Fire & Ambulance |
| 166.1100 | 166.1100 | NFM | Belgium | Fire & Ambulance |
| 166.1300 | 166.1300 | NFM | Belgium | Fire & Ambulance |
| 166.1500 | 166.1500 | NFM | Belgium | Fire & Ambulance |
| 166.1700 | 166.1700 | NFM | Belgium | Fire & Ambulance |
| 166.1900 | 166.1900 | NFM | Belgium | Fire & Ambulance |
| 166.2100 | 166.2100 | NFM | Belgium | Fire & Ambulance |
| 166.2300 | 166.2300 | NFM | Belgium | Fire & Ambulance |
| 166.2700 | 166.2700 | NFM | Belgium | Fire & Ambulance |
| 166.2900 | 166.2900 | NFM | Belgium | Fire & Ambulance |
| 166.3100 | 166.3100 | NFM | Belgium | Fire & Ambulance |
| 166.3300 | 166.3300 | NFM | Belgium | Fire & Ambulance |
| 166.3500 | 166.3500 | NFM | Belgium | Fire & Ambulance |
| 166.3700 | 166.3700 | NFM | Belgium | Disaster Channel 1 |
| 166.3900 | 166.3900 | NFM | Belgium | Fire & Ambulance |
| 166.4100 | 166.4100 | NFM | Belgium | Fire & Ambulance |
| 166.4300 | 166.4300 | NFM | Belgium | Fire & Ambulance |
| 166.4400 | 166.4400 | NFM | Belgium | Disaster Channel 2 |
| 166.4500 | 166.4500 | NFM | Belgium | Fire & Ambulance |
| 166.4700 | 166.4700 | NFM | Belgium | Fire & Ambulance |
| 166.4900 | 166.4900 | NFM | Belgium | Fire & Ambulance |
| 166.5100 | 166.5100 | NFM | Belgium | Fire & Ambulance |
| 166.5300 | 166.5300 | NFM | Belgium | Fire & Ambulance |
| 166.5500 | 166.5500 | NFM | Belgium | Fire & Ambulance |
| 166.5700 | 166.5700 | NFM | Belgium | Fire & Ambulance |
| 166.5900 | 166.5900 | NFM | Belgium | Fire & Ambulance |

| Base | Mobile | Mode | Location | User and Notes |
|------|--------|------|----------|----------------|
| 166.6100 | 166.6100 | NFM | Belgium | Fire & Ambulance |
| 166.6300 | 166.6300 | NFM | Belgium | Fire & Ambulance |
| 166.6500 | 166.6500 | NFM | Belgium | Fire & Ambulance |
| 166.6700 | 166.6700 | NFM | Belgium | Fire & Ambulance |
| 166.6900 | 166.6900 | NFM | Belgium | Fire & Ambulance |
| 166.7100 | 166.7100 | NFM | Belgium | Fire & Ambulance |
| 166.7300 | 166.7300 | NFM | Belgium | Fire & Ambulance |
| 166.7500 | 166.7500 | NFM | Belgium | Fire & Ambulance |
| 166.7700 | 166.7700 | NFM | Belgium | Fire & Ambulance |
| 166.7900 | 166.7900 | NFM | Belgium | Fire & Ambulance |
| 166.8100 | 166.8100 | NFM | Belgium | Fire & Ambulance |
| 166.8300 | 166.8300 | NFM | Belgium | Fire & Ambulance |
| 166.8500 | 166.8500 | NFM | Belgium | Fire & Ambulance |
| 166.8700 | 166.8700 | NFM | Belgium | Disaster Protection |
| 166.9100 | 166.9100 | NFM | Belgium | Disaster Protection |
| 166.9300 | 166.9300 | NFM | Belgium | Disaster Protection |
| 166.9500 | 166.9500 | NFM | Belgium | Disaster Protection |
| 167.0125 | 167.0125 | NFM | Belgium | Disaster Protection |
| 167.0375 | 167.0375 | NFM | Belgium | Disaster Protection |
| 167.0500 | 167.0500 | NFM | Belgium | Disaster Protection |
| 167.0700 | 167.0700 | NFM | Belgium | Disaster Protection |
| 167.0900 | 167.0900 | NFM | Belgium | Disaster Protection |
| 167.1100 | 167.1100 | NFM | Belgium | Ambulance - Hospital |
| 168.5500 | 168.5500 | NFM | Belgium | Gendarmerie Ch 1 |
| 168.5700 | 168.5700 | NFM | Belgium | Gendarmerie Ch 3 |
| 168.5900 | 168.5900 | NFM | Belgium | Gendarmerie Ch 5 |
| 168.6100 | 168.6100 | NFM | Belgium | Gendarmerie Ch 7 |
| 168.6300 | 168.6300 | NFM | Belgium | Gendarmerie Ch 9 |
| 168.6500 | 168.6500 | NFM | Belgium | Gendarmerie Ch 11 |
| 168.6700 | 168.6700 | NFM | Belgium | Gendarmerie Ch 13 |
| 168.6900 | 168.6900 | NFM | Belgium | Gendarmerie Ch 15 |
| 168.7100 | 168.7100 | NFM | Belgium | Gendarmerie Ch 17 |
| 168.7300 | 168.7300 | NFM | Belgium | Gendarmerie Ch 19 |
| 168.7700 | 168.7700 | NFM | Belgium | Gendarmerie Ch 23 |
| 168.7900 | 168.7900 | NFM | Belgium | Gendarmerie Ch 25 |
| 168.8100 | 168.8100 | NFM | Belgium | Gendarmerie Ch 27 |
| 168.8300 | 168.8300 | NFM | Belgium | Gendarmerie Ch 29 |
| 168.8400 | 168.8400 | NFM | Belgium | Gendarmerie Ch 30 |
| 168.8600 | 168.8600 | NFM | Belgium | Gendarmerie Ch 32 |
| 168.8800 | 168.8800 | NFM | Belgium | Gendarmerie Ch 34 |
| 168.9200 | 168.9200 | NFM | Belgium | Gendarmerie Ch 38 |
| 168.9400 | 168.9400 | NFM | Belgium | Gendarmerie Ch 40 |
| 168.9600 | 168.9600 | NFM | Belgium | Gendarmerie Ch 42 |
| 168.9800 | 168.9800 | NFM | Belgium | Gendarmerie Ch 44 |
| 169.0200 | 169.0200 | NFM | Belgium | Gendarmerie Ch 48 |
| 169.0400 | 169.0400 | NFM | Belgium | Gendarmerie Ch 50 |
| 169.0600 | 169.0600 | NFM | Belgium | Gendarmerie Ch 52 |
| 169.0800 | 169.0800 | NFM | Belgium | Gendarmerie Ch 54 |
| 169.1200 | 169.1200 | NFM | Belgium | Gendarmerie Ch 58 |
| 169.1400 | 169.1400 | NFM | Belgium | Gendarmerie Ch 60 |
| 169.1800 | 169.1800 | NFM | Belgium | Gendarmerie Ch 64 |
| 169.2200 | 169.2200 | NFM | Belgium | Gendarmerie Ch 68 |
| 169.2400 | 169.2400 | NFM | Belgium | Gendarmerie Ch 70 |
| 169.2600 | 169.2600 | NFM | Belgium | Gendarmerie Ch 72 |
| 169.2800 | 169.2800 | NFM | Belgium | Gendarmerie Ch 74 |
| 169.3200 | 169.3200 | NFM | Belgium | Gendarmerie Ch 78 |

| Base | Mobile | Mode | Location | User and Notes |
|------|--------|------|----------|----------------|
| 169.3400 | 169.3400 | NFM | Belgium | Gendarmerie Ch 80 |
| 169.3600 | 169.3600 | NFM | Belgium | Gendarmerie Ch 82 |
| 169.3800 | 169.3800 | NFM | Belgium | Gendarmerie Ch 84 |
| 169.4000 | 169.4000 | NFM | Belgium | Gendarmerie Ch 86 |
| 169.4200 | 169.4200 | NFM | Belgium | Gendarmerie Ch 88 |
| 169.4400 | 169.4400 | NFM | Belgium | Gendarmerie Ch 90 |
| 169.4600 | 169.4600 | NFM | Belgium | Gendarmerie Ch 92 |
| 169.4800 | 169.4800 | NFM | Belgium | Gendarmerie Ch 94 |
| 169.5200 | 169.5200 | NFM | Belgium | Gendarmerie Ch 98 |
| 169.5400 | 169.5400 | NFM | Belgium | Gendarmerie Ch 100 |
| 169.5600 | 169.5600 | NFM | Belgium | Gendarmerie Ch 102 |
| 169.5800 | 169.5800 | NFM | Belgium | Gendarmerie Ch 104 |
| 169.6200 | 169.6200 | NFM | Belgium | Gendarmerie Ch 108 |
| 169.6400 | 169.6400 | NFM | Belgium | Gendarmerie Ch 110 |
| 169.6600 | 169.6600 | NFM | Belgium | Gendarmerie Ch 112 |
| 169.6800 | 169.6800 | NFM | Belgium | Gendarmerie Ch 114 |
| 169.7200 | 169.7200 | NFM | Belgium | Gendarmerie Ch 118 |
| 169.7400 | 169.7400 | NFM | Belgium | Gendarmerie Ch 120 |
| 169.7600 | 169.7600 | NFM | Belgium | Gendarmerie Ch 122 |
| 169.7800 | 169.7800 | NFM | Belgium | Gendarmerie Ch 124 |
| 169.8200 | 169.8200 | NFM | Belgium | Gendarmerie Ch 128 |
| 169.8400 | 169.8400 | NFM | Belgium | Gendarmerie Ch 130 |
| 169.8600 | 169.8600 | NFM | Belgium | Gendarmerie Ch 132 |
| 169.8800 | 169.8800 | NFM | Belgium | Gendarmerie Ch 134 |
| 169.9000 | 169.9000 | NFM | Belgium | Gendarmerie Ch 136 |
| 169.9200 | 169.9200 | NFM | Belgium | Gendarmerie Ch 138 |
| 169.9400 | 169.9400 | NFM | Belgium | Gendarmerie Ch 140 |
| 169.9600 | 169.9600 | NFM | Belgium | Gendarmerie Ch 142 |
| 169.9800 | 169.9800 | NFM | Belgium | Gendarmerie Ch 144 |
| 170.0000 | 170.0000 | NFM | Belgium | Gendarmerie Ch 146 |
| 170.0200 | 170.0200 | NFM | Belgium | Gendarmerie Ch 148 |
| 170.0400 | 170.0400 | NFM | Belgium | Gendarmerie Ch 150 |
| 170.0600 | 170.0600 | NFM | Belgium | Gendarmerie Ch 152 |
| 170.0800 | 170.0800 | NFM | Belgium | Gendarmerie Ch 154 |
| 170.1000 | 170.1000 | NFM | Belgium | Gendarmerie Ch 156 |
| 170.1200 | 170.1200 | NFM | Belgium | Gendarmerie Ch 158 |
| 170.1400 | 170.1400 | NFM | Belgium | Gendarmerie Ch 160 |
| 170.1600 | 170.1600 | NFM | Belgium | Gendarmerie Ch 162 |

## Czech Republic

| Base | Mobile | Mode | Location | User and Notes |
|------|--------|------|----------|----------------|
| 66.2000 | | WFM | Brno | Cesko Rozhlas [LBS] |
| 66.3200 | | WFM | Ostrava | Cesko Rozhlas [LBS] |
| 66.4400 | | WFM | Hradec Kralove | Cesko Rozhlas [LBS] |
| 66.8300 | | WFM | Praha | Cesko Rozhlas [LBS] |
| 67.1000 | | WFM | Jesenik | Cesko Rozhlas [LBS] |
| 67.3400 | | WFM | Pizen | Cesko Rozhlas [LBS] |
| 67.6100 | | WFM | Ceske Budejovice | Cesko Rozhlas [LBS] |
| 67.8800 | | WFM | Ostrava | Cesko Rozhlas [LBS] |
| 68.0000 | | WFM | Hradec Kralove | Cesko Rozhlas [LBS] |
| 68.6600 | | WFM | Jesenik | Cesko Rozhlas [LBS] |
| 69.0800 | | WFM | Ostrava | Cesko Rozhlas [LBS] |
| 69.2500 | | WFM | Usti nad Labem | Cesko Rozhlas [LBS] |
| 69.5600 | | WFM | Pizen | Cesko Rozhlas [LBS] |
| 69.9800 | | WFM | Liberec | Cesko Rozhlas [LBS] |

| Base | Mobile | Mode | Location | User and Notes |
|------|--------|------|----------|----------------|
| 70.0700 | | WFM | Ceske Budejovice | Cesko Rozhlas [LBS] |
| 70.1600 | | WFM | Jesenik | Cesko Rozhlas [LBS] |
| 70.3400 | | WFM | Pizen | Cesko Rozhlas [LBS] |
| 70.5800 | | WFM | Usti nad Labem | Cesko Rozhlas [LBS] |
| 71.1800 | | WFM | Liberec | Cesko Rozhlas [LBS] |
| 71.6300 | | WFM | Ceske Budejovice | Cesko Rozhlas [LBS] |
| 71.8700 | | WFM | Brno | Cesko Rozhlas [LBS] |
| 72.2000 | | WFM | Usti nad Labem | Cesko Rozhlas [LBS] |
| 72.7400 | | WFM | Liberec | Cesko Rozhlas [LBS] |

## Denmark

| Base | Mobile | Mode | Location | User and Notes |
|------|--------|------|----------|----------------|
| 129.4750 | 129.4750 | AM | Copenhagen | Copenhagen Information |
| 134.6750 | 134.6750 | AM | Copenhagen | ATC |
| 84.0000 | 85.0000 | NFM | | Police |

## Finland

| Base | Mobile | Mode | Location | User and Notes |
|------|--------|------|----------|----------------|
| 164.1000 | 170.1700 | NFM | | City Police |

## France

| Base | Mobile | Mode | Location | User and Notes |
|------|--------|------|----------|----------------|
| 35.8250 | | NFM | | PMR [LBS] |
| 87.3875 | 87.3875 | AM | | Nuclear Alert Channel |
| 88.3000 | | WFM | Normandy | Melody FM |
| 89.2000 | | WFM | Cherbourg | Culture |
| 89.4000 | | WFM | Brest | Musique |
| 89.9000 | | WFM | Renns | Musique |
| 90.9000 | | WFM | Normandy | CFM |
| 91.4000 | | WFM | Cherbourg | Culture |
| 91.6000 | | WFM | Brest | Musique |
| 92.1000 | | WFM | Renns | Musique |
| 93.000 | | WFM | Brittany | Bretagne Ouest |
| 93.1000 | | WFM | Normandy | Fun Radio |
| 93.4000 | | WFM | Normandy | Radio Manche |
| 93.5000 | | WFM | Rennes | Inter |
| 93.8000 | | WFM | | Inter |
| 94.1000 | | WFM | Cherbourg | Inter |
| 94.2000 | | WFM | Brittany | Culture |
| 94.4000 | | WFM | | Inter |
| 94.5000 | | WFM | Normandy | Fun Radio |
| 94.6000 | | WFM | Brittany | Fun Radio |
| 95.1000 | | WFM | | Cherie FM |
| 95.4000 | | WFM | Brittany | Inter |
| 95.5000 | | WFM | Brest | Inter |
| 95.6000 | | WFM | Caen | Musique |
| 95.9000 | | WFM | | Musique |
| 96.2000 | | WFM | | Radio Cote d' Armor |
| 96.3000 | | WFM | Normandy | Inter |
| 96.4000 | | WFM | Normandy | Nostalgie |
| 96.6000 | | WFM | | Radio France Mayenne |
| 97.5000 | | WFM | Normandy | Radio France Nornandie-Caen |
| 97.9000 | | WFM | Normandy | Melody FM North |

| Base | Mobile | Mode | Location | User and Notes |
|---|---|---|---|---|
| 98.5000 | | WFM | Brittany | Musique |
| 98.9000 | | WFM | Brittany | Musique |
| 98.9000 | | WFM | Normandy | CFM |
| 99.0000 | | WFM | Brest | Musique |
| 99.1000 | | WFM | | Radio Boule |
| 99.3000 | | WFM | Normandy | NRJ |
| 99.4000 | | WFM | France | RFM |
| 99.5000 | | WFM | Renns | Musique |
| 100.1000 | | WFM | Normandy | Radio France Normandie-Rouen |
| 100.4000 | | WFM | Normandy | Radio France, Cherbourg |
| 100.7000 | | WFM | Normandy | Radio France, Cherbourg |
| 101.1000 | | WFM | Normandy | NRJ |
| 102.4000 | | WFM | Normandy | Musique |
| 102.6000 | | WFM | Caen | Radio France Normandie-Caen |
| 103.1000 | | WFM | Renns | Armorique |
| 104.0000 | | WFM | Normandy | RFM |
| 104.3000 | | WFM | | RTL |
| 104.8000 | | WFM | | Europe 1 |
| 105.1000 | | WFM | | NRJ |
| 105.2000 | | WFM | | Nostalgie |
| 105.5000 | | WFM | Normandy | France Info |
| 105.6000 | | WFM | Normandy | France Info |
| 106.1000 | | WFM | Normandy | RTL2 |
| 106.2000 | | WFM | Normandy | RTL2 |
| 106.7000 | | WFM | | Europe 1 |
| 118.1000 | 118.1000 | AM | Calais Airport | Tower |
| 118.2250 | 118.2250 | AM | Paris | Area Radar |
| 118.3000 | 118.3000 | AM | Deauville Airport | Tower |
| 118.3000 | 118.3000 | AM | Le Touquet Airport | Tower |
| 118.3500 | 118.3500 | AM | Brest | ACC |
| 119.0000 | 119.0000 | AM | Dieppe | AFIS |
| 119.3000 | 119.3000 | AM | Toussus Airport | Tower |
| 119.4000 | 119.4000 | AM | St. Brieuc Airport | Tower |
| 119.7000 | 119.7000 | AM | Dinard, | Radar |
| 119.7000 | 119.7000 | AM | Toussus Airport | Approach |
| 119.9000 | 119.9000 | AM | Beauvais Airport | Approach |
| 120.1500 | 120.1500 | AM | Dinard Airport | Approach |
| 120.2500 | 120.2500 | AM | Dinard Airport | Tower |
| 120.3500 | 120.3500 | AM | Deauville Airport | Approach |
| 120.5000 | 120.5000 | AM | Renns Airport | Tower |
| 120.7500 | 120.7500 | AM | Toussus Airport | Approach |
| 121.1500 | 121.1500 | AM | Bordeaux Airport | Approach |
| 121.4000 | 121.4000 | AM | Beauvais Airport | Tower |
| 122.7500 | | AM | Le Bourget | Universal Ops |
| 122.8000 | 122.8000 | AM | Brest | VFR Control |
| 124.0000 | 124.0000 | AM | Paris Airport | ACC/UACC |
| 124.0500 | 124.0500 | AM | Paris Airport | ACC/UACC |
| 124.8000 | 124.8000 | AM | Renns Airport | Approach |
| 124.8500 | 124.8500 | AM | Paris Airport | ACC/UACC |
| 125.1500 | | AM | Paris | VOLMET |
| 125.3000 | 125.3000 | AM | Le Touquet | Approach |
| 125.4500 | 125.4500 | AM | Paris | Control |
| 125.5000 | 125.5000 | AM | Brest | Control |
| 125.5500 | 125.5500 | AM | Brest | IFR Control |
| 125.7000 | 125.7000 | AM | Paris Airport | VFR Control |
| 126.0000 | | AM | Paris | VOLMET |

| Base | Mobile | Mode | Location | User and Notes |
|---|---|---|---|---|
| 126.4000 | | AM | Bordeaux | VOLMET |
| 127.3000 | 127.3000 | AM | Cherbourg Airport | Tower/Approach |
| 127.8500 | 127.8500 | AM | Reims Airport | ACC/UACC |
| 129.0000 | 129.0000 | AM | Brest Airport | ACC/UACC |
| 129.0000 | 129.0000 | AM | Paris Airport | UIR Control |
| 129.3500 | 129.3500 | AM | Paris Airport | ACC/UACC |
| 129.5000 | 129.5000 | AM | Brest Airport | UACC |
| 129.8500 | 129.8500 | AM | Charles de Gaulle | Air France Ops. |
| 130.3250 | 130.3250 | AM | Paris | Leadair Ops. |
| 130.4500 | 130.4500 | AM | Paris | EuroAir Ops. |
| 131.1750 | 131.1750 | AM | Brest Airport | UACC |
| 131.2500 | 131.2500 | AM | Paris Airport | ACC/UACC |
| 131.5500 | 131.5500 | AM | Dinard, | Aurigny Air Service |
| 131.6000 | 131.6000 | AM | Charles de Gaulle | TWA Ops. |
| 131.7750 | 131.7750 | AM | Charles de Gaulle | British Airways |
| 132.0000 | 132.0000 | AM | Paris Airport | ACC/UACC |
| 132.0500 | 132.0500 | AM | Brest Airport | UACC |
| 132.1000 | 132.1000 | AM | Paris Airport | ACC/UACC |
| 132.1250 | 132.1250 | AM | Brest Airport | UACC |
| 132.3750 | 132.3750 | AM | Paris Airport | ACC/UACC |
| 132.5000 | 132.5000 | AM | Reims Airport | ACC/UACC |
| 132.6250 | 132.6250 | AM | Reims Airport | ACC/UACC |
| 132.8250 | 132.8250 | AM | Paris Airport | ACC/UACC |
| 133.0000 | 133.0000 | AM | Brest | ACC/UACC |
| 133.4750 | 133.4750 | AM | Brest | UACC |
| 133.5000 | 133.5000 | AM | Paris Airport | ACC/UACC |
| 133.5750 | 133.5750 | AM | Reims | Control |
| 133.8250 | 133.8250 | AM | Reims Airport | ACC/UACC |
| 133.9250 | 133.9250 | AM | Paris Airport | ACC/UACC |
| 134.2000 | 134.2000 | AM | Brest Airport | ACC |
| 134.4000 | 134.4000 | AM | Reims Airport | ACC/UACC |
| 134.8250 | 134.8250 | AM | Brest Airport | UACC |
| 134.8750 | 134.8750 | AM | Brest Airport | UACC |
| 135.3000 | 135.3000 | AM | Paris Airport | ACC/UACC |
| 135.5000 | 135.5000 | AM | Reims Airport | ACC/UACC |
| 135.6500 | 135.6500 | AM | Brest Airport | UACC |
| 135.8000 | 135.8000 | AM | Paris Airport | ACC/UACC |
| 135.9000 | 135.9000 | AM | Paris Airport | ACC/UACC |
| 136.0750 | 136.0750 | AM | Paris Airport | ACC |
| 145.3250 | 144.7250 | NFM | Caen, Normandy | Amateur Repeater (F5ZBF) |
| 145.3500 | 144.7500 | NFM | Various | Amateur Repeater R9b |
| 145.3750 | 144.7750 | NFM | Tours | Amateur Repeater (FZ0THF) |
| 145.4000 | 145.8000 | NFM | Clermont-Ferrand | Amateur Repeater (FZ8THF) |
| 145.4250 | 144.8250 | NFM | Various | Amateur Repeater R12b |
| 145.6125 | 145.0125 | NFM | Evreux | Amateur Repeater (F5ZBL) |
| 146.6250 | 145.0250 | NFM | Quimper | Amateur Repeater (FZ3VHD) |
| 145.6375 | 145.0375 | NFM | Chateauroux | Amateur Repeater (F5ZDE) |
| 145.6625 | 145.0625 | NFM | Vernon | Amateur Repeater (F5ZCR) |
| 145.6750 | 145.0750 | NFM | Rennes | Amateur Repeater (F1ZBF) |
| 145.7750 | 145.1750 | NFM | Les Herbiers | Amateur Repeater (FZ3VHB) |
| 165.2000 | 168.4000 | NFM | | DGT |
| 166.2000 | 168.3000 | NFM | | TEC |
| 173.0000 | 173.5000 | NFM | | TEC Alphakage |
| 182.5000 | | WFM | | French TV Channel 5 sound |
| 190.5000 | | WFM | | French TV Channel 6 sound |
| 198.5000 | | WFM | | French TV Channel 7 sound |

| Base | Mobile | Mode | Location | User and Notes |
|------|--------|------|----------|----------------|
| 206.5000 | | WFM | | French TV Channel 8 sound |

## Germany

| Base | Mobile | Mode | Location | User and Notes |
|------|--------|------|----------|----------------|
| 38.4600 | 34.3600 | NFM | | Emergency Channel Ch 801 |
| 38.4800 | 34.3800 | NFM | | Emergency Channel Ch 802 |
| 38.5000 | 34.4000 | NFM | | Emergency Channel Ch 803 |
| 38.5200 | 34.4200 | NFM | | Emergency Channel Ch 804 |
| 38.5400 | 34.4400 | NFM | | Emergency Channel Ch 805 |
| 38.5600 | 34.4600 | NFM | | Emergency Channel Ch 806 |
| 38.5800 | 34.4800 | NFM | | Emergency Channel Ch 807 |
| 38.6000 | 34.5000 | NFM | | Emergency Channel Ch 808 |
| 38.6200 | 34.5200 | NFM | | Emergency Channel Ch 809 |
| 38.6400 | 34.5400 | NFM | | Emergency Channel Ch 810 |
| 38.6600 | 34.5600 | NFM | | Emergency Channel Ch 811 |
| 38.6800 | 34.5800 | NFM | | Emergency Channel Ch 812 |
| 38.7000 | 34.6000 | NFM | | Emergency Channel Ch 813 |
| 38.7200 | 34.6200 | NFM | | Emergency Channel Ch 814 |
| 38.7400 | 34.6400 | NFM | | Emergency Channel Ch 815 |
| 38.7600 | 34.6600 | NFM | | Emergency Channel Ch 816 |
| 38.7800 | 34.6800 | NFM | | Emergency Channel Ch 817 |
| 38.8000 | 34.7000 | NFM | | Emergency Channel Ch 818 |
| 38.8200 | 34.7200 | NFM | | Emergency Channel Ch 819 |
| 38.8400 | 34.7400 | NFM | | Emergency Channel Ch 820 |
| 38.8600 | 34.7600 | NFM | | Emergency Channel Ch 821 |
| 38.8800 | 34.7800 | NFM | | Emergency Channel Ch 822 |
| 38.9000 | 34.8000 | NFM | | Emergency Channel Ch 823 |
| 38.9200 | 34.8200 | NFM | | Emergency Channel Ch 824 |
| 38.9400 | 34.8400 | NFM | | Emergency Channel Ch 825 |
| 38.9600 | 34.8600 | NFM | | Emergency Channel Ch 826 |
| 38.9800 | 34.8800 | NFM | | Emergency Channel Ch 827 |
| 39.0000 | 34.9000 | NFM | | Emergency Channel Ch 828 |
| 39.0200 | 34.9200 | NFM | | Emergency Channel Ch 829 |
| 39.0400 | 34.9400 | NFM | | Emergency Channel Ch 830 |
| 39.0600 | 34.9600 | NFM | | Emergency Channel Ch 831 |
| 39.0800 | 34.9800 | NFM | | Emergency Channel Ch 832 |
| 39.1000 | 35.0000 | NFM | | Emergency Channel Ch 833 |
| 39.1200 | 35.0200 | NFM | | Emergency Channel Ch 834 |
| 39.1400 | 35.0400 | NFM | | Emergency Channel Ch 835 |
| 39.1600 | 35.0600 | NFM | | Emergency Channel Ch 836 |
| 39.1800 | 35.0800 | NFM | | Emergency Channel Ch 837 |
| 39.2000 | 35.1000 | NFM | | Emergency Channel Ch 838 |
| 39.2200 | 35.1200 | NFM | | Emergency Channel Ch 839 |
| 39.2400 | 35.1400 | NFM | | Emergency Channel Ch 840 |
| 39.2600 | 35.1600 | NFM | | Emergency Channel Ch 841 |
| 39.2800 | 35.1800 | NFM | | Emergency Channel Ch 842 |
| 39.3000 | 35.2000 | NFM | | Emergency Channel Ch 843 |
| 39.3200 | 35.2200 | NFM | | Emergency Channel Ch 844 |
| 39.3400 | 35.2400 | NFM | | Emergency Channel Ch 845 |
| 39.3600 | 35.2600 | NFM | | Emergency Channel Ch 846 |
| 39.3800 | 35.2800 | NFM | | Emergency Channel Ch 847 |
| 39.4000 | 35.3000 | NFM | | Emergency Channel Ch 848 |
| 39.4200 | 35.3200 | NFM | | Emergency Channel Ch 849 |
| 39.4400 | 35.3400 | NFM | | Emergency Channel Ch 850 |

| Base | Mobile | Mode | Location | User and Notes |
|------|--------|------|----------|----------------|
| 39.4600 | 35.3600 | NFM | | Emergency Channel Ch 851 |
| 39.4800 | 35.3800 | NFM | | Emergency Channel Ch 852 |
| 39.5000 | 35.4000 | NFM | | Emergency Channel Ch 853 |
| 39.5200 | 35.4200 | NFM | | Emergency Channel Ch 854 |
| 39.5400 | 35.4400 | NFM | | Emergency Channel Ch 855 |
| 39.5600 | 35.4600 | NFM | | Emergency Channel Ch 856 |
| 39.5800 | 35.4800 | NFM | | Emergency Channel Ch 857 |
| 39.6000 | 35.5000 | NFM | | Emergency Channel Ch 858 |
| 39.6200 | 35.5200 | NFM | | Emergency Channel Ch 859 |
| 39.6400 | 35.5400 | NFM | | Emergency Channel Ch 860 |
| 39.6600 | 35.5600 | NFM | | Emergency Channel Ch 861 |
| 39.6800 | 35.5800 | NFM | | Emergency Channel Ch 862 |
| 39.7000 | 35.6000 | NFM | | Emergency Channel Ch 863 |
| 39.7200 | 35.6200 | NFM | | Emergency Channel Ch 864 |
| 39.7400 | 35.6400 | NFM | | Emergency Channel Ch 865 |
| 39.7600 | 35.6600 | NFM | | Emergency Channel Ch 866 |
| 39.7800 | 35.6800 | NFM | | Emergency Channel Ch 867 |
| 39.8000 | 35.7000 | NFM | | Emergency Channel Ch 868 |
| 39.8200 | 35.7200 | NFM | | Emergency Channel Ch 869 |
| 39.8400 | 35.7400 | NFM | | Emergency Channel Ch 870 |
| 39.8600 | 35.7600 | NFM | | Emergency Channel Ch 871 |
| 39.8800 | 35.7800 | NFM | | Emergency Channel Ch 872 |
| 39.9000 | 35.8000 | NFM | | Emergency Channel Ch 873 |
| 84.0150 | 74.2150 | NFM | | Emergency Channel Ch 347 |
| 84.0350 | 74.2350 | NFM | | Emergency Channel Ch 348 |
| 84.0550 | 74.2550 | NFM | | Emergency Channel Ch 349 |
| 84.0750 | 74.2750 | NFM | | Emergency Channel Ch 350 |
| 84.0950 | 74.2950 | NFM | | Emergency Channel Ch 351 |
| 84.1150 | 74.3150 | NFM | | Emergency Channel Ch 352 |
| 84.1350 | 74.3350 | NFM | | Emergency Channel Ch 353 |
| 84.1550 | 74.3550 | NFM | | Emergency Channel Ch 354 |
| 84.1750 | 74.3750 | NFM | | Emergency Channel Ch 355 |
| 84.1950 | 74.3950 | NFM | | Emergency Channel Ch 356 |
| 84.2150 | 74.4150 | NFM | | Emergency Channel Ch 357 |
| 84.2350 | 74.4350 | NFM | | Emergency Channel Ch 358 |
| 84.2550 | 74.4550 | NFM | | Emergency Channel Ch 359 |
| 84.2750 | 74.4750 | NFM | | Emergency Channel Ch 360 |
| 84.2950 | 74.4950 | NFM | | Emergency Channel Ch 361 |
| 84.3150 | 74.5150 | NFM | | Emergency Channel Ch 362 |
| 84.3350 | 74.5350 | NFM | | Emergency Channel Ch 363 |
| 84.3550 | 74.5550 | NFM | | Emergency Channel Ch 364 |
| 84.3750 | 74.5750 | NFM | | Emergency Channel Ch 365 |
| 84.3950 | 74.5950 | NFM | | Emergency Channel Ch 366 |
| 84.4150 | 74.6150 | NFM | | Emergency Channel Ch 367 |
| 84.4350 | 74.6350 | NFM | | Emergency Channel Ch 368 |
| 84.4550 | 74.6550 | NFM | | Emergency Channel Ch 369 |
| 84.4750 | 74.6750 | NFM | | Emergency Channel Ch 370 |
| 84.4950 | 74.6950 | NFM | | Emergency Channel Ch 371 |
| 84.5150 | 74.7150 | NFM | | Emergency Channel Ch 372 |
| 84.5350 | 74.7350 | NFM | | Emergency Channel Ch 373 |
| 84.5550 | 74.7550 | NFM | | Emergency Channel Ch 374 |
| 84.5750 | 74.7750 | NFM | | Emergency Channel Ch 375 |
| 84.5950 | 74.7950 | NFM | | Emergency Channel Ch 376 |
| 84.6150 | 74.8150 | NFM | | Emergency Channel Ch 377 |
| 84.6350 | 74.8350 | NFM | | Emergency Channel Ch 378 |
| 84.6550 | 74.8550 | NFM | | Emergency Channel Ch 379 |

| Base | Mobile | Mode | Location | User and Notes |
|---|---|---|---|---|
| 84.6750 | 74.8750 | NFM | | Emergency Channel Ch 380 |
| 84.6950 | 74.8950 | NFM | | Emergency Channel Ch 381 |
| 84.7150 | 74.9150 | NFM | | Emergency Channel Ch 382 |
| 84.7350 | 74.9350 | NFM | | Emergency Channel Ch 383 |
| 84.7550 | 74.9550 | NFM | | Emergency Channel Ch 384 |
| 84.7750 | 74.9750 | NFM | | Emergency Channel Ch 385 |
| 84.7950 | 74.9950 | NFM | | Emergency Channel Ch 386 |
| 84.8150 | 75.0150 | NFM | | Emergency Channel Ch 387 |
| 84.8350 | 75.0350 | NFM | | Emergency Channel Ch 388 |
| 84.8550 | 75.0550 | NFM | | Emergency Channel Ch 389 |
| 84.8550 | | NFM | | Emergency Channel Ch 390 |
| 84.8950 | 75.0950 | NFM | | Emergency Channel Ch 391 |
| 84.9150 | 75.1150 | NFM | | Emergency Channel Ch 392 |
| 84.9350 | 75.1350 | NFM | | Emergency Channel Ch 393 |
| 84.9550 | 75.1550 | NFM | | Emergency Channel Ch 394 |
| 84.9550 | | NFM | | Emergency Channel Ch 395 |
| 84.9950 | 75.1950 | NFM | | Emergency Channel Ch 396 |
| 85.0150 | 75.2150 | NFM | | Emergency Channel Ch 397 |
| 85.0350 | 75.2350 | NFM | | Emergency Channel Ch 398 |
| 85.0550 | 75.2550 | NFM | | Emergency Channel Ch 399 |
| 85.0750 | 75.2750 | NFM | | Emergency Channel Ch 400 |
| 85.0950 | 75.2950 | NFM | | Emergency Channel Ch 401 |
| 85.1150 | 75.3150 | NFM | | Emergency Channel Ch 402 |
| 85.1350 | 75.3350 | NFM | | Emergency Channel Ch 403 |
| 85.1550 | 75.3550 | NFM | | Emergency Channel Ch 404 |
| 85.1750 | 75.3750 | NFM | | Emergency Channel Ch 405 |
| 85.1950 | 75.3950 | NFM | | Emergency Channel Ch 406 |
| 85.2150 | 75.4150 | NFM | | Emergency Channel Ch 407 |
| 85.2350 | 75.4350 | NFM | | Emergency Channel Ch 408 |
| 85.2550 | 75.4550 | NFM | | Emergency Channel Ch 409 |
| 85.2750 | 75.4750 | NFM | | Emergency Channel Ch 410 |
| 85.2950 | 75.4950 | NFM | | Emergency Channel Ch 411 |
| 85.3150 | 75.5150 | NFM | | Emergency Channel Ch 412 |
| 85.3350 | 75.5350 | NFM | | Emergency Channel Ch 413 |
| 85.3550 | 75.5550 | NFM | | Emergency Channel Ch 414 |
| 85.3750 | 75.5750 | NFM | | Emergency Channel Ch 415 |
| 85.3950 | 75.5950 | NFM | | Emergency Channel Ch 416 |
| 85.4150 | 75.6150 | NFM | | Emergency Channel Ch 417 |
| 85.4350 | 75.6350 | NFM | | Emergency Channel Ch 418 |
| 85.4550 | 75.6550 | NFM | | Emergency Channel Ch 419 |
| 85.4950 | 75.6950 | NFM | | Emergency Channel Ch 421 |
| 85.5150 | 75.7150 | NFM | | Emergency Channel Ch 422 |
| 85.5350 | 75.7350 | NFM | | Emergency Channel Ch 423 |
| 85.5550 | 75.7550 | NFM | | Emergency Channel Ch 424 |
| 85.5750 | 75.7750 | NFM | | Emergency Channel Ch 425 |
| 85.6150 | 75.8150 | NFM | | Emergency Channel Ch 427 |
| 85.6350 | 75.8350 | NFM | | Emergency Channel Ch 428 |
| 86.0750 | 76.2750 | NFM | | Emergency Channel Ch 450 |
| 86.0950 | 76.2950 | NFM | | Emergency Channel Ch 451 |
| 86.1150 | 76.3150 | NFM | | Emergency Channel Ch 452 |
| 86.1350 | 76.3350 | NFM | | Emergency Channel Ch 453 |
| 86.1550 | 76.3550 | NFM | | Emergency Channel Ch 454 |
| 86.1750 | 76.3750 | NFM | | Emergency Channel Ch 455 |
| 86.1950 | 76.3950 | NFM | | Emergency Channel Ch 456 |
| 86.2150 | 76.4150 | NFM | | Emergency Channel Ch 457 |
| 86.2350 | 76.4350 | NFM | | Emergency Channel Ch 458 |

| Base | Mobile | Mode | Location | User and Notes |
|------|--------|------|----------|----------------|
| 86.2550 | 76.4550 | NFM | | Emergency Channel Ch 459 |
| 86.2750 | 76.4750 | NFM | | Emergency Channel Ch 460 |
| 86.2950 | 76.4950 | NFM | | Emergency Channel Ch 461 |
| 86.3150 | 76.5150 | NFM | | Emergency Channel Ch 462 |
| 86.3150 | 76.5150 | NFM | | Emergency Channel Ch 462 |
| 86.3350 | 76.5350 | NFM | | Emergency Channel Ch 463 |
| 86.3350 | 76.5350 | NFM | | Emergency Channel Ch 463 |
| 86.3550 | 76.5550 | NFM | | Emergency Channel Ch 464 |
| 86.3750 | 76.5750 | NFM | | Emergency Channel Ch 465 |
| 86.3950 | 76.5950 | NFM | | Emergency Channel Ch 466 |
| 86.4150 | 76.6150 | NFM | | Emergency Channel Ch 467 |
| 86.4350 | 76.6350 | NFM | | Emergency Channel Ch 468 |
| 86.4550 | 76.6550 | NFM | | Emergency Channel Ch 469 |
| 86.4750 | 76.6750 | NFM | | Emergency Channel Ch 470 |
| 86.4950 | 76.6950 | NFM | | Emergency Channel Ch 471 |
| 86.5150 | 76.7150 | NFM | | Emergency Channel Ch 472 |
| 86.5350 | 76.7350 | NFM | | Emergency Channel Ch 473 |
| 86.5550 | 76.7550 | NFM | | Emergency Channel Ch 474 |
| 86.5750 | 76.7750 | NFM | | Emergency Channel Ch 475 |
| 86.5950 | 76.7950 | NFM | | Emergency Channel Ch 476 |
| 86.6150 | 76.8150 | NFM | | Emergency Channel Ch 477 |
| 86.6350 | 76.8350 | NFM | | Emergency Channel Ch 478 |
| 86.6550 | 76.8550 | NFM | | Emergency Channel Ch 479 |
| 86.6750 | 76.8750 | NFM | | Emergency Channel Ch 480 |
| 86.6950 | 76.8950 | NFM | | Emergency Channel Ch 481 |
| 86.7150 | 76.9150 | NFM | | Emergency Channel Ch 482 |
| 86.7350 | 76.9350 | NFM | | Emergency Channel Ch 483 |
| 86.7550 | 76.9550 | NFM | | Emergency Channel Ch 484 |
| 86.7750 | 76.9750 | NFM | | Emergency Channel Ch 485 |
| 86.7950 | 76.9950 | NFM | | Emergency Channel Ch 486 |
| 86.8150 | 77.0150 | NFM | | Emergency Channel Ch 487 |
| 86.8350 | 77.0350 | NFM | | Emergency Channel Ch 488 |
| 86.8550 | 77.0550 | NFM | | Emergency Channel Ch 489 |
| 86.8750 | 77.0750 | NFM | | Emergency Channel Ch 490 |
| 86.8950 | 77.0950 | NFM | | Emergency Channel Ch 491 |
| 86.9150 | 77.1150 | NFM | | Emergency Channel Ch 492 |
| 86.9350 | 77.1350 | NFM | | Emergency Channel Ch 493 |
| 86.9550 | 77.1550 | NFM | | Emergency Channel Ch 494 |
| 86.9750 | 77.1750 | NFM | | Emergency Channel Ch 495 |
| 86.9950 | 77.1950 | NFM | | Emergency Channel Ch 496 |
| 87.0150 | 77.2150 | NFM | | Emergency Channel Ch 497 |
| 87.0350 | 77.2350 | NFM | | Emergency Channel Ch 498 |
| 87.0550 | 77.2550 | NFM | | Emergency Channel Ch 499 |
| 87.0750 | 77.2750 | NFM | | Emergency Channel Ch 500 |
| 87.0950 | 77.2950 | NFM | | Emergency Channel Ch 501 |
| 87.1150 | 77.3150 | NFM | | Emergency Channel Ch 502 |
| 87.1350 | 77.3350 | NFM | | Emergency Channel Ch 503 |
| 87.1550 | 77.3550 | NFM | | Emergency Channel Ch 504 |
| 87.1750 | 77.3750 | NFM | | Emergency Channel Ch 505 |
| 87.1950 | 77.3950 | NFM | | Emergency Channel Ch 506 |
| 87.2150 | 77.4150 | NFM | | Emergency Channel Ch 507 |
| 87.2350 | 77.4350 | NFM | | Emergency Channel Ch 508 |
| 87.2550 | 77.4550 | NFM | | Emergency Channel Ch 509 |
| 131.7500 | 131.7500 | AM | Frankfurt Airport | Lufthansa Ops. |
| 169.8100 | 165.2100 | NFM | | Emergency Services Ch 101 |
| 169.8300 | 165.2300 | NFM | | Emergency Services Ch 102 |

| Base | Mobile | Mode | Location | User and Notes |
|------|--------|------|----------|----------------|
| 169.8500 | 165.2500 | NFM | | Emergency Services Ch 103 |
| 169.8700 | 165.2700 | NFM | | Emergency Services Ch 104 |
| 169.8900 | 165.2900 | NFM | | Emergency Services Ch 105 |
| 169.9100 | 165.3100 | NFM | | Emergency Services Ch 106 |
| 169.9300 | 165.3300 | NFM | | Emergency Services Ch 107 |
| 169.9500 | 165.3500 | NFM | | Emergency Services Ch 108 |
| 169.9700 | 165.3700 | NFM | | Emergency Services Ch 109 |
| 169.9900 | 165.3900 | NFM | | Emergency Services Ch 110 |
| 170.0100 | 165.4100 | NFM | | Emergency Services Ch 111 |
| 170.0300 | 165.4300 | NFM | | Emergency Services Ch 112 |
| 170.0500 | 165.4500 | NFM | | Emergency Services Ch 113 |
| 170.0700 | 165.4700 | NFM | | Emergency Services Ch 114 |
| 170.0900 | 165.4900 | NFM | | Emergency Services Ch 115 |
| 170.1100 | 165.5100 | NFM | | Emergency Services Ch 116 |
| 170.1300 | 165.5300 | NFM | | Emergency Services Ch 117 |
| 170.1500 | 165.5500 | NFM | | Emergency Services Ch 118 |
| 170.1700 | 165.5700 | NFM | | Emergency Services Ch 119 |
| 170.1900 | 165.5900 | NFM | | Emergency Services Ch 120 |
| 170.2100 | 165.6100 | NFM | | Emergency Services Ch 121 |
| 170.2300 | 165.6300 | NFM | | Emergency Services Ch 122 |
| 170.2500 | 165.6500 | NFM | | Emergency Services Ch 123 |
| 170.2700 | 165.6700 | NFM | | Emergency Services Ch 124 |
| 170.2900 | 165.6900 | NFM | | Emergency Services Ch 125 |
| 172.1400 | 167.5400 | NFM | | Emergency Services Ch 200 |
| 172.1600 | 167.5600 | NFM | | Emergency Services Ch 201 |
| 172.1800 | 167.5800 | NFM | | Emergency Services Ch 202 |
| 172.2000 | 167.6000 | NFM | | Emergency Services Ch 203 |
| 172.2200 | 167.6200 | NFM | | Emergency Services Ch 204 |
| 172.2400 | 167.6400 | NFM | | Emergency Services Ch 205 |
| 172.2600 | 167.6600 | NFM | | Emergency Services Ch 206 |
| 172.2800 | 167.6800 | NFM | | Emergency Services Ch 207 |
| 172.3000 | 167.7000 | NFM | | Emergency Services Ch 208 |
| 172.3200 | 167.7200 | NFM | | Emergency Services Ch 209 |
| 172.3400 | 167.7400 | NFM | | Emergency Services Ch 210 |
| 172.3600 | 167.7600 | NFM | | Emergency Services Ch 211 |
| 172.3800 | 167.7800 | NFM | | Emergency Services Ch 212 |
| 172.4000 | 167.8000 | NFM | | Emergency Services Ch 213 |
| 172.4200 | 167.8200 | NFM | | Emergency Services Ch 214 |
| 172.4400 | 167.8400 | NFM | | Emergency Services Ch 215 |
| 172.4600 | 167.8600 | NFM | | Emergency Services Ch 216 |
| 172.4800 | 167.8800 | NFM | | Emergency Services Ch 217 |
| 172.5000 | 167.9000 | NFM | | Emergency Services Ch 218 |
| 172.5200 | 167.9200 | NFM | | Emergency Services Ch 219 |
| 172.5400 | 167.9400 | NFM | | Emergency Services Ch 220 |
| 172.5600 | 167.9600 | NFM | | Emergency Services Ch 221 |
| 172.5800 | 167.9800 | NFM | | Emergency Services Ch 222 |
| 172.6000 | 168.0000 | NFM | | Emergency Services Ch 223 |
| 172.6200 | 168.0200 | NFM | | Emergency Services Ch 224 |
| 172.6400 | 168.0400 | NFM | | Emergency Services Ch 225 |
| 172.6600 | 168.0600 | NFM | | Emergency Services Ch 226 |
| 172.6800 | 168.0800 | NFM | | Emergency Services Ch 227 |
| 172.7000 | 168.1000 | NFM | | Emergency Services Ch 228 |
| 172.7200 | 168.1200 | NFM | | Emergency Services Ch 229 |
| 172.7400 | 168.1400 | NFM | | Emergency Services Ch 230 |
| 172.7600 | 168.1600 | NFM | | Emergency Services Ch 231 |
| 172.7800 | 168.1800 | NFM | | Emergency Services Ch 232 |

| Base | Mobile | Mode | Location | User and Notes |
|------|--------|------|----------|----------------|
| 172.8000 | 168.2000 | NFM | | Emergency Services Ch 233 |
| 172.8200 | 168.2200 | NFM | | Emergency Services Ch 234 |
| 172.8400 | 168.2400 | NFM | | Emergency Services Ch 235 |
| 172.8600 | 168.2600 | NFM | | Emergency Services Ch 236 |
| 172.8800 | 168.2800 | NFM | | Emergency Services Ch 237 |
| 172.9000 | 168.3000 | NFM | | Emergency Services Ch 238 |
| 172.9200 | 168.3200 | NFM | | Emergency Services Ch 239 |
| 172.9400 | 168.3400 | NFM | | Emergency Services Ch 240 |
| 172.9600 | 168.3600 | NFM | | Emergency Services Ch 241 |
| 172.9800 | 168.3800 | NFM | | Emergency Services Ch 242 |
| 173.0000 | 168.4000 | NFM | | Emergency Services Ch 243 |
| 173.0200 | 168.4200 | NFM | | Emergency Services Ch 244 |
| 173.0400 | 168.4400 | NFM | | Emergency Services Ch 245 |
| 173.0600 | 168.4600 | NFM | | Emergency Services Ch 246 |
| 173.0800 | 168.4800 | NFM | | Emergency Services Ch 247 |
| 173.1000 | 168.5000 | NFM | | Emergency Services Ch 248 |
| 173.1200 | 168.5200 | NFM | | Emergency Services Ch 249 |
| 173.1400 | 168.5400 | NFM | | Emergency Services Ch 250 |
| 173.1600 | 168.5600 | NFM | | Emergency Services Ch 251 |
| 173.1800 | 168.5800 | NFM | | Emergency Services Ch 252 |
| 173.2000 | 168.6000 | NFM | | Emergency Services Ch 253 |
| 173.2200 | 168.6200 | NFM | | Emergency Services Ch 254 |
| 173.2400 | 168.6400 | NFM | | Emergency Services Ch 255 |
| 173.2600 | 168.6600 | NFM | | Emergency Services Ch 256 |
| 173.2800 | 168.6800 | NFM | | Emergency Services Ch 257 |
| 173.3000 | 168.7000 | NFM | | Emergency Services Ch 258 |
| 173.3200 | 168.7200 | NFM | | Emergency Services Ch 259 |
| 173.3400 | 168.7400 | NFM | | Emergency Services Ch 260 |
| 173.3600 | 168.7600 | NFM | | Emergency Services Ch 261 |
| 173.3800 | 168.7800 | NFM | | Emergency Services Ch 262 |
| 173.4000 | 168.8000 | NFM | | Emergency Services Ch 263 |
| 173.4200 | 168.8200 | NFM | | Emergency Services Ch 264 |
| 173.4400 | 168.8400 | NFM | | Emergency Services Ch 265 |
| 173.4600 | 168.8600 | NFM | | Emergency Services Ch 266 |
| 173.4800 | 168.8800 | NFM | | Emergency Services Ch 267 |
| 173.5000 | 168.9000 | NFM | | Emergency Services Ch 268 |
| 173.5200 | 168.9200 | NFM | | Emergency Services Ch 269 |
| 173.5400 | 168.9400 | NFM | | Emergency Services Ch 270 |
| 173.5600 | 168.9600 | NFM | | Emergency Services Ch 271 |
| 173.5800 | 168.9800 | NFM | | Emergency Services Ch 272 |
| 173.6000 | 169.0000 | NFM | | Emergency Services Ch 273 |
| 173.6200 | 169.0200 | NFM | | Emergency Services Ch 274 |
| 173.6400 | 169.0400 | NFM | | Emergency Services Ch 275 |
| 173.6600 | 169.0600 | NFM | | Emergency Services Ch 276 |
| 173.6800 | 169.0800 | NFM | | Emergency Services Ch 277 |
| 173.7000 | 169.1000 | NFM | | Emergency Services Ch 278 |
| 173.7200 | 169.1200 | NFM | | Emergency Services Ch 279 |
| 173.7400 | 169.1400 | NFM | | Emergency Services Ch 280 |
| 173.7600 | 169.1600 | NFM | | Emergency Services Ch 281 |
| 173.7800 | 169.1800 | NFM | | Emergency Services Ch 282 |
| 173.8000 | 169.2000 | NFM | | Emergency Services Ch 283 |
| 173.8200 | 169.2200 | NFM | | Emergency Services Ch 284 |
| 173.8400 | 169.2400 | NFM | | Emergency Services Ch 285 |
| 173.8600 | 169.2600 | NFM | | Emergency Services Ch 286 |
| 173.8800 | 169.2800 | NFM | | Emergency Services Ch 287 |
| 173.9000 | 169.3000 | NFM | | Emergency Services Ch 288 |

| Base | Mobile | Mode | Location | User and Notes |
|------|--------|------|----------|----------------|
| 173.9200 | 169.3200 | NFM | | Emergency Services Ch 289 |
| 173.9400 | 169.3400 | NFM | | Emergency Services Ch 290 |
| 173.9600 | 169.3600 | NFM | | Emergency Services Ch 291 |
| 173.9800 | 169.3800 | NFM | | Emergency Services Ch 292 |

## Hungary

| Base | Mobile | Mode | Location | User and Notes |
|------|--------|------|----------|----------------|
| 66.0200 | | WFM | Miskolc | Magyar Radio [LBS] |
| 66.1400 | | WFM | Kemadi | Magyar Radio [LBS] |
| 66.2900 | | WFM | Szentes | Magyar Radio [LBS] |
| 66.6200 | | WFM | Budapest | Magyar Radio [LBS] |
| 66.8000 | | WFM | Miskolc | Magyar Radio [LBS] |
| 66.9200 | | WFM | Kemadi | Magyar Radio [LBS] |
| 67.0400 | | WFM | Gyor | Magyar Radio [LBS] |
| 67.1900 | | WFM | Pecs | Magyar Radio [LBS] |
| 67.4000 | | WFM | Budapest | Magyar Radio [LBS] |
| 67.8500 | | WFM | Szentes | Magyar Radio [LBS] |
| 67.9700 | | WFM | Pecs | Magyar Radio [LBS] |
| 68.2500 | | WFM | Kemadi | Magyar Radio [LBS] |
| 68.3600 | | WFM | Nagykanizsa | Magyar Radio [LBS] |
| 68.4800 | | WFM | Miskolc | Magyar Radio [LBS] |
| 69.3800 | | WFM | Budapest | Magyar Radio [LBS] |
| 69.9800 | | WFM | Nagykanizsa | Magyar Radio [LBS] |
| 70.1000 | | WFM | Kekes | Magyar Radio [LBS] |
| 70.4000 | | WFM | Sopron | Magyar Radio [LBS] |
| 70.4300 | | WFM | Tokaj | Magyar Radio [LBS] |
| 70.6400 | | WFM | Kabhegy | Magyar Radio [LBS] |
| 71.0300 | | WFM | Nagykanizsa | Magyar Radio [LBS] |
| 71.2100 | | WFM | Kekes | Magyar Radio [LBS] |
| 71.3300 | | WFM | Tokaj | Magyar Radio [LBS] |
| 71.4200 | | WFM | Kabhegy | Magyar Radio [LBS] |
| 71.8100 | | WFM | Pecs | Magyar Radio [LBS] |
| 71.8600 | | WFM | Sopron | Magyar Radio [LBS] |
| 72.0800 | | WFM | Sopron | Magyar Radio [LBS] |
| 72.1100 | | WFM | Tokaj | Magyar Radio [LBS] |
| 72.7700 | | WFM | Kekes | Magyar Radio [LBS] |
| 72.9800 | | WFM | Kabhegy | Magyar Radio [LBS] |

## Iceland

| Base | Mobile | Mode | Location | User and Notes |
|------|--------|------|----------|----------------|
| 132.2000 | 132.2000 | AM | Reykjavik ATC | |

## Netherlands

| Base | Mobile | Mode | Location | User and Notes |
|------|--------|------|----------|----------------|
| 86.0750 | 77.6750 | NFM | | Police Ch 804 |
| 86.0875 | 77.6875 | NFM | | Police Ch 805 |
| 86.1000 | 77.7000 | NFM | | Police Ch 806 |
| 86.1125 | 77.7125 | NFM | | Police Ch 807 |
| 86.1250 | 77.7250 | NFM | | Police Ch 808 |
| 86.1375 | 77.7375 | NFM | | Police Ch 809 |
| 86.1500 | 77.7500 | NFM | | Police Ch 810 |
| 86.1625 | 77.7625 | NFM | | Police Ch 811 |
| 86.1750 | 77.7750 | NFM | | Police Ch 812 |

| Base | Mobile | Mode | Location | User and Notes |
|------|--------|------|----------|----------------|
| 86.1875 | 77.7875 | NFM | | Police Ch 813 |
| 86.2000 | 77.8000 | NFM | | Police Ch 814 |
| 86.2125 | 77.8125 | NFM | | Police Ch 815 |
| 86.2250 | 77.8250 | NFM | | Police Ch 816 |
| 86.2375 | 77.8375 | NFM | | Police Ch 817 |
| 86.2500 | 77.8500 | NFM | | Police Ch 818 |
| 86.2625 | 77.8625 | NFM | | Police Ch 819 |
| 86.2750 | 77.8750 | NFM | | Police Ch 820 |
| 86.2875 | 77.8875 | NFM | | Police Ch 821 |
| 86.3000 | 77.9000 | NFM | | Police Ch 822 |
| 86.3000 | 77.9000 | NFM | | Police Ch 822 |
| 86.3125 | 77.9125 | NFM | | Police Ch 823 |
| 86.3125 | 77.9125 | NFM | | Police Ch 823 |
| 86.3250 | 77.9250 | NFM | | Police Ch 824 |
| 86.3250 | 77.9250 | NFM | | Police Ch 824 |
| 86.3375 | 77.9375 | NFM | | Police Ch 825 |
| 86.3375 | 77.9375 | NFM | | Police Ch 825 |
| 86.3500 | 77.9500 | NFM | | Police Ch 826 |
| 86.3625 | 77.9625 | NFM | | Police Ch 827 |
| 86.3750 | 77.9750 | NFM | | Police Ch 828 |
| 86.3875 | 77.9875 | NFM | | Police Ch 829 |
| 86.4000 | 78.0000 | NFM | | Police Ch 830 |
| 86.4250 | 78.0250 | NFM | | Police Ch 832 |
| 86.4375 | 78.0375 | NFM | | Police Ch 833 |
| 86.4500 | 78.0500 | NFM | | Police Ch 834 |
| 86.4625 | 78.0625 | NFM | | Police Ch 835 |
| 86.4750 | 78.0750 | NFM | | Police Ch 836 |
| 86.5000 | 78.1000 | NFM | | Police Ch 838 |
| 86.5125 | 78.1125 | NFM | | Police Ch 839 |
| 86.5250 | 78.1250 | NFM | | Police Ch 840 |
| 86.5375 | 78.1375 | NFM | | Police Ch 841 |
| 86.5500 | 78.1500 | NFM | | Police Ch 842 |
| 86.5625 | 78.1625 | NFM | | Police Ch 843 |
| 86.5750 | 78.1750 | NFM | | Police Ch 844 |
| 86.5875 | 78.1875 | NFM | | Police Ch 845 |
| 86.6000 | 78.2000 | NFM | | Police Ch 846 |
| 86.6125 | 78.2125 | NFM | | Police Ch 847 |
| 86.6250 | 78.2250 | NFM | | Police Ch 848 |
| 86.6375 | 78.2375 | NFM | | Police Ch 849 |
| 86.6500 | 78.2500 | NFM | | Police Ch 850 |
| 86.6625 | 78.2625 | NFM | | Police Ch 851 |
| 86.6750 | 78.2750 | NFM | | Police Ch 852 |
| 86.6875 | 78.2875 | NFM | | Police Ch 853 |
| 86.7000 | 78.3000 | NFM | | Police Ch 854 |
| 86.7125 | 78.3125 | NFM | | Police Ch 855 |
| 86.7250 | 78.3250 | NFM | | Police Ch 856 |
| 86.7375 | 78.3375 | NFM | | Police Ch 857 |
| 86.7500 | 78.3500 | NFM | | Police Ch 858 |
| 86.7625 | 78.3625 | NFM | | Police Ch 859 |
| 86.7750 | 78.3750 | NFM | | Police Ch 860 |
| 86.7875 | 78.3875 | NFM | | Police Ch 861 |
| 86.8000 | 78.4000 | NFM | | Police Ch 862 |
| 86.8125 | 78.4125 | NFM | | Police Ch 863 |
| 86.8250 | 78.4250 | NFM | | Police Ch 864 |
| 86.8375 | 78.4375 | NFM | | Police Ch 865 |
| 86.8500 | 78.4500 | NFM | | Police Ch 866 |

| Base | Mobile | Mode | Location | User and Notes |
|---|---|---|---|---|
| 86.8625 | 78.4625 | NFM | | Police Ch 867 |
| 86.8750 | 78.4750 | NFM | | Police Ch 868 |
| 86.8875 | 78.4875 | NFM | | Police Ch 869 |
| 86.9000 | 78.5000 | NFM | | Police Ch 870 |
| 86.9125 | 78.5125 | NFM | | Police Ch 871 |
| 86.9250 | 78.5250 | NFM | | Police Ch 872 |
| 86.9375 | 78.5375 | NFM | | Police Ch 873 |
| 86.9500 | 78.5500 | NFM | | Police Ch 874 |
| 86.9625 | 78.5625 | NFM | | Police Ch 875 |
| 86.9750 | | NFM | | Water Companies |
| 86.9750 | 78.5750 | NFM | | Police Ch 876 |
| 86.9875 | 78.5875 | NFM | | Police Ch 877 |
| 87.0000 | 78.6000 | NFM | | Police Ch 878 |
| 87.0125 | 78.6125 | NFM | | Police Ch 879 |
| 87.0250 | 78.6250 | NFM | | Police Ch 880 |
| 87.0375 | 78.6375 | NFM | | Police Ch 881 |
| 87.0500 | 78.6500 | NFM | | Police Ch 882 |
| 87.0625 | 78.6625 | NFM | | Police Ch 883 |
| 87.0750 | 78.6750 | NFM | | Police Ch 884 |
| 87.0875 | 78.6875 | NFM | | Police Ch 885 |
| 87.1000 | 78.7000 | NFM | | Police Ch 886 |
| 124.3000 | 124.3000 | AM | Amsterdam Schipol | ACC |
| 124.8750 | 124.8750 | AM | Amsterdam Schipol | ACC |
| 125.7500 | 125.7500 | AM | Amsterdam Schipol | ACC |
| 127.6250 | 127.6250 | AM | Maastricht | Eurocontrol |
| 128.3500 | 128.3500 | AM | Amsterdam Schipol | Dutch Military |
| 129.3000 | 129.3000 | AM | Amsterdam Schipol | ACC |
| 131.4250 | 131.4250 | AM | Amsterdam | KLM Computer Ops. |
| 131.4500 | 131.4500 | AM | Amsterdam | Phillips Ops. |
| 131.4500 | 131.4500 | AM | Amsterdam | Martinair Ops. |
| 131.5500 | 131.5500 | AM | Amsterdam Schipol | Ground Control |
| 131.6000 | 131.6000 | AM | Amsterdam Schipol | TWA Ops. |
| 131.6500 | 131.6500 | AM | Amsterdam Schipol | KLM Ops. |
| 131.8000 | 131.8000 | AM | Amsterdam Schipol | Ogden Aviation Ops. |
| 131.8250 | 131.8250 | AM | Amsterdam Schipol | KLM Maintance |
| 131.8500 | 131.8500 | AM | Amsterdam Schipol | Singapore Airlines Ops. |
| 132.2000 | 132.2000 | AM | Maastricht | UAC |
| 132.3500 | 132.3500 | AM | Amsterdam Schipol | Dutch Mititary |
| 132.5250 | 132.5250 | AM | Amsterdam Schipol | Dutch Military |
| 132.8500 | 132.8500 | AM | Maastricht | UAC |
| 133.1000 | 133.1000 | AM | Amsterdam Schipol | ACC |
| 133.2500 | 133.2500 | AM | Maastricht | UAC |
| 133.3500 | 133.3500 | AM | Maastricht | UAC |
| 133.8500 | 133.8500 | AM | Maastricht | UAC |
| 133.9500 | 133.9500 | AM | Maastricht | UAC |
| 134.3750 | 134.3750 | AM | Maastricht | UAC |
| 135.1500 | 135.1500 | AM | Maastricht | UAC |
| 135.4500 | 135.4500 | AM | Maastricht | UAC |
| 135.9750 | 135.9750 | AM | Maastricht | UACC |
| 145.0875 | 149.4875 | NFM | Reusel | Customs |
| 145.7000 | 145.1000 | NFM | Eindhoven | Amateur Repeater PI3EHV |
| 146.0500 | 146.0500 | NFM | | Disaster Ch 23 |
| 146.0700 | 146.0700 | NFM | | Disaster Ch 24 |
| 146.0900 | 146.0900 | NFM | | Disaster Ch 25 |
| 146.1100 | 146.1100 | NFM | | Disaster Ch 26 |
| 146.1300 | 146.1300 | NFM | | Disaster Ch 27 |

| Base | Mobile | Mode | Location | User and Notes |
|------|--------|------|----------|----------------|
| 146.1500 | 146.1500 | NFM | | Disaster Ch 28 |
| 146.1700 | 146.1700 | NFM | | Disaster Ch 29 |
| 146.1900 | 146.1900 | NFM | | Disaster Ch 30 |
| 146.1900 | 146.1900 | NFM | | Trauma Teams Ch 71 |
| 146.2300 | 146.2300 | NFM | | Disaster Ch 31 |
| 146.2700 | 146.2700 | NFM | | Disaster Ch 33 |
| 146.2900 | 146.2900 | NFM | | Disaster Ch 34 |
| 146.3100 | 146.3100 | NFM | | Trauma Teams Ch 72 |
| 146.3700 | 146.3700 | NFM | | Disaster Ch 36 |
| 146.3900 | 146.3900 | NFM | | Disaster Ch 37 |
| 146.4300 | 146.4300 | NFM | | Disaster Ch 38 |
| 146.4500 | 146.4500 | NFM | | Trauma Teams Ch 73 |
| 146.4700 | 146.4700 | NFM | | Trauma Teams Ch 74 |
| 146.4900 | 146.4900 | NFM | | Disaster Ch 39 |
| 146.5100 | 146.5100 | NFM | | Disaster Ch 40 |
| 146.5300 | 146.5300 | NFM | | Disaster Ch 41 |
| 146.5500 | 146.5500 | NFM | | Disaster Ch 42 |
| 146.5700 | 146.5700 | NFM | | Trauma Teams Ch 75 |
| 146.6100 | 146.6100 | NFM | | Disaster Ch 43 |
| 146.6300 | 146.6300 | NFM | | Disaster Ch 44 |
| 146.6500 | 146.6500 | NFM | | Disaster Ch 45 |
| 146.6700 | 146.6700 | NFM | | Disaster Ch 46 |
| 146.6900 | 146.6900 | NFM | | Disaster Ch 47 |
| 146.7100 | 146.7100 | NFM | | Disaster Ch 48 |
| 146.7300 | 146.7300 | NFM | | Disaster Ch 49 |
| 146.7500 | 146.7500 | NFM | | Disaster Ch 50 |
| 146.7700 | 146.7700 | NFM | | Disaster Ch 51 |
| 146.7900 | 146.7900 | NFM | | Disaster Ch 52 |
| 146.8300 | 146.8300 | NFM | | Disaster Ch 53 |
| 146.8500 | 146.8500 | NFM | | Disaster Ch 54 |
| 146.8700 | 146.8700 | NFM | | Disaster Ch 55 |
| 146.9300 | 146.9300 | NFM | | Disaster Ch 56 |
| 146.9500 | 146.9500 | NFM | | Disaster Ch 57 |
| 147.0500 | 147.0500 | NFM | | Disaster Ch 58 |
| 147.0700 | 147.0700 | NFM | | Disaster Ch 59 |
| 147.0900 | 147.0900 | NFM | | Disaster Ch 60 |
| 147.1700 | 147.1700 | NFM | | Disaster Ch 61 |
| 147.1900 | 147.1900 | NFM | | Disaster Ch 32 |
| 150.5125 | 150.5125 | NFM | Eindhoven | Fire Brigade DAF Trucks |
| 151.7125 | 151.7125 | NFM | | Disaster Ch 62 |
| 151.7375 | 151.7375 | NFM | | Disaster Ch 63 |
| 151.7625 | 151.7625 | NFM | | Disaster Ch 64 |
| 151.7875 | 151.7875 | NFM | | Disaster Ch 65 |
| 151.8375 | 151.8375 | NFM | | Disaster Ch 66 |
| 151.8875 | 151.8875 | NFM | | Disaster Ch 67 |
| 151.9625 | 151.9625 | NFM | | Disaster Ch 68 |
| 151.9875 | 151.9875 | NFM | | Disaster Ch 69 |
| 152.3625 | 152.3625 | NFM | Eindhoven | Animal Ambulance |
| 152.7625 | 152.7625 | NFM | Eindhoven | Fire Brigade DAF Trucks |
| 153.7875 | 153.7875 | NFM | | Fire Brigades Ch 01 |
| 153.8375 | 153.8375 | NFM | | Fire Brigades Ch 02 |
| 153.9375 | 153.9375 | NFM | | Fire Brigades Ch 03 |
| 154.0125 | 154.0125 | NFM | | Fire Brigade Ch 04 |
| 154.2375 | 154.2375 | NFM | | Police Ch 161 |
| 154.2625 | 154.2625 | NFM | | Police Ch 162 |
| 154.2875 | 154.2875 | NFM | | Police Ch 163 |

| Base | Mobile | Mode | Location | User and Notes |
|------|--------|------|----------|----------------|
| 154.3625 | 154.3625 | NFM | | Police Ch 164 |
| 154.3875 | 154.3875 | NFM | | Police Ch 165 |
| 154.4125 | 154.4125 | NFM | | Police Ch 166 |
| 154.4875 | 154.4875 | NFM | | Police Ch 167 |
| 154.6625 | 154.6625 | NFM | | Police Ch 168 |
| 154.8375 | 154.8375 | NFM | | Police Ch 169 |
| 154.8875 | 150.2875 | NFM | Eindhoven | Electricity and Gas Ch 6 |
| 164.1700 | 164.1700 | NFM | Eindhoven | Fire Brigade Philips |
| 164.7500 | 160.2500 | NFM | | Fire Pagers Ch F1 |
| 164.7700 | 164.7700 | NFM | | Fire Pagers Ch F2 |
| 166.6700 | 166.6700 | NFM | Eindhoven | Railway Police Ch 3 |
| 166.8500 | 166.8500 | NFM | Eindhoven | Railway shunters |
| 167.1300 | 167.1300 | NFM | Eindhoven | Railway shunters |
| 167.1700 | 167.1700 | NFM | Eindhoven | Railway Travel Service |
| 167.5500 | 167.5500 | NFM | | Ambulance Service Ch 06 |
| 167.5700 | 167.5700 | NFM | | Ambulance Service Ch 08 |
| 167.5900 | 167.5900 | NFM | | Ambulance Service Ch 09 |
| 167.6100 | 167.6100 | NFM | | Ambulance Service Ch 05 |
| 167.6300 | 167.6300 | NFM | | Ambulance Service Ch 02 |
| 167.6500 | 167.6500 | NFM | | Ambulance Service Ch 01 |
| 167.6700 | 167.6700 | NFM | | Ambulance Service Ch 07 |
| 167.6900 | 167.6900 | NFM | | Ambulance Service Ch 03 |
| 167.7100 | 167.7100 | NFM | | Ambulance Service Ch 04 |
| 167.7300 | 167.7300 | NFM | | Ambulance Service Ch 12 |
| 167.7500 | 167.7500 | NFM | | Fire Brigades Ch 11 |
| 167.7700 | 167.7700 | NFM | | Fire Brigades Ch 13 |
| 167.7900 | 167.7900 | NFM | | Fire Brigades Ch 12 |
| 167.8100 | 167.8100 | NFM | | Fire Brigades Ch 14 |
| 167.8300 | 167.8300 | NFM | | Fire Brigades Ch 16 |
| 167.8500 | 167.8500 | NFM | | Ambulance Service Ch 10 |
| 167.8700 | 167.8700 | NFM | | Fire Brigades Ch 15 |
| 167.8900 | 167.8900 | NFM | | Ambulance Service Ch 13 |
| 167.9100 | 167.9100 | NFM | | Ambulance Service Ch 11 |
| 167.9100 | 167.9100 | NFM | Eindhoven | Ambulance Ch 11 |
| 167.9300 | 167.9300 | NFM | | Fire Brigades Ch 03 |
| 167.9500 | 167.9500 | NFM | | Fire Brigades Ch 04 |
| 167.9700 | 167.9700 | NFM | | Fire Brigades Ch 01 |
| 167.9700 | 167.9700 | NFM | Eindhoven | Fire Brigade Ch 1 |
| 167.9900 | 167.9900 | NFM | | Fire Brigades Ch 07 |
| 168.0100 | 168.0100 | NFM | | Fire Brigades Ch 09 |
| 168.0300 | 168.0300 | NFM | | Fire Brigades Ch 05 |
| 168.0500 | 168.0500 | NFM | | Fire Brigades Ch 06 |
| 168.0700 | 168.0700 | NFM | | Fire Brigades Ch 02 |
| 168.0900 | 168.0900 | NFM | | Fire Brigades Ch 08 |
| 168.0900 | 168.0900 | NFM | Eindhoven | Fire Brigade Ch 8 |
| 168.5900 | 168.5900 | NFM | Airports | Fire Brigades Ch 17 |
| 170.3500 | 170.3500 | NFM | Eindhoven | Fire Brigade Philips |
| 171.0900 | 166.4900 | NFM | Eindhoven | Railway shunters Ch 3 |
| 171.2100 | 166.6100 | NFM | Eindhoven | Railway shunters Ch 9 |
| 171.4500 | 171.4500 | NFM | Eindhoven | Railway information |
| 171.7100 | 171.7100 | NFM | | Police Ch 100 |
| 172.3300 | 172.3300 | NFM | | Police Ch 101 |
| 172.3500 | 172.3500 | NFM | | Police Ch 102 |
| 172.3700 | 172.3700 | NFM | | Police Ch 103 |
| 172.3900 | 172.3900 | NFM | | Police Ch 104 |
| 172.3900 | | NFM | | Riot Police |

| Base | Mobile | Mode | Location | User and Notes |
|---|---|---|---|---|
| 172.4100 | 172.4100 | NFM | | Police Ch 105 |
| 172.4300 | 172.4300 | NFM | | Police Ch 106 |
| 172.4700 | 172.4700 | NFM | | Police Ch 107 |
| 172.4900 | 172.4900 | NFM | | Police Ch 108 |
| 172.5100 | 172.5100 | NFM | | Police Ch 109 |
| 426.5500 | 416.5500 | NFM | Eindhoven | Buses, Hermes |
| 426.6250 | 426.6250 | NFM | Eindhoven | Buses, Hermes |
| 430.1000 | 431.7000 | NFM | Eindhoven | Amateur Repeater PI2EHV |
| 460.1000 | 158.1000 | NFM | Eindhoven | Railways Ch 37 |
| 467.6000 | 457.6000 | NFM | Eindhoven | Railways Ch 17 |
| 467.6750 | 457.6750 | NFM | Eindhoven | Railways Ch 20 |
| 467.7000 | 457.7000 | NFM | Best | Railways Ch 21 |
| 467.7500 | 457.7500 | NFM | Eindhoven | Railways Ch 23 |
| 467.8250 | 457.8250 | NFM | Eindhoven | Railways Ch 26 |
| 468.0000 | 458.0000 | NFM | Eindhoven | Railways Ch 33 |
| 468.0750 | 458.0750 | NFM | Eindhoven | Railways Ch 36 |
| 469.6700 | 459.6700 | NFM | Veldhoven | Wegenwacht (AA) |

## Norway

| Base | Mobile | Mode | Location | User and Notes |
|---|---|---|---|---|
| 120.6500 | 120.6500 | AM | Stavanger Airport | Radar |
| 124.7000 | 124.7000 | AM | Stavanger Airport | Radar |
| 167.0000 | 168.0000 | NFM | | Mobile Phones |
| 172.1250 | 172.2750 | NFM | | Fire Service Ch 2 |

## Poland

| Base | Mobile | Mode | Location | User and Notes |
|---|---|---|---|---|
| 66.4700 | | WFM | Siedice | Polskie Radio I Telewizja [LBS] |
| 66.5600 | | WFM | Poznan | Polskie Radio I Telewizja [LBS] |
| 66.6800 | | WFM | Zamosc | Polskie Radio I Telewizja [LBS] |
| 66.9500 | | WFM | Koszalin | Polskie Radio I Telewizja [LBS] |
| 67.2500 | | WFM | Olsztyn | Polskie Radio I Telewizja [LBS] |
| 67.4000 | | WFM | Poznan | Polskie Radio I Telewizja [LBS] |
| 67.4600 | | WFM | Luban | Polskie Radio I Telewizja [LBS] |
| 67.6100 | | WFM | Zamosc | Polskie Radio I Telewizja [LBS] |
| 67.6400 | | WFM | Klodzko | Polskie Radio I Telewizja [LBS] |
| 67.9400 | | WFM | Warszawa | Polskie Radio I Telewizja [LBS] |
| 68.0300 | | WFM | Siedice | Polskie Radio I Telewizja [LBS] |
| 68.2400 | | WFM | Luban | Polskie Radio I Telewizja [LBS] |
| 68.5100 | | WFM | Kudowa | Polskie Radio I Telewizja [LBS] |
| 68.7800 | | WFM | Jelenia Góra | Polskie Radio I Telewizja [LBS] |
| 69.3800 | | WFM | Zamosc | Polskie Radio I Telewizja [LBS] |
| 69.5600 | | WFM | Luban | Polskie Radio I Telewizja [LBS] |
| 69.5600 | | WFM | Olsztyn | Polskie Radio I Telewizja [LBS] |
| 69.7400 | | WFM | Klodzko | Polskie Radio I Telewizja [LBS] |
| 70.2200 | | WFM | Siedice | Polskie Radio I Telewizja [LBS] |
| 70.7900 | | WFM | Olsztyn | Polskie Radio I Telewizja [LBS] |
| 71.1200 | | WFM | Suwalki | Polskie Radio I Telewizja [LBS] |
| 71.7200 | | WFM | Jelenia Góra | Polskie Radio I Telewizja [LBS] |
| 71.7200 | | WFM | Zielona Góra | Polskie Radio I Telewizja [LBS] |
| 71.8100 | | WFM | Lublin | Polskie Radio I Telewizja [LBS] |
| 71.8400 | | WFM | Bydgoszcz | Polskie Radio I Telewizja [LBS] |

| Base | Mobile | Mode | Location | User and Notes |
|------|--------|------|----------|----------------|
| 72.0200 | | WFM | Bialystok | Polskie Radio I Telewizja [LBS] |
| 72.0200 | | WFM | Pila | Polskie Radio I Telewizja [LBS] |
| 72.4400 | | WFM | Klodzko | Polskie Radio I Telewizja [LBS] |
| 72.5900 | | WFM | Lublin | Polskie Radio I Telewizja [LBS] |
| 72.6200 | | WFM | Bydgoszcz | Polskie Radio I Telewizja [LBS] |
| 72.6800 | | WFM | Suwalki | Polskie Radio I Telewizja [LBS] |
| 72.8000 | | WFM | Bialystok | Polskie Radio I Telewizja [LBS] |
| 72.8000 | | WFM | Pila | Polskie Radio I Telewizja [LBS] |

## Romania

| Base | Mobile | Mode | Location | User and Notes |
|------|--------|------|----------|----------------|
| 65.9600 | | WFM | Gheorgheni | Radioteleviziunea Romana [LBS] |
| 65.9600 | | WFM | Zalau | Radioteleviziunea Romana [LBS] |
| 66.1700 | | WFM | P. Neant | Radioteleviziunea Romana [LBS] |
| 66.3600 | | WFM | Birlad | Radioteleviziunea Romana [LBS] |
| 66.4400 | | WFM | Sibiu | Radioteleviziunea Romana [LBS] |
| 66.5600 | | WFM | Baia Marea | Radioteleviziunea Romana [LBS] |
| 66.7600 | | WFM | Cluj | Radioteleviziunea Romana [LBS] |
| 67.0100 | | WFM | Bacau | Radioteleviziunea Romana [LBS] |
| 67.2500 | | WFM | Vilcea | Radioteleviziunea Romana [LBS] |
| 67.3400 | | WFM | Varatec | Radioteleviziunea Romana [LBS] |
| 67.6700 | | WFM | Zalau | Radioteleviziunea Romana [LBS] |
| 67.7900 | | WFM | Constanta | Radioteleviziunea Romana [LBS] |
| 67.8800 | | WFM | Focsania | Radioteleviziunea Romana [LBS] |
| 68.1200 | | WFM | Baia Mare | Radioteleviziunea Romana [LBS] |
| 68.2500 | | WFM | Bucuresti | Radioteleviziunea Romana [LBS] |
| 68.3600 | | WFM | Cluj | Radioteleviziunea Romana [LBS] |
| 68.5200 | | WFM | Resita | Radioteleviziunea Romana [LBS] |
| 68.8700 | | WFM | Bacau | Radioteleviziunea Romana [LBS] |
| 68.8700 | | WFM | Comanesti | Radioteleviziunea Romana [LBS] |
| 69.1100 | | WFM | Varatec | Radioteleviziunea Romana [LBS] |
| 69.6500 | | WFM | Timisoara, | Radioteleviziunea Romana [LBS] |
| 69.6800 | | WFM | T. Severin | Radioteleviziunea Romana [LBS] |
| 69.7400 | | WFM | Bistrita | Radioteleviziunea Romana [LBS] |
| 69.9200 | | WFM | Iasi | Radioteleviziunea Romana [LBS] |
| 70.0100 | | WFM | Constanta | Radioteleviziunea Romana [LBS] |
| 70.2200 | | WFM | Focsania | Radioteleviziunea Romana [LBS] |
| 70.4000 | | WFM | Bucuresti | Radioteleviziunea Romana [LBS] |
| 70.6100 | | WFM | Suceava | Radioteleviziunea Romana [LBS] |
| 70.6400 | | WFM | Deva | Radioteleviziunea Romana [LBS] |
| 70.7900 | | WFM | Arad | Radioteleviziunea Romana [LBS] |
| 71.0000 | | WFM | Oradea | Radioteleviziunea Romana [LBS] |
| 71.0600 | | WFM | P. Neant | Radioteleviziunea Romana [LBS] |
| 71.0600 | | WFM | Petrosani | Radioteleviziunea Romana [LBS] |
| 71.7200 | | WFM | Timisoara, | Radioteleviziunea Romana [LBS] |
| 71.8400 | | WFM | Iasi | Radioteleviziunea Romana [LBS] |
| 71.9600 | | WFM | Topolog | Radioteleviziunea Romana [LBS] |
| 72.2000 | | WFM | Cimpulung | Radioteleviziunea Romana [LBS] |
| 72.2000 | | WFM | Deva | Radioteleviziunea Romana [LBS] |
| 72.3200 | | WFM | Birlad | Radioteleviziunea Romana [LBS] |
| 72.3600 | | WFM | Resita | Radioteleviziunea Romana [LBS] |
| 72.4400 | | WFM | Bistrita | Radioteleviziunea Romana [LBS] |
| 72.5600 | | WFM | Arad | Radioteleviziunea Romana [LBS] |
| 72.6800 | | WFM | Vilcea | Radioteleviziunea Romana [LBS] |
| 72.7100 | | WFM | T. Severin | Radioteleviziunea Romana [LBS] |

| Base | Mobile | Mode | Location | User and Notes |
|---|---|---|---|---|
| 72.8000 | | WFM | Petrosani | Radioteleviziunea Romana [LBS] |
| 72.9200 | | WFM | Ploesti | Radioteleviziunea Romana [LBS] |
| 72.9800 | | WFM | Bihor | Radioteleviziunea Romana [LBS] |
| 72.9800 | | WFM | Suceava | Radioteleviziunea Romana [LBS] |

## Slovakia

| Base | Mobile | Mode | Location | User and Notes |
|---|---|---|---|---|
| 66.3800 | | WFM | Kosice | Slovensky Rozhlas [LBS] |
| 67.2800 | | WFM | Poprad | Slovensky Rozhlas [LBS] |
| 67.6700 | | WFM | Bratislava, | Slovensky Rozhlas [LBS] |
| 67.9400 | | WFM | Kosice | Slovensky Rozhlas [LBS] |
| 68.0600 | | WFM | Poprad | Slovensky Rozhlas [LBS] |
| 68.8400 | | WFM | Bratislava | Slovensky Rozhlas [LBS] |
| 68.8700 | | WFM | Kosice | Slovensky Rozhlas [LBS] |
| 69.5000 | | WFM | Zilina | Slovensky Rozhlas [LBS] |
| 69.6800 | | WFM | Banska Bystrica | Slovensky Rozhlas [LBS] |
| 70.8200 | | WFM | Zilina | Slovensky Rozhlas [LBS] |
| 70.9400 | | WFM | Banska Bystrica | Slovensky Rozhlas [LBS] |
| 71.1200 | | WFM | Bratislava | Slovensky Rozhlas [LBS] |
| 71.6000 | | WFM | Zilina | Slovensky Rozhlas [LBS] |
| 72.0200 | | WFM | Namestovo | Slovensky Rozhlas [LBS] |
| 72.5000 | | WFM | Banska Bystrica | Slovensky Rozhlas [LBS] |

## Sweden

| Base | Mobile | Mode | Location | User and Notes |
|---|---|---|---|---|
| 79.0000 | 80.0000 | NFM | | Scandanavian Police |
| 167.0000 | 163.0000 | NFM | | Gothenburcreft |

# FREE Books for You!

These new guides list by county the radio frequencies used by the police in Britain, and now include the other emergency services. There are hundreds of frequencies, many have never been published before. The country is covered in four comprehensive parts: London, Southern England, Northern England, and Scotland and Wales.

All you have to do to receive your free copy is to send us 25 or more VHF/UHF frequencies and their users from your area. The frequencies must not be listed in any edition of *The UK Scanning Directory*, and must include location and user. Taxis, telephones and other undefined users are not acceptable. It's that simple!

To get your free book set out your list under these headings:

Base    Mobile
Freq.    Freq.    Mode    Location    User & Notes

*Good luck!*

**Important:**
To qualify for your copy of the *UK Police Radio Guide,* please send the appropriate voucher which is on the last page, for the one you would like along with your frequency list. Please do not send photocopies of the voucher as only the original will be accepted.

# North Atlantic
# Flight Communications

Plot trans Atlantic flights with your HF radio and computer. Enter the flight details and watch in real time as the program plots the flight's progress across the North Atlantic on high resolution charts. From the position reports you receive over the air the flight path can be updated at each waypoint. The accompanying large book clearly explains all the procedures from filing the flight plan right through to landing at the destination, and describes the radio communications system in depth. It also lists hundreds of flight routings, Selcals and all the relevant frequencies. Comprehensive list of geographical waypoints and ICAO codes are also included. Software on two 3.5" disks requires IBM/PC running Widows 3.1 and 95 with min. 8MB RAM.

**Price: £15 + £1.25 UK post. Postage for Europe add £2.25 or £5 airmail to other destinations.**

## INTERPRODUCTS
### 8 Abbot Street, Perth. PH2 0EB, Scotland
### Tel. & Fax: 01738-441199
### e-mail interproducts@netmatters.co.uk

486

# Shortwave Eavesdropper CD-ROM

A huge step forward in the accessibility of shortwave utility information has been made with the *Shortwave Eavesdropper* CD-ROM. It gives instant access to well over 32,000 frequencies, over 42,000 call signs both ITU and military tactical, country by country information containing QSL addresses, schedules, examples of traffic, and maps.

That is not all! The DX Edge shows you in real time where to monitor throughout the day, there are extensive help menus, tutorials and a very large list of aircraft and ARQ SELCAL codes. There are even audio samples of data modes and number stations. *Shortwave Eavesdropper* runs on an IBM PC or compatible computer with CD-ROM drive, at least 4MB of RAM running Microsoft Windows 3.0 or higher and sound board which is optional.

**Price: £16.50 including UK postage and airmail worldwide.**

## Scanning the Maritime Bands
### by FF O'Brian

It is so easy to pick up maritime radio communications on your scanner because transmissions are in the clear and there are so many ships. *Scanning the Maritime Bands* gives you the Channel Number for each port, harbour and coast radio station in the UK, Ireland, Western Europe and right up to Iceland. All you have to do is to key into your scanner the corresponding frequency from the foldout maritime frequency list. When travelling at home or abroad, take along your scanner to hear ports controlling ships and ferries, weather and navigation broadcasts, the supplies and spare parts required, problems they are having with the crew and lots more. From weekend pleasure craft to super tankers all are fitted with VHF radios. By monitoring Channel 16 you can learn when disaster strikes, and then switch to the appropriate channels to hear the whole of the search and rescue operation (156 pages A5).

**Price: £9.50 incl. UK postage. Overseas post add £1.50 for Europe (airmail) and sea mail worldwide, airmail outside Europe add £2.**

## INTERPRODUCTS
### 8 Abbot Street, Perth. PH2 0EB, Scotland
### Tel. & Fax: 01738-441199
### e-mail interproducts@netmatters.co.uk

# Scanner Busters 2

by D. C. Poole

*How to Tune into More Frequencies
and beat new Technology*

The Police continue to scramble more of their frequencies, trunked radio systems are making it harder to eavesdrop on conversations, and there are more and more strange noises heard on the bands. To overcome this new technology *Scanner Busters 2* guides you through the maze, showing you how to deal with these systems, and to tune into the things you really want to hear. The book has clearly explains in simple terms the workings of PMR, new digital telephone systems, spread spectrum, new pager systems, frequency hopping, encryption systems such as MASC used by the Police and the latest communication methods of the emergency services. *Scanner Busters 2* will be of great help to both new scanner owners and veterans.

**Price: £6.00 Special Offer £5 incl. UK postage. Overseas post add £1.25 for Europe (airmail) and sea mail worldwide, airmail outside Europe add £2.**

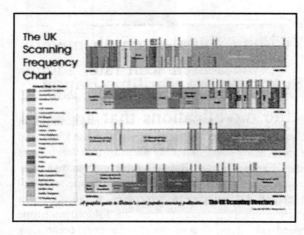

# UK Scanning Frequency Chart

Stunning full colour A3 wall chart covering 25 MHz to 1.8 GHz showing in graphic details all major users of the VHF/UHF spectrum. It will show you quickly where to scan to pick up your favourite transmissions.

*Only £3 including UK postage!*

## INTERPRODUCTS
8 Abbot Street, Perth. PH2 0EB, Scotland
Tel. & Fax: 01738-441199
e-mail interproducts@netmatters.co.uk

## VHF/UHF Airband Frequency & Callsign Guide

This book is a very comprehensive guide to aeronautical frequencies and callsigns in the UK. It lists the every airport and airfield in alphabetical order with their corresponding frequencies in an easy-to-read format, and then goes on to give the frequencies for military ranges, low flying, refuelling, aerobatic displays, UK air defence and AWACS. It also covers air traffic control, Squark codes, Volmet, emergency frequencies and lists other frequencies.

The Callsign section is very extensive for both civil and military. There are over 8,500 military callsigns listed and a vast number of civil ones.

Javiation have put a great deal of work into this book and it will be indispensable for any aircraft enthusiast.

**Price: £12.50 plus £1.25 UK postage. Overseas post Europe £2.25 or £4.50 elsewhere.**

## *Shortwave Maritime Communications*

### by B. E. Richardson

Disasters are quite common, ships are blown onto rocks, run aground or are lost, and each month at least one super tanker breaks up and sinks. *Shortwave Maritime Communications* gives step-by-step instructions on how to monitor these incidents with all the shipping frequencies worldwide.

The book is laid out with both the beginner and the well-seasoned maritime radio enthusiast in mind, providing the most accurate and detailed information in an easy-to-use format. Two mammoth frequency lists include every coastal station from around the world together with the shore and corresponding ship's frequency, and are arranged not only by frequency but by station's name, mode and callsign. Regardless where in the world you live *Shortwave Maritime Communications* provides endless hours of enjoyment. (200 pages A4).

**Price: £14.50 plus £1 UK postage. Overseas post add £2.50 for Europe (airmail) and sea mail worldwide, airmail outside Europe add £6.**

## INTERPRODUCTS
8 Abbot Street, Perth. PH2 0EB, Scotland
Tel. & Fax: 01738-441199
e-mail interproducts@netmatters.co.uk

# Mobile Phones - The Tricks of the Trade

Mobile Phones -
The Tricks of the
Trade

by
Phil Jones

Shows you how to:-
• Save money on your phone
bill

• Avoid connection
charges

• Reconnect your old
phone at less than £10 per
month

• Save money on the cost
of your monthly
subscription and also how
to avoid those nasty restrictive
contracts

Illustrations by Mike Hayne

The mobile telephone is a marvellous invention which gives the freedom to communicate from anywhere and is a Godsend to individuals and businesses large or small. The one great drawback is knowing how to obtain right phone, contract and service provider, and to understand how the system works from the maze of conflicting information that is around.

There are over 7 million mobile phones in Britain and sadly, soon after signing up, almost one in three of these people want to change their network, tariff or phone. Most people feel they receive inadequate performance and service, and many find it prohibitively expensive to use their mobile phone abroad.

Here at last is an A4 book crammed with information in well over 200 pages which will not only explain in simple terms how to get the best from your mobile phone, but will show you :-

√ How to buy the right phone that will match your needs.

√ How to avoid those nasty restrictive contracts.

√ How to connect your own phone to the network.

√ How to find the right service provider.

√ How to re-programme a second hand phone which is

available at a give away price.

√ Explains the difference between analogue and digital phones.

...and much much more.

Most information in the book has not been available to members of the public before.

With the savings you will make from your phone bill, reduced connection charges and monthly subscription  you will easily recoup the cost of this book, and will at last have the most liberating technology in your hands.

**Price: £25 incl UK Postage. Overseas airmail to Europe add £2.70 or elsewhere £6.**

## INTERPRODUCTS
### 8 Abbot Street, Perth. PH2 0EB, Scotland
### Tel. & Fax: 01738-441199
### e-mail interproducts@netmatters.co.uk

# ORDER FORM

To: **Interproducts**
   **8 Abbot Street**
   **Perth,**
   **PH2 0EB,**
   **Scotland.**

**Tel. & Fax: 01738-441199**

International: +44-1738-441199
email:
interproducts@netmatters.co.uk

Name:

Address:

Date:.................................

| Qty | Items | Each £ | Postage £ | Total £ |
|-----|-------|--------|-----------|---------|
|     |       |        |           |         |
|     |       |        |           |         |
|     |       |        |           |         |
|     |       |        |           |         |
|     |       |        |           |         |
|     |       |        |           |         |

Total £

UKSD6

*VISA*

*MasterCard*

I am enclosing a cheque/postal orders/draft for £..........................

Please charge to my
credit card

Expiry date....................... Signature..........................................

Books normally available from stock.

UK credit card orders under £10 have a services charge of 75p.

Please allow 2 weeks for delivery of orders.

# ORDER FORM

To: **Interproducts**
  **8 Abbot Street**
  **Perth,**
  **PH2 0EB,**
  **Scotland.**

**Tel. & Fax: 01738-441199**

International: +44-1738-441199
email:
interproducts@netmatters.co.uk

Name:

Address:

Date:.....................................................

| Qty | Items | Each £ | Postage £ | Total £ |
|-----|-------|--------|-----------|---------|
|     |       |        |           |         |
|     |       |        |           |         |
|     |       |        |           |         |
|     |       |        |           |         |
|     |       |        |           |         |
|     |       |        |           |         |

UKSD6

Total £

**VISA**  **MasterCard**

I am enclosing a cheque/draft for £..........................

Please charge to my
credit card

Expiry date....................... Signature..............................................

Books normally available from stock.

UK credit card orders under £10 have a services charge of 75p.

Please allow 2 weeks for delivery of orders.

## LONDON Edition Voucher

Please send me in return for the 25 or more new frequencies I am enclosing, a FREE copy of the above edition of *The Police Radio Guide*. Please write your name and address overleaf.

## SOUTHERN ENGLAND
### Edition Voucher

Please send me in return for the 25 or more new frequencies I am enclosing, a FREE copy of the above edition of *The Police Radio Guide*. Please write your name and address overleaf.

## NORTHERN ENGLAND
### Edition Voucher

Please send me in return for the 25 or more new frequencies I am enclosing, a FREE copy of the above edition of *The Police Radio Guide*. Please write your name and address overleaf.

## SCOTLAND & WALES
### Edition Voucher

Please send me in return for the 25 or more new frequencies I am enclosing, a FREE copy of the above edition of *The Police Radio Guide*. Please write your name and address overleaf.

Name _____

Address _____

_____

_____


Name _____

Address _____

_____

_____


Name _____

Address _____

_____

_____


Name _____

Address _____

_____

_____